761-5137

9.12 Chpt. 9

1350

23-29-15

658-3121

s

d

														7
		87 Fr	88 Ra	89 Ac	104	105	106	107	108	109	110	111	112	6
85 At	86 Rn	55 Cs	56 Ba	57 La	72 Hf	73 Ta	74 W	75 Re	76 Os	77 Ir	78 Pt	79 Au	80 Hg	5
53 I	54 Xe	37 Rb	38 Sr	39 Y	40 Zr	41 Nb	42 Mo	43 Tc	44 Ru	45 Rh	46 Pd	47 Ag	48 Cd	4
35 Br	36 Kr	19 K	20 Ca	21 Sc	22 Ti	23 V	24 Cr	25 Mn	26 Fe	27 Co	28 Ni	29 Cu	30 Zn	3
17 Cl	18 Ar	11 Na	12 Mg											
9 F	10 Ne	3 Li	4 Be	2										
1		1 H	2 He	1										

Thurs 8:00

Tues. Phys.
Phil. Wed.

D1223860

Chph. 1

$l = \frac{V}{\sqrt{2} N \sigma^2 \pi}$ effusion $= \frac{v_1}{v_2} = \left(\frac{M_2}{M_1}\right)^{1/2}$

v = velocity $= \left(\frac{3RT}{M}\right)^{1/2}$ $E = \frac{3}{2} PV$

$M.W. = \frac{gRT}{PV}$

VDW $\left(P - \frac{An^2}{V^2}\right)(V - nb) = nRT$

B $\left(P - \frac{An^2}{TV^2}\right)(V - nb) = nRT$

$PV = \frac{g}{M_0}(1+\alpha)RT$

D $\left(Pe^{An/RVT}\right)(V - nb) = nRT$

Chph. 2

adiabatic $C_v \ln \frac{T_2}{T_1} = R \ln \frac{V_1}{V_2}$ and $C_p \ln \frac{T_2}{T_1} = R \ln \frac{P_2}{P_1}$ $w = \frac{nR(T_2 - T_1)}{\gamma - 1}$

isothermal $w = nRT \ln \frac{P_2}{P_1}$ $w = nRT \ln \frac{V_1}{V_2}$

Chph. 3

$\Delta H = \Delta H^\circ + \int C_p dt$

$\Delta H = \Delta E + \Delta n_{(g)} RT$

Chph. 4

$\Delta S = nC_p \ln \frac{T_2}{T_1} - nR \ln \frac{P_2}{P_1}$ or $+ nR \ln \frac{V_2}{V_1}$

$\epsilon = \frac{q_2}{q_2} \leq \frac{T_2 - T_1}{T_2}$ $\epsilon = \frac{q_1}{w} \leq \frac{T_1}{T_2 - T_1}$ $\epsilon = \frac{-q_2}{w} \leq \frac{T_2}{T_2 - T_1}$

Chph. 5

Maxwell Relat.

Chpt. 6

$\frac{dp}{dt} = \frac{\Delta S}{\Delta V} \rightarrow \log P_{mm} = \frac{-\Delta H}{2.3RT} \rightarrow \ln \frac{P_2}{P_1} = \frac{\Delta H(T_2 - T_1)}{2.3RT_1T_2}$

SECOND EDITION

PHYSICAL CHEMISTRY

WILLIAM F. SHEEHAN
UNIVERSITY OF SANTA CLARA

SECOND EDITION

PHYSICAL CHEMISTRY

ALLYN AND BACON, INC.
BOSTON

© Copyright 1970 by Allyn and Bacon, Inc., 470 Atlantic Avenue, Boston. All rights reserved. No part of this book may be reproduced in any form, or by any means, without permission in writing from the publisher.

Library of Congress Catalog Card Number: 69-14636

Printed in the United States of America

CONTENTS

PREFACE

The first half of this book consists in general of thermodynamics and classical physical chemistry; the second half consists of chemical physics and quantum chemistry with a microscopic or single-event view of chemistry. This is a new edition in the strictest meaning of the term, for slightly more than one-third of it is new. The old chapters on thermodynamics have been divided and carefully revised by various deletions and additions. Thus this work carries on the thermodynamic reputation of the first edition. However, by generous addition of matter on chemical kinetics, quantum mechanics, and quantum chemistry, a great change in emphasis has been realized. More than half of the text is now devoted to a molecular or electronic view of chemistry in response to many helpful and thoughtful recommendations.

The first chapter on gases is now simple and straightforward, but it has enough matter unfamiliar to the ordinary student to assure him that physical chemistry is not merely elegant general chemistry. Thermodynamics, generally considered the main responsibility of a first course in physical chemistry, is presented in the next eight chapters with exceptional clarity and directness by emphasis on functions of state and the logic of mathematics. There are, however, microscopic explanations of such things as gaseous behavior, entropy and disorder, the third law, and heat capacities. There is also new material on surface chemistry and the Debye-Huckel theory of dilute electrolyte solutions.

The tenth chapter again deals with chemical kinetics, but it now lies in the middle of the book rather than at the end as in the first edition. This chapter on kinetics contains much new matter and smoothly joins the world of thermodynamics to the single events of electrochemistry, quantum theory, structural chemistry, and statistical mechanics in the second half of the book. Chapters 8, 11 and 12 on electrochemistry each contain new matter on surface chemistry to complete the discussion of surface effects begun in Chapter 6. Although it is woven into the main fabric of the book instead of being off in its own chapter, surface chemistry may easily be omitted, for it occurs at the ends of these three chapters.

The final six chapters are mostly new and constitute about half of the book. Chapter 13 is an introduction to wave mechanics by a study of the free particle and the particle in the box. Chapter 14 deals with the harmonic oscillator, the hydrogen atom, and various general theorems and methods of calculation. Chapter 15 applies quantum and wave mechanics to chemical problems: molecular energies, spectroscopy, valence. . . . Ideal and real crystals are fully described geometrically and quantum mechanically in Chapter 16. The next chapter on statistical mechanics is somewhat longer and more thorough than the same chapter of the first edition; equilibrium constants are evaluated from molecular data and there is a section on magnetic properties. The final Chapter 18 deals with chemical kinetics in the light of quantum and statistical mechanics.

Each chapter is begun and summarized with a section intended to orient the student, sometimes by reference to history and sometimes through comparisons to other chapters. This edition, as compared to the first, contains more and shorter chapters, more modern theory, more descriptive matter, more and earlier chemical kinetics, more problems, more figures, and more examples worked out in detail. Yet it is not, and is not intended to be, an encyclopedia of physical chemistry. In fact, one of the most difficult chores of writing a suitable textbook on so broad a subject is deciding what not to say. I hope that deliberate omissions are generally a service to student and professor. The preface of the first edition began:

> Almost everyone has heard that a physical chemist is a mathematician who can blow glass. Not as many unfortunately have heard the description of a physical chemist given by the late Professor Ward V. Evans. He said, in his very special way, that a physical chemist is a chemist who sits behind a big mahogany desk with a platinum slide rule. . . .

With such a characterization of physical chemistry, omissions and inclusions are easily justified. The attitude of the student who has used the book is really of paramount importance.

I have tried very hard to avoid direct or implied scientific, pedagogical, and typographical error. However, faced with this multiply infinite set of possible errors, I know this book cannot be perfect. I will greatly appreciate help from anyone.

This book contains the life work of many scientists; I am very grateful to them all. I regret that it is impossible to acknowledge each of their contributions; even historians have difficulties in this regard. I now thank them individually and offer the references that are explicitly given at various points as a nod in their direction and a reminder to the student that he is expected to join the many people who have contributed to the advancement of science.

Meanwhile, it is appropriate to thank all those students, professors, and reviewers who have generously taken time to point out errors or possible improvements in the first edition and in the manuscript of this edition. Among these, Professor Peter F. Linde has been especially helpful. I am also grateful to Professor David Winkel, who, with the help of Professors W. Byers Brown, C. K. Edmiston, R. G. Parr and students and participants, presented a NSF Summer Conference on Quantum Chemistry at the University of Wyoming in 1965; it was indeed a privilege to attend this conference. And before that, in the fall of 1963, I had the good fortune to attend a conference on chemical kinetics at the University of California; from this I came away grateful to no less than fourteen professors. Of course, I am as ever indebted to my teachers of old and students of today. In particular I should like to thank Professor Verner Schomaker not only for his guidance through graduate work but also for his continual interest; for example, he explained to me what the phase rule is really all about. I should again like to thank Professors Frank P. Cassaretto, J. H. Sturdivant, and the late John G. Kirkwood. Whatever excellence is found here is due to them and their teaching. Professor Joseph F. Deck has greatly encouraged the work on revising the first edition, and as before I am grateful to J. B. Deck and D. P. Waligora for numerous biological examples of osmosis.

Although their contribution is often overlooked or taken for granted, the various learned societies have supported their journals, the primary sources. It is a pleasure to remark, for example, that material reprinted from publications of the American Chemical Society is reprinted by permission of the copyright owner, the American Chemical Society.

The University of Santa Clara has, as always, provided a congenial academic atmosphere for which I am most grateful.

Many thanks are due the publisher and its staff for their expert work and frequent help. As Executive Editor during a major part of this revision, Duane H. Mark is to be thanked for continual interest, much patience, and sound advice on innumerable matters. Gary B. Simonsen and Wilfrid H. Beaubien, as Associate Editors, contributed much to the initial work in obtaining helpful reviews, for which I am grateful. Thanks are due Wayne Barcomb, Editor in Chief, and William M. Roberts, Associate Editor, for their continual interest and help just before and during production. When production finally began, it was my privilege to work with two members of the Editorial-Production Department: James Rigney, who designed the book and ably produced most of it; and Miss Sydney Wheeler, who carried the production carefully to its end. Finally, it is a pleasure to thank Mrs. V. Faye Wharton, as for the first edition, for her most valuable skill in typing much of this manuscript.

W. F. S.

SECOND EDITION

PHYSICAL CHEMISTRY

1

PURE GASES

1.1 INTRODUCTION

Physical chemistry deals with the theoretical basis of chemistry. It is naturally mathematical and as general and universal as its theories are powerful. Physics offers solutions of the same general nature, but usually the number of particles or variables in chemical situations is so great that approximations or averages are required in using the concepts of physics. Mathematics offers a set of rules for manipulating the variables, but again the chemical problem is typically so complex that approximations or empirical methods are used. The ideal, of course, is to calculate all chemically interesting properties in terms of the structure of matter, the forces between or among particles, and their motions.

In order to explain how this ideal may some day be realized, this book begins with an explanation of properties of usual interest to a chemist. The properties of pure gases are the simplest to discuss, and this chapter deals with some that are familiar and some that are not. Then, in subsequent chapters, these and properties of more complicated systems are studied closely in a most economical, orderly, and careful way by thermodynamics. Eventually, in the last half of the book, the thermodynamic properties are shown to be averages of the behavior of electrons, atoms, ions, molecules, and other minute particles and the particular events that they experience. Indeed, some of these microscopic events are woven into the explanation of macroscopic behavior that is so aptly described by thermodynamics.

The first part of this chapter examines a simple model with certain average mechanical properties that can be identified with properties of a nonexistent substance called a perfect gas. Although it deals with an idealization, the model is valuable because it explains something about the nature of gases. Moreover, it is useful because under study it can predict properties of gases and yield unexpected correlations of observed properties. In the light of this ideal discussion, the last part of the chapter discusses the similarities and differences of this perfect gas and real gases.

1.2 MECHANICAL ENERGY

One of the most obvious things of interest about a simple particle is its position at various past and future times. In his three laws of mechanics, Newton summarized possible events for a particle. His first law says that if a particle is not acted upon by other bodies, it remains at rest or, if in motion, it continues to move at the same speed in a straight line. The speed u of a particle is the ratio of distance traveled to time required. If the motion begins at position x_1 at time t_1 and continues without external interference to a position x_2 at time t_2, the value of its speed is

$$u = \frac{x_2 - x_1}{t_2 - t_1} = \frac{\Delta x}{\Delta t}$$

The quantities Δx and Δt are finite differences in position and time. If u is constant, as supposed, then the position of the particle at some time $t = t_2 - t_1$ is $x_2 = ut + x_1$. Thus, position is referred to time.

It is impossible to avoid external interference, if only because of gravitation. Generally both the speed and direction of a particle change through the influence of other particles. Speed and direction are both specified in the particle's velocity, for velocity is a vector. A vector is a directed magnitude and has certain well-known mathematical properties. The rate at which the velocity of a particle changes is called its *acceleration*. While acceleration is also a vector, here it can be treated as a scalar quantity, namely a magnitude without direction. If the rate of change from speed u_1 at time t_1 to u_2 at t_2 is constant, the scalar acceleration is

$$a = \frac{u_2 - u_1}{t_2 - t_1} = \frac{\Delta u}{\Delta t}$$

In general, a and u change continuously so that, at any instant,

$$u = \lim_{\Delta t \to 0} \frac{\Delta x}{\Delta t} = \frac{dx}{dt} \tag{1.1}$$

$$a = \lim_{\Delta t \to 0} \frac{\Delta u}{\Delta t} = \frac{du}{dt} \tag{1.2}$$

Newton's second law of mechanics relates the acceleration experienced by a particle in part to a property of the particle called its *mass*, and in part to outside influences called *forces*. The force F needed to produce an acceleration a is proportional to a and to the mass m of the particle; hence, the mathematical form of the second law of mechanics is

$$F = ma \tag{1.3}$$

Although (1.3) is written as though F and a are merely scalar quantities, both have the same direction and are properly vectors.

At ordinary velocities, the mass of a particle appears to be independent of its speed or velocity. However, at great velocities, m does depend on the particle's speed, and a more general definition of force is

$$F = \frac{d}{dt}(mu) \tag{1.4}$$

That is, force is that rate of change of momentum, where mu is called the particle's momentum. If m is constant, this definition becomes the same as (1.3) for

$$F = \frac{d}{dt}(mu) = m\frac{du}{dt} = ma$$

When several forces act on a particle, the net effect is found by adding forces and accelerations as vectors.

One of two common ways of following the effect of a force as it acts is to calculate the product of the force F and the time Δt that the force acts. This product $F\Delta t$ is called the *impulse*. If F varies with time, the impulse in a time from t_1 to t_2 is, by (1.4),

$$\int_{t_1}^{t_2} F\,dt = \int_{(1)}^{(2)} d(mu) = (mu)_2 - (mu)_1 \tag{1.5}$$

That is, the impulse experienced by a particle is equal to its change of momentum. If the force is zero during a time, then there is no change in the particle's momentum, for $0 = (mu)_2 - (mu)_1$. This, of course, is the situation described by Newton's first law.

A second way of following the effect of a force on a particle is to calculate the quantity called *work*. The product of the force F exerted on a particle and the distance through which it acts is, by definition, the work w done on the particle. In calculating w, the value of the force is F_x, the part of it that is directed along the path, which here is along the x-axis. If F_x varies with position, the total work done on the particle form x_1 to x_2 is, by (1.4), $w = \int_{x_1}^{x_2} F_x\,dx = \int_{x_1}^{x_2} \frac{d(mu)}{dt}\,dx$. With m constant and with $u = dx/dt$ from (1.1), this becomes

$$w = \int_{x_1}^{x_2} F_x dx = m \int_{u_1}^{u_2} u du = \frac{mu_2^2}{2} - \frac{mu_1^2}{2} \tag{1.6}$$

A special case of (1.6) occurs when F_x or dx is zero; then u remains constant, as required by the first law. The important scalar quantity

$$T = \frac{mu^2}{2} \tag{1.7}$$

in (1.6) is called the *kinetic energy* of the particle. According to (1.6), work done on a particle increases its kinetic energy.

The force imposed on a particle, in addition to accelerating the particle as in (1.6), may oppose and overcome gravitational, electrical, magnetic, or other forces that would accelerate the particle if the external force were withdrawn. Such a particle is said to exist in a *field of force*. The field is called *conservative* if the work required to move a particle from one specified place at rest to another place at rest is independent of the intermediate positions. The work linking the initial and final states thus does not depend upon the path actually taken through a conservative field of force. At any point in such a field, the force exerted by the field depends only on position, and the work done on a particle by an external force $F(x)$ is determined solely by the terminal states. The state of a particle at rest in a conservative field is characterized at each point by a quantity called its *potential energy* $V(x)$. The work done on a particle by an external force $F(x)$ that moves the particle from rest at x_1 where $V(x_1) = V_1$ to rest at x_2 where $V(x_2) = V_2$ is

$$w = \int_{x_1}^{x_2} F(x)dx = V_2 - V_1 \tag{1.8}$$

The work done on the particle by a force $F(x)$ originating outside the conservative field is equal to the particle's increase in potential energy in that field.

Newton's third law of mechanics describes a common experience concerning forces: When two bodies exert forces on each other, the forces are equal in magnitude but opposed. A force imposed on a particle not in a field is continuously opposed by an inertial force of magnitude ma, as in (1.3). The externally applied force $F(x)$ in (1.8) is opposed by a force F_i of the field on the particle. In a very small motion in a conservative field, as in (1.8), the work done on the particle by the force $F(x)$ originating outside the field is $dw = F(x)\,dx = dV$. But by the third law of mechanics, $F_i = -F(x)$ so that

$$F_i = -\frac{dV}{dx} \tag{1.9}$$

If motion can occur along several coordinates instead of just along the x-axis, the component of force F_q exerted by the field on the particle along the q-axis is

$$F_q = -\frac{\partial V}{\partial q}$$

where V is some function of all coordinates of position.

The work done on a particle by a conservative field is, by (1.9),

$$w = \int_{x_1}^{x_2} F_i \, dx = -(V_2 - V_1) \tag{1.10}$$

This work is independent of the path because V depends only on position. In general, with no external forces acting, the work done by the field accelerates the particle so that by (1.6) and (1.7),

$$w = T_2 - T_1 \tag{1.11}$$

Because w depends only on position, (1.10) and (1.11) yield $T_2 - T_1 = -(V_2 - V_1)$, or

$$T_2 + V_2 = T_1 + V_1 \tag{1.12}$$

The quantity

$$E = T + V = \frac{mu^2}{2} + V \tag{1.13}$$

is called the *energy* of the particle. According to (1.12), E is constant for a particle anywhere in a conservative field when no nonconservative forces act from outside the field. This is the *law of conservation of energy*. It applies also to a whole system of particles in conservative fields, but not to individual particles of such a system if collisions occur.

1.3 ENERGY OF A PERFECT GAS

The kinetic theory of gases provides a mechanical model with average mechanical properties that are identified with macroscopic properties like pressure. In this model, a pure gaseous substance consists of an aggregation of myriads of minute identical particles called *molecules*. Further division of a molecule is not possible because it would lead to a chemical change of the gas. Repulsive forces, attractive forces tending toward such things as liquefaction or even chemical reaction, and forces due to gravitation or to electric or magnetic fields are assumed to be negligible. Because the molecules do not attract each other and because they repel each other only when in contact, the system is devoid of potential energy.

The molecules are conceived as almost point masses. Each may be so small as to lack rotational energy of its own, but collisions do occur. Each collision can be described by the use of classical mechanics, but here a detailed analysis of events for each molecule by use of the laws of conservation of energy and momentum for the several molecules involved in a collision is not necessary. The total energy E of the system of N molecules, each of mass m, is merely the sum of the average kinetic energies of all, namely,

$$E = N\left[\frac{1}{2}mu^2\right] \tag{1.14}$$

where u^2 is the average of the squares of the velocities of the molecules.

As it suffers continual changes of momentum by collision with other molecules, any individual molecule acquires energies and speeds ranging from zero to very large values. If followed for a sufficiently long time, any molecule exhibits an average velocity of zero, for movement is equally likely in any direction. The square of its velocity is, however, a scalar and always greater than zero; hence, the mean square velocity is greater than zero. If one molecule were followed for a sufficiently long time, its mean square velocity would approach u^2, the mean value for the system of N molecules. In other words, each molecule has an average energy that is equal to the average energy per molecule in the entire system.

The walls of the containing vessel are fixed and any molecule that collides with the wall rebounds with no loss of energy. The changes of momentum that occur at opposite walls will on the average cancel so that the vessel is not accelerated by the impulses. The swarm of molecules exerts a constant outward force on the walls because of the time rate of change of momentum at the walls. The average value of this rate of change of momentum per unit area is the force per unit area, or *pressure*, of the gas. Pressure is thus attributed to mechanical behavior.

Figure 1.1 is a planar section through the center of a spherical vessel of radius r. A molecule that collides with the wall of this vessel rebounds at an angle ϕ equal to its angle of approach. Moreover, since the sphere is symmetrical, one molecule in such a vessel will remain in the same plane, and this plane passes through the center of the sphere. The distance between collisions is $2r \cos \phi$. The time Δt between collisions of a molecule with speed u is $2r \cos \phi/u$.

The component of velocity along the perpendicular to the spherical surface is $u \cos \phi$. Since the component of momentum of a molecule of mass m is $-mu \cos \phi$ before collision, and afterward is $+mu \cos \phi$ because the component of velocity is reversed, the change in momentum Δp per collision is

$$\Delta p = +mu \cos \phi - (-mu \cos \phi) = 2mu \cos \phi$$

This change of momentum occurs on the average N times in a time Δt, for in that time each molecule averages one hit on the vessel wall. The rate of change

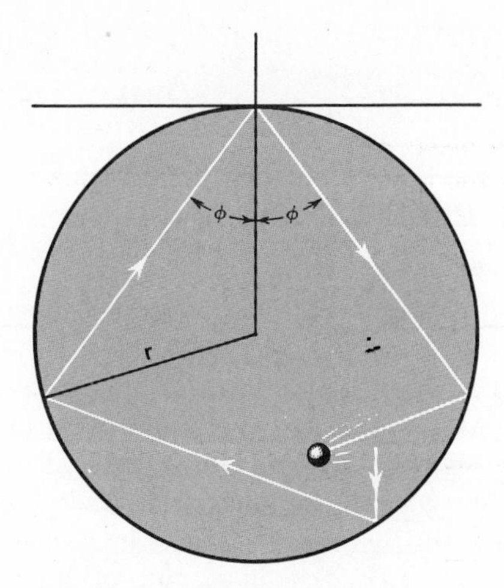

Figure 1.1. Particle in Sphere

of momentum at the walls is therefore

$$N\frac{\Delta p}{\Delta t} = N\frac{2mu\cos\phi}{2r\cos\phi/u} = \frac{Nmu^2}{r}$$

By (1.4), this is the total outward force exerted on the average by all N molecules. If collisions between molecules should prevent any one molecule from traversing a simple path along a chord, its momentum is in any event conserved, and thus ultimately reaches the wall and is there reflected. Since the force is exerted upon the area $4\pi r^2$ of the sphere, the force per unit area, or pressure P, is

$$P = \frac{Nmu^2/r}{4\pi r^2}$$

The volume V of the sphere is $(4/3)\pi r^3$; hence, it follows that

$$PV = \frac{1}{3}Nmu^2 \tag{1.15}$$

It is possible to relate the mechanical variables N, m, and u to the macroscopic quantities P and V in a similar way for a cubic vessel.

The total energy of this idealized gas is all kinetic energy. By (1.14) and (1.15) it is

$$E = N\left[\frac{1}{2}mu^2\right] = \frac{3}{2}\left[\frac{1}{3}Nmu^2\right]$$

$$E = \frac{3}{2}PV \tag{1.16}$$

The theory thus offers a mechanical model with average mechanical properties that are identified as familiar macroscopic properties.

1.4 EQUATION OF STATE OF PERFECT GAS

An *equation of state* is a mathematical relation among macroscopic properties of matter. The first equation of state was discovered in 1662 by Boyle. In one of many series of experiments, this one done in a stairwell, his apparatus was a U-tube with the shorter arm sealed. After adjusting the amount of air in the sealed arm so that the height of mercury in the U was the same in both arms, he or his assistant would pour more mercury into the long open arm and observe the length of the column of air trapped in the short, sealed arm. When the length (or volume) was halved, the difference in levels of mercury in the arms was equal to the height of mercury in a Torricellian barometer. Such a barometer is merely a long straight tube filled with mercury and set upright with its sealed end upwards and its open end still in the reservoir of Hg. The mercury level reaches a characteristic height if nothing besides Hg enters the erect tube. When the reservoir of trapped air in Boyle's bent tube was one-fourth the starting volume, the difference in mercury levels was three times the height in a nearby Torricellian barometer. He was able to show that outside air had pressure by pumping air out of glass containers in which he had placed partly or fully deflated lambs' bladders. Clearly, the total pressure of his trapped air was the sum of the pressure due to the atmosphere and that due to the difference in levels of the mercury. He concluded that air can be compressed and, under the experimental conditions of his laboratory, that the volume of a fixed amount of air is inversely proportional to its total pressure. He also verified this relation at pressures less than atmospheric.

Mathematically, if k_B is the proportionality constant found experimentally for a sample of air by Boyle or for many other gases by other experimenters after him, then Boyle's empirical finding is summarized mathematically as

$$PV = k_B \tag{1.17}$$

The curves of Figure 1.2 show how volume V depends on pressure P as k_B assumes various constant values. Two hundred years in anticipation of the kinetic theory of gases, Boyle had performed experiments on air at constant energy, as (1.16) states. His model of air, however, was a mass of fluffy wool.

Boyle's work depended on others' discovery of the barometer and invention of pumps. Modern gas pumps can generate pressure one thousand times his, and can decrease pressures to 10^{-10} atmospheres. Chemical reaction of any residual gases to produce solids can reduce pressures even lower. Nevertheless, the standard instrument for measuring very low pressures of gases still uses

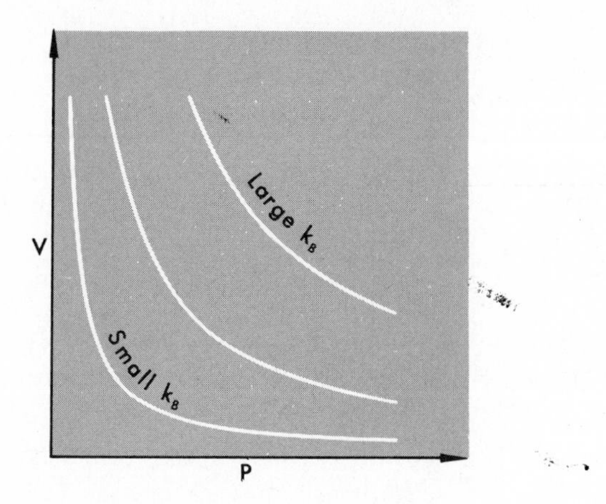

Figure 1.2. Boyle's Law: $PV = k_B$

Boyle's law. Figure 1.3 is an idealized diagram of such a device, called a McLeod gauge. In essence, it traps a fixed volume of gas at a low unknown pressure and compresses it to a measurable pressure and volume. The gauge is connected to a vacuum system at *C*. The gases in the vacuum system fill the gauge to a low pressure *p*. When stopcock *A* is opened, air forces the mercury in the reservoir at the bottom up into the gauge. Eventually the rising mercury traps a sample of the gases at pressure *p* in the vessel of known volume *V*. Air

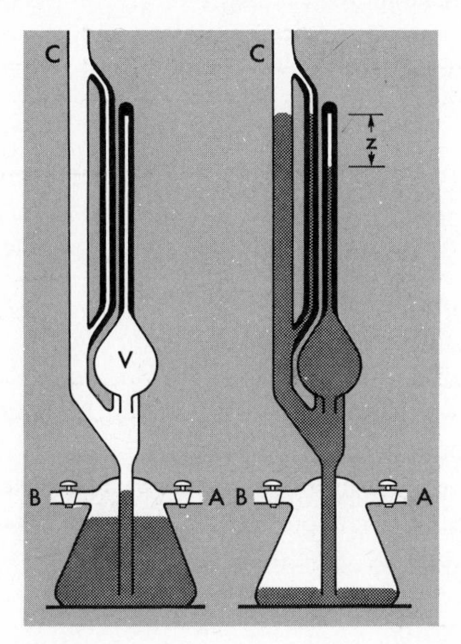

measures very low pressures of gases

Figure 1.3. McLeod Gauge: A Use of Boyle's Law

is admitted until the trapped gas is compressed into the sealed capillary tube above V. This sealed capillary and the open one to its left in Figure 1.3 are of the same bore so that any difference in levels of mercury in them is a direct measure of the difference in pressure between vacuum system and trapped sample. After observing the difference in heights of mercury, stopcock B, which leads to a rough vacuum, is opened to suck out the air and allow the mercury to drain again into the reservoir in anticipation of another measurement.

One way of calculating the low pressure p is to bring the level of mercury in the open capillary to the level of the flat inside end of the sealed capillary, as in the right of Figure 1.3. Then z, the difference in mercury levels, is the difference in pressures between trapped gas and vacuum system. At high vacuum, this is essentially the pressure P of the trapped gas; hence, $P = z$. The volume of trapped gas is $\pi r^2 z$, where r is the radius of the capillary tubing. Applied to the gas when trapped near the end of the capillary, Boyle's law is $P(\pi r^2 z) = \pi r^2 z^2 = k_B$. Applied to the same amount of gas at the moment it is trapped by the rising mercury, Boyle's law is $pV = k_B$; hence, the low pressure to be found is

$$p = \frac{\pi r^2 z^2}{V} \tag{1.18}$$

In practice, a calibrated scale of pressures p based on the constant value of $\pi r^2/V$ for the gauge is attached to the sealed capillary.

A second method of measurement brings the level of mercury in the sealed capillary to a standard level z_0. If z is again the difference in pressure between capillaries, Boyle's law for just trapped and compressed trapped gas reads $pV = z(\pi r^2 z_0)$; hence, on a scale attached to the open capillary, p is the linear function of z:

$$p = \left(\frac{\pi r^2 z_0}{V}\right) z \tag{1.19}$$

1.5 GAS TEMPERATURE SCALE

Boyle was well aware that the flame of a candle destroyed his inverse proportion, but the effects of a change in temperature on gas behavior were only qualitatively understood until more than a century after his discovery. Charles in 1787 and Gay-Lussac in 1802 examined the behavior of gases at constant pressure P. They found that, at constant pressure, the volume V of a fixed amount of gas at temperature τ is related to its volume V_0 at $\tau = 0$ by

$$V = V_0(1 + \alpha\tau) \tag{1.20}$$

In the elegant notation of the calculus, the coefficient of expansion is

$$\alpha = \lim_{\tau \to 0} \left(\frac{V - V_0}{V_0 \tau} \right) = \frac{1}{V} \left(\frac{\partial V}{\partial T} \right)_P \tag{1.21}$$

The subscript P is a reminder that pressure is constant, and temperature τ on the arbitrary scale is replaced by T on another scale of temperature with degrees of the same size. The remarkable thing about α is that it reaches a limiting value that is independent of the kind of gas and its pressure when gases are studied at lower and lower pressures. However, α depends on the temperature T. A choice of α is, then, tantamount to a choice of a scale of temperature in which any gas can be used to define temperature, provided the behavior of the gas can be established at the limit of very low pressures.

The value of α for hot gases is less than for cold gases on any arbitrary temperature scale in which gaseous volume increases with a rise in temperature at constant pressure. A very simple equation for use at constant pressure results if the perfect gas temperature T is set equal to the reciprocal of α, for then (1.21) becomes

$$\frac{1}{V} \left(\frac{\partial V}{\partial T} \right)_P = \frac{1}{T} \tag{1.22}$$

Thus, at constant pressure,

$$\frac{dV}{V} = \frac{dT}{T}$$

$$\ln V = \ln T + f(P)$$

$$\frac{V}{T} = \phi(P) \tag{1.23}$$

The perfect gas scale of temperature that results is such that at constant pressure the volume V of a fixed amount of gas is proportional to its temperature T.

Boyle's law has been verified very exactly for many gases at low pressure when the temperature and amount of gas are constant. Thus (1.17) for a fixed amount of gas is better written

$$PV = k_B(T) \tag{1.24}$$

This implies that the rate of expansion of a gas at constant temperature as its pressure changes is

$$\left(\frac{\partial V}{\partial P} \right)_T = -\frac{k_B(T)}{P^2} = -\frac{V}{P} \tag{1.25}$$

Its coefficient of expansion at constant temperature is thus

$$\kappa = -\frac{1}{V} \left(\frac{\partial V}{\partial P} \right)_T = \frac{1}{P} \tag{1.26}$$

The negative sign keeps κ positive, since V decreases as P increases at constant T.

In general, specifying the pressure and temperature of a fixed amount of a pure gas is sufficient to fix its volume; hence, $V = V(P, T)$. By the rules of calculus and (1.22) and (1.25), it follows that

$$dV = \left(\frac{\partial V}{\partial T}\right)_P dT + \left(\frac{\partial V}{\partial P}\right)_T dP = \frac{V}{T}dT - \frac{V}{P}dP$$

$$\frac{dV}{V} + \frac{dP}{P} = \frac{dT}{T}$$

$$\ln V + \ln P = \ln T + C$$

$$\frac{PV}{T} = e^c \qquad (1.27)$$

This result combines Boyle's law and Charles's law into one equation of state of a perfect gas. For at constant temperature, $PV = Te^c$ = constant; while at constant pressure, $V = (e^c/P)T$ as in (1.23). A comparison of (1.27) and (1.16) also requires that

$$T = PVe^{-c} = \left[\frac{2}{3}e^{-c}\right]E$$

That is, the temperature T of a perfect gas is proportional to the total kinetic energy E of its molecules.

At constant V, (1.27) requires that the perfect gas temperature be proportional to the pressure of a perfect gas. In fact, the ultimate experimental standard of temperature is the constant-volume gas thermometer containing hydrogen. In such a thermometer, H_2 is confined to a known volume. Actually, of course, the volume of the apparatus changes with temperature, but the materials and construction are chosen so that a correction for expansion of the apparatus is very small. The pressure of a fixed amount of H_2 is observed to be P_0 at a standard temperature T_0 and later at another temperature T its pressure is observed to be P. By (1.27) at constant V,

$$\frac{P_0}{T_0} = \frac{P}{T}$$

$$T = T_0\left(\frac{P}{P_0}\right) \qquad (1.28)$$

In this way, a measurement of two pressures allows a calculation of temperature T relative to some standard T_0.

The standard temperature is 273.1600°K. It is the temperature of a mixture of pure ice, pure liquid water, and pure gaseous water. This choice preserves a simple relation between the perfect gas scale T and the Celsius scale τ, where

0°C is the ice point ($T = 273.150$°K) and 100°C is the boiling point of water at one atmosphere pressure. For (1.20) requires

$$V = V_0(1 + \alpha\tau) = V_0\left(\frac{273.150 + \tau}{273.150}\right)$$

while (1.23) requires $V = \phi(P)T$. Hence, a temperature τ on the Celsius scale corresponds to a perfect gas temperature $T = 273.150 + \tau$.

Because a constant-volume hydrogen thermometer is awkward, many secondary temperatures have been established for use in calibrating more convenient thermometers. The three basic types of thermometer are mechanical (e.g., volume of mercury in glass or vapor pressure of He or H_2), electrical (e.g., electrical resistance or thermal EMF), and radiation (pyrometer). Table 1.1 lists some of the secondary standards of temperature established by the National Bureau of Standards. The primary fixed point is the triple-point of water at 0.01°C or 273.1600°K.

Table 1.1 Some Standards of Temperature at One Atmosphere (H. F. Stimson, *J. Res. Nat. Bur. Standards 65A*, 139 [1961]).

Description of system	Phases Present	Temperature	
		°C	°K
Boiling Point of Oxygen	Liquid and Vapor	−182.97	90.18
Melting Point of Mercury	Solid and Liquid	−38.87	234.28
Ice Point	Ice, Water, and Air	0.000	273.150
Transition of $Na_2SO_4 \cdot 10\,H_2O$	Two Solids and Liquid	32.38	305.53
Boiling Point of Water	Liquid and Vapor	100.00	373.15
Melting Point of Tin	Solid and Liquid	231.91	505.06
Melting Point of Zinc	Solid and Liquid	419.505	692.655
Boiling Point of Sulfur	Liquid and Vapor	444.6	717.8
Melting Point of Aluminum	Solid and Liquid	660.1	933.2
Melting Point of Silver	Solid and Liquid	960.8	1234.0
Melting Point of Gold	Solid and Liquid	1063.	1336.
Melting Point of Nickel	Solid and Liquid	1453.	1726.
Melting Point of Platinum	Solid and Liquid	1769.	2042.
Melting Point of Iridium	Solid and Liquid	2443.	2716.

1.6 MOLECULAR WEIGHT

With the synthesis of the unsymmetrical ethers R′OR″ by Williamson in the years following 1850, it became clear that the simple formula HO for water should be H_2O. However, if the smallest chemical combining weight of hydrogen is to be about unity, then the smallest relative weight of oxygen must be about 16 instead of the value of 8 that goes with the formula HO, for water is surely 89% by weight oxygen. Long before Williamson's critical experiment, Avogadro had suggested in 1811 a hypothesis that readily explains the law of combining volumes and at the same time calls for the adjustment of the weight of oxygen from 8 to 16. Avogadro proposed that equal volumes of gases at the same temperature and pressure contain equal numbers of molecules. Since this hypothesis required the formula H_2O, it was unpopular until Williamson's synthesis of the unsymmetrical ethers.

The reason for H_2O instead of HO, if Avogadro's hypothesis is true, is contained in the observations that support the law of combining volumes. Equal volumes of hydrogen and chlorine at the same temperature and pressure unite to yield two volumes of hydrogen chloride. No change in total volume occurs at constant P and T. According to Avogadro, this is the same as saying that one molecule of hydrogen (or one of chlorine) yields two molecules of hydrogen chloride. Since these molecules of hydrogen chloride are alike, each contains half as much hydrogen as one molecule of hydrogen. A molecule of chlorine, for like reasons, must also contain twice as much of the element chlorine as each molecule of hydrogen chloride. The fact that, at constant temperature and pressure, two volumes of hydrogen react with one of oxygen to yield two of water likewise requires that there be twice as much oxygen in each molecule of oxygen as there is in each molecule of water. What Avogadro really did was force a clear distinction between the idea of an atom, the smallest particle of an element to be unchanged during chemical reaction, and the idea of a molecule, the smallest independent unit in a gas. With Avogadro's interpretation, these two chemical reactions require an even number of atoms in each molecule of hydrogen, chlorine, and oxygen. Similar analysis of other reactions requires an even number of atoms in each molecule of nitrogen, bromine, and other elements. Moreover, all the gaseous reactions of these five elements are adequately explained by use of the smallest even number, two. Real proof that their molecules are diatomic has come through spectroscopic measurements that are described in later chapters.

If Avogadro's hypothesis had been accepted earlier than about 1860, much confusion about relative masses of molecules, formulas, and even valence theory would have been avoided. For example, the formula of ether would have been $C_2H_5OC_2H_5$ instead of C_2H_5O. Naturally, with the preparation of methyl ethyl ether, the old formula $C_{1.5}H_4O$ was unacceptable. Until 1960, diatomic oxygen gas with a relative mass of 32 was the standard of comparison for molecular weights. With the discovery of the natural occurrence of three stable isotopes of oxygen atom with relative masses of 16, 17, and 18 by Giauque and Johnston in 1929, two slightly differing scales of atomic weight were used. The natural mixture of isotopes of oxygen, though slightly variable in composition, was assigned a relative mass of 16.0000 by chemists. Physicists, on the other hand, chose the isotope ${}^{16}_{8}O$ as their reference because relative and even absolute masses of atoms can be determined very exactly by mass spectroscopy (Section 14.16). In order to have just one scale of atomic weights with a minimum of change and the full accuracy available through use of mass spectrometric data on isotopic masses and abundances, all scientists agreed in 1960 to let the isotope $^{12}_{6}C$ be exactly 12. On this scale, the atomic weight of oxygen with its usual mixture of isotopes is 15.9994 ± 0.0001, while that of carbon is 12.01115 ± 0.00005.

The differences in these modern scales of atomic weight are seldom of importance in determining relative masses of molecules by Avogadro's hypothesis, now accepted as a law. The reason is that observations on gases can seldom be done with the accuracy of these scales. There are experimental difficulties in weighing large volumes exactly and the gases themselves do not follow the perfect gas law (1.27) exactly. In a way, these handicaps are a blessing, for gaseous $^{12}_{6}C$ is an impractical standard. Naturally occurring carbon contains $^{13}_{6}C$ and $^{14}_{6}C$; carbon vapor contains C, C_2, C_3, and other species; the vapor pressure of carbon is far too low at convenient temperatures. Although readily available gaseous O_2 undoubtedly has a preferred status from history, the interdependence of the best values of the physical constants has become so involved that any pure gas of known molecular weight is acceptable as a standard of comparison.

Table 1.2 Specific Volumes of He at 300.00°K at Various Pressures (D. B. Mann, NBS Technical Note 154, Washington D. C. [1962]).

Pressure (atm)	Specific Volume ($cm^3\ g^{-1}$)	PV (cm^3 atm g^{-1})	ΔPV
0.50000	12303.71	6151.86	
			1.84
1.00000	6153.70	6153.70	
			3.68
2.00000	3078.69	6157.38	
			3.69
3.00000	2053.69	6161.07	
			3.69
4.00000	1541.19	6164.76	
			3.69
5.00000	1233.69	6168.45	

Table 1.2 lists volumes of one gram of He at pressures from 0.5 to 5.0 atm at 300.00°K. These values were calculated by the National Bureau of Standards with the aid of an excellent equation of state and many observations on gaseous He. As expected, Boyle's law is not exact for this real gas. The limiting value of PV at zero pressure, where intermolecular forces are absent, is $6151.86 - 1.84 = 6150.02$ cm³ per gram. Since the atomic and molecular weights of He are 4.0026, the volume of one gram-mole of He, if it were a perfect gas at one atm, would be $4.0026 \times 6150.02 = 24616.1$ cm³. At the ice point (0.000°C), where ice and water exist together at equilibrium with air at one atmosphere, (1.23) predicts a volume

$$V_0 = 24616.1\frac{(273.15)}{(300.00)} = 22413.0 \text{ cm}^3$$

This is the volume of 4.0026 grams of He, if it were a perfect gas at one atm at 0.000°C. With Avogadro's law, it is the volume of one gram-mole of any perfect gas at 0.000°C at one atm. The value of V_0 that best fits all related exact measurements is 22413.6 cm³ mole⁻¹.

The most direct way to observe the molecular weight of a vaporizable substance is to compare the mass of it to the mass of a standard like He or O_2. *Avogadro's law* says that at the same temperature and pressure equal volumes of all gases contain the same number of molecules. Comparing masses of equal volumes at the same T and P is the same as comparing masses of individual molecules, provided both gases are pure. If the observations of volume and mass are made at different T and P, the perfect gas law (1.27) allows one volume to be corrected to the volume it might have had at the other T and P. This correction and similar gas problems are most readily done by the perfect gas law in the form

$$PV = nRT \tag{1.29}$$

Since the volume of a gas at fixed P and T is proportional to the amount of matter in it, the symbol n for the number of gram-moles is added to (1.27). The value of the universal gas constant is then

$$\begin{aligned} R &= \frac{P\left(\frac{V}{n}\right)}{T} = \left(\frac{(1.00000 \text{ atm})\ 22413.6 \text{ cm}^3 \text{ mole}^{-1}}{273.150°\text{K}}\right) \\ &= 82.055 \text{ cm}^3 \text{ atm deg}^{-1} \text{ mole}^{-1} \end{aligned} \tag{1.30}$$

There are several methods of determining the molecular weight M of a substance that can be vaporized. The most direct method is to weigh the amount g of gas in a vessel of volume V at a pressure P and temperature T. Since the effects of the buoyancy of air and adsorption of gases like water on the surfaces of large vessels are noticeable, it is common to use an identical glass vessel as tare to minimize such possible errors. Since the molecular weight M is the mass g of gas per mole, it follows from (1.29) that

$$M = \frac{g}{n} = \frac{gRT}{PV} \tag{1.31}$$

The accuracy of M depends on how perfectly the gas behaves.

Example 1.1. With data from Table 1.2, calculate the apparent molecular weight of helium at 5.00000 atm at 300.00°K.

By (1.31), the molecular weight of He seems to be

$$\begin{aligned} M &= \frac{1.00000 \times 82.055 \times 300.00}{5.00000 \times 1233.69} \\ &= 3.9907 \text{ g/mole} \end{aligned}$$

Very exact values of M can be found by determining the value of the function (g/PV) at various pressures at a constant temperature T. At low pressures and constant T, (g/PV) or (ρ/P) is a linear function of pressure P. This slight dependence on P represents a first-order correction to a function that in zero approximation would be independent of P. Extrapolation from finite low pressures to zero pressure by a straight line as in Figure 1.4 yields a value of (g/PV) or ρ/P at zero pressure where intermolecular forces are nil and all gases are perfect. Then, since R applies to ideal behavior,

$$M = RT \lim_{P \to 0} \left(\frac{g}{PV} \right) \tag{1.32}$$

A similar extrapolation was done in Table 1.2 for He.

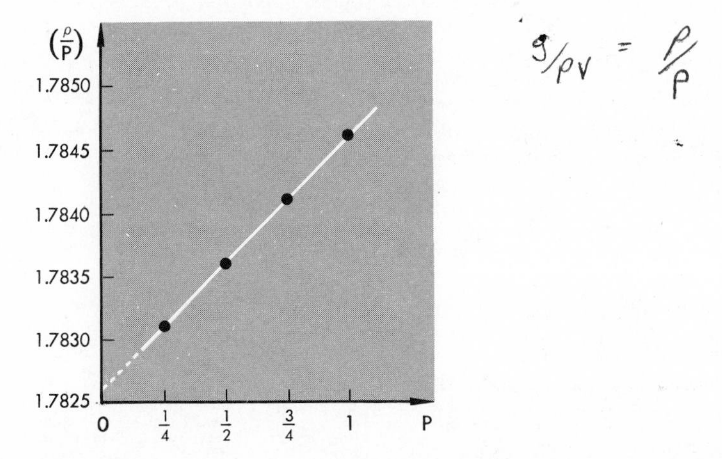

Figure 1.4. Density of Argon as a Function of Pressure at 0.000°C

Example 1.2. At 0.00°C, the limit of (g/PV) at zero pressure for argon is, from Figure 1.4, 1.7826×10^{-3} g cm^{-3} atm^{-1}. What is the molecular weight of argon?

By (1.30) and (1.32), the molecular weight is

$$\begin{aligned} M &= 82.055 \times 273.15 \times 1.7826 \times 10^{-3} \\ &= 39.954 \text{ g mole}^{-1} \end{aligned}$$

If each molecule contains one atom, M is also the atomic weight. Appendix B lists 39.948.

The vapor density of a substance that is liquid or solid at ordinary temperatures and pressures yields in a similar way a molecular weight of the substance as it exists in the gaseous state. In fact, molecular weights are defined only for the gaseous state; their use for condensed states involves a gratuitous assumption about the nature of the liquid or solid. A direct way of measuring vapor density is to add the condensed substance to a rigid weighed vessel with a narrow neck, immerse all but the narrow neck in a thermostat at a temperature high enough that the substance vaporizes at room pressure. If enough of the condensed material has been added at the start, the vessel will have been swept clean of air upon complete vaporization of the substance. When no more condensed material remains, the vessel is sealed off at the known laboratory pressure P and known thermostat temperature T. Weighing the cooled sealed vessel and subsequent calibration of its volume by weighing it empty and filled with water yield g and V on the right of (1.31).

Example 1.3. A 200 ml Dumas bulb was evacuated and sealed; its weight was 40.374 grams. Its narrow tip was broken off and included in subsequent weighings. A few ml of liquid ethyl acetate were sucked into the heated bulb as it cooled with the narrow neck into the liquid. After boiling at 99.6°C at 749.2 mm Hg until the last of the liquid vaporized, the bulb was again sealed. After cooling, it weighed 40.949 g. When it was opened and filled with water, the filled bulb and two tips weighed 241.7 g at 23°C, where the density of water is 0.9978 g cm^{-3}. What is the molecular weight of ethyl acetate?

The weight of the water was 241.7 − 40.4 = 201.3 g; hence, the volume of the bulb was 201.3/0.9978 = 201.7 cm^3. The weight of the ethyl acetate was 40.949 − 40.374 = 0.575 grams. By (1.31), the molecular weight is

$$M = \frac{gRT}{PV} = \frac{0.575 \times 82.05 \times 372.8}{(749.2/760.0) \times 201.7} = 88.6$$

To understand why R works, it is instructive to reason as follows: At 0°C at one atm, without condensation, the gas volume would have become

$$V = 201.7 \times \frac{273.15}{372.8} \times \frac{749.2}{760.0} = 145.7 \text{ cm}^3$$

If the size of the experiment were increased until this volume became 22413 cm^3, the amount of ethyl acetate would be

$$M = 0.575 \frac{(22413)}{(145.7)} = 88.6$$

The reason that R works is that the second calculation uses numbers that were incorporated into R, for in that calculation

$$\begin{aligned} M &= 0.575 \times \frac{22413}{201.7 \times \frac{273.15}{372.8} \times \frac{749.2}{760.0}} \\ &= \frac{0.575 \times 372.8}{749.2/760.0 \times 201.7} \frac{(22413 \times 1)}{(273.15)} \\ &= \frac{gT}{PV}(R) \end{aligned}$$

The Victor Meyer Method of estimating the molecular weight of a volatile liquid or solid is somewhat less direct than the Dumas method. Figure 1.5 is a

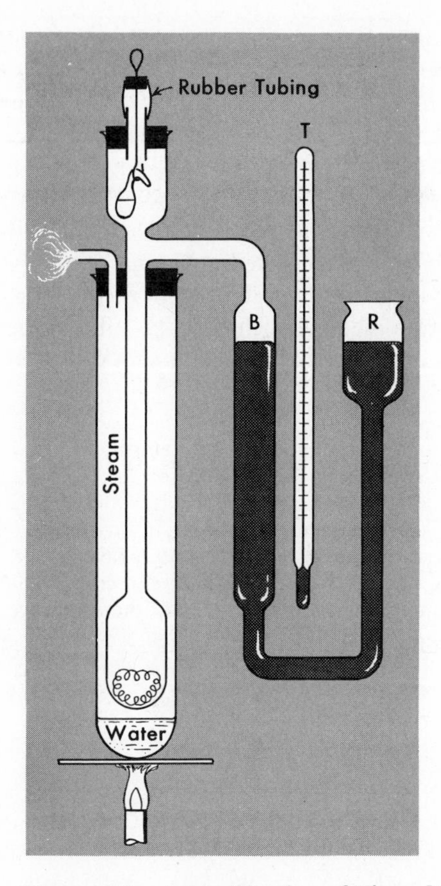

Figure 1.5. A Modification of Victor Meyer Apparatus

schematic diagram of one of many modifications of the apparatus. A jacket containing steam provides a thermostat at about 100°C. A small sealed vial containing about 0.002 mole of liquid weighed accurately as liquid (and thus not subject to noticeable correction for the buoyancy of air) is suspended in the cool zone of the closed constant-volume system. When a stationary state is achieved in which part of the closed system is at about 100°C and the remainder is at room temperature, the mercury levels in gas burette *B* and reservoir *R* are leveled and the reading on the burette is recorded. The barometric pressure of the laboratory, which now is also the pressure within the closed system, is also recorded. The hook on which the sealed vial is hung can be moved vertically into the tube above without admitting air to the system by stretching the rubber joint at the top. Such a vertical movement jams the vial into the tube and breaks it. The opened bulb falls into glass wool in the hot zone and the liquid vaporizes slowly as the vial warms. Warm air, displaced into the cool zone, cools to the temperature of the cool air that it forces ahead into the gas burette. After complete vaporization and before the condensible vapors have diffused out of the hot zone, the reading of the gas burette is once again recorded with leveled mercury levels. The barometric pressure in the laborarory is again recorded. If the pressure has not changed, the increase in volume at the cool end of the sealed system is less than the volume of hot vapor in the hot end. However, if, like the displaced air, that new hot vapor could have been cooled without condensation, as the displaced air in the system was in fact cooled, then that new hot vapor would have occupied the volume change noted at the gas burette. The temperature of the thermostat should exceed the boiling point of the liquid by about 20°C to minimize deviation from ideal gas behavior, and the molecular weight found by this method is that characteristic of the liquid's vapors at the temperature of the thermostat.

Example 1.4. A Victor Meyer glass vial weighed 5.014 g empty. Filled with a pure saturated organic liquid containing only carbon, fluorine, and chlorine, the sealed vial weighed 5.284 g. The vial was broken in a vessel jacketed by steam at 99.8°C. The initial mercury level in the gas burette was 10.46 ml, and the final level was 46.22 ml. The barometric pressure was constant at 754.6 mm Hg, and the temperature of the laboratory was 23.2°C. If the compound contained 57% by weight chlorine, determine its molecular formula and exact molecular weight.

The increase in volume in the cool part of the closed system was $V = 46.22 - 10.46 = 35.76$ ml. The amount of liquid vaporized was $g = 5.284 - 5.014 = 0.270$ g. The approximate molecular weight is, then,

$$M = \frac{gRT}{PV} = \frac{0.270 \times 82.05 \times 296.4}{(754.6/760.0) \times 35.76} = 185$$

The general formula of a saturated compound of this sort is $C_n\,F_x\,Cl_y$, where $x + y = 2n + 2$. But since 57% of it is chlorine, which has an atomic weight of 35.5,

$$y \approx \frac{0.57 \times 185}{35.5} = 2.97 \approx 3$$

Hence, $x = 2n - 1$ and $M = 12n + 19x + 35.5 \times 3$. These two equations yield $x = 3$ and $n = 2$. The molecular formula is, therefore, $C_2\,F_3\,Cl_3$ and its exact molecular weight (see Appendix B) is

$$M = 12.01115 \times 2 + 18.9984 \times 3 + 35.453 \times 3 = 187.376$$

1.7 MOLECULAR VELOCITY

Bernoulli in 1738 was the first to show that the square of the velocity of particles in a system of many particles is proportional to its pressure. An actual value for the root mean square velocity u can be found from (1.15) and (1.29). As they apply to one gram-mole of gas, the molecular weight M is Nm and n is unity.

so that PV equals $\frac{Mu^2}{3} = RT$, or

$$u = \left(\frac{3RT}{M}\right)^{1/2} \tag{1.33}$$

This velocity differs from zero because it is really the square root of the average value of the square of the velocity. The average value of the velocity itself is zero since movement of a gas molecule is equally likely and equally large in all directions.

The value of R in (1.30) is appropriate for the usual P-V-T gas problems, but in (1.33) it yields a velocity with strange dimensions. Because of (1.16) and (1.29), which state that $nRT = PV = (2/3)E$, the dimensions of RT are clearly energy per mole; the definition of R in (1.29) readily yields several values of R when P is expressed on a force per unit area. By definition, one *standard atmosphere* is 1013250 dynes cm^{-2}; hence, since a dyne-cm is an erg,

$$R = P\frac{\left(\frac{V}{n}\right)}{T} = \frac{(1013250 \text{ dynes cm}^{-2})(22413.6 \text{ cm}^3 \text{ mole}^{-1})}{(273.150 \text{ deg})}$$

$$= 8.3143 \times 10^7 \text{ ergs mole}^{-1} \text{ deg}^{-1} \tag{1.34}$$

Since a joule is 10^7 ergs, it follows at once that

$$R = 8.3143 \text{ joules mole}^{-1} \text{ deg}^{-1} \tag{1.35}$$

Furthermore, one *thermodynamic calorie* is defined as 4.1840 joules; so that

$$R = 8.3143 \text{ joules mole}^{-1} \text{ deg}^{-1} \left(\frac{1.00000 \text{ cal}}{4.1840 \text{ joules}}\right)$$

$$= 1.9872 \text{ cal mole}^{-1} \text{ deg}^{-1} \tag{1.36}$$

These values of R are listed in Appendix A.

With R expressed in cgs units as in (1.34), u in (1.33) is given in cgs units of speed, cm sec^{-1}. The reason for this is that kinetic energy (ergs) has dimensions grams $(\text{cm sec}^{-1})^2$ so that (1.33) is dimensionally

$$u = \left(\frac{(\text{ergs mole}^{-1} \text{ deg}^{-1})(\text{deg})}{(\text{grams mole}^{-1})}\right)^{1/2} = \left(\frac{\text{ergs}}{\text{grams}}\right)^{1/2} = \frac{\text{cm}}{\text{sec}}$$

Example 1.5. Calculate and tabulate the root mean square velocities of H_2, N_2, and SF_6 at 0°C and 100°C.

The molecular weights M of these species are 2.016, 28.01, and 146.1. By (1.33) and (1.34) at 0°C, u for N_2 is

$$u = \left(\frac{3 \times 8.314 \times 10^7 \times 273.2}{28.01}\right)^{1/2} = 4.93 \times 10^4 \text{ cm sec}^{-1}$$

At 100°C, u for H_2 is

$$u = \left(\frac{3 \times 8.314 \times 10^7 \times 373.2}{2.016}\right)^{1/2} = 21.49 \times 10^4 \text{ cm sec}^{-1}$$

The table summarizes the six values:

Substance	M	Root Mean Square Velocity (cm sec^{-1} × 10^{-4})	
		$T = 273.2°K$	$T = 373.2°K$
H_2	2.016	18.38	21.49
N_2	28.02	4.93	5.76
SF_6	146.1	2.16	2.52

Even if all molecules of a given sample of a pure gas had velocities exactly equal in absolute magnitude, but differing in direction so that the gas as a whole would not move or behave nonistropically, this extraordinary state would soon be modified by collisions. In a head-on collision, in which the motion of two molecules is along the line between their centers at impact, there is an interchange of velocities if the masses of the two are equal and if the collision is elastic. In an elastic collision, no kinetic energy of translation is transformed into another kind of energy, such as rotation or intramolecular vibration. For example, if a spherical molecule collides head-on and elastically with another at rest, the moving one comes to rest and the struck one moves off with the velocity of the first. As viewed from one of these identical molecules, the process is like bouncing a ball on a fixed surface of infinite inertia. As viewed from a system of coordinates moving with half the velocity of the moving spherical molecule, this process would be a head-on collision of two identical molecules each moving at half speed toward each other. After impact, they separate at the same rate but in the directions from which they first approached the impact.

When trajectories lie in the same plane, similar statements apply to components of velocity. An example is provided in the collision of two identical spherical molecules, each with the same kinetic energy; from this collision, one retires with all their kinetic energy to leave the other at rest. This extreme can occur when a molecule collides elastically with another that is proceeding in the same plane at right angles to its path. If their trajectories are in the same plane and if the collision occurs at the very instant that the center of the second sphere lies along the projected trajectory of the first sphere, the first will stop and the second will possess not only its own original velocity, but it will have gained all the velocity of the first. These two equal perpendicular velocity components act as vectors, and the second molecule proceeds at a 45° angle with a speed $\sqrt{2}$ times that of either molecule before impact. In this collision, linear momentum and kinetic energy are conserved, and the first molecule is stopped while the kinetic energy of the other is doubled. Other types of collision are expected to transfer less energy. Thus, a system of molecules with uniform velocities rapidly achieves a range of velocities from zero to large values that might rarely result from several reinforcing glancing blows.

The reason that the derivation leading to the result

$$\frac{3}{2}PV = E = N\left(\frac{1}{2}mu^2\right)$$

is correct is that the root mean square speed u is the value that gives the actual average kinetic energy of one molecule. In some of the discussions of gaseous behavior that follow, it is necessary to determine averages other than average kinetic energy in systems with molecules of all speeds. The mathematics of finding these averages is sometimes complex; hence, it seems sufficient here to use the root mean square velocity u to establish the general nature of the effect of interest, and then state the exact result that would be found by a proper averaging procedure. The differences in the results are negligible. In fact, some of the calculations involve parameters, like the size of a molecule, that are customarily adjusted to make the rigorously derived results match observation.

1.8 MEAN FREE PATH

If molecules of a gas were really rigid spheres without potential energy, each collision would be a well-defined event. It would take no time to occur because such molecules are either in contact or not. It would, therefore, be impossible for three molecules to collide at once. This extreme view of a collision is, of course, unreal, because molecules really exert their influence with varying intensity over moderate distances. Assigning a definite size to a molecule is thus an arbitrary decision that may even be influenced by the kind of property to be described. Still, for the sake of some insight into molecular processes, an arbitrary molecular radius can be assigned and used without being trusted completely.

The *mean free path* of a molecule among many others is the average distance it moves between collisions. A collision of two molecules occurs when their centers come within a certain critical distance σ of each other. If the molecules are spheres, σ is the sum of their radii. No other molecule is present in the volume swept out by a molecule as it goes from one collision to the next along a path that, on the average, has length l, the mean free path. No other molecule comes within a distance σ of this straight-line trajectory of length l. That is, in the cylindrical volume $\pi\sigma^2 l$, there is an average of only one molecule. This volume is, of course, an average because the mean free path l is an average distance between collisions. If there are N molecules in a volume V, the average volume per molecule is, then,

$$\frac{V}{N} = \pi\sigma^2 l$$

When a proper average over all speeds and directions of motion is taken, the mean free path is found to be

$$l = \frac{V}{\sqrt{2}\, N\pi\sigma^2} \tag{1.37}$$

The factor $\sqrt{2}$ is of negligible importance because real molecules are not hard spheres of radius $\sigma/2$, as supposed in deriving (1.37).

Many molecules will suffer a collision before going a distance l, and some few will go much farther than l without collision. Out of a flight of N molecules, the number that meet another molecule in a short distance dx is proportional to that distance dx and to the number N that are watched. Mathematically, the number that collide is

$$-dN = kN dx \tag{1.38}$$

The negative sign on dN keeps the proportionality constant k positive, for dN is negative because there is a decrease in the number of molecules. The distance dx must be short, for the number N is continually decreasing as collisions occur. The proportionality constant k depends only on the obstacles in the path of the N molecules under study. In a uniform gas, k is then independent of N and x so that (1.38) can be integrated easily.

$$\int \frac{dN}{N} = -k \int dx$$

$$\ln N = -kx + C \tag{1.39}$$

If N_0 molecules started their flight at $x = 0$, then the integration constant C is $\ln N_0 + k(0)$ and (1.39) becomes

$$\ln N = -kx + \ln N_0$$

$$\ln N - \ln N_0 = \ln \frac{N}{N_0} = -kx$$

$$N = N_0 e^{-kx} \tag{1.40}$$

This same result can be obtained at once from (1.38) by definite integration with N_0 molecules at $x = 0$ and N molecules at x, for

$$\int_{N_0}^{N} \frac{dN'}{N'} = -k \int_0^x dx'$$

$$\ln \frac{N}{N_0} = -kx$$

$$N = N_0 e^{-kx} \tag{1.40}$$

Since k and x are positive, the number N that go a distance x without collision is less than N_0, as expected.

The proportionality constant k has the dimensions of a reciprocal length, if (1.38) and (1.40) are to be dimensionally correct equations. The relation k has to the mean free path can be found by calculating the average distance gone by N_0 molecules until they undergo a collision. By (1.40), the number that collide between x and $x + dx$ is $dN = N_0 e^{-kx}(-k)dx = -kNdx$, as in (1.38). Out of N_0 collisions that must ultimately occur between $x = 0$ and $x = \infty$, the number that occur between x and $x + dx$ is $kNdx$. That is, within an uncertainty of $(1/2)dx$, the distance x is reached $kNdx$ times by $kNdx$ molecules out of the flight of N_0. The average distance achieved in a set of five events would be

$$\bar{x} = \frac{x_1 + x_2 + x_3 + x_4 + x_5}{5}$$

If the distance x_1 were observed twice so that $x_1 = x_2$, the mean distance $\bar{x}$ would be

$$\bar{x} = \frac{2x_1 + x_3 + x_4 + x_5}{5}$$

Similarly, if a distance of about x is reached $kNdx$ times out of N_0 chances, the average value of x, which here is also the mean free path, is the sum

$$l = \frac{\int_0^\infty xkNdx}{N_0} = \int_0^\infty xke^{-kx}\,dx$$

$$= \frac{1}{k}\int_0^\infty (kx)e^{-kx}\,d(kx) = \frac{1}{k}\int_0^\infty ye^{-y}\,dy$$

Integration by parts yields

$$l = \frac{1}{k}[-ye^{-y}]_{y=0}^{y=\infty} + \frac{1}{k}\int_0^\infty e^{-y}\,dy = \frac{1}{k}[-e^{-y}]_{y=0}^{y=\infty}$$

$$l = \frac{1}{k} \tag{1.41}$$

The integral above may also be evaluated by use of the gamma functions, as explained in Appendix C. Here,

$$l = \frac{1}{k}\int_0^\infty ye^{-y}\,dy = \frac{1}{k}\Gamma(2) = \frac{1}{k}$$

Thus, (1.40) becomes

$$N = N_0 e^{-x/l} \tag{1.42}$$

where l is the mean free path. The number that travel a distance of one mean free path without a collision is, therefore, by (1.42) with $x = 1$,

$$N = N_0 e^{-1} = 0.36788 N_0$$

Only about one molecule in twenty goes three mean free paths without collision; one in one thousand goes almost seven mean free paths.

1.9 EFFUSION AND DIFFUSION

The mean free path of a system of molecules tells much about the distances through which single molecules are likely to move. With the root mean square velocity, it also tells much about the frequency of collisions. If a significant fraction of molecules can reach a vessel wall without collision, the wall may influence the properties of the gas. However, if the mean free path is small compared to the dimensions of the container, the effect of the walls will usually be negligible. The result of a small difference in concentration or temperature or the result of a massed motion of many molecules can be considered as a small disturbance of a gas at equilibrium when the walls are several collisions away.

If an imaginary plane of area $\mathscr{A}$ is inserted into a gas at equilibrium, the frequency of collisions on each side of the plane will be equal on the average, for the gas is the same on both sides. Moreover, at any instant, one-third of the molecules will be moving along the axis perpendicular to the plane. Of these, half will be moving toward the plane and half away. The average distance a molecule travels without collision to hit this plane is the mean free path l. Hence, the time it takes one-sixth of the molecules within the distance l of the plane to hit the plane on one side is approximately l/u, where u is their root mean square velocity. If there are c molecules per unit volume, then the total number of molecules in the volume $l\mathscr{A}$ is $cl\mathscr{A}$, and the number that hit one side of the plane of area $\mathscr{A}$ in the time l/u is $1/6\ cl\mathscr{A}$. In other words, the number of collisions per unit time on one side of the plane of area $\mathscr{A}$ is about $(1/6)cl\mathscr{A}(u/l) = (1/6)u\mathscr{A}c$. These molecules originate within a distance of about l.

If the imaginary plane of area $\mathscr{A}$ represents a hole with dimensions of the order of the mean free path, then the rate at which molecules leak or effuse one by one through the tiny hole is $(1/6)u\mathscr{A}c$. Rates of effusion of different gases can be compared at constant concentration by holding pressure and temperature of the gas constant. The effective value of $\mathscr{A}$ can be fixed for several gases by using one piece of apparatus for all. Under these conditions, the ratio of effusion rates v_1 and v_2 for two gases is, by (1.33),

$$\frac{v_1}{v_2} = \frac{\left(\frac{1}{6}\right)u_1\mathscr{A}c}{\left(\frac{1}{6}\right)u_2\mathscr{A}c} = \frac{u_1}{u_2} = \left(\frac{M_2}{M_1}\right)^{1/2} \tag{1.43}$$

At a constant number of molecules per unit volume, (1.43) is equivalent to saying that the rates are inversely proportional to gas density, a fact first discovered by Graham in 1829. Graham's law finds use in the separation of isotopes, such as in the separation of $^{235}UF_6$ from the slower $^{238}UF_6$, and as a possible means of recovering He from hydrocarbon gases in which it occurs.

Example 1.6. Calculate the relative rates of effusion of $^{235}UF_6$ and $^{238}UF_6$ and of $^{12}CH_4$ and ^4He.

By (1.43), for UF_6,

$$\frac{v_1}{v_2} = \left(\frac{238 + 6(19)}{235 + 6(19)}\right)^{1/2} = \left(\frac{352}{349}\right)^{1/2} = 1.0043$$

and for CH_4 and He,

$$\frac{v_1}{v_2} = \left(\frac{12 + 4}{4}\right)^{1/2} = \left(\frac{16}{4}\right)^{1/2} = 2.00$$

In both, the less massive molecules diffuse faster.

Example 1.7. At what temperature will argon ($M = 40$) at one atm effuse through a certain orifice at the same rate (moles sec^{-1}) as He ($M = 4.0$) at 0.100 atm at 300°K?

Equal rates of effusion require that $(1/6)\, u_1 \mathscr{A} c_1 = (1/6) u_2 \mathscr{A} c_2$, where $\mathscr{A}$ is the same for both because the same orifice is used. The condition $u_1 c_1 = u_2 c_2$, with the use of (1.29) and (1.33), is

$$\left(\frac{3RT_1}{M_1}\right)^{1/2}\left(\frac{P_1}{RT_1}\right) = \left(\frac{3RT_2}{T_2}\right)^{1/2}\left(\frac{P_2}{RT_2}\right)$$

$$T_2 = T_1\left(\frac{M_1 P_2^2}{M_2 P_1^2}\right)$$

The temperature of the argon must therefore be

$$T_2 = 300\left(\frac{4.0 \times 1.00^2}{40 \times 0.100^2}\right) = 3000°\mathrm{K}$$

The preceding discussion on *effusion*, wherein molecules leak out of a vessel one by one, leads naturally to *diffusion*, wherein molecules mix by interpenetration. A difference in concentration on each side of the imaginary plane at z_0 in Figure 1.6 would lead to a net transfer of molecules across that plane. If c_1 is the concentration at plane z_1, which is a distance l below plane z_0, the rate at which molecules move upward across plane z_0 is $(1/6)u\mathscr{A}c_1$. Similarly, if c_2 is the concentration at plane z_2, a distance l above plane z_0, then the rate at which molecules move downward across plane z_0 is $(1/6)u\mathscr{A}c_2$. The net number of molecules passing upward through plane z_0 per unit time is, therefore,

$$\frac{dN}{dt} = \frac{1}{6}u\mathscr{A}(c_1 - c_2) \tag{1.44}$$

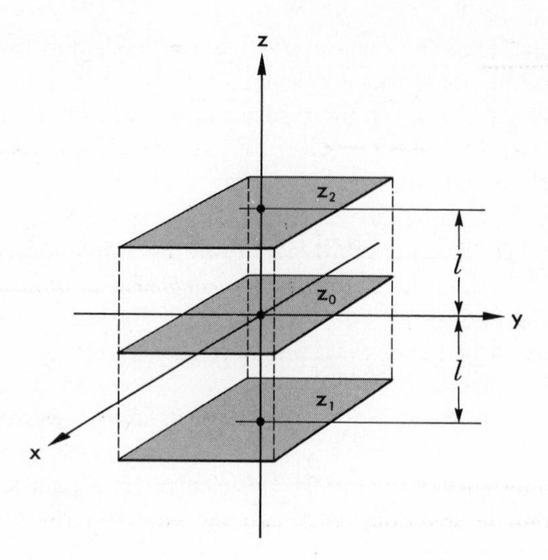

Figure 1.6. Transport of Molecules, Momentum, and Energy from z_1 to z_2

The difference in concentration is assumed to be so small that no other equilibrium properties of the gas are affected noticeably. Moreover, the concentrations at z_1 and z_2 are then given with sufficient accuracy by

$$c_i = c_0 + (z_i - z_0)\left(\frac{dc}{dz}\right)_0 \tag{1.45}$$

where c_0 is the concentration at plane z_0. The right side of (1.45) is just the first part of a Taylor's series expansion. When z_i approaches z_0, (1.45) is almost a tautology, for then

$$\lim_{z_i \to z_0} \frac{c_i - c_0}{z_i - z_0} = \lim_{\Delta z \to 0} \frac{\Delta c}{\Delta z} = \left(\frac{dc}{dz}\right)_0$$

The derivative in (1.45) is called the *gradient* of the concentration; it offers a first-order correction to c_0. There is no change in concentration in the z-direction when this gradient is zero.

Substitution of c_2 and c_1 from (1.45) into (1.44) yields

$$\frac{dN}{dt} = \frac{1}{6} u\mathscr{A}[(z_1 - z_0) - (z_2 - z_0)]\left(\frac{dc}{dz}\right)_0$$

Since $z_2 - z_1 = 2l$, this is

$$\frac{dN}{dt} = -\frac{1}{3} ul\mathscr{A}\left(\frac{dc}{dz}\right)_0 \tag{1.46}$$

The coefficient of $\mathscr{A}$ and the gradient in (1.46) is $\mathscr{D}$, the *coefficient of self-diffusion*, in Fick's *first law of diffusion*

$$\frac{dN}{dt} = -\mathscr{D}\mathscr{A}\left(\frac{dc}{dz}\right)_0 \tag{1.47}$$

This law can be used without a knowledge of the mass of single molecules, if N is a mass and c is a mass per unit volume. Diffusion of one gas into another is also described by (1.46), but then $\mathscr{D}$ is called simply the *coefficient of diffusion*, and its value depends upon the natures of both gases. For pure gases of molecular weight about 30 at one atmosphere pressure at room temperature, $\mathscr{D}$ is of the order of 0.2 $cm^2\ sec^{-1}$. Two approximate ways of determining $\mathscr{D}$ of a pure gas are to follow the movement of isotopically labeled molecules or of molecules that differ chemically but are similar in molecular weight and size. Examples of the latter are homologues of high molecular weight, or N_2 and CO. When gases differ, $\mathscr{D}$ for a pair is generally more like the self-diffusion coefficient of the more rapidly diffusing one.

Comparison of (1.46) and (1.47) yields, of course,

$$\mathscr{D} = \frac{1}{3}ul \tag{1.48}$$

A proper average of speeds and angles gives, however, for rigid spheres,

$$\mathscr{D} = \frac{\sqrt{6\pi}}{8}ul = 0.543\ ul \tag{1.49}$$

where u and l are given by (1.33) and (1.37).

Example 1.8. A self-diffusion coefficient of 0.200 $cm^2\ sec^{-1}$ at 300°K for a gas of molecular weight 30 implies what mean free path?

By (1.33), the root mean square velocity is

$$u = \left(\frac{3 \times 8.314 \times 10^7 \times 300}{30}\right)^{1/2} = 5.00 \times 10^4\ \text{cm sec}^{-1}$$

From (1.49), the mean free path l is then

$$l = \frac{8\mathscr{D}}{u\sqrt{6\pi}} = \frac{8 \times 0.200}{5.00 \times 10^4\sqrt{6\pi}} = 7.37 \times 10^{-6}\ \text{cm}$$

1.10 VISCOSITY

Diffusion is one of the basic gaseous properties that depend on the transport of matter. Diffusion itself deals with the transport of molecules. Viscosity, another transport property, deals with the steady-state transfer of momentum between adjacent layers moving at different speeds. If the flow can be described as movement of layers that are parallel to each other, the flow is called *laminar*. Viscosity is a measure of the force required to maintain the flow, and thus is a measure of a fluid's steady resistance to steady flow. The force F required to maintain a difference in velocity dv between layers of area $\mathscr{A}$ separated from each other by a distance dz is

$$F = -\eta \mathscr{A} \frac{dv}{dz} \tag{1.50}$$

This equation is of the same form as Fick's first law (1.47). The proportionality constant η is the coefficient of viscosity. In the cgs system, when F is measured in dynes, $\mathscr{A}$ in cm^2, and the gradient of velocity in sec^{-1}, the units of η are gram cm^{-1} sec^{-1}, or poises.

Figure 1.6 again describes the transport phenomenon; the parallel layers at z_1, z_0, and z_2 represent swarms of molecules moving together parallel to the x-y plane. In addition to its momentum due to random motion in any direction, each molecule has an average momentum mv in a steady state of laminar flow at speed v. In the layer represented by the plane at z_0, this additional average momentum associated with macroscopic flow perpendicular to the z-axis is mv_0 per molecule. At the layer z_i the flow momentum has the same direction as in the z_0 layer, but its magnitude is

$$mv_i = mv_0 + (z_i - z_0)\left(\frac{d(mv)}{dz}\right)_0 \tag{1.51}$$

because the layer at z_i moves at a speed v_i.

In addition to the parallel flow velocities v_i and v_0, the molecules possess the usual randomly oriented velocities characteristic of a gas at equilibrium. Because these random movements can transfer a molecule along the z-axis from layer to layer, there is on the average an exchange of momentum among neighboring levels whenever a molecule moves from layer to layer. It is like the change of momentum that would occur if helmsmen of racing shells were to play catch as they pass. When the distance $z_2 - z_0$ is l, the average rate at which molecules cross the z_0 plane from above is about $\frac{1}{6}u\mathscr{A}c_2$, as in the previous section. The rate at which they carry their flow momentum down across the z_0 plane is, therefore, $\frac{1}{6}u\mathscr{A}c_2mv_2$, where mv_2 is the flow momentum of one typical molecule in layer z_2. The rate at which molecules from the z_1 layer carry flow momentum upwards across the z_0 plane is, similarly, $\frac{1}{6}u\mathscr{A}c_1mv_1$. The net rate at which momentum crosses the plane at z_0 from the z_2 layer to the z_1 layer is thus $\frac{1}{6}u\mathscr{A}m(c_2v_2 - c_1v_1)$. All properties except flow velocity are supposed to be uniform in this treatment so that $c_2 = c = c_1$. Hence, with $2l = z_2 - z_1$ in (1.51), the viscous force that maintains the rate of transport of momentum across the area $\mathscr{A}$ at z_0 is

$$\begin{aligned} F &= -\frac{1}{6}u\mathscr{A}c(mv_2 - mv_1) \\ &= -\frac{1}{6}u\mathscr{A}c(z_2 - z_1)\left(\frac{d(mv)}{dz}\right)_0 \\ &= -\frac{1}{3}uclm\mathscr{A}\left(\frac{dv}{dz}\right)_0 \end{aligned} \tag{1.52}$$

Comparison of (1.50) and (1.52) gives for the coefficient of viscosity

$$\eta = \frac{1}{3}uclm \tag{1.53}$$

As usual, u is the root mean square velocity of (1.33), c is the number of molecules per unit volume, l is the mean free path, and m is the mass of one molecule. Care for the distribution of speeds of molecules in their random motion and account of the various angles at which molecules cross the plane at z_0 gives

$$\eta = \frac{5}{8}\left(\frac{\pi}{6}\right)^{1/2} uclm = 0.452uclm \tag{1.54}$$

where l is given by (1.37).

The theoretical result (1.53) or (1.54) for η was found by Maxwell in 1860. It had two important effects. It offered an unexpected experimental test of the kinetic theory of gases and it gave the first indication of the size of gas molecules and the number of them in one gram-mole. If there are N molecules in a volume V, their concentration is $c = N/V$ and (1.37) can be written $l = (\sqrt{2}\,\pi\sigma^2 c)^{-1}$. This result and (1.33) transform (1.53) into

$$\eta = \frac{1}{3}\left(\frac{3RT}{M}\right)^{1/2} \frac{m}{\sqrt{2}\,\pi\sigma^2} \tag{1.55}$$

If this result of the kinetic theory is reliable, it predicts for a gas with definite molecular weight M and molecules of definite size σ and mass m that its viscosity should increase with temperature. Completely at odds with everyday experience with liquids like water and molasses, the viscosities of which decrease as T rises, this amazing result was soon verified qualitatively for many gases. This experimental confirmation of a prediction of the kinetic theory was, of course, important in its infancy.

In 1865, a few years before the first periodic table, Loschmidt used gaseous viscosity to establish roughly the number of molecules in one cubic centimeter of gas at standard conditions (1 atm, 0°C). Nowadays, the same sort of calculation would be done for 22413.6 cm³ of gas, namely a gram-mole. This kind of estimate begins with the assumption that molecules are the same size in gases, liquids, and solids, and that in any condensed phase they are more or less close-packed. The volume of a gram-mole of a substance of density ρ and molecular weight M is M/ρ. If, as a gas or condensed phase, a gram-mole consists of N_0 molecules, each of volume $(4/3)\pi(\sigma/2)^3$, then the volume of a gram-mole of it when condensed is roughly

$$\frac{M}{\rho} = N_0\left(\frac{\pi}{6}\right)\sigma^3 \tag{1.56}$$

Typical values might be $\rho = 2g\ \text{cm}^{-3}$ and $M = 30$ so that, approximately,

$$N_0\sigma^3 \approx 30\ \text{cm}^3 \tag{1.57}$$

At one atmosphere pressure at room temperature, gases with $M \approx 30$ have $\eta \approx 2 \times 10^{-4}$ poise. With $M = N_0 m$ in (1.55) a second approximate condition on N_0 and σ is

$$2 \times 10^{-4} = \frac{1}{3}\left(\frac{3 \times 8.3 \times 10^7 \times 300}{30}\right)^{1/2} \frac{30}{\sqrt{2}\,\pi N_0 \sigma^2}$$

$$N_0\sigma^2 = 5.6 \times 10^8\ \text{cm}^2 \tag{1.58}$$

Division of (1.57) by (1.58) yields for a typical molecular diameter $\sigma = 5 \times 10^{-8}$ cm. Moreover, the number of molecules in one gram-mole from (1.58) is of the order of

$$N_0 \approx \frac{5.6 \times 10^8}{(5 \times 10^{-8})^2} \approx 0.2 \times 10^{24}$$

More sophisticated determinations of Avogadro's number N_0 have been based on other uses of the kinetic theory and especially also on measurements of single-particle events since about 1900, but this first indication of the size of N_0 and σ is a remarkable achievement. At the present time, information on N_0 from many different kinds of experiments is pooled with other observations on other physical constants. A most probable and self-consistent set of physical constants that best fits all reliable data from all acceptable sources is then found by statistical methods. Among the values of this kind listed in Appendix A is

$$\frac{N}{n} = N_0 = 0.602252 \times 10^{24} \tag{1.59}$$

With this value of Avogadro's number N_0 it is possible to predict accurate values of mean free path, diffusion coefficients, and viscosity coefficients, as the following examples illustrate. Without N_0, the connection between theory and experiment is often lacking.

Example 1.9. What is the mean free path of a gas at a pressure of 1.00×10^{-3} mm Hg at 27°C if $\sigma = \sqrt{10} \times 10^{-8}$ cm?

By the perfect gas equation (1.29) and the fact that there are N_0 molecules in one gram-mole, $V/N = nRT/NP = RT/N_0P$. According to (1.37), the mean free path is then

$$l = \frac{V}{\sqrt{2}\,N\pi\sigma^2} = \frac{RT}{\sqrt{2}\,\pi\sigma^2 N_0 P}$$

Hence, under the conditions specified here,

$$l = \frac{82.05 \times 300}{\sqrt{2}\,\pi 10 \times 10^{-16} \times 0.602 \times 10^{24} \times \dfrac{1.00 \times 10^{-3}}{760}} = 6.99 \text{ cm}$$

In a vacuum system having vessels with dimensions of the order of 7 cm, collisions with the vessel walls would be very important at pressure less than about 1×10^{-3} mm Hg.

Example 1.10. Predict the coefficient of self-diffusion of argon ($\sigma = 4 \times 10^{-8}$ cm) at 0.010 atm at 300°K.

As in the preceding example,

$$l = \frac{82.05 \times 300}{\sqrt{2}\,\pi \times 16 \times 10^{-16} \times 0.602 \times 10^{24} \times 0.010} = 5.8 \times 10^{-5} \text{ cm}$$

By (1.33),

$$u = \left(\frac{3 \times 8.314 \times 10^7 \times 300}{40}\right)^{1/2} = 4.32 \times 10^4 \text{ cm sec}^{-1}$$

Finally, by the exact formula (1.49),

$$\mathscr{D} = 0.543 \times 4.32 \times 10^4 \times 5.8 \times 10^{-5} = 1.36 \text{ cm}^2 \text{ sec}^{-1}$$

Example 1.11. What is the viscosity of N_2 ($M = 28.0$; $\sigma^2 = 10 \times 10^{-16}$ cm^2) at 300°K?

From the discussion that culminates in (1.55),

$$cl = \frac{1}{\sqrt{2}\,\pi\sigma^2} = \frac{1}{\sqrt{2}\,\pi \times 10 \times 10^{-16}} = 0.225 \times 10^{15} \text{ cm}^{-2}$$

The mass of one molecule is

$$m = \frac{M}{N_0} = \frac{28.0}{0.602 \times 10^{24}} = 46.5 \times 10^{-24} \text{ gram}$$

The root mean square velocity of N_2 at 300°K is

$$u = \left(\frac{3RT}{M}\right)^{1/2} = \left(\frac{3 \times 8.314 \times 10^7 \times 300}{28.0}\right)^{1/2} = 5.17 \times 10^4 \text{ cm sec}^{-1}$$

Hence, by the rigorous result in (1.54),

$$\eta = 0.452 \times 5.17 \times 10^4 \times 0.225 \times 10^{15} \times 46.5 \times 10^{-24}$$
$$= 2.45 \times 10^{-4} \text{ gram cm}^{-1} \text{ sec}^{-1} = 0.245 \text{ millipoise}$$

The observed value is about two-thirds as great. Changing σ from 3.16×10^{-8} cm to 3.83×10^{-8} cm would yield a theoretical value close to the observed η.

1.11 COLLISIONS

Accurate description of a real collision is greatly simplified by imagining that a collision is as definite an event as contact between spheres when their centers are a distance σ apart. The molecular diameter σ remains to the end a parameter for matching theory and experiment. This indefiniteness of σ allows the kinetic theory to be developed here without excessive care about details like the distribution of molecular speeds.

A molecule is expected to collide once in a distance l, its mean free path. The time it takes to go the distance l between collisions at a speed u is lu^{-1}. The rate at which a typical molecule suffers collision is, therefore, $Z_1 = ul^{-1}$. Each of the N molecules in a volume V averages the same rate Z_1 of collision. However, the rate of two-molecule, or bimolecular, collisions is half the rate of collision noted by individual molecules because each collision involves two molecules. Accordingly, the rate at which collisions occur between the N molecules in the volume V is $(1/2)NZ_1$ and the rate of bimolecular collisions per unit volume in a pure gas is $Z_{11} = NZ_1/2V = Nu/2Vl$. With the root mean square velocity u from (1.33) and the mean free path l from (1.37), the frequency of double collisions per unit volume becomes

$$Z_{11} = \frac{1}{2}\left(\frac{N}{V}\right)\left(\frac{3RT}{M}\right)^{1/2}\left(\frac{\sqrt{2}\,N\pi\sigma^2}{V}\right)$$
$$= \left(\frac{3}{2}\right)^{1/2}\left(\frac{N}{V}\right)^2(\pi\sigma^2)\left(\frac{RT}{M}\right)^{1/2}$$

A more painstaking analysis with account of the range of molecular speeds in a gas at equilibrium at T yields

$$Z_{11} = \left(\frac{4}{\pi}\right)^{1/2}\left(\frac{N}{V}\right)^2(\pi\sigma^2)\left(\frac{RT}{M}\right)^{1/2} \tag{1.60}$$

If there are N_1 molecules of kind 1 in the volume V with N_2 of kind 2, the frequency of collision of kind 1 with kind 2 per unit volume is rigorously

$$Z_{12} = \left(\frac{8}{\pi}\right)^{1/2}\left(\frac{N_1}{V}\right)\left(\frac{N_2}{V}\right)(\pi\sigma_{12}^2)\left(\frac{RT}{M_{12}}\right)^{1/2} \tag{1.61}$$

where $2\,\sigma_{12} = \sigma_1 + \sigma_2$ is the sum of the molecules' diameters, and where $M_{12}^{-1} = M_1^{-1} + M_2^{-1}$ is the reduced molecular weight of the colliding pair. In this same mixture, the rate per unit volume at which like molecules collide is given by (1.60). When mixed gases become alike (so that $\sigma_{12} = \sigma_1 = \sigma_2 = \sigma$

and $N_1 + N_2 = N$ and $2M_{12} = M_1 = M_2 = M$), the total rate of collision per unit volume becomes

$$
\begin{aligned}
Z &= Z_{11} + Z_{12} + Z_{22} \\
&= \left(\frac{4}{\pi}\right)^{1/2}\left(\frac{N_1}{V}\right)^2(\pi\sigma^2)\left(\frac{RT}{M}\right)^{1/2} + \left(\frac{8}{\pi}\right)^{1/2}\left(\frac{N_1}{V}\right)\left(\frac{N_2}{V}\right)(\pi\sigma^2)\left(\frac{2RT}{M}\right)^{1/2} \\
&\quad + \left(\frac{4}{\pi}\right)^{1/2}\left(\frac{N_2}{V}\right)^2(\pi\sigma^2)\left(\frac{RT}{M}\right)^{1/2} \\
&= \left(\frac{4}{\pi}\right)^{1/2}(\pi\sigma^2)\left(\frac{RT}{M}\right)^{1/2}\left(\frac{N_1^2 + 2N_1N_2 + N_2^2}{V^2}\right) \\
&= \left(\frac{4}{\pi}\right)^{1/2}(\pi\sigma^2)\left(\frac{RT}{M}\right)^{1/2}\left(\frac{N_1 + N_2}{V}\right)^2
\end{aligned}
$$

which is like (1.60). These expressions for Z are of interest in describing the rates of chemical reactions.

At large distances there is generally a weak attraction between molecules; only at small distances of the order of σ does a strong repulsion gradually dominate the interaction. The characteristic collision diameter σ represents a kind of average distance of interaction; it may vary with the kind of interaction. As soon as molecules are thought of as deformable or of varying size, or as soon as any bimolecular collision endures for a finite time, there is a possibility of a triple collision. Such an event is conceived as a collision of a third molecule with two others that are actually colliding. The time that a double collision lasts is of the order of σu^{-1}, namely, the time it takes a molecule of speed u to pass a molecule of size σ. The free time of a molecule between collisions is about lu^{-1}. Therefore, the fraction of the time lu^{-1} that a third molecule is near one of the two that approach collision from a distance l is about $(\sigma u^{-1})/(lu^{-1}) = \sigma l^{-1}$. Thus, the ratio of the rate of triple collisions to the rate of double collisions is of the order of σl^{-1}. Even at 1 atm where l is about 10^{-5} cm, triple collisions represent less than 1% of the collisions in a gas.

Example 1.12. Calculate the total number of bimolecular collisions per sec in 1 ml of pure He ($\sigma = 2 \times 10^{-8}$ cm) and pure N_2 ($\sigma = 4 \times 10^{-8}$ cm) at 300°K at 1 atm.

At $P = 1$ atm and $T = 300$°K, by (1.29) and (1.59)

$$\frac{N}{V} = \frac{NP}{nRT} = \frac{N_0P}{RT} = \frac{0.602 \times 10^{24} \times 1}{82.05 \times 300} = 2.45 \times 10^{19} \text{ molecules cm}^{-3}$$

By (1.60) with $M = 4.00$ for He,

$$
\begin{aligned}
Z_{11} &= \left(\frac{4}{\pi}\right)^{1/2}(2.45 \times 10^{19})^2\,\pi(2 \times 10^{-8})^2\left(\frac{8.314 \times 10^7 \times 300}{4.00}\right)^{1/2} \\
&= 7 \times 10^{28} \text{ collisions sec}^{-1}\text{ cm}^{-3}
\end{aligned}
$$

Similarly, for N_2 with $M = 28.0$, $Z_{11} = 10 \times 10^{28}$ sec^{-1} cm^{-3}.

1.12 EQUATIONS OF STATE OF REAL GAS

The perfect gas law fails to describe the behavior of a real gas for two reasons. It takes no account of the actual volume of the molecules and it ignores the attractive energies that cause any real gas to condense as a liquid or solid. The perfect gas law is adequate when the volume occupied by the molecules themselves is a very small part of the volume of the gas and when the kinetic energy of the molecules is great relative to attractive intermolecular energies.

When the unoccupied volume is not great relative to the very volume of the molecules, the compressibility of a gas is less than expected because the unoccupied volume is significantly less than the apparent volume of the gas. If b is the volume proper to 1 mole of molecules, then the unoccupied volume of n moles with an apparent total volume V is $(V - nb)$. This unoccupied volume $(V - nb)$ is the volume that can be lost by compression.

The feeble intermolecular attraction that culminates at low T in condensation extends over a distance of several σ. When the mean free path is also several σ, each molecule has a lower energy than might be expected because it tends to be held by its neighbors in a favorable position. In other words, in addition to kinetic energy it exhibits potential energy. Compared to a perfect gas, its energy is low, and thus its impacts on the walls of its container are less violent than those of a molecule of a perfect gas.

In 1873, van der Waals proposed as the equation of state of n moles of a real gas at a pressure P in a volume V at a temperature T

$$\left(P + \frac{an^2}{V^2}\right)(V - nb) = nRT \tag{1.62}$$

The empirical constant b represents the effective collisional volume of a mole of molecules themselves; this volume b is actually somewhat greater than the molar volume of the liquid. The empirical constant a is a proportionality constant linking a "pressure-that-might-have-been" to the number of collisions, all of which are considered as attractive.

There are for real gases two other simple equations of state with just two arbitrary constants. Berthelot's equation, somewhat like (1.62), is

$$\left(P + \frac{an^2}{TV^2}\right)(V - nb) = nRT \tag{1.63}$$

where a and b are new empirical constants characteristic of the gas. The last of these common two-constant equations is Dieterici's equation

$$(Pe^{an/VRT})(V - nb) = nRT \tag{1.64}$$

All three of these equations of state have the general form of the perfect gas law, but the volume is the unoccupied volume $(V - nb)$ and the ideal pressure is replaced by two parts: the observed pressure P and a pseudopressure that is lost to intermolecular attractions.

All three of these equations can be expressed approximately in the common form

$$\frac{PV}{nRT} = 1 + \frac{nB}{V} + \frac{n^2C}{V^2} + \cdots \tag{1.65}$$

called the *virial equation of state*, wherein B is called the *second virial coefficient*, C the *third*, and so on. Generally, the third and succeeding terms are negligible. According to van der Waals' equation (1.62),

$$PV + \frac{an^2}{V} - Pnb - \frac{abn^3}{V^2} = nRT$$

$$\begin{aligned}
\frac{PV}{nRT} &= 1 + \frac{Pb}{RT} - \frac{an}{VRT} + \frac{abn^2}{V^2RT} \\
&= 1 + \frac{b}{RT}\left(\frac{nRT}{V - nb} - \frac{an^2}{V^2}\right) - \frac{an}{VRT} + \frac{abn^2}{V^2RT} \\
&= 1 + \frac{nb}{V}\left(1 - \frac{nb}{V}\right)^{-1} - \frac{an}{VRT} \\
&= 1 + \frac{nb}{V}\left[1 + \frac{nb}{V} + \left(\frac{nb}{V}\right)^2 + \cdots\right] - \frac{an}{VRT} \\
&= 1 + \frac{n}{V}\left(b - \frac{a}{RT}\right) + \frac{n^2}{V^2}(b^2) + \cdots
\end{aligned}$$

By comparison with (1.65) it is clear that for the van der Waals equation

$$B = b - \frac{a}{RT} \quad \text{and} \quad C = b^2 \tag{1.66}$$

Sometimes it is convenient to express the virial equation as a power series in P in the form

$$PV = nRT + nBP + \cdots \tag{1.67}$$

While B has the same value as in (1.65), the third virial coefficients of (1.65) and (1.67) differ. Thus, a second approximate form of (1.62), useful when V is to be found, is

$$PV = nRT + n\left(b - \frac{a}{RT}\right)P \tag{1.68}$$

Similarly, Berthelot's equation (1.63) yields

$$B = b - \frac{a}{RT^2} \quad \text{and} \quad C = b^2 \tag{1.69}$$

Finally, expansion of $e^{-an/VRT}$ as a power series yields for Dieterici's equation

$$\left.\begin{aligned} B &= b - \frac{a}{RT} \\ C &= b^2 - \frac{ab}{RT} + \frac{a^2}{2R^2T^2} \end{aligned}\right\} \tag{1.70}$$

The values of a and b for a substance differ for each equation. Table 1.3 lists values for use in the equations of van der Waals (1.62) and Dieterici (1.64).

Table 1.3 Dieterici and van der Waals Constants. (Calculated from P_c and T_c as reported in C. D. Hodgman et al., eds. *Handbook of Chemistry and Physics*, Cleveland, Ohio: Chemical Rubber Publishing Co., 1953, pp. 2121–2123.)

Dieterici		Fluid	van der Waals	
a	b		a	b
(cm^6 atm mole^{-2})	(cm^3 mole^{-1})		(cm^6 atm mole^{-2})	(cm^3 mole^{-1})
1.73×10^6	34.9	Ar	1.35×10^6	32.2
0.316	28.8	H_2	0.246	26.6
1.73	41.9	N_2	1.35	38.6
1.75	34.5	O_2	1.36	31.9
8.33	61.0	Cl_2	6.49	56.2
1.87	42.5	CO	1.46	39.2
4.70	44.2	HCl	3.66	40.8
7.02	33.0	H_2O	5.47	30.5
5.38	40.4	NH_3	4.19	37.3
8.70	61.6	SO_2	6.77	56.9
4.62	46.3	CO_2	3.60	42.8
25.1	137.5	CCl_4	19.6	126.9
2.89	46.3	CH_4	2.25	42.7
6.97	69.4	C_2H_6	5.43	64.1
11.5	95.	C_3H_8	8.99	88.0
18.3	131.	C_4H_{10}	14.3	121.
24.4	158.	C_5H_{12}	19.0	146.
31.8	191.	C_6H_{14}	24.8	177.
39.5	224.	C_7H_{16}	30.9	207.
5.73	61.8	C_2H_4	4.46	57.0
5.62	55.4	C_2H_2	4.37	51.1
15.4	91.0	C_2H_5OH	12.0	84.0
20.0	120.2	CH_3COCH_3	15.6	111.0
24.0	130.6	C_6H_6	18.78	120.7
30.8	158.4	$C_6H_5CH_3$	24.06	146.4

When observations of P, V, n, and T are at hand for a gas, the value of B is found by determining from (1.65) at constant T the limit

$$B = \lim_{P \to 0} \left(\frac{PV}{nRT} - 1 \right) \frac{V}{n} \tag{1.71}$$

This limit is at large V, for PV is finite at fixed T. With the dimensions of volume per mole, B is a function of T. At high temperatures it is greater than zero, but as T decreases B also decreases continuously until eventually it becomes less than zero. The *Boyle temperature of a gas* is the temperature at which B is zero. For He, Ne, Ar, N_2, and O_2 these temperatures are 25°K, 210°K, 420°K, 325°K, and 425°K. For a van der Waals or Dieterici gas, the Boyle temperature is, by (1.66) and (1.70),

$$T_B = \frac{a}{Rb} \tag{1.72}$$

The compressibility factors for ethane shown in Figure 1.7 indicate that T_B for ethane exceeds 250°C. By (1.72) and Table 1.3, T_B for ethane is about 1100°K. At sufficiently high T and P, the compressibility factor exceeds unity because the actual volume of the molecules cannot be neglected while intermolecular forces can.

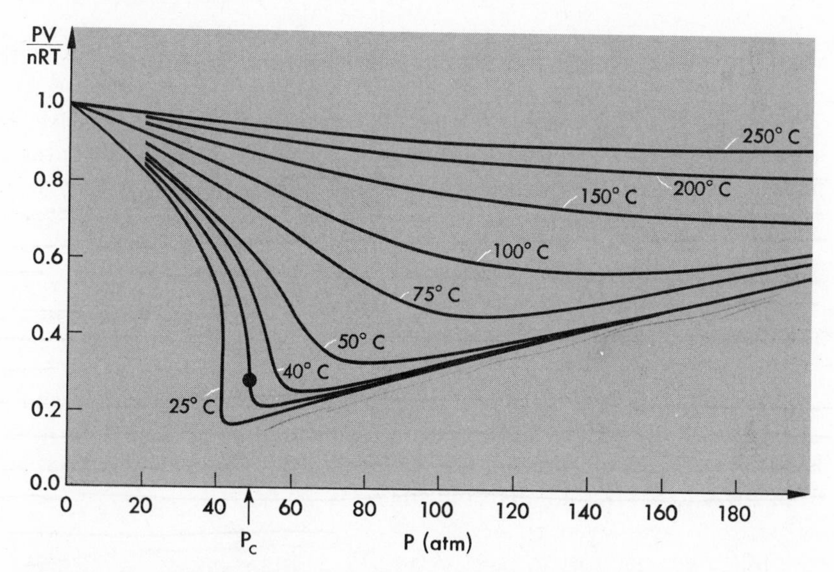

Figure 1.7. Compressibility Factor PV/nRT for Ethane at Various Temperatures and Pressures†

The *Boyle point of a gas* occurs when PV has a minimum value as a function of P. It differs from the Boyle temperature. Figure 1.7 shows the Boyle point of ethane at 100°C to occur at about 140 atm. At the Boyle point of a gas, B in (1.67) is less than zero; hence, the Boyle point occurs at temperatures less than T_B.

†Values calculated from data of J. A. Beattie, C. Hadlock, and N. Poffenberger, *J. Chem. Phys.* **3,** 93 (1935) and B. H. Sage, D. C. Webster, and W. N. Lacey, *Ind. and Eng. Chem.* **29,** 658 (1937).

Table 1.4 Beattie-Bridgeman Constants [Equation (1.73)]. (From H. S. Taylor and S. Glasstone, *A Treatise on Physical Chemistry*, **2**, Copyright 1951, D. Van Nostrand Company, Inc., Princeton, N.J.)

Gas	$A_0 \times 10^4$	$a \times 10^4$	$B_0 \times 10^4$	$b \times 10^4$	$c \times 10^{-4}$
H_2	1975	−50.6	209.6	−435.9	0.504
N_2	13445	261.7	504.6	−69.1	4.20
O_2	14911	256.2	462.4	42.08	4.80
NH_3	23930	1703.1	341.5	1911.2	476.87
CH_4	22769	185.5	558.7	−158.70	12.83
CO_2	50065	713.2	1047.6	723.5	66.0
n-C_5H_{12}	282600	1509.9	3940.0	1396.0	400.00

As the number of parameters like a and b of the two-constant equations of state is increased, more and more accurate equations are possible. By far the best empirical equation is that of Beattie and Bridgeman[1]

$$PV = RT\left(1 - \frac{c}{VT^3}\right)\left(1 + \frac{B_0}{V} - \frac{bB_0}{V^2}\right) - \frac{A_0}{V}\left(1 - \frac{a}{V}\right) \tag{1.73}$$

The volume V is for one mole. Table 1.4 lists the values of the five constants for several gases when P, V, and T have units that match $R = 0.08206$ l atm deg^{-1} mole^{-1}. This equation is accurate up to about 250 atm. In virial form it is

$$\frac{PV}{RT} = 1 + \frac{1}{V}\left(B_0 - \frac{c}{T^3} - \frac{A_0}{RT}\right) + \frac{1}{V^2}\left(\frac{aA_0}{RT} - \frac{cB_0}{T^3} - B_0 b\right) + \frac{1}{V^3}\left(\frac{cB_0 b}{T^3}\right) \tag{1.74}$$

Equations of state may become quite complex and yet remain useful when calculations are done by an automatic high-speed computer. A form of the Benedict-Webb-Rubin equation of state, modified for liquid and gaseous helium from 2.2°K to 574°K and up to 140 atm,[2] is

$$\begin{aligned} P = (RT)\rho &+ \left(Rn_1T + n_2 + \frac{n_3}{T} + \frac{n_4}{T^2} + \frac{n_5}{T^4}\right)\rho^2 \\ &+ (Rn_6T + n_7)\rho^3 + (n_8)\rho^4 \\ &+ \left(\frac{n_9}{T^2} + \frac{n_{10}}{T^3} + \frac{n_{11}}{T^4}\right)\rho^3 \exp\left(-\frac{n_{12}\rho^2}{T}\right) \\ &+ \left(\frac{n_{13}}{T^2} + \frac{n_{14}}{T^3} + \frac{n_{15}}{T^4}\right)\rho^5 \exp\left(-\frac{n_{12}\rho^2}{T}\right) + n_{16}\rho^5 + n_{17}\rho^6 \end{aligned}$$

In it, the pressure P in atmospheres is given as a function of the gas constant R

[1] J. A. Beattie and O. C. Bridgeman, *J. Am. Chem. Soc.* **49**, 1665 (1927)
[2] D. B. Mann, "The Thermodynamic Properties of Helium from 3 to 300°K Between 0.5 and 100 Atmospheres," Washington, D.C.: NBS Technical Note 154, Jan. 1962.

(here 0.0820575 l atm deg^{-1} mole^{-1}), the temperature T, the density ρ (moles liter^{-1}), and seventeen constants which were found by a statistical method of adjustment to achieve a best fit to 695 points of known P, T, and ρ. The errors in P and ρ are less than 3% except that an error of 5% is possible in P at high P or in ρ below 10°K. The constants:

$n_1 = 0.01627693557$ | $n_2 = -0.03700903492$
$n_3 = 0.007567259965$ | $n_4 = -0.01887566673$
$n_5 = 0.04792344640$ | $n_6 = 0.0001560344984$
$n_7 = 0.0009274298542$ | $n_8 = -0.00002833997045$
$n_9 = -0.005002871627$ | $n_{10} = 0.03451283837$
$n_{11} = 0.1008924438$ | $n_{12} = 0.0065$
$n_{13} = -0.00001851562535$ | $n_{14} = 0.00004204351888$
$n_{15} = -0.0001712445150$ | $n_{16} = 0.7739390202 \times 10^{-6}$
$n_{17} = -0.2870693948 \times 10^{-8}$

It is obvious why a computer is needed. It is also probably clear what can be expected of accurate equations of state for fluids less ideal than He.

Example 1.13. Ten moles of ethane are confined to a volume of 4860 cm^3 at 300°K. Under these conditions, predict the pressure by means of these equations of state:
(a) perfect gas; (b) van der Waals; (c) Dieterici; (d) virial.
(Beattie-Bridgeman constants of ethane from J. A. Beattie, C. Hadlock, and N. Pofenberger, *J. Chem. Phys.* **3,** 93 (1935) are $A_0 = 5.8800$, $a = 0.05861$, $B_0 = 0.09400$, $b = 0.01915$, $c = 90.00 \times 10^4$ with P in atm, V in liters mole^{-1}.)
(The observed value of B. H. Sage, D. C. Webster, and W. N. Lacey, *Ind. Eng. Chem.* **29,** 658 (1937) is 34.0 atm.)

(a) For this perfect gas, (1.29) yields

$$P = \frac{nRT}{V} = \frac{10.0 \times 82.06 \times 300}{4860} = 50.7 \text{ atm}$$

(b) For ethane considered as a van der Waals gas, with $a = 5.43 \times 10^6$ cm^6 atm mole^{-2} and $b = 64.1$ cm^3 mole^{-1} from Table 1.3, (1.62) yields

$$P = \frac{nRT}{V - nb} - \frac{an^2}{V^2} = \frac{10.0 \times 82.06 \times 300}{4860 - 641} - \frac{5.43 \times 10^6 \times 10.0^2}{(4.86 \times 10^3)^2}$$
$$= 58.4 - 23.0 = 35.4 \text{ atm}$$

(c) For ethane considered as a Dieterici gas, with $a = 6.97 \times 10^6$ cm^6 atm mole^{-2} and $b = 69.4$ cm^3 mole^{-1} from Table 1.3, (1.64) yields

$$P = \frac{nRT}{V - nb} \exp\left(-\frac{an}{VRT}\right)$$
$$= \frac{10.0 \times 82.06 \times 300}{4860 - 694} \exp\left(-\frac{6.97 \times 10^6 \times 10.0}{4860 \times 82.06 \times 300}\right)$$
$$= 59.09\, e^{-0.583} = 59.09 \times 0.5584 = 33.0 \text{ atm}$$

(d) According to (1.74), the virial coefficients are unity and

$$B = B_0 - \frac{c}{T^3} - \frac{A_0}{RT} = 0.09400 - \frac{90.00 \times 10^4}{300^3} - \frac{5.8800}{0.08206 \times 300}$$

$$= -0.1781 \text{ l mole}^{-1} = -178.1 \text{ cm}^3 \text{ mole}^{-1}$$

$$C = \frac{aA_0}{RT} - \frac{cB_0}{T^3} - bB_0$$

$$= \frac{0.05861 \times 5.8800}{0.08206 \times 300} - \frac{90.00 \times 10^4 \times 0.09400}{300^3} - 0.01915 \times 0.09400$$

$$= +0.00907 \text{ l}^2 \text{ mole}^{-2} = 9070 \text{ cm}^6 \text{ mole}^{-2}$$

$$D = \frac{cB_0 b}{T^3} = \frac{90.00 \times 10^4 \times 0.09400 \times 0.01915}{300^3}$$

$$= +6.00 \times 10^{-5} \text{ l}^3 \text{ mole}^{-3} = 6.00 \times 10^4 \text{ cm}^9 \text{ mole}^{-3}$$

With these values, (1.65) with $V = 486.0$ cm^3 mole^{-1} yields

$$\frac{PV}{RT} = 1 - \frac{178.1}{486.0} + \frac{9070}{486.0^2} + \frac{60000}{486.0^3}$$

$$= 1 - 0.3665 + 0.0384 + 0.000522 = 0.6724$$

$$P = 0.6724\left(\frac{RT}{V}\right) = 0.6724 \times 50.7 = 34.1 \text{ atm}$$

The Beattie-Bridgeman result is the same as observed. Since the volume effectively occupied by the molecules of ethane is about one-seventh of the 4860 cm^3, and since this fraction acts as though it is incompressible, the pressure on this account might have been predicted to be about

$$P \approx \frac{nRT}{V - nb} \approx \frac{10 \times 82 \times 300}{4800 - 700} \approx 60 \text{ atm}$$

This exceeds even the estimate of 50.7 atm for a perfect gas of point molecules. However, because of intermolecular attraction, this value of about 60 atm is decreased to 35.4 atm (VDW) and 33.0 atm (Dieterici). At 300°K and 34.0 atm, as indicated roughly by Figure 1.7,

$$\frac{PV}{nRT} = 0.672 = \frac{34.0 \times 4860}{10 \times 82.06 \times 300}$$

1.13 CRITICAL STATE

As the temperature of a system containing both liquid and gas is increased, the density of the liquid decreases as it expands and the density of the gas increases. The *critical temperature* of a substance is that temperature at which liquid and vapor become so similar that they can no longer be distinguished as individuals. The indexes of refraction, densities, and molar volumes of the two phases become identical in the critical state. The *critical state* of a fluid is its condition at its critical temperature, pressure, and volume. In this state, the mean free path of a molecule is approximately equal to its diameter. Figure 1.8 illustrates how P and V are related near the critical state of a typical fluid. Each curve, called an *isotherm*, tells how P depends on the total volume V of a fixed amount of the substance when T is constant. At high T, the curve is like Boyle's law. At intermediate temperatures, the curves are no longer hyperbolas $PV = k_B$ because of deviations from ideal behavior. Still, the pressure decreases continuously at constant temperature as the volume increases. At low T, there is a range of V in which P is constant at constant T. In these circumstances, the horizontal part of the isotherm specifies the fluid's vapor pressure at T for the isotherm. If Figure 1.8 is drawn for one mole, the ends of these horizontal parts of the isotherms specify the volumes of one mole of liquid and saturated gas. The boundaries of the gray dome-shaped region of Figure 1.8 mark the limits of P and V within which liquid and gas coexist at equilibrium; within the dome-shaped region, the liquid and gaseous states exist together.

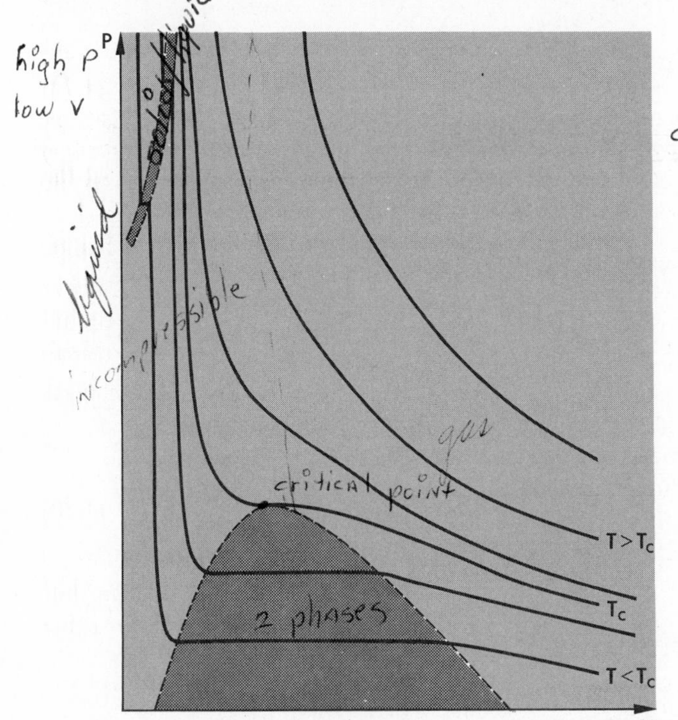

Figure 1.8. Typical Variation of Pressure with Volume at Various Constant Temperatures

The isotherm that goes through the very top of the dome-shaped region is called the *critical isotherm*. At this T, the critical temperature T_c, the volumes of coexisting liquid and gas have become alike. The pressure at the top of the dome is the *critical pressure* of the substance, and the volume there is its *critical volume per mole*. The two isotherms for which $T < T_c$ extend into the liquid region of low compressibility to the left of and above the domed liquid-gas region. At sufficiently high P, almost all substances solidify; the steps in the isotherm for $T < T_c$ show this change, and a slim gray region at high P and low V tells when solid and liquid coexist.

At the critical state, the slope of the critical isotherm is zero. In fact, no fluid isotherm for a temperature above T_c achieves zero slope, while all isotherms for $T < T_c$ have zero slope within the dome-shaped region of Figure 1.8. When the slope is zero, a small change in volume ΔV at constant pressure does not cause a change ΔP in pressure. That is, P is not a function of V at constant T. Mathematically, with the subscript T to indicate explicitly that temperature is constant along an isotherm, the slope is zero when

$$\lim_{\Delta V \to 0} \left(\frac{\Delta P}{\Delta V}\right)_T = \left(\frac{\partial P}{\partial V}\right)_T = 0 \tag{1.75}$$

Equation (1.75) holds within the dome-shaped region of Figure 1.8 and at the critical point.

The critical isotherm is distinguished from those at lower T in that its slope increases continuously to zero at the critical point, then decreases, and finally at large V increases continuously once again. That is, the slope reaches a maximum value of zero at one point, the critical point. Mathematically, when the slope $(\partial P/\partial V)_T$ is a maximum, the rate of change of the slope with respect to changes in V is zero so that, at the critical point,

$$\frac{\partial}{\partial V}\left(\frac{\partial P}{\partial V}\right)_T = \left(\frac{\partial^2 P}{\partial V^2}\right)_T = 0 \tag{1.76}$$

Equations (1.75) and (1.76) are true also within the dome-shaped region, but there the points at which the slope becomes zero do not coincide and the value of zero is not attained continuously.

The two conditions (1.75) and (1.76) define the critical state. As conditions on an equation of state of a fluid, (1.75) and (1.76) fix the two parameters a and b of the equations of state of van der Waals, Dieterici, or Berthelot. (The parameter R is never varied from the value it has at low P and large V.) Since Dieterici's equation (1.64) is the best of these two-constant equations in the neighborhood of the critical state, it is worth applying (1.75) and (1.76) to it. Solution of (1.64) for P yields

$$P = \frac{nRT}{V - nb} e^{-an/VRT} \tag{1.77}$$

When T, R, n, a, and b are constant, it follows that

$$\left(\frac{\partial P}{\partial V}\right)_T = nRT\,e^{-an/VRT}\left[\frac{an}{V^2RT(V-nb)} - \frac{1}{(V-nb)^2}\right]$$

$$= P\left[\frac{an}{V^2RT} - \frac{1}{V-nb}\right] \qquad (1.78)$$

At the critical state, where the pressure is P_c and the volume is V_c and the temperature is T_c, (1.75) requires

$$0 = P_c\left(\frac{an}{V_c^2RT_c} - \frac{1}{V_c - nb}\right) \qquad (1.79)$$

That is,

$$a = \frac{V_c^2RT_c}{n(V_c - nb)} \qquad (1.80)$$

A second condition on a and b comes from (1.76). This requires the second derivative, which, by use of (1.78) as needed, has the value

$$\left(\frac{\partial^2 P}{\partial V^2}\right)_T = -\frac{2Pan}{V^3RT} + \frac{P}{(V-nb)^2} + \left(\frac{an}{V^2RT} - \frac{1}{V-nb}\right)^2 P$$

Accordingly, at the critical point, (1.76) requires

$$0 = P_c\left[\left(\frac{an}{V_c^2RT_c} - \frac{1}{V_c - nb}\right)^2 - \frac{2an}{V_c^3RT_c} + \frac{1}{(V_c - nb)^2}\right]$$

With the aid of (1.79), this becomes simply

$$0 = -\frac{2an}{V_c^3RT_c} + \frac{1}{(V_c - nb)^2}$$

That is,

$$a = \frac{V_c^3RT_c}{2n(V_c - nb)^2} \qquad (1.81)$$

Simultaneous solution of (1.80) and (1.81) for a and b in terms of P_c, V_c, and T_c yields, upon division of (1.81) by (1.80),

$$1 = \frac{V_c}{2(V_c - nb)}$$

$$b = \frac{V_c}{2n} \qquad (1.82)$$

When (1.82) in the form $nb = V_c/2$ is substituted into (1.80) the result is

$$a = \frac{V_c^2 RT_c}{n(V_c - V_c/2)} = \frac{2V_c RT_c}{n} \tag{1.83}$$

At the critical point, the Dieterici equation with (1.82) and (1.83) is then

$$\begin{aligned} P_c &= \left(\frac{nRT_c}{V_c - nb}\right) e^{-an/V_c RT_c} \\ &= \frac{nRT_c e^{-2}}{V_c - V_c/2} = \frac{2nRT_c}{V_c e^2} \\ &= \frac{2nR\left(\dfrac{an}{2V_c R}\right)}{V_c e^2} = \frac{n^2 a}{e^2 V_c^2} \end{aligned}$$

$$P_c = \frac{a}{4b^2 e^2} \tag{1.84}$$

Any two of the equations (1.82), (1.83), and (1.84) are sufficient to fix a and b in terms of the critical constants. The values of a and b in Table 1.3 were found from P_c and T_c by eliminating V_c from (1.82) and (1.83) to get $a = 4bRT_c$, which, with (1.84), yields $P_c = RT_c b^{-1} e^{-2}$ or

$$b = \frac{RT_c}{P_c e^2} \tag{1.85}$$

$$a = \frac{4R^2 T_c^2}{P_c e^2} \tag{1.86}$$

Since Dieterici's equation is not perfect, the values of a and b depend somewhat upon which two of the three critical constants (P_c, V_c, and T_c) are chosen.

It has been customary to base calculations of a and b on P_c and T_c because these have usually been more easily observed than V_c. However, Hakala[3] has discovered a remarkably accurate empirical rule linking densities of liquid and saturated vapor at temperatures much less than T_c to the critical density. For many substances of varied chemical and physical nature, the liquid density $\boldsymbol{\rho}$ and vapor density ρ, as these two phases coexist at equilibrium at various T, are related to the critical density ρ_c by the Hakala relation

$$\frac{\boldsymbol{\rho} + \rho}{2} = \rho_c + K(\boldsymbol{\rho} - \rho)^{10/3} \tag{1.87}$$

The left-hand member is the average density of coexisting liquid and vapor at T. At T_c, $\boldsymbol{\rho} = \rho$ and the average density becomes the critical density ρ_c. Figures 1.9 and 1.10 illustrate (1.87) for ethanol from 80°C to a few degrees below its T_c at 243°C and for chlorobenzene from 140°C to 220°C. The critical density

[3] R. W. Hakala, *Chem. and Eng. News*, March 16, 1959, p. 43, and May 4, 1959, p. 13.

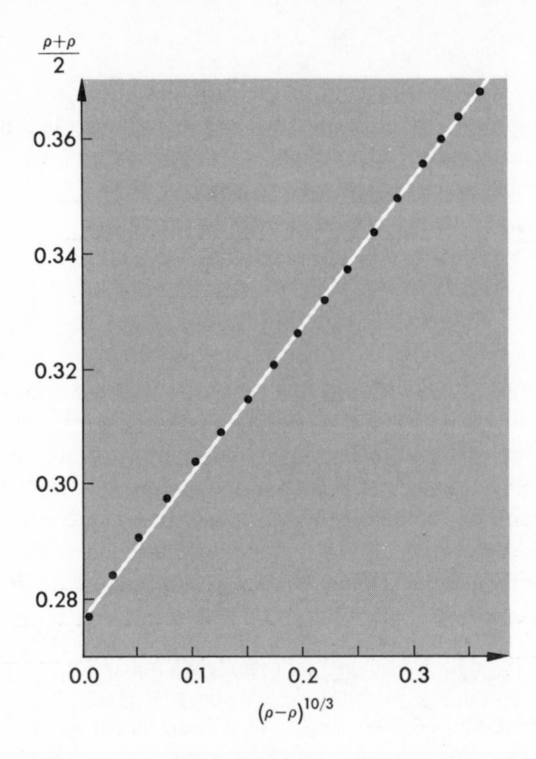

Figure 1.9. Critical Density of Ethanol by Hakala's Method†

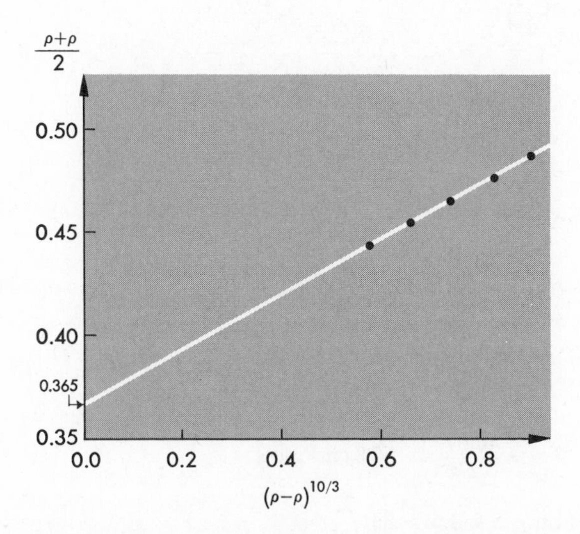

Figure 1.10. Critical Density of Chlorobenzene by Hakala's Method‡

---

†Data from Lange's *Handbook of Chemistry*, New York: McGraw-Hill Book Co., Inc. 1967, p. 1455.

‡Data from Lange's *Handbook of Chemistry*, New York: McGraw-Hill Book Co., Inc. 1967, p. 1454.

of ethanol is 0.276 g cm^{-3} by this method and others; that of chlorobenzene at its T_c of 359.2°C is 0.365 g cm^{-3} by this method and by others that use density data close to T_c. In general, values of ρ_c found by this linear extrapolation agree with traditional methods; even when the densities are one hundred degrees from T_c, the values of ρ_c are correct within one percent.

The critical molar volume V_c can be calculated from ρ_c by

$$V_c = \frac{M}{\rho_c} \tag{1.88}$$

where M is the molecular weight of the vapor at low pressures where it behaves as a perfect gas. If T_c is not known, it can also be estimated like ρ_c, for the temperature T at which $\boldsymbol{\rho}$ and ρ are observed is approximately a linear function of $(\boldsymbol{\rho} - \rho)^{10/3}$. Values of a and b can thus be based ultimately on densities of liquid and vapor at low pressures and at temperatures much less than T_c. Since P_c is high and sometimes difficult to observe, and since many substances decompose at T_c, the remarkable function $(\boldsymbol{\rho} - \rho)^{10/3}$ offers valuable assistance in equations of state for fluids.

Example 1.14. Evaluate the van der Waals a and b of ethanol by the use of (1.75) and (1.76) and the facts that $\rho_c = 0.276$ g cm^{-3} and $T_c = 516$°K.

A van der Waals gas has $P = nRT(V-nb)^{-1} - an^2V^{-2}$ so that at the critical point, (1.75) requires

$$0 = \left(\frac{\partial P}{\partial V}\right)_T = -\frac{nRT_c}{(V_c - nb)^2} + \frac{2an^2}{V_c^3}$$

while (1.76) requires

$$0 = \left(\frac{\partial^2 P}{\partial V^2}\right)_T = \frac{2nRT_c}{(V_c - nb)^3} - \frac{6an^2}{V_c^4}$$

Division of these equations yields $V_c - nb = (2/3)V_c$ or $b = (V_c/3n)$. With this result in (1.75),

$$a = \frac{V_c^3 nRT_c}{2n^2[(2/3)V_c]^2} = \frac{9RV_cT_c}{8n}$$

Since $T_c = 516$°K, $R = 82.06$ cm^3 atm mole^{-1} deg^{-1}, and M of C_2H_5OH is 46.07, it follows from (1.88) that

$$\frac{V_c}{n} = \frac{46.07}{0.276} = 166.8 \text{ cm}^3 \text{ mole}^{-1}$$

and from the results above it follows that

$$a = \left(\frac{9}{8}\right) 82.06 \times 166.8 \times 516 = 7.95 \times 10^6 \text{ cm}^6 \text{ atm mole}^{-2}$$

$$b = \left(\frac{1}{3}\right) 166.8 = 55.6 \text{ cm}^3 \text{ mole}^{-1}$$

The values of Table 1.3, based on P_c and T_c, are 12.0×10^6 and 84.0. Both sets in (1.72) predict that the Boyle temperature T_B is 1740°K, while the second virial coefficients B predicted by (1.66) are noticeably different. For example, by (1.66) at 500°K, B based on P_c and T_c is -209 cm^3 mole^{-1}, while B based on V_c and T_c is -138 cm^3 mole^{-1}. Actually B is about -200 cm^3 mole^{-1} at 500°K.

1.14 PRINCIPLE OF CORRESPONDING STATES

The ambiguity in evaluating a and b arises from the fact that they are just two adjustable constants that must satisfy three equations at the critical point. One equation is the equation of state itself; the other two equations are (1.75) and (1.76), which call at the critical point for a maximum slope of zero when P is a function of V at constant T. It would perhaps be possible to avoid this dilemma by introducing a third parameter, but it would not be generally advisable to vary R to fit the critical constants because R is specified by the common behavior of gases at low pressure.

A remarkable fact is hidden in this seemingly ambiguous set of three simultaneous equations for a and b. If a and b are eliminated from (1.84) by use of (1.82) and (1.83), the result is

$$P_c = \frac{a}{4b^2e^2} \tag{1.84}$$

$$= \left(\frac{2V_cRT_c}{n}\right)\left(\frac{1}{4e^2}\right)\left(\frac{2n}{V_c}\right)^2$$

$$\frac{P_cV_c}{nRT_c} = \frac{2}{e^2} = 0.2707 \tag{1.89}$$

That is, Dieterici's equation predicts that at the critical point the compressibility factor of every fluid has the same universal value 0.2707! The value for ethane at the large dot in Figure 1.7 is 0.275, and some indication of the agreement of this general prediction with observation is offered in Table 1.5, where fluids are arbitrarily classified into five groups. Fluids with small (slightly polarizable) symmetrical (nonpolar) molecules have critical state compressibility factors close to 0.29. Polarity or polarizability almost always lowers this value to about 0.27, while hydrogen-bonding so dominates intermolecular attractions that low values near 0.24 result for water and similar substances. In the same way, the van der Waals and Berthelot equations predict all compressibility factors at the critical point to be

$$\frac{P_cV_c}{nRT_c} = \frac{3}{8} = 0.375 \tag{1.90}$$

Hence, they are less satisfactory than the Dieterici equation near the critical point. Any two-constant equation can be treated similarly to yield a value of the compressibility factor at the critical point.

Table 1.5. Observed Values of the Compressibility Factor at the Critical State[a]

Substance	P_c (atm)	V_c (ml mole^{-1})	T_c (°K)	$\frac{P_cV_c}{RT_c}$	General Characteristics of Fluid
He	2.261	57.8	5.23	0.305	Nonpolar; slightly polarizable
Ne[b]	25.9	41.7	44.5	0.296	
Ar	48.0	75.3	150.7	0.292	
Kr[c]	54.1	92.1	209.4	0.290	
Xe	58.2	113.8	289.8	0.279	
H_2	12.8	65.0	33.2	0.306	
N_2[b]	33.5	90.1	126.1	0.292	
O_2	50.1	74.4	154.8	0.293	
CH_4	45.8	99.4	191.1	0.290	
CO_2	72.9	94.9	304.3	0.277	
Cl_2	76.1	123.8	417.	0.275	Nonpolar; polarizable
CS_2	78	173.	552.	0.298	
CCl_4	45.0	262.	556.3	0.258	
C_2H_2	61.6	113.	309.2	0.272	
C_2H_4	50.6	134.	282.8	0.292	
C_2H_6[d]	48.7	141.7	305.7	0.275	
C_6H_6	48.6	260.	562.	0.274	
SO_3	83.8	126.5	491.4	0.263	
CO[c]	34.5	93.2	133.0	0.295	Polar; slightly polarizable
HCl	81.6	86.0	324.6	0.263	
N_2O	71.7	96.2	309.7	0.271	
CH_3Cl	65.9	143.0	416.3	0.276	Polar; polarizable
SO_2	77.8	123.8	430.7	0.273	
CH_3COCH_3	46.6	213.	508.5	0.238	
n-C_5H_{12}	33.3	310.3	469.8	0.268	
n-C_6H_{14}	29.9	367.5	507.9	0.264	
n-C_7H_{16}	27.0	428.	543.2	0.259	
C_6H_5F	44.6	271.2	559.8	0.263	
C_6H_5Cl	44.6	308.0	632.4	0.265	
NH_3	111.3	72.9	405.5	0.244	Hydrogen-bonded
H_2O	219.5	58.8	647.6	0.243	
CH_3OH	78.5	117.7	513.2	0.220	
C_2H_5OH	63.0	167.2	516.	0.249	

[a] Data calculated from Lange's *Handbook of Chemistry*. New York: McGraw-Hill Book Co., Inc., 1967, pp. 1451–1464, 1485 unless noted otherwise.

[b] Hirschfelder, J.O., C.F. Curtiss, and R. B. Bird, *Molecular Theory of Gases and Liquids*. New York: John Wiley and Sons, Inc., 1954, p. 245.

[c] Guggenheim, E. A., *Thermodynamics*, Amsterdam: North-Holland Publ. Co., 1957, p. 167.

[d] Sage, B.H., D.C. Webster, and W. N. Lacey, *Ind. Eng. Chem.*, **29**, 658 (1937).

The compressibility factor is just one of many dimensionless combinations of the physical quantities that are correlated in an equation of state. Any properly written equation linking physical quantities is dimensionally homogeneous; that is, the variables in it have the correct units. It is always possible to transform such an equation to dimensionless variables that are products of dimensioned quantities. For example, when a and b in Dieterici's equation (1.64) are eliminated by (1.82) and (1.83), the result is

$$Pe^{2V_cRT_c/VRT}\left(V - \frac{nV_c}{2n}\right) = nRT$$

Division by (1.89) yields

$$\frac{P}{P_c}e^{2(V_c/V)(T_c/T)}\left(\frac{V}{V_c} - \frac{1}{2}\right) = \left(\frac{e^2}{2}\right)\left(\frac{T}{T_c}\right)$$

$$P_re^{2/V_rT_r}(2V_r - 1) = e^2T_r \qquad (1.91)$$

where the dimensionless variables are

$$P_r = \frac{P}{P_c} \qquad V_r = \frac{V}{V_c} \qquad T_r = \frac{T}{T_c} \qquad (1.92)$$

the reduced pressure P_r, the reduced volume V_r, and the reduced temperature T_r. Within the limitations of the Dieterici equation, all fluids have the same equation of state (1.91).

The dimensionless form of van der Waals equation is

$$\left(P_r + \frac{3}{V_r^2}\right)(3V_r - 1) = 8T_r \qquad (1.93)$$

What (1.91) and (1.93) both state is that only two of the three reduced variables in (1.92) are independent. In general, then, if the form of the equation of state is not known, it follows that

$$P_r = \phi(V_r, T_r) \qquad (1.94)$$

A more useful form that is really equivalent to (1.94) is

$$\frac{PV}{nRT} = F(P_r, T_r) \qquad (1.95)$$

Both (1.94) and (1.95) say that two of three dimensionless variables are independent. This formulation implies, of course, if $F(P_r, T_r)$ is the same for some substance and for ethane, that Figure 1.7 may be used for both provided the isotherms are labeled with the variable T_r and the abscissa is labeled P_r. The principle of corresponding states is a formal statement of these ideas. It says that similar substances have a common functional form of their reduced equation of state like (1.94) or (1.95). That functional form may be (1.91), or (1.93), or some graphical summary like the well-known charts of Hougen and Watson.[4]

The most general statement of the law of corresponding states is[5]

$$\frac{PV}{nRT} = f(Z_c, P_r, T_r) \tag{1.96}$$

where

$$Z_c = \frac{P_c V_c}{nRT_c} \tag{1.97}$$

That is, the function ϕ in (1.94) or the function F in (1.95) is the same only for those substances with the same compressibility factor Z_c at the critical point, provided that the only important variables are P, V, n, R, T, P_c, V_c, and T_c. Standard methods are known[5] for extending the principle to equations of state involving more variables or to any kind of equation with physical meaning.

Example 1.15. With Figure 1.7 and critical data from Table 1.5, estimate the compressibility factor of N_2 at 100 atm at $-100°C$.

Since T_c of N_2 is 126.1°K in Table 1.5, at $-100°C$ $T_r = 173.2/126.1 = 1.373$. For C_2H_6, T_c is 305.7°K in Table 1.5; hence, the appropriate isotherm is $T = T_r T_c = 1.373 \times 305.7 = 420°K = 147°C$. Similarly, for N_2, $P_r = 100/33.5 = 2.98$; hence, for C_2H_6 at the same P_r, $P = 2.98 \times P_c = 2.98 \times 48.7 = 145$ atm. From Figure 1.7, at $P = 145$ atm near the 150°C isotherm, PV/nRT is 0.725. The observed value for N_2 is 0.708. Much of the discrepancy can be ascribed to the difference in compressibility factors at the critical point and consequent expected failure of the principle of corresponding states. Moreover, at large P, differences in b become important.

1.15 SUMMARY

This chapter on pure gases does several things. It relates chemistry to physics; it explains by example the value of a model and a theory in organizing and even predicting observables; it deals with simple ideas with the elegance of mathematics; it sketches as simply as possible the history of the modern kinetic theory; it defines such things as temperature, R, and molecular weights; it develops equations of state for use in the equations of thermodynamics; it presents a limited field of observation as a basis for the somewhat abstract methods of thermodynamics; and it offers incomplete answers to vexing questions that may be answered in what follows.

[4] O. A. Hougen and K. M. Watson, *Chemical Process Principles*, New York: John Wiley and Sons, Inc. (1947) Part II.

[5] R. W. Hakala, *J. Chem. Ed.* **41**, 380 (1964).

PROBLEMS

Note: Each of the three sets of questions deals with the entire chapter. The first set is easiest; the third is most challenging.

1. Calculate in ergs and in joules the kinetic energy of one neon molecule with a velocity of 5.00×10^4 cm sec^{-1} if its mass is 3.35×10^{-23} gram.
   Answer: 4.19×10^{-14} erg $= 4.19 \times 10^{-21}$ j.

2. Calculate the change in energy of a perfect gas that undergoes a change that can be described by Boyle's law.
   Answer: No change in E.

3. If 40,000 cm³ of N_2 at 27°C at 0.900 atm are cooled to 4°C at 1.000 atm, what will be the final volume? How many gram-moles of N_2 are present?
   Answer: 33,200 cm³; 1.461 moles.

4. A sample of H_2 at the ice-point (0.000°C = 273.150°K) has a pressure sufficient to support a column of Hg 83.50 cm long. In a vessel of constant volume, the same H_2 at another temperature supported a column of Hg that was 48.33 cm long. What was the second temperature?
   Answer: 158.2°K.

5. What is the density of gaseous C_2H_5Cl at 50°C at 2.20 atm?
   Answer: 0.00535 g cm^{-3}.

6. At 100°C, 1.83 g of a pure gas with empirical formula CH_2 occupies a volume of 950 cm³ at 0.691 atm. What is its formula?
   Answer: C_6H_{12}.

7. Calculate the root mean square velocities of O_2 and CO_2 molecules at 37°C.
   Answer: 4.91×10^4 and 4.19×10^4 cm sec^{-1}.

8. At what temperature will SO_3 have the same root mean square velocity as N_2 at 0°C?
   Answer: 780°K.

9. Calculate the mean free path of pure gaseous Cl_2 at 0°C at 1.000 atm if $\sigma = 3 \times 10^{-8}$ cm. Do the same for H_2 if $\sigma = 3 \times 10^{-8}$ cm.
   Answer: 9.3×10^{-6} cm.

10. Calculate the relative rates of effusion of He and CH_4 through the same orifice at the same temperature if the pressure of CH_4 is twice that of He.
    Answer: Rates equal.

11. A gas of molecular weight 28 effuses from a tiny hole in 75 sec. What is the molecular weight of another gas that takes 120 sec under the same experimental conditions?
    Answer: 72.

12. How many molecules are there per cubic centimeter of a perfect gas at a pressure of 1.0×10^{-6} mm Hg at 27°C?
    Answer: 3.2×10^{10} molecules.

13. Find σ^2 for H_2 if its viscosity at 300°C is 1.40×10^{-4} poise.
    Answer: $\sigma^2 = 6.45 \times 10^{-16}$ cm².

14. Calculate the number of double and triple collisions per second in 1000 cm³ of N_2 at 50°C at 0.500 atm if $\sigma = \sqrt{10} \times 10^{-8}$ cm.
Answer: $Z_{11} = 1.41 \times 10^{31}$ sec⁻¹; $Z_{111} = 2.26 \times 10^{28}$ sec⁻¹.

15. If two moles of gaseous CO_2 are confined to a volume of 4000 cm³ at 27°C, the pressure according to the van der Waals equation is what?
Answer: 11.7 atm.

16. What pressure is really exerted by a mole of gaseous NH_3 at 25°C if confined to a volume of 150 cm³?
Answer: Ca. 30 atm.

17. One hundred grams of normal heptane in a volume of 500 cm³ at 300°C has what pressure?
Answer: Ca. 35 atm.

18. What pressure is really expected of two moles of ethene (C_2H_4) confined to 1400 cm³ at −20°C?
Answer: 23.2 atm (VDW); 22.0 atm (D).

19. Estimate the Boyle temperatures of CH_4 and CCl_4.
Answer: Ca. 700°K (CH_4) and 2000°K (CCl_4).

20. Show that the Boyle temperature of a Dieterici gas is four times its critical temperature.

21. If a gaseous hydrocarbon with a Boyle point of 1700°K has a pressure of 50.0 atm at 300°C when two moles of it are confined to a volume of 1500 cm³, what are its critical pressure and critical molar volume?
Answer: 32 atm; 300 cm³ mole⁻¹.

---

22. What is the total kinetic energy of 1000 cm³ of a perfect monatomic gas at 1.00 atm?
Answer: 1.52×10^9 ergs.

23. The height to which Hg rose in a Torricellian barometer happened to be 75.81 cm. If the density of Hg in the barometer was 13.54 g cm⁻³ and the acceleration of gravity was 980.5 cm sec⁻², what pressure was exerted by the Hg column?
Answer: 1.007×10^6 dynes cm⁻².

24. Exactly ten cm³ NH_3 at 0°C were compressed to a volume of 7.50 cm³ at 100°C. If the initial pressure was 1.00×10^{-3} atm, what was the final pressure?
Answer: 1.82×10^{-3} atm.

25. Exactly one gram of each of two metals was oxidized to yield a pure volatile oxide whose gaseous density was observed at 100°C at 0.200 atm. Find the equivalent weight of the metal, the approximate and exact molecular weights of the oxide, and the formula of the oxide if each molecule has one metal atom when
(a) from one metal 1.629 g of oxide were produced and its vapor density was 1.08 milligrams per cm³;
(b) from the other metal 1.337 g of oxide were produced and its vapor density was 1.65 mg cm⁻³.
Answer: (a) RuO_4; (b) OsO_4.

26. Exactly one gram of element X was burned in air to form 2.29 grams of pure gaseous oxide that occupied 2070 cm³ at a pressure of 200 mm Hg at 550°C.
a. What is the molecular weight of the oxide?

b. If each molecule of the oxide contains four atoms of X, what is the atomic weight of X?
Answer: a. 284.2; b. 31.05.

27. If the actual volume of one gram-mole of O_2 at 1.00000 atm at 0.00°C is 22395 cm³, what volume is expected of O_2 at 0.50000 atm at 0.00°C?
Answer: 44808 cm³.

28. What is the root mean square velocity of gaseous WCl_6 at 300°C at 0.100 atm?
Answer: 1.90×10^4 cm sec^{-1}.

29. The best vacuum pump can generate a vacuum with a pressure of about 1×10^{-9} mm Hg. At 20°C, how many molecules are present in one cm³ at this pressure? Estimate the mean free path.
Answer: 3.22×10^7 molecules cm^{-3}; $\sim 10^7$ cm.

30. If a hole with a radius or diameter of the order of 0.1 cm is to be used as an effusion orifice (without streaming flow of the gas), what is the order of magnitude of the maximum number of molecules allowable per cm³?
Answer: 10^{15}.

31. What is the rate of self-diffusion in a gas at 300°K with a mean free path of 1.00×10^{-5} cm, a molecular weight of 30, and a σ of $\sqrt{10} \times 10^{-8}$ cm if the concentration gradient is 1.00×10^{-7} moles cm^{-4}?
Answer: 2.72×10^{-8} moles cm^{-2} sec^{-1}.

32. At 100°C, the viscosity of gaseous Br_2 is 0.188 millipoise at one atm. Determine the mean free path, the coefficient of self-diffusion, and the collisional diameter σ of Br_2 molecules at 100°C at one atm.
Answer: $l = 3.30 \times 10^{-6}$ cm; $\mathscr{D} = 0.0433$ cm² sec^{-1}; $\sigma = 5.88 \times 10^{-8}$ cm.

33. What chance does a molecule have of going one cm without collision through a gas at one atm at 27°C if $\sigma = \sqrt{10} \times 10^{-8}$ cm?
Answer: One in $10^{470,000}$.

34. At a height of 300 km, the temperature of the atmosphere is about 1100°K and the pressure is about 5.0×10^{-10} atm. Estimate for a gas of average molecular weight 25, the density of molecules, their mean free path, and the frequency of double collisions if $\sigma = \sqrt{10} \times 10^{-8}$ cm.
Answer: $c = 0.33 \times 10^{10}$ molecules cm^{-3}; $l = 670$ m; $Z_{11} = 2.4 \times 10^9$ cm^{-3} sec^{-1}.

35. A molecule of F_2 with a speed of 3.00×10^4 cm sec^{-1} collides head-on with a molecule of IF proceeding in the opposite direction with a speed of 4.00×10^4 cm sec^{-1}. Both speeds are calculated relative to stationary laboratory coordinates. What is the kinetic energy of the system after collision as noted by an observer in the laboratory and by another on F_2? Relative to an observer in the laboratory, what are the speeds of F_2 and IF after collision?
Answer: In lab, $E = 22.24 \times 10^{-14}$ erg; on F_2, $E = 59.9 \times 10^{-14}$ erg. IF moves on at 1.10×10^4 cm sec^{-1}; F_2 rebounds at 8.10×10^4 cm sec^{-1}.

36. At what temperature will gaseous acetone at 20.0 atm pressure have a density of 0.0350 g cm^{-3}?
Answer: (VDW) 484°K; (Dieterici) 501°K.

37. What is the pressure of gaseous HCl at −40°C if its density is 0.00800 g cm^{-3}?
Answer: 4.20 atm (perf. gas); 4.06 atm (VDW).

38. Estimate the actual density of gaseous normal pentane at 1.50 atm at 40°C.
Answer: By (1.67), 4.36×10^{-3} g cm^{-3}.

39. Estimate the pressure really expected of gaseous Cl_2 at 120°C at a density of 0.220 g cm^{-3}.
Answer: Ca. 57 atm.

40. By means of several isotherms, explain graphically how PV for a van der Waals gas depends on P when (a) $a = 0$; (b) $b = 0$; (c) $a = b = 0$.

41. With the Dieterici or van der Waals b as a guide to the actual volume of matter in one mole of steam, determine Avogadro's number and σ for H_2O if the viscosity of steam at 150°C is 0.145 millipoise.
Answer: $\sigma = 6.21 \times 10^{-8}$ cm; $N_0 = 2.50 \times 10^{23}$.

42. With P_c and T_c from Table 1.5 for SO_3, predict by Dieterici's equation the pressure of SO_3 at 200°C when its density is 0.200 g cm^{-3}.
Answer: $a = 10.52 \times 10^6$ cm^6 atm mole^{-2}; $b = 65.2$ cm^3 mole^{-1}; $P = 58.8$ atm.

43. The volumes of one mole of liquid and gaseous ethane as they exist together at various temperatures and pressures are given in the table. Find the critical molar volume, critical pressure, and critical temperature of ethane. (Data from B. H. Sage, D.C. Webster, and W. N. Lacey, *Ind. Eng. Chem.* **29,** 658 (1937)).

Temperature (°C)	Pressure (atm)	Volume (cm^3 mole^{-1})	
		Gas	Liquid
17.6	35.7	373.9	86.2
19.8	37.4	345.0	88.31
21.9	39.1	318.2	90.00
23.9	40.8	294.1	92.35
25.8	42.5	269.0	95.33
27.7	44.2	242.7	99.35
29.6	45.9	214.4	105.37
31.4	47.6	182.8	116.00

Answer: Obs. $\rho_c = 0.2121$ g cm^{-3}.

44. At 1000 atm at 300°C, the compressibility factor of N_2 is $PV/nRT = 1.581$. At what temperature and pressure will C_2H_6 and Cl_2 have similar values of PV/nRT? What practical matters may interfere with direct observations on C_2H_6 and Cl_2 at these conditions?
Answer: Cl_2: 2270 atm and 1890°K; C_2H_6:1450 atm and 1390°K; decomposition.

---

45. A McLeod gauge with a bulb-capillary volume V of 200 cm^3 has a capillary-tube radius of 0.10 cm. The length of the sealed capillary is 20 cm. Over what range of low pressures can it be useful?
Answer: If (1.18), $p < 6.3 \times 10^{-2}$; if (1.19), range depends on height of sealed capillary above Hg reservoir.

46. A Victor Meyer vial weighed 4.332 g empty. When filled with a pure liquid containing about 74.0% by weight fluorine, the sealed vial weighed 4.786 g. As in the usual procedure, the vial was broken in a vessel jacketed by a water bath at 99.8°C. The volume of air displaced was measured over Hg at 27°C at 745 mm Hg; it occupied 44.6 ml. If the liquid contains only two elements, determine its molecular weight and possible formulas.
Answer: 256; M_nF_{10}, $nM = 66$, e.g. S_2F_{10} or C_5F_{10}.

47. If a gas of molecular weight 50 has a density of 0.00200 g cm^{-3} at 0.750 atm, what is the root mean square velocity of its molecules?
Answer: 3.37×10^4 cm sec^{-1}.

48. Explain why the root mean square free path of a molecule exceeds its mean free path.
Answer: Long distances, when squared, assume great importance.

49. In terms of the mean free path l, how far will half of a set of molecules move before suffering a second collision?
Answer: $l \ln 2$.

50. By calculating the net rate at which molecules at level z_0 in Figure 1.6 gain momentum from adjacent layers z_1 and z_2 in laminar flow, show that typical molecules near the plane at z_0 are not accelerated by the continuous transfer of momentum across the plane at z_0 in a steady state of viscous flow.

51. The viscosities of gaseous He and Hg at 300°C are 0.312 and 0.537 millipoise at 1 atm. What is the ratio of their collisional cross sections?
Answer: $\sigma(\text{Hg}) = 2.03\ \sigma(\text{He})$.

52. Two gases with collision diameters $\sigma_1 = 3.00 \times 10^{-8}$ cm and $\sigma_2 = 4.00 \times 10^{-8}$ cm and with molecular weights $M_1 = 64.0$ and $M_2 = 100$ are thoroughly mixed. What concentration ratio is needed to make the frequency of bimolecular collisions of unlike molecules equal to the total frequency of bimolecular collisions of like molecules ($Z_{11} + Z_{22} = Z_{12}$)?
Answer: $c_1 = 0.925c_2$ or $c_1 = 1.538c_2$.

53. By the perfect gas law and by the Dieterici equation, predict the volume of 10.0 g gaseous H_2 at 27°C at 3.32 atm. Do the same for 10.0 g gaseous SO_2.
Answer: For H_2, 36,700 cm^3 (P.G.) and 36,800 cm^3 (D); for SO_2, 1158 cm^3 (P. G.) and 1146 cm^3 (D).

54. By expanding the exponential function in the Dieterici equation, show that it is like the van der Waals equation when T is high and gas density is low.

55. Compare the pressures predicted by the Dieterici and Beattie-Bridgeman equations for one mole of CH_4 at -60°C at a density of 0.200 g ml^{-1}.
Answer: 62.2 atm (D); 62.0 atm (B-B).

56. With regard to van der Waals equation,
(a) show that b exceeds the actual volume of a mole of molecules;
(b) explain mathematically why a substance with $a = 0$ cannot be liquefied.

57. Criticize the statement: At its Boyle temperature, every gas follows Boyle's law exactly.

58. What is wrong with the second virial coefficient of the equation of state $Pe^{fn/V}(1 + qn/V)(V - nb) = nRT$?
Answer: $B = b - g - f$ is independent of T.

59. Determine the critical density and estimate the critical pressure of diethyl ether at its critical temperature of 193.8°C from these densities of saturated vapor and liquid: at 50°C, 0.6764 and 0.005079 g cm^{-3}; at 70°C, 0.6532 and 0.00892 g cm^{-3}; at 90°C, 0.6250 and 0.01477 g cm^{-3}; at 110°C, 0.5942 and 0.02349 g cm^{-3}. (Data from Lange's *Handbook of Chemistry*, New York: McGraw-Hill Book Co., Inc., 1967, p. 1455.)
Answer: Obs. $\rho_c = 0.264$ g cm^{-3}; $P_c = 35.6$ atm.

60. Suggest a way of generalizing the Dieterici or van der Waals equation to take full advantage of the generality in (1.96).

ENERGY AND ENTHALPY

2.1 INTRODUCTION

Thermodynamics is the exact mathematical science that describes the interrelationship of heat and work. The kinetic theory and statistical mechanics describe how the mechanics of molecules and atoms and other tiny bits of matter is responsible for seemingly continuous and homogeneous behavior. Observed as a whole, myriads of such bits of matter exhibit steady average properties. These averages are made over times that are long compared to times between collisions or times of vibration; they are made over regions of space that contain many molecules; they are made for energies of so many molecules that any change of energy of one molecule is itself insignificant to the average. Thermodynamics describes transformations of matter and energy when the atomistic constitution of matter can be ignored. The mechanical energy of thermodynamics may be closely related to the mechanical energy of the elementary bits of matter, but thermodynamics treats of matter as a continuum that displays thermal and mechanical properties on a visible or molar basis.

That part of the physical universe that is under study is the *system;* everything else in the universe constitutes the *surroundings*. A *closed system* cannot exchange matter with the surroundings, but an *open system can*. If a system cannot exchange matter or energy of any kind with its surroundings, it is called an *isolated system*. Because there is no barrier to gravitation a perfectly isolated system is impossible, but the influence of gravity is often negligible. The boundary of a closed system must be unpenetrated by matter, while the boundary of an isolated system is not crossed by flow of matter, heat, radiation, or other forms of energy, and is not displaced against a force. These definitions require that mass and energy be conserved separately. In this nonrelativistic view of the universe, mass and energy are not interconvertible; each is itself conserved in any change.

The *state of a system* is defined when a certain number of properties of the system are specified. The properties chosen are ordinarily *intensive properties*, that is, properties that do not depend upon the amount of matter in the system. When two systems have each of their several intensive properties alike, they are said to be *in the same state*. For example, the temperature and pressure of a gas are intensive properties, for each can be measured whether 1 mole or 1000 moles are in the system. The pressure and temperature in two systems containing different amounts of matter can be equal and are in no way restricted or determined by the amount of matter in each. Similarly, the mole fractions of all the molecular species present and the index of refraction of a mixture would be classed as intensive properties, but volume or mass would not. It is also possible to specify the state of a system by a mixture of intensive and extensive properties, or even by extensive properties alone. The most suitable choice of a set of properties may be indicated by experimental expediency or theoretical elegance. What is important here is the fact that only a select few of the many, many properties of a system are sufficient to fix its state and all its other properties.

If in a system the intensive properties like density and pressure are continuous functions of position, then the system is said to be *homogeneous;* if they are discontinuous, then *inhomogeneous* or *heterogeneous*. The distinction *continuous or discontinuous* depends upon the scale of measurement. For thermodynamics, the scale is the wavelength of visible light: if a body looks to be continuous even under the best optical microscope, it is taken to be continuous on the macroscopic scale. Water and oil ordinarily form two phases; that is, there is a region rich in water where the density and elemental composition correspond closely to the values for water, and there is another region where the intensive properties correspond closely to those for oil. At the interface between the two liquid phases various intensive properties appear discontinuous to the eye, but on a molecular scale the apparent discontinuity is perhaps a thin layer of very rapidly changing molecular population. Exactly which intensive thermodynamic properties are to be specified is often a matter of experimental convenience. However, the number of such independent properties that must be specified in any set of circumstances in order to fix the state of the system is a matter that can be answered by thermodynamics, namely, by the phase rule.

As a system changes from an initial well-defined state, wherein enough intensive properties are specified to fix the state of the system, to a final well-defined state, the various intensive properties assume intermediate values. Sometimes these intermediate values are ill defined. Generally, however, in this simple treatment of thermodynamics, the process or path by which such a change is effected will be sufficiently well defined to permit calculation of required thermodynamic functions. *Equilibrium thermodynamics*, the kind to be discussed here, is not concerned with the effects of time or the difficulties associated with such ill-defined intermediate states. Thermodynamics does assume, as experience readily verifies, that of all possible processes some come to equilibrium in a finite time while others do not.

Many kinds of *process*, *path*, or *change* are possible. A *reversible process* is a series of equilibrium states. A system is in a state of thermodynamic *equilibrium* if its intensive properties are independent of time and if there are no currents of matter or energy within the system or at its boundaries. Another way of defining a reversible process is to say that the process can be stopped or reversed by infinitesimal changes in the variables that control the state of the system. Squeezing a rubber ball slowly and within its elastic limits is reversible, but squeezing a tube of toothpaste usually is not. In a *cyclic process*, like a game of golf, the initial and final states of the system are the same, at the clubhouse. An *isothermal process* proceeds at constant temperature, as in a thermostat; an *isobaric process* proceeds at constant pressure, as open to the atmosphere in a laboratory in a short time; an *adiabatic process* proceeds without exchange of heat energy between system and surroundings, as in a thermos bottle. Other kinds of process will be met from time to time.

2.2 WORK

Work is defined as the product of the distance by which a body is moved and of the component of force along the direction of movement. It is a scalar quantity with the units of energy. Work done on a system by the surroundings is energy gained by the system by virtue of the movement of its parts by an external force.

The infinitesimal work dw done on a body of mass m as it is lifted vertically against the force of gravity is the product of the infinitesimal vertical distance dz and the force mg that is exerted on the body to lift it.

$$dw = mg\,dz \tag{2.1}$$

As the height z increases, the amount of work increases and is proportional to the mass m and the acceleration of gravity g.

Work done in a gravitational field is performed in one dimension, vertically. Work can be done in increasing the exposed surface of a phase. The force that must be overcome is the force that tends to maximize the contacts among parts of one phase and minimize the contacts among different phases. The proportionality factor between the work dw done on a system and the increase in area $d\mathscr{A}$ effected by the work is called the *surface tension* or *surface energy* γ.

$$dw = \gamma\,d\mathscr{A} \tag{2.2}$$

As the area of the system increases by the amount $d\mathscr{A}$, a positive amount of work dw must be done on the system. In order that (2.2) be dimensionally homogeneous, γ is given the units of force per unit length or energy per unit area.

Work done in three dimensions involves changes in volume. A positive amount of work done on a system will decrease its volume; that is, $+dw$ is the infinitesimal work done on a system as its volume changes by dV, where dV is less than zero. Symbolically,

$$dw = -P\,dV \tag{2.3}$$

where the negative sign keeps the proportionality constant P positive. The units of P are energy per unit volume or force per unit area. This latter choice of units establishes P as pressure. In fluid systems, P is a uniform normal pressure; work done in deforming or compressing solids requires more complicated mathematical treatment that cannot be undertaken here. Since dw is observed in the surroundings, P is the pressure exerted by the surroundings on the system as the work is performed. During a compression of the system wherein dw is positive, P is at least equal to the pressure within the system, but P may exceed this minimum value if, for example, the piston is massive, if it moves swiftly enough to cause a stirring or shock wave within the system, or if it is not frictionless. In other words, the work dw done on a system may not appear to be simply a force acting through a distance in the view of an observer within the system. Difficulties and uncertainties of these kinds are best avoided by careful specification of the process.

The infinitesimal electric work done in generating a charge of dQ at a potential $\mathscr{E}$ or in moving a charge dQ through a potential difference $\mathscr{E}$ is

$$dw = +\mathscr{E}\,dQ \tag{2.4}$$

The convention on the signs of $\mathscr{E}$ and Q (Chapter 12) requires the positive sign. If $\mathscr{E}$ is measured in volts and dQ in coulombs, then dw is the number of joules of electric work energy that is done on the system. Although work can be performed under circumstances other than those described above, the gravitational, surface, volume, and electrical kinds of work are generally sufficient for chemical thermodynamics.

The initial and final states that exist before and after a process involving work may be the same for several processes, but the amount of work involved in the change depends on how the work is done. That is, w depends on the intermediate states or on the path followed during the process as well as on the initial and final states of the process.

For example, the work done by 1 mole of gas as it changes from a pressure of 10 atm to a pressure of 1 atm at constant temperature depends on how the change in pressure occurs. In fact, the work done on the surroundings by the gas can range from none to a definite maximum value. Suppose that the gas expands isothermally from a pressure of 10 atm to a pressure of 1 atm by expansion into an evacuated chamber of just the right size to give a final pressure of 1 atm, or in a second isothermal process by expansion against the essentially constant atmospheric pressure present in a laboratory, or again in a third isothermal process by forcing a piston slowly outward against a constantly diminishing pressure that differs only infinitesimally from the pressure of the gas itself. This third process is reversible, for the expansion could be stopped or reversed by an infinitesimal change in pressure in the surroundings. Since the force against which the displacement occurs is a maximum (for a greater force would stop or reverse the change), the work done by the system in this third process is a maximum.

For the free expansion into a vacuum, the boundary of the surroundings is not displaced if the boundary of the surroundings is chosen to exclude the evacuated space, as is correct. That is, there is no work done by the surroundings on the system, the gas, for the surroundings were unchanged in the process. Nor is it correct to say that the gas did work on itself. Even if there were residual van der Waals attractive forces tending to hold the gas molecules together, there is no work done by the system on the surroundings. There is, of course, energy required to overcome these attractive intermolecular forces, but this energy must be supplied as heat from the surroundings or from the gas itself. For this free expansion, then

$$w_1 = 0 \tag{2.5}$$

For the expansion at constant pressure, as seen in the surroundings, P is constant at 1 atm. The absolute magnitude of the work done by the gas on the surroundings equals that done on the gas by the surroundings when no other change occurs, but these two works differ in algebraic sign. If w_2 is the work done on the expanding gas, then the work done by the gas in going from a volume V_1 to a volume V_2 is

$$\begin{aligned} -w_2 &= \int_{V_1}^{V_2} P\,dV = P(V_2 - V_1) \\ &= (1 \text{ atm})\left(\frac{RT}{1.0 \text{ atm}} - \frac{RT}{10.0 \text{ atm}}\right) \\ &= \frac{9}{10}RT \end{aligned} \tag{2.6}$$

For the reversible expansion against a constantly decreasing pressure, P is given by the equation of state of the gas. If the gas is ideal, $PV = RT$ and the work done by the gas is

$$\begin{aligned} -w_3 &= \int_{V_1}^{V_2} P\,dV = \int_{V_1}^{V_2} \frac{RT}{V}\,dV \\ &= RT \ln\left(\frac{V_2}{V_1}\right) = RT \ln\left(\frac{P_1}{P_2}\right) \\ &= RT \ln 10 \end{aligned} \tag{2.7}$$

An alternate way of calculating (2.7) is to find dV as a function of P thus:

$$V = \frac{RT}{P}, \qquad dV = -RT\frac{dP}{P^2}$$

$$-w_3 = \int_{P_1}^{P_2} P\left(-\frac{RT}{P^2}\right)dP = -RP \ln\left(\frac{P_2}{P_1}\right)$$

$$= RT \ln 10 \tag{2.7}$$

These three different expansion processes between identical pairs of initial and final states illustrate that work is a line integral that depends upon the path of integration. (See Appendix D for a discussion of line integrals.) Despite the implications of the notation used, dw is an inexact differential form. That is, there is no function w that depends on the state of the system so that w or the change in w depends merely upon the initial and final states. Rather, w generally depends upon the process and the initial and final states.

At constant temperature Boyle's law $PV = k_B = RT$ is the equation of state of a fixed amount of a perfect gas. Figure 2.1 shows three hyperbolas of

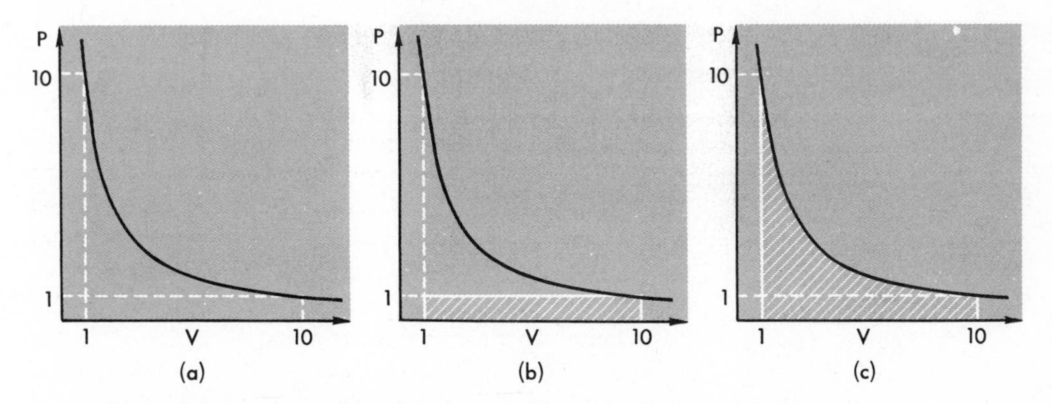

Figure 2.1. Work as a Line Integral. (a) Free Expansion into a Vacuum [$P = 0$]; (b) Expansion at Constant Pressure [$P = 1$]; (c) Reversible Isothermal Expansion [$P = k_B/V$]

the form $PV = k_B$. The shaded portions are the areas $\int P\,dV$, which by (2.3) are the values of the work done by the system on the surroundings ($-w$). Although P in (2.3) cannot exceed (k_B/V) for any value of V, it can be less than this value. Figure 2.2 shows a somewhat more complicated expansion, isobaric at $P = 5$ and then reversible. The shaded region is again the work done by the system, somewhat less than the reversible work of Figure 2.1(c). In both figures, the expansions occur at constant temperature from the same initial state to the same final state, but the amounts of work differ because the processes differ.

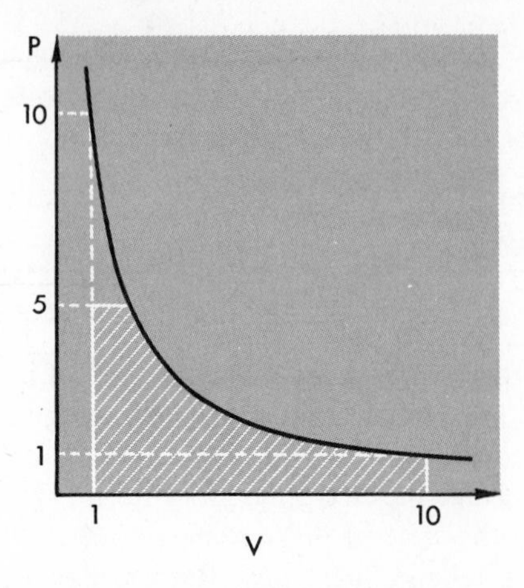

Figure 2.2 Isobaric and Reversible Expansion Work at Constant Temperature

2.3 FUNCTIONS OF STATE

A thermodynamic system is in a definite and well-defined state if a certain subset of its set of intensive properties is specified. Since these certain intensive properties are the independent variables that determine the state of the system, they become exact differentials in their infinitesimal form. (See Appendix D for a discussion of exact and inexact differentials.) Temperature and pressure are two such properties of matter. The change in temperature for a certain change in state is the final value T_2 diminished by the initial value T_1. Thus $\Delta T = T_2 - T_1$. For an infinitesimal change, where ΔT approaches zero as a limit, ΔT becomes dT. Similarly, a finite change in pressure would be $\Delta P = P_2 - P_1$: namely, the final pressure P_2 less the initial pressure P_1. For an infinitesimal process, ΔP becomes dP. In any cyclic process, the values of such independent variables as T or P return to the initial value, and thus the increment of each such variable is zero for the cycle. If the change is accomplished isothermally, the temperature is constant for any small part of the change and $dT = 0$. Similarly, for an isobaric process, $dP = 0$.

Temperature and pressure are functions of state almost by definition because they are ordinarily chosen by the experimenter as the intensive properties that he can control or specify readily. By experience it has been found that the energy of a system is also a function of state. Each well-defined state of matter has its own definite energy. Although this fact concerning energy is part of the first law of thermodynamics, the mathematical implications of this fact are worth discussing in anticipation of the final law. Regardless of how many changes a portion of matter undergoes, when it is returned to its initial state its energy E

is found to be the same as it was before the changes. In mathematical language, for any process,

$$\oint dE = 0 \tag{2.8}$$

As shown in Appendix D, the necessary and sufficient condition that an integral $\int dE$ depend only on the initial and final states is that (2.8) be true, which it is by the first law of thermodynamics. That is, for any process by which state 1 becomes state 2, the change in energy is

$$\Delta E = E_2 - E_1 = \int_{E_1}^{E_2} dE \tag{2.9}$$

where E_1 is the energy of the initial state and E_2 is the energy of the final state. The unique increase in energy that accompanies any change between the specified terminal states is ΔE. The function E exists and dE is an exact differential. The reference point of zero energy is arbitrary, but this is of little or no importance for it is the increment in energy ΔE that is observable.

An example of energy as a function of state is appropriate here. A person at the Ferry Building in San Francisco can go to the post office in Reno several ways: by air; by bus through Donner Pass; by car over Sonora Pass; by train; by walking. On reaching Reno his potential energy in the gravitational field of the earth is increased for Reno is several thousand feet above sea level. Once he has arrived, the length or height or difficulty of the passage over the Sierra Nevada is unimportant. The increase in energy is a unique function of initial and final positions. Returning to the initial state at the Ferry Building in San Francisco brings the traveler once again to his initial state and completes a cycle of movement. His energy is what it was at the start, just as though he had not traveled.

2.4 THE FIRST LAW OF THERMODYNAMICS

When a thermometer, such as a constant-volume hydrogen thermometer, indicates that two separated bodies have the same temperature, it is a matter of experience that no energy is transferred between these two systems if they are placed in thermal contact and if they do not work on each other. On the other hand, if the thermometer had shown a difference in temperature while they were separated, placing the two systems in thermal contact would have allowed a transfer of energy. At the same time, their different initial temperatures would have been observed to approach a single intermediate temperature on achieving equilibrium. As it cools, the hotter body transfers energy to the cooler body. Generally both reach a new intermediate temperature, but if some change like melting or boiling occurs in one, the temperature of that one need not change as the other's temperature changes. These observations about processes that reach thermal equilibrium without work or transfer of matter from system to system are sometimes formalized in what has come to be known as the zeroth law of thermodynamics. This law says that when each of two bodies is in thermal equilibrium with a third test body, they would be in thermal equilibrium with each other if placed in thermal contact. This law really establishes the usefulness of a thermometer and its accompanying scale of temperature. It also calls attention to a special form of energy. Energy that is transferred from one system to another by virtue of a temperature difference is called *heat.* In terms of the kinetic theory, heat is disorganized molecular and atomic movement, while work is the energy of visibly organized movement that accompanies the forced movement of the parts of a system.

The amount of heat transferred is a function of the initial and final temperatures of some standard body, like a certain mass of water, when it absorbs or evolves energy in the form of heat. In particular, 1 calorie of heat is the energy absorbed by 1 gram of water, the standard body, when its temperature increment is 1 centigrade degree. The calorie used in this text has been defined as 4.18400 joules, but in ordinary applications the difference between the two definitions is quite negligible.

The amount of heat absorbed by matter different from that of the standard body, water, is measured by comparing the temperature change observed to the temperature change that the standard body would have suffered on absorbing the same amount of heat. For example, 1 g copper would undergo a temperature change of 10° if it absorbed the same amount of heat as 1 g water that suffered a temperature change of 1°. For a given temperature change, say, 1°, copper need absorb only one-tenth as much heat as the same amount of water. The extensive factor by which the temperature increment is multiplied to express the heat involved in a certain process is called the *specific heat* or *heat capacity*. Copper has a specific heat of 0.1 cal g^{-1} deg^{-1}. That is, the heat required to increase the temperature of 1 g copper by 1°C is one-tenth as much as would have been required to increase the temperature of 1 g water by 1°. In general, if the temperature is increased from T_1 to T_2, the heat absorbed by n moles of a substance with a molar heat capacity of C is

$$q = n \int_{T_1}^{T_2} C \, dT \tag{2.10}$$

If the molar heat capacity is independent of temperature, (2.10) becomes

$$\begin{aligned} q &= nC \int_{T_1}^{T_2} dT \\ &= nC \, \Delta T \end{aligned} \tag{2.11}$$

While (2.10) and (2.11) are suitable for calculation of heat, the fundamental measurement is a measurement of a temperature increment, either in the standard body or some other body. The temperature of a body is measured by means of an infinitesimal test body that has some obvious property that can be related to the more subtle property called *temperature*. The obvious property may be the volume of a gas at a low constant pressure, or it may be the volume of mercury in a rigid container or the voltage developed by a thermocouple. In any case, the temperature must be a single valued, continuous, monotonic function of the property to be measured. The volume of 1 g water would not be suitable near 4°C.

The first law of thermodynamics originated in the wonderings of Count Rumford (Benjamin Thompson of Massachusetts) as he directed the boring of cannons in the Munich arsenal at the end of the eighteenth century. The shavings were hot, perhaps because of a chemical or physical change as they were generated or came into contact with the air, but perhaps because the work done by the bit during boring heated them. He observed, in answer to various objections, that the shavings were physically and chemically the same as the original piece and that using a dull bit made fewer and hotter shavings, There was no correspondence between the thermal energy and the amount of shavings. It was friction that was changing work into thermal energy. Sir Humphrey Davy verified this by rubbing two pieces of ice together at 29°F until they melted.

In the meantime, several physicians were debating the source of animal work. Mayer, who was one of them, even stated that heat was a form of energy that was to be conserved. However, verification of this fact came from experiments of James Joule of England. In many experiments after 1840, he dissipated both electrical and mechanical (stirring) energy in various liquids and noted the accompanying temperature rises. His accurate determinations of the ratio of thermal energy in calories to mechanical energy were generalized by Helmholtz in 1847 into the first law of thermodynamics. The kinetic theory eventually dispelled the notion that heat might be a fluid and interpreted temperature as a measure of random motion of minute particles.

The first law of thermodynamics is the law of conservation of energy for the science of thermodynamics. The increase in energy ΔE of a system is equal to the heat q absorbed by the system plus the work w done on the system. In mathematical terms, the first law is

$$\Delta E = E_2 - E_1 = q + w \tag{2.12}$$

In its infinitesimal form, provided dq and dw are understood to be inexact differentials, (2.12) reads

$$dE = dq + dw \tag{2.13}$$

The first part of (2.12), $\Delta E = E_2 - E_1$, implies that E is a function of state, which it is. However, since the work done on a system by the surroundings depends upon the path, heat absorbed by the system from the surroundings also depends upon the path. Like w, q is not a function of state. That is, (2.10) and (2.11) are in general line integrals of inexact differentials, and as such depend upon initial and final states and the process connecting them.

Equation (2.12) can be considered as an alternate definition of heat. If so, heat becomes the energy that is not accounted for in terms of work or the initial and final energy states of the system. Quite often it is easy to evaluate ΔE and w, but quite difficult to calculate the heat absorbed in some process. The first law provides the means of calculating q. That these two definitions of heat are really alike and that the first law is true have been verified experimentally many times. The difference $\Delta E - w$ is always found to be the energy transferred or transferable by virtue of a temperature difference. (Many texts and thermodynamic treatises state the first law as $\Delta E = q - w$ or $dE = dq - dw$. In these books, w refers to work done *by* the system.)

2.5 ADIABATIC PROCESSES

The first law of thermodynamics has been stated as the law of conservation of energy for thermodynamics. Another statement is given by Guggenheim[1] in terms of any process that involves no heat: "The work required to bring a *thermally insulated* system from one completely specified state to a second completely specified state is independent of the source of the work and of the path through which the system passes from the initial to the final state." The process undergone by the thermally insulated system is an adiabatic process; it involves no heat. For an adiabatic process, $q = 0$, and (2.13) becomes

$$dE = dw \tag{2.14}$$

Any change that does not involve heat, such as most problems in classical mechanics, is an illustration of an adiabatic process and (2.14) and (2.15).

$$\Delta E = w \tag{2.15}$$

Indeed, these equations are the basis of the definition that energy is the ability to do work. While (2.14) and (2.15) are always true, this description as the ability to do work is thermodynamically unsatisfactory. As soon as a non-conservative force like friction is encountered, energy is better described as a measure of work done. It is possible to deal with friction by conservative mechanics by shifting to a microscopic or molecular description, but this is outside the scope of thermodynamics. On the macroscopic or thermodynamic scale, when a bow is drawn, some of the work done on it is dissipated within the bow. The kinetic energy of the newly released arrow is less than the work done in drawing the

(1) Guggenheim, E. A., *Thermodynamics*. Amsterdam: North-Holland Publishing Co., 1957, p. 11.

bow. Some of the loss is in the bow and some is in the twang of the string. Even as the arrow moves through the air, it is slowed by friction as it stirs the air. Finally, it hits the target and dissipates its energy into vibrations of various kinds. As in Joule's or Rumford's experiments, which can be thought of as adiabatic if the system is properly chosen, the archer has increased the temperature of other bodies in the system (bow + arrow + air + target). The second law of thermodynamics (Chapter 4) deals with the recovery of this energy as work.

2.6 PROCESSES WITHOUT WORK

Expansion work due to changes in volume is perhaps the most common form of work in chemical processes. It would be a rare chemical or physical change in which the volume of the final state is identical with the volume of the initial state. Experimentally to achieve a constant volume is perhaps impossible, for even the strongest vessel suffers a slight displacement due to pressure changes within or without. However, for some process in which all work done on the system is pressure-volume work [Equation (2.3)], the first law of thermodynamics [Equations (2.12) and (2.13)] becomes more definite and is given by

$$\Delta E = q - \int_{V_1}^{V_2} P\, dV \tag{2.16}$$

$$dE = dq - P\, dV \tag{2.17}$$

In (2.16) and (2.17) P is the uniform normal pressure of the surroundings, and V_1 and V_2 are the initial and final volumes of the system. If the volume V is held constant during the process, dV is everywhere zero, and the increase in energy of the system equals q_V or dq_V, the heat absorbed by the system at constant volume. That is, by (2.16) and (2.17), at constant volume,

$$\Delta E = q_V \tag{2.18}$$

$$dE = dq_V \tag{2.19}$$

Since E is a function of state, q_V is also a function of state. For any process, whether it is chemical or physical, that involves only pressure-volume work and that is performed at constant volume, ΔE or q_V is the unique increase in energy that accompanies the change.

2.7 PROCESSES AT CONSTANT PRESSURE

It is very easy to perform experiments at constant pressure. Ordinary apparatus like beakers, furnaces, and burettes is open to the atmosphere of the laboratory.

Provided the experiment is completed before the diurnal variation in barometric pressure becomes important, such an experiment can be said to occur in a huge barostat, the atmosphere of the laboratory and earth. It is fitting, therefore, that some thermodynamic function be defined to acknowledge the value of this barostat and its influence on common processes. If only pressure-volume work is involved, the first law [Equation (2.16)] for an isobaric process is restated in (2.20), for P is constant.

$$\begin{aligned} q_P &= \Delta E + \int_{V_1}^{V_2} P\,dV \\ &= \Delta E + P\,\Delta V \end{aligned} \tag{2.20}$$

The subscript on q indicates that q_P is the heat absorbed by the system for a process that occurs at constant pressure.

By definition, the enthalpy H of a system is given by

$$H = E + PV \tag{2.21}$$

Since E, P, and V are functions of state, H is also a function of state. That is, changes in enthalpy are independent of the path or process, and dH is an exact differential. Equation (2.20) can be restated thus, since $P = P_1 = P_2$:

$$\begin{aligned} q_P &= \Delta E + P\,\Delta V \\ &= E_2 - E_1 + P(V_2 - V_1) \\ &= E_2 + P_2V_2 - (E_1 - P_1V_1) \end{aligned} \tag{2.20}$$

But by (2.21),

$$q_P = H_2 - H_1$$

That is,

$$q_P = \Delta H \tag{2.22}$$

Enthalpy is a convenient thermodynamic function for describing thermal effects that accompany isobaric changes, for the increase in enthalpy ΔH is equal to the heat absorbed by the system at constant pressure for changes that involve only expansion work.

For a change that involves a pressure change from P_1 to P_2, a volume change from V_1 to V_2, and an energy change from E_1 to E_2, the increase in enthalpy is

$$\begin{aligned} \Delta H = H_2 - H_1 &= E_2 + P_2V_2 - (E_1 + P_1V_1) \\ &= E_2 - E_1 + P_2V_2 - P_1V_1 \\ &= \Delta E + \Delta(PV) \end{aligned} \tag{2.23}$$

Equation (2.23) is perfectly general. For many chemical changes, the magnitude of the $\Delta(PV)$ term is small compared with the ΔH and ΔE terms. Situations in which this is true are illustrated in Examples 2.5 and 2.6 and in Chapter 3.

If a particular isobaric change involves work other than pressure-volume work, then recourse to the first law (2.12) and the expression for a change in enthalpy (2.23) leads to (2.24), which relates all the work other than pressure-volume work to the enthalpy change ΔH and the heat absorbed by the system q_P.

$$\Delta H = \Delta E + \Delta(PV) \tag{2.23}$$

$$= q_P + w_{PV} + w_0 + P\,\Delta V \qquad \text{[by (2.12)]}$$

$$= q_P + w_0 \tag{2.24}$$

since, by (2.3), $w_{PV} = -\int_{V_1}^{V_2} P\,dV = -P\,\Delta V$. Equation (2.24), which is more general than (2.22), states merely that the increase in enthalpy of a system is equal to the heat absorbed at constant pressure plus all the isobaric work done on the system provided such work is not pressure-volume work.

The determination of the mechanical equivalent of thermal energy is an example of the use of (2.24) when $q_P = 0$. The orderly movement of a paddle-wheel that stirs a thermally insulated fluid into disorganized eddies and vortices increases the enthalpy of the system, the fluid. The amount of energy that enters the system as work is measured by the rise in temperature that results in the fluid. Similarly, the organized movement of electrons that flow in a conductor becomes the disorganized movement of the atoms of the conductor as electric work is transformed into energy that can be measured by a rise in temperature of a fluid in contact with the conductor but thermally insulated from the surroundings.

Example 2.1. Calculate the increase in enthalpy of one mole H_2O when it is changed from ice at 0°C at 0.0060 atm to water vapor at 0°C at 0.0060 atm. The thermal energy necessary to transform one g liquid H_2O to gaseous H_2O at 0°C at 0.0060 atm is 596 cal. The thermal energy to melt one g ice at 0°C at 0.0060 atm is 80 cal.

The problem can be clarified by a diagram.

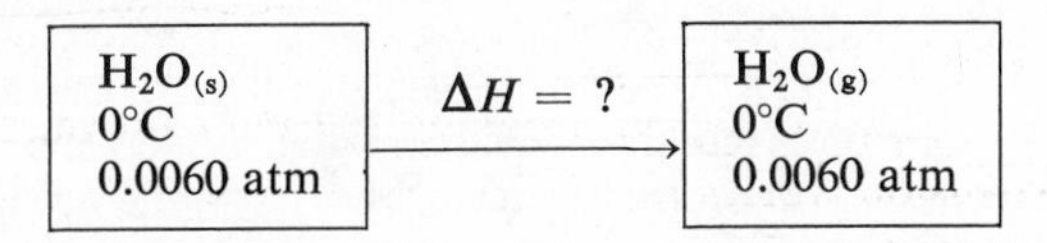

The system is one mole H_2O. The subscripts (s), (l), or (g) indicate the state of aggregation, solid, liquid, or gas. The information that is given can be summarized in a similar way.

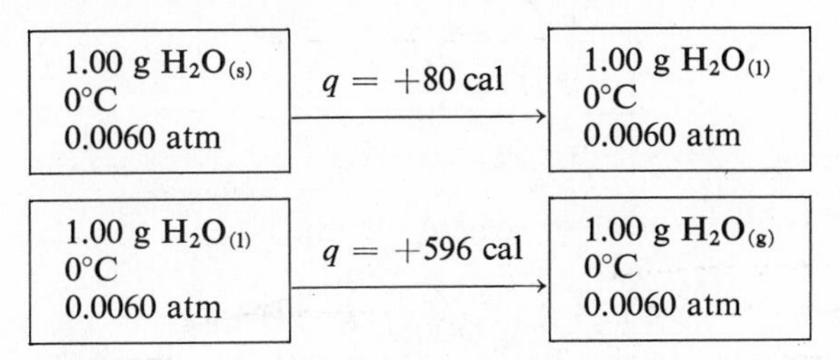

All the processes diagrammed are isothermal ($dT = 0$) and isobaric ($dP = 0$). Since the pressure is constant at 0.0060 atm and since all work is pressure-volume work, the thermal energies are q_P. By Equation (2.22), $q_P = \Delta H$. For 1 mole, the heat of fusion ΔH_f is 18.0×80 cal and the heat of vaporization ΔH_v is 18.0×596 cal. Since H is a function of state, the diagrams can be combined, for the enthalpy of a mole of water does not depend on its previous history as ice, its future state as vapor, or the process by which it was brought to or will leave its liquid state at 0°C at 0.0060 atm.

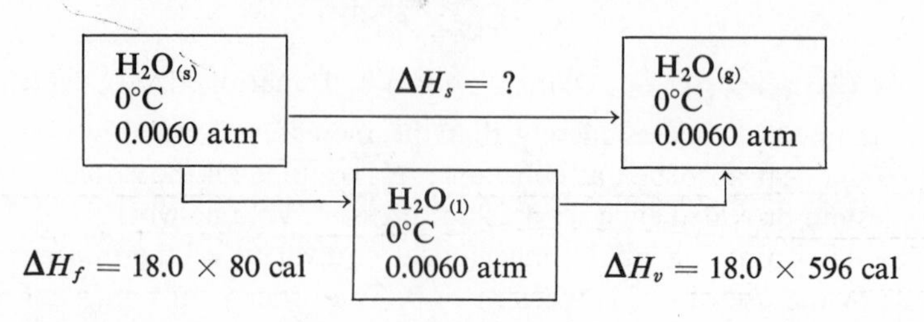

The heat of sublimation ΔH_s is clearly the sum of the enthalpy changes with water as intermediate species. That is, $\Delta H_s = 18.0 \times 80 + 18.0 \times 596$ cal $= 12{,}170$ cal. That this follows from the fact that H is a function of state can be shown mathematically by assigning an absolute molar enthalpy $H_{(s)}$ to ice, $H_{(l)}$ to water, and $H_{(g)}$ to steam. Then,

$$\Delta H_f = H_{(l)} - H_{(s)}, \qquad \Delta H_v = H_{(g)} - H_{(l)}$$

$$\Delta H_s = H_{(g)} - H_{(s)} = H_{(g)} - H_{(l)} + (H_{(l)} - H_{(s)}) = \Delta H_v + \Delta H_f$$

It is not important how the process by which ice became steam occurred. It might have been irreversible with water existing temporarily at 3°C, but for the change under study, $\Delta H = 12{,}170$ cal. Since ΔH is greater than zero, the enthalpy of steam is greater than that of ice when both steam and ice are at 0°C at 0.0060 atm.

Example 2.2. Calculate the increase in energy ΔE for the isobaric condensation of one mole steam at 0°C at 0.0060 atm to water at 0°C at 0.0060 atm. The heat of vaporization of H_2O is 10,730 cal mole^{-1} at 0°C at 0.0060 atm.

Since vaporization requires that thermal energy be absorbed by the water, condensation must require that water evolve the same amount of energy. For the process $H_2O_{(g)} \rightarrow H_2O_{(l)}$, $\Delta H = q_P = -10{,}730$ cal. The work done on the steam as it condenses at 0°C at 0.0060 atm is given by (2.3).

$$\begin{aligned}
w &= -\int_{V(g)}^{V(l)} P\,dV \\
&= -P(V_{(l)} - V_{(g)}) \\
&= -(0.0060 \text{ atm})\left[0.018\text{ l} - \left(22.4 \times \frac{1}{0.0060}\right)\text{ l}\right] \\
&= (22.4 - 0.0060 \times 0.018) \text{ l-atm} = 22.4 \text{ l-atm} \\
&= 22.4 \times \left(\frac{1.987}{0.08206}\right) \text{cal} = 543 \text{ cal}
\end{aligned}$$

By the first law [Equation (2.12)],

$$\Delta E = q + w = -10{,}730 + 543 \text{ cal} = -10{,}187 \text{ cal}$$

The energy of the liquid is less than that of the vapor since ΔE is less than zero. The same result might have been obtained by (2.23), where the $\Delta(PV)$ term is -543 cal and is dominated by the PV product of the gas phase.

2.8 HEAT CAPACITY

For processes that do not occur at constant temperature it is necessary to account for energy involved in changing the temperature. Indeed, it was the temperature change suffered by a standard body of standard heat capacity that was chosen as the measure of thermal energy transferred. Acocrding to (2.10) and (2.11), the heat capacity C is a proportionality factor with the value

$$C = \frac{dq}{dT} \tag{2.25}$$

It is customary to let C refer to 1 mole of matter that absorbs the heat.

The thermodynamic definition of C_V, the heat capacity for constant-volume processes, is

$$C_V = \left(\frac{\partial E}{\partial T}\right)_V \tag{2.26}$$

That this definition is reasonable in view of (2.25) is shown by substitution of (2.25) into the first law (2.17) where all work is expansion work.

$$\begin{aligned} dE &= dq - P\,dV \\ &= C\,dT - P\,dV \end{aligned} \tag{2.17}$$

If the volume is constant, $dV = 0$ and (2.26) is justified.

Similarly, for processes at constant pressure, the heat capacity C_P is defined as

$$C_P = \left(\frac{\partial H}{\partial T}\right)_P \tag{2.27}$$

This is reasonable, for by (2.21) $dH = d(E + PV) = dE + P\,dV + V\,dP$. Whence, by (2.17) and (2.25), when only expansion work is involved,

$$dH = dq - P\,dV + P\,dV + V\,dP = dq + V\,dP = C\,dT + V\,dP$$

If the pressure is constant, $dP = 0$ and (2.27) results, where the subscript P indicates that the pressure is constant.

For finite temperature changes, (2.26) and (2.27) must be integrated. The results are

$$dE = C_V\,dT \qquad (dV = 0)$$

$$\int_{E_1}^{E_2} dE = \int_{T_1}^{T_2} C_V\,dT$$

heat capacity for c.v.

$$\Delta E = \int_{T_1}^{T_2} C_V\,dT \quad (dV = 0) \tag{2.28}$$

$$dH = C_P\,dT \qquad (dP = 0)$$

$$\int_{H_1}^{H_2} dH = \int_{T_1}^{T_2} C_P\,dT$$

$$\Delta H = \int_{T_1}^{T_2} C_P\,dT \quad (dP = 0) \tag{2.29}$$

Example 2.3. In determining the thermal equivalent of electric energy, an electric current of 1.00 amp flowed through a conductor with a resistance of 2.00 ohms. The conductor had a specific heat of 0.10 cal g^{-1} deg^{-1} and it weighed one g. The conductor was immersed in 100.0 g pure water, which were in turn held in a vessel with a heat capacity of 5.0 cal deg^{-1}. The vessel and its contents were thermally insulated from the surroundings. The rise in temperature of the system (conductor, water, and vessel) was 2.73°C after the current had flowed 10.0 min. What is the conversion factor between electric work in joules and thermal energy in calories?

By (2.4) and Ohm's law ($\mathscr{E} = \mathscr{I}\mathscr{R}$), the electric work done on the system was

$$w = \int \mathscr{E}\,dQ = \int_0^t \mathscr{E}\mathscr{I}\,dt' = \mathscr{E}\mathscr{I}t = \mathscr{I}^2\mathscr{R}t$$

$$= (1.00 \text{ amp})^2 \times (2.00 \text{ ohms}) \times (600 \text{ sec}) = 1200 \text{ j}$$

Since the system was thermally insulated, $q_P = 0$. The increase in enthalpy of the system for this isobaric process is given by (2.29).

$$\Delta H = \int_{T_1}^{T_2} C_P\,dT = C_P\,\Delta T$$

$$= [(0.1 + 100.0 + 5.0) \text{ cal deg}^{-1}] \times [2.73°] = 287 \text{ cal}$$

By Equation (2.24),

$$\Delta H = q_P + w_E, \quad 287 \text{ cal} = 0 + 1200 \text{ j}$$

That is, one calorie is equivalent to 4.18 joules.

Example 2.4. In determining the specific heat of mercury, an electric current of 0.200 amp flowed through a conductor with a resistance of 2.00 ohms. The conductor had a specific heat of 0.10 cal g^{-1} deg^{-1} and it weighed one g. The conductor was immersed in 1300 g pure Hg, which were in turn held in a vessel with a heat capacity of 5.00 cal deg^{-1}. The vessel and its contents were thermally insulated from the surroundings at one atm. The rise in temperature of the system (conductor, Hg, and vessel) was 0.166°C after the current had flowed 420 sec. What is the specific heat of Hg?

As in Example 2.3, the electric work done on the system is $w_E = \mathscr{I}^2 \mathscr{R} t = 0.200^2 \times 2.00 \times 420 = 33.6$ j. Since the system was thermally insulated at constant pressure, $q_P = 0$. For this isobaric process, the increase in enthalpy of the system is, by (2.29),

$$\Delta H = (0.10 + 1300 c_P + 5.00)(0.166)$$

where c_P is the specific heat of Hg. But by (2.24)

$$\Delta H = q_P + w_E = 0 + 33.6\ \text{j}$$

Equating values of ΔH yields $c_P = 0.0333$ cal g^{-1} deg^{-1}.

Example 2.5. Between 20°C and 100°C the isobaric specific heat of Hg depends on the Celsius temperature τ approximately thus: $c_P = 0.03323 - 0.00007$ $(\tau - 20)$ cal g^{-1} deg^{-1}. Calculate ΔH and ΔE for the isobaric change of one gram-atom (200.6 g) of Hg from 20°C to 100°C if the density of Hg at 20°C is 13.546 g cm^{-3} while at 100°C it is 13.352 g cm^{-3}.

As in (2.29), for this change of state

$$\Delta H = 200.6 \int_{20}^{100} [c_P] d\tau = 200.6 \int_{20}^{100} [0.03323 - 0.00007(\tau - 20)\, d\tau$$

$$= 200.6 \int_{0}^{80} [0.03323 - 0.00007(\tau - 20) d(\tau - 20)$$

$$= 200.6 \times 0.03323 \times 80 - 0.00007 \frac{80^2 - 0}{2} = 533.3 - 0.2 = 533.1 \text{ cal}$$

As 200.6 g Hg change from 20°C to 100°C at one atm

$$\Delta(PV) = P\Delta V = 1.000 \text{ atm} \left(\frac{200.6}{13.352} - \frac{200.6}{13.546}\right)\left(\frac{1.987}{82.06}\right) = 0.00521 \text{ cal}$$

By (2.23), $\Delta E = \Delta H - \Delta(PV) = 533.1 - 0.005 = 533.1$ cal.

In this isobaric process, $q_P = \Delta H = 533.1$ cal by (2.22). The work done on the Hg is $w = -P\Delta V = -0.00521$ cal. By the first law (2.12), $\Delta E = q + w = 533.1 - 0.005 = 533.1$ cal, as found by (2.23). In other words, the difference $\Delta H - \Delta E = \Delta(PV) = -w = 0.00521$ cal is the expansion work done by the Hg on the surroundings as it expands isobarically at one atm. For condensed phases, such expansion work is generally negligible relative to ΔH and ΔE.

2.9 THERMODYNAMIC PROPERTIES OF A PERFECT GAS

When the equation of state of a perfect gas $PV = nRT$ was described in Chapter 1, the temperature scale T was defined in terms of the behavior of a perfect gas.

The constant-volume hydrogen gas thermometer is in fact the primary standard of the absolute temperature scale. The second law of thermodynamics will introduce a thermodynamic temperature scale that can be shown to be identical with the perfect gas scale of temperature. The definition of a perfect gas is most aptly put in terms that are consistent with but different from conformity with the perfect gas equation.

A perfect gas must obey Boyle's law and its energy must be independent of its volume at constant temperature. In mathematical terms, a gas is perfect if it conforms to (2.30).

$$\left.\begin{aligned} PV &= f(n, T) \\ \left(\frac{\partial E}{\partial V}\right)_T &= 0 \end{aligned}\right\} \tag{2.30}$$

For a specified amount of gas at a specified temperature, $f(n, T)$ is a constant. The second criterion was determined experimentally by Gay-Lussac in 1807 and by Joule in 1844. Their system was a compressed gas held in part of a rigid container. When the gas was allowed to expand freely into the unoccupied part of the rigid container, the temperature of the expanding gas decreased and the temperature of the gas streaming into the previously evacuated part of the container increased. When a final uniform temperature of the gas was achieved, it was clear that there was no net transfer of heat between gas and surroundings. The final temperature was the same as the initial temperature; no heat or work was exchanged between system and surroundings. By the first law, since $q = 0$ and $w = 0$,

$$\Delta E = q + w = 0$$

The experiment showed that the energy of a gas was independent of its volume at constant temperature, and the second criterion is a mathematical statement of this observation.

The surroundings used in the early experiments were a water bath that, because of its high heat capacity, could not record by its temperature changes the exchange of slight amounts of thermal energy. Isolation by means of a vacuum and use of thin metal containers does much to refine this type of experiment. Since the Joule-Thomson experiment is quite suitable for noting deviations from ideal behavior in this regard, the matter of experimental elegance is here of small concern. All real gases generally fail to satisfy part or all of (2.30), but often the degree of failure is of little importance.

The energy of a system can be considered to be a function of its composition, volume, and temperature. That is, for a closed system of fixed composition,

$$E = E(V, T) \tag{2.31}$$

By the rules of calculus, the differential of E from (2.31) is

$$dE = \left(\frac{\partial E}{\partial T}\right)_V dT + \left(\frac{\partial E}{\partial V}\right)_T dV \qquad (2.32)$$

But for a perfect gas, the coefficient of dV is zero by (2.30) and the coefficient of dT is C_V, or nC_V if there be n moles in the system. Then (2.32) becomes

$$dE = nC_V\, dT \qquad (2.33)$$

By virtue of Equations (2.30) to (2.33), the energy of a fixed amount of a perfect gas is a function only of its temperature. This result was obtained in Chapter 1 by the kinetic theory. Moreover, in any isothermal change, there is no change in the energy of a perfect gas. That is, if $dT = 0$ in (2.33),

$$dE = 0 \qquad \Delta E = 0 \qquad E = E(T) \qquad (2.34)$$

The enthalpy of a perfect gas is also dependent only on its temperature. By (2.30) and (2.34) and the definition of H,

$$H = E + PV = E(T) + f(n, T) = H(T)$$

Any isothermal change of a perfect gas involves no change in enthalpy if the system is closed. Moreover, the enthalpy of a perfect gas at constant temperature is independent of its pressure. That is, at constant temperature,

$$dH = 0 \qquad \Delta H = 0 \qquad H = H(T) \qquad (2.35)$$

$$\left(\frac{\partial H}{\partial P}\right)_T = 0 \qquad (2.36)$$

Equations (2.35) and (2.36) are the natural results of and the counterparts of Equations (2.34) and (2.30). Just as E is customarily and conveniently taken as a function of volume and temperature, H is taken as a function of pressure and temperature.

$$H = H(P, T) \qquad (2.37)$$

By the rules of calculus,

$$dH = \left(\frac{\partial H}{\partial T}\right)_P dT + \left(\frac{\partial H}{\partial P}\right)_T dP \qquad (2.38)$$

For any kind of process of a perfect gas, the coefficient of dP in (2.38) is zero and the coefficient of dT is nC_P; so that

$$dH = nC_P\, dT \qquad (2.39)$$

Equations (2.33) and (2.39) not only are useful for perfect gases but also generally dominate other terms in circumstances where behavior of gases is not quite perfect.

2.10 HEAT CAPACITIES OF GASES

The heat capacity of a gas at constant pressure exceeds the heat capacity of that gas at constant volume because the gas performs work on its surroundings as it expands at constant pressure. If its volume is held constant, such expansion work by the gas as it is heated is impossible. The difference between C_P and C_V for a perfect gas is easily evaluated from (2.34) and (2.35). By the several definitions of C_P, C_V, and H,

$$C_P - C_V = \left(\frac{\partial H}{\partial T}\right)_P - \left(\frac{\partial E}{\partial T}\right)_V$$

$$= \left[\frac{\partial}{\partial T}(E + PV)\right]_P - \left(\frac{\partial E}{\partial T}\right)_V$$

$$= \frac{dE}{dT} + \left[\frac{\partial}{\partial T}(RT)\right]_P - \frac{dE}{dT}$$

where total derivatives replace partial derivatives since E is a function only of T by (2.34). Accordingly,

$$C_P - C_V = R \tag{2.40}$$

For any substance, perfect gas or not, the difference between C_P and C_V is somewhat more complicated. By (2.32), which is true for any substance,

$$dE = \left(\frac{\partial E}{\partial T}\right)_V dT + \left(\frac{\partial E}{\partial V}\right)_T dV \tag{2.32}$$

Division by dT at constant pressure gives

$$\left(\frac{\partial E}{\partial T}\right)_P = \left(\frac{\partial E}{\partial T}\right)_V + \left(\frac{\partial E}{\partial V}\right)_T\left(\frac{\partial V}{\partial T}\right)_P$$

By definition,

$$C_P - C_V = \left(\frac{\partial H}{\partial T}\right)_P - \left(\frac{\partial E}{\partial T}\right)_V = \left(\frac{\partial E}{\partial T}\right)_P + \left(\frac{\partial (PV)}{\partial T}\right)_P - \left(\frac{\partial E}{\partial T}\right)_V$$

The first term of the right-hand member is given above; thus

$$C_P - C_V = \left(\frac{\partial E}{\partial V}\right)_T\left(\frac{\partial V}{\partial T}\right)_P + \left(\frac{\partial (PV)}{\partial T}\right)_P = \left[\left(\frac{\partial E}{\partial V}\right)_T + P\right]\left(\frac{\partial V}{\partial T}\right)_P \tag{2.41}$$

When the value of $(\partial E/\partial V)_T$ is known, (2.41) provides a convenient way to find C_V from C_P and the equation of state, $V = V(P, T)$. While $(\partial V/\partial T)_P$ is often small for condensed phases, $(\partial E/\partial V)_T$ may be large enough to make C_P differ from C_V by 25%.

Example 2.6. Show that Equation (2.40) is a special case of (2.41).

The equation of state of 1 mole of a perfect gas is $PV = RT$. Substitution in (2.41) and account of (2.30) yield the desired result.

$$C_P - C_V = \left[\left(\frac{\partial E}{\partial V}\right)_T + P\right]\left(\frac{\partial V}{\partial T}\right)_P = [0 + P]\left[\frac{\partial}{\partial T}\left(\frac{RT}{P}\right)\right]_P = R$$

The kinetic theory equation from Chapter 1 explicitly evaluates the energy of a perfect gas as a function of temperature. For 1 mole monatomic gas,

$$E = \frac{3}{2}RT$$

By Equations (2.26) and (2.40), the molar heat capacities of a perfect monatomic gas are

$$\left.\begin{aligned} C_V &= \left(\frac{\partial E}{\partial T}\right)_V = \frac{3}{2}R \\ C_P &= C_V + R = \frac{5}{2}R \end{aligned}\right\} \tag{2.42}$$

The heat capacities of real gases are in general functions of the absolute temperature, for as the temperature rises the various degrees of freedom within the molecule—rotations, bendings, vibrations, and electronic changes—are excited. This excitation requires energy that is added as heat. Moreover, additional thermal energy is required to keep the whole molecule's rotational energy commensurate with its translational energy at T, for collisions cause one to become the other. The average rotational energy of a mole of rigid linear molecules at T is RT, while that of a mole of rigid nonlinear molecules is $\frac{3}{2}RT$. Accordingly, for a mole of rigid linear molecules at T, the average energy of translation and rotation is $E = (\frac{3}{2})RT + RT = (\frac{5}{2})RT$ so that, with (2.40) if the gas is perfect,

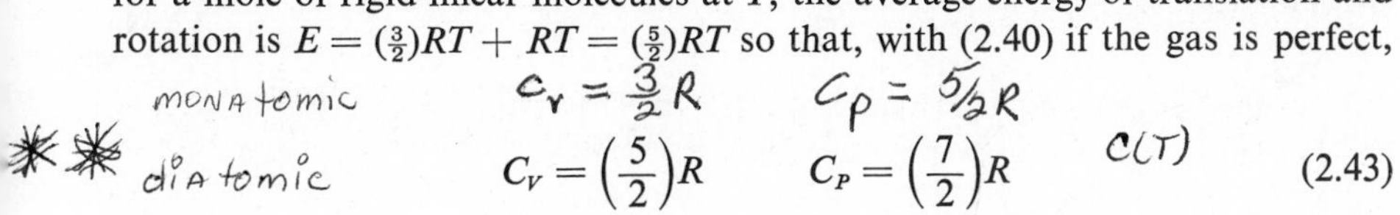

$$C_V = \left(\frac{5}{2}\right)R \qquad C_P = \left(\frac{7}{2}\right)R \tag{2.43}$$

Diatomic molecules with strong bonds (e. g., CO, N_2, O_2, H_2) follow (2.43) at moderate T. Similarly, for a rigid nonlinear molecule, $E = (\frac{3}{2})RT +$

$(\frac{3}{2})RT$ so that $C_V = 3R$, with $C_P = 4R$ if it is perfect. Figure 2.3 illustrates these values as lower limits to heat capacities of really vibrating molecules. For example, H_2 and N_2 have $C_P = (\frac{7}{2})R$ below about 500°K, and C_P for H_2O approaches the limit $4R$ near 300°K. Figure 2.3 also illustrates how the complexity and suppleness of a molecule enhances C_P as T rises.

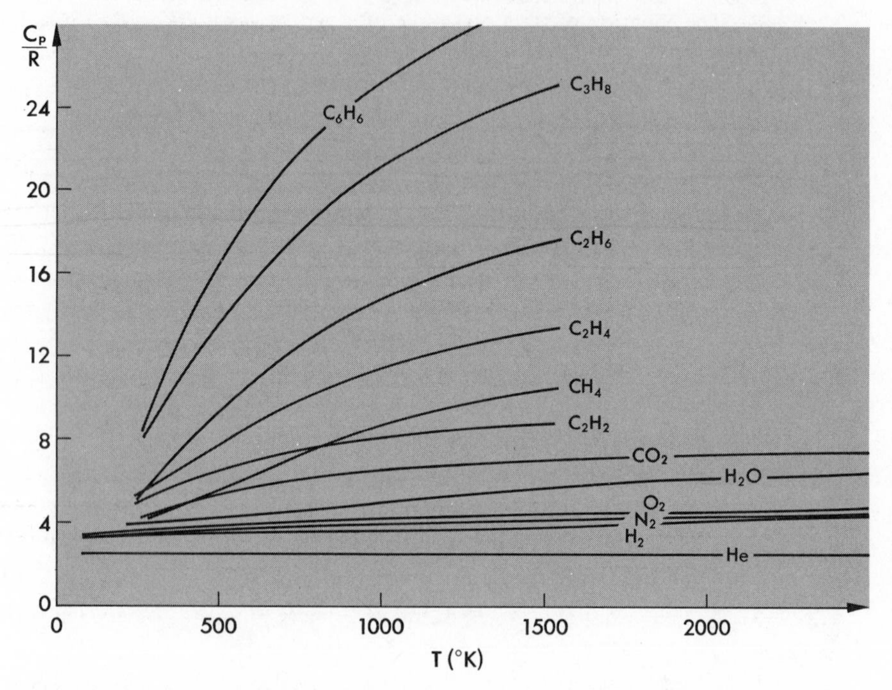

Figure 2.3. Gaseous Heat Capacities at Constant Pressure as Functions of Temperature†

Heat capacities can be calculated by the methods of statistical mechanics, and at high temperatures such calculated heat capacities are often more accurate than observed values. It has long been customary to express the molar heat capacity of a gas empirically as a power series in the temperature, as in

$$C_P = C_P^{(0)} + C_P^{(1)}T + C_P^{(2)}T^2 + \cdots \tag{2.44}$$

The value of C_V can be found from C_P at any temperature by (2.40) or (2.41). Table 2.1 contains the constants $C_P^{(i)}$ for some common gases.

†Data from *Selected Values of Properties of Hydrocarbons, Circular of the National Bureau of Standards C461* by F. D. Rossini et al., Washington, D. C.; U. S. Government Printing Office, November, 1947.

Table 2.1 Molar Heat Capacities of Gases at Constant Pressure For Temperatures of 300°K to 1500°K (H. M. Spencer and J. L. Justice, *J. Am. Chem. Soc.* **56,** 2311 [1934]; H. M. Spencer and G. N. Flannagan, *J. Am. Chem. Soc.* **64,** 2511 [1942]; H. M. Spencer, *J. Am. Chem. Soc.* **67,** 1859 [1945].)

$$C_P = C_P^{(0)} + C_P^{(1)}T + C_P^{(2)}T^2 \text{ (cal mole}^{-1}\text{ deg}^{-1}\text{)}$$

Gas	$C_P^{(0)}$	$C_P^{(1)} \times 10^3$	$C_P^{(2)} \times 10^6$
Ammonia	6.189	7.887	−0.728
Benzene	−0.283	77.936	−26.296
n-Butane	4.357	72.552	−22.145
cis-2-Butene	2.047	64.311	−19.834
Bromine	8.4228	0.9739	−0.3555
Carbon dioxide	6.214	10.396	−3.545
Carbon monoxide	6.420	1.665	−0.196
Chlorine	7.5755	2.4244	−0.9650
Ethane	2.195	38.282	−11.001
Hydrogen	6.9469	−0.1999	0.4808
Hydrogen bromide	6.5776	0.9549	0.1581
Hydrogen chloride	6.7319	0.4325	0.3697
Methane	3.381	18.044	−4.300
Nitrogen	6.524	1.250	−0.001
Oxygen	6.148	3.102	−0.923
Propane	2.258	57.636	−17.594
Water	7.256	2.298	0.283

Example 2.7. Calculate the heat required to increase the temperature of 1.00 mole gaseous oxygen from 0.0°C to 100.0°C, (a) at constant pressure, and (b) at constant volume. Account for the difference in the heat absorbed in (a) and (b). The heat capacity of O_2 is given in Table 2.1 and O_2 may be assumed to be a perfect gas.

A diagram of the processes follows, where P_i and V_i signify the pressure and volume of the oxygen at state *i*.

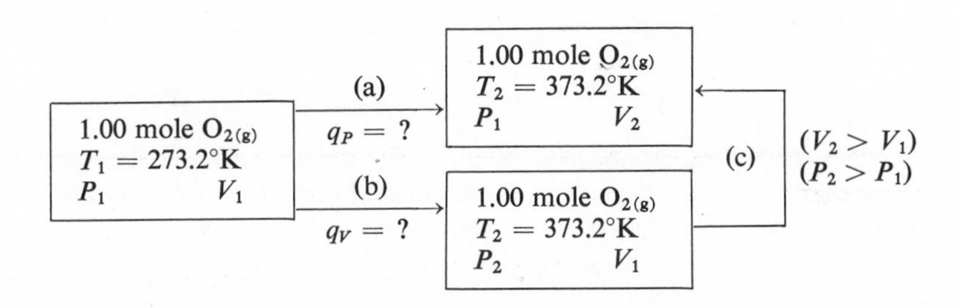

(a) When only pressure-volume work is involved in an isobaric process, Equation (2.22) or (2.24) and Equation (2.29) or (2.39) are applicable.

$$q_P = \int_{T_1}^{T_2} C_P \, dT$$

$$= \int_{T_1}^{T_2} [C_P^{(0)} + C_P^{(1)}T + C_P^{(2)}T^2] \, dT$$

$$q_P = C_P^{(0)} \int_{T_1}^{T_2} dT + C_P^{(1)} \int_{T_1}^{T_2} T\,dT + C_P^{(2)} \int_{T_1}^{T_2} T^2\,dT$$

$$= C_P^{(0)}(T_2 - T_1) + C_P^{(1)}\left(\frac{T_2^2 - T_1^2}{2}\right) + C_P^{(2)}\left(\frac{T_2^3 - T_1^3}{3}\right)$$

$$= 614.8 + 3.102 \times 10^{-3}\left(\frac{373.2^2 - 273.2^2}{2}\right)$$

$$- 0.923 \times 10^{-6}\left(\frac{373.2^3 - 273.2^3}{3}\right)$$

$$= 614.8 + 3.102 \times 10^{-3}\left(\frac{(373.2 + 273.2)(373.2 - 273.2)}{2}\right)$$

$$- \frac{0.923}{3}(52.0 - 20.4)$$

$$= 614.8 + 100.2 - 9.72 = 705.3 \text{ cal}$$

(b) Similarly, by Equations (2.18), (2.33), and (2.40),

$$q_V = \Delta E = \int_{T_1}^{T_2} C_V\,dT = \int_{T_1}^{T_2} (C_P - R)dT = \Delta H - R(T_2 - T_1)$$

$$= 705.3 - 1.987 \times 100.0 = 506.6 \text{ cal}$$

More heat is absorbed in the isobaric process than in the process at constant volume because the gas does work as it expands at constant pressure, and this work energy is supplied as heat. The work done by the gas on the surroundings in the process labeled (a) is done at constant pressure P_1, and is calculated thus:

$$-w_P = \int_{V_1}^{V_2} P\,dV = \int_{V_1}^{V_2} P_1\,dV = P_1(V_2 - V_1)$$

$$= P_1\left(\frac{RT_2}{P_1} - \frac{RT_1}{P_1}\right) = R(T_2 - T_1) = 1.987 \times 100.0 = 198.7 \text{ cal}$$

For process (a), then,

$$\Delta E = q + w = q_P + w_P = 705.3 - 198.7 = 506.6 \text{ cal}$$

Since O_2 is here assumed to be a perfect gas, H and E are functions only of temperature. Since process (c) is isothermal, for it $\Delta H = \Delta E = 0$. For processes (b) and (c), then,

$$\Delta E = \Delta E_{(b)} + \Delta E_{(c)} = 506.6 + 0 = 506.6 \text{ cal}$$

The same change in energy results for either path that ends at T_2, P_1, and V_2 because the initial and final states are alike and E is a function of state.

It is not possible to calculate the work involved in the process labeled (c), for the process is not specified. The work done by the gas if it had expanded isothermally and reversibly from V_1 to V_2 could be calculated thus:

$$-w = \int_{V_1}^{V_2} P\,dV = RT_2 \int_{V_1}^{V_2} \frac{dV}{V} = RT_2 \ln\left(\frac{V_2}{V_1}\right)$$

But $P_1V_1 = RT_1$ and $P_1V_2 = RT_2$; hence,

$$-w = RT_2 \ln\left(\frac{T_2}{T_1}\right) > 0$$

Since $\Delta E = 0$ for process (c), heat would have to be absorbed by the gas since

$$q = \Delta E - w = 0 + RT_2 \ln\left(\frac{T_2}{T_1}\right) > 0$$

If, however, process (c) had been performed irreversibly, less work would have been done by the gas. For example, isothermal expansion into a vacuum could have led to no work, and thus to an adiabatic process since ΔE for process (c) is zero. Since many other processes could be imagined, in the absence of an explicit definition of the process, it is impossible to evaluate the work done by the gas in process (c).

2:11 REVERSIBLE ISOTHERMAL WORK

Although the amount of work involved in a process depends both upon initial and final states and upon the path followed by the process, the qualifications that the work be done reversibly and isothermally so restrict the process as to make such work unique. If the process is reversible, an infinitesimal change in the pressure that causes the process could stop or reverse the process. For a reversible expansion, an infinitesimal increase in the pressure in the surroundings would halt the expansion by which the system works. It is clear, then, that the driving and opposing forces in such a process are everywhere a maximum. Any such work done by the system must also be a maximum. If the pressures on each side of the boundary of the system differ at most by an infinitesimal, they are in the limit equal. It is for this reason that the pressure calculated from the equation of state of the system can be used in place of the pressure exerted by the surroundings.

The specification *isothermal* is not readily explained before development of the second law of thermodynamics. Briefly, such a specification must be made in order to prevent transfer of energy by virtue of a difference in temperature. The second law will also clarify the fact that isothermal reversible work is a function of state.

The work done reversibly and isothermally on a system by the surroundings is given by (2.3), which can be stated in the integrated form

$$w = -\int_{V_1}^{V_2} P\,dV \tag{2.45}$$

Here V_1 is the initial volume of the system, V_2 is the final volume of the system, and P is the pressure of the system or surroundings as the process occurs. The volume changes of the system are assumed to be equal in magnitude but opposite in sign to the changes in volume of the surroundings. The maximum work done by the system is equal in magnitude but opposite in sign to the work done on the system. That is, the work done by the system is $-w$, where, as above,

$$-w = \int_{V_1}^{V_2} P\,dV \tag{2.45}$$

There are two common ways in which isothermal reversible work can be done. The pressure may vary as the change in volume occurs, or the pressure may remain constant as the volume changes. This latter situation arises in phase changes, as in equilibrium between vapor and a condensed phase at a fixed temperature. The constant pressure is the vapor pressure at the fixed temperature. In (2.45), since the value of P is constant, the integral becomes

$$w = -P \int_{V_1}^{V_2} dV = -P\,\Delta V \tag{2.46}$$

It is obvious here that w is a function of state, for P, V_1, and V_2 are themselves functions of state.

A process described by (2.46) might be a condensation. If water vapor at 100°C contains an infinitesimal drop of liquid water, the conditions for equilibrium between liquid and vapor are satisfied. When the pressure exerted on the vapor by the surroundings through a piston is infinitesimally greater than 1 atm, the piston will move inward upon the water vapor and cause it to condense to liquid water at 100°C. The condensation could be stopped or reversed by an infinitesimal decrease in the pressure of the surroundings or an infinitesimal increase in the pressure of the water vapor. This increase in pressure could perhaps be caused by an infinitesimal increase in the temperature of the water. The process is reversible because its direction can be altered by infinitesimal changes in the temperature or pressure. While the weight of the piston, its friction with the cylinder walls, or condensation in a time less than eternity would make the real process irreversible, the essence of the process is not changed when the magnitude of each of these experimental difficulties is imagined to be less and less important. Lighter and lighter alloys could be used in the piston, better and better lubricants and machining could reduce friction, and time is of no concern to equilibrium thermodynamics.

Example 2.8. Calculate the work done on one mole of steam as it is condensed reversibly at 120.0°C.

At 120.0°C, the vapor pressure of water is 1489 mm Hg and the molar volumes of vapor and liquid are 16.07 l and 0.019 l. By (2.46), the work done on the steam is

$$w = -P\Delta V = -\left(\frac{1489}{760.0}\right)(0.02 - 16.07) \times \left(\frac{1.987}{0.08206}\right) = 761 \text{ cal}$$

If 1 mole liquid water is vaporized reversibly at 120.0°C, it would do +761 cal of work on the atmosphere, for reversing the process and worker causes two changes in sign.

If two phases do not coexist at a fixed temperature, the pressure of the system will depend upon its volume. When the system consists of a perfect gas at a constant temperature T, (2.45) is readily evaluated in explicit form for the work done on the system.

$$w = -\int_{V_1}^{V_2} P\,dV = -\int_{V_1}^{V_2} \left(\frac{nRT}{V}\right) dV = -nRT \int_{V_1}^{V_2} \frac{dV}{V}$$

$$= nRT \ln\left(\frac{V_1}{V_2}\right) \tag{2.47}$$

Since the conditions for Boyle's law obtain, $P_1V_1 = P_2V_2$, and (2.47) becomes

$$w = nRT \ln\left(\frac{P_2}{P_1}\right) \tag{2.48}$$

Equations (2.47) and (2.48) say that a positive amount of work w must be done on a system if its volume is decreased from V_1 to V_2 or if its pressure is increased from P_1 to P_2. Equation (2.7) and Example 2.7 have anticipated (2.47) and (2.48).

Example 2.9. Calculate the minimum work that must be done at 25°C on 2 moles CO_2 to compress them from a volume of 20.0 l to a volume of 1.00 l, when CO_2 is assumed (a) to be a perfect gas; and (b) to follow van der Waals' equation.

If the pressure exerted by the surroundings should momentarily exceed the pressure of the CO_2, the work done by the surroundings would not be a minimum. The excess over the minimum would appear as a shock wave or as kinetic energy of CO_2 molecules and, of course, ultimately as thermal energy. Thus the minimum work, with no wasted energy, is the reversible work at 25°C. (a) By (2.45) or (2.47),

$$w = -\int_{V_1}^{V_2} P\,dV = -nRT \ln\left(\frac{V_2}{V_1}\right) = 2 \times 1.987 \times 298.2 \times 2.303 \times \log_{10}\left(\frac{20.0}{1.00}\right)$$

$$= 3553 \text{ cal}$$

(b) By (2.45) and van der Waals' equation,

$$w = -\int_{V_1}^{V_2} P\,dV = -\int_{V_1}^{V_2} \left(\frac{nRT}{V - nb} - \frac{an^2}{V^2}\right) dV$$

$$= nRT \ln\left(\frac{V_1 - nb}{V_2 - nb}\right) - an^2 \left(\frac{1}{V_2} - \frac{1}{V_1}\right)$$

For CO_2, $a = 3.60 \times 10^6$ cm^6 atm mole^{-2} and $b = 42.8$ cm^3 mole^{-1}.

$$w = \left[2 \times 82.06 \times 298.2 \times 2.303 \times \log_{10}\left(\frac{20000 - 86}{1000 - 86}\right) - 3.60 \times 10^6 \times 2^2\left(\frac{20000 - 1000}{1000 \times 20000}\right)\right]$$

$$= (151.0 - 13.7) \times 10^3 \times \frac{1.987}{82.06} = 3325 \text{ cal}$$

Less work is done on the CO_2 when the attractive forces between molecules are estimated by van der Waals' equation than when the attractive forces are neglected with use of the perfect gas equation.

2.12 ADIABATIC PROCESSES OF A PERFECT GAS

In an adiabatic process there is no heat exchanged between system and surroundings: $dq = 0$. If the system is assumed to approximate a perfect gas in its behavior, the conditions of Equation (2.30) and their consequences obtain, namely,

$$\left.\begin{aligned} PV &= f(n, T) \\ \left(\frac{\partial E}{\partial V}\right)_T &= 0 \end{aligned}\right\} \tag{2.30}$$

$$\left(\frac{\partial H}{\partial P}\right)_T = 0 \tag{2.36}$$

Use of these equations and the adiabatic condition with the first law provides differential equations from which the adiabatic gas laws can be derived.

By Equations (2.32), (2.30), and (2.26),

$$dE = nC_V\, dT \tag{2.33}$$

But for an adiabatic process that involves only pressure-volume work, the first law says $dE = dw = -P\,dV$. Equating the two expressions for dE gives (2.49), which is a suitable differential equation when temperature and volume are the variables specified.

$$C_V\, dT = -P\, dV \tag{2.49}$$

Similarly, when temperature and pressure are the variables specified for an adiabatic process of a perfect gas involving only pressure-volume work, Equations (2.38), (2.36), and (2.27), give

$$dH = nC_P\, dT \tag{2.39}$$

But

$$dH = dE + P\,dV + V\,dP = dq - P\,dV + P\,dV + V\,dP = V\,dP$$

That is,

$$C_P\, dT = V\, dP \tag{2.50}$$

When the adiabatic process is reversible, the equation of state of the system can be used in the right of (2.49) or (2.50). The variables are easily separated preparatory to integration when $PV = nRT$, and Equations (2.51) and (2.52) result. By (2.49),

$$C_V\, dT = -P\, dV = -\frac{RT}{V}\, dV$$

$$C_V \frac{dT}{T} = -R\frac{dV}{V}$$

If C_V is independent of temperature, and if V_1 is the volume of the gas at temperature T_1 and V_2 is the volume of the gas at temperature T_2, then

$$C_V \int_{T_1}^{T_2} \frac{dT}{T} = -R \int_{V_1}^{V_2} \frac{dV}{V}$$

$$C_V \ln\left(\frac{T_2}{T_1}\right) = R \ln\left(\frac{V_1}{V_2}\right) \tag{2.51a}$$

That is,

$$\frac{C_V}{R} \ln\left(\frac{T_2}{T_1}\right) = \ln\left(\frac{V_1}{V_2}\right)$$

$$V_1 T_1^{(C_V/R)} = V_2 T_2^{(C_V/R)} \tag{2.51b}$$

Similarly, if C_P is independent of temperature, (2.50) becomes

$$C_P\, dT = V\, dP = \frac{RT}{P}\, dP, \qquad C_P \frac{dT}{T} = R\frac{dP}{P}$$

$$C_P \int_{T_1}^{T_2} \frac{dT}{T} = R \int_{P_1}^{P_2} \frac{dP}{P}$$

$$C_P \ln\left(\frac{T_2}{T_1}\right) = R \ln\left(\frac{P_2}{P_1}\right) \tag{2.52a}$$

That is,

$$P_1 T_2^{(C_P/R)} = P_2 T_1^{(C_P/R)} \tag{2.52b}$$

Equations (2.51) and (2.52) can be transformed in various ways. For such changes it is convenient to define a quantity γ as the ratio of the two heat capacities as in

$$\gamma = \frac{C_P}{C_V} \tag{2.53}$$

The value of γ always exceeds unity. Since $R = C_P - C_V$ by (2.40), $R/C_V = \gamma - 1$. Equation (2.51b) can be rewritten as

$$V_1^{(R/C_V)}T_1 = V_2^{(R/C_V)}T_2$$

That is,

$$T_1 V_1^{\gamma-1} = T_2 V_2^{\gamma-1} \tag{2.54}$$

Elimination of T from (2.54) by the relations $P_1V_1 = RT_1$ and $P_2V_2 = RT_2$ that hold at the initial and final states gives (2.55), a common form of the adiabatic perfect gas law.

$$\left(\frac{P_1V_1}{R}\right)V_1^{\gamma-1} = \left(\frac{P_2V_2}{R}\right)V_2^{\gamma-1}$$

$$P_1V_1^{\gamma} = P_2V_2^{\gamma} \tag{2.55}$$

Work done on a perfect gas along a reversible adiabatic path is found from (2.3) and (2.55).

$$dw = -P\,dV \tag{2.3}$$

$$w = -\int_{V_1}^{V_2} P\,dV$$

Since state (2) in (2.55) is any state for the fixed amount of gas, PV^{γ} is a constant; that is, $PV^{\gamma} = C_0$.
Then,

$$w = -\int_{V_1}^{V_2} \frac{C_0}{V^{\gamma}}dV = -C_0 \int_{V_1}^{V_2} V^{-\gamma}\,dV$$

$$= -\frac{C_0}{1-\gamma}(V_2^{1-\gamma} - V_1^{1-\gamma})$$

$$= \frac{P_2V_2 - P_1V_1}{\gamma - 1} \tag{2.56}$$

$$= \frac{nR(T_2 - T_1)}{\gamma - 1} \tag{2.57}$$

Equation (2.57) says that T_2 is greater than T_1 if a positive amount of work w is done adiabatically and reversibly on a perfect gas. Conversely, if a perfect gas works reversibly and adiabatically on its surroundings, its temperature will fall, for the work that it does is $-w$ and thus its final temperature T_2 is less than its initial temperature T_1.

Example 2.10. Three moles of a perfect gas with C_V equal to 5.00 cal mole^{-1} deg^{-1} are to be compressed adiabatically and reversibly from a volume of

75.0 l at 1.00 atm to a pressure of 100 atm. Predict (a) the final volume of the gas; (b) the final temperature of the gas; and (c) the work that must be done on the gas to compress it.

Since $C_V = 5.00$, $C_P = 5.00 + R$ by (2.40). Whence, by (2.53)

$$\gamma = \frac{C_P}{C_V} = \frac{6.99}{5.00} = 1.397$$

(a) Let $V_2 =$ the final volume; by (2.55),

$$1.00 \times 75.0^{1.397} = 100 \times V_2^{1.397}$$

$$\left(\frac{75.0}{V_2}\right)^{1.397} = 100; \qquad \frac{75.0}{V_2} = 27.0; \qquad V_2 = 2.78 \text{ l}$$

(b) Let $T_2 =$ the final temperature; then $P_2V_2 = nRT_2$ and

$$T_2 = \frac{P_2V_2}{nR} = \frac{100 \times 2780}{3.00 \times 82.06} = 1130°\text{K}$$

(c) By Equation (2.56),

$$w = \frac{100 \times 2780 - 1.00 \times 75000}{1.397 - 1} = \frac{203 \times 10^3}{0.397} \times \frac{1.987}{82.06} = 12{,}400 \text{ cal}$$

Example 2.11. Three moles of an ideal gas with C_V equal to 5.00 cal mole^{-1} deg^{-1} at an initial pressure of 100 atm at a temperature of 1130°K were suddenly allowed to escape into the atmosphere at a constant pressure of one atm. For this irreversible adiabatic change, calculate ΔE and ΔH.

Since this adiabatic change is irreversible, most of the equations of this section are not applicable. The work done by the gas is $-w$, where by (2.3)

$$-w = \int_{V_1}^{V_2} P\,dV = P\,\Delta V$$

$$= 1.00\left(\frac{3.00 \times 82.06 \times T_2}{1.00} - \frac{3.00 \times 82.06 \times 1130}{100}\right) \times \left(\frac{1.987}{82.06}\right)$$

For the same change, by (2.33),

$$\Delta E = \int_{T_1}^{T_2} nC_V\,dT = 3.00 \times 5.00 \times (T_2 - 1130)$$

By the first law of thermodynamics, for this adiabatic change, $\Delta E = w$, whence

$$5.00(T_2 - 1130) = -1.99\left(T_2 - \frac{1130}{100}\right)$$

$$T_2 = 812°\text{K}$$

Hence,

$$\Delta E = w = 3.00 \times 5.00 \times (812 - 1130) = -4770 \text{ cal}$$

$$\Delta H = \Delta E + \Delta(PV) = \Delta E + nR\Delta T$$

$$= -4770 + 3.00 \times 1.99 \times (812 - 1130) = -6670 \text{ cal}$$

Although the process occurs at a constant pressure of 1.00 atm, the initial state is not at this pressure. Thus the equation $\Delta H = q_P = 0$ does not apply for this adiabatic change of state. It is worth noting that the work done by the gas in its irreversible isobaric expansion is less than that which it might have performed reversibly, 12,400 cal. As a result, the final state of this example (812°K) differs from the initial state of the preceding example (305°K).

Example 2.12. Show that the rate of change of fluid pressure with respect to volume in an adiabatic change is γ times the rate in an isothermal change.

The problem asks for a proof of the equation

$$\left(\frac{\partial P}{\partial V}\right)_q = \gamma \left(\frac{\partial P}{\partial V}\right)_T$$

Since P and V are the variables of interest, it is best to choose them as independent. In an adiabatic change wherein $E = E(P, V)$, the rules of the calculus and the first law (2.17) with $dq = 0$ require

$$dE = \left(\frac{\partial E}{\partial V}\right)_P dV + \left(\frac{\partial E}{\partial P}\right)_V dP = -P\,dV$$

$$\left[P + \left(\frac{\partial E}{\partial T}\right)_P \left(\frac{\partial T}{\partial V}\right)_P\right] dV + \left(\frac{\partial E}{\partial T}\right)_V \left(\frac{\partial T}{\partial P}\right)_V dP = 0$$

That is, with the adiabatic condition indicated by subscript q,

$$\left(\frac{\partial P}{\partial V}\right)_q = -\frac{\left(\frac{\partial T}{\partial V}\right)_P \left[P\left(\frac{\partial V}{\partial T}\right)_P + \left(\frac{\partial E}{\partial T}\right)_P\right]}{\left(\frac{\partial T}{\partial P}\right)_V \left[\left(\frac{\partial E}{\partial T}\right)_V\right]} = -\frac{\left(\frac{\partial T}{\partial V}\right)_P \left(\frac{\partial H}{\partial T}\right)_P}{\left(\frac{\partial T}{\partial P}\right)_V \left(\frac{\partial E}{\partial T}\right)_V}$$

wherein the substitution

$$\left(\frac{\partial H}{\partial T}\right)_P = \left[\frac{\partial(E + PV)}{\partial T}\right]_P = \left(\frac{\partial E}{\partial T}\right)_P + P\left(\frac{\partial V}{\partial T}\right)_P$$

has been used. The equation of state of any fluid is of the form $T = T(P, V)$ so that by the rules of the calculus at constant T

$$dT = \left(\frac{\partial T}{\partial P}\right)_V dP + \left(\frac{\partial T}{\partial V}\right)_P dV = 0$$

$$\left(\frac{\partial P}{\partial V}\right)_T = -\frac{\left(\frac{\partial T}{\partial V}\right)_P}{\left(\frac{\partial T}{\partial P}\right)_V}$$

With this result and the definitions of γ, C_P, and C_V in (2.53), (2.26), and (2.27), the proof is complete. The value of the proof lies in the fact that $\gamma > 1$ so that adiabatics in P-V space have a greater slope (more negative) than isotherms.

Example 2.13. What final pressure results if reversible adiabatic compression of a perfect rigid diatomic gas initially at 300°K at 1.00 atm is to reach a final temperature of 3000°K? What pressure, if the adiabatic compression is irreversible?

By (2.43), a rigid diatomic gas has $C_V = (\frac{5}{2})R$ and, when it is perfect, $C_P = (\frac{7}{2})R$. With $P_1 = 1.00$ atm, $T_1 = 300$°K, and $T_2 = 3000$°K, the final pressure P_2 for the reversible compression is found thus by (2.52a).

$$R \log \frac{P_2}{P_1} = \left(\frac{7}{2}\right) R \log \frac{3000}{300} = \left(\frac{7}{2}\right) R \log 10 = \left(\frac{7}{2}\right) R$$

$$P_2 = P_1 \times 10^{7/2} = P_1 \times 10^{1/2} \times 10^3 = 3162 \text{ atm}$$

Since the final state at T_2 is supposedly an equilibrium state, for the reversible compression ending at pressure P_2 and volume V_2 the perfect gas law is $P_2V_2 = nRT_2$, while for the irreversible compression ending at pressure P_2' and volume V_2', similarly, $P_2' V_2' = nRT_2$. In any adiabatic change, the first law (2.14) reads $w = \Delta E$. Because ΔE is a function of the initial and final states and not of the path or process, the work done on the gas is the same in either process, namely

$$w = \Delta E = n \int_{T_1}^{T_2} C_V \, dT = \left(\frac{5}{2}\right) R(3000 - 300) = 13410 \text{ cal mole}^{-1}$$

In terms of $w = -\int P \, dV$, this work is the area below the adiabatic reversible curve of Figure 2.4a. If irreversible, the pressure P' experienced in the surroundings exceeds P so that the path in Figure 2.4b has a higher pressure. To keep the area w constant, the extra gray region above the dashed reversible pressure P must equal the gray area between V_2' and V_2. Necessarily, V_2' exceeds V_2; whence it follows that P_2 exceeds P_2' because at T_2 there exists the condition $P_2 V_2 = nRT = P_2' V_2'$. That is, the final pressure after irreversible adiabatic compression is less than that after reversible adiabatic compression of a perfect gas to the same temperature. The reason is that stirring or shock waves in the

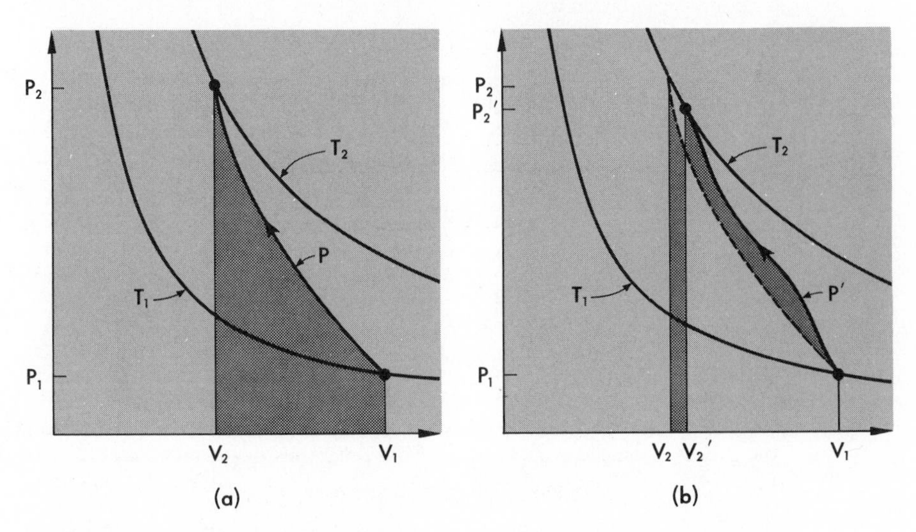

Figure 2.4. Caricature of Reversible (a) and Irreversible (b) Adiabatic Compression of a Perfect Gas

gas or friction in the piston dissipates work into thermal energy (increased T) of the gas while the compressing piston moves less for a fixed amount of work.

Analytic proof of this same result begins with the equality of the two works.

$$w = -\int_{V_1}^{V_2} P\,dV = -\int_{V_1}^{V_2'} P'\,dV$$

Since the irreversible pressure P' exceeds the reversible pressure P, and since for V_2' of any size $V_2 - V_1 = (V_2 - V_2') + (V_2' - V_1)$, the condition on w requires

$$0 = -\int_{V_1}^{V_2'} P'\,dV + \int_{V_1}^{V_2'} P\,dV + \int_{V_2'}^{V_2} P\,dV$$

$$\int_{V_1}^{V_2'} (P' - P)\,dV = \int_{V_2'}^{V_2} P\,dV < 0$$

where the inequality comes from the facts that $P' > P$ and $V_1 > V_2'$. But since $P > 0$, it follows that $V_2 < V_2'$, which is the result found by Figure 2.4. This, of course, again yields $P_2 > P_2'$ because Boyle's law holds at T_2.

Example 2.14. One mole of methane at 200°C and 10.0 atm expanded adiabatically and reversibly until its temperature was 0°C. If methane is a perfect gas with C_P as given in Table 2.1, calculate (a) the work done by the methane; (b) the final pressure of the methane.

(a) The work done by the methane, $-w$, can be calculated through the first law since the process is adiabatic and ΔE is readily evaluated.

$$-w = -\Delta E \qquad (2.14)$$

$$= -\int_{T_1}^{T_2} C_V\,dT = \int_{T_2}^{T_1} (C_P - R)\,dT \qquad (2.28)(2.40)$$

$$= \int_{273}^{473} (1.394 + 18.044 \times 10^{-3}T - 4.300 \times 10^{-6}T^2)\,dT$$

$$= 1.394(473 - 273) + \frac{18.044 \times 10^{-3}}{2}(473^2 - 273^2)$$

$$- \frac{4.300 \times 10^{-6}}{3}(473^3 - 273^3)$$

$$= 279 + 1346 - 123 = 1502 \text{ cal}$$

(b) Since C_P is a function of temperature, finding the final pressure must be begun with (2.49) or (2.50).

$$C_P\,dT = V\,dP = \frac{RT}{P}\,dP, \qquad \int_{473}^{273} \frac{C_P\,dT}{T} = R\int_{10}^{P_2} \frac{dP}{P}$$

$$3.381 \ln\left(\frac{273}{473}\right) + 18.044 \times 10^{-3}(273 - 473) - \frac{4.300 \times 10^{-6}}{2}(273^2 - 473^2)$$

$$= 1.987 \ln\left(\frac{P_2}{10}\right)$$

$$1.858 + 3.609 - 0.321 = 1.987 \ln\left(\frac{10}{P_2}\right)$$

$$\log\left(\frac{10}{P_2}\right) = 1.125, \qquad P_2 = 0.75 \text{ atm}$$

2.13 ADIABATIC PROCESSES OF A REAL GAS

The salient feature of the previous section of adiabatic processes of a perfect gas was that the energy E or enthalpy H depended only on the temperature. For real gases this is not generally true. Accordingly, in general for real gases, E and H depend on variables other than the temperature, and

$$\left(\frac{\partial E}{\partial V}\right)_T \neq 0 \quad \text{and} \quad \left(\frac{\partial H}{\partial P}\right)_T \neq 0$$

Until the second law of thermodynamics presents a more suitable independent variable than temperature, it is generally best to speak of temperature and volume as the independent variables for energy, and of temperature and pressure as the independent variables for enthalpy. This is in accord with

$$dE = \left(\frac{\partial E}{\partial T}\right)_V dT + \left(\frac{\partial E}{\partial V}\right)_T dV \tag{2.32}$$

$$dH = \left(\frac{\partial H}{\partial T}\right)_P dT + \left(\frac{\partial H}{\partial P}\right)_T dP \tag{2.38}$$

It is the aim of this section to evaluate the coefficients of dV and dP in (2.32) and (2.38).

Let a volume V_1 of gas at a constant pressure P_1 be forced by a piston through a porous barrier or plug that serves merely to establish a pressure difference. As it passes through the barrier, the gas pushes against a piston at a constant pressure P_2 and gradually fills a volume V_2. The work done on the gas is P_1V_1 and the work done by the gas is P_2V_2. The net work done on the gas is then $P_1V_1 - P_2V_2$. If the porous plug and the pistons and cylinders (see Figure 2.5) are very poor conductors of heat, the process can be made essentially

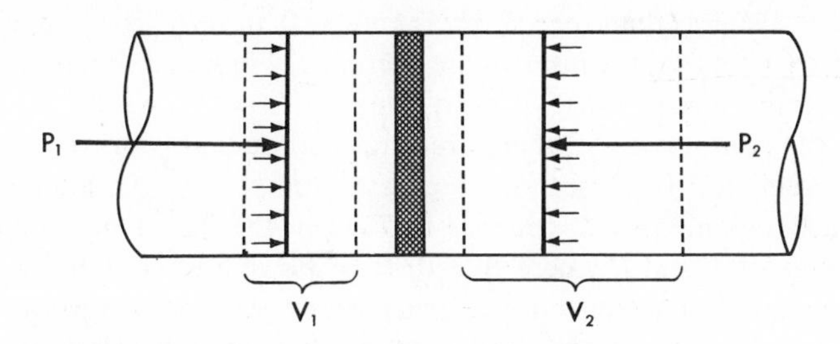

Figure 2.5. Joule-Thomson Porous Plug Experiment

adiabatic. It is found experimentally that the final temperature T_2 of a real gas that undergoes this process generally differs from its initial temperature T_1.

This means, of course, that $P_1V_1 - P_2V_2$ may not be zero. The change in enthalpy is, however, zero. By (2.23) and the first law

$$\begin{aligned}\Delta H &= \Delta E + \Delta(PV) \\ &= q + w + (P_2V_2 - P_1V_1) \qquad (2.23)\end{aligned}$$

But $q = 0$ since the process is adiabatic and $w = P_1V_1 - P_2V_2$. By substitution,

$$\Delta H = 0 + (P_1V_1 - P_2V_2) + (P_2V_2 - P_1V_1) = 0$$

Since ΔH is zero, the enthalpy of the gas is constant, and $dH = 0$. Equation (2.38) then becomes

$$0 = \left(\frac{\partial H}{\partial T}\right)_P dT + \left(\frac{\partial H}{\partial P}\right)_T dP \qquad (2.58)$$

Division of (2.58) by dP gives

$$\left(\frac{\partial H}{\partial P}\right)_T = -\mu C_P \qquad (2.59)$$

where $C_P = (\partial H/\partial T)_P$ by (2.27) and where the Joule-Thomson coefficient μ is defined by (2.60).

$$\mu = \left(\frac{\partial T}{\partial P}\right)_H \qquad (2.60)$$

The value of μ is given experimentally by the observed change ΔT in temperature caused by the observed change ΔP in pressure when a real gas is allowed to expand adiabatically through the porous plug. Here ΔP is less than zero when the final pressure is less than the initial pressure; if the temperature of the gas decreases then ΔT is also less than zero and μ is greater than zero. The temperature at which μ is zero is called the *inversion temperature*. Figure 2.6 summarizes how μ and the inversion temperature of N_2 depend on T and P. Within the region bounded by the contour $\mu = 0$ there are three contours at positive values of μ; outside this region, T increases as P decreases and $\mu < 0$. An adiabatic decrease in P is accompanied by a decrease in T when the initial state of N_2 lies within this range of T and P where $\mu > 0$. It is possible to cool and even liquefy a gas by adiabatic expansion when its μ is positive. At room temperature, H_2 and He have $\mu < 0$; they become hotter upon adiabatic expansion. However, since low-pressure inversion temperatures are about seven times the absolute critical temperature, most gases become cooler upon adiabatic expansion. Table 2.2 lists some observed values of μ for ethane, and the second law will provide a method of caluclating μ from the equation of state.

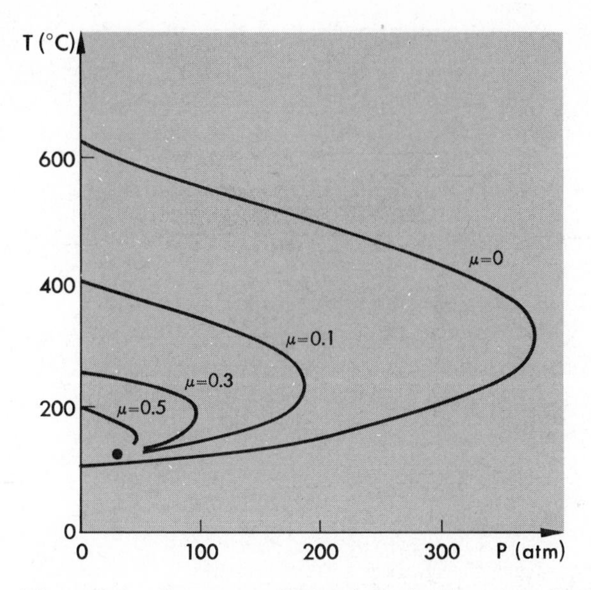

Figure 2.6. Contours of Equal Joule-Thomson Coefficients of N_2 as Functions of Pressure and Temperature†

Table 2.2. Joule-Thomson Coefficients of Ethane at Various Temperatures and Pressures (deg C/atm). (B. H. Sage, D. C. Webster, and W. N. Lacey, *Ind. Eng. Chem.* **29,** 658 [1937].)

Pressure	25°C	40°C	50°C	75°C	100°C
1 atm	0.932	0.828	0.771	0.644	0.523
20 atm	1.23	1.05	0.956	0.752	0.604
40 atm	—	1.28	1.13	0.830	0.628

2.14 LIQUEFACTION OF GASES BY ADIABATIC EXPANSION

A gas below its inversion temperature becomes cooler as its pressure is reduced adiabatically. Commercial processes for the liquefaction of gases use gas cooled by expansion to lower the temperature of incoming compressed gas until the incoming gas is so cold that part of it liquefies during the expansion. With neglect of the pressure drops and kinetic energy due to flow in such a process, the fraction of incoming high pressure gas that liquefies can be calculated quite easily.

Figure 2.7 is a simplified schematic diagram of the apparatus used in liquefying gases. Let 1 mole of gas at high pressure P_1 and temperature T_1 be delivered

†J. R. Roebuck and H. Osterberg, *Phys. Rev.* **48,** 450 (1935).

to the expansion nozzle through a heat exchanger that allows the expanded gases that flow upward to cool the unexpanded gases that flow downward. The process is adiabatic, for 1 mole of gas, expanded and unexpanded, is the system. When the temperature falls to the boiling point T_2 at the pressure P_2, a fraction X of the gas that issues from the nozzle condenses and a fraction $(1 - X)$ will proceed upward and out of the heat exchanger at a pressure of P_2 and temperature T_1.

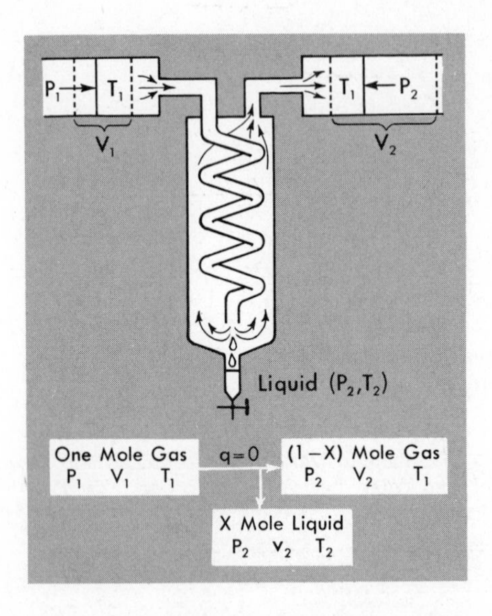

Figure 2.7. Simplified Schematic Diagram of Common Process for Liquefying Gases by Adiabatic Expansion

As in the Joule-Thomson experiment, the net work done in the system at the constant pressures P_1 and P_2 is

$$w = P_1V_1 - [(1 - X)P_2V_2 + XP_2v_2]$$

By the first law of thermodynamics, since the process is adiabatic,

$$\Delta E = w = P_1V_1 - [(1 - X)P_2V_2 + XP_2v_2]$$

But for the assumed changes of state,

$$\Delta E = (1 - X)E(V_2, T_1) + XE(v_2, T_2) - E(V_1, T_1)$$

where $E(V_2, T_1)$ is the energy of the expanded gas,
where $E(v_2, T_2)$ is the energy of the liquid, and
where $E(V_1, T_1)$ is the energy of the incoming compressed gas.

When these two expressions for ΔE are equated and their terms are rearranged, the following equations result.

$$P_1V_1 - P_2V_2 + X(P_2V_2 - P_2v_2) = E(V_2, T_1) - E(V_1, T_1) + X[E(v_2, T_2) - E(V_2, T_1)]$$

$$[E(V_1, T_1) + P_1V_1] + X[E(V_2, T_1) + P_2V_2] = [E(V_2, T_1) + P_2V_2] + X[E(v_2, T_2) + P_2v_2]$$

But by the definition of enthalpy, the various terms in brackets are identified with enthalpies of the three states of the system; that is, the equations become the following:

$$H(P_1, T_1) + XH(P_2, T_1) = H(P_2, T_1) + XH(P_2, T_2)$$

where $H(P_1, T_1)$ is the molar enthalpy of the incoming compressed gas,
where $H(P_2, T_1)$ is the molar enthalpy of the exit gas, and
where $H(P_2, T_2)$ is the molar enthalpy of the liquid. The fraction X of liquid that is formed is then found by solving for X.

$$X = \frac{H(P_2, T_1) - H(P_1, T_1)}{H(P_2, T_1) - H(P_2, T_2)} \tag{2.61}$$

The numerator of (2.61) is the change in enthalpy of 1 mole of gas at temperature T_1 when its pressure falls from P_1 to P_2. The value of this numerator is a function of state and can be evaluated from (2.38) and (2.59) when $dT_1 = 0$.

$$dH = C_P\,dT + \left(\frac{\partial H}{\partial P}\right)_T dP$$

$$= -\mu C_P\,dP$$

$$\Delta H = \int_{P_1}^{P_2} (-\mu C_P)\,dP = \int_{P_2}^{P_1} \mu C_P\,dP$$

The denominator of (2.61) is the change in enthalpy of 1 mole of liquid at temperature T_2 to 1 mole of gas at temperature T_1 when the pressure is constant at P_2. The value of this denominator can be found by dividing the process into a vaporization at P_2, T_2 and a heating of the gas from T_2 to T_1.

$$\Delta H = H_{(g)}(P_2, T_1) - H_{(l)}(P_2, T_2)$$

$$= H_{(g)}(P_2, T_1) - H_{(g)}(P_2, T_2) + H_{(g)}(P_2, T_2) - H_{(l)}(P_2, T_2)$$

$$= \int_{T_2}^{T_1} C_P\,dT + \Delta H_v$$

With these evaluations of numerator and denominator, (2.61), which gives the fraction X of gas that condenses in an adiabatic expansion, becomes

$$X = \frac{\int_{P_2}^{P_1} \mu C_P \, dP}{\int_{T_2}^{T_1} C_P \, dT + \Delta H_v} \tag{2.62}$$

where the value of μ is the value at T_1.

Example 2.15. The molar heat of vaporization of oxygen at its boiling point of $-183°C$ is 1600 cal and its Joule-Thomson coefficient is about 0.30°C atm^{-1}. If the molar heat capacity of oxygen at constant pressure is $7R/2$, estimate the fraction of liquid expected when oxygen gas is allowed to expand adiabatically from a pressure of 100 atm at 0°C to a pressure of 1 atm.

By (2.62)

$$X = \frac{\int_{1}^{100} 0.30 \times \frac{7}{2}R \times dP}{\int_{90}^{273} \frac{7}{2}R \, dT + 1600} = \frac{0.30 \times \frac{7}{2} \times 1.99 \times (100 - 1)}{\frac{7}{2} \times 1.99 \times 183 + 1600}$$

$$= \frac{207}{1275 + 1600} = 0.072$$

For every mole of oxygen pumped in at 100 atm at 0°C, there could be produced 0.072 mole liquid oxygen at its normal boiling point. A more accurate estimate would take account of the way μ and C_P depend on P and T.

2.15 PHYSICAL PROCESSES

The physical processes of interest in this section are restricted to those which accompany a change of temperature, pressure, and volume. For a perfect gas the equation of state $PV = nRT$ says that pressure, volume, and temperature are not all independent variables if the number of moles of gas is fixed. Every substance—gas, liquid, or solid—has an equation of state that summarizes the results of simultaneous equilibrium measurement of pressure, volume, and temperature. Only two of the three variables are independent. When a calculation involves E, usually it is best to choose V and T as independent variables with $E = E(V, T)$. Similarly, in dealing with H, usually P and T are most convenient with $H = H(P, T)$ and

$$dH = \left(\frac{\partial H}{\partial T}\right)_P dT + \left(\frac{\partial H}{\partial P}\right)_T dP \tag{2.38}$$

$$= C_P \, dT + \left(\frac{dH}{\partial P}\right)_T dP \tag{2.63}$$

Since the enthalpy H of the system is a function of state, the initial and final states being specified by P and T, the process by which a system changes in pressure and temperature from P_1 and T_1 to P_2 and T_2 can for convenience be divided into two processes, one at constant pressure and one at constant temperature. The diagram of such a process and its division into simpler processes would look like this.

$H(P_1, T_2)$

$dP_1 = 0$ $\quad$ $dT_2 = 0$

$H(P_1, T_1)$ $\xrightarrow{\Delta H}$ $H(P_2, T_2)$

$dT_1 = 0$ $\quad$ $dP_2 = 0$

$H(P_2, T_1)$

$$\begin{aligned}\Delta H &= H(P_2, T_2) - H(P_1, T_1)\\ &= [H(P_1, T_2) - H(P_1, T_1)] + [H(P_2, T_2) - H(P_1, T_2)]\\ &= \int_{T_1}^{T_2} C_{P_1}\, dT + \int_{P_1}^{P_2} \left(\frac{\partial H}{\partial P}\right)_{T_2} dP \end{aligned} \tag{2.64}$$

Or, by the alternate route, which may be more convenient,

$$\Delta H = \int_{P_1}^{P_2} \left(\frac{\partial H}{\partial P}\right)_{T_1} dP + \int_{T_1}^{T_2} C_{P_2}\, dT \tag{2.65}$$

The differential equation (2.63) was used to evaluate the coefficient of dP in terms of the Joule-Thomson coefficient and C_P when dH was zero. In considering the liquefaction of gases, a somewhat more general situation than that described by (2.64) and (2.65) was encountered. The general situation involving a phase change, like liquefaction, vaporization, and so forth, is diagramed as

$H_1(P_1, T_1)$ $\xrightarrow{\Delta H}$ $H_2(P_2, T_2)$

$dP_1 = 0$ $\quad$ $dP_2 = 0$

$H_1(P_1, T)$ $\xrightarrow{dT=0}$ $H_1(P, T)$ $\xrightarrow{\Delta H_{tr}}$ $H_2(P, T)$ $\xrightarrow{dT=0}$ $H_2(P_2, T)$

The phase change from state 1 of aggregation to state 2 involves the enthalpy change $\Delta H_{tr} = H_2(P, T) - H_1(P, T)$. For this kind of overall process, whether it be reversible or not, followed or not,

$$\begin{aligned}\Delta H = \int_{T_1}^{T} C_{P_1}\, dT' &+ \int_{P_1}^{P} \left(\frac{\partial H_1}{\partial P'}\right)_T dP' + \Delta H_{tr}\\ &+ \int_{P}^{P_2} \left(\frac{\partial H_2}{\partial P'}\right)_T dP' + \int_{T}^{T_2} C_{P_2}\, dT' \end{aligned} \tag{2.66}$$

It is important to realize that *any* path, whether or not it is actually traversed in the net change from a well defined initial state to a well defined final state, is satisfactory for the calculation of ΔH or of the increment in any other function of state. Thus, exactly analogous diagrams involving isothermal ($dT = 0$) and isochoric ($dV = 0$) processes in some convenient sequence are useful for linking specified initial and final states when ΔE is to be calculated by

$$dE = C_V\, dT + \left(\frac{\partial E}{\partial V}\right)_T dV \tag{2.67}$$

The dependence of E on V or of H on P can be neglected for the present because it is usually small for gases at low P.

Example 2.16. Calculate ΔE and ΔH when one mole water at 25°C at one atm becomes one mole steam at 130°C at two atm.

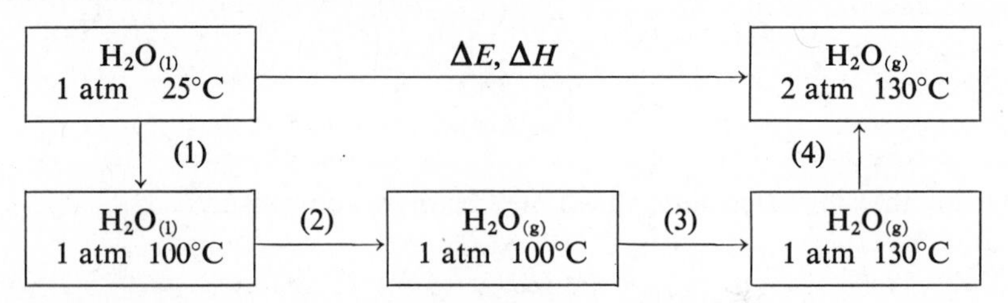

For change (1),

$$\Delta H_1 = \int_{298}^{373} C_P\, dT = 18.0(373 - 298) = 1350 \text{ cal}$$

$$\Delta E_1 = \Delta H_1 - \Delta(PV)_1 = \Delta H_1 - P_1\, \Delta V_1 \approx \Delta H_1$$

For change (2),

$$\Delta H_2 = \Delta H_{\text{vap}} = 9713 \text{ cal}$$

$$\Delta E_2 = \Delta H_2 - P\Delta V_2 = \Delta H_2 - P(V_{(g)} - V_{(l)})$$

$$\approx \Delta H_2 - RT = 9713 - 1.987 \times 373.2 = 8971 \text{ cal}$$

For change (3),

$$\Delta H_3 = \int_{373.2}^{403.2} C_P\, dT = \int_{373.2}^{403.2} (7.256 + 2.298 \times 10^{-3}T + 0.283 \times 10^{-6}T^2)\, dT$$

$$= 7.256(403.2 - 373.2) + \frac{2.298 \times 10^{-3}}{2}(403.2^2 - 373.2^2)$$

$$+ \frac{0.283 \times 10^{-6}}{3}(403.2^3 - 373.2^3)$$

$$= 217.7 + 26.8 + 1.3 = 245.8 \text{ cal}$$

$$\Delta E_3 = \int_{373.2}^{403.2} C_V\, dT = \int_{373.2}^{403.2} (C_P - R)\, dT$$

$$= 245.8 - 1.987(403.2 - 373.2) = 186.2 \text{ cal}$$

For change (4), since it is isothermal and since perfect gas behavior has been assumed, $\Delta H_4 = \Delta E_4 = 0$.

For the overall change of state,

$$\Delta H = \sum_{i=1}^{4} \Delta H_i = 1350 + 9713 + 246 + 0 = 11{,}309 \text{ cal}$$

$$\Delta E = \sum_{i=1}^{4} \Delta E_i = 1350 + 8971 + 186 + 0 = 10{,}507 \text{ cal}$$

2.16 SUMMARY

This chapter begins thermodynamics after a brief introduction to equations of state and the kinetic theory of gases. To the familiar idea of conservation of energy, this chapter adds the concept of a function of state. This idea and accompanying maneuvers of inventing processes and using the mathematics of exact differentials are fundamental to the methods of thermodynamics. So also are careful definition and the ideas of reversibility and functions of path. If heat and work were not dependent on the process as well as the initial and final states, thermodynamics would be much less demanding and interesting. In fact, it might not exist. The device of adding PV to E to get the more convenient enthalpy state-function H is to be repeated profitably in other circumstances with other variables. It is almost as if this one chapter embodies the spirit of all of thermodynamics, even though it represents only the first one-tenth of this book's modest introduction to the subject.

The terse language of mathematics fits thermodynamics very well. As an undergaduate student making his first acquaintance with this science of heat and work, the author found it helpful to base his study of physical chemistry on the few key thermodynamic equations of the widest validity and generality. The first law is surely one of these, but $C_P\,dT = V\,dP$ is not. Special and even familiar equations for particular situations, with their frequently multitudinous conditions, are best derived when needed so that no accidentally overlooked condition can invalidate a prediction. Such continual review of derivations is also a study aid. As in glassblowing, it is wise to make a good start, especially on a discipline as exacting, discriminating, and even fastidious as thermodynamics.

Finally, for a true appreciation and understanding of thermodynamics, there is absolutely no substitute for working many particular problems with careful attention to such details as algebraic signs. Coupled with an on-the-spot derivation, such work does not degenerate into a memory contest or lucky substitution of numerical values. It should always be possible to describe a result verbally, as is often done at the end of the worked examples in this book, by translating the mathematical result into ordinary language. After using the logic of mathematics, if it is ever impossible to justify a calculated result verbally and perhaps by a mental picture of the process or at least to verify roughly or by its relation to zero the result of a calculation, then something essential is lacking in the exercise. Every correct thermodynamic equation, part by part, has physical meaning, often for a wide range of circumstances. The problem is thoroughly to appreciate this meaning by living thermodynamics as a way of scientific life.

PROBLEMS

1. Calculate the work required to compress reversibly two moles of a perfect gas from a volume of 50.0 l to 10.0 l:
(a) At 0°C.
(b) At 100°C.
Answer: (a) 1750 cal; (b) 2390 cal.

2. How hot will a 2.59-g lead bullet at 50°C become if it is suddenly and adiabatically stopped from a velocity of 3.00×10^4 cm sec^{-1}?
Answer: 327°C, the melting point of Pb.

3. Thirty g bromine at 100°C at one atm did 200 cal work and achieved a final temperature of 100°C at one atm. Find ΔE, ΔH, q, and w for the process.
Answer: $\Delta E = \Delta H = 0$; $q = 200$ cal; $w = -200$ cal.

4. One mole of a perfect gas expands isothermally at 50°C from a pressure of 3.00 atm to 2.0×10^{-3} atm. Find q, w, ΔE, and ΔH.
Answer: If reversible, $w = -q = -4700$ cal; $\Delta E = \Delta H = 0$.

5. Forty g propane at 25°C are heated to 100°C. If the initial and final pressures are 2.00 atm, find q, w, ΔE, and ΔH if the process is:
(a) Reversible, at constant pressure.
(b) Irreversible and yields no work.
Answer: $\Delta H = 1362$ cal; $\Delta E = 1227$ cal; (a) $q = 1362$ cal and $w = -135$ cal; (b) $q = 1227$ cal and $w = 0$.

6. Two moles steam at 120°C are condensed isothermally and reversibly to water at 120°C. At this temperature, the vapor pressure of water is 1490 mm Hg and its heat of vaporization is 526 cal g^{-1}. Find w, q, ΔE, and ΔH for this condensation.
Answer: $q = \Delta H = -18{,}960$ cal; if perfect gas, $w = 1560$ cal; if van der Waals gas, $w = 1550$ cal.

7. Calculate the work done by one mole of a liquid as it vaporizes reversibly at its normal boiling point of:
(a) 200°C.
(b) 400°C.
Answer: (a) 940 cal; (b) 1338 cal.

8. Three identical gaseous samples, each of one mole of a perfect diatomic gas at 150°C at 10.0 atm, are each allowed to expand to a volume of 30.0 l. Calculate the final pressure that results and the work done by the gas when:
(a) The first sample expands adiabatically into a vacuum.
(b) The second sample expands isothermally and reversibly.
(c) The third sample expands adiabatically and reversibly.
Answer: (a) 1.157 atm, $w = 0$; (b) 1.157 atm, $-w = 1814$ cal; (c) 0.489 atm, $-w = 1215$ cal.

9. One mole of a perfect rigid diatomic gas (e.g., N_2 or CO) expands reversibly and adiabatically until its volume is tripled. Find the final temperature of the gas if its initial temperature was 227°C.
Answer: 322°K.

10. One mole of a perfect gas consisting of rigid diatoms is compressed reversibly and adiabatically from 27°C at one atm to a volume of 3.00 liters. Calculate the final temperature of the gas, its increase in enthalpy, and the work done on it.
Answer: 696°K; $\Delta H = 2750$ cal; $w = 1969$ cal.

11. Calculate ΔE, ΔH, q, and w for the reversible isobaric process by which one mole liquid water at 1 atm at 25°C becomes one mole steam at 1 atm at 150°C.
Answer: $q = \Delta H = 11{,}471$ cal; $\Delta E = 10{,}630$ cal; $w = -841$ cal.

12. One mole of liquid water at 100°C and one atm is isothermally and reversibly converted to one mole of gaseous water at 100°C at 0.500 atm. If the heat of vaporization of water is 9720 cal mole^{-1} at 100°C, find ΔE, q, w, and ΔH for this change.
Answer: $\Delta E = 8980$ cal; $q = 10{,}230$ cal; $w = -1256$ cal; $\Delta H = 9720$ cal.

13. Estimate the yields of liquid N_2 if a final temperature of 77°K at one atm is reached from 0°C at either 50 atm or 100 atm. The heat of vaporization of N_2 is 1350 cal mole^{-1}.
Answer: 0.025 or 0.050.

---

14. What is the least work that must be done to divide one spherical drop of water of mass of 50 mg into identical spherical droplets with diameters of 1000 A?
Answer: 0.218 joules.

15. Calculate the work done on a gas when it is forced isothermally, isobarically, and reversibly through one mile of horizontal pipe at ten atm if the inner diameter of the pipe is one inch.
Answer: $w = 197.4$ kcal.

16. Calculate the increase in energy and the heat absorbed by one mole of an ideal monatomic crystalline solid (such as a metal) with $C_V = 6.0$ cal mole^{-1} deg^{-1} as it goes from 0°C to 200°C at constant pressure of one atm if the solid does not expand.
Answer: $\Delta E = q = 1200$ cal.

17. Calculate the increase in energy of one mole of a perfect monatomic gas that is heated at constant pressure from 100°C to 200°C and is also elevated one mile if its molecular weight is 30. What is ΔH for this process?
Answer: $\Delta E = 411$ cal; $\Delta H = 610$ cal.

18. Calculate the values of ΔE and ΔH for the changes of state:
(a) Two moles nitrogen ($C_V = 5R/2$) are heated from 0°C to 100°C at one atm.
(b) Three moles steam ($C_P = 8.2$ cal mole^{-1} deg^{-1}) are cooled from 150°C to 100°C at one atm.
Answer: (a) $\Delta E = 994$ cal, $\Delta H = 1392$ cal; (b) $\Delta E = -932$ cal, $\Delta H = -1230$ cal.

19. One-half mole gaseous chlorine expands isothermally and reversibly at 30°C from a volume of two l to a volume of ten l. Calculate the work done by the chlorine:
(a) If it is a perfect gas.
(b) If it is a van der Waals gas.
Explain the difference in the amount of work done by the chlorine.
Answer: (a) 485 cal; (b) 473 cal.

20. Show that the molar heat capacity at constant volume (C_V) of a perfect gas does not depend upon the volume of the gas in the absence of fields.

21. Two moles of a perfect gas at 27°C at ten atm expand isothermally and reversibly until the pressure is one atm. Calculate the heat absorbed by the gas in this process.
Answer: 2750 cal.

22. One mole N_2 ($C_V = 5R/2$) expands adiabatically from a pressure of 75.0 atm at 100°C to a volume of 12.0 l. Calculate the final temperature and q, w, ΔE, and ΔH for this process if the adiabatic expansion:
(a) Is reversible.
(b) Involves 300 cal work done by the gas.
Answer: (a) 96.6°K; $q = 0$; $w = \Delta E = -1374$ cal; $\Delta H = -1922$ cal; (b) 312.8°K; $q = 0$; $w = \Delta E = -300$ cal; $\Delta H = -420$ cal.

23. Calculate the final pressure that results from reversible adiabatic compression of two moles gaseous NH_3 from 0.500 atm at 27°C until its temperature reaches 100°C. How much work is done on the ammonia?
Answer: If perfect gas, 1.305 atm and $w = 990$ cal.

24. One mole of methane at 50.0 atm at 200°C expanded reversibly and adiabatically until its volume was 15.0 liters. If $C_P = 8.54$ cal mole^{-1} deg^{-1}, what are q, w, ΔE, and ΔH for this process?
Answer: $q = 0$; $w = \Delta E = -1840$ cal; $\Delta H = -2400$ cal.

25. One mole of helium at 427°C at 5.00 atm expanded adiabatically until its final pressure was 1.00 atm. Find ΔE and ΔH for this change of state if the adiabatic expansion was:
(a) Reversible.
(b) Irreversible and isobaric at 1.00 atm.
Answer: (a) $\Delta E = -989$ cal, $\Delta H = -1650$ cal; (b) $\Delta E = -918$ cal, $\Delta H = -1530$ cal.

26. One mole of gaseous nitrogen ($C_P = 6.50 + 0.001\,T$ cal mole^{-1} deg^{-1}) is reversibly and adiabatically compressed from 25°C at one atm to a pressure of ten atm. State any assumption needed to obtain a definite final temperature of the nitrogen.
Answer: If a perfect gas, 578°K.

27. The approximate Joule-Thomson coefficients of air at 0°C and 100°C are 0.25 and 0.15° atm^{-1}. If air at 100 atm at each of these temperatures expands adiabatically to a pressure of one atm, what yields of liquid air are expected from each process? The heat of vaporization of air may be taken as 50 cal g^{-1} and its boiling point as −185°C.
Answer: At 0°C, 0.0632; at 100°C, 0.0302.

28. One mole of a perfect diatomic gas ($C_P = 7R/2$) at 127°C expands irreversibly through a Joule-Thomson porous plug and its pressure falls from three atm to one atm. Then, at constant pressure of one atm, its temperature is changed reversibly to 27°C. Calculate w, q, ΔE, and ΔH for the overall change.
Answer: $w = 199$ cal; $q = -696$ cal; $\Delta E = -497$ cal; $\Delta H = -696$ cal.

29. Twenty l of an ideal rigid diatomic gas at 400°C and 7.00 atm expand until the pressure of the gas is 2.00 atm. Calculate w, ΔE, and ΔH for the process if the expansion is:
(a) Isothermal and reversible.
(b) Reversible and adiabatic.

(c) Isothermal and adiabatic.

(d) Isobaric at two atm and adiabatic.

(e) Isobaric at two atm and isothermal.

Answer: Zero except: (a) $w = -4250$ cal; (b) $w = \Delta E = -2555$ cal and $\Delta H = -3580$ cal; (d) $w = \Delta E = -1725$ cal and $\Delta H = -2415$ cal; (e) $w = -2420$ cal.

30. One mole of gaseous SO_2 at 3.00 atm at 25°C is liquefied, its final state being liquid SO_2 at -10°C at one atm. If C_P for SO_2 is 9.51 cal mole^{-1} deg^{-1}, if its heat of vaporization at one atm at -10°C is 5960 cal mole^{-1}, and if -10°C is its boiling point at one atm, calculate for the overall liquefaction the values of w, ΔE, and ΔH.
Answer: $\Delta E = -5701$ cal; $\Delta H = -6293$ cal; a fuller description of the process is needed to find w.

---

31. Calculate the work done on one mole of a perfect gas at 27°C in these circumstances:
(a) Reversible compression from one atm to five atm.
(b) Reversible expansion from five atm to one atm.
(c) Irreversible expansion from the final state of (a) to the initial state of (a).
Answer: (a) 961 cal; (b) -961 cal; (c) $w > -961$ cal.

32. The potential energy possessed by a body by virtue of its position in a gravitational field is independent of the path by which it acquired the potential energy. In terms of the first law of thermodynamics, discuss what happens to this potential energy when:
(a) A body is dropped in a vacuum.
(b) A falling body suddenly is halted so that its kinetic energy becomes thermal energy.
(c) A body is dropped in a viscous fluid.

33. Calculate the work done on a spring in stretching it by three cm if its Hooke's law force constant is 1000 dyne cm^{-1}. Calculate the increase in its potential energy. If 2% of the mechanical energy is dissipated as heat, recalculate the work and change in potential mechanical energy.
Answer: $w = \Delta E = 4500$ ergs; $w = 4500$ ergs and $\Delta E = 4410$ ergs.

34. Calculate ΔH, ΔE, q, and w for the reversible vaporization of one mole of NH_3 at one atm at its normal boiling point of -33.4°C, where its heat of vaporization at constant pressure is 5580 cal mole^{-1}.
Answer: $\Delta H = q_P = 5580$ cal; $\Delta E = 5100$ cal; $w = -477$ cal.

35. The heat of vaporization of water at 100°C is 539 cal g^{-1}. If steam is a perfect gas and the volume of the liquid is negligible, find w, q, ΔE, and ΔH for the vaporization of ten g H_2O at 100°C if the process is:
(a) Reversible.
(b) Irreversible to the extent that the work really done by the H_2O is 40.0 cal less than the reversible work. Explain how step (b) might occur.
Answer: $\Delta H = 5390$ cal; $\Delta E = 4978$ cal; (a) $w = -412$ cal; $q = \Delta H$; (b) $w = -372$ cal, $q = 5350$ cal.

36. Calculate the minimum work to be done in compressing two moles ammonia from 20.0 to 8.00 l at 10°C. Use the ideal gas law and van der Waals' equation and explain any difference in the results.
Answer: 1031 cal; 1008 cal.

37. What work is done on two moles of a perfect monatomic gas as it is compressed from a volume of 98.4 liters to 49.2 liters:

(a) Reversibly and isothermally at 27°C?
(b) Irreversibly and isobarically at one atm?
Answer: (a) 826 cal; (b) 1191 cal.

38. Two moles of neon at 27°C in a volume of 98.4 liters are compressed irreversibly and adiabatically until their volume is 49.2 liters. If the pressure experienced in the surroundings is constant at one atm because of friction (the results of which are felt only within the gas), what final temperature is reached by the neon?
Answer: 500°K.

39. One mole of a perfect gas with $C_V = 9.00$ cal mole^{-1} deg^{-1} expanded from a volume of 20.0 liters at 200°C until its pressure was 0.500 atm. Calculate the final temperature, the work done by the gas, and ΔE of the gas for the change of state if the expansion was adiabatic and:
(a) Reversible.
(b) Irreversible and isobaric at 0.500 atm.
Answer: (a) 370°K; 927 cal; $\Delta E = -927$ cal; (b) 410°K; 567 cal; $\Delta E = -567$ cal.

40. One mole of a rigid perfect diatomic gas is initially in a volume of 30.0 l at 400°K. It then experiences the following *successive* processes:
(a) From its initial state it is compressed isothermally and reversibly until its pressure is 10.0 atm.
(b) Then it is allowed to expand into an evacuated vessel until its pressure is 5.00 atm.
(c) Then it is allowed to expand adiabatically and reversibly until its volume is 10.0 l.
(d) Then it is allowed to expand irreversibly and adiabatically until it returns to its initial state.
For each process and the whole cycle find w, q, ΔE, and ΔH, and tabulate results in calories.
Answer: (in cal) (a) 1759, −1759, 0, 0; (b) 0, 0, 0, 0; (c) −1499, 0, −1499, −2098; (d) 1499, 0, 1499, 2098; for cycle, 1759, −1759, 0, 0.

41. Let a perfect gas be forced isobarically through an orifice into an evacuated rigid vessel until its pressure in that vessel rises to the isobaric value and the process stops. Show that the final temperature of the gas in the vessel before it loses heat to the walls of the vessel is γ times its initial temperature before entering the vessel.

42. Calculate the temperature that would result from adiabatic compression of one mole of a perfect gas from 2.00 atm to 200 atm if the initial temperature is 227°C. Assume that $C_V = 5R/2$. Also state and explain any other assumption required to obtain a unique answer.
Answer: If reversible, 1864°K.

43. One mole of a perfect gas consisting of rigid diatomic molecules is compressed from 1.00 atm at 127°C to a pressure of 10.00 atm. Calculate w, q, ΔE, and ΔH if the process is:
(a) Reversible and adiabatic.
(b) Reversible and isothermal.
(c) Irreversible and isothermal.
Answer: (a) $q = 0$; $w = \Delta E = 1847$ cal; $\Delta H = 2587$ cal. (b) $q = -w = -1831$ cal; $\Delta E = \Delta H = 0$. (c) $\Delta E = \Delta H = 0$. The process must be more fully described to calculate q and w.

44. A rubber balloon filled with O_2 at 25°C at 1.10 atm is exploded adiabatically in a large room where the atmospheric pressure is 0.98 atm. What is the temperature of the oxygen immediately after the explosion before it mixes with room air if the pop dissipates no energy?
(a) Assume that O_2 is a perfect gas with $C_V = 5R/2$.
(b) Assume that O_2 is itself a real gas.
Answer: (a) 15.73°C; (b) 15.70°C.

45. Two moles hydrogen at 16.00 atm at 0.00°C are allowed to expand adiabatically as in a Joule-Thomson experiment until their pressure falls to 2.00 atm. Estimate the temperature of the final state if the Joule-Thomson coefficient of H_2 is constant at $-0.013°$ atm^{-1}.
Answer: 0.182°C.

3

THERMOCHEMISTRY

3.1 INTRODUCTION

This chapter deals with the heats of chemical reaction. Although there is no natural division between chemical and physical change, it is appropriate because of the general importance of the subject to reserve a special chapter for the heat effects in changes that can be described by balanced chemical equations. This chapter is for the most part just an application of the first law of thermodynamics to isobaric ($dP = 0$) processes that involve only expansion work ($dw = -P\,dV$). The volume change is the almost inevitable difference in volume of products and reactants if, as ordinarily happens, the boundary between system and surroundings is seen in the surroundings to move at finite pressure as the chemical change occurs. In brief, this chapter explores the equation

$$\Delta H = q_P \tag{2.22}$$

for chemical changes of state.

The concept of a function of state entered mechanics at an early date with the idea of potential energy. Before the first law was clearly stated by Helmholtz in 1847 and before Joule's classic measurements of the thermal equivalent of electric and mechanical work, Hess in 1840 observed that the heat absorbed or evolved in a chemical reaction done in open vessels depends only on the initial and final states of the chemicals. The heat of reaction does not depend on the process by which the net chemical change is effected nor on the existence or number of supposed or observed intermediate species.

There was some hint of this valuable hypothesis in the work of Wilcke, Black, and Cavendish on the heat of fusion of ice in the 1750's and in the work of Lavoisier and Laplace on certain heats of solution and combustion in the 1780's. However, Hess's clear statement of 1840 initiated much experimental work on heats of reaction by several investigators. In fact, in their enthusiasm for thermochemistry, Thomsen in 1854 and Berthelot in 1873 were each misled into formulating the false hypothesis that the measure of the driving force of a chemical reaction is the amount of heat liberated by that reaction. Although the heat of a reaction does not by itself determine the tendency of a reaction to occur or its point of equilibrium at the cessation of reaction, the heat of a reaction is of interest in any study of fuels. This chapter also introduces the idea of a standard thermodynamic state as an arbitrary point of reference.

3.2 HEAT OF REACTION

For any change between thermodynamically well defined states there is a unique and definite change in energy or enthalpy, for each of these functions is a function of state. All the examples that have been used to illustrate the calculation of changes in energy or enthalpy have been of the kind that are usually classified as physical changes of state. These included fusion, vaporization, expansion, and so forth. But the illustrations dealt not only with elements but with compounds. If a compound of several elements has a definite state when involved in physical processes, it must also have a definite state in any process, chemical or physical. To its definite state there is to be attributed a definite value of energy and enthalpy, except perhaps for an additive constant that would depend upon the zero of energy chosen.

It is possible to measure the heat evolved or absorbed in a chemical or physical process. If the process occurs at constant pressure, as in a laboratory in open vessels, the heat absorbed by the system in the change would be q_P, and by (2.22) or (2.24) this must equal the increase in enthalpy ΔH if only pressure-volume work is done. That is, in the derivation of (2.22) or (2.24) or in the various definitions of the variables, there is no restriction that would serve to exclude chemical processes from consideration. Similarly, if the chemical change occurred at constant volume, as in a closed rigid vessel, the heat absorbed by the system would be q_V or ΔE, as in (2.18). When only condensed phases are involved as reactants and products, the magnitude of the $\Delta(PV)$ term by which ΔH and ΔE differ is often quite negligible compared to the chemical energies ΔH and ΔE. Thus, for reactions involving no gases, ΔH and ΔE are generally almost equal.

When gases do partake in a chemical change, the $\Delta(PV)$ usually leads to a measurable difference between the heats absorbed by the system at constant volume and pressure.

$$\Delta H = \Delta E + \Delta(PV) \tag{2.23}$$

Each mole of gaseous product will contribute to $\Delta(PV)$ a term

$$P_2V_2 = n_2RT_2$$

while each mole of gaseous reactant will contribute a term

$$-P_1V_1 = -n_1RT_1$$

The values of ΔH and ΔE are customarily quoted for reactants and products at the same temperature; hence, the $\Delta(PV)$ term for the gases involved can be expressed in terms of $\Delta n_{(g)}$, the increase in the number of gas molecules in the reaction, by factoring RT from each PV term. Since the $\Delta(PV)$ term for condensed phases is ordinarily negligible, (2.23) can be restated as

gaseous ✱ $$\Delta H = \Delta E + \Delta n_{(g)}RT \tag{3.1}$$

The values of ΔH and ΔE for a chemical reaction depend only on the states of the reactants and products. They do not depend upon how the change is effected. Whether or not the change is reversible is of no concern. The values of ΔH and ΔE do not depend on the existence of intermediates that can or cannot be isolated. They do not depend upon the presence or absence of a catalyst, a species which is unchanged in the overall reaction. They do depend only on the initial and final states of the species that appear in the stoichiometric equation. If the reaction is reversed, the initial and final states are interchanged and ΔH and ΔE change sign. This means that reversing a reaction will require the absorption of just as much heat as is liberated when it proceeds forward. This independence of path is Hess's law.

The value of ΔH or ΔE that is attributed to a particular reaction assumes that the reactants in their specified states are converted completely into the products in their specified states. There are many chemical reactions that do indeed react essentially to completeness. Theoretically, of course, no reaction will go spontaneously to absolute completeness. But even for those reactions which are incomplete at equilibrium, it is possible to calculate the heat that would be absorbed if the reaction began with pure reactants and left no reactants. At one time, the heat of a reaction was considered to be a measure of the completeness of a reaction. This is false. The explanation must await discussion of free energy and the second law of thermodynamics, but it is easy to illustrate the fact that evolution of heat is not a necessary and sufficient condition for a spontaneous physical or chemical change. Perfect gases mix spontaneously without heat; solid ammonium nitrate dissolves readily at constant temperature with absorption of heat or, what is essentially the same thing, in dissolving adiabatically the final temperature of the solution is less than the common temperature of the solid NH_4NO_3 and water before solution; at sufficiently high T

the bonds in any stable molecule are spontaneously broken with absorption of heat as the molecules disintegrate into atoms.

Hess's law is useful in calculating the heat absorbed in reactions that cannot be performed directly in the laboratory because the reaction does not go to completeness or because it produces more than one product. For example, burning graphite in an inadequate supply of oxygen in the hope of producing just carbon monoxide fails because some carbon dioxide is inevitably produced. The heat of the reaction must therefore be calculated by an indirect method, Hess's law. It is possible, however, to burn either graphite or purified carbon monoxide completely to carbon dioxide. For these reactions, values of ΔH with reactants and products at 25°C at one atm from Rossini, F. D., *et al.*, *Selected Values of Chemical Thermodynamic Properties*, Washington, D. C.: Circular 500 of the U. S. National Bureau of Standards, 1952, are

$$C_{(s)} + O_{2(g)} \longrightarrow CO_{2(g)}, \qquad \Delta H = -94.0518 \text{ kcal} \tag{3.2}$$

$$CO_{(g)} + \tfrac{1}{2}O_{2(g)} \longrightarrow CO_{2(g)}, \qquad \Delta H = -67.6361 \text{ kcal} \tag{3.3}$$

Since (3.2) and (3.3) both proceed to the same final state, gaseous CO_2 at 25°C at 1 atm, the difference in enthalpies of their intial states can be found by subtraction. It is just as though CO_2 were an intermediate state in the diagram

$C_{(s)} + O_{2(g)}$ 25°C 1 atm	$\Delta H =$ -94.0518 kcal → (3.2)	$CO_{2(g)}$ 25°C 1 atm	$\Delta H =$ -67.6361 kcal ← (3.3)	$CO_{(g)} + \frac{1}{2}O_{2(g)}$ 25°C 1 atm
└───────	────────	$\Delta H = ?$	────────	───────→

Since ΔH is independent of the path, from the diagram

$$\Delta H - 67.6361 = -94.0518$$

$$\Delta H = -26.4157 \text{ kcal} \tag{3.4}$$

for the net reaction

$$C_{(s)} + \tfrac{1}{2}O_{2(g)} \longrightarrow CO_{(g)} \tag{3.4}$$

The same result (3.4) could have been found by treating (3.2) and (3.3) as four algebraic equations and by subtracting the pair labeled (3.3) from the pair labeled (3.2). This is equivalent to reversing (3.3), which of course changes the sign of its ΔH, and proceeding from $C_{(s)}$ and $\frac{1}{2}O_{2(g)}$ to $CO_{(g)}$ via $CO_{2(g)}$. The $\frac{1}{2}O_{2(g)}$, which is unchanged in the overall reaction $C_{(s)} + O_{2(g)} \longrightarrow CO_{(g)} + \frac{1}{2}O_{2(g)}$, can be ignored (that is, subtracted from both sides of the equation) because it is in fact unchanged and thus contributes nothing to ΔH or the reaction.

Example 3.1. When 1 mole $MgSO_{4(s)}$ is dissolved in water at 25°C, 21.8 kcal of heat are evolved. When 1 mole $MgSO_4 \cdot 7H_2O_{(s)}$ is dissolved in water at 25°C to form the same final solution, 3.3 kcal are absorbed. (Data from Rossini, F. D., *et al.*, Circular 500, N. B. S., 1952.) Calculate ΔH for the reaction:

$$MgSO_{4(s)} + 7\,H_2O_{(1)} \longrightarrow MgSO_{(4)} \cdot 7H_2O_{(s)}.$$

Since the solution of $MgSO_{4(s)}$ liberates heat, it must absorb a negative amount of heat, and thus ΔH is less than zero.

$$MgSO_{(4)s} + (n + 7)\,H_2O_{(1)} \longrightarrow Mg^{++}SO_4^{--} \text{ in } (n + 7)\,H_2O_{(1)}, \quad \Delta H = -21.8 \text{ kcal}$$

Similarly, for the solution of $MgSO_4 \cdot 7\,H_2O_{(s)}$, which involves the absorption of a positive amount of heat,

$$MgSO_4 \cdot 7\,H_2O_{(s)} + n\,H_2O_{(1)} \longrightarrow Mg^{++}SO_4^{--} \text{ in } (n + 7)\,H_2O_{(1)}, \quad \Delta H = +3.3 \text{ kcal}$$

By subtraction, in which the solution is eliminated,

$$MgSO_{4(s)} + 7\,H_2O_{(1)} \longrightarrow MgSO_4 \cdot 7\,H_2O_{(s)}, \quad \Delta H = -21.8 - (+3.3) = -25.1 \text{ kcal}$$

Example 3.2. Calculate the heat of hydrogenation of acetylene to ethylene at constant volume from the following heats of reaction (Rossini, F. D., *et al.*, Circular 500, N. B. S., 1952) at 25°C, in which reactants and products are each at one atm: (a) burning completely one mole $H_{2(g)}$ to liquid water evolves 68.3174 kcal; (b) burning completely one mole acetylene gas to liquid water and gaseous CO_2 evolves 310.615 kcal; (c) burning completely one mole ethylene gas to liquid water and gaseous CO_2 evolves 337.234 kcal.

From the given information:

$$H_{2(g)} + \tfrac{1}{2}\,O_{2(g)} \longrightarrow H_2O_{(l)}, \qquad \Delta H = -68.317 \text{ kcal}$$
$$C_2H_{2(g)} + \tfrac{5}{2}\,O_{2(g)} \longrightarrow H_2O_{(l)} + 2\,CO_{2(g)}, \qquad \Delta H = -310.615 \text{ kcal}$$
$$C_2H_{4(g)} + 3\,O_{2(g)} \longrightarrow 2\,H_2O_{(l)} + 2\,CO_{2(g)}, \qquad \Delta H = -337.234 \text{ kcal}$$

By subtracting the third pair of equations from the sum of the first two pairs, the result is obtained.

$$C_2H_{2(g)} + H_{2(g)} \longrightarrow C_2H_{4(g)}, \qquad \Delta H = -41.698 \text{ kcal}$$

By (3.1), since $\Delta n_{(g)} = 1 - (1 + 1) = -1$ for the hydrogenation of acetylene,

$$\Delta E = -41.698 - (-1) \times 1.987 \times 298.2 \times 10^{-3} = -41.105 \text{ kcal}$$

More heat is absorbed by the system when acetylene is hydrogenated at constant volume than at constant pressure because ΔE is greater than ΔH. That is, more heat is evolved by the system in the constant-pressure process because the pressure exerted by the surroundings on the system favors the reduction in volume as the reaction occurs. The surroundings actually compress the system as the isothermal reaction occurs at constant P; this work-energy is evolved as heat in addition to the heat that is evolved even in the constant-volume change.

3.3 STANDARD STATES

The 100 or so elements constitute the simplest complete set of independent species from which any chemical compound can be prepared. Since the chemist ordinarily is not interested in separating isotopes or in nuclear reactions, his independent set is comprised of the isotopic mixtures found in nature. On the other hand, a physicist or physical chemist could appropriately choose as his simplest set the several hundred stable isotopes or the 1000 known isotopes, or even the 30-odd fundamental particles, if his interests led him to the separation of stable isotopes, the preparation of radioactively tagged compounds, or the preparations or reactions of nucleuses. The many possible heats of reaction can similarly be catalogued with reference to the energies or enthalpies of the elements as they naturally exist in some standard reference state.

The state of a system is said to be *thermodynamically well defined* if its composition, amount, state of aggregation (solid, liquid, gas, concentrations, surface states, etc.), temperature, and pressure are specified and if positions in and the intensities of fields (electric, magnetic, gravitational, etc.) are also specified. The composition and amount of 1 mole or formula weight of a compound are specified by its chemical formula. Its state of aggregation is commonly noted by a subscript: s for solid; l for liquid; g for gas; aq for infinitely dilute solution in water; and so forth. By common agreement, the standard pressure is one atmosphere, and the various fields are absent in the standard state. The standard state of a substance may occur at any clearly specified temperature such as the temperature of the thermostat in which the system is supposed to exist. It is most common to choose 25°C as the temperature of the standard state.

By definition, the standard state of an element or compound is its real stable thermodynamically well defined state of aggregation as a pure substance at equilibrium in the absence of external fields at a pressure of one atmosphere at the agreed standard temperature. If its stable state of aggregation under standard conditions is a gas, the preceding definition is slightly modified. The standard state of a real gas is a hypothetical reference state of unit fugacity; in this state its enthalpy is equal to the enthalpy it would have or approach at zero pressure, and its fugacity is an effective or idealized pressure that becomes equal to pressure as the limit of zero pressure is approached. The distinction between pressure and fugacity will be explained in Section 5.13; for the present, fugacity and pressure are essentially alike and the equation of state for correcting observable thermodynamic quantities from zero pressure to the hypothetical standard state at unit fugacity is the perfect gas equation of state. The standard state of a perfect gas comes at one atmosphere pressure.

The standard states of solvents and solutes are often taken to be certain unrealizable or hypothetical states of unit concentration because, like the laws of gases, the laws of solutions generally assume simple forms only in the limit of zero concentration. It is very important to be sure of the standard state in use, for there is some variety, especially for solutions. When there is no change in isotopic abundance of an element during reaction, it is unnecessary to classify the element as a nearly ideal solution. Tables for chemical use ignore the fact that elements are generally solutions of isotopes unless a specific notation is made to the contrary; this problem is deferred to Sections 4.12 and 7.5 and to Chapter 17. For the usual solutions of chemicals in chemicals, there are two widely used conventions for the standard state at T at a pressure of one atmosphere in the absence of fields. The first treats all substances in the solution on an equal basis; the standard state of each is the pure stable state of each component of the solution. The second convention, commonly used for aqueous solutions, treats the solvent (generally more common than any other substance in the solution) differently from the solutes; here the standard state of the solvent is its pure state and the standard states of the solutes are hypothetical states of unit concentration (often molality). In these generally unrealizable states of unit concentration, the solute has the same enthalpy it would be observed to have in the limit of zero concentration, while those observable thermodynamic properties that would depend on concentration even if the solution were ideal are corrected to standard state values by the particular ideal law of solution in use. These subtle definitions of standard states become of direct concern after Chapter 6, for here all solutions are extremely dilute aqueous solutions whose enthalpies are not altered by further dilution.

3.4 HEAT OF FORMATION

The enthalpy of an element in its standard state is zero by definition. The enthalpy of a compound is then referred to the several zeros of enthalpy of its constituent elements. For the reaction by which a compound in a specified state is formed from its elements in their standard states, the increase in enthalpy is called the *heat of formation of the compound* in that state. Enthalpies rather than energies are the basis of this kind of systematization because constant pressure processes are much more common in the ordinary laboratory than are constant volume processes.

The molar heat of formation of water is the increase in enthalpy of the reaction that produces 1 mole water from hydrogen and oxygen that are gases in their standard states at 25°C. If the water is liquid, then the heat of formation is the increase in enthalpy ΔH of the reaction

$$H_{2(g)} + \tfrac{1}{2}O_{2(g)} \longrightarrow H_2O_{(l)}. \qquad \Delta H_f^0 = -68.3174 \text{ kcal} \tag{3.5}$$

If the water is gaseous, an unstable but well-defined state at 25°C at one atm, the heat of formation is the value of ΔH for the reaction

$$H_{2(g)} + \tfrac{1}{2}O_{2(g)} \longrightarrow H_2O_{(g)}, \qquad \Delta H_f^\circ = -57.7979 \text{ kcal} \qquad (3.6)$$

The superscript $^\circ$ indicates that reactants and products exist in their standard states, and when that state is not the most stable state, as for $H_2O_{(g)}$ in (3.6), it is clearly noted by a subscript or otherwise.

Similarly, the heats of formation of $CO_{(g)}$ and $CO_{2(g)}$ are

$$C_{(s)} + \tfrac{1}{2}O_{2(g)} \longrightarrow CO_{(g)}, \qquad \Delta H_f^\circ = -26.4157 \text{ kcal} \qquad (3.4)$$

$$C_{(s)} + O_{2(g)} \longrightarrow CO_{2(g)}, \qquad \Delta H_f^\circ = -94.0518 \text{ kcal} \qquad (3.2)$$

The standard state of carbon is graphite, not diamond, for diamond is less stable than graphite under standard conditions.

The heat of formation of a compound is often calculated indirectly through the application of Hess's law. For example, graphite and hydrogen do not form ethylene rapidly in significant amounts, yet from the heat of combustion of ethylene its heat of formation can be calculated as follows:

$$C_2H_{4(g)} + 3\,O_{2(g)} \longrightarrow 2\,CO_{2(g)} + 2\,H_2O_{(l)}, \qquad \Delta H^\circ = -337.234 \text{ kcal} \qquad (3.7)$$

$$2\,H_{2(g)} + O_{2(g)} \longrightarrow 2\,H_2O_{(l)}, \qquad 2\,\Delta H_f^\circ = 2(-68.317 \text{ kcal}) \qquad (3.5)$$

$$2\,C_{(s)} + 2\,O_{2(g)} \longrightarrow 2\,CO_{2(g)}, \qquad 2\,\Delta H_f^\circ = 2(-94.052 \text{ kcal}) \qquad (3.2)$$

If Equations (3.7) are subtracted from the sums of (3.5) and (3.2), the heat of formation of ethylene is found.

$$2\,C_{(s)} + 2\,H_{2(g)} \longrightarrow C_2H_{4(g)} \qquad (3.8)$$

$$\Delta H_f^\circ = 2(-68.317) + 2(-94.052) - (-337.234)$$

$$= +\,12.496 \text{ kcal} \qquad (3.8)$$

Reversing the calculation would allow the calculation of the heat of combustion, $\Delta H^\circ = -337.234$ kcal, of ethylene from the heats of formation of $C_2H_{4(g)}$, $CO_{2(g)}$, and $H_2O_{(l)}$. Similarly the heat absorbed in any chemical or physical change can be calculated from the heats of formation of the various reactants and products, for the kinds and numbers of atoms are preserved in an ordinary chemical or physical change.

Example 3.3. How much heat is evolved when the thermite reaction occurs?

$$\begin{array}{ccccccc} Fe_2O_{3(s)} & + & 2Al_{(s)} & \longrightarrow & 2Fe_{(s)} & + & \alpha\text{-}Al_2O_{3(s)} \\ \Delta H_f^\circ = -196.5 \text{ kcal} & & \Delta H_f^\circ = 0 & & \Delta H_f^\circ = 0 & & \Delta H_f^\circ = -399.1 \text{ kcal} \end{array}$$

$$\Delta H^\circ = -399.1 - (-196.5) = -202.6 \text{ kcal}$$

For every formula weight of $Fe_2O_{3(s)}$ that is reduced to 2 $Fe_{(s)}$ at 25°C at 1 atm, 202,600 cal are evolved. If the reaction is really performed, this heat will generally increase the temperature of the products and melt the iron metal.

When dilute ionic solutions are mixed very little heat is evolved or absorbed, for, if interionic attractions and repulsions and dilution effects can be neglected, the final states of the ions do not differ from the initial states. For example, mixing dilute aqueous solutions of KCl and NaF produces no chemical reaction and no heat.

$$K^+_{(aq)} + Cl^-_{(aq)} + Na^+_{(aq)} + F^-_{(aq)} \longrightarrow K^+_{(aq)} + F^-_{(aq)} + Na^+_{(aq)} + Cl^-_{(aq)} \qquad \Delta H^\circ = 0 \qquad (3.9)$$

However, when there is a change of state or a chemical reaction, as in dissolution, precipitation, or the production or reaction of slightly ionized substances, then the change in enthalpy is obviously not zero. Example 2.1 contains examples of heats of solution. Perhaps the most fundamental ionic reaction in aqueous solutions is the production of un-ionized water from hydrogen ions and hydroxide ions. When any strong acid reacts in dilute solution with any strong base, about 13,360 cal are evolved for each mole of liquid water produced at 25°C at 1 atm. Equations (3.10) state this fact.

$$H^+_{(aq)} + OH^-_{(aq)} \longrightarrow H_2O_{(l)}, \qquad \Delta H^\circ = -13.360 \text{ kcal} \qquad (3.10)$$

From this fact and the heat of formation of $H_2O_{(l)}$ it is possible to calculate the sum of the heats of formation of $H^+_{(aq)}$ and $OH^-_{(aq)}$.

$$H_{2(g)} + \tfrac{1}{2}O_{2(g)} \longrightarrow H_2O_{(l)}, \qquad \Delta H_f^\circ = -68.317 \text{ kcal} \qquad (3.5)$$

From (3.5) and (3.10),

$$H_{2(g)} + \tfrac{1}{2}O_{2(g)} \longrightarrow H^+_{(aq)} + OH^-_{(aq)}$$
$$\Delta H^\circ = -68.317 - (-13,360) = -54.957 \text{ kcal} \qquad (3.11)$$

By convention, the standard heat of formation of $H^+_{(aq)}$ is taken to be zero at any T. The only heat of formation that is not defined at zero in (3.11) is that of $OH^-_{(aq)}$. Thus (3.11) fixes ΔH_f° of $OH^-_{(aq)}$ as -54.957 kcal. With these two ions' heats of formation determined, the heat of formation of any other ion can be found from the heats of formation and solution of its pure compound with H^+ or OH^-. For example, ΔH_f° of $NaOH_{(s)}$ is -101.99 kcal. As n approaches infinity,

$$NaOH_{(s)}(+\, n\, H_2O_{(l)}) \longrightarrow Na^+_{(aq)} + OH^-_{(aq)}, \qquad \Delta H^\circ = -10.25 \text{ kcal} \qquad (3.12)$$

Since there are equal numbers of moles of water on both sides of (3.12), the two infinities give no net effect and the heat of formation of $Na^+_{(aq)}$ is found thus:

$$\begin{aligned} -10.25 &= \Delta H_f^\circ[OH^-_{(aq)}] + \Delta H_f^\circ[Na^+_{(aq)}] - \Delta H_f^\circ[NaOH_{(s)}] \\ &= -54.957 + \Delta H_f^\circ[Na^+_{(aq)}] - (-101.99) \\ \Delta H_f^\circ[Na^+_{(aq)}] &= -57.28 \text{ kcal} \end{aligned}$$

Similarly, from $NaCl_{(aq)}$ or $HCl_{(aq)}$ the heat of formation of $Cl^-_{(aq)}$ can be found. And so on to all ions. The changes in enthalpy of any ionic reaction can then be found from these ionic heats of formation and the usual heats of formation of compounds by performing similar calculations in reverse.

Example 3.4. Calculate ΔH° for the reaction at 25°C:

$$\begin{array}{lccc} & Ba^{++}_{(aq)} + & SO_{4\,(aq)}^{--} \longrightarrow & BaSO_{4\,(s)} \\ \Delta H_f^\circ & -128.67 & -216.90 & -350.2 \end{array}$$

$$\Delta H^\circ = -350.2 - (-128.67 - 216.90) = -4.6 \text{ kcal}$$

Example 3.5. Calculate the heat evolved when one mole $HCl_{(g)}$ is dissolved in a very large amount of water at 25°C. The change in state is

$$\begin{array}{lccc} & HCl_{(g)} \longrightarrow & H^+_{(aq)} + & Cl^-_{(aq)} \\ \Delta H_f^\circ & -22.063 & 0.000 & -40.023 \end{array}$$

$$\Delta H^\circ = -40.023 - (-22.063) = -17.960 \text{ kcal}$$

The heat evolved is $-\Delta H^\circ$, or 17,960 cal.

The standard heat of formation of a gaseous ion differs from that of an aqueous ion in several respects. For a gaseous ion, ΔH_f° refers to reactions like

$$\begin{aligned} \tfrac{1}{2}H_{2\,(g)} &\longrightarrow H^+_{(g)} + e^-_{(g)} & \Delta H^\circ = \Delta H_f^\circ &= +367.088 \text{ kcal} \qquad (3.13) \\ Zn_{(s)} &\longrightarrow Zn^{2+}_{(g)} + 2e^-_{(g)} & \Delta H^\circ = \Delta H_f^\circ &= +664.902 \text{ kcal} \\ e^-_{(g)} + \tfrac{1}{2}Cl_{2\,(g)} &\longrightarrow Cl^-_{(g)} & \Delta H^\circ = \Delta H_f^\circ &= -58.3 \text{ kcal} \\ 2e^-_{(g)} + S_{(s)} &\longrightarrow S^{2-}_{(g)} & \Delta H^\circ = \Delta H_f^\circ &= +125.2 \text{ kcal} \end{aligned}$$

In these reactions, every species with subscript g, including the electron, contributes a significant $PV = RT$ term to the difference between ΔE and ΔH.

The heats of formation and isobaric heat capacities of compounds and ions are listed in Table 3.1. The values used in this section and those of Table 3.1 were taken from Rossini, Wagman, Evans, Levine, and Jaffe, *Selected Values of Chemical Thermodynamic Properties;* Washington, D. C.: Circular 500 of the National Bureau of Standards, U. S. Government Printing Office, 1952, and

Table 3.1. Standard Heats of Formation ΔH_f^0 (kcal per gram-formula-weight) of Compounds and Ions At 25°C and Their Isobaric Heat Capacities C_P (cal per degree per gram-formula weight) at 25°C (NBS Circulars 500 [1952] and C461 [1947].)

Substance	ΔH_f^0	C_P	Substance	ΔH_f^0	C_P
$O_{3(g)}$	34.0	9.12	$C_6H_{6(g)}$	19.820	19.52
$H^+_{(aq)}$	0.000		cyclo $C_6H_{12(g)}$	−29.43	25.40
$H^+_{(g)}$	367.088		$Pb^{2+}_{(aq)}$	0.39	
$OH^-_{(aq)}$	−54.957		$PbS_{(s)}$	−22.54	11.83
$H_2O_{(g)}$	−57.7979	8.025	$PbSO_{4(s)}$	−219.50	24.9
$H_2O_{(l)}$	−68.3174	17.996	$Zn^{2+}_{(g)}$	664.902	
$F^-_{(g)}$	−79.5		$Zn^{2+}_{(aq)}$	−36.43	
$F^-_{(aq)}$	−78.66		$ZnSO_{4(s)}$	−233.88	28.
$HF_{(g)}$	−64.2	6.95	$ZnSO_4\cdot H_2O_{(s)}$	−310.6	34.7
$Cl^-_{(g)}$	−58.3		$ZnSO_4\cdot 6H_2O_{(s)}$	−663.3	80.8
$Cl^-_{(aq)}$	−40.023		$ZnSO_4\cdot 7H_2O_{(s)}$	−735.1	93.7
$HCl_{(g)}$	−22.063	6.96	$Ag^+_{(g)}$	245.274	
$Br^-_{(g)}$	−55.3		$Ag^+_{(aq)}$	25.31	
$Br^-_{(aq)}$	−28.90		$Ag_2O_{(s)}$	−7.306	15.67
$Br_{2(g)}$	7.34	8.60	$AgCl_{(s)}$	−30.362	12.14
$HBr_{(g)}$	−8.66	6.96	$AgBr_{(s)}$	−23.78	12.52
$I_{2(g)}$	14.876	8.81	$Ag_2CO_{3(s)}$	−120.97	26.8
$HI_{(g)}$	6.20	6.97	$Fe_2O_{3(s)}$	−196.5	25.0
$S_{(g)}$	53.25	5.66	$Fe_3O_{4(s)}$	−267.0	
$S^{2-}_{(g)}$	125.2		$CrO^{2-}_{4(aq)}$	−206.3	
$SO_{2(g)}$	−70.96	9.51	$Cr_2O^{2-}_{7(aq)}$	−349.1	
$SO_{3(g)}$	−94.45	12.10	$HCrO^-_{4(aq)}$	−212.8	
$SO^{2-}_{4(aq)}$	−216.90		$H_2CrO_{4(aq)}$	−213.5	
$H_2S_{(g)}$	−4.815	8.12	$Ag_2CrO_{4(s)}$	−170.15	34.00
$H_2SO_{4(l)}$	−193.91	32.88	$TiO_{2(s)}$(rut)	−218.0	13.16
$NO_{(g)}$	21.600	7.137	$TiCl_{4(g)}$		22.88
$NO_{2(g)}$	8.091	9.06	$TiCl_{4(l)}$	−179.3	37.5
$NO^-_{3(aq)}$	−49.372		$Al_2O_{3(s)}(\alpha)$	−399.09	18.88
$NH_{3(g)}$	−11.04	8.523	$MgCl_{2(s)}$	−153.40	17.04
$NH_{3(aq)}$	−19.32		$Ca^{2+}_{(aq)}$	−129.77	
$NH^+_{4(aq)}$	−31.74		$CaF_{2(s)}$	−290.3	16.02
$NH_4OH_{(aq)}$	−87.64		$Ba^{2+}_{(aq)}$	−128.67	
$C_{(diamond)}$	0.4532	1.449	$BaCl_{2(s)}$	−205.56	18.0
$CO_{(g)}$	−26.4157	6.965	$BaCl_2\cdot H_2O_{(s)}$	−278.4	28.2
$CO_{2(g)}$	−94.0518	8.874	$BaCl_2\cdot 2H_2O_{(s)}$	−349.35	37.10
$CO^{2-}_{3(aq)}$	−161.63		$BaSO_{4(s)}$	−350.2	24.32
$CH_{4(g)}$	−17.889	8.536	$Na^+_{(g)}$	146.015	
$HCO^-_{3(aq)}$	−165.18		$Na^+_{(aq)}$	−57.279	
$CH_3OH_{(g)}$	−48.08		$NaOH_{(s)}$	−101.99	19.2
$CH_3NO_{2(l)}$	−21.28	25.3	$NaCl_{(s)}$	−98.232	11.88
$C_2H_{2(g)}$	54.194	10.499	$NaBr_{(s)}$	−86.030	12.5
$C_2H_{4(g)}$	12.496	10.41	$Na_2SO_{4(s)}$	−330.90	30.50
$C_2H_{6(g)}$	−20.236	12.585	$Na_2SO_4\cdot 10H_2O_{(s)}$	−1033.48	140.4
$C_3H_{8(g)}$	−24.820	17.57	$Na_2CO_{3(s)}$	−270.3	26.41
n-$C_6H_{14(g)}$	−39.96	35.06	$NaHCO_{3(s)}$	−226.5	20.94

Rossini, Pitzer, Taylor, Ebert, Kilpatrick, Beckett, Williams, and Werner, *Selected Values of Properties of Hydrocarbons;* Washington, D. C.: Circular C461 of the National Bureau of Standards, U. S. Goverment Printing Office, 1947. The arbitrary convention that ΔH_f° of $H^+_{(aq)}$ is zero makes all standard heats of formation of aqueous ions only indirectly related to observation. This convention, of course, causes no trouble for net ionic reactions like

$$Zn_{(s)} + 2\,Ag^+_{(aq)} \longrightarrow Zn^{2+}_{(aq)} + 2\,Ag_{(s)}$$

However, it does lead to fictitious values of ΔH for half-reactions involving electrons and aqueous ions and for reactions in which ions move between phases.

Example 3.6. With the aid of Table 3.1, calculate ΔH° for the reaction

$$TiCl_{4(l)} + 2\,H_2O_{(g)} \longrightarrow TiO_{2(s)} + 4\,HCl_{(g)}$$

The calculation involves subtracting the heats of formation of reactants from those of the products or, what is equivalent, adding the values of ΔH° for the reactions of formation of products and the reversed reactions of formation of reactants. Hence,

$$\Delta H^\circ = 4(-22.06) + (-218.0) - (-179.3) - 2(-57.8) = -11.3 \text{ kcal.}$$

When one mole of $TiCl_{4(l)}$ hydrolyzes thus, 11,300 cal are evolved at one atm at 25°C.

3.5 HEAT OF REACTION AT ANY TEMPERATURE

Calculation of a heat of reaction at any temperature other than the standard temperature for which heats of formation are tabulated is nothing more than the extension of the principles of Section 2.15. A path is invented to make the calculations as convenient as possible. The temperature of the reactants is changed to the standard temperature, the chemical or physical process is effected isothermally, and the temperature of the products is then changed from the standard temperature to the initial temperature of the reactants. The value of ΔE or ΔH for the overall change is, then, the heat of reaction at the arbitrary temperature and is calculated by summing the three values of ΔE or ΔH for the three invented processes.

Any isothermal changes of pressure or volume required to bring the reactants or products to a standard state of pressure or volume are readily calculated. Since the method of finding ΔE is analogous to that for finding ΔH, the problem is most practically stated as the determination of the heat of reaction at constant pressure at any temperature, given ΔH_0 at some reference temperature T_0. A diagram clarifies the issue.

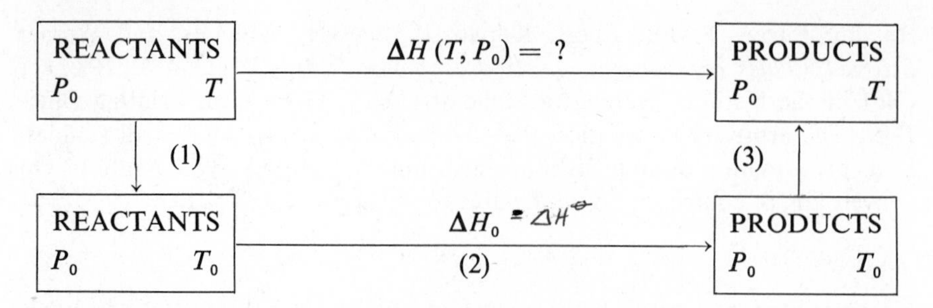

Change (1) is accomplished at the standard pressure P_0, and for this change in the temperature of all of the reactants, by (2.64) or (2.65),

$$\Delta H_1 = \int_T^{T_0} \sum_{\text{reactants}} C_{P_0} dT' \tag{3.14}$$

Change (2) is accomplished at the reference temperature T_0. Generally T_0 will be the standard temperature and P_0 will be the standard pressure at which standard heats of formation of reactants and products are known and tabulated. The value of $\Delta H_2 = \Delta H_0 = \Delta H^\ominus$ is found with the use of Table 3.1. Change (3) is accomplished at the standard pressure P_0, and for it, as for Change (1),

$$\Delta H_3 = \int_{T_0}^{T} \sum_{\text{products}} C_{P_0} dT' \tag{3.15}$$

For the general reaction

$$a\text{A} + b\text{B} + \cdots \longrightarrow d\text{D} + e\text{E} + \cdots$$

the increase in enthalpy at any temperature T is

$$\begin{aligned}
\Delta H(T, P_0) &= \Delta H_1 + \Delta H_2 + \Delta H_3 \\
&= \int_T^{T_0} \sum_{\text{reactants}} C_{P_0} dT' + \Delta H(T_0, P_0) + \int_{T_0}^{T} \sum_{\text{products}} C_{P_0} dT' \\
&= \Delta H(T_0, P_0) + \int_{T_0}^{T} \left[\sum_{\text{products}} C_{P_0} - \sum_{\text{reactants}} C_{P_0} \right] dT' \\
&= [d\Delta H_f^\ominus(\text{D}) + e\Delta H_f^\ominus(\text{E}) + \cdots] \\
&\quad -[a\Delta H_f^\ominus(\text{A}) + b\Delta H_f^\ominus(\text{B}) + \cdots] + \int_{T_0}^{T} [dC_{P_0}(\text{D}) \\
&\quad + eC_{P_0}(\text{E}) + \cdots - aC_{P_0}(\text{A}) - bC_{P_0}(\text{B}) - \cdots] dT'
\end{aligned} \tag{3.16}$$

where $\Delta H_f^\ominus(\text{A})$ is the standard heat of formation of 1 mole A, where $C_{P_0}(\text{A})$ is the molar heat capacity of A at pressure P_0, and so on for B, . . . , D, E, ...

Equation (3.16) can be abbreviated by defining ΔC_{P_0}, ΔH_0, and ΔH by (3.17), (3.18), and (3.19).

$$\Delta C_{P_0} = \sum_{\text{products}} C_{P_0} - \sum_{\text{reactants}} C_{P_0}$$
$$= dC_{P_0}(\text{D}) + eC_{P_0}(\text{E}) + \cdots - aC_{P_0}(\text{A}) - bC_{P_0}(\text{B}) - \cdots \tag{3.17}$$

and

$$\Delta H_0 = \Delta H(T_0, P_0)$$
$$= d\Delta H_f^0(\text{D}) + e\Delta H_f^0(\text{E}) + \cdots - a\Delta H_f^0(\text{A}) - b\Delta H_f^0(\text{B}) \cdots \tag{3.18}$$
$$\Delta H = \Delta H(T, P_0) \tag{3.19}$$

Equation (3.16) then assumes the simple appearance of (3.20).

$$\Delta H = \Delta H_0 + \int_{T_0}^{T} \Delta C_{P_0}\, dT' \tag{3.20}$$

Equation (3.20) can be transformed from its integral form to the equivalent differential form of (3.21) as $T - T_0$ approaches dT and $\Delta H - \Delta H_0$ approaches $d(\Delta H)$ at constant pressure P_0.

$$\left(\frac{\partial \Delta H}{\partial T}\right)_{P_0} = \Delta C_{P_0} \tag{3.21}$$

In view of the detailed derivation of Kirchhoff's law, (3.20) and (3.21), the following purely formal derivation of (3.21) has sufficient meaning despite its terseness to warrant mention. Let H_2 represent the enthalpy of the products and H_1 the enthalpy of the reactants at the same temperature T and pressure P_0. Then, for the complete conversion of products into reactants at T and P_0, the increase in enthalpy is

$$\Delta H = H_2 - H_1$$

From this, with the aid of (2.27) and (3.17),

$$\left(\frac{\partial \Delta H}{\partial T}\right)_{P_0} = \left(\frac{\partial H_2}{\partial T}\right)_{P_0} - \left(\frac{\partial H_1}{\partial T}\right)_{P_0}$$
$$= \Delta C_{P_0} \tag{3.21}$$

Definite integration of (3.21) leads to (3.20); thus, at a constant pressure of P_0, if ΔH is the heat of reaction at T and ΔH_0 is the heat of reaction at T_0,

$$\int_{\Delta H_0}^{\Delta H} d(\Delta H)' = \int_{T_0}^{T} \Delta C_{P_0} dT'$$

$$\Delta H - \Delta H_0 = \int_{T_0}^{T} \Delta C_{P_0} dT' \tag{3.20}$$

It is clear that the energy equations analogous to (3.20) and (3.21) are

$$\Delta E - \Delta E_0 = \int_{T_0}^{T} \Delta C_{V_0} dT' \tag{3.22}$$

$$\left(\frac{\partial \Delta E}{\partial T}\right)_{V_0} = \Delta C_{V_0} \tag{3.23}$$

In (3.22) and (3.23), ΔE and ΔE_0 are the heats of reaction at constant volume V_0 at the temperatures T and T_0.

Example 3.7. At 355°K, $\Delta H = -28{,}570$ cal for the hydrogenation of one mole of cis-butene-2 (G. B. Kistiakowsky, *et al.*, *J. Am. Chem. Soc.* **57,** 876 (1935). What is $\Delta H^\ominus$ at 25°C?

The reaction is $C_4H_{8(g)} + H_{2(g)} \rightarrow C_4H_{10(g)}$. According to Table 2.1 and (3.17),

$$\begin{aligned}\Delta C_P &= C_P(C_4H_{10}) - C_P(H_2) - C_P(C_4H_8)\\ &= \Delta C_P^{(0)} + T\Delta C_P^{(1)} + T^2\,\Delta C_P^{(2)}\\ &= (4.357 - 6.947 - 2.047) + T \times 10^{-3}\,[72.552 - (-0.200) - 64.311]\\ &\quad + T^2 \times 10^{-6}\,[(-22.145) - (0.481) - (-19.834)]\\ &= -4.637 + 8.441 \times 10^{-3}\,T - 2.792 \times 10^{-6}\,T^2\end{aligned}$$

With $T = 355$°K when $\Delta H = -28{,}570$ cal, it follows that, at $T_0 = 298$°K, $\Delta H_0 = \Delta H^\ominus$ and by (3.20)

$$\begin{aligned}-28{,}570 - \Delta H^\ominus &= \int_{298}^{355} (-4.637 + 8.441 \times 10^{-3}T - 2.792 \times 10^{-6}T^2)dT\\ &= -264 + 157 - 17 = -124 \text{ cal}\\ \Delta H^\ominus &= -28{,}570 + 124 = -28{,}446 \text{ cal}\end{aligned}$$

Hydrogenation of a mole of cis-butene-2 at 25°C at one atm evolves 28,446 cal.

Example 3.8. Estimate ΔH at one atm at 850°C for the reaction

$$TiCl_{4(g)} + 2\,Mg_{(l)} \longrightarrow Ti_{(s)} + 2\,MgCl_{2(l)}$$

Circular 500 of the National Bureau of Standards provides some data in Table 3.1 and the additional facts that at its boiling point of 135.8°C at one atm the heat of vaporization of $TiCl_4$ is 8.4 kcal mole^{-1}, that Mg melts at 650°C at one atm with a heat of fusion of 2.2 kcal mole^{-1}, and that $MgCl_2$ melts at 714°C at one atm with a heat of fusion of 10.3 kcal mole^{-1}. For this example, assume the following C_P's (cal mole^{-1} deg^{-1}): 38 ($TiCl_{4(l)}$); 23 ($TiCl_{4(g)}$); 6 ($Mg_{(s)}$ and $Ti_{(s)}$); 11 ($Mg_{(l)}$); 17 ($MgCl_{2(s)}$); and 28 ($MgCl_{2(l)}$).

During change (1) in which reactants are cooled isobarically from 850°C (1123°K) to 25°C (298°K), $TiCl_4$ is condensed at 409°K and 2 Mg are crystallized at 923°K. For this decrease in T, by a form of (2.66) at one atm,

$$\begin{aligned}\Delta H_1 &= \int_{1123}^{409} 23\,dT + (-8400) + \int_{409}^{298} 38\,dT + \int_{1123}^{923} 2(11)\,dT\\ &\quad + 2(-2200) + \int_{923}^{298} 2(6)\,dT\\ &= -45{,}300 \text{ cal}\end{aligned}$$

At 25°C at one atm for the second change $TiCl_{4(l)} + 2\ Mg_{(s)} \longrightarrow 2\ MgCl_{2(s)} + Ti_{(s)}$, data from Table 3.1 yield

$$\Delta H^{\ominus} = 0 + 2\,(-153.40) - 2\,(0) - (-179.3) = -127.5 \text{ kcal}$$

During change (3) in which products are heated isobarically from 25°C to 850°C, 2 $MgCl_2$ melt at 987°K; hence, by a form of (2.66),

$$\Delta H_3 = \int_{298}^{1123} 6\,dT + \int_{298}^{987} 2(17)\,dT + 2(10300) + \int_{987}^{1123} 2(28)\,dT$$
$$= 56{,}600 \text{ cal}$$

Thus, for the isobaric change of state at 850°C,

$$\Delta H = \Delta H_1 + \Delta H^{\ominus} + \Delta H_3 = -45{,}300 - 127{,}500 + 56{,}600$$
$$= -116{,}200 \text{ cal}$$

Example 3.9. Develop an equation for ΔH as a function of T for the reaction

$$2\ H_{2(g)} + O_{2(g)} \longrightarrow 2\ H_2O_{(g)}$$

The calculation of ΔC_P and $\Delta H^{\ominus}$ of (3.20) is facilitated by good organization. Values of the following table are drawn from Tables 2.1 and 3.1.

Item	2 H_2	O_2	2 H_2O	Increment in Item
$\Delta H_f^{\ominus}$	0	0	2 (−57.7979)	−115.5958
$C_P^{(0)}$	2 (6.9469)	6.148	2 (7.256)	−5.530
$C_P^{(1)} \times 10^3$	2 (−0.1999)	3.102	2 (2.298)	1.894
$C_P^{(2)} \times 10^6$	2 (0.4808)	−0.923	2 (0.283)	−1.319

By (3.20), ΔH at any temperature T can be found if the value of ΔH_0 is known at one temperature T_0. Since $\Delta H_0 = -115{,}595.8$ cal at $T_0 = 298.2$°K, it follows that

$$\Delta H = -115{,}595.8 + \int_{298.2}^{T'} (-5.530 + 1.894 \times 10^{-3}\,T - 1.319 \times 10^{-6}\,T^2)\,dT$$
$$= -115{,}595.8 - 5.530\,(T' - 298.2) + \frac{0.001894}{2}(T'^2 - 298.2^2)$$
$$- \frac{1.319 \times 10^{-6}}{3}(T'^3 - 298.2^3)$$
$$= -115{,}595.8 + 1649.0 - 84.2 + 11.6 - 5.530T' + 0.947 \times 10^{-3}\,T'^2$$
$$- 0.440 \times 10^{-6}(T')^3$$
$$= -114{,}019.4 - 5.530\,T' + 0.947 \times 10^{-3}T'^2 - 0.440 \times 10^{-6}\,T'^3$$

For example, ΔH at 1000°K is found by substituting $T' = 1000$; the result is $\Delta H = -119{,}042$ cal at 1000°K. The value −114,019.4 does not apply at absolute zero because the heat capacities are valid only between 300°K and 1500°K.

Example 3.10. According to Circular 500 of the National Bureau of Standards, spectroscopic observations show that at 0°K the minimum energy needed to dissociate a mole of H_2 molecules to atoms is 103.240 kcal and that at 0°K the minimum energy needed to ionize H atoms is 313.518 kcal mole^{-1}. Show how (3.13) depends on these facts.

To convert an energy change at 0°K to one at 298°K by (3.23) requires C_V for all species in the reaction (3.13), namely, $\frac{1}{2}H_{2(g)} \longrightarrow H^+_{(g)} + e^-_{(g)}$. Since the products are as simple as monatomic molecules, (2.42) suggests $C_V = (\frac{3}{2})R$ for each; since H_2 may perhaps be assumed to be a rigid diatom, for it $C_V = (\frac{5}{2})R$; hence, for the reaction of interest, $\Delta C_V = (\frac{3}{2})R + (\frac{3}{2})R - \frac{1}{2}(\frac{5}{2}R) = (\frac{7}{4})R$. Furthermore, the spectroscopic results in conventional form are

$$\begin{array}{lll} \frac{1}{2}H_{2(g)} \longrightarrow H_{(g)} & \Delta E^\circ_0 = & 51.620 \text{ kcal} \\ H_{(g)} \longrightarrow H^+_{(g)} + e^-_{(g)} & \Delta E^\circ_0 = & 313.518 \text{ kcal} \\ \hline \frac{1}{2}H_{2(g)} \longrightarrow H^+_{(g)} + e^-_{(g)} & \Delta E^\circ_0 = & 365.138 \text{ kcal} \end{array}$$

Thus (3.22) yields

$$\Delta E^\circ_{298} = \Delta E^\circ_0 + \int_0^{298} \Delta C_V \, dT = 365{,}138 + (\tfrac{7}{4})1.987 \times 298 = 366{,}174 \text{ cal}$$

Then, by (3.1) at 298°K,

$$\Delta H^\circ_{298} = \Delta E^\circ_{298} + (1 + 1 - \tfrac{1}{2})RT = 366{,}174 + 889 = 367{,}063 \text{ cal}$$

The slight difference in values is attributable to inaccuracy in the assumed C_V for H_2 and to the fact that all C_V's approach zero at $T = 0$.

3.6 FINAL TEMPERATURE OF AN ADIABATIC REACTION

It frequently happens that a reaction occurs in circumstances in which thermal contact between the reacting system and the surroundings is restricted or even absent by design. However, because ΔE or ΔH is not zero, the products of the reaction and any unconsumed reactants must change in temperature because the heat of reaction has no other place to go. The positive amount of heat liberated by an *exothermic* reaction, wherein ΔE or ΔH is less than zero, would increase the temperature of the products. Conversely, an *endothermic* reaction, wherein ΔE or ΔH is greater than zero, would be accompanied by a decrease in the temperature of the products.

For example, when $NaOH_{(s)}$ or $H_2SO_{4(l)}$ is dissolved in water, the resulting solution is at a higher temperature than the water and pure solute if they were initially at the same temperature. For isothermal solution processes of this kind, ΔE and ΔH are less than zero. Similarly, when a mixture of hydrogen and oxygen at uniform temperature is ignited, the temperature of the water produced is greater than that of the unignited mixture. As commonly performed, these processes cannot dissipate their heats of reaction swiftly enough to their surroundings to maintain the initial temperature. Performed under control with adequate stirring in good thermal contact with a large thermostat, these reactions could be performed isothermally, or nearly so.

A diagram of the changes that occur when a reaction proceeds essentially to completion under isobaric ($dP_0 = 0$) adiabatic ($dq = dH = 0$) conditions follows:

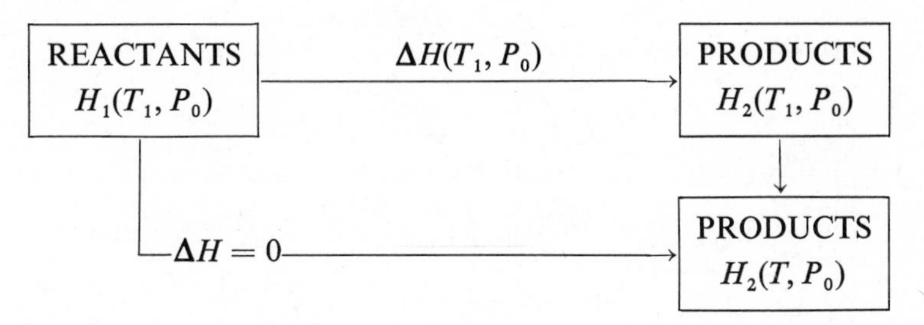

In view of Equation (3.20) and its derivation in the preceding section, the convenient path of the diagram yields (3.24) where $\Delta H(T_1, P_0)$ is the increase in enthalpy for the reaction at constant temperature T_1.

$$\Delta H = \Delta H(T_1, P_0) + \int_{T_1}^{T} \sum_{\text{products}} C_{P_0} dT' \tag{3.24}$$

But ΔH really is zero since the change is effected adiabatically and isobarically. By (3.24), since $\Delta H = 0$,

$$\Delta H(T_1, P_0) = \int_{T}^{T_1} \sum_{\text{products}} C_{P_0} dT' \tag{3.25}$$

If $\Delta H(T_1, P_0)$ is known through calculation by the methods of the preceding section, and if the heat capacities at constant pressure of the products are known, then the final temperature T achieved is readily found from (3.25).

Another possible route for the same change of state involves changing the temperature of the reactants from T_1 to T and then performing the reaction at T and P_0 as in the next diagram.

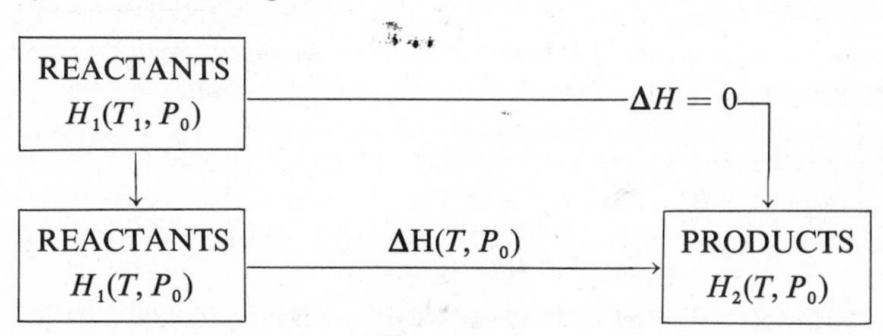

This scheme is somewhat less convenient because the temperature T is not known beforehand to facilitate the calculation of $\Delta H(T, P_0)$. To use this scheme,

ΔH must be expressed as a function of T, but this inconvenience could perhaps be compensated for by the simplicity of the change of state of the reactants between T_1 and T.

Example 3.11. What is the maximum temperature achievable by a methane-air flame? For the purposes of this problem and not because the real situation warrants such approximations, assume that:

(1) The only reaction is

$$CH_{4(g)} + 2\,O_{2(g)} \longrightarrow CO_{2(g)} + 2\,H_2O_{(g)}.$$

(2) The reaction goes to completion.
(3) Air is 20% vol O_2 and 80% vol N_2.
(4) No energy is lost by radiation or kinetic energy of flow or otherwise.
(5) All gases are perfect.
(6) The change is adiabatic and isobaric.
(7) The methane-air mixture is initially at 25°C.

The diagram of the change is this,

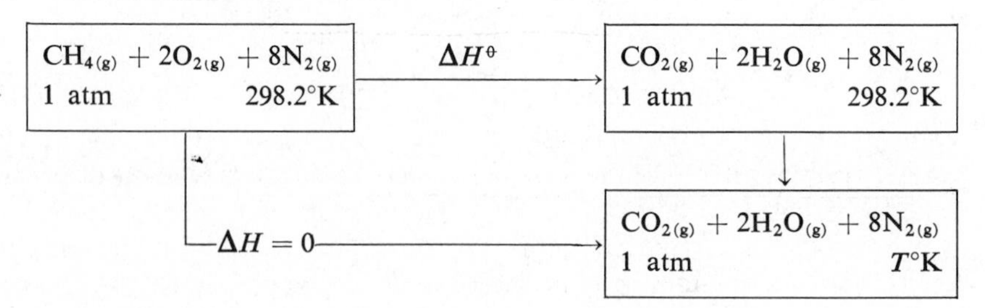

From Table 3.1,

$$\begin{aligned}\Delta H^\ominus &= \Delta H_f^\ominus[CO_{2(g)}] + 2\,\Delta H_f^\ominus[H_2O_{(g)}] - \Delta H_f^\ominus[CH_{4(g)}]\\ &= -94.0518 + 2(-57.7979) - (-17.889) = -191.759 \text{ kcal}\end{aligned}$$

From Table 2.1,

$$\begin{aligned}\sum_{\text{products}} C_{P_0} &= C_{P_0}[CO_{2(g)}] + 2C_{P_0}[H_2O_{(g)}] + 8C_{P_0}[N_{2(g)}]\\ &= 72.918 + 24.992 \times 10^{-3}\,T - 2.987 \times 10^{-6}\,T^2\end{aligned}$$

By (3.25)

$$-191{,}759 = \int_T^{298.2} [72.918 + 24.992 \times 10^{-3}\,T' - 2.987 \times 10^{-6}\,T'^2]\,dT'$$

$$\begin{aligned}191{,}759 &= 72.918(T - 298.2) + 12.496 \times 10^{-3}(T^2 - 298.2^2)\\ &\quad - 0.996 \times 10^{-6}(T^3 - 298.2^3)\end{aligned}$$

$$214{,}585 = 72.918T + 12.496 \times 10^{-3}T^2 - 0.996 \times 10^{-6}T^3$$

Since the observed value is 2150°K, this cubic equation in T is best solved by trial and error near $T = 2150$. The required solution is $T = 2240$°K, but the value of this answer is doubtful not only because some of the assumptions may be in error but also because the heat capacities of Table 2.1 are expected to hold only from 300°K to 1500°K.

3.7 ADIABATIC CALORIMETRY

Calorimeters measure thermal energy when the flow of heat is somehow controlled. The observations of heat capacities, heats of transition, and heats of reaction are fundamental to thermodynamics. Much ingenuity and care are required in the design and use of calorimeters because heat is an elusive kind of energy.

Cavendish determined the heat of vaporization of water with a calorimeter in which several burners were supposedly providing heat at a constant rate. Although the water boiled at constant temperature, from the time it took to boil away he calculated the temperature it would have reached as water if it had not boiled. Thus, he compared the heat of vaporization to the rise in temperature of water. As explained in Section 2.4, the primary observation in a calorimeter has usually been a rise in temperature of water. However, because electrical work can be controlled and measured very exactly, the modern unit of heat is the joule, with the thermodynamic calorie defined as 4.1840 joules.

In 1784 Lavoisier and Laplace used an isothermal calorimeter in which the amount of thermal energy generated by a physical or chemical process was determined by weighing the amount of water produced from ice. Drainage of water from ice is not reproducible; hence, this kind of calorimeter was not generally accepted until 1947, when Ginnings and Corruccini showed that the amount of ice melted or frozen by a change could be measured exactly by observing the change in volume of the ice-water mixture in the calorimeter. Phase changes of other substances are also used in isothermal calorimeters away from 0°C.

Figure 3.1 is a diagram of an ice calorimeter used to study isobaric heat capacities up to 1200°K. The ice I is deposited on tinned copper vanes F by inserting a tube of dry ice into the well A. A hot sample in container D is dropped into the calorimeter through the central well A, which is made of inconel, an alloy of low thermal conductivity. The liquid mercury dilatometer for measuring the change in volume of the ice I as it melts consists of a reservoir R, a glass capillary C, a beaker B of Hg, and a needle valve V. An external ice bath E serves to keep the pyrex glass calorimeter vessel P essentially adiabatic and to cool the Hg that enters the dilatometer. A gate G prevents furnace radiation from entering the calorimeter via the delivery tube A before and after the sample container D is dropped. The temperature T of the sample in the furnace is observed by resistance thermometers or thermocouples in wells N. If n moles of sample of molar heat capacity C_P in a container of heat capacity C are cooled suddenly and adiabatically at constant pressure from a temperature T to

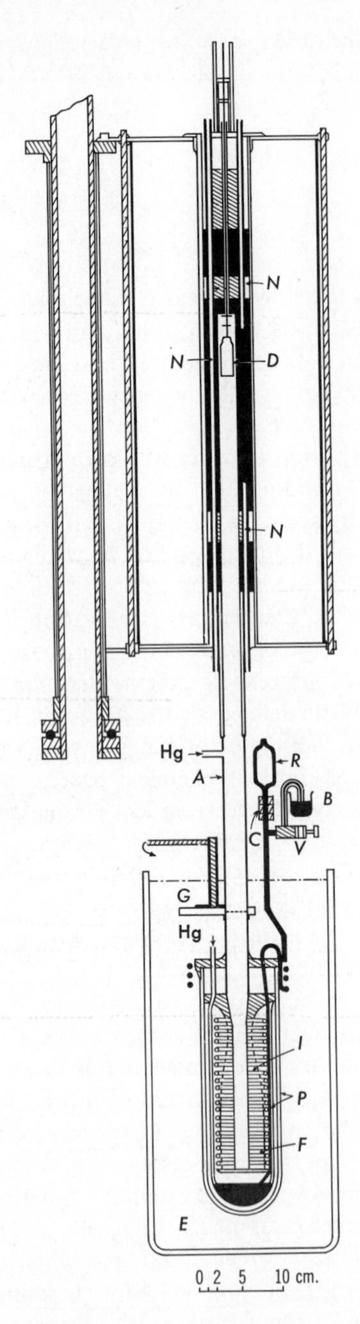

Figure 3.1. Ice Calorimeter with Furnace from Which Hot Sample is Dropped†

†Fig. 6 of G. T. Furukawa et al., *J. Res. Nat. Bur. Stds*, **57**, 67, (1956).

273.150°K while the level of Hg in the dilatometer capillary moves a distance z, then for the adiabatic calorimeter

$$0 = q_P = \int_T^{273.150} (nC_P + C)\, dT' + Kz \tag{3.26}$$

The quantity Kz is the heat of fusion of the ice that melts at I in the calorimeter. The value of K is found by dissipation of electric work in the calorimeter during a preliminary calibration, and C is found by dropping the heated empty container. Thus, for several related T's, (3.26) yields C_P, the isobaric molar heat capacity of the sample. It is possible to reduce the error in C_P to about 0.2%.

A very simple and elegant calorimeter in which heat was reduced to negligible proportions by careful design was made by Eucken and Nernst in about 1910 to determine heat capacities at very low T. The sample was suspended in an evacuated chamber by wires whose resistance could be used to determine the sample's temperature. These same wires were used to heat the sample electrically while the sample itself acted as the thermally most important part of the calorimeter. An outer dewar flask containing liquid air, H_2, or other substance at constant temperature made this calorimeter an isothermal jacket type. It was, of course, necessary to take account of the small transfer of thermal energy because of radiation and conduction between sample and vessel walls, for they were generally at different T.

Modern research calorimeters are almost always adiabatic calorimeters in which the jacket is automatically heated to almost the same temperature as the calorimeter. As a further guarantee of adiabatic conditions, several radiation shields lie between jacket and calorimeter, and thermal contact through heating and temperature-sensing wires is minimized by making them very thin and of metals of low thermal conductivity. Figure 3.2 is a diagram of an adiabatic calorimeter for use from 30°C to 500°C. The sample container C is a cylinder of solid aluminum two inches long and two inches in diameter; in it many small holes were drilled to hold the sample and thus, by close contact of sample and metal, speed the attainment of one temperature by all of the sample. The thermometer is a platinum resistance thermometer. Many thermocouples T_t sample the temperature of the silver radiation shields at various points so as to allow the average temperature of the jacket's shields S_2 and L_2 to be kept almost equal to that of the calorimeter's shields S_1 and L_1 as electric work is done on the heaters H_{1A} and H_{1B}. Gaseous CO_2 flows around everything within the aluminum guard G, which is kept about 0.3°C below jacket temperature; this flow aids in equalizing the temperatures of various thermally connected parts of jacket or calorimeter, especially during heating. A vacuum would have isolated jacket from calorimeter more effectively, but each would not have been as isothermal without the CO_2.

Ultimately, even in this excellent device, small exchanges of heat are corrected by empirical means. The care with which this calorimeter is made is ample

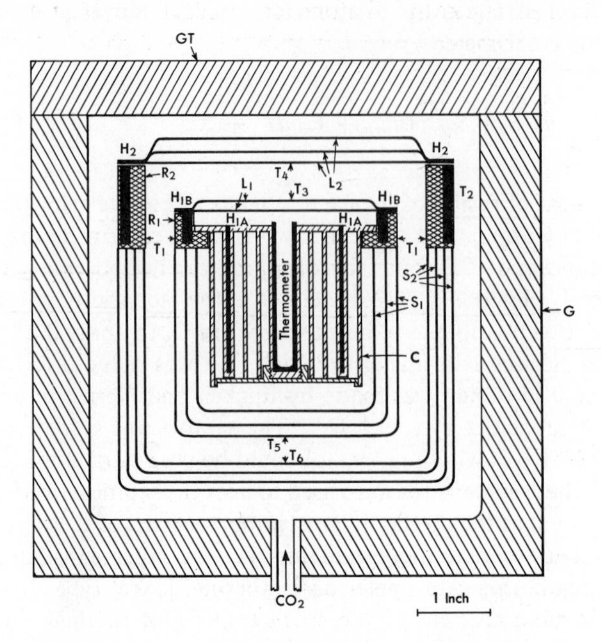

Figure 3.2. Adiabatic Calorimeter for Heat Capacities†

indication of how elusive heat is. Most calorimeters merely attempt to keep a much larger flow of heat constant from experiment to experiment in the hope that due allowance can be made for the loss. One way to do this is to use twin calorimeters, one containing the unknown and the other a standard. With a standard mode of operation, losses many times as great as those of the calorimeter of Figure 3.2 can be tolerated. The errors of the calorimeter of Figure 3.2 are of the order of 0.1%.

3.8 SUMMARY

This chapter offers a simple set of applications of elementary thermodynamics. Although much still remains to be said of standard states, it also introduces the idea of and need for standard states of elements, compounds, and ions. Careful specification of exactly what change is under study and what things constitute the system are clearly needed in every problem. The chapter ends with a description of one of the fundamental tools of experimental thermodynamics, the calorimeter. As a blend of the thermometer (zeroth law) and Hess's law (first

†Fig. 1 of E. D. West and D. C. Ginnings, *J. Res. Nat. Bur. Stds.* **60**, 309 (1958).

law), the calorimeter compares changes in thermal energy due to heat. The chapters that follow extract the fullest measure of physical and chemical information from the observations that can be made with calorimeters.

PROBLEMS

1. One mole methane explodes at 25°C in an excess of oxygen to produce $CO_{2(g)}$ and $H_2O_{(l)}$. If the heat of mixing of gases is negligible and if the reaction goes to completion, will more heat be evolved if the explosion occurs in a rigid closed vessel or in a nonrigid vessel such that initial and final pressures are both one atm? If all gases are ideal, calculate any difference.
Answer: At 25°C, 1185 cal more evolved at constant P.

2. Calculate the molar heat of solution of solid NaCl as it dissolves in a great quantity of water.
Answer: $\Delta H = 930$ cal.

3. When one g liquid benzene at 25°C burns in an open vessel to yield gaseous CO_2 and water at 25°C at atmospheric pressure, 10.0 kcal heat are liberated. What is the molar heat of formation of benzene?
Answer: $\Delta H_f^{\ominus} = +11.9$ kcal mole^{-1}.

4. If one mole of gaseous propene burns at one atm at 25°C to liquid water and gaseous CO_2 with evolution of 492.0 kcal of heat, what is the standard heat of formation of propene?
Answer: 4.9 kcal mole^{-1}.

5. Calculate values of $\Delta E^{\ominus}$ and $\Delta H^{\ominus}$ at 25°C:
(a) $Ag_2O_{(s)} \longrightarrow 2\,Ag_{(s)} + \frac{1}{2}O_{2(g)}$.
(b) $H_{2(g)} + Cl_{2(g)} \longrightarrow 2\,HCl_{(g)}$.
(c) $2\,SO_{2(g)} + O_{2(g)} \longrightarrow 2\,SO_{3(g)}$.
(d) $C_2H_{6(g)} + H_{2(g)} \longrightarrow 2\,CH_{4(g)}$.
(e) $2\,C_2H_{6(g)} + 7\,O_{2(g)} \longrightarrow 4\,CO_{2(g)} + 6\,H_2O_{(l)}$.
(f) $2\,C_2H_{6(g)} + 5\,O_{2(g)} \longrightarrow 4\,CO_{(g)} + 6\,H_2O_{(l)}$.
Answer: (a) $\Delta H^{\ominus} = 7306$ cal; $\Delta E^{\ominus} = 7010$ cal; (b) $\Delta H^{\ominus} = \Delta E^{\ominus} = -44{,}126$ cal; (c) $\Delta H^{\ominus} = -46{,}980$ cal; $\Delta E^{\ominus} = -46{,}390$ cal; (d) $\Delta H^{\ominus} = \Delta E^{\ominus} = -15{,}542$ cal; (e) $\Delta H^{\ominus} = -745{,}640$ cal; $\Delta E^{\ominus} = -742{,}677$ cal; (f) $\Delta H^{\ominus} = -475{,}095$ cal; $\Delta E^{\ominus} = -473{,}317$ cal.

6. What are ΔH and ΔE at 25°C for the change

$$H_{2(g)}(0.200\text{ atm}) + Cl_{2(g)}(5.00\text{ atm}) \longrightarrow 2\,HCl_{(g)}(1.00\text{ atm})?$$

Answer: $\Delta E = \Delta H = -44.126$ kcal.

7. What would be the standard heat of formation of gaseous ethane at 25°C if diamond were the standard state of carbon?
Answer: -21.142 kcal mole^{-1}.

8. Account for the difference in the standard heats of formation of aqueous
(a) NH_3 and NH_4OH;
(b) NH_4^+ and NH_4OH.
Answer: (a) $\Delta H_f^{\ominus}(H_2O_{(l)})$; (b) $\Delta H^{\ominus} = 940$ cal for ionization of NH_4OH.

9. Calculate ΔH° at 10°C for the reaction

$$3\,NO_{2(g)} + H_2O_{(l)} \longrightarrow 2\,HNO_{3(aq)} + NO_{(g)}$$

if C_P for dilute HNO_3 is 4.0 cal mole^{-1} deg^{-1}.
Answer: −32,650 cal.

10. With the heats of formation from Table 3.1 and the heat capacities C_P for SO_2, O_2, and SO_3 listed below, calculate ΔH and ΔE at 425°C for the reaction $2\,SO_{2(g)} + O_{2(g)} \longrightarrow 2\,SO_{3(g)}$.

Gas	C_P (cal mole^{-1} deg^{-1})
O_2	$6.50 + 0.0010\,T$
SO_2	$7.50 + 0.0065\,T$
SO_3	$10.10 + 0.0065\,T$

Answer: $\Delta H = -47{,}700$ cal; $\Delta E = -46{,}310$ cal.

11. How much heat is evolved at 1000°K at one atm by the gaseous reaction $2\,H_2S + 3\,O_2 \longrightarrow 2\,SO_2 + 2\,H_2O$? Assume that the heat capacities of H_2S and H_2O are equal, that C_P of O_2 is constant at 3.50 R, and that C_P of SO_2 is constant at 9.51 cal mole^{-1} deg^{-1}.
Answer: $-\Delta H^{\circ} = 249{,}180$ cal.

12. If the molar isobaric heat capacities of the gases involved in this problem are constant at all T, what temperature will be reached by a mixture of $2\,SO_2 + O_2 + 4\,N_2$ initially at one atm at 200°C when all SO_2 is burned adiabatically to SO_3 at constant pressure?
Answer: 1109°C.

13. When 16.3346 g $Al_2O_{3(s)}$ at various furnace temperatures were dropped so as to become part of the ice calorimeter of Figure 3.1, the change in enthalpy ΔH of container and alumina was observed by the volume change of the mixture of ice and water. In separate experiments, the enthalpy change $\Delta H'$ of the empty container was also noted. From the selected data of the table (G. T. Furukawa *et al.*, *J. Res. Nat. Bur. Std.* **57**, 67 (1956)), calculate a formula for the molar isobaric heat capacity of alumina of the form $C_P^{(0)} + C_P^{(1)}T + C_P^{(2)}T^2$ valid from 0°C to 350°C and determine with it the heat capacity at 250°C.

Furnace Temperature	100°C	200°C	300°C
$-\Delta H'$ (empty container)	546 j	1129 j	1732 j
$-\Delta H$ (container + Al_2O_3)	1890 j	4052 j	6380 j

Answer: $C_P = 9.1 + 0.3007\,T + (-2.12 \times 10^{-4})T^2$ j deg^{-1} mole^{-1} ; 108.4 j mole^{-1} deg^{-1}.

---

14. How much heat is evolved at 25°C when 50.0 g pure solid lead dissolve in an excess of dilute aqueous silver nitrate?
Answer: 12,100 cal

15. Calculate values of ΔH° and ΔE° for these reactions at 25°C:
(a) $H_2SO_{4(l)} \longrightarrow 2\,H^+_{(aq)} + SO^{--}_{4(aq)}$.
(b) $H_2O_{(l)} + CO_{2(g)} \longrightarrow 2H^+_{(aq)} + CO^{--}_{(aq)}$.
(c) $Ag^+_{(aq)} + Br^-_{(aq)} \longrightarrow AgBr_{(s)}$.
(d) $Ag_2CO_{3(s)} \longrightarrow Ag_2O_{(s)} + CO_{2(g)}$.
(e) $4\,NH_{3(g)} + 5\,O_{2(g)} \longrightarrow 4\,NO_{(g)} + 6\,H_2O_{(g)}$.

Answer: (a) -22.99 kcal; (b) $\Delta H^\ominus = +0.74$ kcal; $\Delta E^\ominus = +1.33$ kcal; (c) $\Delta E^\ominus = \Delta H^\ominus = -20.19$ kcal; (d) $\Delta H^\ominus = +19.61$ kcal; $\Delta E^\ominus = +19.02$ kcal; (e) $\Delta H^\ominus = -216.23$ kcal; $\Delta E^\ominus = -216.82$ kcal.

16. What is the heat of vaporization of one mole water at 150°C? Use data of Table 3.1. The observed value is 9.10 kcal $mole^{-1}$.

17. Calculate ΔH at 850°C for the reaction $4\,NH_{3(g)} + 5\,O_{2(g)} \longrightarrow 4\,NO_{(g)} + 6\,H_2O_{(g)}$. For NO, let $C_P = 6.665 + 1.420 \times 10^{-3}T$.
Answer: $\Delta H = -215{,}970$ cal.

18. Find an expression for ΔH as a function of temperature for the reaction $N_{2(g)} + O_{2(g)} \longrightarrow 2\,NO_{(g)}$. Assume $C_P = 6.50 + 0.0010T$ for each gas.
Answer: $\Delta H = 2\,\Delta H_f^\ominus = 43{,}200$ cal.

19. Find an expression for ΔH as a function of temperature for the reaction $2\,NH_{3(g)} \longrightarrow 3\,H_{2(g)} + N_{2(g)}$.
Answer: $\Delta H = 18254 + 14.987T - 7.562 \times 10^{-3}T^2 + 0.966 \times 10^{-6}T^3$

20. How much heat is evolved at 1200°K when ten grams of CO burn completely to CO_2 at constant pressure?
Answer: 24,070 cal.

---

21. What is $\Delta H^\ominus$ at 25°C for the change

$$NH^+_{4(aq)} + HCO^-_{3(aq)} + Na^+_{(aq)} + Cl^-_{(aq)} \longrightarrow NaHCO_{3(s)} + NH_4Cl_{(aq)}$$

Answer: -4.0 kcal.

22. At what temperature is $\Delta H = 0$ for the isobaric reaction:
(a) $H_2O_{(l)} \longrightarrow H_2O_{(g)}$?
(b) $H_{2(g)} + Br_{2(g)} \longrightarrow 2\,HBr_{(g)}$?
Answer: (a) 647.6°K; (b) if $\Delta C_P = 0$, no temperature.

23. What circumstance causes the evolution of heat from a certain chemical reaction to increase as the temperature of reaction is increased if the reaction is performed:
(a) At constant pressure?
(b) At constant volume?

24. The heat evolved by the gaseous reaction $NH_3 + \frac{3}{2}F_2 \longrightarrow 3\,HF + \frac{1}{2}N_2$ is observed at 25°C at one atm to be 759.7 kilojoules [G. T. Armstrong and R. S. Jessup, *J. Res. Nat. Bur. Std. 64A*, 49 (1960)]. From the standard heat of formation of NH_3 in Table 3.1, determine that of gaseous HF.
Answer: -64.2 kcal $mole^{-1}$.

25. From these observations [A. A. Gilliland and W. H. Johnson, *J. Res. Nat. Bur. Std. 65A*, 67 (1961)] at 25°C at one atm with three solutions labeled I, II, and III,

$NaClO_{4(s)}$ + I $\longrightarrow$ II + $KClO_{4(ppt)}$ $\Delta H = -21.166$ kilojoules
$KCl_{(s)}$ + III $\longrightarrow$ I $\Delta H = +\ 3.850$ kj
$NaCl_{(s)}$ + III $\longrightarrow$ II $\Delta H = +\ 7.002$ kj
$KClO_{4(s)}$ + I $\longrightarrow$ I + $KClO_{4(ppt)}$ $\Delta H = -\ 0.075$ kj

and the further observation at 25°C at one atm that (W. H. Johnson and A. A. Gilliland, ibid., p 63)

$$KClO_{4(s)} \longrightarrow KCl_{(s)} + 2\,O_{2(g)} \quad \Delta H = -4.02 \text{ kj}$$

determine the standard heat of formation of solid $NaClO_4$.
Answer: -382.75 kj $mole^{-1}$.

26. Calculate the heat of hydrogenation of acetylene to ethylene at 200°C when the reaction is carried out at:
(a) Constant volume.
(b) Constant pressure.
Assume that C_P of H_2 is $7R/2$ and that C_P of each hydrocarbon is $5R$. How hot could the reaction at constant volume become if left unattended at 200°C if the reaction goes to completion and no excess H_2 is present?
Answer: (a) $\Delta E = -41{,}978$ cal; (b) $\Delta H = -42{,}918$ cal; up to 5480°C.

27. Calculate the increase in enthalpy at 175°C for the gaseous reaction

$$Cl_2 + 2\,HBr \longrightarrow Br_2 + 2\,HCl$$

Answer: $-19{,}410$ cal.

28. At 0°K the dissociation energies of H_2 and Br_2 are 103.24 and 45.46 kcal mole^{-1}. If the isobaric heat capacities of monatoms are 2.50 R and of diatoms are 3.50R, what is ΔH at 200°C for the gaseous reaction

$$H_2 + Br \longrightarrow HBr + H$$

Answer: 16.56 kcal.

29. What final temperature is reached when one mole of gaseous chlorine at 450°C is mixed adiabatically with two moles of gaseous HBr at 0°C if they react at constant pressure to yield only Br_2 and 2 HCl? Assume that all C_P's are 3.50 R and that no heat accompanies mixing of the gases.
Answer: 1356°K.

4
ENTROPY

4.1 INTRODUCTION

The first law of thermodynamics does two things: it states the law of conservation of energy for heat and work; it systematizes thermochemistry. In doing these things, it points out that it is impossible to get something for nothing and that the energy of a well-defined thermodynamic state is independent of its past or future because energy is a function of state.

The second and third laws of thermodynamics, which deal with the thermodynamic state-function called entropy, treat heat in a different and somewhat more subtle way. Work done on a system may not appear to be work to an observer within the system. In fact, the fundamental experiments of Joule in the 1840's were founded on the transformation of work entirely into thermal energy, a form of energy that is all too readily transferred by virtue of a difference in temperature. It is noteworthy that he did not establish the mechanical equivalent of thermal energy by converting thermal energy into work. The first law would not forbid this. The second law, however, deals with this asymmetric behavior of energy: work can be converted fully to thermal energy, but the reverse is not as generally possible. When thermal energy is in fact converted into work, the conversion is not complete without special help from other agencies.

In 1824 Carnot made an intensive study of steam engines in order to understand their efficiency for converting the thermal energy of fuels into useful mechanical work. His ideas were later put into mathematical form by Clapeyron. The second law was formally stated in terms of an ideal engine, called a Carnot engine, by Clausius in 1850 and by Thomson (Lord Kelvin) in 1851. Although Clausius had first used the mathematics of entropy in 1845, he did not actually use the name *entropy* until 1865. Horstmann was the first to use the second law in a truly chemical investigation; this was in 1869, a year famous for the origin of the periodic table. There were, of course, many statements of the first and second laws of thermodynamics before this time. One of the most famous and most quoted of these is that of Clausius in 1865: The energy of the universe is constant; the entropy of the universe forges on to a maximum. A large part of the rest of this book is devoted to understanding these two ideas about energy and entropy.

4.2 REVERSIBLE PROCESSES

While reversibility was of interest in the first law only in regard to work, and thus indirectly in regard to heat, reversibility of a process is of paramount importance in the second law. Indeed, reversibility and irreversibility are part of the statement of this law. The words *reversible* and *irreversible* may not be mentioned, but always present is the idea of a process that can be continued, stopped, or reversed through infinitesimal changes in the variables that control or specify the states of the system and surroundings. Not only must the process occur by virtue of infinitesimal differences in the controlling variables, but it must be possible to restore the system and surroundings to their initial states merely by reversing the process through infinitesimal changes.

While performing a process through intermediate states necessarily involves a sequence of events in time, time is of no concern for equilibrium thermodynamics. A reversible process is conceived as a series of related equilibrium states. As such, it is a limit, just as an infinitesimal is a limit. A really reversible process would require eons and eons for its performance, if it ever really got started, because each step in the process could differ from equilibrium at most by an infinitesimal. A reversible process is, then, a convenient abstraction and a limiting type of process that can be approximated by a real process if its driving force is reduced sufficiently. Often the difference between a real process and a *series of equilibrium states* can be made negligible. If so, the concept has value.

If energy is exchanged between system and surroundings by virtue of an infinitesimal difference in temperature, heat is absorbed or evolved reversibly. If a liquid vaporizes because a confining ideal piston (frictionless to avoid losses of thermal energy, weightless to avoid losses in kinetic energy, and so forth) experiences an infinitesimal pressure difference, reversible expansion work is performed and the vaporization process is reversible. On the other hand, if the difference in temperature that causes the exchange of energy is not an infinitesimal, but is rather a finite difference in temperature, the heat is not reversible. Nor is the vaporization reversible if the pressure difference is finite.

It is interesting to note that the reversible vaporization could be controlled by an infinitesimal temperature difference rather than by an infinitesimal pressure difference. Suppose the ideal piston at first experiences exactly equal pressures on both sides. But if the temperature of the surroundings and thus of the system, consisting of liquid and vapor, is increased infinitesimally, the vapor pressure rises infinitesimally and drives the piston outward. The energy required to perform this expansion work and to vaporize the liquid is absorbed from the thermostated surroundings by virtue of the supposed infinitesimal increase in their temperature. Thus the process proceeds reversibly.

The terms *real, actual, spontaneous,* and *natural* each label a process as one that proceeds of its own accord if left unattended. Some thermodynamicists prefer to describe a spontaneous process as a change that is potentially able to do work on the surroundings and thus can in fact occur reversibly or irreversibly. Here, however, the terms *real, actual, spontaneous,* and *natural* are taken to be synonymous with *irreversible*. The time rate of a process is sometimes an indication of the degree to which it approximates a reversible process. The slower the process, usually the closer it approximates reversibility. A sluggish river can be stopped by a dam (or even reversed like the Chicago River) much more easily than can a towering waterfall (like Yosemite Falls). The true criterion of the degree to which a process approaches reversibility is the magnitude of the increment in the controlling variables. A sluggish river falls less rapidly than a waterfall. The river's flow is easily reversed, for the increment in altitude per mile of sluggish river is small.

Hydrogen and oxygen can exist mixed at room temperature for years, but the slow rate of reaction does not indicate the distance from equilibrium or the difficulty of preventing an exploding mixture from exploding completely. In certain circumstances, a system like a mixture of hydrogen and oxygen can be treated as though it were at equilibrium even though it is nowhere near equilibrium and even though there is no infinitesimal adjustment that could reverse the very slow changes that occur spontaneously. Such a mixture of hydrogen and oxygen has a well-defined pressure and volume at specified temperature, a definite heat capacity, and so on. But avoid finely divided platinum or a spark! If any perturbation or change can be undone or reversed so that the system is restored to its original state by infinitesimal readjustments, then a long-lived state can be assumed to be at true equilibrium. However, the illustration of hydrogen and oxygen shows that to be long-lived is not always to be at equilibrium, for what infinitesimal readjustment could undo the effect of a spark in an explosive mixture?

4.3 THE SECOND LAW OF THERMODYNAMICS

There are many ways of stating the second law of thermodynamics. If it is stated in words, the law states what men are convinced cannot be done. For example, the statement that perpetual motion of the first kind is impossible could be taken as a crude and unwieldy statement of the conservation of energy. The most tractable statement of the second law, as for the first, is mathematical rather than verbal, for the language of mathematics is precise and its rules of logic, embodying allowed operations, are definite and simple. In this discussion after an abstract and axiomatic mathematical statement will come several statements in words which explain the meaning of the law. Although these verbal statements will here be proved from the mathematical statement, the reasoning processes of the proofs can be reversed. In fact, these statements of what cannot be done were originally taken as the fundamental statements by their originators, who then developed this terse mathematical statement or its equivalent.

Equations (4.1), (4.2), and (4.3) and the definitions of the symbols constitute together the second law of thermodynamics. For reversible processes,

$$dq_{\mathrm{rev}} = T\,dS \tag{4.1}$$

For actual or irreversible or spontaneous processes,

$$dq < T\,dS \tag{4.2}$$

For any change of state,

$$\Delta S = S_2 - S_1 \tag{4.3}$$

In these equations, dq is the infinitesimal heat absorbed by the system from the surroundings, T is the thermodynamic temperature of the isothermal surroundings, S_1 is the entropy of the initial state, and S_2 is the entropy of the final state. The entropy S is a function of state and thus dS is an exact differential.

With the understanding that S is a function of state and that T is the thermodynamic temperature of the surroundings, these three equations can be combined neatly into one, (4.4), wherein the equality refers to reversible processes or equilibrium states and the inequality refers to irreversible processes.

$$dq \leqslant T\,dS \tag{4.4}$$

To find a definite value for the increase in entropy ΔS for a change from state 1 to state 2, it is necessary merely to invent *any* reversible path that connects states 1 and 2 or to follow the reversible path experienced by the system and to use the equality of (4.4). That is,

$$\Delta S = \int_{S_1}^{S_2} dS = S_2 - S_1 = \int_{(1)}^{(2)} \frac{dq_{rev}}{T} \tag{4.5}$$

Since S is a function of state and since ΔS is independent of the path, any invented or experienced reversible path yields the same unique value of ΔS. Experience in evaluating ΔS under various circumstances often suggests one path as easiest for the calculation, even though the actual or reversible path followed by the system may have been quite another.

It will be proved in Section 5.4 that the thermodynamic temperature of the second law is the same as the absolute temperature of the perfect gas. Actually, the second law provides the best way of defining temperature, for any real substance is suitable as thermometric substance. Hence, temperature is no longer defined in terms of ideal behavior of a special class of substance.

4.4 ADIABATIC PROCESSES

Any spontaneous or reversible adiabatic process is a process for which dq is zero during the process. For any reversible adiabatic process, $T\,dS = 0$ by (4.1). Since T is greater than zero (as can be shown),

$$dS = 0 \tag{4.6}$$

$$\Delta S = \int_{S_1}^{S_2} dS = S_2 - S_1 = 0 \tag{4.7}$$

The entropy of any system is constant in a reversible adiabatic process, for $S_1 = S_2$ by (4.7) and the initial and final states are restricted only in being joined by a reversible adiabatic path.

If an adiabatic process is not reversible, then the infinitesimal increment of entropy is given by (4.2) when $dq = 0$.

$$T\,dS > dq = 0$$

Since T is greater than zero, for any irreversible adiabatic process,

$$dS > 0 \tag{4.8}$$

$$\Delta S = \int_{S_1}^{S_2} dS = S_2 - S_1 > 0 \tag{4.9}$$

The entropy is not constant in an irreversible adiabatic process, for $S_2 > S_1$ by (4.9). That is, the entropy of the final state exceeds that of the initial state if the process is irreversible and adiabatic. Thus it is said that the entropy of an isolated system, which cannot exchange matter or energy with its surroundings and cannot be worked upon by its surroundings, tends to increase. Once at equilibrium, however, the isolated system maintains a maximum entropy that is constant by virtue of (4.7).

The inequality of the second law for irreversible processes is really a summary of how things happen in time. That is, the one-way flow of time is related to the steady increase in entropy. In general, thermodynamic processes are of two kinds: those that reach equilibrium within a finite time and those that are assumed not to do so. A system that has reached an assumed equilibrium state within a certain time has achieved a state of maximum entropy. The rate of production of entropy is nil in that state, for entropy is a function of state. If a longer time interval for the attainment of equilibrium is considered or if certain constraints are relaxed, a change previously deemed impossible now is of thermodynamic interest as an allowable change. The system may now approach a new state of equilibrium. If the new state is reached by an irreversible adiabatic process, the entropy of the system rises to a new and higher maximum value until, at equilibrium, no further increase in entropy occurs.

Irreversible thermodynamics deals, among other things, with steady states. In these, certain thermodynamic variables like density or temperature are constant because an experimenter in the surroundings fixes these values arbitrarily at nonequilibrium values despite other changes that continue to occur in the system. It is a general principle of irreversible thermodynamics that in a steady state the system behaves in such a way that the time-rate of production of entropy is a minimum. Other possible steady states consistent with the constraints would cause a more rapid increase in the entropy of the system. That is, the one really existing steady state produces less entropy per unit time than would other unrealized steady states that might also not contradict the externally imposed constraints. Entropy production is thus the key to irreversible thermodynamics. In the strictest sense, temperature has meaning only at equilibrium, but for steady states rather close to equilibrium, the concept of temperature still can be used to advantage. The demands of the science of irreversible thermodynamics are often so great, however, that the simple inequality in (4.2) or (4.9) must suffice. If an allowed adiabatic change should be accompanied by an increase in entropy, the process will be considered spontaneous or real. The rate at which it occurs is not a question for equilibrium thermodynamics or the second law.

Although an inequality would appear to be awkward mathematically and much less definite than an equality, the second law for irreversible changes has much physical meaning. It is helpful to think of changes of state in terms of a geometrical analogy with well defined states of the system at points; between points, paths or processes are represented by curves in a space of as many dimensions as there are thermodynamic variables of interest. With such a geometrical analogy, Caratheodory in 1909 found that near any state-point there are many other state-points that cannot be reached from that point by any reversible or irreversible adiabatic process. Mathematically, if $dq = dE - dw = 0$ when there exist such inaccessible state-points, he found that dq can be transformed into the exact differential dS. For example, suppose that by path A from state 1 to state 2 a system reversibly evolves a positive amount of heat. Since this heat is evolved, $dq < 0$. By (4.1), $T\,dS < 0$. Since $T > 0$, $dS < 0$, and for a finite process in which a finite amount of heat is evolved reversibly by the system,

$$\Delta S = \int_{S_1}^{S_2} dS = S_2 - S_1 < 0 \tag{4.10}$$

Equation (4.10) says that S_2 is less than S_1; that is, the entropy of the final state is less than that of the initial state. If the same change of state were effected irreversibly and adiabatically by another path B, (4.9) insists that ΔS, the same ΔS since the terminal states are unchanged, be greater than zero. That is, (4.9) insists that the entropy of the final state is greater than that of the initial state. Even if the same change of state were effected by a reversible and adiabatic path C, (4.7) would require $S_1 = S_2$. In short, (4.10) contradicts (4.7) and (4.9). The second law says, then, that state 2 cannot be reached from state 1 by *any* kind of adiabatic process, reversible (C) or irreversible (B), if the system evolves a positive amount of heat in the reversible process (path A) by which state 1 becomes state 2. This limitation is imposed by the second law and not by the first law, which calls merely for conservation of energy in any form.

A definite example of this situation exists when a perfect gas is reversibly and isothermally compressed. As work is done on the gas by the surroundings, heat is evolved by the gas since the change of energy is zero at constant temperature. State 2, the final compressed state, cannot be reached from state 1 by any kind of adiabatic process, reversible or not. The second law is silent, however, on the possibility of proceeding adiabatically and isothermally from state 2, the compressed state, to state 1. This reverse process is the Joule-Thomson experiment for expansion of a perfect gas into a vacuum. The fact that the gas is here assumed to be perfect is of no importance, for the energy required to overcome van der Waal's attractions is not work. What is important and what the second law says is that there is no adiabatic process for the compression. This is a new limitation upon possible changes of state. And indeed, one does not expect ever to be quick enough to catch all or even most of the molecules of gas in a room when they happen to be in one corner of the room. To compress them there, it takes work that must be evolved as heat to keep T constant, as along path A.

Another definite example of this new limitation is one of Joule's classic experiments. As water at 18.0°C at one atm is stirred adiabatically at constant pressure, its temperature is observed to rise after a time to a higher value, say 18.1°C. The entropy of the water increases in this change of state because the same change of state could have been effected by the absorption of heat described by a convenient invented reversible process linking the same initial and final states. If $\Delta S > 0$ for the forward process, then $\Delta S < 0$ for the reverse process by which water at 18.1°C cools to 18.0°C at one atm. Since (4.7) and (4.9) require $\Delta S \geqslant 0$ for any adiabatic process, the second law as a summary of experience says that the reverse process (cooling the water adiabatically and isobarically) cannot be observed if the forward process (warming the water adiabatically and isobarically) is observed, The first law merely says for the forward adiabatic process that $w = \Delta E$ and for the reverse adiabatic process that the work done on the system is $-w = -\Delta E$. Hence, for a cycle (18.0°C $\rightarrow$ 18.1°C $\rightarrow$ 18.0°C) the total work done isobarically and adiabatically on the system might be $w + (-w) = \Delta E + (-\Delta E) = 0$. Thus, by the first law alone, it is not impossible to recover in full any work done on a system adiabatically; this is temperatureless and heatless mechanics. If atoms and other small particles could be seen and dealt with individually in each experiment, the first law would suffice. For it is their disorganized movements or positions that soak up or retain the organized work-motion done on them, and it is their disorganization that prevents the recovery of organized motion as work. It is just not likely that myriads of random movements will occur in coordination, or that a disorganized structure will of itself become ordered.

4.5 HEAT ENGINES

A heat engine is a device that can convert heat into work. It is commonly considered to work in cycles so that periodically the engine, commonly thought of as a working substance like a fluid, is restored to some standard state from which it can once again begin its operation. The second law of thermodynamics places certain restrictions on the performance of heat engines. The first law of thermodynamics requires merely that work produced by such a device should not exceed the heat furnished to the engine. But conservation of energy is not enough. It has been found impossible, for example, to withdraw heat at constant temperature from such huge heat reservoirs as the oceans and the atmosphere by a cyclic process and perform an equivalent amount of work. While the first law prohibits perpetual motion of the first kind, creation of energy, the second law prohibits perpetual motion of the second kind, isothermal or complete transformation of heat into work and nothing more.

The two common ways of stating the second law verbally state what cannot be done by matter, considered as an engine of some sort. The first, due to Clausius in 1854, says: It is impossible for an engine that operates in cycles to transfer heat from one reservoir to another at a higher temperature if the surroundings do not suffer a net change. From this could be deduced the mathematical statements (4.1) to (4.3). It is sufficient for this treatment to show that this verbal statement is contained in the mathematical statement.

If the surroundings do not suffer a net change in one cycle of operation, their initial and final states are the same. Because E and S are functions of state, by (2.8) and (4.3) for the surroundings

$$\left.\begin{aligned} \Delta E_s &= 0 \\ \Delta S_s &= 0 \end{aligned}\right\} \tag{4.11}$$

The subscript s indicates in (4.11) and below that the increment is for the surroundings. Since the engine works in a cycle, again by (2.8) and (4.3), for the engine in one cycle

$$\left.\begin{aligned} \Delta E_e &= 0 \\ \Delta S_e &= 0 \end{aligned}\right\} \tag{4.12}$$

In (4.12) and below, the subscript e refers to the engine. Conservation of energy requires that the heat evolved by the low-temperature reservoir be equal to the heat absorbed by the high-temperature reservoir since the engine and reservoirs are unaffected by the surroundings, which are supposed not to change. That is, for all three, if ΔE_r is the increase in the energy of the reservoirs per cycle,

$$\Delta E = \Delta E_e + \Delta E_r + \Delta E_s = 0 \tag{4.13}$$

Whence, by (4.11) and (4.12),

$$\Delta E_r = 0 \tag{4.14}$$

From (4.14), since no work is done by engine, reservoirs, or surroundings,

$$\Delta E_r = q_1 + q_2 = 0 \tag{4.15}$$

where q_1 is the heat absorbed by the low-temperature reservoir at temperature T_1 and q_2 is the heat absorbed by the high-temperature reservoir at temperature T_2. From (4.15),

$$q_2 = -q_1 \tag{4.16}$$

That is, the heat absorbed by the high-temperature reservoir equals the heat evolved by the low-temperature reservoir, as was concluded intuitively above.

The entropy change per cycle for the reservoirs is, by (4.5) and (4.16),

$$\Delta S_r = \frac{q_1}{T_1} + \frac{q_2}{T_2} = \frac{q_1}{T_1} - \frac{q_1}{T_2} \tag{4.17}$$

But the engine, reservoirs, and surroundings comprise an isolated system for which (4.7) and (4.9) give

$$\Delta S = \Delta S_e + \Delta S_r + \Delta S_s \geqslant 0 \tag{4.18}$$

Substitution of (4.11), (4.12), and (4.17) into (4.18) gives

$$\Delta S_r = q_1\left(\frac{1}{T_1} - \frac{1}{T_2}\right) \geqslant 0 \tag{4.19}$$

If a positive amount of heat is evolved by the low-temperature reservoir, as Clausius supposed, $q_1 < 0$ and (4.19) requires that

$$\frac{1}{T_1} - \frac{1}{T_2} \leqslant 0 \tag{4.20}$$

which is equivalent to

$$T_1 \geqslant T_2 \tag{4.21}$$

That is, (4.21) says that the low-temperature reservoir with temperature T_1 really has the higher temperature if it evolves a positive amount of heat to the engine and if the mathematical statement of the second law is true. That is, the supposed operations are indeed impossible as stated verbally, because they lead inexorably to the contradiction (4.21). Moreover, this proof shows that the transfer of heat is reversible if $T_1 = T_2$ and spontaneous if $T_1 > T_2$. Briefly said, heat flows spontaneously from a high to a low temperature.

If heat does flow spontaneously from a high to a low temperature, it should be put to work. In their statement of the second law Thomson and Planck say: A process the final result of which is merely a transformation of heat into work is impossible.

In order to deduce this verbal statement from the mathematical statement (4.1) to (4.3), let the heat engine perform a positive amount of work w on the surroundings by absorbing a positive amount of heat q from a thermal reservoir at temperature T. A graphic summary of the situation might be

Since the interaction of engine and surroundings is adiabatic, for the surroundings

$$\left.\begin{aligned} \Delta E_s &= w \\ \Delta S_s &= 0 \end{aligned}\right\} \tag{4.22}$$

Since the engine operates cyclically, for one cycle, as for (4.12),

$$\left.\begin{aligned} \Delta E_e &= 0 \\ \Delta S_e &= 0 \end{aligned}\right\} \tag{4.23}$$

But the engine absorbs heat q from the heat reservoir in order to do work w in one cycle; hence, by the first law,

$$\Delta E_e = q - w = 0 \tag{4.24}$$

The energy of the reservoir, engine, and surroundings is conserved; hence, for them $0 = \Delta E_r + \Delta E_e + \Delta E_s = \Delta E_r + 0 + w$. Then, by (4.24)

$$\Delta E_r = -w = -q \tag{4.25}$$

Since the reservoir evolves the heat q at the temperature T, for it, by (4.5) and (4.25),

$$\Delta S_r = -\frac{q}{T} = -\frac{w}{T} \tag{4.26}$$

For the system, which consists of engine and reservoir, and the surroundings, (4.7) and (4.9) yield

$$\Delta S = \Delta S_e + \Delta S_r + \Delta S_s \geqslant 0 \tag{4.27}$$

Substitution of (4.22), (4.23), and (4.26) into (4.27) gives

$$-\frac{w}{T} \geqslant 0 \tag{4.28}$$

For values of T greater than zero, there is no positive value of w that satisfies (4.28). That is, the second law says that there is no engine that can do work on the surroundings by operating in cycles if it merely absorbs heat at one temperature. Only if there were irreversible or noncyclic changes in the surroundings or withdrawal of extra heat from the reservoir or other hidden changes could such an engine do work. The second verbal statement of the second law is justified.

The qualification that the engine operate in a cycle is important. It is possible to transform heat isothermally completely into work, as in the isothermal reversible expansion of a perfect gas for which $\Delta E = 0$. If the pressure fell to one-half its initial value, the work done reversibly at the constant temperature T by a mole of gas would be $RT \ln 2$ by (2.48). But the gas (heat engine) would not have returned to its initial state after doing the work and absorbing heat at the constant temperature as it worked.

A very well-known cyclic process in which a heat engine transforms into work *some* of the heat which is put at its disposal is the *Carnot cycle*. Although the Carnot cycle is reversible, it is convenient to develop the mathematics for an irreversible process that involves the same steps. The four parts of the cycle as experienced by the engine (the working substance, which is commonly supposed to be a compressible fluid) are: (a) *isothermal absorption* by the working substance of a positive amount of heat q_2 from the heat reservoir at the constant temperature T_2; (b) *adiabatic expansion* in which the temperature of the working substance falls from T_2 to T_1; (c) *isothermal evolution* by the working substance of a positive amount of heat $-q_1$ to the heat reservoir at the constant temperature T_1 such that (d) *adiabatic compression* in which the temperature of the work-

ing substance rises from T_1 to T_2 completes the cycle and returns the working substance to its initial state.

Translation of these four steps of the cycle into mathematical symbols yields (4.29) for the heats absorbed by the working substance.

$$q_2 \text{ at } T_2, \qquad dT_2 = 0 \tag{4.29a}$$

$$dq = 0, \qquad T_2 \longrightarrow T_1 \tag{4.29b}$$

$$q_1 \text{ at } T_1, \qquad dT_1 = 0 \tag{4.29c}$$

$$dq = 0, \qquad T_1 \longrightarrow T_2 \tag{4.29d}$$

A graphic summary of the relation of reservoirs, engine, and surroundings with account of the energy flow is

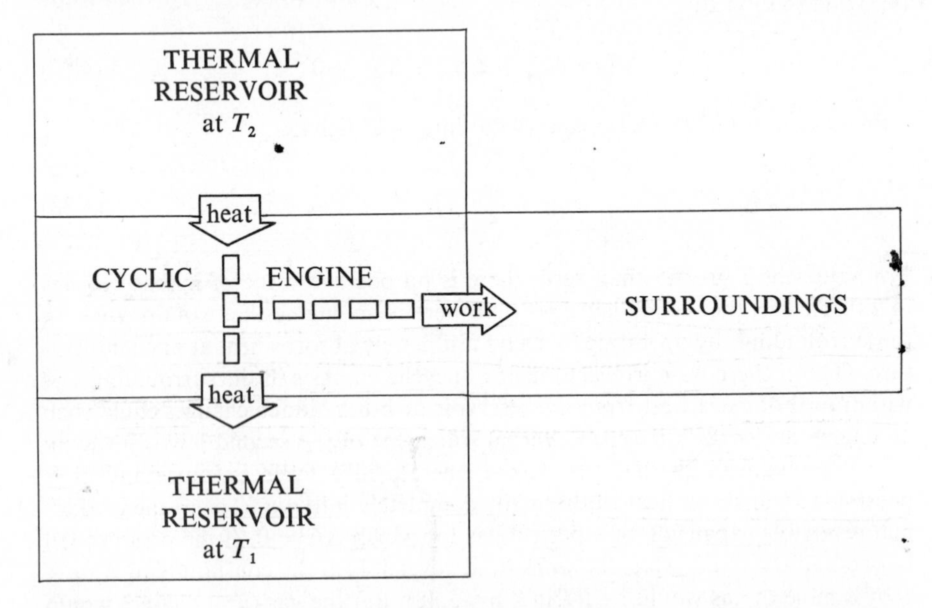

If the work w done on the surroundings by the engine in one cycle is equal in absolute value to the work $-w$ done on the engine by the surroundings in one cycle of the engine, then for the engine in one cycle

$$0 = \oint dE = q_1 + q_2 - w \tag{4.30}$$

$$0 = \oint dS \geqslant \frac{q_1}{T_1} + \frac{q_2}{T_2} \tag{4.31}$$

The efficiency ϵ_{eng} of the engine is the ratio of w, the work done by the engine or working substance, to the heat q_2 absorbed by the system at the higher temperature T_2. Elimination of q_1 from (4.30) and (4.31) yields (4.34) by the following manipulations. By (4.31),

$$0 \geqslant \frac{q_1}{T_1} + \frac{q_2}{T_2}, \qquad 0 \geqslant \frac{1}{T_2} + \frac{q_1}{q_2 T_1}$$

$$\frac{q_1}{q_2} \leqslant -\frac{T_1}{T_2} \begin{Bmatrix} T_1 > 0 \\ q_2 > 0 \end{Bmatrix} \tag{4.32}$$

By (4.30),

$$w = q_1 + q_2$$

$$\frac{w}{q_2} = 1 + \frac{q_1}{q_2} \tag{4.33}$$

Addition of (4.32) and (4.33) gives the desired result, where ϵ_{eng} is equal to the ratio of w to q_2 by definition.

$$\epsilon_{eng} = \frac{w}{q_2} \leqslant 1 - \frac{T_1}{T_2}$$

$$\epsilon_{eng} = \frac{w}{q_2} \leqslant \frac{T_2 - T_1}{T_2} \tag{4.34}$$

maximum for a reversible cycle

The efficiency ϵ of this kind of reversible cycle, the Carnot cycle, is equal to the right-hand member of (4.34). It is independent of everything except the temperatures of the two heat reservoirs. The efficiency of an irreversible cycle is less than that of a reversible one, for then the inequality obtains.

Many kinds of reversible cycles are possible. If there are, however, a maximum temperature T_2 and a minimum temperature T_1 between which any reversible cycle is confined, it can be shown that Equation (4.34) gives the maximum efficiency for any such reversible cycle. Even a reversible cycle may have an efficiency less than the greatest difference in temperatures divided by the highest temperature if some of the heat is transferred at intermediate temperatures.

Example 4.1. Calculate the maximum efficiency with which heat from these reservoirs can be converted into work. Assume that the thermodynamic temperature scale is the same as the perfect gas temperature scale. (a) Steam at 100°C and water at 25°C; (b) steam at 150°C and water at 25°C; (c) mercury vapor at 357°C and liquid mercury at 100°C; (d) helium at 2000°C and helium at 500°C; (e) helium at 5×10^6°C and helium at 1000°C.

With the use of Equation (4.34), $\epsilon_{eng} = (T_2 - T_1)/T_2$, and

(a) $$\epsilon_{eng} = \frac{373 - 298}{373} = 0.20$$

(b) $$\epsilon_{eng} = \frac{423 - 298}{423} = 0.30$$

(c) $$\epsilon_{eng} = \frac{630 - 373}{630} = 0.41$$

(d) $$\epsilon_{eng} = \frac{2273 - 773}{2273} = 0.66$$

(e) $$\epsilon_{\text{eng}} = \frac{5 \times 10^6 - 0.001 \times 10^6}{5 \times 10^6} = 1.0.$$

4.6 REFRIGERATOR

A refrigerator causes heat to flow from a low temperature to a high temperature. Since this process is nonspontaneous or unnatural because heat spontaneously flows from a high to a low temperature, work must be done on the system. A graphic summary of the situation is this.

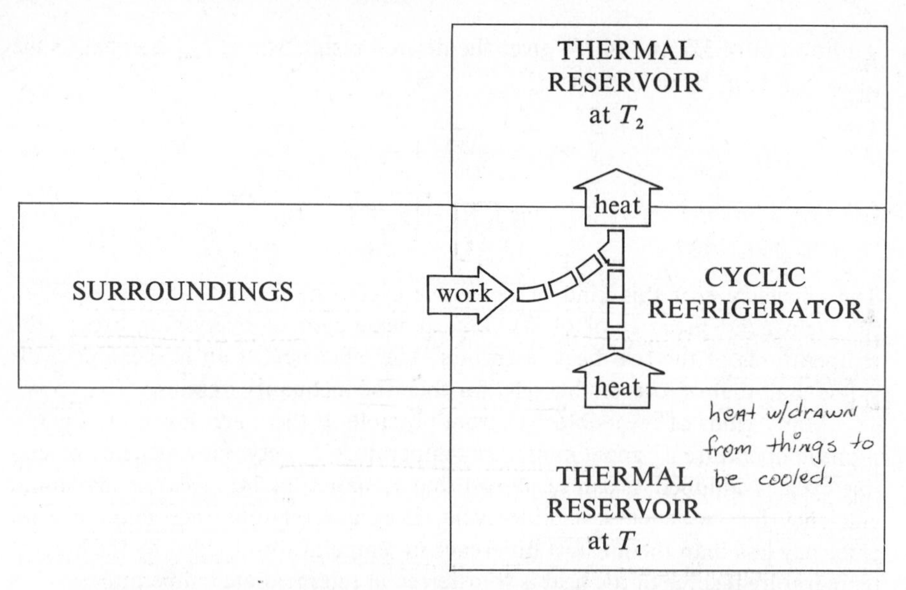

Let w be the work done on the refrigerator, let q_1 be the heat absorbed by the working substance of the refrigerator at the low temperature T_1, and let $-q_2$ be the positive heat evolved by the working substance of the refrigerator at the high temperature T_2. These energies are related to zero by (4.35).

$$\left.\begin{aligned} w &> 0 \\ q_1 &> 0 \\ q_2 &< 0 \end{aligned}\right\} \tag{4.35}$$

The efficiency of a refrigerator is the ratio of the heat withdrawn from the things to be cooled, the thermal reservoir at T_1, to the work done on the working substance of the refrigerator. By definition, then, the efficiency of a refrigerator is

$$\epsilon_{\text{ref}} = \frac{q_1}{w} \tag{4.36}$$

One cycle of operation carries the working substance of the refrigerator through an isothermal absorption of heat q_1 at T_1, an adiabatic compression in which the temperature rises from T_1 to T_2, an isothermal rejection of heat $-q_2$ at T_2, and an adiabatic expansion in which the temperature falls from T_2 to T_1 and in which the cycle is completed. For one cycle, the energy and the entropy of the refrigerator do not increase; as in the previous section,

$$0 = \oint dE = q_1 + q_2 + w \tag{4.37}$$

$$0 = \oint dS \geqslant \frac{q_1}{T_1} + \frac{q_2}{T_2} \tag{4.38}$$

Since $T_2 > 0$, (4.37) and (4.38) become

$$w = -q_1 - q_2 \tag{4.39}$$

and

$$0 \geqslant q_1\left(\frac{T_2}{T_1}\right) + q_2 \tag{4.40}$$

Addition of (4.39) and (4.40) yields

$$w \geqslant q_1\left(\frac{T_2}{T_1} - 1\right) \tag{4.41}$$

Since $T_2 > T_1 > 0$ by hypothesis, with the aid of (4.36), (4.41) becomes (4.42),

$$\epsilon_{\text{ref}} = \frac{q_1}{w} \leqslant \frac{T_1}{T_2 - T_1} \tag{4.42}$$

Example 4.2. For a refrigerator that operates between 20°C and −10°C, (a) what is the maximum efficiency ϵ_{ref} predicted? (b) What is the minimum work that must be done to withdraw 1000 cal of heat from the thermal reservoir at −10°C and reject them to the room at 20°C?

Equation (4.42) provides the solutions.

(a) $$\epsilon_{\text{ref}} = \frac{263}{293 - 263} = \frac{263}{30} = 8.8\ (!!)$$

(b) $$w \geqslant \left(\frac{T_2 - T_1}{T_1}\right) q_1 = \frac{30}{263} \times 1000 = 114 \text{ cal}$$

4.7 HEAT PUMP

A heat pump is a refrigerator the purpose of which is to heat the surroundings at the high temperature T_2 by cooling the surroundings at the low temperature T_1. It "pumps" heat to a higher temperature in the hope of doing so with an efficiency greater than unity. The efficiency of a heat pump is defined as the ratio of the heat $-q_2$ evolved by the heat pump at the high temperature T_2 to the work w done on the heat pump. That is, by definition

$$\epsilon_{\text{pump}} = \frac{-q_2}{w} \tag{4.43}$$

Although the definitions of efficiency differ for the refrigerator and heat pump because of a difference in purpose, Equations (4.35), (4.37), and (4.38) again obtain for the same kind of process, refrigeration. Since q_1 rather than q_2 is to be eliminated from the equations, (4.38) must be manipulated in a slightly different way. If $T_1 > 0$, (4.38) becomes

$$0 \geqslant q_1 + q_2\left(\frac{T_1}{T_2}\right) \tag{4.44}$$

As above,

$$w = -q_1 - q_2 \tag{4.39}$$

Whence, by addition and (4.43), if $T_2 > T_1 > 0$,

$$w \geqslant -q_2\left(1 - \frac{T_1}{T_2}\right)$$

$$\epsilon_{\text{pump}} = \frac{-q_2}{w} \leqslant \frac{T_2}{T_2 - T_1} \tag{4.45}$$

Although (4.45) holds the promise of cheap heat for dwellings, especially in mild climates where the difference in inside temperature T_2 and outside heat source T_1 is small, there are engineering difficulties associated with heat transfer.

4.8 THE FUNDAMENTAL RELATION OF THERMODYNAMICS

In Section 2.13 the statement was made that there exist independent variables more natural than volume and temperature for the energy of closed systems. Since a closed system by definition cannot gain or lose matter, the first law (2.13) involves only heat and work.

$$dE = dq + dw \tag{2.13}$$

An abbreviated form of the second law, (4.4) provides a way of combining the first and second laws.

$$dq \leqslant T\,dS \tag{4.4}$$

Addition of (2.13) and (4.4) yields the fundamental relation of thermodynamics for closed systems:

$$dE \leqslant T\,dS + dw \tag{4.46}$$

The inequality (4.46) describes in a limited way the thermodynamic behavior of a closed system when the changes are natural or spontaneous. Of greater importance to this treatment, however, is the equality (4.46), which applies to reversible changes and equilibrium. When all work is expansion work, $dw = -P\,dV$ and (4.46) assumes the very important special form

$$dE = T\,dS - P\,dV \tag{4.47}$$

From (4.46) or (4.47) come many other useful equations; much of what follows is built upon them.

The independent variables in (4.47) appear to be the entropy S and the volume V of the system. These are the natural thermodynamic variables for the energy of a closed system when only expansion work is involved. That is,

$$E = E(S, V) \tag{4.48}$$

4.9 REVERSIBLE WORK IN A CYCLIC PROCESS

The work that must be done reversibly on a closed system to carry it through a cycle is, by (4.46),

$$w = \oint dw = \oint dE - \oint T\,dS$$

There is no energy change of the system after a cycle is complete, for the initial and final states of a cycle are alike and energy is a function of state; hence, $\oint dE = 0$. However, $\oint dw$ may not be zero because dw is not an exact differential. Hence, for a reversible cycle, the work done on the system is

$$w = -\oint T\,dS \tag{4.49a}$$

Figure 4.1 shows a refrigeration cycle in temperature-entropy space. In a cycle, the working substance (a) absorbs heat q_1 at T_1, (b) suffers a reversible adiabatic rise in temperature from T_1 to T_2, (c) evolves such a positive amount of heat $-q_2$ at T_2 that, in step (d), it can suffer a reversible adiabatic decrease in temperature from T_2 to T_1 to complete the cycle. In the isothermal steps (a) and (c), T is constant; in the reversible adiabatic steps (b) and (d), S is constant by (4.7). This refrigeration path as it is performed encircles the rectangular area of Figure 4.1 in the positive sense (area on the left, as in Appendix D). Thus, the right side of (4.49a) is the (positive) area of the rectangle. By (4.49a), this area is the work done on the working substance in one cycle.

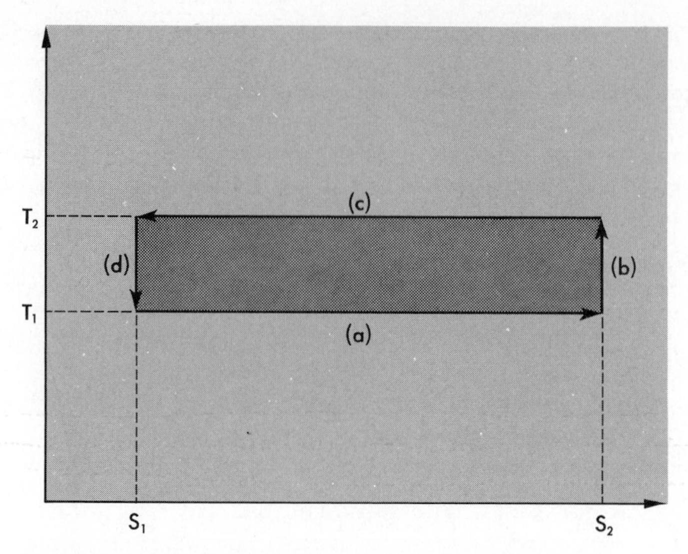

Figure 4.1. The Refrigeration Cycle in *T-S* Space

Figure 4.2 illustrates a Carnot cycle with labels as in (4.29); the sequence of steps is the reverse of the refrigeration cycle of Figure 4.1. By (4.49a), the work done by the Carnot engine in one cycle is

$$-w = -\left(-\oint T\,dS\right) \tag{4.49b}$$

The area of the rectangle on Figure 4.2 is the quantity in parentheses, and the negative sign before the parentheses reverses the sense of the refrigeration cycle

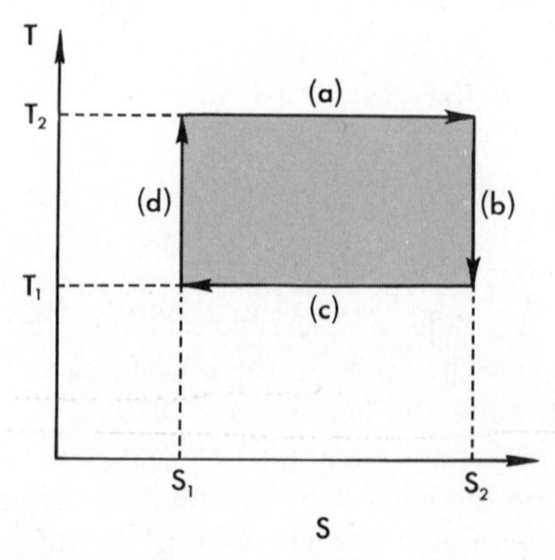

Figure 4.2. The Carnot Cycle in *T-S* Space

(for which $-\oint T\,dS$ exceeds zero) to match the sense of the Carnot cycle. That is, $-w$ is the (positive) work done by the Carnot engine in one cycle of operation. Alternatively, if the symbol $\oint$ is interpreted thermodynamically rather than mathematically so that it indicates the forward sense of the Carnot cycle, then Figure 4.2 shows that $-w = \oint T\,dS$ exceeds zero because step (a) is the large area below T_2 while step (c) is the negative of the area below T_1 since along T_1 the value of dS is negative as the engine evolves heat.

The work done by the working substance of a Carnot engine can be described in terms of variables somewhat more vivid in their physical significance. If the working substance of the Carnot engine is a compressible fluid like a perfect gas, two variables suitable for work and for the specification of the state of the fluid are pressure and volume. In a two-dimensional space where P and V are the variables, the Carnot cycle then looks like Figure 4.3, where once again the labels on the four parts of the cycle correspond with the labels of (4.29). The first and third parts of the cycle are isothermal so that the lines in P-V space are hyperbolas in accord with Boyle's law, $PV =$ constant. The second and fourth parts of the cycle are adiabatics; if the working substance is a

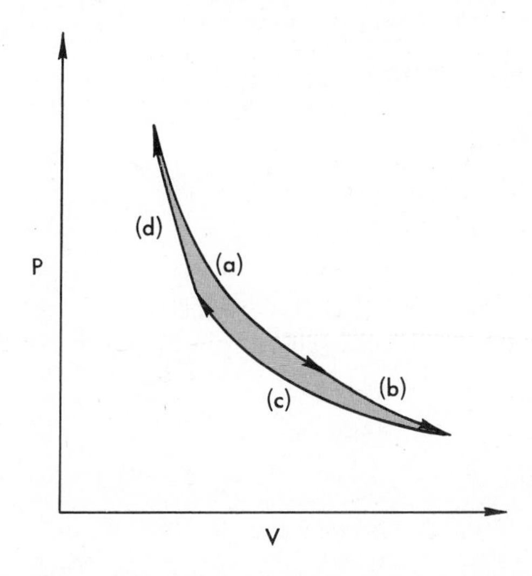

Figure 4.3. The Carnot Cycle in P-V Space

fluid, as supposed in Figure 4.3, these adiabatics have a more negative slope than the isotherms, as shown in Example 2.12. The line integral around the closed path of Figure 4.3 is the area of the bounded figure, as it was in Figure 4.2. Thus (4.49b) says that the reversible work $-w$ done by the working substance is the bounded area of Figure 4.3. That this is true is confirmed by

$$-w = \int_{V_1}^{V_2} P\,dV \qquad (2.45)$$

Along the first and second parts of the cycle, the integral of (2.45) is the area bounded by the V-axis and the upper curves. Along the third and fourth parts of the cycle, this integral is the area bounded by the V-axis and the lower curves, but its sign is negative since V decreases along the lower curves as the process occurs. The sum of these two areas with account of their signs is just the bounded area of Figure 4.3.

Example 4.3. One mole of a perfect gas with a molar heat capacity at constant pressure of $7R/2$ is the working substance in a Carnot cycle. The high temperature is 1000°K, the low temperature is 400°K, and in the isothermal expansion at 1000°K the work done by the gas is 1000 cal. Calculate (a) the net work done by the gas in one cycle of operation; (b) the work done on the gas, the heat absorbed by the gas, and the increments in energy, enthalpy, and entropy for each of the four parts of the cycle.

(a) For the isothermal expansion at 1000°K, $\Delta E = 0$ since the energy of a perfect gas depends only on its temperature by (2.34). It is given that $w_2 = -1000$ cal for this part of the cycle. Whence,

$$\Delta E_2 = q_2 + w_2 = q_2 - 1000 = 0$$

$$q_2 = 1000 \text{ cal}$$

By (4.34), wherein w' is the net work done by the gas in one cycle,

$$w' = q_2\left(\frac{T_2 - T_1}{T_2}\right)$$

$$= 1000\left(\frac{1000 - 400}{1000}\right) = 600 \text{ cal}$$

The work done on the gas is $w = -600$ cal per cycle.

(b) For the complete cycle, $\Delta E = 0$ so that

$$\Delta E = q_2 + q_1 - w' = 0$$

$$q_1 = w' - q_2 = 600 - 1000 = -400 \text{ cal}$$

Because the third part of the cycle is isothermal like the first part,

$$\Delta E_1 = q_1 + w_1 = 0$$

$$w_1 = -q_1 = 400 \text{ cal}$$

For the isothermal parts, $\Delta H = 0$ by (2.35), since the enthalpy of a perfect gas is a function only of its temperature. Again, for the reversible adiabatic parts of the cycle, the entropy is constant. It is profitable at this point to summarize what is known.

Part	Reversible process	w	q	ΔE	ΔH	ΔS
a	Isothermal expansion (T_2)	−1000	1000	0	0	$\frac{q_2}{T_2} = \frac{1000}{1000}$
b	Adiabatic expansion		0			0
c	Isothermal compression (T_1)	400	−400	0	0	$\frac{q_1}{T_1} = \frac{-400}{400}$
d	Adiabatic compression		0			0
(All)	Net value for cycle	−600	600	0	0	0

The values of ΔE and ΔH for the second part of the cycle are readily calculated by the methods of Chapter 2 thus:

1 mole $T_2 = 1000°K$	⟶	1 mole $T_1 = 400°K$

By (2.40), $$C_V = C_P - R = \tfrac{7}{2}R - R = \tfrac{5}{2}R.$$

By (2.30), (2.36), (2.67), and (2.65),

$$\Delta E = \int_{T_2}^{T_1} C_V dT = \tfrac{5}{2}R(400 - 1000) = -1500R \text{ cal}$$

$$\Delta H = \int_{T_2}^{T_1} C_P dT = \tfrac{7}{2}R(400 - 1000) = -2100R \text{ cal}$$

The values of ΔE and ΔH for the fourth part of the cycle are equal in magnitude but opposite in sign because initial and final temperatures are interchanged.

The value of w for the second and fourth parts of the cycle can be found by the first law. For example, for the second part, by (2.12),

$$w = \Delta E - q = -1500R - 0 = -1500R \text{ cal}$$

And so the table of values is complete.

Part	Reversible Process	w	q	ΔE	ΔH	ΔS
a	Isothermal expansion (T_2)	-1000	1000	0	0	1.00
b	Adiabatic expansion	$-1500R$	0	$-1500R$	$-2100R$	0
c	Isothermal compression (T_1)	400	-400	0	0	-1.00
d	Adiabatic compression	$1500R$	0	$1500R$	$2100R$	0
(All)	Net value for cycle	-600	600	0	0	0

The values for w have been found indirectly without integration. As a check, the value of w for the adiabatic compression can be found by (2.57).

$$w = \frac{nR(T_2 - T_1)}{\gamma - 1} = \frac{R(1000 - 400)}{\frac{7}{5} - 1} = 1500R$$

4.10 REVERSIBLE PROCESSES AT CONSTANT TEMPERATURE AND PRESSURE

By the definition (2.21) of H and the rules of calculus, $dH = d(E + PV) = dE + P\,dV + V\,dP$. A reversible process that involves only expansion work obeys (4.47), namely $dE = T\,dS - P\,dV$; hence, together these yield

$$dH = T\,dS + V\,dP \qquad (4.50)$$

only expansion work

If the reversible process is also isobaric, then dP is zero and

$$dH = T\,dS \tag{4.51}$$

Integration of (4.51) between states 1 and 2 is easy if T is constant; thus

$$\int_{H_1}^{H_2} dH = \int_{S_1}^{S_2} T\,dS = T\int_{S_1}^{S_2} dS$$

$$\Delta H = T\,\Delta S \tag{4.52}$$

Equation (4.52) is applicable to isothermal isobaric reversible changes like phase transitions: fusion, vaporization, sublimation, and so forth.

It is instructive to consider some values of ΔS for physical changes in which isothermal isobaric absorption of heat causes an increase in the disorder of the system, which here is taken to be a pure substance. Solution processes at constant P and T generally are accompanied by an increase in entropy as the substance goes from the order of its crystal to the relative disorder of the solution. An increase of about 2 cal mole^{-1} deg^{-1} is typical of the melting of a monatomic solid, while an entropy of fusion less than about 5 cal mole^{-1} deg^{-1} for a molecular crystal is exceptional. An entropy of fusion less than this indicates less than the usual disordering upon fusion, perhaps because the crystal is disordered with rotating molecules (e.g., CH_4 or WF_6, both of which are almost spherical) or perhaps because the liquid has special order (e.g., H_2O or CH_3OH, both of which are organized by hydrogen bonds). Furthermore, with regard to substances that boil at one atm without obvious dissociation or polymerization, out of the 500 such substances listed in NBS Circular 500 (F. D. Rossini *et al.*, *Selected Values of Chemical Thermodynamic Properties*, Washington, D.C., 1952), half have an entropy of vaporization calculated by (4.52) from 21 to 23 cal mole^{-1} deg^{-1}. This is Trouton's rule, and as expected, the extent of the disorder caused by vaporization generally exceeds that of fusion. Table 4.1 illustrates that even great differences in chemical nature do not cause great

Table 4.1. Some Entropies of Vaporization at One Atm (Data from NBS Circular 500)

Substance	ΔH_v (cal mole^{-1})	T_b (°K)	$\Delta S_v = \frac{\Delta H_v}{T_b}$ (cal mole^{-1} deg^{-1})
CH_4	1,960	112	17.5
Ar	1,560	87.3	17.9
Cl_2	4,880	239	20.4
AgBr	37,000	1806	20.5
C_2H_3Cl	5,500	259	21.2
Zn	27,400	1180	23.2
Ag	60,700	2466	24.6
H_2O	9,720	373	26.0
$ZnCl_2$	30,900	1029	30.0

deviations from Trouton's empirical rule. Another form of this rule is the Nernst-Bingham rule for the entropy of vaporization (cal mole^{-1} deg^{-1})

$$\Delta S = 17 + 0.011\,T$$

where T is the absolute boiling point at one atm.

4.11 ENTROPY AS A FUNCTION OF TEMPERATURE

Equation (4.51) provides the means of calculating the change in entropy attendant upon a change in temperature. One of the restrictions on (4.51) is that the process for which it is written be isobaric. Division by dT and explicit statement of this restriction by a subscript leads to (4.53) if recourse is had to the definition of C_P in (2.27).

$$\left(\frac{\partial H}{\partial T}\right)_P = T\left(\frac{\partial S}{\partial T}\right)_P = C_P \tag{4.53}$$

By the very meaning of the derivative, the increment in entropy for any reversible isobaric process that involves only expansion work on a closed system is

$$\Delta S = \int_{(1)}^{(2)} \left(\frac{\partial S}{\partial T}\right)_P dT$$

With (4.53), this becomes

$$\Delta S = \int_{T_1}^{T_2} \frac{C_P}{T}\,dT \tag{4.54}$$

Even if the actual process is not reversible, (4.54) is the proper way to calculate the value of ΔS for the process that transforms the well-defined state (1) with the temperature T_1 into the well-defined state (2) with the temperature T_2. Since Table 2.1 contains C_P as a power series in T, the integration is easily performed along an invented reversible isobaric path.

In a similar way, (4.47) provides the means of calculating ΔS for a reversible process that involves no work of any kind. If the volume is constant, $dw = -P\,dV = 0$ since $dV = 0$. Then, by (4.47), the analogue of (4.51) is

$$dE = T\,dS \tag{4.55}$$

Division by dT and explicit statement that the volume is constant leads to (4.56), where the definition of C_V is given by (2.26).

$$\left(\frac{\partial E}{\partial T}\right)_V = T\left(\frac{\partial S}{\partial T}\right)_V = C_V \tag{4.56}$$

The unique increment in entropy for any process by which state (1) with temperature T_1 and volume V becomes state (2) with temperature T_2 and the same volume V is given by (4.57) if the system is closed.

$$\Delta S = \int_{(1)}^{(2)} \left(\frac{\partial S}{\partial T}\right)_V dT$$

$$* \quad = \int_{T_1}^{T_2} \frac{C_V}{T} dT \tag{4.57}$$

Both (4.54) and (4.57) are readily integrated if the heat capacity C_P or C_V is independent of temperature. Then,

$$\begin{aligned} \Delta S &= \int_{T_1}^{T_2} \frac{C}{T} dT \\ &= C \int_{T_1}^{T_2} \frac{dT}{T} \\ &= C \ln\left(\frac{T_2}{T_1}\right) \end{aligned} \tag{4.58}$$

The increase in entropy ΔS is an extensive property and if n moles constitute the system with molar heat capacity C, (4.58) becomes (4.59) and similar adjustments can be made for the other equations of this section.

$$\Delta S = \int_{T_1}^{T_2} \frac{nC}{T} dT = nC \ln\left(\frac{T_2}{T_1}\right) \tag{4.59}$$

Example 4.4. Calculate the increment in entropy suffered by two moles gaseous oxygen when its temperature is changed from 300.00°K to 400.00°K (a) at constant pressure; and (b) at constant volume.

From Table 2.1, for oxygen, $C_P = 6.148 + 3.102 \times 10^{-3}T - 0.923 \times 10^{-6}T^2$. And from (2.40), $C_V = C_P - R$.

(a) At constant pressure, by (4.53) or (4.54),

$$\begin{aligned} \Delta S &= 2 \int_{300.00}^{400.00} (6.148 + 3.102 \times 10^{-3}T - 0.923 \times 10^{-6}T^2)\frac{dT}{T} \\ &= 2\left[6.148 \ln\left(\frac{400.00}{300.00}\right) + 3.102 \times 10^{-3}(400.00 - 300.00)\right. \\ &\qquad \left. - \frac{0.923 \times 10^{-6}}{2}(400.00^2 - 300.00^2)\right] \\ &= 2(1.7687 + 0.3102 - 0.0323 = 4.0932 \text{ cal deg}^{-1}. \end{aligned}$$

(b) At constant volume, by (4.57),

$$\begin{aligned} \Delta S &= 2\int_{T_1}^{T_2} \frac{C_V}{T} dT = 2\int_{T_1}^{T_2} \left(\frac{C_P - R}{T}\right) dT \\ &= 4.0932 - 2R \ln\left(\frac{T_2}{T_1}\right) \\ &= 4.0932 - 2 \times 1.9872 \ln\left(\tfrac{4}{3}\right) = 4.0932 - 1.1434 \\ &= 2.9498 \text{ cal deg}^{-1}. \end{aligned}$$

4.12 THE MOST PROBABLE DISTRIBUTION OF ENERGIES

In order to calculate entropy changes accompanying changes in T, it is necessary to know C_P or C_V as a function of T. Summarizing observed C_P's by an empirical power series in T, as in Table 2.1, is adequate but theoretically unsatisfying. What is needed is an understanding of why heat capacities vary with T and from substance to substance. This implies a knowledge of E and H at equilibrium at any T so that the definitions of C_P and C_V in (2.26) and (2.27) can be used.

An equilibrium state has a maximum entropy when the system is isolated. At equilibrium or during reversible processes a system maintains that state of disorder commensurate with its temperature and energy. A perfect monatomic gas has no order; a diatomic gas has only the order of atom-pairs; a solid has the order of its lattice, the mathematical array of an infinite set of points repeated regularly throughout space; a liquid has that remnant of crystalline order that prevents its molecules from moving independently as in a gas. The preceding section clearly states that any substance suffers an increase in S and thermal disorder as its T rises. An understanding of heat capacities through an appreciation of thermal disorder and order calls for a microscopic picture of what the atoms and molecules are doing. Such a description is foreign to thermodynamics with its macroscopic view of matter as a continuum.

Chapter 1 established the fact that a perfect gas at equilibrium at T has molecules with many different velocities and energies. The same can be said of any system at equilibrium; its energy is an average of the various differing energies of its parts. According to kinetic theory, collisions or the action of various fields of force cause a continual exchange of energy among the parts. There is in classical mechanics no restriction on how small or how great the energy change can be for any one part, provided the total energy in an isolated event or system is conserved.

For the purposes of counting and averaging, it is, however, convenient, despite the view that energy may be continually variable, to divide the N particles of a system into groups of similar energy: N_1 particles, each of energy ε_1; N_2, each of energy ε_2; and so on. Clearly, in a closed system without chemical reaction, the total number of particles is constant at

$$N = N_1 + N_2 + N_3 + \cdots = \sum_i N_i \tag{4.60}$$

The numbers N_i are each supposed to be very great and yet the energy ranges $\varepsilon_j - \varepsilon_i$ are sufficiently small when $j \approx i$ that use of these arbitrary energy ranges for the sake of mathematical convenience is of negligible importance in any calculation of a thermodynamic property such as the total energy E of the system

$$E = N_1\varepsilon_1 + N_2\varepsilon_2 + N_3\varepsilon_3 + \cdots = \sum_i N_i\,\varepsilon_i \tag{4.61}$$

The task of following the trajectory of each of the N particles is in principle possible according to classical mechanics, but in practice it is impossible because N is huge. That is, a thermodynamic state is well defined by a few variables like P, V, and T, whereas many different microscopic states are treated alike thermodynamically. Everyone recognizes this, at least implicitly, for several specimens of a substance can be brought to the same thermodynamic state in different ways by different observers who, of course, know very well that the microscopic parts of the several samples are not moving in phase. This lack of microscopic knowledge is compensated for by statistics. It is unimportant which of identical particles has a certain position and momentum if only about the right number have about the right values. It is also clear that there is considerable latitude in the number N_i of energy ε_i if only N and E are known.

The number of ways of rearranging N numbered or distinguishable particles of the same kind and energy is $N!$, for there are N choices for the first, $(N - 1)$ choices for the second, and so on to the unique choice of the last. The number of ways is less than $N!$, however, if the particles differ in energy. Within the group of N_1 of energy ε_1, there are $N_1!$ ways of rearranging the particles without in any way affecting E; within the group of energy ε_2, there are likewise $N_2!$ ways of rearranging the N_2 particles, and so on. Hence, the number of distinguishable ways in which N particles can be taken in groups of N_i is

$$G = \frac{N!}{N_1!\, N_2!\, N_3! \cdots N_i! \cdots}$$

This great number measures the number of different microscopic states that are consistent with the macroscopic or thermodynamic state with energy E. The probability P that the system does in fact have N_i particles of energy ε_i is proportional to the number of ways the arrangement can occur out of all possible arrangements; hence,

$$P = C\,G = \frac{C\,N!}{N_1!\, N_2!\, N_3! \cdots N_i! \cdots} \tag{4.62}$$

The physical problem is to find the most probable value of P consistent with the energy E and the total number N of particles that an experimenter might specify thermodynamically. Finding this P is tantamount to bringing an arbitrary dynamic state of N particles to equilibrium and to maximum S while holding E and N constant.

The most probable value of P is its maximum value. It is more convenient, however, to maximize $\ln P$ because for large N there exists the Stirling approximation

$$\ln N! = N \ln N - N + \tfrac{1}{2} \ln(2\pi N)$$

When N is large, the last term of the Stirling approximation is negligible so that

$$\ln N! \approx N \ln N - N \tag{4.63}$$

With (4.63), it follows from (4.62) that

$$\ln P = \ln C + \ln N! - \ln N_1! - \ln N_2! - \cdots$$
$$= \ln C + (N \ln N - N) - \sum_i (N_i \ln N_i - N_i) \qquad (4.64)$$

By analogy with the requirement that the derivative be zero at a maximum or minimum, the condition that P or $\ln P$ be an extreme or stationary value is that the variation $\delta(\ln P)$ be zero. Treating the variation of $\ln P$ in (4.64) like a first differential thus gives the condition

$$0 = \delta(\ln C) + \delta(N \ln N - N) - \sum_i \delta(N_i \ln N_i - N_i)$$
$$= 0 + \left(N\frac{\delta N}{N} + \ln N\, \delta N - \delta N\right) - \sum_i \left(N_i \frac{\delta N_i}{N_i} + \ln N_i\, \delta N_i - \delta N_i\right)$$
$$= (\ln N)\, \delta N - \sum_i (\ln N_i)\, \delta N_i \qquad (4.65)$$

This extreme (maximum) value of $\ln P$ is achieved subject to two conditions: (1) N in (4.60) must be constant; and (2) E in (4.61) must be constant. Hence,

$$0 = \delta N = \sum_i \delta N_i \qquad (4.66)$$
$$0 = \delta E = \sum_i \varepsilon_i \delta N_i \qquad (4.67)$$

The adjustment to equilibrium is conceived in (4.67) as an adjustment in the numbers N_i of particles each of energy ε_i and not as an adjustment in the very energies ε_i which are fixed by certain physical properties like the position of the vessel walls if the system is a gas or the nature of the lattice if the system is a solid. The condition (4.66) also simplifies (4.65) to the form

$$0 = -\delta(\ln P) = \sum_i (\ln N_i)\delta N_i \qquad (4.68)$$

Lagrange's method of undetermined multipliers allows (4.66), (4.67), and (4.68) to be satisfied simultaneously by the use of two adjustable constants α and β in the one condition

$$0 = -\delta(\ln P) + \alpha\, \delta N + \beta\, \delta E$$
$$0 = \sum_i (\ln N_i + \alpha + \beta\, \varepsilon_i)\delta N_i \qquad (4.69)$$

The values of α and β are to be adjusted to fit the fixed values of N and E in (4.66) and (4.67). Since the δN_i in (4.69) are arbitrary,

$$\ln N_i + \alpha + \beta\, \varepsilon_i = 0$$
$$N_i = e^{-\alpha} e^{-\beta \varepsilon_i} \qquad (4.70)$$

The condition that N be constant is satisfied if

$$\sum_j N_j = \sum_j e^{-\alpha} e^{-\beta\varepsilon_j} = e^{-\alpha} \sum_j e^{-\beta\varepsilon_j} = N \tag{4.71}$$

Similarly, the condition that E be constant is satisfied if

$$\sum_i \varepsilon_i N_i = \sum_i e^{-\alpha} \varepsilon_i e^{-\beta\varepsilon_i} = e^{-\alpha} \sum_i \varepsilon_i e^{-\beta\varepsilon_i} = E \tag{4.72}$$

Elimination of α from (4.70) and (4.72) by division of each by (4.71) yields

$$\frac{N_i}{N} = \frac{e^{-\beta\varepsilon_i}}{\sum_j e^{-\beta\varepsilon_j}} \tag{4.73}$$

and

$$\frac{E}{N} = \frac{\sum_i \varepsilon_i e^{-\beta\varepsilon_i}}{\sum_j e^{-\beta\varepsilon_j}} \tag{4.74}$$

Actually there are so many particles N in any ordinary macroscopic system that the probability that E will fluctuate significantly from its average is negligible. That is, P is effectively zero except when it gives the correct E. Hence, as indicated in Figure 4.4, the adjustment to the most probable P is practically the same as adjusting to the P that would give the average energy observable thermodynamically. Thus the average energy per particle is, by (4.73) and (4.74),

$$\bar{\varepsilon} = \frac{E}{N} = \frac{\sum_i \varepsilon_i e^{-\beta\varepsilon_i}}{\sum_j e^{-\beta\varepsilon_j}} = \sum_i \varepsilon_i \left(\frac{N_i}{N}\right) \tag{4.75}$$

The terms $\varepsilon_i N_i/N$ in (4.75) are called the expected values of the energy ε_i, and N_i/N is the probability that a particle sampled from the total of N will have the energy ε_i. Equation (4.75) is like that for the average value of a roll of a die as a sum of the expected values of the various outcomes: $1(\frac{1}{6}) + 2(\frac{1}{6}) + 3(\frac{1}{6}) + 4(\frac{1}{6}) + 5(\frac{1}{6}) + 6(\frac{1}{6})$. The distribution (4.73) is the most probable distribution consistent with N particles of total energy E; it is the well known Boltzmann distribution.

Equation (4.75) offers a way to evaluate β, for it can be applied to a perfect gas. By (1.16) and (1.29), the average energy per particle of a perfect gas is already known to be

$$\bar{\varepsilon} = \frac{E}{N} = \frac{3}{2}\left(\frac{PV}{N}\right) = \frac{3}{2}\left(\frac{RT}{N}\right) = \left(\frac{3}{2}\right)kT \tag{4.76}$$

where $k = R/N$. If $\bar{\varepsilon}$ can be calculated by (4.75), the result, which will involve β, can be set equal to $(3/2)kT$ to give β as a function of T.

The energy of a free molecule of mass m having components of linear momentum $p_x = m\,v_x$, $p_y = m\,v_y$, and $p_z = m\,v_z$ along the Cartesian axes is

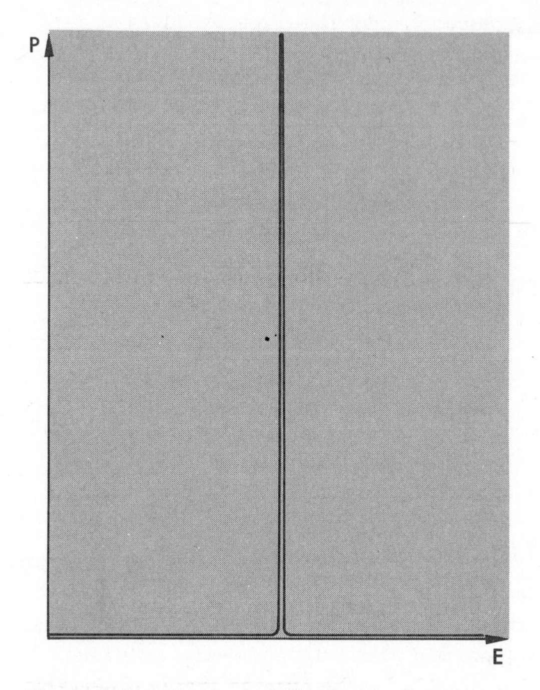

Figure 4.4. The Probability $P(E)$ of an Energy E of a System of Many Particles. (Note that the maximum value of P is practically the same as any non-zero value of P.)

$$\varepsilon = \frac{mv^2}{2} = \frac{m}{2}(v_x^2 + v_y^2 + v_z^2) = \frac{p_x^2 + p_y^2 + p_z^2}{2m} \tag{4.77}$$

As a perfect gas, it has no potential energy and no interaction with other molecules. Like every other molecule of the N in the system, this one's energy consists of three parts. Indeed, there are $3N$ separate contributions to the energy of N molecules, each contribution being of the form $p_{xi}^2/2m$.

Classically, ε and each p may take any value because ε and p are conceived as continuous variables. It is proper, then, to formulate the sums in (4.75) as integrals with each classical momentum p ranging from $-\infty$ to $+\infty$. Although a more rigorous discussion is given in Chapter 17, it is sufficient here to note that all coordinates for other molecules and even p_{yi} and p_{zi} for this molecule cancel when the summations of (4.75) are done if (4.77) is true for every molecule. Thus (4.75) becomes simply

$$\bar{\varepsilon}_m = \frac{\displaystyle\int_{-\infty}^{+\infty} \left(\frac{p_{xi}^2}{2m}\right) e^{-\beta(p_{xi}^2/2m)}\, dp_{xi}}{\displaystyle\int_{-\infty}^{+\infty} e^{-\beta(p_{xi}^2/2m)}\, dp_{xi}} \tag{4.78}$$

That is, for this part of $\bar{\varepsilon}$, the integrals over the other variables are alike and cancel. Inspection of (4.78) yields the simplification

$$\bar{\varepsilon}_m = -\frac{1}{I_m}\frac{\partial I_m}{\partial \beta} = -\frac{\partial \ln I_m}{\partial \beta} \tag{4.79}$$

where

$$I_m = \int_{-\infty}^{+\infty} e^{-\beta(p^2/2m)}\, dp \tag{4.80}$$

With $y = \beta p^2/2m$, (4.80) becomes

$$I_m = 2\int_0^{\infty} \left(\frac{\beta}{2my}\right)^{1/2} e^{-y} \left(\frac{m}{\beta}\right) dy = \left(\frac{2m}{\beta}\right)^{1/2} \int_0^{\infty} y^{1/2-1}\, e^{-y}\, dy$$

$$= \left(\frac{2m}{\beta}\right)^{1/2} \Gamma\left(\frac{1}{2}\right) = \left(\frac{2\pi m}{\beta}\right)^{1/2} \tag{4.81}$$

Accordingly, (4.81) in (4.79) yields

$$\bar{\varepsilon}_m = -\frac{\partial}{\partial \beta}\left[\frac{1}{2}\ln\left(\frac{2\pi m}{\beta}\right)\right] = -\frac{1}{2}\frac{\partial}{\partial \beta}(\ln(2\pi m) - \ln \beta) = \frac{1}{2\beta} \tag{4.82}$$

With equal contributions from $p_{yi}^2/2m$ and $p_{zi}^2/2m$ for this molecule i, it is clear from (4.82), (4.77), and (4.76) that

$$\bar{\varepsilon} = \frac{3}{2\beta} = \frac{3kT}{2} \tag{4.83}$$

Hence

$$\beta = \frac{1}{kT} \tag{4.84}$$

According to (4.76) the Boltzmann constant k has the value

$$k = \frac{R}{N_0} = \frac{8.3143 \times 10^7 \text{ erg mole}^{-1} \text{ deg}^{-1}}{6.02252 \times 10^{23} \text{ mole}^{-1}}$$

$$= 1.38054 \times 10^{-16} \text{ erg deg}^{-1} \tag{4.85}$$

Thus, with the perfect monatomic gas as thermometer, β is found in (4.84) to be a statistical temperature related inversely to the more familiar thermodynamic or absolute temperature T.

4.13 EQUIPARTITION OF ENERGY

The energy of an atom of mass m in a crystal is

$$\varepsilon = \frac{p_x^2 + p_y^2 + p_z^2}{2m} + \frac{b_x}{2}x^2 + \frac{b_y}{2}y^2 + \frac{b_z}{2}z^2 \tag{4.86}$$

Avg. energy is $E = N\bar{\varepsilon} = N\left(\frac{6}{2}\right)kT = 3RT$

THEN, $C_v = 3R$

where the Hooke's law force constants b describe the intensity of the forces that tend to hold the atom in place near its equilibrium position $x = y = z = 0$. Any calculation of $\bar{\varepsilon}$ by (4.75) must include contributions from kinetic energy by allowing momenta p to range from $-\infty$ to $+\infty$ as well as contributions from potential energy by allowing positions to range from $-\infty$ to $+\infty$ in each direction. As before, each coordinate $(p_{xi}, p_{yi}, p_{zi}, x_i, y_i, z_i)$ of atom i makes its own separate contribution. For each component of momentum there will be, as in (4.79) and (4.80), a contribution to $\bar{\varepsilon}$ for each atom of the form

$$\bar{\varepsilon}_m = -\frac{\partial \ln I_m}{\partial \beta} = \frac{1}{2\beta} \tag{4.87}$$

Similarly, for each direction there will be a contribution to $\bar{\varepsilon}$ with a term of the form

$$\bar{\varepsilon}_b = \frac{\int_{-\infty}^{+\infty} \left(\frac{b_x x^2}{2}\right) e^{-\beta(b_x x^2/2)}\, dx}{\int_{-\infty}^{+\infty} e^{-\beta(b_x x^2/2)}\, dx} \tag{4.88}$$

As in (4.79) and (4.80), it is convenient to evaluate (4.88) by the ruse

$$\bar{\varepsilon}_b = -\frac{\partial \ln I_b}{\partial \beta} \tag{4.89}$$

where

$$I_b = \int_{-\infty}^{+\infty} e^{-\beta(b_x x^2/2)}\, dx \tag{4.90}$$

If $\beta b/2$ in (4.90) is replaced by $\beta/2m$, it is clear that I_b equals I_m of (4.80); hence, with $b = 1/m$ in (4.81),

$$I_b = \left(\frac{2\pi}{\beta b}\right)^{1/2} \tag{4.91}$$

From (4.89) and (4.91) then comes

$$\bar{\varepsilon}_b = -\frac{\partial}{\partial \beta}\left[\frac{1}{2}\ln\left(\frac{2\pi}{b}\right) - \frac{1}{2}\ln \beta\right] = \frac{1}{2\beta} \tag{4.92}$$

The amazing feature of (4.92) and (4.82) is that each additive energy term that involves the square of a momentum or position coordinate contributes $1/2\beta = (1/2)kT$ to the average energy of the particle. Clearly, for N particles, the contribution is $N(1/2)kT$ for each square term in a particle's energy expression. The *principle of equipartition of energy* summarizes this thus: The average energy due to each coordinate that contributes a quadratic term to the total particle energy ε is $(1/2)kT$, regardless of the kind of coordinate.

Both momentum and position coordinates must be counted. For a mole of monatomic gas with particle energies given by (4.77), the energy per mole is $E = N\bar{\varepsilon} = N(3/2)kT = (3/2)RT$; hence, its heat capacity at constant volume is $C_V = (\partial E/\partial T)_V = (3/2)R$. For a mole of atoms in a crystal with particle energy given by (4.86), the average energy is $E = N\bar{\varepsilon} = N(6/2)kT = 3RT$; hence, $C_V = 3R$.

The power of the principle becomes evident from some further applications to heat capacities. The energy of a rigid diatomic molecule of mass M and moment of inertia I is the translational and rotational energy:

$$\varepsilon = \frac{p_x^2 + p_y^2 + p_z^2}{2M} + \frac{1}{2} I(\omega_x^2 + \omega_y^2)$$

Accordingly, the average energy of a mole containing N_0 molecules is

$$E = N_0\bar{\varepsilon} = N_0\left(\frac{3}{2}kT + \frac{2}{2}kT\right) = \frac{5}{2}RT$$

and, as in (2.43), its heat capacity is $C_V = \frac{5}{2}R$. Similarly, the energy of a gas consisting of rigid nonlinear molecules is $\frac{6}{2}RT$ because there is one more rotational kinetic energy term. Table 4.2 lists these and other results when the molecules vibrate. The configuration of a vibrating molecule of a atoms is specified by $3a$ position coordinates, namely x, y, and z for each of the a atoms. If the molecule is linear, five of these $3a$ coordinates are used to specify the position of the center of mass and two angles of rotation; hence, the number of independent internal coordinates is $3a - 5$. Each of these contributes $\frac{1}{2}kT$ in kinetic energy through the components of momentum along each internal coordinate, and, if the motions are sufficiently small that Hooke's law holds, $\frac{1}{2}kT$ in potential energy. If the molecule of a atoms is nonlinear, the number of internal coordinates is $3a - 6$ because three angles are needed to specify the orientation of the whole molecule and, as usual, three position coordinates fix the center of mass. Each of the $3a - 6$ internal coordinates contributes $\frac{1}{2}kT$ as kinetic energy and, if the motions are sufficiently small, $\frac{1}{2}kT$ in potential energy. If all $3a$ coordinates had potential energies, C_V of a mole of gas with a atoms per molecule would be $3aR$, but the five or six coordinates of translation and rotation of the whole molecule lack potential energy and thus contribute only $\frac{1}{2}kT$ to $\bar{\varepsilon}$ rather than kT.

Table 4.2. Some Applications of the Principle of Equipartition of Energy to Perfect Gases.

Kind of Molecule	$E = N_0\bar{\varepsilon}$	C_V
One atom	$N_0(\frac{3}{2})kT$	$\frac{3}{2}R$
Rigid Linear Molecule	$N_0(\frac{3}{2} + \frac{2}{2})kT$	$\frac{5}{2}R$
Nonrigid Linear Molecule of a Atoms	$N_0(\frac{3}{2} + \frac{2}{2} + (3a - 5))kT$	$(3a - \frac{5}{2})R$
Rigid Nonlinear Molecule	$N_0(\frac{3}{2} + \frac{3}{2})kT$	$3R$
Nonrigid Nonlinear Molecule of a Atoms	$N_0(\frac{3}{2} + \frac{3}{2} + (3a - 6))kT$	$3(a - 1)R$

Example 4.5. By the principle of equipartition of energy, estimate C_V of a crystal containing nonlinear molecules held at each site by Hooke's law forces if each molecule is

(a) rigid and rotates freely at its site in the crystal;
(b) rigid and rotates slightly and periodically at its site;
(c) nonrigid and rotates slightly and periodically at its site.

In addition to the crystalline energy $E = 3RT$ that by (4.92) describes the vibration of each molecule at its lattice site:

(a) Each freely rotating rigid molecule has the rotational kinetic energy

$$\tfrac{1}{2}I_x\omega_x^2 + \tfrac{1}{2}I_y\omega_y^2 + \tfrac{1}{2}I_z\omega_z^2$$

For each term $\bar{\varepsilon}$ gets $\frac{1}{2}kT$ so that $E = (3 + \frac{3}{2})RT$ and $C_V = \frac{9}{2}R$.

(b) Each rigid molecule has rotational and vibrational kinetic energy. The periodic rotation is slight and may be assumed to be harmonic (Hooke's law) so that the average kinetic energy of rotation at a site is $\frac{3}{2}kT$ and the average potential energy of rotation at a site is $\frac{3}{2}kT$. Thus the energy of the crystal is $E = (\frac{6}{2} + \frac{6}{2})RT$ and $C_V = 6R$.

(c) Each molecule has the rotational energy $3kT$ as in (b) plus internal vibrational energy $(3a - 6)kT$, half of which is kinetic and half of which is potential. Hence, $E = (\frac{6}{2} + 3 + (3a - 6))N_0kT = 3aRT$ and $C_V = 3aR$. Since all atoms are vibrating harmonically either against intramolecular forces or crystalline forces, it is clear that each atom might have been treated individually, as for a monatomic solid for which $C_V = 3R$ by (4.92). (This result, an extension of the Dulong-Petit rule that $C = 3R$ for monatomic solids, is *Kopp's law*, which assigns additive values to C_V for each atom or ion in a formula.)

4.14 REAL HEAT CAPACITIES

There are several unsatisfactory features of the principle of equipartition of energy despite its obvious simplicity and generality. Heat capacities of solids and gases are not really independent of T; they are observed to increase with T in general. No molecule should be deemed rigid if the principle obtains, for any bond, regardless of its kind or strength, must vibrate at sufficiently high T. But if it vibrates at high T, then it must vibrate classically at any T. However small the amplitude may be at low T, the contribution to $\bar{\varepsilon}$ of each squared coordinate in ε(and ε can always be so expressed for small amplitudes) is a full $\frac{1}{2}kT$. The only other alternative is absolutely no vibration with no contribution whatsoever to E and no gradual variation from seemingly rigid to seemingly nonrigid. Thus C_V for a real diatom should be $\frac{7}{2}R$ because for it there is average translational energy of $\frac{3}{2}kT$, average rotational energy of $\frac{2}{2}kT$, and average internal energy of kT due to the kinetic and potential energy of the vibrating bond. However, C_V, for N_2, O_2, NO, and other diatoms is observed to be $\frac{5}{2}R$ at low T and up to about $\frac{7}{2}R$ at high T.

Heat capacities of solids are even more puzzling at very low T, for as $T \longrightarrow 0$ many C's obviously decrease toward zero! Figure 4.5 shows a typical

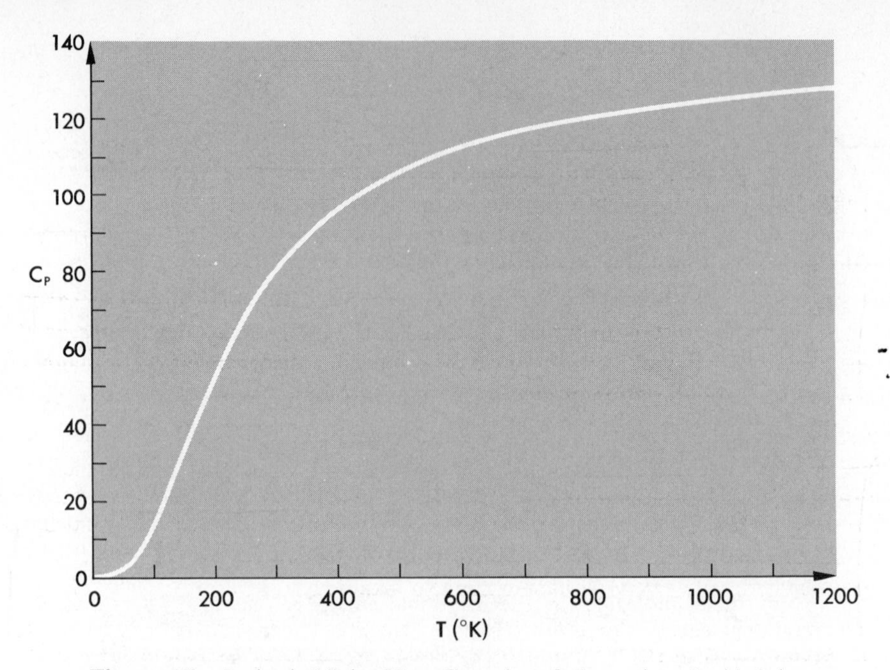

Figure 4.5. Isobaric Molar Heat Capacity of Corundum (α-Al_2O_3) as a Function of Temperature (joules mole^{-1} deg^{-1})†

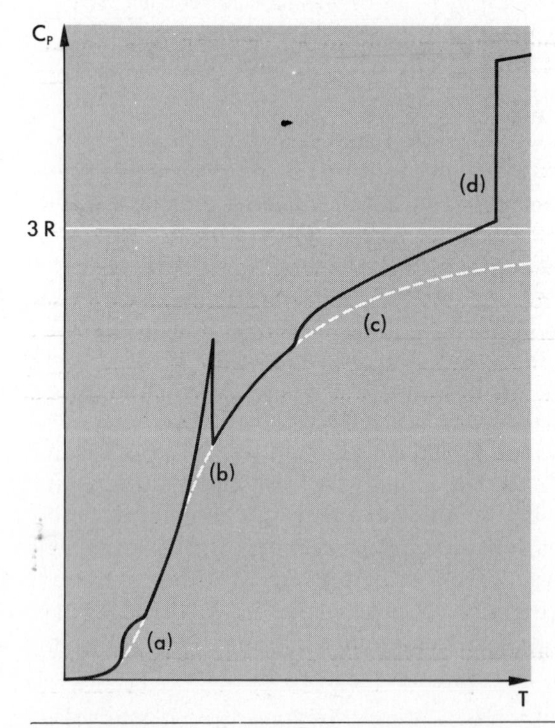

Figure 4.6. Three Common Types of Anomaly in Isobaric Heat Capacity of a Solid. (a) Excitation of Electrons; (b) Disordering of Dipoles; (c) Rotation of Part or All of Molecule; (d) Change of Phase.

†G. T. Furukawa, T. B. Douglas, R. E. McCoskey, and D. C. Ginnings, *J. Res. Nat. Bur. Stds.* **57**, 67 (1956).

case. At high T, the limit is about $15R$, which corresponds to five simple ions in the formula Al_2O_3, each with kinetic and potential energy at its site. However, C_P and C_V fall continuously toward zero as T decreases.

In addition to these discrepancies, the utter simplicity of C_V's calculated by the principle is unrealistic. Figure 4.6 illustrates three kinds of deviation from the simple C_P of ideal crystals that merely vibrate. The small hump at (a) is typical of many crystals in which electrons can be excited to new states as T rises. The so-called lambda point at (b) originates in a disorganization of magnetic or electric dipoles that may exist on ions, atoms, or whole molecules. A lambda point very close to $T = 0$ would perhaps be due to reorganization of nuclear magnetic dipoles. The anomaly at (c) is due to some motion besides a lattice vibration; often it is a rotation of a whole molecule at its site or even of a part of a molecule. Each anomaly of Figure 4.6 represents an increase in disorder as T rises; each contributes an extraordinary bit of entropy to the process of warming the crystal. With sufficient time to attain equilibrium at low T, where many processes are quite slow, these changes can be reversed during cooling. The discontinuity at (d) is caused by a change of phase or by fusion; of all the anomalies, only that at (d) has a non-zero ΔH at constant T.

With or without the peculiarities of Figure 4.6, the inexorable decline in C_P as T decreases contradicts the tenet of classical mechanics that any amplitude of vibration, large or small, contributes equally to E. This contradiction and several others of a different nature (e.g., the frequency distribution and intensities of thermal radiation) are very easily resolved by assuming, as Planck did in 1900, that a system and its parts change energy in steps or bits. That is, a change in energy is of definite size for a given system; it occurs if enough energy is supplied, but it does not occur at all if insufficient energy is made available. In other words, the development of the Boltzmann distribution (4.73) in terms of discrete energy states is, after all, correct if the energies ε_i are reinterpreted as states that may or may not be realized. As T tends toward zero and as β rises, the most stable states of low energy are realized by the system. Finally, at $T = 0$ all N particles would be in the most stable state $\varepsilon_1 = 0$; with $N_1 = N$, (4.75) gives $\bar{\varepsilon} = \varepsilon_1 = 0$. As $E = N_0\bar{\varepsilon}$ tends to zero at low T, C_V and C_P also decrease to zero in accord with experience. In this remarkable way, a *discrete* spectrum of energy states leads to a *continuous* variation in heat capacity and energy!

4.15 THE THIRD LAW OF THERMODYNAMICS

It is easy to look back historically and explain the preceding facts about heat capacities. Without low-temperature observations of C_P, it was not easy for Richards in 1902 and Nernst in 1906 to realize the great significance of their discovery that, as $T \rightarrow 0$, ΔS for certain reversible isothermal chemical reactions also approaches zero. They had discovered the *third law of thermodynamics*.

In 1912, Planck stated it thus: At any pressure, the entropy of every crystalline solid in thermodynamic equilibrium at absolute zero is zero. Since substances other than perfect crystals (whatever perfect may mean in this regard) also behave as though they have no entropy at $T = 0$, a still more general statement of the third law is now appropriate. Moreover, just as there are several ways of stating the second law, so are there also several ways of stating the third. For the sake of directness, the mathematically most tractable way is presented first. For the sake of clarity, the physical meaning of this law is then discussed and, from the mathematical statement, a verbal statement of an impossibility will be derived in the next section.

The third law of thermodynamics says: At any pressure, every substance that approaches a unique stable or metastable state reversibly as T decreases toward absolute zero has an entropy that is zero at absolute zero. The state that would then be reached at $T = 0$ is clearly the one of least disorder consistent with the chemical nature of the substance. The third law thus establishes a common reference value of S for many substances. (There is no one reference value for E or H.) The value zero is chosen for the reference value of S because of its mathematical simplicity and because it makes good sense when thermodynamic properties are calculated from the mechanical properties of atoms and molecules by the methods of statistical mechanics (Chapter 17).

Some of the susbtances that have zero entropy at equilibrium at $T = 0$ are:

1. crystalline elements
2. crystalline compounds, including alloys with organized positions (superlattice) for differing atoms
3. liquid helium, and perhaps all pure liquids
4. perfect gases
5. electrons in a metal or non-metal.

The temperatures at which it is obvious that C_P and S are on the way to zero differ for these categories; for solids it may vary from of the order of one to several hundred degrees Kelvin, while for perfect gases it is less than 10^{-6} degrees Kelvin, the present limit of observation. The energy of the substance at $T = 0$ is not important in this classification, for stable and metastable states may both have $S = 0$ at $T = 0$. For example, both crystalline modifications of S (monoclinic and orthorhombic) and ZnS (cubic and hexagonal) have zero entropy at $T = 0$, and solid C_2H_2—as well as solid C and solid H_2 to which C_2H_2 might decompose with a great decrease in chemical energy—also has zero entropy at $T = 0$.

As soon as the element of disorder enters the description of a state of a substance, its S increases. The tiniest bit of impurity, if not somehow formally acknowledged in a stoichiometric formula, renders the substance a solution. For this reason, alloys that are solid solutions have positive entropy at $T = 0$. Similarly, a substance like solid S or ZnS, if made of sulfur containing the usual mixture of isotopes, is a solid solution having nonzero entropy at $T = 0$. Only if the isotopes were somehow organized upon a grand scale (like atoms in a superlattice) so that the position of each distinguishable isotope could be predicted from observable regularity elsewhere in the crystal would it be justifiable to assign zero entropy to S and ZnS at $T = 0$. The disorder that invalidates the third law for a substance may be only geometrical, as in finely divided substances with high surface area or as in glasses, even when the composition is described exactly by a simple formula like SiO_2. In a glass, for example, there is no long-range order of the kind that could be found in ordinary crystals of the substance.

Another kind of disorder may be caused by the way a crystal is grown. For example, the ends of molecules of NO and CO are so similar and the rate and tendency for their ends to be distinguished at low T is so small that, at the temperatures at which such molecules are organized into a crystalline lattice, pure solid CO or NO may have a solution-like disorder in which half of the molecules point north while half point south, with no organization of either set into a superlattice. Similar disorder occurs in ice, where whole molecules of H_2O are fixed in any one of six possible orientations; the only order of the H's, which lie along straight lines between two O's, is that only one exists between any two O's and it is nearer one O than the other so as to preserve whole molecules of H_2O. With such disorder locked in by the slow rate of change at low T, solid H_2O, NO, CO, and similar substances have nonzero entropy at $T = 0$.

Still another kind of disorder may be based on the magnetic moments of unpaired electrons or of nuclei. If the spins of electrons or nuclei are not regularly organized so that a prediction of the spin state cannot be made upon further progression through the lattice, then a superlattice is lacking and $S > 0$ at $T = 0$.

From this recital of awkward possibilities, it would appear that the third law has no ordinary use. Fortunately, this is not true. The reason is that the residual or *zero-point entropy* that remains at $T = 0$ can often be ignored. If isotopes are not separated by the processes for which a thermodynamic calculation is made (e.g., chemical reactions of S or ZnS), then the existing mixture of isotopes is for practical purposes pure and composed of just one species. Thus, the entropy associated with the mixing of the isotopes can be ignored because it is the same for all states considered (e.g., SO_2 or $ZnSO_4$). Similarly, if any impurity always goes along for the ride, it too can be ignored. If the substance of a glass could not be crystallized, the glass at $T = 0$ could have or be assigned zero entropy without affecting any value of ΔS in which the glass was involved. If no test of electronic or nuclear spin states is made, the property might as well not exist and the entropy of disorganization of the spins can be ignored. The real culprit, in all of these cases, is the well-informed scientist who insists on calculating the entropy of a system from the correct formula

$$S = k \ln \Omega \tag{4.93}$$

where Ω is the number of states in which the system might exist and still be in accord with what is known of it. He may know about things that an experimenter can easily ignore. What may seem to one to be single state with $\Omega = 1$ at $T = 0$ may to the other (generally the more theoretical one) to be a state with $\Omega > 1$ and $S > 0$ at $T = 0$.

Suppressing certain entropies of disorder is equivalent to ignoring a hump in the C_P curve of Figure 4.6. If, for example, the electrons are excited in the same way throughout an experiment, the contribution of hump (*a*) to the entropy is ignorable. In the same way, if a lambda point for nuclear spin exists well below 1°K, and if nuclear spins are random throughout a chemical transformation, it is of little use to attempt to measure C_P so exactly below 1°K that the lump in C_P can be found. It might as well be ignored, and the curve relating C_P to T might as well be extrapolated in ignorance smoothly to $T = 0$. Indeed, faced with the possibility of innumerable lumps in C_P at still lower T, one must in practice ignore the unknown but be ready for it should a calculated and experimental ΔS disagree.

It is generally believed that there is only one most stable equilibrium state for crystals, liquids, and gases at $T = 0$. The many energy states that differ by the very weak interaction of randomly oriented H_2O's or nuclear spin moments would in time probably interact among themselves and with their lattice to form one most stable state for which $\Omega = 1$. How this could be true for fluids in a finite volume, especially for a pure perfect gas, is best left to a discussion of the particle in a box and the quantum conditions involved (Section 13.9). Even if just one most stable state does not occur, however, the entropy at $T = 0$ may be effectively zero for thermodynamic calculations if the number of such states in a mole is much less than Avogadro's number (Section 17.11). It is probably fortunate that ordinarily S is effectively zero near $T = 0$, for in his 1906 statement of the third law Nernst said: As the absolute temperature approaches zero, the increment in entropy for reversible isothermal processes in crystalline solids approaches zero as a limit.

As a system goes from a thermodynamic state with Ω_1 microscopic states to one with Ω_2 microscopic states that are consistent with its macroscopic state, (4.93) gives

$$\Delta S = S_2 - S_1 = k \ln \Omega_2 - k \ln \Omega_1 = k \ln\left(\frac{\Omega_2}{\Omega_1}\right) \tag{4.94}$$

If this change of state can be effected adiabatically and irreversibly, then $\Delta S > 0$ and $\Omega_2 > \Omega_1$. Thus, irreversible adiabatic changes like the isothermal mixing of perfect gases or adiabatic expansion of a gas into a vacuum proceed to states of greater disorder. The result in (4.94) is also reminiscent of (4.58), for if ΔS is the same positive value in both, then $T_2 > T_1$ and $\Omega_2 > \Omega_1$, which is true if a higher T implies less certainty about the order of a system.

There is a direct connection between (4.93) and the Boltzmann distribution (4.73).[1] The entropy of N distinguishable particles of which N_i have energy

ε_i is, by (4.62),

$$S_1 = k \ln \frac{CN!}{N_1!\,N_2!\cdots}$$

As one particle of energy ε_1 absorbs thermal energy from isothermal surroundings at T and achieves a state of higher energy ε_2, the entropy of the particles changes to

$$S_2 = k \ln \frac{CN!}{(N_1 - 1)!\,(N_2 + 1)!\cdots} = k \ln \frac{CN!\,N_1}{N_1!\,(N_2 + 1)\,N_2!\cdots}$$

The entropy change of the particles is therefore

$$\Delta S_p = S_2 - S_1 = k \ln \frac{N_1}{N_2 + 1} \approx k \ln \frac{N_1}{N_2}$$

where the approximation holds because $N_2 \gg 1$. During the same process, the entropy change of the isothermal reservoir, which does no work as it suffers an energy change $\Delta\varepsilon = q = \varepsilon_1 - \varepsilon_2 < 0$, is

$$\Delta S_r = \frac{q}{T} = \frac{\Delta\varepsilon}{T} = -\frac{\varepsilon_2 - \varepsilon_1}{T} < 0$$

But for the particles and reservoir, because they constitute an isolated system, (4.6) and (4.8) require

$$\Delta S_p + \Delta S_r = k \ln \frac{N_1}{N_2} - \frac{\varepsilon_2 - \varepsilon_1}{T} \geqslant 0$$

That is,

$$-\frac{\varepsilon_2 - \varepsilon_1}{kT} \geqslant \ln \frac{N_2}{N_1}$$

$$N_2 \leqslant N_1 \exp\left(-\frac{\varepsilon_2 - \varepsilon_1}{kT}\right) \qquad (4.95)$$

If the change is reversible, the equality of (4.95) is the same as (4.73), the Boltzmann distribution. If the inequality of (4.95) describes the actual change, it says that the number N_2 of particles of higher energy must be less than the number expected by (4.73) if their number is to be increased by spontaneous absorption of energy $\varepsilon_2 - \varepsilon_1$ from the reservoir at T.

4.16 THE APPROACH TO ABSOLUTE ZERO

A verbal statement of the third law in terms of an impossibility is this: It is impossible to reduce the temperature of any system to absolute zero by any finite process. Although it is possible to derive from this statement the fact that the entropies of any two substances at equilibrium at absolute zero are equal,

(1) Gurney, R. W., *Introduction to Statistical Mechanics*, New York: McGraw-Hill Book Co., Inc. 1949, Chapter I.

it is sufficient for this treatment to follow the style of treatment of the second law and prove this verbal statement of an impossibility from the mathematical statement.[2]

Suppose that a reversible process by which state (1) becomes state (2) is to be used to achieve absolute zero. Such a process might be adiabatic demagnetization, in which state (1) is a paramagnetic salt like gadolinium sulfate that is cooled in liquid helium in a strong magnetic field and state (2) is achieved by removing the magnetic field slowly when the salt is isolated from its surroundings. Since the atomic spins become disordered as the field is removed, the energy required for the disordering process comes from the crystal lattice and the salt is cooled. Whether this or some other process is used, the entropies of the initial and final states are given, as in (4.54), by

$$S_1(T_1) - S_1(0) = \int_0^{T_1} \frac{C_P^{(1)}}{T} dT \tag{4.96}$$

$$S_2(T_2) - S_2(0) = \int_0^{T_2} \frac{C_P^{(2)}}{T} dT \tag{4.97}$$

And by the third law, as stated mathematically,

$$S_2(0) = S_1(0) \tag{4.98}$$

Since there is no heat reservoir at a lower T to accept heat from the system ($q < 0$) if it is the best attempt to reach absolute zero, the system must absorb heat ($q > 0$) or any change must be adiabatic ($q = 0$). It would be folly to allow $q > 0$, for this would increase T. Hence, the only acceptable process is

$$\boxed{T_1} \xrightarrow{\text{reversible adiabatic}} \boxed{T_2}$$

Pressure is unimportant since the third law holds at any pressure. But for any adiabatic reversible process, by (4.7),

$$\Delta S = S_2(T_2) - S_1(T_1) = 0 \tag{4.99}$$

Substitution of (4.96), (4.97), and (4.98) into (4.99) yields

$$\int_0^{T_1} \frac{C_P^{(1)}}{T} dT = \int_0^{T_2} \frac{C_P^{(2)}}{T} dT \tag{4.100}$$

If T_2 is to be zero, then the right side of (4.100) is zero because the limits of the definite integral are equal, and

$$\int_0^{T_1} \frac{C_P^{(1)}}{T} dT = 0 \tag{4.101}$$

But if the process starts at a real positive temperature T_1, it is impossible to satisfy (4.101) because $C_P^{(1)}$ is greater than zero at all temperatures. Since a simi-

[2] Guggenheim, E. A., *Thermodynamics*, Amsterdam: North-Holland Publishing Co. 1957, pp. 192–4.

lar argument holds when T_1 is to be forced to zero, even the reverse process is of no use. In other words, it is impossible to achieve absolute zero by a reversible process performed a finite number of times.

An appealing alternative to a reversible process is an irreversible one, for its spontaneity may perhaps succeed like a downhill tumble. As before, only an adiabatic process is reasonable. Thus, the process that might succeed in changing a positive T_1 to $T_2 = 0$ is to be

$$\boxed{T_1} \xrightarrow{\text{irreversible adiabatic}} \boxed{T_2}$$

According to (4.9), for any irreversible adiabatic process

$$\Delta S = S_2(T_2) - S_1(T_1) > 0 \tag{4.102}$$

In a similar way it is found as for (4.100) that

$$\int_0^{T_2} \frac{C_P^{(2)}}{T}\, dT > \int_0^{T_1} \frac{C_P^{(1)}}{T}\, dT \tag{4.103}$$

If $T_2 = 0$, the left side of (4.103) is zero, while the right side exceeds zero because T_1 and $C_P^{(1)}$ both are positive. Since (4.103) cannot then be satisfied, an irreversible adiabatic process will not succeed in reaching absolute zero.

A third possibility is to start toward absolute zero from the possible vantage of a metastable state. However, if $S_1(0) = 0$ for this state, then (4.101) or (4.103) again obtain, with no success.

It is therefore impossible to reach $T_2 = 0$ by a process that is reversible or irreversible, whether it begins with a stable or metastable state that has zero entropy at absolute zero, in accord with the third law. Even if these attempts are repeated again and again, each repetition suffers from the same limitation. Pumping off vapor from liquid helium produces temperatures down to about 0.3°K. With a reservoir at such a temperature, adiabatic demagnetization of electron spins can reduce the temperature of a system to about 0.001°K. With such a reservoir at 0.001°K, used for cooling a system containing nuclear spins aligned by a strong magnetic field, another adiabatic demagnetization of nuclear spins can yield a temperature of the order of 0.000001°K, still above the unattainable absolute zero.

There remain two more possibilities outside the domain of the third law because they deal with substances with such disorder at absolute zero that for them $S(0) > 0$. If only the initial state would violate the third law, then

$$S_1(0) > S_2(0) \tag{4.104}$$

Since (4.7) and (4.9) require of an adiabatic process that

$$S_2(T_2) \geqslant S_1(T_1) \tag{4.105}$$

then addition of (4.104) and (4.105) leads to

$$S_2(T_2) + S_1(0) > S_1(T_1) + S_2(0)$$

$$S_2(T_2) - S_2(0) > S_1(T_1) - S_1(0) \tag{4.106}$$

which as before yields the impasse at (4.103). However, the final state may be generated in so disordered a state that (4.104) is reversed and

$$S_1(0) < S_2(0) \tag{4.107}$$

Then, if (4.107) dominates (4.105) upon addition to give

$$S_2(T_2) - S_2(0) < S_1(T_1) - S_1(0) \tag{4.108}$$

there results, by (4.96) and (4.97),

$$\int_0^{T_2} \frac{C_P^{(2)}}{T}\, dT < \int_0^{T_1} \frac{C_P^{(1)}}{T}\, dT$$

which is the reverse of (4.103) and allows T_2 to be zero without contradiction. The vexing problem, however, is by an adiabatic process to achieve a final state that really has residual entropy at $T_2 = 0$. Adiabatic demagnetization is an attempt to do this by going from a state with ordered spins to one of disordered spins, but the final state obeys the third law.

4.17 STANDARD ENTROPIES

In fixing a common reference point for entropies of all cystalline solids at equilibrium, the third law permits the calculation of absolute values of entropy. In brief, it supplies a universal integration constant for (4.53) and (4.56). With the use of the third law for an imagined reversible process in which a crystalline solid with molar heat capacity C_P at the pressure P is warmed from absolute zero to temperature T, (4.53) yields (4.109) on integration.

$$\Delta S = S(T, P) - S(0, P) = \int_0^T \left(\frac{\partial S}{\partial T'}\right)_P dT' = \int_0^T \frac{C_P}{T'}\, dT'$$

Or, since $S(0, P) = 0$ by the third law,

$$S(T, P) = \int_0^T \frac{C_P}{T'}\, dT' \tag{4.109}$$

For a similar reversible process at constant volume, (4.56) yields

$$S(T, V) = \int_0^T \frac{C_V}{T'}\, dT' \tag{4.110}$$

The values of C_P for many solids have been measured at low temperatures and have been calculated theoretically by the methods of statistical mechanics. Near absolute zero, where measurements are difficult or impossible, it is common practice to extrapolate observed values to zero with theoretical expressions as guides. For many crystals, lattice vibrations are dominant in determining the heat capacity; for these, C_P is proportional to the cube of the absolute temperature. Theoretically, near $T = 0$, a crystal that contains sturdy two-dimensional layers, like graphite, is expected to have C_P vary as T^2, while crystals containing long chains of atoms, as in polymers, are expected to have C_P vary as T; experimentally, the T^3 law seems to hold for all. In addition to a term proportional to T^3, metals exhibit a term proportional to the temperature itself and due to the conduction electrons. Solids that exhibit quantum effects may have additive contributions to their heat capacities that vary as another power of T, like $T^{3/2}$ for spin waves. The heat capacity at low temperatures may depend measurably upon the state of division or the surface area. The most common dependence, however, is that of (4.111), where $\gamma = 0$ for nonconductors.

$$C_P \approx C_V = \gamma T + BT^3 \tag{4.111}$$

The value of γ ranges from about 1 to 40×10^{-4} cal mole^{-1} deg^{-2} and B is given by

$$B = \frac{12\pi^4 R}{5\Theta^3} \tag{4.112}$$

In (4.72), Θ is the Debye characteristic temperature, which generally varies from 50 to 500°K. Figure 4.7 illustrates the behavior of heat capacities of conductors and nonconductors near absolute zero.

The absolute entropy of a substance at any temperature can be calculated if its heat capacity and its various heats of transition are known. Suppose that the absolute entropy of a gas at the temperature T is to be calculated. Below the temperature T_{tr}, the solid exists at equilibrium as the α modification with the heat capacity $C_P^{(\alpha)}$. At T_{tr}, the α form is transformed reversibly at the pressure P into the β form, the heat of transition being $\Delta H_{\alpha,\beta}$. Between T_{tr} and T_f, the heat capacity of the stable β form is $C_P^{(\beta)}$. At T_f, the β form melts reversibly with a heat of fusion ΔH_f. The liquid has the heat capacity $C_P^{(l)}$ and the heat of vaporization is ΔH_v at the pressure P at the boiling point T_b, and the heat ca-

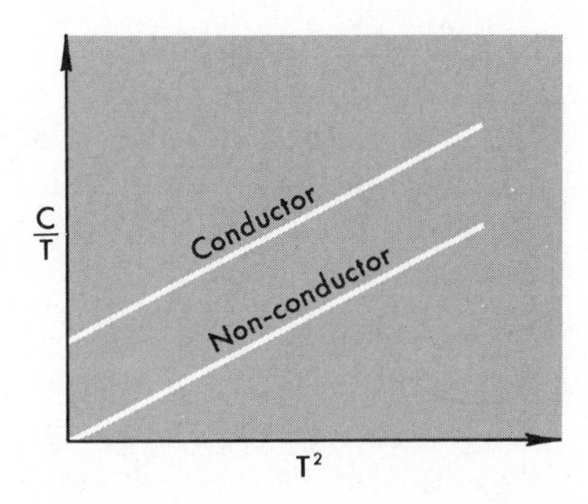

Figure 4.7. Typical Behavior of Heat Capacity C Below About 10°K

pacity of the gas is $C_P^{(g)}$. The reversible isobaric process by which the absolute entropy is evaluated is diagrammed:

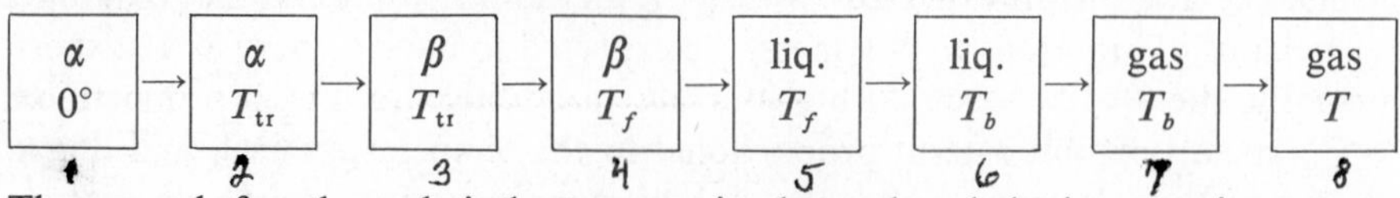

The second, fourth, and sixth steps are isothermal and the increase in entropy for each can be found by (4.52). The odd-numbered processes are not isothermal and the increase in entropy for each can be found by (4.54). For the diagrammed changes, then, since S is a function of state,

$$\Delta S = S(T, P) - S(0, P) \tag{4.113}$$

where $S(T, P)$ is the absolute entropy of the gas at the temperature T and pressure P and where $S(0, P)$, the absolute entropy of the stable crystalline solid at equilibrium at 0°K, is zero by the third law. Thus,

$$S(T, P) = \int_0^{T_{tr}} \frac{C_P^{(\alpha)}}{T}\, dT + \frac{\Delta H_{\alpha,\beta}}{T_{tr}} + \int_{T_{tr}}^{T_f} \frac{C_P^{(\beta)}}{T}\, dT + \frac{\Delta H_f}{T_f} + \int_{T_f}^{T_b} \frac{C_P^{(l)}}{T}\, dT + \frac{\Delta H_v}{T_b} + \int_{T_b}^{T} \frac{C_P^{(g)}}{T'}\, dT' \tag{4.114}$$

If the substance exists as a condensed phase at T, some of the last terms of (4.114) are to be omitted.

The integrals of (4.114) are ordinarily performed graphically because of the difficulty of expressing the heat capacities by an explicit function of T that fully reflects the experimental accuracy. For example, the first integral can be expressed in two convenient ways, namely,

$$S(T, P) = \int_0^T \left(\frac{C_P}{T'}\right) dT' \tag{4.115}$$

$$S(T, P) = \int_{T'=0}^{T'=T} C_P\, d(\ln T') \tag{4.116}$$

If the former method were used, (C_P/T') would be plotted as a function of T'; and the area bounded by the curve, the T' axis, and the line $T' = T$ would be $S(T)$. If the latter method were used, C_P would be plotted as a function of $\ln T'$ and the area bounded by $\ln T' = \ln T$, the curve, the abscissa axis, and $\ln T'$ for some small value of T' would be calculated. The value of this integral in the immediate neighborhood of absolute zero is readily found through (4.117) or a similar equation. For a nonconductor, at these lowest temperatures where experimental values of C_P are lacking,

$$S(T, P) = \int_0^T \frac{B(T')^3}{T'}\, dT' = B\int_0^T (T')^2\, dT' = \frac{B}{3}T^3 = \frac{C_P}{3} \tag{4.117}$$

where C_P is the value at the lowest observed temperature T.

Table 4.3 lists the absolute entropies of various substances at the standard temperature of 298.16°K. The standard entropy of $H^+_{(aq)}$ is sometimes taken to be zero, but for reasons that are thoroughly explained elsewhere,[3] the conven-

Table 4.3 Standard Entropies of Elements, Compounds, and Ions at 25°C. [cal deg^{-1} (gram-formula-weight)$^{-1}$] (F. D. Rossini *et al.*, *Selected Values of Chemical Thermodynamic Properties*, NBS Circular 500, Washington, D. C., 1952, and *Selected Values of Properties of Hydrocarbons*, NBS Circular C461, Washington, D. C., 1947.)

		(cal per degree per gram-formula-weight)			
Substance	$S^\ominus$	Substance	$S^\ominus$	Substance	$S^\ominus$
$O_{2(g)}$	49.003	$NH_{3(g)}$	46.01	$Ag_2CO_{3(s)}$	40.0
$O_{3(g)}$	56.8	$NH_{3(aq)}$	26.3	$Fe_{(s)}$	6.49
$H^+_{(g)}$	†	$NH^+_{4(aq)}$	42.58	$Fe_2O_{3(s)}$	21.5
$H^+_{(aq)}$	15.606	$C_{(s)}$(graphite)	1.3609	$Fe_3O_{4(s)}$	35.0
$H_{2(g)}$	31.211	$C_{(s)}$(diamond)	0.5829	$Cr_{(s)}$	5.68
$OH^-_{(aq)}$	−18.125	$CO_{(g)}$	47.301	$CrO^{2-}_{4(aq)}$	−22.0
$H_2O_{(g)}$	45.106	$CO_{2(g)}$	51.061	$Cr_2O^{2-}_{7(aq)}$	19.9
$H_2O_{(l)}$	16.716	$CO^{2-}_{3(aq)}$	−43.9	$HCrO^-_{4(aq)}$	0.9
$F^-_{(g)}$	†	$CH_{4(g)}$	44.50	$H_2CrO_{4(aq)}$	17.5
$F^-_{(aq)}$	−17.9	$HCO^-_{3(aq)}$	7.1	$Ag_2CrO_{4(s)}$	51.8
$F_{2(g)}$	48.6	$CH_3OH_{(g)}$	56.8	$Ti_{(s)}$	7.24
$HF_{(g)}$	41.47	$CH_3NO_{2(l)}$	41.1	$TiO_{2(s)}$(rutile)	12.01
$Cl^-_{(g)}$	†	$C_2H_{2(g)}$	47.997	$TiCl_{4(g)}$	84.4
$Cl^-_{(aq)}$	−2.44	$C_2H_{4(g)}$	52.45	$TiCl_{4(l)}$	60.4
$Cl_{2(g)}$	53.286	$C_2H_{6(g)}$	54.85	$Al_{(s)}$	6.769
$HCl_{(g)}$	44.617	$C_3H_{8(g)}$	64.51	$Al_2O_{3(s)}$(alpha)	12.186
$Br^-_{(g)}$	†	n-$C_6H_{14(g)}$	92.45	$Mg_{(s)}$	7.77
$Br^-_{(aq)}$	3.68	$C_6H_{6(g)}$	64.34	$MgCl_{2(s)}$	21.4
$Br_{2(g)}$	58.639	cyclo-$C_6H_{12(g)}$	71.28	$Ca_{(s)}$	9.95
$Br_{2(l)}$	36.4	$Pb_{(s)}$	15.51	$Ca^{2+}_{(aq)}$	18.0
$HBr_{(g)}$	47.437	$Pb^{2+}_{(aq)}$	36.3	$CaF_{2(s)}$	16.46
$I_{2(g)}$	62.280	$PbS_{(s)}$	21.8	$Ba_{(s)}$	16.
$I_{2(s)}$	27.9	$PbSO_{4(s)}$	35.2	$Ba^{2+}_{(aq)}$	34.
$HI_{(g)}$	49.314	$Zn_{(s)}$	9.95	$BaCl_{2(s)}$	30.
$S_{(g)}$	40.085	$Zn^{2+}_{(g)}$	†	$BaCl_2 \cdot H_2O_{(s)}$	40.
$S_{(s)}$(rhombic)	7.62	$Zn^{2+}_{(aq)}$	5.76	$BaCl_2 \cdot 2H_2O_{(s)}$	48.5
$S_{(s)}$(monoclinic)	7.78	$ZnSO_{4(s)}$	29.8	$BaSO_{4(s)}$	31.6
$S^{2-}_{(g)}$	†	$ZnSO_4 \cdot H_2O_{(s)}$	34.9	$Na_{(s)}$	12.2
$SO_{2(g)}$	59.40	$ZnSO_4 \cdot 6H_2O_{(s)}$	86.8	$Na^+_{(g)}$	†
$SO_{3(g)}$	61.24	$ZnSO_4 \cdot 7H_2O_{(s)}$	92.4	$Na^+_{(aq)}$	30.0
$SO^{-2}_{4(aq)}$	−27.1	$Ag_{(s)}$	10.206	$NaCl_{(s)}$	17.30
$H_2S_{(g)}$	49.15	$Ag^+_{(g)}$	†	$Na_2SO_{4(s)}$	35.73
$N_{2(g)}$	45.767	$Ag^+_{(aq)}$	33.28	$Na_2SO_4 \cdot 10H_2O_{(s)}$	141.7
$NO_{(g)}$	50.339	$Ag_2O_{(s)}$	29.09	$Na_2CO_{3(s)}$	32.5
$NO_{2(g)}$	57.47	$AgCl_{(s)}$	22.97	$NaHCO_{3(s)}$	24.4
$NO^-_{3(aq)}$	19.4	$AgBr_{(s)}$	25.60	$He_{(g)}$	†

† At 25°C at one atm the translational entropy of a monatomic gas with no internal energy states is $1.5000R \ln M + 25.991$, where M is the gram-formula-weight. For example, for $He_{(g)}$, $S^\ominus = 1.500 R \ln 4.003 + 25.991 = 30.126$ cal deg^{-1} mole^{-1}.

[3] R. M. Noyes, *J. Chem. Ed.* **40,** 2 (1963); R. M. Noyes, *J. Am. Chem. Soc.* **86,** 971 (1964).

tion of the NBS Circular 500 has been changed to

$$S^{\ominus}(H^{+}_{(aq)}) = \tfrac{1}{2}S^{\ominus}(H_{2\,(g)}) = 15.606 \text{ cal mole}^{-1} \text{ deg}^{-1} \tag{4.118}$$

with appropriate changes of the standard entropies of other aqueous ions. Example 4.6 illustrates how $S^{\ominus}$ is calculated.

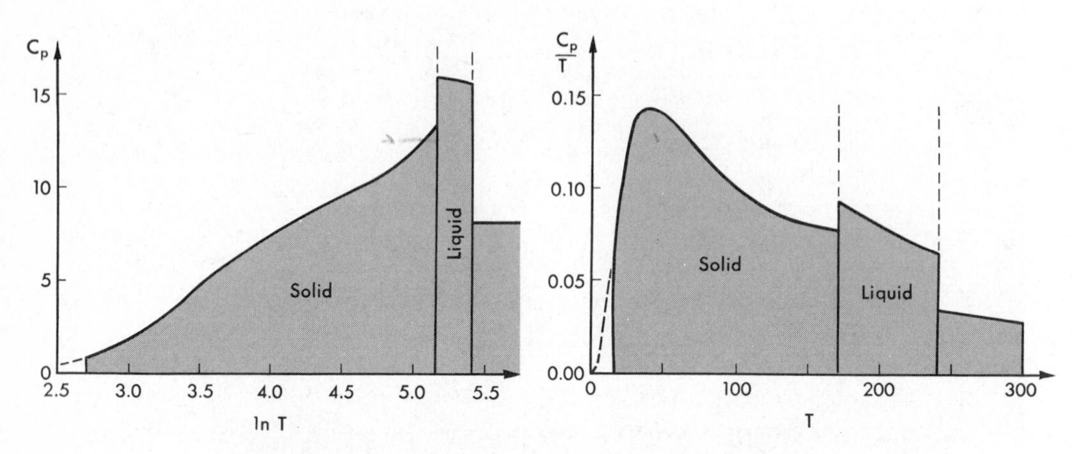

Figure 4.8. Alternate Graphical Integrations to Obtain Absolute Entropy of Chlorine

Example 4.6. From the data presented below, the third law and the assumption that $Cl_{2(g)}$ is a perfect gas with $C_P = 8.18$ cal mole^{-1} deg^{-1}, calculate the absolute standard entropy of $Cl_{2(g)}$ at 298.16°K at 1 atm. The data are taken from Giauque, W. F. and T. M. Powell, *J. Am. Chem. Soc.* **61**, 1970 (1939).
Fusion: $\Delta H_f = 1.531$ kcal mole^{-1} at $T = 172.12$°K.
Vaporization: $\Delta H_v = 4.878$ kcal mole^{-1} at $T = 239.05$°K.

T(°K)	C_P (cal mole^{-1} deg^{-1})	T(°K)	C_P (cal mole^{-1} deg^{-1})	T(°K)	C_P (cal mole^{-1} deg^{-1})
15	0.89	80	9.23	172.12	13.27
20	1.85	90	9.71	172.12	16.03
25	2.89	100	10.10	180	16.02
30	3.99	110	10.47	190	15.99
35	4.97	120	10.87	200	15.95
40	5.73	130	11.29	210	15.89
45	6.39	140	11.73	220	15.84
50	6.99	150	12.20	230	15.77
60	8.00	160	12.68	240	15.70
70	8.68	170	13.17		

With the aid of Figure 4.8 and equations from above, the absolute entropy of $Cl_{2(g)}$ is readily found by the steps indicated in the table.

Item	Value	Source
Entropy of $Cl_{2(s)}$ at 15°K	0.30	(4.117)
Increase in entropy of $Cl_{2(s)}$ (15° − 172.12°K)	16.77	Figure 4.8
Entropy of fusion	8.90	(4.52)
Increase in entropy of $Cl_{2(l)}$ (172.12° − 239.05°K)	5.32	Figure 4.8
Entropy of vaporization	20.40	(4.52)
Increase in entropy of $Cl_{2(g)}$ (239.05° − 298.16°K)	1.81	(4.58)
Total = standard entropy of $Cl_{2(g)}$ (298.16°K; 1 atm)	53.50	(4.114)

The difference between this value, 53.50 cal mole^{-1} deg^{-1}, and the value from Table 4.1, 53.286 cal mole^{-1} deg^{-1}, can be ascribed to the assumptions that the gas is perfect and has a constant heat capacity of 8.18 cal mole^{-1} deg^{-1}, and to the fact that the value of the table is based on different data.

Example 4.7. With Table 4.3, calculate the increase in entropy at standard conditions for the reactions

(a) $$2\,O_{3(g)} \longrightarrow 3\,O_{2(g)}$$

(b) $$N_{2(g)} + O_{2(g)} \longrightarrow 2\,NO_{(g)}$$

(c) $$BaSO_{4(s)} \longrightarrow Ba^{2+}_{(aq)} + SO^{2-}_{4(aq)}$$

Since entropy is an extensive property like enthalpy,

(a) $\Delta S^\ominus = 3\,S^\ominus(O_2) - 2\,S^\ominus(O_3) = 3(49.0) - 2(56.8) = 33.4$ cal deg^{-1}

(b) $\Delta S^\ominus = 2\,S^\ominus(NO) - S^\ominus(N_2) - S^\ominus(O_2) = 5.908$ cal deg^{-1}

(c) $\Delta S^\ominus = S^\ominus(Ba^{2+}) + S^\ominus(SO_4^{2-}) - S^\ominus(BaSO_4) = -25$ cal deg^{-1}

Example 4.8. What is the absolute entropy of a mole of solid silver at one atm at 500°K if $C_P = 3R$?

As one mole of $Ag_{(s)}$ is warmed reversibly at one atm from 298°K to 500°K, by (4.54)

$$\Delta S = \int_{298}^{500} \frac{C_P\,dT}{T} = 3R \ln\left(\frac{500}{298}\right) = 3.08 \text{ cal mole}^{-1}\text{ deg}^{-1}$$

Since Table 4.3 gives $S^\ominus_{298} = 10.206$ cal mole^{-1} deg^{-1}, it follows that

$$S^\ominus_{500} = S^\ominus_{298} + \Delta S = 10.21 + 3.08 = 13.29 \text{ cal mole}^{-1}\text{ deg}^{-1}$$

4.18 SUMMARY

This challenging and comprehensive chapter deals with the peculiar properties of heat and thermal disorder in macroscopic systems. Concern for the limitations of engines as converters of heat into work led naturally to the exact differential dS that comes from the inexact differential dq by use of a factor T^{-1}. The second law provides T as a universal property of matter containing many particles and as the intensive factor for S and q, just as pressure P is the intensive factor for volume in $dw = -P\,dV$.

As a function of state, S is useful for discussing physical changes and the performance of reversible heat engines that operate in cycles and do work, but it is even more important, at least for chemists, as a guide to what can be done in chemical changes. The criterion that S tends to a maximum value that remains constant at equilibrium in an isolated system is adequate but not the most elegant way to discuss chemical changes because it is difficult to realize isolated or even adiabatic conditions. For the time being, then, interest has centered on entropy changes in physical processes like changes in temperature or in state of aggregation. One of the results of a study of this chapter is a familiarity with entropy S as a mathematical quantity to be calculated along a nearly experienced or invented reversible path linking specific initial and final states.

An even more important result is an understanding of S as a meaningful physical quantity that measures the disorder of a system relative to the perfect order that all substances would exhibit at equilibrium at absolute zero. Even a crystalline alloy that is a solid solution at low T is expected at $T = 0$, if the third law holds and absolute zero is in fact unattainable, either to separate into pure phases or to become organized as a definite chemical with a stoichiometric formula and a structure based on the long-range order of a superlattice. The kinetic theory, in its insistence on arbitrarily small vibrations of classical mechanics, contradicts observations of heat capacities that indicate a universal trend toward perfect order at $T = 0$, where $S = 0$. Quite unexpectedly, then, one is face to face with quanta of energy that are as real as Dalton's atoms and the quanta of charge and mass of the fundamental particles whose statistical (i.e., partly unknown or unspecified) behavior is measured by S. The full meaning of all this does not come all at once or easily, but working problems helps. The following articles may also be helpful:

(a) R. H. Wright, *J. Chem. Ed.* **18**, 263 (1941)
(b) S. E. Wood, *J. Chem. Ed.* **20**, 80 (1943)
(c) W. F. Luder, *J. Chem. Ed.* **21**, 265, 600 (1944)
(d) A. E. Martell, *J. Chem. Ed.* **23**, 166 (1946)
(e) R. C. Tolman and P. C. Fine, *Revs. Modern Phys.* **20**, 51 (1948)
(f) E. M. Loebl, *J. Chem. Ed.* **37**, 361 (1960)
(g) G. E. MacWood and F. H. Verhoek, *J. Chem. Ed.* **38**, 334 (1961)
(h) G. J. Bockhoff, *J. Chem. Ed.* **39**, 340 (1962)
(i) E. F. Westrum, Jr., *J. Chem. Ed.* **39**, 443 (1962)
(j) H. A. Bent, *J. Chem. Ed.* **39**, 491 (1962)

PROBLEMS

1. A certain engine that operates in a Carnot cycle absorbs 800 cal at 400°C in one cycle. If it rejects heat at 100°C, how much work is done by the engine per cycle and how much heat is evolved at 100°C in each cycle?
Answer: 357 cal of work; 443 cal of heat.

2. Develop the Carnot cycle for a perfect gas.

3. What must be the upper temperature of a Carnot engine that evolves 700 cal heat per cycle at the lower temperature of 100°C if the engine does 400 cal work per cycle?
Answer: 314°C.

4. What happens to a household refrigerator on a very hot day?
Answer: Efficiency falls as T_2 rises; rate of heat transfer falls.

5. The heat of fusion of water is 80 cal g^{-1} at 0°C. For one gram-mole H_2O at constant temperature of 0°C, calculate ΔS when:
(a) The water freezes.
(b) The ice melts reversibly.
(c) The ice melts irreversibly because the temperature is not always 0°C during melting, but is 0°C at start and finish.
Answer: (a) $\Delta S = -5.28$ cal deg^{-1}; (b) and (c) $\Delta S = 5.28$ cal deg^{-1}.

6. Calculate the increase in entropy of one gram-mole of a monatomic crystalline solid like Cu or Mo as it changes from 300°K to 600°K at constant volume.
Answer: $\Delta S = 4.13$ cal deg^{-1}.

7. Calculate the increase in entropy of one kg steam as it changes isobarically from 100°C to 200°C.
Answer: 108.4 cal deg^{-1}.

8. Calculate the absolute entropy of one mole methane at 400°C at one atm.
Answer: 53.24 cal $mole^{-1}$ deg^{-1}.

9. According to NBS Circular 500, AgCl melts at 728°K with absorption of 3160 cal of heat per mole. If C_P of solid AgCl is 12.1 cal $mole^{-1}$ deg^{-1} while C_P of liquid AgCl is 18.5 cal $mole^{-1}$ deg^{-1}, what is the increase in entropy for the isobaric transformation of two moles of solid AgCl at 25°C at one atm into two moles of liquid AgCl at 500°C at one atm?
Answer: 33.70 cal deg^{-1}.

10. What is the ratio of the number of molecules in state A to the number in state B at equilibrium at 300°K if the energies of these states above the lowest state are 5.00×10^{-14} erg $molecule^{-1}$ for state A and 10.00×10^{-14} erg $molecule^{-1}$ for state B?
Answer: $N_A = 3.34\ N_B$.

11. According to Table 3.1, $C_P = 10.5$ cal $mole^{-1}$ deg^{-1} for gaseous acetylene at 25°C. If the molecules are linear, about how many internal vibrations are effectively rigid if the principle of equipartition of energy holds?
Answer: 5.

12. By the principle of equipartition of energy, estimate the heat capacity of a solid having rigid linear molecules that rotate freely at each lattice site to which they are bound by Hooke's law forces.
Answer: $C_V = 4R$.

13. What is the zero-point entropy of a mole of solid CO in which any molecule has an equal chance of being in one of two orientations?
Answer: $N_0\, k \ln 2$.

14. If the number of states of ice consistent with ordinary thermodynamic information is $(\frac{3}{2})^{N_0}$ per mole, what is the zero-point entropy of ice?
Answer: $N_0\, k \ln \frac{3}{2}$.

mt, wt xsp. ht = c. ht

15. What is the absolute entropy of one mole of gaseous O_2 at 100°C if its molar heat capacity is $C_P = 6.50 + 0.0010\ T$?
Answer: 50.535 cal mole^{-1} deg^{-1}.

16. What is $\Delta S^{\ominus}$ for the change $H_2S_{(g)} + Pb^{2+}_{(aq)} \longrightarrow PbS_{(s)} + 2\ H^{+}_{(aq)}$?
Answer: -32.4 cal deg^{-1}.

---

17. Can the pressure of gaseous argon be increased isothermally and adiabatically?
Answer: No, for the entropy of the argon decreases, contrary to the second law.

18. What is the greatest and least amount of heat that must be rejected per hour to the ocean at 4°C if a nuclear reactor provides 1000 kw (as heat) at 200°C for use in a Carnot-like cycle? Assume reactor is not shut down when ship stops.
Answer: 8.61 to 5.03×10^8 cal hr^{-1}.

19. An engine operates in a Carnot cycle between 300°K and 900°K and does 600 joules of work on the surroundings per cycle. For this engine in one cycle, calculate if possible
(a) the heat absorbed at $T_2 = 900°K$;
(b) the heat evolved at $T_1 = 300°K$;
(c) ΔE and ΔS for the isothermal expansion at T_2;
(d) ΔE and ΔS for the adiabatic compression from T_1 to T_2.
Answer: (a) 900 j; (b) 300 j; (c) $\Delta S_2 = 1.00$ j deg^{-1}, but $\Delta E_2 = ?$; (d) $\Delta S = 0$, but $\Delta E = ?$

20. How much work must be done to freeze one kg H_2O at 0°C if the refrigerator rejects its heat at 25°C?
Answer: 7.32 kcal.

21. A heat pump operating in a reversible Carnot cycle is to deliver thirty kilowatts at 20°C by transferring energy from a heat reservoir at 4°C. Find
(a) the net work per second that must be done on the working substance of the heat pump;
(b) the rate at which heat is to be absorbed from the cool reservoir.
Answer: (a) 1.640 kj sec^{-1}; (b) 28.36 kj sec^{-1}.

22. Explain graphically why the effciency or work of an engine that operates irreversibly in a Carnot-like cycle is less than that for an engine that operates reversibly under similar conditions.

23. Trouton's rule says that the molar entropy of vaporization of normal liquids at their boiling points are about 21 cal deg^{-1}. In terms of randomness and disorder, explain the following exceptions to this rule:
(a) Associated or hydrogen-bonded liquids generally have entropies of vaporization in excess of 25 cal mole^{-1}.
(b) Liquids like S, P, and HF, which vaporize to form associated or polymerized gases, have entropies of vaporization much less than 21 cal mole^{-1}.
Answer: (a) gas normal, but liquid ordered; (b) gas unusually ordered.

24. Calculate the increase in entropy of three moles of H_2 as they change from 300°K to 1000°K at one atm.
Answer: 25.328 cal deg^{-1}.

25. With the aid of Figure 4.5, calculate the increases in S and H for the change of state of a mole of Al_2O_3 at one atm at absolute zero to one atm at (a) 298.15°K and (b) 1200°K.
Answer: (a) 50.9 j mole^{-1} deg^{-1} and 10.0 kj mole^{-1}; (b) 203.2 j mole^{-1} deg^{-1} and 113.3 kj mole^{-1}.

26. Derive an approximate formula that makes it obvious that there is an increase in entropy when equal amounts of a pure liquid at slightly different temperatures are mixed adiabatically and isobarically.

27. In terms of the Boltzmann distribution and discrete energy states, discuss the meaning of a negative absolute temperature. Is this colder or hotter than ordinary temperatures, and why?
Answer: Hotter, with excited states overpopulated (e.g., $N_2 > N_1$).

28. Find the temperature at which C_P of methane is a maximum. Justify the possible existence of such a maximum in terms of equipartition of energy even though the equation for C_P is not expected to be valid in this range of T.
Answer: 2100°K; C_P of atoms is less than C_P of molecule because they have no potential energy of vibration.

29. At what temperature, as judged by the C_P's of Table 2.1 and the principle of equipartition, do half of the internal vibrations of NH_3 and n-C_4H_{10} become seemingly nonrigid?
Answer: 1093°K for NH_3; 684°K for butane.

30. For large values of N_i, show that $k \ln (N!/N_1!N_2! \ldots N_i! \ldots) = -Nk \sum_i (N_i/N) \cdot \ln (N_i/N)$.

31. With the result of the preceding problem, calculate the (usually suppressed) entropy of mixing of isotopes in a mole of diamond at $T = 0$ if the ratio of ^{12}C to ^{13}C is 989 to 11.
Answer: 0.0606 R.

32. Calculate the absolute standard molar entropy of gaseous SO_2 from these data [Giauque, W. F. and C. C. Stephenson, *J. Am. Chem. Soc.* **60,** 1389 (1938)]:

$T_f = 197.64°K \qquad 1.769 \text{ kcal mole}^{-1} = \Delta H_f$

$T_b = 263.08°K \qquad 5.960 \text{ kcal mole}^{-1} = \Delta H_v$

For gaseous SO_2 assume $C_P = 9.7$ cal mole^{-1} deg^{-1}.

T(°K)	C_P (cal mole^{-1} deg^{-1})	T(°K)	C_P (cal mole^{-1} deg^{-1})
15	0.83	130	12.83
20	1.66	140	13.31
25	2.74	150	13.82
30	3.79	160	14.33
35	4.85	170	14.85
40	5.78	180	15.42
45	6.61	190	16.02
50	7.36	197.64	M.P.
55	8.02	200	20.97
60	8.62	210	20.91
70	9.57	220	20.86
80	10.32	230	20.81
90	10.93	240	20.76
100	11.49	250	20.71
110	11.97	260	20.66
120	12.40	263.08	B.P.

Answer: 59.20 cal mole^{-1} deg^{-1}.

33. At 25°C find $\Delta S^\ominus$ at 1 atm for these changes:
(a) $3\ O_{2(g)} \longrightarrow 2\ O_{3(g)}$.
(b) $Ag_2O_{(s)} \longrightarrow 2\ Ag_{(s)} + \frac{1}{2}O_{2(g)}$.

(c) $C_{(s)} + 2\,H_{2(g)} \longrightarrow CH_{4(g)}$.
(d) $H_2O_{(l)} \longrightarrow H_2O_{(g)}$.

Justify the sign of ΔS for each reaction in terms of randomness and disorder.
Answer: (a) -33.4; (b) 15.82; (c) -19.28; (d) 28.390 cal deg^{-1}.

34. What is the entropy of a mole of monatomic Hg vapor at one atm at 1000°C? According to NBS Circular 500, the heat of vaporization at its boiling point at one atm of 356.57°C is 13.89 kcal mole^{-1}, and at 25°C the standard entropy of liquid Hg is 18.5 cal mole^{-1} deg^{-1}. Assume $C_P = 6.6$ cal mole^{-1} deg^{-1} for the liquid at all T.
Answer: 49.0 cal mole^{-1} deg^{-1}.

---

35. A certain chemical change has $\Delta S^{\ominus} = -10.0$ cal deg^{-1} at all T at one atm. What is the temperature range over which this change can occur spontaneously, isothermally, isobarically, and adiabatically if at all T its $\Delta H^{\ominus}$ is
(a) $+5000$ cal
(b) -5000 cal
Answer: (a) at no T; (b) below 500°K.

36. An engine that is to operate in a Carnot cycle is to do 1000 cal work per cycle. If the upper and lower temperatures are 100°C and 4°C, what must be the minimum difference in entropies of the working substance for these two temperatures? Could water be a suitable working substance? Explain.
Answer: $S_2 - S_1 = 10.42$ cal deg^{-1}; yes, if engine is big enough.

37. Calculate the amount of heat absorbed from the surroundings at 50°F by a heat pump in one cycle of operation if it must yield one BTU per cycle at 75°F. What is the work done on the pump per cycle? What is its greatest efficiency?
Answer: $q_1 = 0.9533$ BTU cycle^{-1}; $w = 0.0467$ BTU cycle^{-1}; 21.40.

38. Calculate the heat of vaporization of $TiCl_4$ at 25°C from the standard entropies of Table 4.3. Why might the observed value differ from this value?
Answer: 7.16 kcal mole^{-1}; standard states assume gas is perfect.

39. Calculate the increase in entropy of a system consisting of one mole water at 30°C and one mole water at 20°C when they are mixed and achieve equilibrium adiabatically and isobarically.
Answer: $\Delta S = 0.0051$ cal deg^{-1}.

40. Two bodies of equal heat capacity but different temperature are placed in thermal contact with each other but out of thermal contact with their surroundings. In terms of their initial temperatures, find the final common temperature of both at equilibrium when:
(a) No work is done by them.
(b) They produce work reversibly by means of a heat engine that operates cyclically.
Answer: (a) mean T; (b) $T_{\text{final}} = (T_1T_2)^{1/2}$.

41. With the aid of Table 2.1, calculate the increment in S for the warming of a mole of gaseous chlorine from 239.05°K at one atm to 298.15°K at one atm.
Answer: 1.800 cal mole^{-1} deg^{-1}.

42. If the energies of all states of a subsystem are given by $\varepsilon_i = (n_i + \frac{1}{2})\varepsilon$ where ε is constant and $n_i = 0, 1, 2, 3, \ldots \infty$, what is the average energy of a system of N_0 of these subsystems?
Answer: $E = N_0(\varepsilon/2)$ ctnh $(\beta\varepsilon/2)$.

43. By the principle of equipartition, estimate the heat capacity of gaseous dimethyl acetylene if there are four nonrigid vibrations (bendings) and if both methyl groups rotate freely about the axis of the molecule.
Answer: $C_V = 7.500$ R.

44. What is the (usually suppressed) entropy of mixing due to isotopes in a pure elemental solid in which diatomic molecules occupy equivalent lattice sites if there are two isotopes with relative abundances in the ratio 3 to 1?
Answer: 2.1179 R.

45. In 1904, van't Hoff showed that if a substance exists in two pure forms (e.g., two different crystalline modifications) the stable form at any low temperature is the one with the larger C_P. Prove this with the second and third laws.

46. Calculate the absolute molar entropy of gaseous chlorine at 300°C at three atm if it is a perfect gas.
Answer: 56.604 cal mole^{-1} deg^{-1}.

47. A certain miser had ten moles of hot gold at one atm; it had an absolute entropy of 200 cal deg^{-1}. Someone mentioned that his gold contained more than the standard amount of entropy, namely, 114 cal deg^{-1} at 25°C. At once, considering the possible value of entropy, the miser asked for advice about how to eke as much entropy as possible out of his fortunate circumstances by letting his hot gold interact isobarically with the surroundings until it returned to its standard state. Since he offered a "generous" commission based on the production of entropy, what advice is appropriate?
Answer: For the gold, upon cooling always $\Delta S = -86$ cal deg^{-1}; however, quenching it in cold surroundings (e.g., liquid He) greatly increases the total production of entropy, . . . and the commission.

5

FREE ENERGY

5.1 INTRODUCTION

Entropy is the key to both a microscopic and a macroscopic understanding of matter. It links the disorder of many single events to heat. The meaning of work or the average energy of many particles is straightforward in terms of mechanics, but other familiar macroscopic variables like pressure and temperature do not have as obvious a connection to the mechanics of single particles. The kinetic theory provides a ready interpretation of pressure as bombardment of vessel walls by a very special kind of substance, the perfect gas, and leaves pressures manifested by other substances either to the intuition or to more comprehensive theoretical description. Similarly, heat and hotness have clear qualitative meaning, but the connection to single mechanical events is less direct.

Entropy, as the fundamental thermodynamic source of the variable T through the second law, and as the measure of order and disorder through the third law, is clearly of critical importance for an understanding of matter. This chapter is limited mostly to pure substances for the sake of clarity, but its results are of much greater generality than this limitation implies. This chapter explains how the rather impractical criterion of equilibrium and spontaneity in terms of adiabatic constancy or growth in entropy can be maneuvered, by simple mathematical transformation, into criteria that are more directly connected to the senses and ordinary laboratory practice.

Mechanics would suggest the minimum energy of a system as the state of repose at equilibrium. After an adiabatic change, thermodynamics would suggest the most disordered state as the natural finale, even though it involves states of energy above the minimum. A compromise is reached at constant temperature by use of free energy.

5.2 DEFINITIONS OF FREE ENERGIES

A chemist or physicist seldom finds it convenient in his experiments to control or specify some of the independent thermodynamic variables that quite naturally accompany the usual statements of the laws of thermodynamics. An example of this kind of awkward situation arose in thermochemistry. When, as often happens, only expansion work is involved in a process, the first law says directly that heat of reaction is a function of state only if the volume is constant (or rather, if no work is done on the system by the surroundings). Since no vessel is perfectly rigid, theoretically it would be difficult to correlate theory and experiment even if it were common to perform experiments in almost rigid containers. However, by the mathematical trick presented in Section 2.7, namely, by inventing the function H, thermochemistry was simplified. In essence, the enthalpy H is more directly measured for it is easier to hold the pressure constant by operating in vessels open to the atmosphere than it is to try to experiment at constant volume. The invention of H transformed the first law into Hess's law, $q_P = \Delta H$.

A similar mathematical transformation of variables allows the fundamental equation (4.46) to be expressed in terms of independent variables more readily specified in the laboratory. As was done in Section 2.7, add $d(PV)$ to both sides of (4.47).

$$dE = T\,dS - P\,dV \tag{4.47}$$

$$dE + d(PV) = T\,dS - P\,dV + d(PV)$$

$$d(E + PV) = T\,dS - P\,dV + P\,dV + V\,dP$$

$$dH = T\,dS + V\,dP \tag{4.50}$$

By this, pressure P has been maneuvered into the position previously held by the volume V, the awkward variable. By adding $d(-TS)$, the temperature T replaces entropy S as the second independent variable. By (4.46),

$$dE + d(-TS) = T\,dS - P\,dV + d(-TS)$$

$$d(E - TS) = -S\,dT - P\,dV$$

By definition, the Helmholtz free energy function A is

$$A = E - TS \tag{5.1}$$

Since E, T, and S are each functions of state, the Helmholtz free energy A is also a function of state. Substitution of (5.1) into the preceding expression yields

$$dA = -S\,dT - P\,dV \tag{5.2}$$

Similarly, by (4.50),

$$dH + d(-TS) = T\,dS + V\,dP + d(-TS)$$
$$d(H - TS) = -S\,dT + V\,dP$$

By definition, the Gibbs free energy function G is

$$G = H - TS \tag{5.3}$$

Most Americans use F instead of G for the Gibbs free energy function. However, since most Europeans use F for the Helmholtz free energy function, the symbol F is not used for either free energy in this book. Table 5.1 is an attempt to clarify a needlessly confused situation. Since H, T, and S are each functions of state, the Gibbs free energy G is also a function of state. Substitution of (5.3) into the preceding expression yields

$$dG = -S\,dT + V\,dP \tag{5.4}$$

In order to emphasize the importance of the functions just set forth, they are presented together in Table 5.1. These four definitions are always true.

These free energy functions originated with Gibbs in 1875–8 and Helmholtz in 1882. However, in 1869 Massieu had introduced for similar reasons the functions $-A/T$ and $-G/T$; these are sometimes used in statistical mechanics.

Table 5.1 A List of Symbols and Names of Thermodynamic Functions

This Work			Other Common Usage	
Symbol	Definition	Name	Symbol	Name
E	(first law)	Energy	U	Internal Energy Total Energy
H	$E + PV$	Enthalpy		Heat Function Heat Content Total Heat
S	(second law)	Entropy		
A	$E - TS$	Helmholtz Free Energy	F	Free Energy Work Function Helmholtz Function
G	$H - TS$	Gibbs Free Energy	F, Z	Free Enthalpy Thermodynamic Potential Gibbs Function

The four relations (4.47), (4.50), (5.2), and (5.4) apply to closed systems that have only expansion work done on them. These four relations are the differential equations that express the four common thermodynamic functions as functions of the independent variables S, V, P, and T. It was shown in (4.48) that energy is a function of S and V by its nature. In a similar way, the other thermodynamic functions depend on two of these four variables in the manner.

$$E = E(S, V) \tag{4.48}$$

$$H = H(S, P) \tag{5.5}$$

$$A = A(T, V) \tag{5.6}$$

$$G = G(T, P) \tag{5.7}$$

Although these variables are natural for E, H, A, and G, and thus are generally the most convenient, it is still quite correct to treat E as a function of T and V or of some other suitable set of variables.

Because its volume is immense compared to the volume changes in laboratory experiments, the atmosphere constitutes an ideal barostat for processes that can be performed in open vessels in a time so short that the diurnal variation in barometric pressure or variations due to unsettled weather are negligible. It is also relatively easy to perform experiments in thermostats in which a fluid like water or a molten salt is maintained at a constant temperature by heating or cooling devices and in which the reaction vessel is immersed. For the chemist, then, the most appropriate thermodynamic function is the Gibbs free energy $G(T, P)$. Equations (5.4) and (5.7) indicate that G is constant in any closed system that undergoes any reversible isothermal isobaric process in which all work is expansion work. There is also no change in G in any process in which the system returns to its initial state, for G is a function of state.

5.3 SOME USEFUL EQUALITIES

The equations of the previous section not only are useful in their own right for the calculation of increments in A and G but also provide convenient definitions of T and P for statistical mechanics and convenient ways of evaluating, from equations of state, isothermal changes in E, H, and S when the volume or pressure is changed.

By the rules of calculus and the definitions of the symbols involved, (4.48) for closed systems undergoing expansion work yields

$$dE = \left(\frac{\partial E}{\partial S}\right)_V dS + \left(\frac{\partial E}{\partial V}\right)_S dV \tag{5.8}$$

However, substitution of (4.47) into (5.8) yields

$$T\,dS - P\,dV = \left(\frac{\partial E}{\partial S}\right)_V dS + \left(\frac{\partial E}{dV}\right)_S dV \tag{5.9}$$

For arbitrary variations in S and V, it is necessary that

$$T = \left(\frac{\partial E}{\partial S}\right)_V \tag{5.10}$$

$$-P = \left(\frac{\partial E}{\partial V}\right)_S \tag{5.11}$$

Although (5.11) is seldom of use, (4.10) provides a convenient definition of temperature for statistical mechanics (see Chapter 17).

Equation (5.10) is the best definition of temperature and it now replaces all others. With any substance as thermometer, the absolute temperature T is merely the limit at constant volume of the ratio of a small energy change to a small entropy change for any reversible process involving no work. Because $T > 0$, the isochoric changes in E and S have the same sign. Moreover, as T rises, there is a steady decrease in the entropy change that accompanies a constant change in energy at constant volume.

In a similar way, (5.5) and (4.50) yield

$$T\,dS + V\,dP = \left(\frac{\partial H}{\partial S}\right)_P dS + \left(\frac{\partial H}{\partial P}\right)_S dP \tag{5.12}$$

In turn, for arbitrary variations in S and P, (5.12) yields

$$T = \left(\frac{\partial H}{\partial S}\right)_P \tag{5.13}$$

$$V = \left(\frac{\partial H}{\partial P}\right)_S \tag{5.14}$$

Although (5.14) is seldom used, (5.13) is in reality the important Equation (4.51). In any reversible isobaric change involving only expansion work, ΔH and ΔS have the same sign, and as T rises there is a steady decrease in the entropy change that accompanies a constant change in enthalpy in a reversible isobaric process that involves only expansion work.

Again, (5.2) and (5.6) yield

$$-S\,dT - P\,dV = \left(\frac{\partial A}{\partial T}\right)_V dT + \left(\frac{\partial A}{\partial V}\right)_T dV \tag{5.15}$$

which in turn leads to

$$-S = \left(\frac{\partial A}{\partial T}\right)_V \tag{5.16}$$

$$-P = \left(\frac{\partial A}{\partial V}\right)_T \tag{5.17}$$

Equation (5.17) provides a convenient definition of pressure for statistical mechanics and (5.16) is useful for processes that occur at constant volume.

Lastly, for the Gibbs free energy, (5.4) and (5.7) yield (5.18), which then yields (5.19) and (5.20) for arbitrary variations in T and P.

$$-S\,dT + V\,dP = \left(\frac{\partial G}{\partial T}\right)_P dT + \left(\frac{\partial G}{\partial P}\right)_T dP \tag{5.18}$$

$$-S = \left(\frac{\partial G}{\partial T}\right)_P \tag{5.19}$$

$$V = \left(\frac{\partial G}{\partial P}\right)_T \tag{5.20}$$

Equation (5.19), the Gibbs-Helmholtz equation, finds many uses, chiefly in electrochemistry and in the dependence of G on temperature, and (5.20) is most important in regard to equilibrium constants and osmotic pressure.

Equations (4.48), (5.5), (5.6), and (5.7) state that E, H, A and G are functions of state and that increments in them are calculable along any reversible path that joins the initial and final states. The equations derived in this section thus assume that the increments are independent of the path. However, these four innocent-looking equations contain much more information. For physical systems, functions like E, H, A, and G seldom display pathological peculiarities that are the delight of the discriminating mathematician. For physically meaningful quantities like these, the two second mixed partial derivatives are equal. That is,

$$\frac{\partial^2 E}{\partial S\,\partial V} = \frac{\partial^2 E}{\partial V\,\partial S}$$

and so on for H, A, and G. If the order of such differentiation is indeed unimportant, then the eight relations just derived can be differentiated properly to give four more equalities, which are known as the *Maxwell relations*. The second mixed partial derivatives of E with respect to S and V yield, with the aid of (5.10) and (5.11),

$$\left(\frac{\partial T}{\partial V}\right)_S = -\left(\frac{\partial P}{\partial S}\right)_V \tag{5.21}$$

In a similar way, with (5.13) and (5.14), the second mixed partial derivatives of H with respect to S and P yield

$$\left(\frac{\partial T}{\partial P}\right)_S = \left(\frac{\partial V}{\partial S}\right)_P \tag{5.22}$$

Equations (5.21) and (5.22) are seldom used because entropy is awkward to control experimentally. For the calculation of changes in entropy at constant temperature from equation-of-state data, the following two Maxwell relations are, however, very valuable. The second mixed partial derivatives of A with respect to T and V yield, from (5.16) and (5.17),

$$\left(\frac{\partial S}{\partial V}\right)_T = \left(\frac{\partial P}{\partial T}\right)_V \tag{5.23}$$

If the pressure of a substance is given by its equation of state as a function of V and T, it is a simple matter to evaluate the right-hand member of (4.23) and thus find how entropy varies with volume at constant temperature. Finally, the second mixed partial derivatives of G with respect to T and P together with (5.19) and (5.20) yield the isothermal pressure dependence of entropy in terms that can be found from the equation of state, $V = V(T, P)$.

$$\left(\frac{\partial S}{\partial P}\right)_T = -\left(\frac{\partial V}{\partial T}\right)_P \tag{5.24}$$

Example 5.1. The entropy of a paramagnetic salt containing ions with magnetic moments depends, in addition to the usual variables, on the intensity of the magnetic field $\mathscr{H}$ to which it is subjected. However, as T rises, the alignment of the magnetic moments by a constant field $\mathscr{H}$ is disturbed by lattice vibrations so that the magnetic moment M of the salt decreases. If expansion work is negligible and if the magnetic work done on a paramagnetic salt is $\mathscr{H}\,dM$

(a) find an expression for the exact differential $d(A - \mathscr{H}M)$; and

(b) show that isobaric reversible adiabatic demagnetization of a paramagnetic salt causes its temperature to decrease.

(a) According to the first and second laws, as in (4.46),

$$dE = T\,dS + dw = T\,dS + \mathscr{H}\,dM$$

Addition of $d(-TS - \mathscr{H}M)$ to both sides of this result gives at once

$$d(E - TS - \mathscr{H}M) = d(A - \mathscr{H}M) = -S\,dT - M\,d\mathscr{H}$$

(b) A reversible adiabatic change occurs at constant S by (4.6). The task thus is to show that T decreases as $\mathscr{H}$ decreases at constant S, or, in other terms, it is to show that the derivative $(\partial T/\partial \mathscr{H})_S$ is positive. One clue comes from the fact that if $S = S(P, T, \mathscr{H})$, then at constant P

$$dS = \left(\frac{\partial S}{\partial T}\right)_{\mathscr{H}} dT + \left(\frac{\partial S}{\partial \mathscr{H}}\right)_T d\mathscr{H}$$

If S is constant so that $dS = 0$, then

$$\left(\frac{\partial T}{\partial \mathscr{H}}\right)_S = -\frac{\left(\dfrac{\partial S}{\partial \mathscr{H}}\right)_T}{\left(\dfrac{\partial S}{\partial T}\right)_{\mathscr{H}}}$$

The denominator is positive because of (4.53), wherein $\mathscr{H}$ was not mentioned because it was constant. The problem thus comes to a determination of the sign of the numerator. As in the derivation of the Maxwell relations, the second mixed derivative of $A - \mathscr{H}M$ with respect to T and $\mathscr{H}$ gives

$$\left(\frac{\partial S}{\partial \mathscr{H}}\right)_T = \left(\frac{\partial M}{\partial T}\right)_{\mathscr{H}}$$

But both these derivatives are negative since it is given that M decreases as T increases when $\mathscr{H}$ is constant. Hence, $(\partial T/\partial \mathscr{H})_S$ is positive, and reversible adiabatic ($dS = 0$) demagnetization ($d\mathscr{H} < 0$) leads to a decrease in $T(dT < 0)$.

5.4 THERMODYNAMIC EQUATION OF STATE

If derivatives of the kind in the right-hand members of (5.23) and (5.24) are to be found, there must be some justification that the thermodynamic temperature of the derivative is indeed the perfect gas temperature of the equation of state. Proof that the thermodynamic temperature T, defined by the second law, is the perfect gas temperature T' follows.

The usual combined form of the first and second laws is $dE = T\,dS - P\,dV$. Division by dV at constant temperature yields

$$\left(\frac{\partial E}{\partial V}\right)_T = T\left(\frac{\partial S}{\partial V}\right)_T - P$$

and subsequent use of (5.23) leads to (5.25), an equation that relates the energy of any system directly to the variables of the equation of state.

$$\left(\frac{\partial E}{\partial V}\right)_T = T\left(\frac{\partial P}{\partial T}\right)_V - P \tag{5.25}$$

Equation (5.25) applies to all substances and has been called the *thermodynamic equation of state*. It says that the observable pressure P of a substance is the net effect of two opposing effective pressures, for

$$P = T\left(\frac{\partial P}{\partial T}\right)_V - \left(\frac{\partial E}{\partial V}\right)_T$$

The first of these is called the *kinetic pressure;* it may be pictured as the result of thermal vibrations confined to a constant volume but increased in amplitude and intensity because of a rise in T. For a perfect gas, the kinetic pressure is simply

$$T\left(\frac{\partial P}{\partial T}\right)_V = T\left[\frac{\partial}{\partial T}\left(\frac{nRT}{V}\right)\right]_V = \frac{nRT}{V} = P$$

The second term, which counters the kinetic pressure, is called the *internal pressure* of the substance; it is the rate at which energy must be expended isothermally on a substance to increase its volume against its cohesive forces. For a perfect gas, the internal pressure $(\partial E/\partial V)_T$ is zero by (2.30) or because there are no intermolecular forces of attraction. For a liquid at low P, however, both terms may be of an order of magnitude greater than P. And when molecules are jammed together at high P, the internal pressure may become negative because molecules are then actually repelling each other.

For a perfect gas, the energy of which is independent of its volume for isothermal changes by (2.30), it follows from (5.25) that

$$0 = T\left(\frac{\partial P}{\partial T}\right)_V - P$$

That is, at constant volume,

$$\frac{dP}{P} = \frac{dT}{T}$$

which, on definite integration from the state with pressure P_1 and temperature T_1 to the state with pressure P_2 and temperature T_2, yields

$$\int_{P_1}^{P_2} \frac{dP}{P} = \int_{T_1}^{T_2} \frac{dT}{T}$$

$$\ln\left(\frac{P_2}{P_1}\right) = \ln\left(\frac{T_2}{T_1}\right)$$

$$\frac{P_2}{P_1} = \frac{T_2}{T_1}, \qquad (dV = 0) \tag{5.26}$$

However, the measurement of a pressure at constant volume in a hydrogen thermometer constitutes the standard of the perfect gas temperature scale through

$$\frac{P_2}{P_1} = \frac{T_2'}{T_1'} \tag{5.27}$$

where T_2' is the absolute gas temperature of the gas at pressure P_2 while T_1' is its gas temperature at P_1. By (5.26) and (5.27), which is really Charles's law,

$$\frac{T_2'}{T_1'} = \frac{T_2}{T_1} \tag{5.28}$$

However, (5.28) says nothing more or less than that the second law's thermodynamic temperature scale T agrees with and is identical to the perfect gas temperature scale T'.

While C_V is readily calculated, it is C_P that is easily observed. It is thus valuable to know how C_P and C_V differ to check theory or observation. By (2.41) and (5.25)

$$C_P - C_V = \left[\left(\frac{\partial E}{\partial V}\right)_T + P\right]\left(\frac{\partial V}{\partial T}\right)_P = T\left(\frac{\partial V}{\partial T}\right)_P\left(\frac{\partial P}{\partial T}\right)_V \tag{5.29}$$

The last factor is easily expressed in terms of the commonly observed isobaric and isothermal coefficients of expansion, which are defined as

$$\alpha = \frac{1}{V}\left(\frac{\partial V}{\partial T}\right)_P \quad \text{and} \quad \beta = -\frac{1}{V}\left(\frac{\partial V}{\partial P}\right)_T \tag{5.30}$$

For if $V = V(P, T)$, setting dV equal to zero yields

$$0 = \left(\frac{\partial V}{\partial P}\right)_T dP + \left(\frac{\partial V}{\partial T}\right)_P dT \tag{5.31}$$

which is the same as the well known mathematical result

$$-1 = \left(\frac{\partial P}{\partial T}\right)_V \left(\frac{\partial V}{\partial P}\right)_T \left(\frac{\partial T}{\partial V}\right)_P \tag{5.32}$$

Substitution of (5.30) and either (5.31) or (5.32) into (5.29) yields

$$C_P - C_V = \frac{TV\alpha^2}{\beta} \tag{5.33}$$

Any substance in any state of aggregation follows (5.33). This difference is often small for condensed phases because typically $V = 50$ cm³ mole⁻¹, $\alpha = 10^{-4}$ deg⁻¹, $\beta = 10^{-5}$ atm⁻¹, and at 300°K $C_P - C_V = 15$ cm³ atm mole⁻¹ deg⁻¹ $= 0.3$ cal mole⁻¹ deg⁻¹. Values of $C_P - C_V$ of the order of ten cal mole⁻¹ deg⁻¹ are sometimes observed for liquids and solids.

5.5 ENERGY OF A REAL GAS

The van der Waals equation attempts in a simple way to describe the behavior of a real gas. Explicit solution for the pressure leads to

$$P = \frac{nRT}{V - nb} - \frac{an^2}{V^2}$$

Then, toward fitting (5.25),

$$\left(\frac{\partial P}{\partial T}\right)_V = \frac{nR}{V - nb}$$

so that (5.25) becomes (5.34) in the following way.

$$\left(\frac{\partial E}{\partial V}\right)_T = T\left(\frac{nR}{V - nb}\right) - \left(\frac{nRT}{V - nb} - \frac{an^2}{V^2}\right)$$

$$\left(\frac{\partial E}{\partial V}\right)_T = \frac{an^2}{V^2} \tag{5.34}$$

For a Dieterici fluid, the right side of (5.34) is $(an^2/V^2)(PV/nRT)$. From (5.34) with $n = 1$ at a constant temperature T, it follows that the actual energy $E(T)$

of a van der Waals gas at volume V differs from the ideal or reference energy $E_0(T)$ at large volumes by the amount

$$\int_{E_0}^{E} dE' = E(T) - E_0(T) = \int_{\infty}^{V} \frac{a}{V'^2}\,dV' = -\frac{a}{V} \tag{5.35}$$

Figure 5.1 compares (5.35) for argon at 0°C to observation and similar theoretical results from the Dieterici and Beattie-Bridgeman equations.

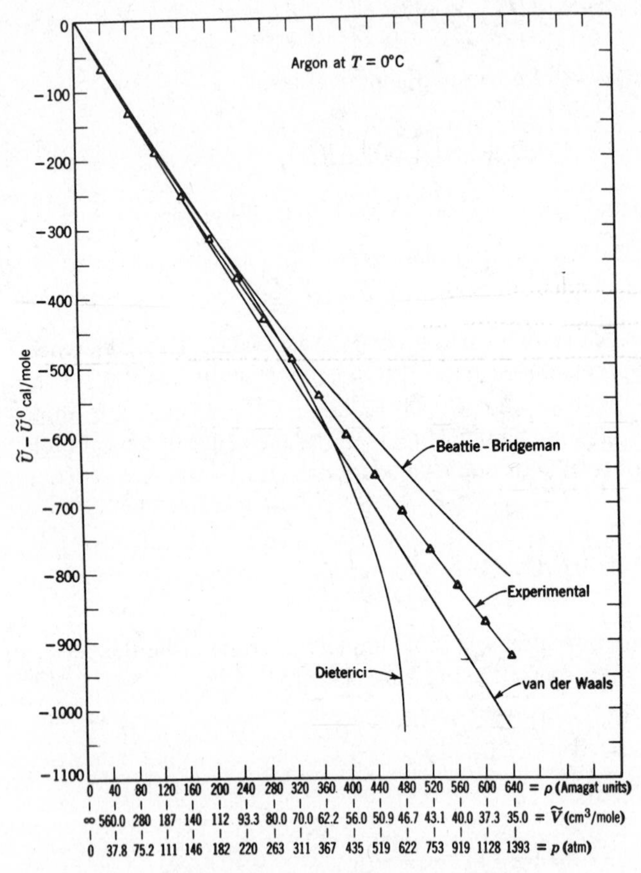

Figure 5.1. Difference in Actual Energy E and Ideal Energy E_0 of Argon at 0°C†

5.6 ENTHALPY OF A REAL GAS

The second law, through (5.24), permits the calculation of the Joule-Thomson coefficient μ from the equation of state. In Sections 2.13 and 2.14 this coefficient

†J. O. Hirschfelder, C. F. Curtiss, and R. B. Bird, *Molecular Theory of Gases and Liquids*, New York: John Wiley and Sons, Inc. 1954, p. 256.

was presented as an empirically observed ratio of change of temperature to change of pressure. Now, however, values of μ can be calculated.

Varying the pressure isothermally for a system the enthalpy of which is described by (4.50) leads, by the equivalent formal operation of dividing by dP at constant temperature, to (5.36).

$$dH = T\,dS + V\,dP \tag{4.50}$$

$$\left(\frac{\partial H}{\partial P}\right)_T = T\left(\frac{\partial S}{\partial P}\right)_T + V \tag{5.36}$$

By (5.24), it follows that

$$\left(\frac{\partial H}{\partial P}\right)_T = V - T\left(\frac{\partial V}{\partial T}\right)_P \tag{5.37}$$

$$= V(1 - \alpha T) \tag{5.38}$$

where α is given by (5.30). With $PV = nRT$, it is easy to verify that the enthalpy of a perfect gas is independent of its pressure. The enthalpy of a real gas, however, does depend upon its pressure, and the expression of this dependence in (5.37) permits the calculation of μ, the Joule-Thomson coefficient. By (2.59),

$$\mu = -\frac{1}{C_P}\left(\frac{\partial H}{\partial P}\right)_T = \frac{1}{C_P}\left[T\left(\frac{\partial V}{\partial T}\right)_P - V\right] \tag{5.39}$$

With the van der Waals or Dieterici equation in the convenient approximate form

$$PV = nRT + n\left(b - \frac{a}{RT}\right)P$$

it follows that

$$P\left(\frac{\partial V}{\partial T}\right)_P = nR + \frac{naP}{RT^2}$$

so that, by (5.39),

$$\mu = \frac{1}{C_P}\left[\frac{nRT}{P} + \frac{na}{RT} - \frac{nRT}{P} - n\left(b - \frac{a}{RT}\right)\right]$$

$$= \frac{1}{C_P}\left(\frac{2na}{RT} - nb\right) \tag{5.40}$$

At the inversion temperature T_i, μ is zero, so that by (5.40),

$$T_i = \frac{2a}{bR} \tag{5.41}$$

Typically, T_i is about 2 T_B and about 7 T_C.

Example 5.2. Compare the Joule-Thomson coefficient of ethane predicted by (5.40) to the accurate values of Table 2.2.

By Table 1.3, ethane has $a \approx 6.2 \times 10^6$ cm^6 atm mole^{-2} and $b \approx 67$ cm^3 mole^{-1}; by Table 3.1, C_P at 25°C is 12.6 cal mole^{-1} deg^{-1}, which, upon conversion by the R-ratio (82.0/1.99), is 520 cm^3 atm deg^{-1} mole^{-1}. Hence, in (5.40),

$$\mu = \frac{1}{520}\left(\frac{2 \times 6.2 \times 10^6}{82.0 \times 298} - 67\right) = 0.85 \text{ deg atm}^{-1}$$

In Table 2.2, at 25°C μ falls from 1.23 deg atm^{-1} at 20 atm to 0.932 deg atm^{-1} at 1 atm. Part of the difference between calculated and observed values is caused by use of a low-pressure form of the equations of state.

5.7 ENTROPY CHANGES

Increments in entropy for reversible isothermal processes and for processes that involve only a change in temperature and could in principle be executed reversibly were calculated above in order to evaluate absolute entropies at 25°C and at the standard pressure of one atm. In order to find the increase in entropy for a process that begins or ends with an arbitrary state, it is most convenient to analyze the process into two parts, one of which is isothermal and the other not isothermal. That is, if one considers the entropy of a closed system as a function of pressure P and temperature T, such that $S = S(P, T)$, by the rules of calculus,

$$dS = \left(\frac{\partial S}{\partial T}\right)_P dT + \left(\frac{\partial S}{\partial P}\right)_T dP$$

But from (4.53) and (5.24),

$$dS = \frac{C_P}{T}\,dT - \left(\frac{\partial V}{\partial T}\right)_P dP \qquad (5.42)$$

Any path that could in principle be performed reversibly is just as good as any other because S is a function of state and dS is an exact differential. For the change of state from pressure P_1 to P_2 and from temperature T_1 to T_2, it is convenient to choose the following reversible path:

$$S(P_1, T_1) \xrightarrow[(1)]{dP_1 = 0} S(P_1, T_2) \xrightarrow[(2)]{dT_2 = 0} S(P_2, T_2)$$

$$\Delta S = \,?$$

For the isobaric process, (5.42) becomes

$$\Delta S_1 = \int_{T_1}^{T_2} \frac{C_P}{T}\,dT$$

For the isothermal process, (5.42) yields

$$\Delta S_2 = -\int_{P_1}^{P_2} \left(\frac{\partial V}{\partial T}\right)_P dP$$

Then, for the overall change of state,

$$\Delta S = \Delta S_1 + \Delta S_2 = \int_{T_1}^{T_2} \frac{C_P}{T} dT - \int_{P_1}^{P_2} \left(\frac{\partial V}{\partial T}\right)_P dP \tag{5.43}$$

If the equation of state of the system is $V = V(P, T)$, the integrals of (5.43) are readily evaluated. For n moles of a perfect gas with constant molar heat capacity C_P,

$$\begin{aligned}\Delta S &= nC_P \int_{T_1}^{T_2} \frac{dT}{T} - \int_{P_1}^{P_2} \left[\frac{\partial}{\partial T}\left(\frac{nRT}{P}\right)\right]_P dP \\ &= nC_P \ln\left(\frac{T_2}{T_1}\right) - nR \int_{P_1}^{P_2} \frac{dP}{P} \\ &= nC_P \ln\left(\frac{T_2}{T_1}\right) + nR \ln\left(\frac{P_1}{P_2}\right) \end{aligned} \tag{5.44}$$

If the pressure decreases, $P_1 > P_2$ and the second term of (5.44) is positive, in accord with the concept that a decrease in pressure involves a regression from the order of condensed states towards the disorder and increased entropy of a more random state.

When $S = S(V, T)$, a similar development using (4.57) and (5.23) yields

$$\Delta S = \int_{T_1}^{T_2} \frac{C_V}{T} dT + \int_{V_1}^{V_2} \left(\frac{\partial P}{\partial T}\right)_V dV \tag{5.45}$$

Example 5.3. Calculate the increase in entropy of two moles of a perfect gas that is suddenly released into an evacuated vessel of such size that its pressure falls from 4/3 atm to one atm.

This sudden change is irreversible and adiabatic. Since no work is done, $\Delta E = 0$ for the gas and its temperature is constant because it is perfect. The value of ΔS can be calculated from the initial and final states by (5.44).

$$\Delta S = 2 \times 1.9872 \times \ln\left(\tfrac{4}{3}\right) = 1.1434 \text{ cal deg}^{-1}$$

This is the difference in entropy of the final states of the oxygen in Example 4.4:

$$\Delta S = 4.0932 - 2.9498 = 1.1434 \text{ cal deg}^{-1}$$

Example 5.4. One mole H_2 at 127°C and 10 atm was cooled to 27°C at constant pressure, and then was allowed to expand irreversibly into an evacuated chamber so that its final pressure was 0.5 atm. Then it was compressed reversibly and adiabatically until its temperature was 127°C. Finally, its pressure was adjusted isothermally at 127°C until it was 10 atm. If hydrogen is a perfect gas with $C_P = 6.82$ cal mole^{-1} deg^{-1}, calculate the total change in entropy of the hydrogen.

Since the initial and final states are alike, $\Delta S = 0$. (The enterprising student may wish to verify this by actual step-by-step calculation.)

Example 5.5. Calculate the increase in entropy of a mole of a perfect diatomic gas ($C_P = 7R/2$) the initial state of which is 25°C at 1.00 atm and the final state of which is 100°C at (a) 1.00 atm; (b) 10.0 atm.

In terms of randomness and disorder, explain the difference in these two entropy changes for these two different changes of state.

(a) If the perfect diatomic gas is heated reversibly at constant pressure of 1.00 atm, (4.59) yields

$$\Delta S = \frac{7}{2} R \ln \left(\frac{373}{298}\right) = 1.56 \text{ cal deg}^{-1}$$

(b) If the perfect diatomic gas is heated reversibly at 1.00 atm to 100°C and then is compressed isothermally to 10.0 atm, (5.44) yields

$$\Delta S = \frac{7}{2} R \ln \left(\frac{373}{298}\right) + R \ln \left(\frac{1}{10}\right) = 1.56 - 4.58 = -3.02 \text{ cal deg}^{-1}$$

The isobaric change of state involves only an increase in temperature, which is easily interpreted as increased agitation, increased disorder, or increased entropy. The second change of state, however, involves two influences. The increase in temperature again leads to a modest increase in entropy, but the subsequent compression increases the packing and order of the molecules to such an extent that there is a net decrease in entropy.

5.8 CONDITIONS FOR EQUILIBRIUM AND SPONTANEITY

A state of equilibrium or a reversible process is considered to be a limiting situation; it exists if there is no small change that could occur spontaneously. On the other hand, a reversible process is said to be performed if a small change would cause the occurrence of a spontaneous process that differs as little as desired from the limiting reversible process. A process that tends away from equilibrium is unnatural, or nonspontaneous, because it does not occur in nature.

A simple trial-and-error method of determining whether a specified system in a specified state is at equilibrium or not would be to calculate some appropriately chosen thermodynamic property at several points in the immediate neighborhood of the specified state. If the supposed changes satisfied or failed to satisfy a suitably chosen criterion of equilibrium or spontaneity, then a definite statement concerning the state of the system or kind of process could be made. Melted snow quite naturally seeks the lowest level in a valley. Once in a valley, the water flows to the lowest point. If all points in the immediate neighborhood of this lowest point are higher, a body of water collects. The size and conformation of the neighborhood determine whether the body of water is a puddle, a lake, or an ocean. If all possible changes are upward, water is in its most stable position: in the ocean. Even its position in a puddle would be stable relative to immediately adjacent regions. Similarly, the manner of choice or the number of choices for calculation may give assurance that a certain thermodynamic property always decreases or increases in the neighborhood of a state whose stability is to be determined. If so, a maximum or minimum relative to adjacent states has been found.

In Section 4.4 it was concluded that the entropy of an isolated system tends naturally and spontaneously to a maximum. In view of the discussion just ended, a suitable criterion of equilibrium in an isolated system would be that any virtual change in entropy δS leads away from the maximum and thus is less than zero. The abbreviated statement of the second law in (4.4) suggests a similar criterion for any closed system in contact with isothermal surroundings at the temperature T. For a process that is not spontaneous, and thus does not involve the inequality of (4.4), any virtual change of state that would be accompanied by a change in entropy δS and an absorption of heat δq would satisfy the relation

$$T\,\delta S \leqslant \delta q \tag{5.46}$$

That is, if (5.46) is satisfied for any arbitrary variation in the neighborhood of the state of a closed system in contact with isothermal surroundings, then the state is an equilibrium state. What (5.46) really says is that there is no variation possible in the state of the system (as restricted) such that $T\,\delta S > \delta q$.

There are other equally fundamental but much more easily used criteria of equilibrium. These are derived from (5.46) and the first law in the form $\delta E = \delta q - P\,\delta V$. For arbitrarily chosen virtual variations, these relations can be stated as criteria of equilibrium thus:

$$\delta E + P\,\delta V - T\,\delta S \geqslant 0 \tag{5.47}$$

$$\delta H - V\,\delta P - T\,\delta S \geqslant 0 \tag{5.48}$$

$$\delta A + P\,\delta V + S\,\delta T \geqslant 0 \tag{5.49}$$

$$\delta G - V\,\delta P + S\,\delta T \geqslant 0 \tag{5.50}$$

These are clearly like (4.47), (4.50), (5.2), and (5.4). In particular, for virtual variations made with the volume V and entropy S held constant so the δV and δS are zero, (5.47) says that any variation of energy δE involves no change in or an increase in energy. Symbolically for this situation,

$$(\delta E)_{S,V} \geqslant 0 \tag{5.51}$$

From the mode of derivation, it is clear that an unnatural change at constant entropy and volume would involve an increase in energy, like water running uphill.

The other three analogous criteria of equilibria in closed systems all of whose work is expansion work are:

$$(\delta H)_{S,P} \geqslant 0 \tag{5.52}$$

$$(\delta A)_{V,T} \geqslant 0 \tag{5.53}$$

$$(\delta G)_{P,T} \geqslant 0 \tag{5.54}$$

The last two relations are by far the most useful, for entropy is awkward to control experimentally, while pressure, volume, and temperature are easily controlled. The last relation, (5.54), is most suitable for chemists. If any supposed isothermal isobaric change in a system leads to an increase in the Gibbs free energy, that system is at equilibrium. Again, if the supposed isothermal isobaric change does not change the Gibbs free energy, the system is at equilibrium.

In a similar way these are the criteria of spontaneity for closed systems doing expansion work:

$$(\delta E)_{S,V} < 0 \tag{5.55}$$

$$(\delta H)_{S,P} < 0 \tag{5.56}$$

$$(\delta A)_{V,T} < 0 \tag{5.57}$$

$$(\delta G)_{P,T} < 0 \tag{5.58}$$

Inequality (5.58), which is commonly used by chemists, says that natural or spontaneous changes that occur isothermally and isobarically involve a decrease in Gibbs free energy. In other words, the Gibbs free energy tends to a minimum in such changes in closed systems, just as water flows to the lowest elevation in the neighborhood.

With these four criteria of spontaneity must, of course, be placed the fundamental one proposed directly by the second law in (4.2):

$$(\delta S)_q > 0 \tag{5.59}$$

where the subscript q indicates adiabatic conditions. The four criteria above are just restatements of this. For example, the first law and (4.2) in the form $\delta q < T\delta S$ yield the precursor of (5.55), namely $\delta E + P\,\delta V - T\,\delta S < 0$. However, if $\delta E = \delta V = 0$ in a system that can undergo only expansion work, the first law requires $\delta q = 0$ so that (5.59) can be restated

$$(\delta S)_{E,V} > 0 \tag{5.60}$$

It is clear that (5.60) comes from the converse of (5.47), namely $\delta E + P\delta V - T\delta S < 0$. The converse of (5.47) also gives a third less useful criterion of spontaneity, $(\delta V)_{E,S} < 0$. Indeed, the converses of (5.47), (5.48), (5.49), and (5.50) each yield three equivalent criteria. These say nothing about the rate at which the virtual change could or will grow. They merely indicate the natural sequence of thermodynamic states.

The operation of a bubble counter illustrates the tendency for the entropy of a system to increase in spontaneous processes. In a bubble counter, a superheated liquid like hydrogen or ether is caused to boil at the incidence of ionizing radiation like a cosmic ray. Since this irreversible boiling along the particle's track is quite sudden, the process may be considered adiabatic. For the purposes of this illustration, the process shall be assumed to be isobaric so that for this adiabatic isobaric process involving only expansion work, by (2.22), $0 = q_P = \Delta H$. A diagram of the change of state in which 1 mole of superheated liquid at a temperature T_1 becomes a mixture of X moles of gas and $(1 - X)$ moles of liquid at the boiling point T_2 is drawn with a reversible path in order to calculate the increase in entropy.

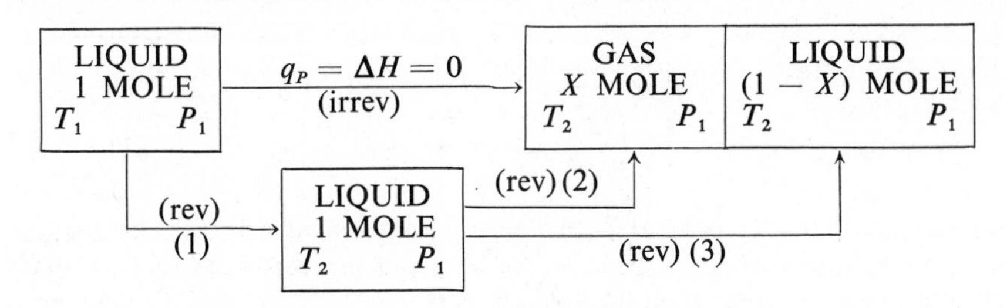

Let τ be the number of degrees by which the liquid is superheated; hence, $T_1 = T_2 + \tau$. For process (1),

$$\Delta H_1 = \int_{T_1}^{T_2} C_P \, dT = C_P(T_2 - T_1) = -C_P\tau$$

The second process involves the vaporization of X moles with a molar heat of vaporization ΔH_v. For process (2),

$$\Delta H_2 = X \, \Delta H_v$$

The third process involves no change of state of the $(1 - X)$ moles of liquid so that $\Delta H_3 = 0$. The overall increase in enthalpy is zero; hence,

$$\Delta H = \Delta H_1 + \Delta H_2 + \Delta H_3$$
$$0 = -C_P\tau + X \, \Delta H_v$$

The three increases in entropy along the reversible path are calculated in a similar way. By (4.58) and then (4.52)

$$\Delta S_1 = \int_{T_1}^{T_2} \frac{C_P}{T} \, dT = C_P \ln\left(\frac{T_2}{T_1}\right)$$

$$\Delta S_2 = \frac{X \, \Delta H_v}{T_2}$$

$$\Delta S_3 = 0$$

For the irreversible change, then, with $X\,\Delta H_v = C_P\tau$,

$$\Delta S = \Delta S_1 + \Delta S_2 + \Delta S_3 = C_P \ln\left(\frac{T_2}{T_1}\right) + \frac{X\,\Delta H_v}{T_2}$$

$$= -C_P \ln\left(\frac{T_2+\tau}{T_2}\right) + \frac{X\,\Delta H_v}{T_2} = -C_P \ln\left(1+\frac{\tau}{T_2}\right) + \frac{C_P\tau}{T_2}$$

If τ is much less than T_2, the logarithm can be approximated by

$$\ln(1+x) = x - \frac{x^2}{2} + \cdots$$

Accordingly,

$$\Delta S = -C_P\left[\frac{\tau}{T_2} - \frac{1}{2}\left(\frac{\tau}{T_2}\right)^2 + \cdots\right] + C_P\left(\frac{\tau}{T_2}\right) \approx \frac{C_P}{2}\left(\frac{\tau}{T_2}\right)^2$$

This expression for ΔS is greater than zero, in agreement with the expectations of the variation form of (5.56) for spontaneous processes: $T\,\delta S + V\,\delta P - \delta H > 0$. For at constant H and P, $(\delta S)_{H,P} > 0$.

Example 5.6. What is the change in entropy of one mole H_2O when a tiny crystal of ice is dropped into an open Dewar flask of negligible heat capacity if the flask initially contains one mole supercooled water at $-5.00°C$? Assume that the final state achieved spontaneously is an equilibrium state. The molar C_P for water is 18.0 cal deg^{-1}; the molar C_P for ice is 9.0 cal deg^{-1}; and the molar of fusion ΔH_f of H_2O is 1440 cal.

This irreversible change is isobaric and adiabatic since it occurs in an open Dewar flask. Since all work is expansion work, $q_P = \Delta H = 0$ by (2.22). A diagram of the process as it achieves the final temperature T_2 is amplified by a convenient reversible path.

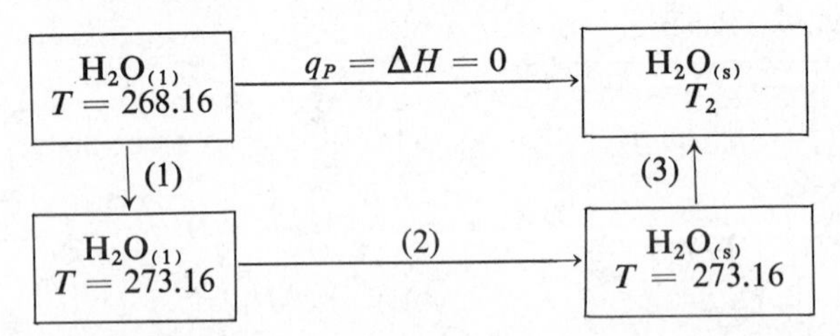

In order to verify that T_2 is 273.16°K, or that some water remains in equilibrium with the ice that crystallizes in the seeding process, the increase in enthalpy by processes (1), (2), and (3) is calculated.

$$\Delta H_1 = \int_{268.16}^{273.16} C_P\,dT = 18.0\,(273.16 - 268.16) = 18.0 \times 5.00 \text{ cal}$$

$$\Delta H_2 = -1440 \text{ cal}$$

$$\Delta H_3 = \int_{273.16}^{T_2} C_P\,dT = 9.0\,(T_2 - 273.16)$$

$$\Delta H = \Delta H_1 + \Delta H_2 + \Delta H_3$$
$$0 = 18.0 \times 5.00 - 1440 + 9.0\,(T_2 - 273.16)$$
$$T_2 = 423$$

But ice cannot exist at 423°K at equilibrium at 1 atm. Hence, not all water solidifies and the diagram should have been this, where X is the fraction of a mole water that becomes ice.

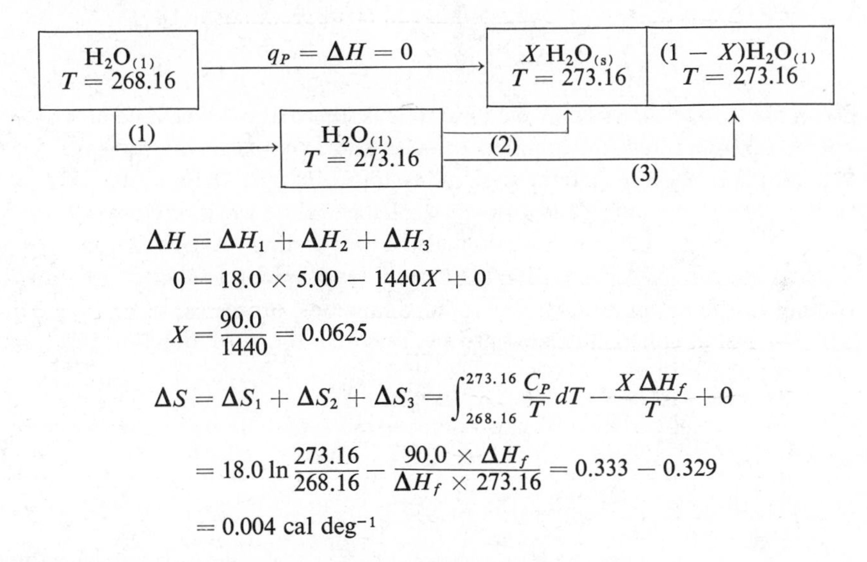

$$\Delta H = \Delta H_1 + \Delta H_2 + \Delta H_3$$
$$0 = 18.0 \times 5.00 - 1440X + 0$$
$$X = \frac{90.0}{1440} = 0.0625$$
$$\Delta S = \Delta S_1 + \Delta S_2 + \Delta S_3 = \int_{268.16}^{273.16} \frac{C_P}{T}\,dT - \frac{X\,\Delta H_f}{T} + 0$$
$$= 18.0 \ln \frac{273.16}{268.16} - \frac{90.0 \times \Delta H_f}{\Delta H_f \times 273.16} = 0.333 - 0.329$$
$$= 0.004 \text{ cal deg}^{-1}$$

Once again for a spontaneous process, $(\delta S)_{H,P} > 0$.

5.9 REVERSIBLE WORK

In Section 2.11 on reversible isothermal work there appeared an argument based on plausibility in support of the fact that reversible isothermal work is a function of state. The forms of the equations for the reversible expansion work performed by perfect gases and performed during isobaric phase transitions suggested that such work depends only on the initial and final states of the system. Moreover, the idea that a reversible process proceeds by virtue of a pressure difference that in the limit becomes zero suggested that such reversible work is an extremum, and as such should be a unique function of state. Now that the concept of entropy has been developed, a rigorous mathematical proof of these facts is possible. The proof begins with the fundamental relation of thermodynamics

$$dE \leqslant T\,dS + dw \qquad (4.46)$$

By the methods of Section 5.2,

$$d(E - TS) \leqslant T\,dS + dw - d(TS)$$
$$dA \leqslant -S\,dT + dw$$

For an isothermal process $dT = 0$, so that

$$dA \leqslant dw, \qquad (dT = 0) \tag{5.61}$$

Or

$$\Delta A \leqslant w, \qquad (dT = 0) \tag{5.62}$$

These two equations say that the reversible isothermal work w done on a system by the surroundings is a function of state and is equal to the increase ΔA in Helmholtz free energy of the system. Because of this, A has been called the *work function;* but since A is a function of state while work often is not, such a name is avoided here because it may be misleading. As inequalities, (5.61) and (5.62) state that irreversible isothermal work is not a function of state because A is a function of state.

For a reversible isothermal process in which the work done on the system is w_{rev}, (5.62) is simply

$$w_{rev} = \Delta A \tag{5.63}$$

For the same change of state accomplished by an irreversible isothermal process, (5.62) is

$$\Delta A < w \tag{5.64}$$

Addition of (5.63) and (5.64) yields

$$w_{rev} < w \tag{5.65}$$

which states that reversible work done isothermally on a system is always less than irreversible work done isothermally on a system when the same change in state is effected. In terms of work done by the system, $-w_{rev}$ and $-w$, multiplication of (5.65) by -1 reverses the sense of the inequality so that

$$-w_{rev} > -w \tag{5.66}$$

That is, the isothermal reversible work done by a system is greater than the irreversible isothermal work done by the system when the same change of state of the system occurs. Such isothermal reversible work is in fact a maximum. The discussions and examples of work in the first part of Chapter 2, particularly Sections 2.2 and 2.11, provide several examples of these ideas and of the fact that w depends upon the path.

Physicists and engineers are often able to use or perform work with some sort of expansion device and thus are quite content with the function A. Chemists however, seldom are interested in the almost inevitable expansion work that accompanies chemical change, but are often preoccupied with electric work or other kinds of nonexpansion work. If such nonexpansion work done on the system by the surroundings is given the symbol w_0 as in (2.24), then, when w_{PV} is the expansion work, the first law becomes in infinitesimal form: $dE = dq + dw_{PV} + dw_0$. With the use of the second law, this becomes $dE \leqslant T\,dS + dw_{PV} + dw_0$. By (2.3) and the usual methods of Section 4.13, $d(E + PV - TS) \leqslant T\,dS - P\,dV + dw_0 + d(PV - TS)$. That is,

$$dG \leqslant -S\,dT + V\,dP + dw_0 \tag{5.67}$$

For any isothermal ($dT = 0$) and isobaric ($dP = 0$) process,

$$dG \leqslant dw_0, \qquad (dT = dP = 0) \tag{5.68}$$

Or

$$\Delta G \leqslant w_0, \qquad (dT = dP = 0) \tag{5.69}$$

As for reversible isothermal work, these last two equations say that reversible isothermal isobaric nonexpansion work done on a system is a function of state, since G is a function of state. Moreover, such work is equal to the increase ΔG in Gibbs free energy of the system. And, as shown above, such reversible work is less than the irreversible work that must be done on the system to effect the specified change in state of the system.

If a system is subdivided so as to increase its surface area despite the action of surface tension, which tends to minimize the exposed surface area of the system, the work of subdivision leads by (5.69) to an increase in the Gibbs free energy of the system. Similarly, if electric work is done on a system, as in electrolysis to produce chemically active species like sodium or chlorine, such electric work serves to increase the Gibbs free energy of the system. If the electrolysis is performed reversibly, a minimum of electric work is done. But if the electrolysis is performed rapidly and irreversibly, the extra electric work does not appear in the activity of the chemicals, but is rather dissipated within the system and its presence is noted by a rise in the temperature of the system.

Example 5.7. Calculate the minimum work to be done on a mole of a substance at constant volume and temperature in order to raise it to a height Z in a uniform gravitational field.

If the volume and temperature are constant, the equation of state of the system, $P = P(V, T)$, assures that the pressure is also constant in this reversible process. By (2.1), (5.63), and (5.69), if the mass of 1 mole is M,

$$w = \Delta A = \Delta G = \int_0^Z Mg\,dz' = MgZ$$

If any work in excess of MgZ were done on the system in elevating it, such extra work due to irreversibility would appear as kinetic energy of the system or the surroundings.

5.10 PROCESSES AT CONSTANT TEMPERATURE

The preceding section on reversible work is a discussion of isothermal processes for which the work is calculable as work. That section could well have been included in this section. Since free energy is a function of state, any change of state has associated with it a definite change in free energy regardless of whether work is done or not in that change. Quite generally, a change from state 1 to state 2 has associated with it an increase in Helmholtz free energy ΔA, where by the definition of A in (4.79), $\Delta A = A_2 - A_1 = (E_2 - T_2S_2) - (E_1 - T_1S_1) = \Delta E - \Delta(TS)$. If $T_1 = T_2$, as in an isothermal process,

$$\Delta A = \Delta E - T\,\Delta S \tag{5.70}$$

where ΔA, ΔE, and ΔS are the increases in A, E, and S when the initial and final states are at the same temperature T. In a similar way, for the Gibbs free energy, by the definition of G in (5.3), $\Delta G = G_2 - G_1 = (H_2 - T_2S_2) - (H_1 - T_1S_1) = \Delta H - \Delta(TS)$. If $T_1 = T_2$, as in an isothermal process,

$$\Delta G = \Delta H - T\,\Delta S \tag{5.71}$$

A special case of the application of (5.71) concerns an isothermal phase transition like fusion or evaporation. If ΔH is the heat of transition, (4.52) yields for ΔS for such a change,

$$\Delta S = \frac{\Delta H}{T} \tag{4.52}$$

Substitution in (5.71) yields

$$\Delta G = \Delta H - T\left(\frac{\Delta H}{T}\right) = 0 \tag{5.72}$$

That is, for any isobaric isothermal reversible change in a closed system that, if it does work, does only expansion work, there is no change in the Gibbs free energy. The Gibbs free energies G_1 and G_2 of phases in equilibrium through such a process are equal, for $\Delta G = 0$ and $G_2 - G_1 = 0$ so that

$$G_2(T, P) = G_1(T, P) \tag{5.73}$$

Equations (5.72) and (5.73) are merely another way of expressing the equality (5.54), one of the criteria of equilibrium, now a criterion of equilibrium between coexisting phases like ice and water: $(\delta G)_{P,T} = 0$.

As discussed with regard to heats of formation and Hess's law, a chemical transformation may involve well-specified initial and final states. If so, there is for such a transformation a definite increase in free energy ΔG. Equation (5.71) provides the means of calculating numerical values of $\Delta G^\ominus$ for reactions which involve reactants and products in their standard (or specified) states if the various chemical species are listed in Table 3.1 (Heats of Formation) and Table 4.3 (Standard Absolute Entropies).

Example 5.8. Calculate $\Delta G^\ominus$ at 25°C for the change of state

$$H_2O_{(l)}\ (1\text{ atm}) \longrightarrow H_2O_{(g)}\ (1\text{ atm})$$

From Table 3.1, $\Delta H^\ominus = -57.7979 - (-68.3174) = 10{,}519.5$ cal.
From Table 4.3, $\Delta S^\ominus = 45.106 - 16.716 = 28.390$ cal deg^{-1}.
By (5.71), $\Delta G^\ominus = 10{,}519.5 - 298.16 \times 28.390 = 2054.7$ cal.
The fact that $\Delta G^\ominus > 0$ for the reaction as written is a sign that it is unnatural for water to have a vapor pressure of 1 atm at 25°C. Everyone knows that this reaction is not spontaneous, for water vapor at 25°C at 1 atm would condense to form water.

Example 5.9. Calculate $\Delta G^\ominus$ at 25°C for the reaction

$$2\,H_{2(g)} + O_{2(g)} \longrightarrow 2\,H_2O_{(l)}$$

where reactants and products are in their standard states at 1 atm.
From Table 3.1, $\Delta H^\ominus = 2(-68{,}317.4) = -136{,}634.8$ cal.
From Table 4.3, $\Delta S^\ominus = 2(16.716) - [49.003 + 2(31.211)] = -77.993$ cal deg^{-1}.
By (5.71), $\Delta G^\ominus = -136{,}634.8 - 298.16(-77.993) = -113{,}380.4$ cal.
Application of a spark to a mixture of hydrogen and oxygen would suggest to most people, in agreement with (5.58) and the fact that $\Delta G^\ominus < 0$, that the reaction is spontaneous, even though the initial and final states of the fire or explosion might not be quite those specified in the chemical equation.

Example 5.10. The production of energy by controlled fusion of deuterium nuclei may be accompanied by the production of cheap hydrogen if the deuterium is separated from ocean water by electrolysis. Perhaps then iron will be prepared thus:

$$3\,H_{2(g)} + Fe_2O_{3(s)} \longrightarrow 2\,Fe_{(s)} + 3\,H_2O_{(g)}$$

Is this reaction spontaneous at 25°C at 1 atm?
From Table 3.1, $\Delta H^\ominus = 3(-57.7979) - (-196.5) = +23.1$ kcal.
From Table 4.3, $\Delta S^\ominus = 3(45.106) + 2(6.49) - 21.5 - 3(31.211) = 33.2$ cal deg^{-1}.
By (5.71),

$$\Delta G^\ominus = 23{,}100 - 298.16 \times 33.2 = 13{,}200 \text{ cal}$$

The reaction is not spontaneous. The idea is not promising unless some change in pressure or temperature leads to a much lower value of $\Delta G^\ominus$ (see Example 9.14).

The entropy of a system is sometimes defined or described as the energy per degree of absolute temperature that cannot be made available as work. Terms of the form $T\,\Delta S$ are then called the *unavailable energy* of the system at the temperature T. In support of this idea, the following argument is set forth. At constant temperature,

$$\begin{cases} \Delta E = w + q \\ \Delta E = \Delta A + T\,\Delta S \\ \Delta A = w \end{cases}$$

The $T\,\Delta S$ term, as suggested by the second law Equation (4.1), is obviously a reversible heat term that seems not to be available as work at the temperature T. Indeed, it was proved in Section 4.5 that, as Thomson and Planck aver, a process the final result of which is merely a transformation of heat into work is impossible. Or again, there is no engine that can do work by operating in cycles if it merely absorbs heat at one temperature. But the qualifications *merely* and *cyclic* are the crux of the matter. Without these qualifications the concept "unavailable energy" is devoid of meaning (unavailable under what circumstances? unavailable for what?) and even incorrect and misleading.

Consider these two simple reversible processes by which an energy term $T\,\Delta S$ can be converted isothermally into work:

(a) One mole of a perfect gas expands isothermally and reversibly at the temperature T from a volume V_1 to a volume V_2. By (2.3), the work done by the gas is $-w$, where

$$-w = \int_{V_1}^{V_2} P\,dV = RT \int_{V_1}^{V_2} \frac{dV}{V} = RT \ln\left(\frac{V_2}{V_1}\right)$$

Since the energy of a perfect gas depends only on its temperature, $\Delta E = 0$ so that by the first law,

$$q = -w = RT \ln\left(\frac{V_2}{V_1}\right)$$

That is, all the heat q absorbed by the gas is used by the gas as it performs positive work. For this same isothermal change in state, by (5.45),

$$\Delta S = \int_{V_1}^{V_2} \left(\frac{\partial P}{\partial T}\right)_V dV = \int_{V_1}^{V_2} \frac{R}{V}\,dV = R \ln\left(\frac{V_2}{V_1}\right)$$

Accordingly, the value of $T\,\Delta S$ is that of q; hence, the "isothermally unavailable energy" $T\,\Delta S$ has in fact been converted entirely into work. *But the system and surroundings have not been restored to their original states.*

(b) One mole of liquid water is isothermally and reversibly vaporized at its normal boiling point. By (2.3), the isobaric work done by the system is $-w$, where

$$-w = \int_{V_1}^{V_2} P\,dV = P \int_{V_1}^{V_2} dV = P\,\Delta V \approx RT \approx 1.987 \times 373.2 \approx 742 \text{ cal}$$

Since the process is isobaric and involves only expansion work, if ΔH_v is the molar heat of vaporization, (2.22) yields $q_P = \Delta H_v$. But for the same change in state, by (4.52), $T\,\Delta S$ is ΔH_v, the isobaric reversible heat absorbed by the system. Of this "isothermally unavailable energy," about 742 cal have been recovered as work. *Again, the system and surroundings have not been restored to their original states.* It seems preferable to avoid discussion of a concept that requires so many qualifications that it becomes cumbersome and yet can be greatly abused. It is perhaps suitable for those whose engines and surroundings run reversibly and only in completed cycles.

5.11 FREE ENERGY AS A FUNCTION OF TEMPERATURE

It was possible to derive Kirchhoff's law, (3.20) or (3.21), in two ways.

$$\Delta H = \Delta H_0 + \int_{T_0}^{T} \Delta C_{P_0}\, dT' \tag{3.20}$$

$$\left(\frac{\partial \Delta H}{\partial T}\right)_{P_0} = \Delta C_{P_0} \tag{3.21}$$

One involved a vivid but long and detailed consideration of two routes by which a process could be performed. The other, a purely formal mathematical operation, involved interchanging the order of subtraction and differentiation. For the sake of brevity, the Gibbs-Helmholtz equation (5.19) is transformed by this latter process into a more meaningful form.

Let the Gibbs free energy of the final state of a closed system be G_2 and let its entropy be S_2. Similarly, let G_1 and S_1 refer to the Gibbs free energy and entropy of the initial state of the same closed system. It is clear that each of these symbols may consist of a sum of many terms. Then (5.19) reads for each

$$\left(\frac{\partial G_2}{\partial T}\right)_P = -S_2, \quad \text{and} \quad \left(\frac{\partial G_1}{\partial T}\right)_P = -S_1$$

Subtraction of the latter from the former and interchanging the order of subtraction and differentiation yields the Gibbs-Helmholtz equation in a common form:

$$\left(\frac{\partial \Delta G}{\partial T}\right)_P = -\Delta S \tag{5.74}$$

where $\Delta G = G_2 - G_1$ and $\Delta S = S_2 - S_1$. At any temperature, however, (5.71) requires $\Delta G = \Delta H - T\,\Delta S$. Hence, elimination of ΔS yields the usual form of the Gibbs-Helmholtz equation:

$$\left(\frac{\partial \Delta G}{\partial T}\right)_P = \frac{\Delta G - \Delta H}{T} \tag{5.75}$$

This equation gives the variation of the change in Gibbs free energy with respect to variations in temperature at constant pressure for any process that can in principle be performed reversibly in a closed system.

The mark of a spontaneous process is $(\delta G)_{P,T} < 0$ by (5.58); that is, a spontaneous process at constant T and P tends toward ever lower G. According to (5.74), ΔS for a certain isobaric process measures the rate at which ΔG of that process decreases as T rises. If $\Delta S > 0$, then a rise in T decreases ΔG and increases the tendency of the isobaric process to occur. If $\Delta S < 0$, a rise in T decreases that tendency. Conversely, if $\Delta S > 0$, then a fall in T increases ΔG and decreases the tendency of the isobaric process to occur. For example, reversible vaporization has $\Delta S^{\ominus} > 0$ by (4.52) and $\Delta G^{\ominus} = 0$ by (5.72). As T falls below the boiling point, (5.74) says that $\Delta G^{\ominus} > 0$, as already noted in Example 5.8.

There are several ways of integrating (5.75) or (5.74). The usual way is to transform (5.75) thus,

$$\left[\frac{\partial}{\partial T}\left(-\frac{\Delta G}{T}\right)\right]_P = -\frac{1}{T}\left(\frac{\partial \Delta G}{\partial T}\right)_P + \frac{\Delta G}{T^2}$$

By (5.75),

$$\left[\frac{\partial}{\partial T}\left(-\frac{\Delta G}{T}\right)\right]_P = -\frac{1}{T}\left(\frac{\Delta G - \Delta H}{T}\right) + \frac{\Delta G}{T^2}$$

Hence,

$$-\left[\frac{\partial}{\partial T}\left(\frac{\Delta G}{T}\right)\right]_P = \frac{\Delta H}{T^2} \tag{5.76}$$

If ΔH is known as a function of temperature through (3.20), then (5.76) is readily integrated at constant pressure. If ΔG_2 is the increase in Gibbs free energy at temperature T_2 while ΔG_1 is the increase in Gibbs free energy at temperature T_1 at the same pressure P for two changes in state that differ only in T_1 and T_2, then (5.76) becomes

$$-d\left(\frac{\Delta G}{T}\right) = \frac{\Delta H}{T^2}\,dT, \qquad (dP = 0)$$

$$-\int_{(\Delta G_1/T_1)}^{(\Delta G_2/T_2)} d\left(\frac{\Delta G}{T^2}\right) = \int_{T_1}^{T_2} \frac{\Delta H}{T^2}\,dT$$

$$-\frac{\Delta G_2}{T_2} + \frac{\Delta G_1}{T_1} = \int_{T_1}^{T_2} \frac{\Delta H}{T^2}\,dT, \qquad (dP = 0) \tag{5.77}$$

If the value of the integral and any three of the four quantities ΔG_1, ΔG_2, T_1 and T_2 are known, the fourth quantity can be found. In general, this fourth quantity is ΔG_2, when ΔG_1, T_1 and T_2 are known or specified. It is common, for example, to know ΔG_1 at 25°C and by (3.20) to know ΔH as a function of temperature from 25°C to the temperature $T = T_2$ at which ΔG_2 is sought.

A second way of solving for ΔG at any T is to find ΔS as a function of T. As in the derivation of (5.74), if the differentiation is interchanged in order with substraction as (4.53) applies to final state with entropy S_2 and initial state with entropy S_1, there results from

$$\left(\frac{\partial S_2}{\partial T}\right)_P = \frac{C_{P_2}}{T} \quad \text{and} \quad \left(\frac{\partial S_1}{\partial T}\right)_P = \frac{C_{P_1}}{T}$$

the general equation

$$\left(\frac{\partial \Delta S}{\partial T}\right)_P = \frac{\Delta C_P}{T} \tag{5.78}$$

where $\Delta S = S_2 - S_1$ and $\Delta C_P = C_{P_2} - C_{P_1}$, which occurred in Kirchhoff's law (3.21). If ΔS holds at T while ΔS_0 holds at T_0, then at P

$$\int_{\Delta S_0}^{\Delta S} d(\Delta S)' = \Delta S - \Delta S_0 = \int_{T_0}^{T} \frac{\Delta C_P}{T'}\, dT' \tag{5.79}$$

Then, with ΔS known as a function of T by (5.79), it follows from (5.74) that

$$\int_{\Delta G_1}^{\Delta G_2} d(\Delta G) = \Delta G_2 - \Delta G_1 = -\int_{T_1}^{T_2} \Delta S\, dT \tag{5.80}$$

which gives ΔG_2 at T_2.

A third way to find ΔG_2 at any T_2 is to find ΔH_2 by Kirchhoff's law (3.21) and ΔS_2 at T_2 by (5.78) or (5.79) and then use (5.71) in the form $\Delta G_2 = \Delta H_2 - T_2\, \Delta S_2$.

All three methods become very simple if $\Delta C_P = 0$, for then, by (3.21) and (5.78), ΔH and ΔS are constant at all T. The third method, with $\Delta H_2 = \Delta H_1$ and $\Delta S_2 = \Delta S_1$ then becomes

$$\Delta G_2 = \Delta H_1 - T_2\, \Delta S_1 \tag{5.81}$$

The second method's (5.80) then yields

$$\Delta G_2 - \Delta G_1 = -\Delta S_1(T_2 - T_1)$$

$$\Delta G_2 - (\Delta H_1 - T_1\, \Delta S_1) = T_1\, \Delta S_1 - T_2\, \Delta S_1$$

$$\Delta G_2 = \Delta H_1 - T_2\, \Delta S_1 \tag{5.81}$$

Finally, the first method's (5.77) gives

$$-\frac{\Delta G_2}{T_2} + \frac{\Delta G_1}{T_1} = \Delta H_1 \int_{T_1}^{T_2} \frac{dT}{T^2} = \Delta H_1 \left(-\frac{1}{T_2} + \frac{1}{T_1}\right)$$

$$-\frac{\Delta G_2}{T_2} + \frac{\Delta H_1}{T_1} - \Delta S_1 = -\frac{\Delta H_1}{T_2} + \frac{\Delta H_1}{T_1}$$

$$\Delta G_2 = \Delta H_1 - T_2\, \Delta S_1 \tag{5.81}$$

All the equations of this section apply to physical or chemical changes, just as a change like vaporization, which is commonly considered to be physical, can be described by quasi-chemical equations like

$$H_2O_{(l)} \longrightarrow H_2O_{(g)} \quad \text{or} \quad Br_{2(l)} \longrightarrow Br_{2(g)}$$

This presentation of the dependence of free energy upon temperature is meant to show that it does indeed depend upon temperature and that its calculation at any temperature is possible. Adequate treatment of the increments in free energy at any temperature for chemical reactions would extend this presentation unduly. Accordingly, here only changes generally classified as physical will be studied. Chemical changes must wait for discussion in succeeding chapters.

A brief remark about ΔH and ΔG for any change, physical or chemical, at low T is, however, appropriate here. As $T \longrightarrow 0$, (5.71) requires that the difference between ΔG and ΔH gradually vanish. If $\Delta S = 0$ at $T = 0$ and if $\Delta C_P > 0$, (5.78) requires $\Delta S > 0$ at $T > 0$. But then (5.74) requires that ΔG increase as T decreases. On the other hand, if still $\Delta C_P > 0$, then (3.21) requires that ΔH decrease as T decreases. Figure 5.2 shows how ΔH and ΔG thus converge to their common value at $T = 0$. If all the C_P's vary as T^3 near absolute zero, the curves for ΔH and ΔG vary as T^4. Figure 5.2 summarizes qualitatively what Richards discovered in 1902 about certain chemical reactions that could be run reversibly in electric cells.

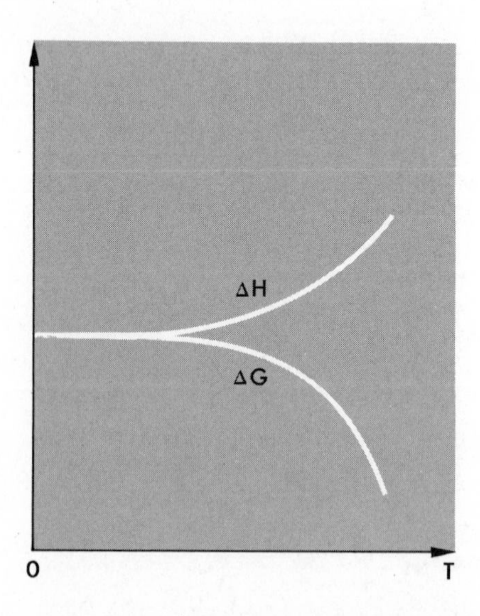

Figure 5.2. ΔH and ΔG at Low Temperature

Example 5.11. Calculate ΔG° at 100.00°C for the change of state $H_2O_{(l)} \longrightarrow H_2O_{(g)}$ with data from Tables 2.1, 3.1, and 4.3 if $C_P = 17.430 + 1.813 \times 10^{-3}T$ for $H_2O_{(l)}$.

An orderly summary of data eases the solution.

Item	$H_2O_{(l)}$ $\longrightarrow$	$H_2O_{(g)}$	Increment in Item
ΔH_f° (cal mole^{-1})	−68,317.4	−57,797.9	ΔH° = 10,519.5 cal
S° (cal mole^{-1} deg^{-1})	16.716	45.106	ΔS° = 28.390 cal deg^{-1}
$C_P^{(0)}$ (cal mole^{-1} deg^{-1})	17.430	7.256	$\Delta C_P^{(0)}$ = −10.174
$C_P^{(1)} \times 10^3$	1.813	2.298	$\Delta C_P^{(1)}$ = 0.485 × 10^{-3}
$C_P^{(2)} \times 10^6$	0.000	0.283	$\Delta C_P^{(2)}$ = 0.283 × 10^{-6}

By Kirchhoff's law (3.20),

$$\Delta H^\circ = \Delta H_0^\circ + \int_{T_0}^{T} \Delta C_P \, dT'$$

$$= 10{,}519.5 + \int_{298.15}^{T} (-10.174 + 0.485 \times 10^{-3} T' + 0.283 \times 10^{-6} T'^2) \, dT'$$

$$= 13{,}528.8 - 10.174 T + 2.42 \left(\frac{T}{100}\right)^2 + 0.0943 \left(\frac{T}{100}\right)^3$$

By (5.79),

$$\Delta S^\circ = \Delta S_0^\circ + \int_{T_0}^{T} \frac{\Delta C_P}{T'} \, dT'$$

$$= 28.390 + \int_{298.15}^{T} \left(\frac{-10.174 + 0.485 \times 10^{-3} T' + 0.283 \times 10^{-6} T'^2}{T'}\right) dT'$$

$$= 86.199 - 10.174 \ln T + 0.485 \left(\frac{T}{1000}\right) + 0.1415 \left(\frac{T}{1000}\right)^2$$

By (5.71) at $T_1 = 298.15$,

$$\Delta G_1^\circ = \Delta H_1^\circ - T_1 \Delta S_1^\circ$$

$$= 10{,}519.4 - 298.15(28{,}390) = 2054.9 \text{ cal}$$

A first method of solution by (5.77) with ΔH° from above and $T_2 = 373.15$:

$$-\frac{\Delta G_2^\circ}{373.15} + \frac{2054.9}{298.15} = \int_{298.15}^{373.15} \left[\frac{13528.8 - 10.174 T + \left(\frac{2.42}{10^4}\right) T^2 + \left(\frac{0.0943}{10^6}\right) T^3}{T^2}\right] dT$$

$$-\frac{\Delta G_2^\circ}{373.15} + 6.8922 = \frac{13528.8 \times 75.00}{373.15 \times 298.15} - 10.174 \ln \frac{373.15}{298.15} + \left(\frac{2.42}{10^4}\right)(75.00)$$

$$+ \frac{0.0943}{2 \times 10^6} (373.15^2 - 298.15^2)$$

$$\Delta G_2^\circ = +13 \text{ cal}$$

A second method of solution by (5.80) with ΔS° from above:

$$\Delta G_2^\ominus = 2054.9 - \int_{298.15}^{373.15} \left[86.199 - 10.174 \ln T + 0.485 \left(\frac{T}{1000}\right) + 0.1415 \left(\frac{T}{1000}\right)^2 \right] dT$$

$$= 2054.9 - 86.199(75.00) + 10.174 \left[T \ln T - T \right]_{298.15}^{373.15} - \frac{0.485}{2 \times 1000}(373.15^2 - 298.15^2) - \frac{0.1415}{3 \times 10^6}(373.15^3 - 298.15^3)$$

$$= 2054.9 - 6465.0 + 4436.9 - 12.2 - 1.3$$

$$= +13 \text{ cal}$$

A third method of solution with $T_2 = 373.15$ in the general expressions for $\Delta H^\ominus$ and $\Delta S^\ominus$:

$$\Delta H_2^\ominus = 13{,}528.8 - 10.174(373.15) + 2.42 \times 3.73^2 + 0.0943(3.73)^3$$

$$= 9771.9 \text{ cal}$$

$$\Delta S_2^\ominus = 86.199 - 10.174 \ln (373.15) + 0.485 \times 0.373 + 0.1415 \times 0.373^2$$

$$= 26.150 \text{ cal deg}^{-1}$$

By (5.81),

$$\Delta G_2^\ominus = 9771.9 - 373.15(26.150) = +13 \text{ cal}$$

According to (5.54) or (5.73), $\Delta G = 0$ at one atm at 100.00°C because water and steam are in equilibrium under these conditions. However, because the steam is not a perfect gas at 100°C, the standard state has a free energy that is about 5 cal greater than that of the real state of steam at 100°C at a pressure of one atm (see Example 5.16). The rest of the discrepancy is due to poor C_P's.

5.12 FREE ENERGY AS A FUNCTION OF PRESSURE

Infinitesimal changes in G of a closed system depend on infinitesimal changes in P and T and whatever other independent variables specify the nonexpansion work through the basic relation

$$dG \leqslant -S\,dT + V\,dP + dw_0 \tag{5.67}$$

If no nonexpansion work occurs ($dw_0 = 0$) and if T is constant ($dT = 0$), (5.67) for a reversible change is $dG = V\,dP$. In the elegant notation of the calculus, this is simply

$$\left(\frac{\partial G}{\partial P}\right)_T = V \tag{5.20}$$

Increasing the pressure of a real system isothermally always increases its Gibbs free energy if (5.20) holds, for $V > 0$.

This equation is readily solved for finite increments in G if the volume V is known as a function of the pressure P at the temperature T. That is, if $V = V(P, T)$, then, by (5.20),

$$\Delta G = \int_{P_1}^{P_2} V(P, T)\, dP, \qquad (dT = 0) \tag{5.82}$$

The terms of the form PV by which E and H differ have long been recognized as small in size when P is of the order of a few atmospheres and when V is the volume of a condensed phase. It is true here also that the magnitude of (5.82) for condensed phases is generally negligible when gases are also involved or when chemical changes occur to produce appreciable changes in G. When account must be taken of (5.82) for changes in condensed phases, it is often quite adequate to assume that the condensed phases are incompressible. Since their volumes are then independent of pressure, V is a constant for each phase, and the increase in Gibbs free energy for each phase that suffers a change in pressure from P_1 to P_2 is

$$\Delta G = V \int_{P_1}^{P_2} dP = V\, \Delta P. \tag{5.83}$$

If $V = 50$ ml mole^{-1} and if $\Delta P \approx 10$ atm, the value of ΔG is only about 12 cal per mole of condensed phase.

The magnitude of ΔG is generally not negligible when gases are involved. For n moles of a perfect gas compressed reversibly and isothermally from a pressure P_1 to a pressure P_2, by (5.82),

$$\begin{aligned} \Delta G &= \int_{P_1}^{P_2} \frac{nRT}{P}\, dP \\ &= nRT \ln\left(\frac{P_2}{P_1}\right) \end{aligned} \tag{5.84}$$

For gas at 273°K, an increase in pressure from 1 to 11 atm requires

$$\Delta G = 1.987 \times 273 \times \ln\left(\tfrac{11}{1}\right) = 1300 \text{ cal mole}^{-1}$$

These 1300 cal constitute about a hundredfold increase over the 12 cal for a mole of a typical incompressible condensed phase as its pressure is increased by 10 atm. For the sake of performing the calculation, a reversible path was followed. However, for the same isothermal pressure change, ΔG would be given by (5.84) whether or not the change really occurred reversibly because G is a function of state.

It happens that for a perfect gas at constant temperature,

$$d(PV) = d(RT), \qquad P\, dV + V\, dP = 0, \qquad V\, dP = -P\, dV$$

That is, the increase $V\, dP$ in Gibbs free energy of a perfect gas is equal to the reversible work $dA = -P\, dV$ done on it at constant temperature. In order to compress reversibly 1 mole of a perfect gas at 273°K from a pressure of 1 to 11 atm, the work done on the gas is

$$\Delta A = w = -\int_{V_1}^{V_2} P\,dV = -RT\ln\left(\frac{V_2}{V_1}\right)$$

But by Boyle's law, $P_1V_1 = P_2V_2$; hence,

$$w = RT\ln\left(\frac{P_2}{P_1}\right)$$

which is (5.84) because of the special form of the equation of state of a perfect gas.

Example 5.12. As one mole $CO_{2(g)}$ at 27°C expands, its pressure falls from 3.00 atm to 1.00 atm. Calculate for this change values of ΔG, ΔA, and w if (a) CO_2 is assumed to be a perfect gas; and (b) CO_2 is assumed to behave as a van der Waals gas with $a = 3.61$ l^2 atm mole^{-2} and $b = 0.0428$ l mole^{-1}.

Since the process is not sufficiently well defined, it is impossible to calculate w, the work involved. However, with the invention of a suitable reversible path, namely, an isothermal reversible expansion, it is possible to find ΔG and ΔA.

(a) If CO_2 is a perfect gas, by (5.82) or (5.84)

$$\Delta G = \int_{3.00}^{1.00}\left(\frac{RT}{P}\right)dP = 1.987 \times 300 \times \ln\left(\frac{1.00}{3.00}\right) = -655 \text{ cal}$$

Similarly, by (5.61)

$$\Delta A = -\int_{V_1}^{V_2} P\,dV = -\int_{3.00}^{1.00} P\left(-\frac{RT}{P^2}\right)dP = RT\ln\left(\frac{1.00}{3.00}\right) = -655 \text{ cal}$$

(b) If CO_2 is a van der Waals gas, by (5.82) and (1.67),

$$\Delta G = \int_{P_1}^{P_2}\left[\frac{RT}{P} + \left(b - \frac{a}{RT}\right)\right]dP = RT\ln\left(\frac{P_2}{P_1}\right) + \left(b - \frac{a}{RT}\right)(P_2 - P_1)$$

$$= -655 + \left(0.0428 - \frac{3.61}{0.08205 \times 300}\right)(1.00 - 3.00)\left(\frac{1.987}{0.08205}\right)$$

$$= -655 + 5 = -650 \text{ cal}$$

By (5.61)

$$\Delta A = -\int_{V_1}^{V_2} P\,dV = -\int_{V_1}^{V_2}\left[\frac{RT}{V + \dfrac{a}{RT} - b}\right]dV$$

$$= RT\ln\left[\frac{V_1 + \dfrac{a}{RT} - b}{V_2 + \dfrac{a}{RT} - b}\right] = 1.987 \times 300 \times \ln\left(\frac{P_2}{P_1}\right) = -655 \text{ cal}$$

It is an accident of the method of calculation that the values of ΔA are alike for the two equations of state. It is clear, however, that deviations from ideal behavior influence ΔG.

Example 5.13. Calculate the value of the standard entropy $S^\ominus_{(l)}$ of $Br_{2\,(l)}$ at 25°C from the accurate theoretical value of $S^\ominus$ of the vapor in Table 4.3. The density of $Br_{2\,(l)}$ is 3.12 g cm^{-3} and its Dieterici constants are $a = 12.94 \times 10^6$ atm cm^6 mole^{-2} and $b = 67.5$ cm^3 mole^{-1}. According to NBS Circular 500 (ref. Table 4.3), the vapor pressure of Br_2 at 25.00°C is 214 mm Hg (0.282 atm) and its standard heat of formation is 7.34 kcal mole^{-1}.

Consider the reversible process at 25°C:

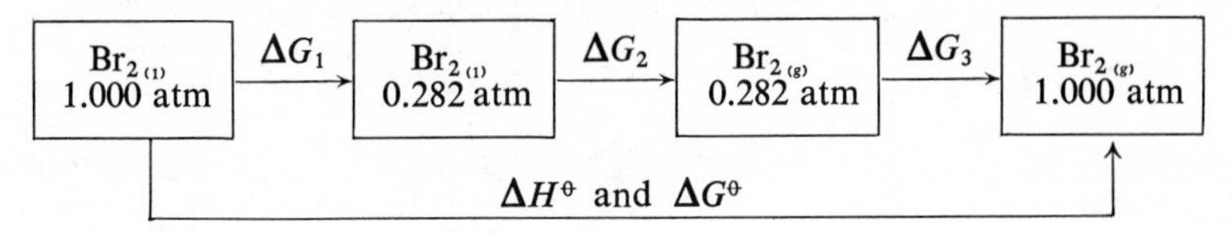

By (5.83), since $M = 2 \times 79.9$ for Br_2,

$$\Delta G_1 = \int_{1.000}^{0.282} V\,dP = \frac{2 \times 79.9}{3.12}(0.282 - 1.000)\frac{1.987}{82.06} = -0.891 \text{ cal}$$

Because vaporization at 25.00°C at 0.282 atm is reversible, $\Delta G_2 = 0$ by (5.73). Finally, by (5.82) and (1.67), as in the preceding example,

$$\begin{aligned}
\Delta G_3 &= RT \ln\left(\frac{P_2}{P_1}\right) + \left(b - \frac{a}{RT}\right)(P_2 - P_1) \\
&= 1.987 \times 298.2 \times 2.303 \times \log_{10}\left(\frac{1.000}{0.282}\right) \\
&\quad + \left(67.5 - \frac{12.94 \times 10^6}{82.0 \times 298.2}\right) \times (1.000 - 0.282)\left(\frac{1.987}{82.0}\right) \\
&= 750 - 8 = 742 \text{ cal}
\end{aligned}$$

For the overall process, then, $\Delta H^\ominus = 7340$ cal and $\Delta G^\ominus = \Delta G_1 + \Delta G_2 + \Delta G_3 = -1 + 0 + 742 = 741$ cal. Hence, by (5.71),

$$\Delta S^\ominus = S^\ominus_{(g)} - S^\ominus_{(l)} = \frac{\Delta H^\ominus - \Delta G^\ominus}{T} = \frac{7340 - 741}{298.2} = 22.1_2$$

By Table 4.3, then, $S^\ominus_{(l)} = S^\ominus_{(g)} - \Delta S^\ominus = 58.639 - 22.1_2 = 36.5_2$ cal mole^{-1} deg^{-1}. It is clear that a more accurate value of the heat of vaporization would allow a more accurate value of $S^\ominus_{(l)}$ to be found without C_P's at low T. (The effect of pressure on $\Delta H^\ominus$ is negligible in this problem.)

Example 5.14. Calculate the net work that must be done reversibly and isothermally on a mole of a perfect gas to transport it from its equilibrium state at the surface of the earth to its equilibrium state at a height z.

As the gas rises, its pressure decreases continuously from P_o at the surface to P at the altitude z. An infinitesimal vertical movement requires, by (2.1), that gravitational work $Mg\,dz$ be done on the gas, where M is the mass of 1 mole of gas and dz is the infinitesimal vertical movement. But for an infinitesimal movement, $dG = 0$ since the gas is at equilibrium with its immediate surroundings with respect to temperature and pressure. Hence, by (5.67), the pressure varies with altitude thus:

$$dG = V\,dP + Mg\,dz = 0$$

Definite integration yields the equation for the dependence of pressure on altitude in a uniform gravitational field if the temperature of the closed system of 1 mole is constant.

$$-\int_{P_o}^{P} V\,dP = \int_0^z Mg\,dz', \qquad RT\ln\left(\frac{P_o}{P}\right) = Mgz, \qquad P = P_o e^{-Mgz/RT}$$

The diagram for the isothermal change of state is this:

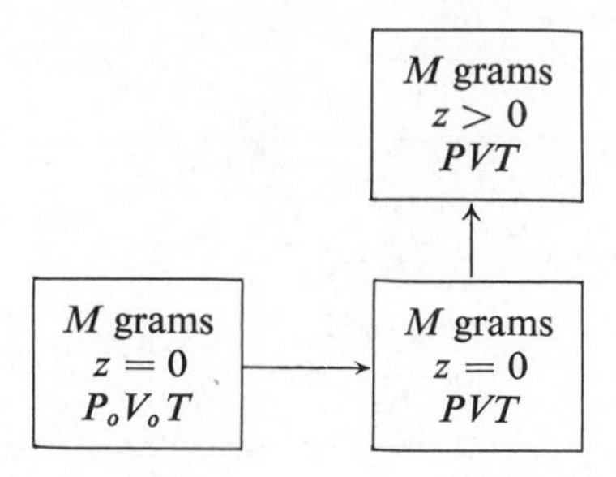

The state of the system is specified not only by three of the four variables of the perfect gas equation but also by the altitude z. With account of Boyle's law, $P_oV_o = PV$, the isothermal reversible work done on the gas at the surface of the earth where $z = 0$ is

$$w = -\int_{V_o}^{V} P\,dV' = -RT\int_{V_o}^{V} \frac{dV'}{V'} = -RT\ln\left(\frac{V}{V_o}\right) = RT\ln\left(\frac{P}{P_o}\right)$$

The isothermal reversible work done on the gas as it is elevated at constant volume V is, as in Example 5.7,

$$w = \int_0^z Mg\,dz' = Mgz$$

The net isothermal work ΔA is, by (5.62), the sum of the expansion and gravitational work, namely,

$$\Delta A = RT\ln\left(\frac{P}{P_o}\right) + Mgz$$

But from the previous results concerning the dependence of pressure on altitude, $P = P_o \exp(-Mgz/RT)$, it follows that $\Delta A = 0$. Whatever work the gas could do by expansion is used to raise it against the force of gravity. This last statement of the law of conservation of energy could, of course, have been used to obtain the dependence of pressure on altitude without recourse to the Gibbs free energy.

5.13 FUGACITY

Fugacity is a mathematical device invented by G. N. Lewis in 1901 to preserve the simple appearances of Equation (5.84) even for real gases. All gases tend to behave like perfect gases at low pressures and at high temperature. The modest size of the second virial coefficient B in the virial expansion $V = nRT/P + nB$ assures that a small enough value of P or a large enough value of T will yield the perfect gas equation within the accuracy of the measurements of P, V, and T.

Associated with any specified change of state of a gas there is a definite increment in Gibbs free energy ΔG. If there is ascribed to the initial state a fugacity f_1 and to the final state a fugacity f_2, then preservation of the form of (5.84) for an isothermal process yields (5.85).

$$\Delta G = nRT \ln \left(\frac{P_2}{P_1}\right) \tag{5.84}$$

$$\Delta G = nRT \ln \left(\frac{f_2}{f_1}\right) \tag{5.85}$$

The fugacity of a gas is defined by (5.85) and the condition that, at low pressures, the values of the fugacity and observed pressure become alike. That is, fugacity f is defined by (5.85) and (5.86).

$$\lim_{P \to 0} \left(\frac{f}{P}\right) = 1 \tag{5.86}$$

Since free energy is a well-defined property of a system and since an arbitrary zero of energy or free energy can be set, suppose that the molar Gibbs free energy of a system in some standard state is $G^{\circ}(f^{\circ}, T)$. Then, for isothermal change of state involving n moles from this standard state to some other state with molar free energy $G(f, T)$, let

$$\Delta G = G(f, T) - G^{\circ}(f^{\circ}, T) = nRT \ln \left(\frac{f}{f^{\circ}}\right)$$

If the units of f are such that the numerical value of f° is unity, the value of $G^{\circ}(f^{\circ}, T)$ is independent of f°. Then,

$$G(f, T) = nRT \ln f + G^{\circ}(T) \tag{5.87}$$

For an isothermal change between states that are not standard, by (5.87)

$$\Delta G = G(f_2, T) - G(f_1, T) = nRT \ln \left(\frac{f_2}{f_1}\right)$$

which is (5.85) with its desired simplicity. In this way, the arbitrary but quite definite reference free energy $G^{\circ}(T)$ will always be suppressed for any observed change of state. Here $G^{\circ}(T)$ is the free energy of the gas in its standard state, which until now has been taken to be a pressure of one atm. Now, however, it is clear that this standard state is the hypothetical reference state with a fugacity of one atm at the standard temperature.

A convenient way of evaluating G as a function of pressure is the following, in which the major dependence of G on the pressure is explicitly acknowledged in order that attention may be focused on the correction term. For 1 mole, by (5.20)

$$\left[\frac{\partial}{\partial P}(G - nRT\ln P)\right]_T = V(P, T) - \frac{nRT}{P} \tag{5.88}$$

But by (5.87),

$$G - nRT\ln P = nRT\ln\left(\frac{f}{P}\right) + G^{\circ}(T)$$

Hence, by (5.86),

$$\lim_{P\to 0}\,[G - nRT\ln P] = G^{\circ}(T)$$

Despite the embarrassing infinity that seems to come from the logarithm of zero, this limit exists because all the other terms of Equation (5.89) below exist. Integration of (5.88) from a very low pressure to a finite pressure yields

$$\int_{G^{\circ}}^{G-nRT\ln P} d(G - nRT\ln P)' = \int_0^P \left(V - \frac{nRT}{P'}\right) dP'$$

$$G(P, T) - nRT\ln P - G^{\circ}(T) = \int_0^P \left(V - \frac{nRT}{P'}\right) dP' \tag{5.89}$$

When the virial expansion (1.67) is adequate as the equation of state,

$$G(P, T) = G^{\circ}(T) + nRT\ln P + n\int_0^P \left(\frac{RT}{P'} + B - \frac{RT}{P'}\right) dP'$$

$$= G^{\circ}(T) + nRT\ln P + nBP \tag{5.90}$$

$$= G^{\circ}(T) + nRT\ln f \tag{5.87}$$

If (5.90) is to assume the same form as the desired (5.87) for the same state, then

$$\ln f = \ln P + \frac{BP}{RT}$$

or

$$f = Pe^{BP/RT} \tag{5.91}$$

Figure 5.3 illustrates values of f and P for typical values of B. The fugacity f has the units of pressure P and is numerically equal to P for perfect gases since for them $B = 0$. Often f is almost equal to P since B is small. If T becomes great or P becomes small, the value of the fugacity approaches that of the pressure. Evaluation of the fugacity is in no way easier because of its invention. Rather,

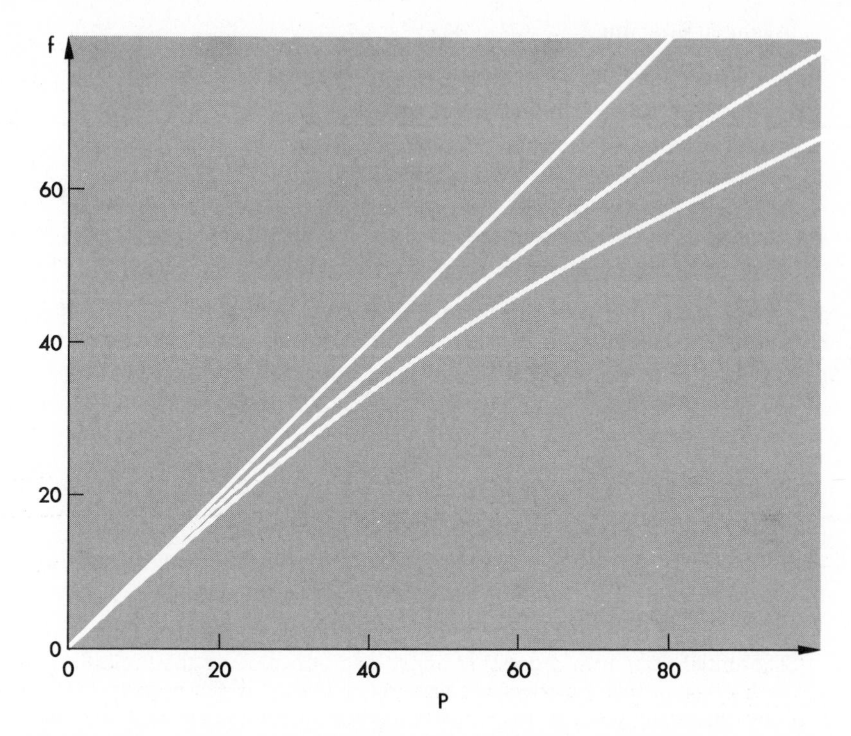

Figure 5.3. Fugacity as a Function of Pressure According to Equation (5.91) When B/RT is Zero, -400^{-1}, and -250^{-1} $\text{cm}^3\ \text{mole}^{-1}$

its main justification is in (5.91), which suggests that pressure, although strictly incorrect, is often a satisfactory approximation to the true thermodynamic variable fugacity.

Example 5.15. What are the fugacities of N_2 and CO_2 at 25°C at pressures of one and fifty atm?

With the van der Waals approximation to the second virial coefficient $B = b - a/RT$,

$$B(N_2) = 38.6 - \frac{1.35 \times 10^6}{0.08205 \times 298.2} = -16.5\ \text{cm}^3\ \text{mole}^{-1}$$

$$B(CO_2) = 42.8 - \frac{3.60 \times 10^6}{82.05 \times 298.2} = -104.3\ \text{cm}^3\ \text{mole}^{-1}$$

By (4.171), at a pressure of one atm,

$$f(N_2) = 1.000 \exp\left(\frac{-16.5 \times 1.000}{82.05 \times 298.2}\right) = 0.999\ \text{atm}$$

$$f(CO_2) = 1.000 \exp\left(\frac{-104.3 \times 1.000}{82.05 \times 298.2}\right) = 0.996\ \text{atm}$$

Again, at fifty atm,

$$f(N_2) = 50.00 \exp\left(\frac{-16.5 \times 50.00}{82.05 \times 298.2}\right) = 48.34 \text{ atm}$$

$$f(CO_2) = 50.00 \exp\left(\frac{-104.3 \times 50.00}{82.05 \times 298.2}\right) = 40.40 \text{ atm}$$

Example 5.16. Calculate the increment in Gibbs free energy as one mole of steam at 100°C is changed isothermally from a fugacity of 1.00 atm to a pressure of one atm.

By Table 1.3, $a = 7.02 \times 10^6$ cm^6 atm mole^{-2} and $b = 33.0$ cm^3 mole^{-1} (Dieterici). Hence,

$$B = b - \frac{a}{RT} = 33.0 - \frac{7.02 \times 10^6}{82.0 \times 373} = -196 \text{ cm}^3 \text{ mole}^{-1}$$

If G_1 is described by (5.87) and G_2 by (5.90), then

$$\Delta G = RT \ln P_2 + BP_2 - RT \ln f_1 = BP_2$$

$$= -196 \times 1.00 \left(\frac{1.987}{82.0}\right) = -4.74 \text{ cal mole}^{-1}$$

The initial state is at a pressure above one atm because the molecules attract each other in this imperfect gas and thus reduce f, which measures their thermodynamic activity or interaction with their surroundings. Since $P_1 > P_2$ and $f_1 > f_2$, (5.84) or (5.85) requires $\Delta G < 0$ as calculated.

5.14 SUMMARY

This chapter's very general theoretical developments that lead to free energy have been illustrated for very simple changes of state. These applications have justified, at least for physical changes, the definitions of free energy. Several kinds of thermodynamic proof and definition have also been presented.

Much of the practical numerical work has dealt with ideal and real gases because for them simple equations of state are available and because moderate changes in pressure have so great an effect on their free energies. The next four chapters turn free energy and the various criteria of spontaneity and equilibrium to a description of the parts of a system suffering physical and chemical change. In other words, the generality and breadth of this chapter as it deals with a system as a unit are to be specialized for more particular events and circumstances within a system.

Free energy has taken the dominant role from entropy as the thermodynamic function of most value in describing equilibrium and the approach to it, even though fundamentally both rank equally. The importance of the equations

$$\left(\frac{\partial G}{\partial T}\right)_P = -S \quad \text{and} \quad \left(\frac{\partial G}{\partial P}\right)_T = V$$

will become obvious in the chapters that follow.

PROBLEMS

1. What function of state is constant during isothermal isobaric processes of closed systems that do expansion work in a uniform gravitational field?
Answer: $G - Mgz$.

2. Show that $(\partial S/\partial P)_T = -R/P$ for a perfect gas at pressure P and interpret the negative sign in terms of randomness and disorder.

3. Show that $(\partial E/\partial V)_T = T^2[\partial/\partial T(P/T)]_V$ and with this result show that the thermodynamic and perfect gas scales of T are alike.

4. Estimate the fall in temperature of O_2 ($C_V = \frac{5}{2}R$ and $a = 1.55 \times 10^6$ cm^6 atm mole^{-2}) as it escapes from a small rigid vessel where its temperature is 25.000°C at 5.00 atm adiabatically into a very large evacuated, rigid chamber.
Answer: 1.545°.

5. Show that the inversion temperature of a Dieterici or van der Waals gas is twice its Boyle temperature.

6. Calculate the inversion temperatures of H_2, N_2, Cl_2, and SO_2.
Answer: (H_2) 225°K; (N_2) 850°K; (Cl_2) 2800°K; (SO_2) 2900°K.

7. Show that for n moles of a perfect gas that change from a volume V_1 at T_1 to a volume V_2 at T_2

$$\frac{\Delta S}{n} = \int_{T_1}^{T_2} \frac{C_P}{T}\, dT - R \ln \frac{T_2}{T_1} + R \ln \frac{V_2}{V_1}$$

8. Derive (5.42) from (4.50).

9. Explain the condensation of supersaturated vapor (e.g., in a cloud chamber) by recourse to the increase in entropy as a particle causes condensation nuclei to form.

10. What is the change in entropy of H_2O when a tiny crystal of ice is dropped into an open Dewar flask of negligible heat capacity if the flask initially contains one mole supercooled liquid water at -10.00°C? What fraction of the mole of H_2O crystallizes?
Answer: $\Delta S = 0.013$ cal deg^{-1}; 0.1250 mole.

11. Calculate ΔG° at 25°C for the reactions
(a) $3\ O_{2\,(g)} \longrightarrow 2\ O_{3\,(g)}$
(b) $I_{2\,(s)} \longrightarrow I_{2\,(g)}$
Answer: (a) 78.0 kcal; (b) 4.62 kcal.

12. Show that

$$\Delta H = \left[\frac{\partial(\Delta G/T)}{\partial(1/T)}\right]_P$$

and use it to find $\Delta G^{\ominus}$ at 2000°K for the gaseous reaction 2 HCl $\longrightarrow$ $H_2 + Cl_2$ if $\Delta C_P = 0$.
Answer: $\Delta G^{\ominus} = 53{,}614$ cal.

13. What pressure change is required to increase the Gibbs free energy of a mole of liquid ($V = 50$ cm^3 mole^{-1}) by 20.0 cal mole^{-1} at 0°C? At 100°C?
Answer: 16.5 atm.

14. Calculate the fugacity and molar free energy of gaseous H_2 at 25°C at ten atm.
Answer: 10.0678 atm; 1368.3 cal mole^{-1}.

15. At what pressure does O_2 have a fugacity of one atm at 25°C?
Answer: 1.000978 atm.

---

16. In words, as is done in the text for (5.10) and (5.14), restate (5.11), (5.14), (5.16), (5.17), (5.18), and (5.19).

17. Calculate the heat absorbed by one mole of water as it changes from 20.00°C at one atm to 80.00°C, first at constant pressure, and, secondly, at constant volume. Assume that C_P is 18.016 cal mole^{-1} deg^{-1}. The volume of a mole of water at 20.00°C at one atm is 18.047 cm^3; at 80.00°C at one atm it is 18.537 cm^3 mole^{-1}; at 80.00°C it is 18.047 cm^3 mole^{-1} at 1464 atm.
Answer: $q_P = 1081$ cal; $q_V = 987$ cal.

18. Predict the final temperature of CO_2 that escapes adiabatically into an evacuated chamber of such size that its final volume is twenty times its initial volume at 25°C and 1.00 atm.
Answer: 24.53°C.

19. Calculate the Joule-Thomson coefficients of H_2 and SO_2 at 25°C. For SO_2, $C_P = 9.7$ cal mole^{-1} deg^{-1}.
Answer: (H_2) $-$ 0.023 deg atm^{-1}; (SO_2) 1.24 deg atm^{-1}.

20. Show that the inversion temperature of a real gas is about seven times its absolute critical temperature.

21. Calculate the absolute entropy of one mole gaseous hydrogen at -20°C at 0.200 atm.
Answer: 33.275 cal mole^{-1} deg^{-1}.

22. Two moles argon, a perfect monatomic gas, at 2.000 atm are compressed reversibly at 25°C until their pressure is 10.00 atm. Then the argon expands freely and irreversibly into an evacuated vessel of such size that the final pressure is 2.000 atm. Calculate and tabulate ΔE, ΔH, ΔA, ΔG, ΔS, q, and w for the compression, for the expansion, and for the whole process.
Answer: Compression: $\Delta A = \Delta G = w = -q = 1907$ cal; $\Delta S = -6.396$ cal deg^{-1};
Expansion: $\Delta A = \Delta G = -1907$ cal; $\Delta S = 6.396$ cal deg^{-1};
Cycle: $w = -q = 1907$ cal; all others zero.

23. Calculate the increase in entropy of a mole of $CO_{2(g)}$ that expands isothermally at 0°C from a volume of 7.000 liters to a volume of 21.000 liters if CO_2 is a
(a) perfect gas.
(b) van der Waals gas.
Answer: (a) $R \ln 3.0000$; (b) $R \ln 3.0123$.

24. The Massieu functions of 1869 are $(-A/T)$ and $(-G/T)$. Express the general conditions of spontaneity for these functions for closed systems.
Answer: $\delta(-A/T)_{T,V} > 0$; $\delta(-G/T)_{T,P} > 0$.

25. By two proofs show that

$$(P/T) = (\partial S/\partial V)_E$$

for any substance in internal equilibrium in the absence of nonexpansion work.

26. Calculate $\Delta G^\ominus$ and $\Delta A^\ominus$ at 25°C for these changes:
(a) $H_{2(g)} + F_{2(g)} \longrightarrow 2HF_{(g)}$.
(b) $HF_{(g)} \longrightarrow H^+_{(aq)} + F^-_{(aq)}$.
(c) $H_{2(g)} + F_{2(g)} \longrightarrow 2H^+_{(aq)} + 2F^-_{(aq)}$.
(d) $2Ag_{(s)} + Cl_{2(g)} \longrightarrow 2AgCl_{(s)}$.
(e) $ZnSO_4 \cdot 7H_2O_{(s)} \longrightarrow ZnSO_4 \cdot 6H_2O_{(s)} + H_2O_{(g)}$.
Answer: (a) $\Delta G^\ominus = \Delta A^\ominus = -129.4$ kcal; (b) $\Delta G^\ominus = -1.4$ kcal; $\Delta A^\ominus = -0.8$ kcal; (c) $\Delta G^\ominus = -132.16$ kcal, $\Delta A^\ominus = -130.98$ kcal, (d) $\Delta G^\ominus = -52.44$ kcal; $\Delta A^\ominus = -51.85$ kcal; (e) $\Delta G^\ominus = +2.2$ kcal; $\Delta A^\ominus = +1.6$ kcal.

27. At about what temperature does Br_2 boil at one atm? Use data from Tables 3.1 and 4.3.
Answer: 59°C.

28. Calculate ΔG and ΔA for two moles of a perfect gas that changes isothermally and irreversibly from a pressure of 10.0 atm to 0.200 atm at 0°C. Recalculate ΔG and ΔA for the same process when the gas is a real van der Waals gas, namely, methane.
Answer: $\Delta G = \Delta A = -4247$ cal (P.G.); $\Delta G = -4269$ cal and $\Delta A = -4298$ cal (CH_4).

29. What is the fugacity of steam at 150°C at a pressure of 4.000 atm?
Answer: 3.942 atm.

---

30. In order to estimate the low temperature T_1 reached by adiabatic demagnetization of a paramagnetic salt, the following experiments were done:
(a) Reversible adiabatic demagnetization of salt from a temperature of 1.20°K in a magnetic field of $\mathscr{H}$ to a low temperature T_1 in essentially zero field.
(b) Slight warming of the salt by gamma radiation for t minutes from T_1 to T_2 in essentially zero magnetic field, which was constant during warming.
(c) Reversible adiabatic magnetic work done on salt, initially at T_2 in zero field, until the temperature is T_3 and the magnetic field is again $\mathscr{H}$.
(d) Slight warming of salt by gamma radiation for a much longer time nt minutes in constant magnetic field $\mathscr{H}$ until the temperature rises from 1.20°K to T_3.
If $T_3 \approx 1.2$°K and if $T_1 \approx T_2$, calculate ΔS for a cycle that includes these four steps in forward or reverse sense. Then find T_1 as a function of n.
Answer: $nT_1 = 1.20$

31. The normal boiling point of SO_2 is -10°C, and its vapor pressure at 25°C is 3.80 atm. Calculate the absolute molar entropies of liquid and saturated gaseous SO_2 at 0°C from $S^\ominus$ in Table 4.1. For gaseous SO_2, $C_P = 9.7$ cal mole^{-1} deg^{-1}.
Answer: 33.14 cal deg^{-1}, 57.62 cal deg^{-1}.

32. One mole N_2, a perfect gas with $C_P = 7R/2$, is caused to change its state from 3.00 atm at 200°C to 1.00 atm at 0°C by three different processes. Find and tabulate q, w, ΔE, ΔH, and ΔS for this change of state for these processes:
(a) The gas expands reversibly and adiabatically until its temperature is 0°C; then it is brought reversibly and isothermally to the final state.

(b) By expanding irreversibly through a Joule-Thomson porous plug, the pressure of the gas falls to 1 atm; then it is brought isobarically to the final state.
(c) The gas expands freely into an evacuated vessel; then it is cooled suddenly without expansion work until the final state is reached.
Answer: $\Delta E = -994$ cal; $\Delta H = -1391$ cal; $\Delta S = -1.64$ cal deg^{-1}; $w = \Delta E - q$; (a) $q = -445$ cal; (b) $q = 1391$ cal; (c) $q = -994$ cal.

33. It is observed that a tiny bit of light can cause the reaction $H_{2(g)} + Cl_{2(g)} \longrightarrow 2HCl_{(g)}$ to occur suddenly and to an extent quite out of proportion to the cause. In terms of the entropy change for such an adiabatic process, explain the spontaneity of this reaction at 25°C.
Answer: $\Delta S > 0$.

34. Find ΔE, ΔH, ΔS, and w for one mole of an ideal gas with $C_V = 5R/2$ as it changes from an initial state at 4.00 atm at 250°C:
(a) To 1.00 atm by reversible adiabatic expansion.
(b) To 1.00 atm at 200°C by irreversible adiabatic expansion (if this is possible).
(c) To 1.00 atm at 50°C by irreversible adiabatic expansion (if this is possible).
What is the maximum work that could be done by the gas between these same three pairs of terminal states in any kind of process done once? Find ΔE, ΔH, and ΔS for these processes that produce more work.
Answer: In the order $\Delta E = w$(cal), ΔH(cal), ΔS(cal deg^{-1}): (a) -850, -1189, zero; (b) -248, -348, 2.121; (c) impossible if adiabatic.

35. Calculate $\Delta G^{\ominus}$ and $\Delta A^{\ominus}$ at 25°C for these changes:
(a) $C_2H_{4(g)} + H_{2(g)} \longrightarrow C_2H_{6(g)}$
(b) $2Al_{(s)} + Fe_2O_{3(s)} \longrightarrow Al_2O_{3(s)} + 2Fe_{(s)}$
Answer: (a) $\Delta G^{\ominus} = -24.142$ kcal, $\Delta A^{\ominus} = -23.549$ kcal; (b) $\Delta A^{\ominus} \approx \Delta G^{\ominus} = -199.7$ kcal.

36. For the changes of the preceding problem, what happens to $\Delta G^{\ominus}$ as T rises and as P rises?
Answer: As T rises, both $\Delta G^{\ominus}$'s increase. As P rises, $\Delta G^{\ominus}$ of (a) decreases while $\Delta G^{\ominus}$ of (b) is about constant since $\Delta V \approx 0$.

37. Compare ΔG at 227°C for these sudden (i.e., adiabatic) changes:
(a) Two moles of a nonvolatile, incompressible liquid with molar volume 40 cm^3 mole^{-1} at 100 atm pressure go to a pressure of one atm.
(b) Two moles of a volatile, incompressible liquid with molar volume 40 cm^3 mole^{-1} at 100 atm pressure go to vapor at one atm. The vapor pressure of the liquid is 10.0 atm at 227°C.
Answer: (a) -192 cal; (b) -2251 cal.

38. Calculate ΔG at 100°C for isothermal compression of a mole of gas from a pressure of one atm to a pressure of ten atm if its equation of state is $PV = nRT - 200nP$, where P is in atm and V is in cm^3 mole^{-1}. How much reversible isothermal work must be done at 100°C on this mole of gas to compress it from one to ten atm pressure?
Answer: $\Delta G = 1663$ cal; $w = 1707$ cal.

39. Calculate the increase in enthalpy when one mole of gaseous O_2 at 25°C changes from a pressure of one atm to a fugacity of one atm.
Answer: $\Delta H = -0.0079$ joule.

6
CHEMICAL POTENTIAL

6.1 INTRODUCTION

The chemical potential of a substance in a system is a convenient measure of its tendency to act chemically or thermodynamically, just as the altitude of a weight, the tension of a spring, or the pressure of a gas are measures of the intensity of their tendencies to cause mechanical changes. At a certain fixed temperature and pressure, the chemical potential of a substance is the rate at which the Gibbs free energy of the system increases as one mole of the substance is added to the system, the system being so large and the relative amount of substance actually added being so small that the composition of the system remains unchanged.

Before solutions are investigated, however, it is appropriate to consider in more detail than in the previous chapter how free energy of a pure substance depends on its pressure, temperature, and state of aggregation. Then, after a discussion of solutions and a mathematical definition of chemical potential, it will be possible in this chapter to consider how the chemical potential of a pure or dissolved substance may depend on fine division or existence in thin layers between macroscopically observable phases. This chapter, in a way, is a practical summary of the last few sections of the preceding chapter and a prelude to the phase rule of the following chapter. The purpose of this chapter is to make chemical potential a reasonable and familiar thermodynamic variable.

6.2 VAPOR PRESSURE AS A FUNCTION OF PRESSURE

Almost every general chemistry textbook contains a table with the vapor pressure of water as a function of temperature. After providing numerical values as an example of dynamic equilibrium between liquid and gaseous phases, the data of this table are commonly used to correct the observed pressure of a gas collected over water to the pressure that the gas would exert if dry. This kind of tabulation and use implies that the vapor pressure of water and probably the vapor pressures of all liquids are independent of the total pressure exerted on the liquids. This implication is not quite true.

The dependence of vapor pressure on total pressure is most easily seen in a system that is ideal in two ways. The gaseous phase is a mixture of two kinds of noninteracting molecule; alone or mixed, each species is a perfect gas. Secondly, one of these two gases is insoluble in the liquid phase of the other. If, at constant T, the total pressure P of the gases upon the pure liquid is increased, the vapor pressure p of the liquid increases above the value it would be if the liquid and its pure vapor were alone at the same temperature. According to Section 5.12, the increase in Gibbs free energy of the liquid of molar volume v as the pressure on it rises by dP is $v\,dP$, while the increase in Gibbs free energy of its vapor of molar volume V as its pressure rises by dp is $V\,dp$. At equilibrium at constant T, there is no tendency for the dynamic equilibrium of liquid and its vapor to be upset if the Gibbs free energy of the condensible species changes equally in both phases. Equilibrium is thus maintained at constant T for that species if $V\,dp = v\,dP$. That is,

$$\left(\frac{\partial p}{\partial P}\right)_T = \frac{v}{V} \tag{6.1}$$

This derivative, which gives the isothermal rate of change of vapor pressure with respect to changes in the total pressure on the condensed phase, is very small since the molar volume v of a condensed phase is much less than the molar volume V of a gas.

Equation (6.1) is readily integrated at constant temperature if the condensed phase is incompressible and if the vapor behaves as a perfect gas so that $V = RT/p$. Then,

$$RT \int_{p_1}^{p_2} \frac{dp}{p} = v \int_{P_1}^{P_2} dP$$

$$RT \ln\left(\frac{p_2}{p_1}\right) = v(P_2 - P_1) \tag{6.2}$$

In (6.2), p_2 is the vapor pressure at the total pressure P_2 while p_1 is the vapor pressure at the total pressure P_1. In the commonly used tables of vapor pressure $p_1 = P_1$.

Example 6.1. Calculate the vapor pressure of water at 25°C when the total pressure exerted on the water is one, ten, and one hundred atm. At 25°C under the pressure of its own vapor, water has a vapor pressure of 23.756 mm Hg. (*Handbook of Chemistry* [10th Edition] ed. by N. A. Lange and G. M. Forker, New York: McGraw-Hill Book Co., Inc., 1967, p. 1471.)

In (6.2), $p_1 = P_1 = 23.756/760.00 = 0.0313$ atm; hence,

$$\log p_2 = \log p_1 + \frac{v(P_2 - P_1)}{2.303RT}$$

$$= \log 23.756 + \frac{18.07(P_2 - 0.0313)}{2.303 \times 82.05 \times 298.2}$$

$$= 1.37577 + 0.0003207(P_2 - 0.0313)$$

If $P_2 = 1.0000$ atm,

$$\log p_2 = 1.37577 + 0.0003207 \times 0.9687 = 1.37608$$

$$p_2 = 23.773 \text{ mm Hg at 1 atm}$$

If $P_2 = 10.0000$ atm,

$$\log p_2 = 1.37577 + 0.0003207 \times 9.9687 = 1.37897$$

$$p_2 = 23.932 \text{ mm Hg at 10 atm}$$

If $P_2 = 100.0000$ atm,

$$\log p_2 = 1.37577 + 0.0003207 \times 99.9687 = 1.40783$$

$$p_2 = 25.576 \text{ mm Hg at 100 atm}$$

At 1, 10, and 100 atm, the vapor pressure is increased from its value at its vapor pressure by 0.07%, 0.74%, and 7.7%.

6.3 EQUILIBRIUM OF ONE COMPONENT IN TWO PHASES

When two phases remain at equilibrium despite changes in pressure or temperature common to both phases, (5.54) or (5.73) requires that their Gibbs free energies remain equal. If dG_2 is the infinitesimal change in Gibbs free energy of phase 2, then by (5.4), when any work done on the closed system is expansion work, $dG_2 = -S_2\,dT_2 + V_2\,dP_2$. Similarly, for the other phase, $dG_1 = -S_1\,dT_1 + V_1\,dP_1$. It will be proved below in Section 6.8 that the pressure and temperature everywhere assume common values P and T in a system of the sort considered here. Hence $dP_2 = dP_1 = dP$, the common infinitesimal change in pressure; and $dT_2 = dT_1 = dT$, the common infinitesimal change in temperature that maintains equilibrium as the pressure changes. But $dG_2 = dG_1$ so that

$$-S_2\,dT + V_2\,dP = -S_1\,dT + V_1\,dP$$

$$(V_2 - V_1)\,dP = (S_2 - S_1)\,dT$$

$$\frac{dP}{dT} = \frac{\Delta S}{\Delta V} \tag{6.3}$$

In (6.3), which is called the *Clapeyron equation*, ΔS is the increase in entropy attendant upon the change from phase 1 to phase 2, and ΔV is the increase in volume for the same change of state for the same amount of matter. The change of state is any reversible change that can be performed isobarically, equilibrium being maintained with respect to pressure, and isothermally, equilibrium being maintained with respect to temperature. The change may involve only work that is expansion work. Briefly, the Clapeyron equation (6.3) applies to reversible phase changes and describes the way pressure and temperature must vary simultaneously if both phases are to continue to coexist so that $dG_1 = dG_2$.

The Clapeyron equation is seldom used as stated. At any temperature T,

$$\Delta H = T\,\Delta S \tag{4.52}$$

Substitution of (4.52) into (6.3) gives

$$\frac{dP}{dT} = \frac{\Delta H}{T\Delta V} \tag{6.4}$$

where ΔH is the heat of transition from phase 1 to phase 2. If ΔH and ΔV could be expressed explicitly as functions of T and P, (6.4) could be integrated. When both states are condensed phases, it is often sufficient to approximate the derivative by a ratio of finite differences. Then,

$$\frac{\delta P}{\delta T} = \frac{P_2 - P_1}{T_2 - T_1} = \frac{\Delta H}{T\Delta V} \tag{6.5}$$

where $P_2 - P_1$ is the change in pressure that accompanies the change in temperature from T_1 to T_2. It should be noted that δP and δT apply to this simultaneous adjustment of P and T, while ΔH and ΔV apply to the change of state of the phases in equilibrium.

Example 6.2. What pressure is required to decrease the freezing point of ice by 2.00°C?

The heat of fusion of ice is 1436.3 cal mole^{-1} at 0.00°C. The density of water at 0.00°C is 0.9999 g ml^{-1}; that of ice is 0.9168 g ml^{-1}. For one g,

$$\Delta V = \frac{1.0000}{0.9999} - \frac{1.0000}{0.9168} = -0.0907 \text{ ml}$$

$$\Delta H = \frac{1436.3}{18.02} \times \frac{82.05}{1.987} = 3290 \text{ ml atm}$$

If $\delta T = T_2 - T_1 = -2.00$°C, by (6.5),

$$\delta P = \frac{3290 \times (-2.00)}{273 \times (-0.0907)}$$

$$P_2 - P_1 = 266 \text{ atm}$$

That is, an absolute pressure of 267 atm would be required to maintain equilibrium between ice and water at -2.00°C.

6.4 VAPORIZATION AND SUBLIMATION

When one of the phases at equilibrium is a gas, the Clapeyron equation (6.4) assumes a rather simple approximate form. Let phase 2 be the gas, while phase 1 is a condensed phase. If the condensed phase is, for example, a liquid, the differential equation to be derived will give the dependence of vapor pressure on temperature. Then,

$$\Delta V = V_2 - V_1 = \frac{RT}{P} - V_1 \approx \frac{RT}{P}$$

where the approximation is reasonable since the molar volume V_2 of the vapor phase is about 1000 times V_1, that of the condensed phase. When this value of ΔV is substituted into the Clapeyron equation, the resulting equation is

$$\frac{dP}{dT} = \frac{P\Delta H}{RT^2} \tag{6.6}$$

The Clausius-Clapeyron equation (6.6) is readily integrated if ΔH is known as a function of temperature, for then

$$R\int_{P_1}^{P_2} \frac{dP}{P} = R\ln\left(\frac{P_2}{P_1}\right) = \int_{T_1}^{T_2} \frac{\Delta H}{T^2}\,dT \tag{6.7}$$

where P_2 is the vapor pressure at T_2 and P_1 is the value at T_1.

A very simple case occurs when ΔH is independent of temperature, or if a suitable average value of ΔH for the temperature range of interest can be found, for by (6.6)

$$\int \frac{dP}{P} = \frac{\Delta H}{R}\int \frac{dT}{T^2}$$

$$\ln P = -\frac{\Delta H}{RT} + C_o \tag{6.8}$$

$$\log P = -\frac{\Delta H}{2.303RT} + \frac{C_o}{2.303} \tag{6.9}$$

The constant of integration in (6.8) or (6.9) can be evaluated if ΔH is known and if the vapor pressure P is known at one temperature T. These equations then fix the vapor pressure at other temperatures for which the assumptions in its derivation are valid. Definite integration of (6.6) when ΔH is independent of temperature and pressure yields

$$\int_{P_1}^{P_2} \frac{dP}{P} = \frac{\Delta H}{R}\int_{T_1}^{T_2} \frac{dT}{T^2} = \frac{\Delta H}{R}\left(-\frac{1}{T_2} + \frac{1}{T_1}\right)$$

$$\ln\left(\frac{P_2}{P_1}\right) = \frac{\Delta H(T_2 - T_1)}{RT_2T_1} \tag{6.10}$$

$$\log\left(\frac{P_2}{P_1}\right) = \frac{\Delta H(T_2 - T_1)}{2.303RT_2T_1} \tag{6.11}$$

These equations relate the five variables: ΔH, the vapor pressure P_1 at temperature T_1, and the vapor pressure P_2 at temperature T_2. If any four are known, the fifth is readily found by (6.10) or (6.11).

Example 6.3. The normal boiling point of CCl_4 is 76.8°C, and its vapor pressure at 25.0°C is 115 mm Hg. (*Handbook of Chemistry* [10th Edition], ed. by N. A. Lange and G. M. Forker, New York: McGraw-Hill Book Co., Inc., 1967, p. 1438.) What is the molar heat of vaporization of CCl_4?

By (6.11), with $P_2 = 760$ mm Hg at $T_2 = 350.0$ and $P_1 = 115$ mm Hg at $T_1 = 298.2$,

$$\Delta H = \frac{2.303RT_1T_2}{T_2 - T_1}\log\left(\frac{P_2}{P_1}\right)$$

$$= \frac{2.303 \times 1.987 \times 298.2 \times 350.0}{51.8}\log\left(\frac{760}{115}\right)$$

$$= 7560 \text{ cal mole}^{-1}$$

This is an effective mean value of ΔH_v over the temperature range 25.0°C to 76.8°C.

Example 6.4. If the heat of vaporization of water is 540 cal gram^{-1}, what is its vapor pressure at 95°C?

$$\Delta H = 18.0 \times 540 = 9720 \text{ cal mole}^{-1}$$

At $T_2 = 373.16$°K, $P_2 = 760$ mm Hg. By (6.11),

$$\log\left(\frac{760}{P_1}\right) = \frac{9720(373.16 - 368.16)}{2.303 \times 1.987 \times 373.2 \times 368.2}$$

$$= 0.0773 = \log(1.195)$$

$$P_1 = \frac{760}{1.195} = 636 \text{ mm Hg}$$

The observed value is 633.90 mm Hg.

Example 6.5. From (6.6), estimate the vapor pressure of water at 95°C if $\Delta H_v = 9720$ cal mole^{-1}.

$$\frac{dP}{dT} = \frac{P\Delta H}{RT^2} = \frac{9720 \times 1.000}{1.987 \times 373^2} = 0.0352 \text{ atm deg}^{-1}$$

If $\delta T = -5.00°$, $\delta P = 0.0352 \times (-5.00) = -0.176$ atm. At 95°C, $P = 1.000 - 0.176 = 0.824$ atm $= 626$ mm Hg.

Example 6.6. With data from Example 5.11, estimate the vapor pressure of water at 95.00°C if steam is a perfect gas.

With $T = 368.15$°K in the general expressions for ΔH° and ΔS°, one finds $\Delta H^\circ = 9820.7$ cal and $\Delta S^\circ = 26.284$ cal deg^{-1} at 95.00°C. Hence, by (5.71), $\Delta G^\circ = 144$ cal. By the same data, $\Delta G^\circ = 13$ cal at 100.00°C. In order to rid these results of the effects of nonideal behavior of the vapor and errors in the C_P's, both should be reduced by 13 cal so that ΔG is effectively zero at 100°C at one atm. Thus ΔG is effectively 131 cal at 95°C at one atm. Towards calculating the vapor pressure P, a suitable state diagram is

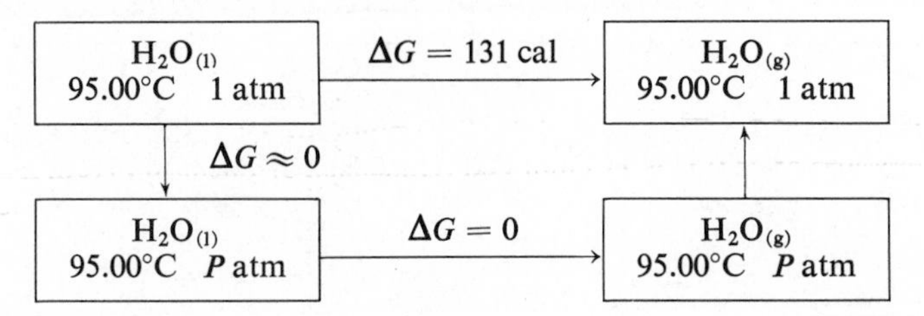

The value of ΔG for the change in which the pressure on the water is reduced to less than 1 atm is less than 1 cal since the molar volume of water is small. For the isothermal compression of water vapor, (5.84) yields

$$\Delta G = RT \ln\left(\frac{1.000}{P}\right)$$

Since ΔG is independent of the path,

$$\log P = -\frac{\Delta G}{2.303RT} = -\frac{131}{2.303 \times 1.987 \times 368.2} = -0.0778$$

$$P = 0.836 \text{ atm} = 636 \text{ mm Hg.}$$

Tables 6.1 and 6.2 list vapor pressures and heats of vaporization and sublimation at one atm. Although these ΔH's really depend on T, they may be

Table 6.1 Vapor Pressures (*Handbook of Chemistry* [10th Edition], ed. by N. A. Lange and G. M. Forker, New York: McGraw-Hill Book Co., Inc., 1967, pp. 1470–73, 1451–2, 1463, 1465.)

Temperature (°C)	H_2O (mm Hg)	NH_3 (atm)	SO_2 (atm)	Hg (mm Hg)
−75	0.00090(s)	0.0738		
−50	0.0296(s)	0.4034	0.11411	
−30	0.2859(s)	1.1799	0.3759	4.78×10^{-6}
−20	0.776(s)	1.8774	0.6274	1.81×10^{-5}
−10	1.950(s)			
−10	2.149(liq)	2.8703	0.9995	6.06×10^{-5}
0	4.579	4.2380	1.529	1.85×10^{-4}
10	9.209	6.0685	2.256	4.90×10^{-4}
20	17.535	8.4585	3.228	1.201×10^{-3}
25	23.756	9.8955		
30	31.824	11.512	4.498	2.777×10^{-3}
40	55.324	15.339	6.125	6.079×10^{-3}
50	92.51	20.059	8.176	0.01267
60	149.38	25.797	10.729	0.02524
70	233.7	32.687	13.867	0.04825
80	355.1	40.902	17.682	0.08880
90	525.76	50.558	22.268	0.1582
100	760.00	61.816	27.714	0.2729

Table 6.2 Heats of Vaporization and Sublimation at One Atm (F. D. Rossini *et al.*, *Selected Values of Chemical Thermodynamic Properties*, NBS Circular 500, Washington, D. C., 1952.)

Substance	ΔH (kcal mole^{-1})	T (°K)	Substance	ΔH (kcal mole^{-1})	T (°K)
O_2	1.630	90.18	CO	1.444	81.65
H_2	0.216	20.38	CO_2(subl.)	6.031	194.67
H_2O	9.7171	373.15	CH_4	1.955	111.66
Ar	1.558	87.28	CH_3OH	8.43	337.9
F_2	1.51	85.23	C_2H_2(subl.)	5.1	189.2
HF	1.8	293.1	C_2H_4	3.237	169.44
Cl_2	4.878	239.09	C_2H_6	3.517	184.52
HCl	3.86	188.10	Pb	43.0	2023.
HBr	4.210	206.42	Ag	60.72	2466.
HI	4.724	237.79	AgCl	43.7	1830.
S	2.5	717.75	AgBr	37.0	1806.
SO_2	5.955	263.13	Fe_3O_4	33.	1867.
H_2S	4.463	212.81	$TiCl_4$	8.4	409.0
N_2	1.333	77.33	Al	67.9	2600.
NO	3.293	121.38	Mg	31.5	1393.
NH_3	5.581	239.72	$MgCl_2$	32.7	1691.

used in (6.9) and (6.11) over restricted ranges of T. When $\log P$ is graphed as a function of T^{-1}, (6.9) is a straight line with slope $(-\Delta H/2.303\,R)$. Actually the slope changes with T; this gradual change is sometimes noted in an equation of the form

$$\log P = -\frac{A}{T-B} + C$$

where A, B, and C are empirical constants characteristics of a substance. Figure 6.1 greatly exaggerates the usual curvature of the $\log P$ vs T^{-1} curve.

An equation that reproduces the whole $\log P$ vs T^{-1} curves of several substances with an average deviation of 0.3% is

$$\log P = A + \frac{B}{T} + C\log T + \frac{DP}{T^2} \tag{6.12}$$

where A, B, C, and D are empirical constants[1]. A few of these constants are listed in Table 6.3 when P is in mm Hg. This kind of equation can be derived

Table 6.3 Some Vapor Pressure Constants [Equation (6.12)] (A. A. Frost and D. R. Kalkwarf, *J. Chem. Phys.* **21**, 264 (1953).)

Substance	A	B	C	D
Methane	13.44740	−567.5868	−2.681065	0.191423
Ethane	16.74451	−1068.273	−3.566685	0.457881
Carbon Dioxide	23.06810	−1374.064	−5.634143	0.305254
Water	22.75017	−2908.894	−4.695517	0.424676

[1] A. A. Frost and D. R. Kalkwarf, *J. Chem. Phys.* **21**, 264 (1953).

from the Clapeyron equation (6.4) if ΔH is a linear function of T and if, by the van der Waals equation, $\Delta V \approx V - b$.

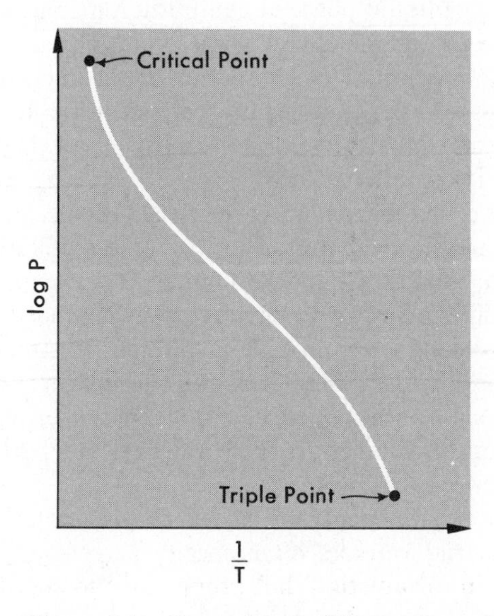

Figure 6.1. Dependence of Vapor Pressure P on Temperature T (Curvature Exaggerated)

6.5 SOLUTIONS

A *solution* is a physically homogeneous mixture that changes continuously in composition on the formation of a new phase. A portion of matter that is physically homogeneous acts as a continuum in the experiment at hand. Many experiments, but not all, with monochromatic X rays would evidence a lack in homogeneity because the wavelengths of X rays and sizes of atoms are of comparable magnitude and thus sometimes interact to show diffraction phenomena. The circumstances in which visible light exhibits its wave nature and the discreteness and inhomogeneity of matter are generally confined to colloid chemistry and spectroscopy. Accordingly, when the experiment at hand is a commonplace vaporization of fusion, the visible portions of matter in the experiment appear alike in every part in each phase and each phase is then termed *physically homogeneous*. In other words, physically homogeneous in general means having dimensions of the order of or greater than the wavelength of light. A *mixture* is a portion of matter that does not obey the law of multiple or definite proportions. Air, gasoline, and a crystalline defect structure like that of FeS_{1+x} are examples of mixtures, for accurate chemical or elemental analysis of each would show varying results from sample to sample. Air, gasoline, and iron sulfide are solutions because by a physical process like fractional distillation each can be changed continuously in composition as a gas phase of nitrogen, pentane, or sulfur forms. Salt and water form one liquid phase at equilibrium if somewhat less than 40 g salt are mixed with 100 g water at room temperature. The amount of salt could be 20 g, 2 g, or 2 micrograms. When such a liquid mixture is frozen, pure solid water crystallizes and the concentration of salt in the liquor increases continuously to a certain maximum value, the solubility of salt ($NaCl \cdot 2\,H_2O$) in water. That is, salt water is a solution.

There are certain aggregations of matter that are properly solutions and yet behave like pure substances in a physical separation process like distillation. Constant-boiling hydrochloric acid, used as a standard in analytical chemistry, boils at a definite temperature and pressure without change in composition. But a change in pressure or crystallizing ice from such a solution does indeed cause the composition to vary continuously. Similarly, eutectic mixtures and racemic mixtures behave like pure substances on melting, but some other physical process would betray their nonstoichiometry. These vagaries are part of the matter of this chapter.

The proportions in which pure components are mixed to form solutions are specified in many ways. Industrial workers often specify percentages by weight or volume for convenience in formulation, but proportions so specified seldom if ever have chemical significance. Analytical chemists find it convenient to measure volumes and thus specify a chemically meaningful amount per unit volume. The molarity C_i of a solution is the number of gram-moles of solute i per liter of solution; the formality F_i of a solution is the number of gram-formula weights of solute i per liter of solution; the normality N_i of a solution is the number of gram-equivalent weights of solute i per liter of solution. In mathematical terms, if V is the actual volume in milliliters of solution that results when W_i grams of species i are dissolved, then

$$C_i = \frac{W_i}{M_i} \times \frac{1000}{V} \tag{6.13}$$

$$F_i = \frac{W_i}{M_i} \times \frac{1000}{V} \tag{6.14}$$

$$N_i = \frac{nW_i}{M_i} \times \frac{1000}{V} \tag{6.15}$$

In these equations, M_i is the molecular or formula weight of the pure solute i in grams and n is the number of protons, electrons, or their equivalent (divided, of course, by Avogadro's number) that are lost or gained by M_i grams of solute in the particular reaction of interest. The normality is always an integral multiple of the formality or molarity.

If a solution expands with an increase in temperature, the number by which its normality, formality, or molarity is expressed decreases as the temperature rises for the amount of solute is unchanged by supposition. In order to avoid this dependence on temperature, which is as unpredictable as changes in density, physical chemists commonly express concentrations in terms of molality. The molality m_i of a solution is the number of gram-molecular weights per kilogram of solvent, which is here called species 1. Mathematically,

$$m_i = \frac{W_i}{M_i} \times \frac{1000}{W_1} \tag{6.16}$$

where W_i grams of solute with gram molecular weight M_i are dissolved in W_1 grams of solvent. If no new phases are generated or if no matter is transferred to phases already in contact with the solution, m_i is independent of temperature and pressure, in the absence of decomposition by chemical reaction of solute or solvent. That is,

$$\frac{dm_i}{dT} = 0; \quad \frac{dm_i}{dP} = 0 \tag{6.17}$$

The numerical value of m_i often fails to exhibit fully the chemical nature of a solution; hence, mole fraction was invented. If W_i grams of species i with gram molecular weight M_i are mixed with $(\mathsf{C} - 1)$ other components, then the mole fraction X_i of species i is

$$X_i = \frac{\dfrac{W_i}{M_i}}{\sum_{j=1}^{\mathsf{C}} \dfrac{W_j}{M_j}} \tag{6.18}$$

By (5.6),

$$\sum_{i=1}^{\mathsf{C}} X_i = \frac{\sum_{i=1}^{\mathsf{C}} \dfrac{W_i}{M_i}}{\sum_{j=1}^{\mathsf{C}} \dfrac{W_j}{M_j}} = 1 \tag{6.19}$$

since the summations merely count, perhaps in a different order, the numbers of gram-moles of the C components. As for m_i, if the phase under consideration loses no matter to other phases and does not undergo chemical changes such as reaction or dissociation of molecules,

$$\frac{dX_i}{dT} = 0; \qquad \frac{dX_i}{dP} = 0 \tag{6.20}$$

As defined for gaseous solutions, M_i has a definite measurable value. As applied to liquid or solid solutions, the molecular weight of the solvent may sometimes have any arbitrary value, but in this treatment simplicity and indeed common use ordinarily require that M_i for solute and solvent be the molecular weight of the vapor.

Example 6.7. At 20°C, the density of an aqueous solution containing 15.00% by weight H_2SO_4 is 1.102 g ml^{-1}. Calculate its formality, normality, and molality.

The number of grams of pure H_2SO_4 in 1 l of this solution are $1.102 \times 1000 \times 0.1500$, or 165.3 g. Since the formula weight of H_2SO_4 is 98.08, this is 1.685 gram formula weights per liter. That is, the formality is 1.685. And if both protons are lost in an acid-base reaction, the normality is $2 \times 1.685 = 3.370$.

The molality of the solution is readily found by (6.16), for $W_1 = 1102 - 165 = 937$ g water.

$$m_2 = \frac{165.3}{98.08} \times \frac{1000}{937} = 1.799$$

6.6 HOMOGENEOUS FUNCTIONS

The function $f(x, y, \cdots)$ is said to be a homogeneous function of degree n in $x, y, \ldots$ if $f(\lambda x, \lambda y, \cdots) = \lambda^n f(x, y, \cdots)$. In particular, for two independent variables, $f(x, y)$ is a homogeneous function of degree n if

$$f(\lambda x, \lambda y) = \lambda^n f(x, y) \tag{6.21}$$

For example, $x^2 + 4xy + 4y^2$ is homogeneous of the second degree in x and y, for

$$\begin{aligned} f(x, y) &= x^2 + 4xy + 4y^2 \\ f(\lambda x, \lambda y) &= \lambda^2 x^2 + 4\lambda^2 xy + 4\lambda^2 y^2 \\ &= \lambda^2(x^2 + 4xy + 4y^2) = \lambda^2 f(x, y) \end{aligned}$$

Total differentiation with respect to λ transforms (6.21) into (6.22), since $f(\lambda x, \lambda y)$ depends on λ while $f(x, y)$ does not.

$$\frac{df}{d\lambda} = n\lambda^{n-1} f(x, y) \tag{6.22}$$

Symbolic statement of the operation of taking the derivative of $f(\lambda x, \lambda y)$ is

$$\begin{aligned} \frac{df}{d\lambda} &= \frac{\partial f}{\partial(\lambda x)}\frac{d(\lambda x)}{d\lambda} + \frac{\partial f}{\partial(\lambda y)}\frac{d(\lambda y)}{d\lambda} \\ &= x\left[\frac{\partial f}{\partial(\lambda x)}\right] + y\left[\frac{\partial f}{\partial(\lambda y)}\right] \end{aligned} \tag{6.23}$$

If $\lambda = 1$, (6.22) and (6.23) yield

$$nf(x, y) = x\frac{\partial f}{\partial x} + y\frac{\partial f}{\partial y} \tag{6.24}$$

Equation (6.24) is Euler's theorem on homogeneous function in its simplest form[2]. The proof for functions of many variables $x, y, z, \ldots$ is quite straightforward. When $f(\lambda x, \lambda y, \lambda z, \ldots) = \lambda^n f(x, y, z, \ldots)$ (6.24) becomes

$$nf(x, y, z, \cdots) = x\frac{\partial f}{\partial x} + y\frac{\partial f}{\partial y} + z\frac{\partial f}{\partial z} + \cdots \tag{6.25}$$

Euler's theorem (6.25) or (6.24) is of much thermodynamic value when $x, y, z, \ldots$ represent moles or grams of the various chemical species in a system. The partial derivatives on the right sides of (6.24) and (6.25) then take the form

$$\bar{W}_i = \frac{\partial W}{\partial n_i} = \left(\frac{\partial W}{\partial n_i}\right)_{T, P, n_j} \qquad (j \neq i) \tag{6.26}$$

where n_i is the number of moles of species i, T is temperature, P is pressure, and W is a thermodynamic property of the system. If, for example, W is the volume of the system, then $\bar{W}_i = \bar{V}_i$ is called the *partial molar volume* of species i.

The values of some thermodynamic properties are independent of the amount of matter in the system. The temperature of a mass of water can be taken provided the disturbance due to the heat absorbed or evolved by the thermometer affects the temperature of the water only in a negligible way. But it is of no importance whether 1 cu mile sea water has a temperature of 7.00°C or 1 liter sea water has a temperature of 7.00°C. Their temperatures have the same numerical measure and the same value. The same thermometer exhibits the same reading in each. Similarly, if gravitational effects are neglected, the pressure of a gas can be measured anywhere in a large volume of gas at equilibrium and is found to be the same everywhere. Indeed, one measurement of pressure on a small sample of the gas would have yielded the same value for the pressure if the measurement were properly made. Concentrations within a homogeneous region of a system are also independent of the size of the system. Still further properties of this kind are index of refraction, density, viscosity, standard molar heat of formation, molar heat capacity, and molar entropy. This kind of property is called an *intensive property*. An intensive property is defined as a property whose value does not change when it is observed in each of two identical systems or in the one system that would result from physically combining the two identical systems. Since an intensive property is independent of mass or moles, the partial molar quantity associated with an intensive property is zero.

The thermodynamic state of a system can be fixed by specifying a certain few of all its possible properties. Because properties like $(P^3 + V/T)$ or arctan $[\ln(\rho\sqrt{T})]$ are inconvenient, thermodynamics uses just two kinds: intensive and extensive. It is possible to specify fully the state of a system with just extensive properties, but it is not possible to do so with just intensive properties

[2] Woods, F. S., *Advanced Calculus*, Boston: Ginn and Co., 1934, pp. 73–4.

because they cannot tell the size of a system. An *extensive property* is a property whose value for two identical systems is exactly twice as great as it is for just one of the identical systems. Usually it does not matter whether the two identical systems are physically combined or not when the doubled value of the property is noted. For example, the mass, energy, entropy, . . . of a system is ordinarily doubled when an identical system is physically added to it. If so, the extensive property W is homogeneous of degree unity in the number of moles, n is unity in (6.24) and (6.25), and $\bar{W}_i$ has a nonzero value. For example, the volume of a perfect gas is a homogeneous function of degree unity in the moles of gas at constant T and P, for $V = (RT/P)n$. In general, E, H, S, A, and G are like volume in being homogeneous of first degree in mass or moles.

However, not all extensive properties are homogeneous of first degree in mass or moles. Some extensive properties vary according to the geometrical arrangement of the parts of the system. For example, the potential energy of a fixed number of ions depends on their positions, and the mechanical energy stored in a spring depends on its state of extension or compression. These potential energies are extensive because they are twice as great for two identical systems as for one system, but may not be twice as great when the two systems are combined because the mass of the ions or of the springs is not of direct interest. Surface energy and surface area are likewise extensive but not necessarily proportional to mass or moles. Indeed, even the volume of a fluid or solid at constant T and externally observed P will not be exactly halved when its mass is divided into two equal parts, for the molecules at the new surface between halves now exist in unsymmetrical environments and thus may occupy different effective volumes. Even gravitational attraction would cause less constriction within the separated halves than within the whole, but the T and P observed outside halves or whole might be the same. Despite these difficulties, it is common practice to treat all extensive properties as homogeneous of first order in mass or moles.

The situation that arises when the system is considered to be composed of two chemical species is mathematically quite tractable. The volumes of various mixtures of alcohol and water, which deviate from the volumes that might be predicted by assuming additivity of volumes, would provide a concrete example of an extensive property W that is some function of the numbers of moles of species 1 and 2. In general, for any extensive property W, $W = W(n_1, n_2)$, where n_1 is the number of moles of species 1 and n_2 is the number of moles of species 2. By (6.24) and (6.26), if W is indeed an extensive property so that $n = 1$,

$$W = n_1\bar{W}_1 + n_2\bar{W}_2 \tag{6.27}$$

It is convenient to define a mean molar quantity W_m as

$$W_m = \frac{W}{n_1 + n_2} = \frac{n_1\bar{W}_1 + n_2\bar{W}_2}{n_1 + n_2} = X_1\bar{W}_1 + X_2\bar{W}_2 \tag{6.28}$$

But $X_1 + X_2 = 1$; hence

$$\left.\begin{aligned} W_m &= (1 - X_2)\bar{W}_1 + X_2\bar{W}_2 \\ \frac{\partial W_m}{\partial X_2} &= -\bar{W}_1 + \bar{W}_2 \end{aligned}\right\} \tag{6.29}$$

Solution of the simultaneous equations (6.29) yields values for the partial molar quantities $\bar{W}_1$ and $\bar{W}_2$.

$$\bar{W}_1 = W_m - X_2\left(\frac{\partial W_m}{\partial X_2}\right) \tag{6.30}$$

$$\bar{W}_2 = W_m + (1 - X_2)\left(\frac{\partial W_m}{\partial X_2}\right) \tag{6.31}$$

The value of W_m and its rate of change with respect to X_2, $(\partial W_m/\partial X_2)$, can be evaluated analytically, or graphically from a plot of W_m as a function of X_2 as in Figure 6.2. The resultant values of $\bar{W}_1$ or $\bar{W}_2$ for the various compositions X_2 represent the changes expected in the extensive property W when 1 mole of one of the species is added to a huge amount of solution of composition X_2. The amount of solution is so large that X_2 is practically the same before and after the addition. From $\bar{W}_1$ and $\bar{W}_2$ the value of W for a mixture of n_1 and n_2 moles can be calculated by (6.27).

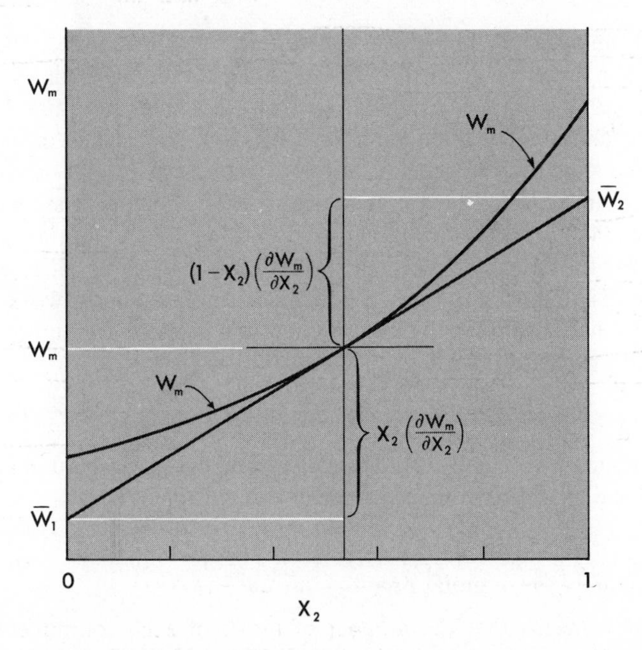

Figure 6.2. Partial Molar Quantities from Mean Molar Quantity W_m

Changes in the partial molar quantities of a system are related to each other. If any extensive property V is considered to be a function only of T, P, and the numbers n_i of moles of the various components of the system, then $V = V(T, P, n_1, n_2, n_3, \ldots, n_i, \ldots)$ and by (6.26) and the rules of the calculus

$$dV = \left(\frac{\partial V}{\partial T}\right)_{P,n} dT + \left(\frac{\partial V}{\partial P}\right)_{T,n} dP + \sum_{i=1}^{\mathsf{C}} \bar{V}_i \, dn_i \tag{6.32}$$

However, Euler's theorem (6.25) for an extensive ($n = 1$) property V requires $V = \sum_i n_i \bar{V}_i$ so that

$$dV = \sum_{i=1}^{\mathsf{C}} \bar{V}_i \, dn_i + \sum_{i=1}^{\mathsf{C}} n_i \, d\bar{V}_i \tag{6.33}$$

where C is the number of components. Subtracting (6.33) from (6.32) yields

$$0 = \left(\frac{\partial V}{\partial T}\right)_{P,n} dT + \left(\frac{\partial V}{\partial P}\right)_{T,n} dP - \sum_{i=1}^{\mathsf{C}} n_i \, d\bar{V}_i \tag{6.34}$$

Equation (6.34), which is a restriction upon the possible variations in the $\bar{V}_i$'s, is very important when V is the Gibbs free energy.

6.7 CHEMICAL POTENTIAL

Let C be the minimum number of chemical substances out of which the several coexisting phases of a system can each be made separately. In addition to the usual independent thermodynamic variables like pressure and temperature there will then be up to C more independent variables that must be specified in order to define the size and state of the system. These C variables are usually taken to be the numbers of gram-moles of the C components out of which the system can be prepared. Just as (4.48) established entropy and volume as the natural independent variables for the energy of a closed system that, if it works, does only expansion work, so also for open systems experiencing only expansion work the energy is a natural function of entropy and volume as well as of the number n_i of gram-moles of the various components. That is,

$$E = E(S, V, n_1 \, n_2, \cdots n_i, \cdots n_{\mathsf{C}}) \tag{6.35}$$

Infinitesimal changes in these $\mathsf{C} + 2$ variables will lead to an infinitesimal change dE in the energy of the system. By the usual rule of calculus,

$$dE = \left(\frac{\partial E}{\partial S}\right)_{V,n} dS + \left(\frac{\partial E}{\partial V}\right)_{S,n} dV + \sum_{i=1}^{\mathsf{C}} \left(\frac{\partial E}{\partial n_i}\right)_{S,V,n_j} dn_i \tag{6.36}$$

where the subscript n means that the number of moles of each component is held fixed and where the subscript n_j indicates that the number of moles of each component except for the ith component is held constant. If all dn_i were zero, (6.36) would apply to a closed system as

$$dE = T\,dS - P\,dV \tag{4.46}$$

Comparison of (6.36) with (4.46) for a closed system then yields

$$dE = T\,dS - P\,dV + \sum_{i=1}^{C} \mu_i\,dn_i \tag{6.37}$$

where the chemical potential μ_i of species i is defined by

$$\mu_i = \left(\frac{\partial E}{\partial n_i}\right)_{S,V,n_j} \tag{6.38}$$

By the usual methods of Section 4.13 it is possible to obtain from (6.37) analogous expressions for dH, dA, and dG in the following way.

$$dE + d(PV) = d(PV) + T\,dS - P\,dV + \sum_{i=1}^{C} \mu_i\,dn_i$$

$$dH = T\,dS + V\,dP + \sum_{i=1}^{C} \mu_i\,dn_i \tag{6.39}$$

$$dE - d(TS) = -d(TS) + T\,dS - P\,dV + \sum_{i=1}^{C} \mu_i\,dn_i$$

$$dA = -S\,dT - P\,dV + \sum_{i=1}^{C} \mu_i\,dn_i \tag{6.40}$$

$$dE + d(PV - TS) = d(PV - TS) + T\,dS - P\,dV + \sum_{i=1}^{C} \mu_i\,dn_i$$

$$dG = -S\,dT + V\,dP + \sum_{i=1}^{C} \mu_i\,dn_i \tag{6.41}$$

From the method of derivation and from the definition of the chemical potential in (6.38), it is clear that

$$\mu_i = \left(\frac{\partial E}{\partial n_i}\right)_{S,V,n_j} = \left(\frac{\partial H}{\partial n_i}\right)_{S,P,n_j} = \left(\frac{\partial A}{\partial n_i}\right)_{T,V,n_j} = \left(\frac{\partial G}{\partial n_i}\right)_{T,P,n_j} \tag{6.42}$$

Moreover, as in (6.35),

$$G = G(T, P, n_1, n_2, \cdots n_i, \cdots n_C) \tag{6.43}$$

and so on for H and A. The really important feature of (6.42) and (6.43) is that the chemical potential μ_i is a partial molar quantity as in (6.26) when the Gibbs free energy G is the extensive property. Hence, by the natural extension of (6.27) from two to C components,

$$G(T, P, n_i) = \sum_{i=1}^{C} n_i \mu_i(T, P) \tag{6.44}$$

The order in which mixed partial derivatives are taken is unimportant in thermodynamics. When partial derivatives with respect to n_i and T are taken of (6.44) only the i-th term of the summation remains and the result is

$$\left[\frac{\partial}{\partial n_i}\left(\frac{\partial G}{\partial T}\right)_{P,n}\right]_{T,P,n_j} = \left[\frac{\partial}{\partial T}\left(\frac{\partial n_i \mu_i}{\partial n_i}\right)_{T,P,n_j}\right]_{P,n} \tag{6.45}$$

Since (5.19) was derived for a closed system, it can be rewritten

$$-S = \left(\frac{\partial G}{\partial T}\right)_{P,n} \tag{6.46}$$

But by (6.26) and (6.46), the left side of (6.45) is $-\bar{S}_i$; hence, upon performing the operations on the right, (6.45) becomes

$$-\bar{S}_i = \left(\frac{\partial \mu_i}{\partial T}\right)_{P,n} \tag{6.47}$$

Similarly, by use of (6.26) and (5.20), partial differentiation with respect to n_i and P yields

$$\bar{V}_i = \left(\frac{\partial \mu_i}{\partial P}\right)_{T,n} \tag{6.48}$$

Equations (6.47) and (6.48) are intensive forms of (5.19) and (5.20); they apply to species i as one of several species in a system at equilibrium. Without the subscript i and bar, they apply to one mole of a pure substance.

The chemical potential of a pure gas is readily found from (5.87) to be

$$\mu = \left(\frac{\partial G}{\partial n}\right)_{T,P} = RT \ln f + \mu^{\ominus}(T) \tag{6.49}$$

where

$$\mu^{\ominus}(T) = \left(\frac{\partial G^{\ominus}}{\partial n}\right)_{T,P} = \frac{dG^{\ominus}}{dT}$$

For a mixture of gases, the expression analogous to (6.49) is

$$\mu_i = \mu_i^{\ominus} + RT \ln f_i \tag{6.50}$$

where $\mu_i^{\ominus}$ is the chemical potential of species i in its standard state ($f_i = 1$) at T.

When species i is not a gas, the expression analogous to (6.50) is

$$\mu_i = \mu_i(T, P) = \mu_i^{\ominus}(T, P) + RT \ln a_i \tag{6.51}$$

where a_i is the activity of species i at T and P. The standard chemical potential $\mu_i^{\ominus}(T, P)$ of i at T and P in the standard state ($a_i = 1$) is the standard molar Gibbs free energy of formation of i, the value of which will be given in Section 9.4.

6.8 SPECIFIC CONDITIONS FOR THERMODYNAMIC EQUILIBRIUM

The criterion of equilibrium of (5.51) as stated for a closed system is a convenient starting point for the development of specific conditions for equilibrium. With explicit statement of the fact that the system is closed by the use of the subscript n, (5.51) becomes

$$(\delta E)_{S,V,n} \geqslant 0 \tag{6.52}$$

If surface effects can be neglected, each of the extensive properties of a system of P homogeneous phases is the sum of the values of the extensive property in each phase. In other words, the energy or volume of a system is the sum of the energies or volumes of its parts, the P phases. And the same applies to entropy and the moles of each of the C components out of which the system is made. Mathematically, if a superscript indicates the phase,

$$E = \sum_{j=1}^{\mathrm{P}} E^{(j)} \tag{6.53}$$

$$\left.\begin{aligned} V &= \sum_{j=1}^{\mathrm{P}} V^{(j)} \\ S &= \sum_{j=1}^{\mathrm{P}} S^{(j)} \\ n_i &= \sum_{j=1}^{\mathrm{P}} n_i^{(j)}, \qquad (i = 1, 2, \cdots, \mathrm{C}) \end{aligned}\right\} \tag{6.54}$$

Equation (6.53) says that the energy of the system is the sum of the energies of its phases, and (6.54) says the same for volumes, entropies, and moles of each of the C components. The values of V, S, and n_i in (6.54) are to be held constant in order to apply the criterion (6.52) of equilibrium. For some small variation $\delta V^{(j)}$ in the volume of phase j, for some small variation $\delta S^{(j)}$ in the entropy of phase j, and for some small variation $\delta n_i^{(j)}$ in the number of moles of component i in phase j, there will be by (6.37) a small change $\delta E^{(j)}$ in the energy of phase j such that

$$\delta E^{(j)} = T^{(j)}\,\delta S^{(j)} - P^{(j)}\,\delta V^{(j)} + \sum_{i=1}^{\mathrm{C}} \mu_i^{(j)}\,\delta n_i^{(j)} \tag{6.55}$$

Equation (6.55) assumes that there are no force fields (e.g., gravitational, electric, magnetic) affecting the system and that there is only a uniform normal external pressure $P^{(j)}$ on each phase. The temperature of phase j is $T^{(j)}$ and in it the chemical potential of component i is $\mu_i^{(j)}$. In other words, (6.55) treats phase j as a system in itself.

In order to preserve equilibrium in the system of P phases there must be simultaneous coordinated changes in entropy, volume, and numbers of moles of the various components if the total values of (6.54) for the system of phases are to remain constant. That is, if the volume of phase j increases by $\delta V^{(j)}$, there must be a decrease in volume of one or more of the other phases if the volume V of the whole system is constant. The same applies to a loss of moles $\delta n_i^{(j)}$ from phase j; these moles of i must appear elsewhere in the system. The same applies to $\delta S^{(j)}$ and S. By (6.53) and (6.55), the energy change that results (in the absence of other extraordinary restraints such as osmotic membranes that prevent the transfer of some component from one phase to another) is

$$\delta E = \sum_{j=1}^{\mathsf{P}} \delta E^{(j)} = \sum_{j=1}^{\mathsf{P}} T^{(j)}\, \delta S^{(j)} + \sum_{j=1}^{\mathsf{P}} [-P^{(j)}]\, \delta V^{(j)} + \sum_{j=1}^{\mathsf{P}} \sum_{i=1}^{\mathsf{C}} \mu_i^{(j)} \delta n_i^{(j)}$$

If equilibrium is to be maintained in the system, this variation in energy δE must be greater than or equal to zero by (6.52). In other words,

$$\left.\begin{aligned} &\sum_{j=1}^{\mathsf{P}} T^{(j)}\, \delta S^{(j)} + \sum_{j=1}^{\mathsf{P}} [-P^{(j)}]\delta V^{(j)} + \sum_{j=1}^{\mathsf{P}} \sum_{i=1}^{\mathsf{C}} \mu_i^{(j)} \delta n_i^{(j)} \geqslant 0 \\ &\text{provided} \\ &\delta V = \sum_{j=1}^{\mathsf{P}} \delta V^{(j)} = 0 \\ &\delta S = \sum_{j=1}^{\mathsf{P}} \delta S^{(j)} = 0 \\ &\delta n_i = \sum_{j=1}^{\mathsf{P}} \delta n_i^{(j)} = 0, \qquad (i = 1, 2, \cdots, \mathsf{C}) \end{aligned}\right\} \quad (6.56)$$

In order to show that at equilibrium the temperatures of any two phases labeled 1 and 2 are equal, let there be no changes in volume of any phase [$\delta V^{(j)} = 0$ for all j] and no transfer of matter across phase boundaries [$\delta n_i^{(j)} = 0$ for all i and j], and let the only entropy change occur in phases 1 and 2 [$\delta S^{(j)} = 0$ of $1 \neq j \neq 2$]. By (6.56),

$$\begin{aligned} T^{(1)}\, \delta S^{(1)} + T^{(2)}\, \delta S^{(2)} &\geqslant 0 \\ \delta S^{(1)} + \delta S^{(2)} &= 0 \end{aligned}$$

Elimination of $\delta S^{(2)}$ from these two relations yields

$$[T^{(1)} - T^{(2)}]\, \delta S^{(1)} \geqslant 0$$

If $\delta S^{(1)}$ is greater than zero, $T^{(1)} \geqslant T^{(2)}$; if $\delta S^{(1)}$ is less than zero, $T^{(1)} \leqslant T^{(2)}$. Since $\delta S^{(1)}$ is not zero, these two relations are satisfied only if $T^{(1)} = T^{(2)}$.

A spontaneous increase in the entropy of phase 1 such that $\delta S^{(1)}$ is greater than zero, perhaps by absorption of a positive amount of heat from phase 2, requires that $[T^{(1)} - T^{(2)}]\delta S^{(1)} < 0$ or that $T^{(1)} < T^{(2)}$. This is nothing more than a statement that heat flows spontaneously from a high to a low temperature.

In order to show that at equilibrium in the absence of such things as fields and membranes the pressures of any two phases labeled 1 and 2 are equal, let there be no changes in entropy in any phase [$\delta S^{(j)} = 0$ for all j] and no transfer of matter from phase to phase [$\delta n_i^{(j)} = 0$ for all i and j], and let the only volume change occur between phases 1 and 2 [$\delta V^{(j)} = 0$ for $1 \neq j \neq 2$]. By (6.56),

$$-P^{(1)}\,\delta V^{(1)} - P^{(2)}\,\delta V^{(2)} \geqslant 0$$

$$\delta V^{(1)} + \delta V^{(2)} = 0$$

Elimination of $\delta V^{(2)}$ yields

$$[P^{(2)} - P^{(1)}]\,\delta V^{(1)} \geqslant 0$$

If the volume of phase 1 increases, $\delta V^{(1)} > 0$ and $P^{(2)} \geqslant P^{(1)}$. If the volume of phase 1 decreases, $\delta V^{(1)} < 0$ and $P^{(2)} \leqslant P^{(1)}$. But since the volume of phase 1 must change, these two relations are satisfied only if $P^{(1)} = P^{(2)}$ so that the pressure is uniform throughout the system.

A spontaneous increase in the volume of phase 1 requires $[P^{(2)} - P^{(1)}]\delta V^{(1)} < 0$ and since $\delta V^{(1)}$ is supposed to be greater than zero, $P^{(2)} < P^{(1)}$. That is, the volume of a phase with a high pressure increases spontaneously and at the expense of a phase with a low pressure.

In order to show that the chemical potential of any species i is the same anywhere in the system, let there be no changes in volume or entropy of any phase [$\delta V^{(j)} = dS^{(j)} = 0$ for all j] and let the only transfer of any component be a transfer of δn_i moles of component i between the arbitrarily chosen phases 1 and 2, each of which contains component i. Then, as before, by (6.56),

$$\delta V = \sum_{j=1}^{P} \delta V^{(j)} = 0$$

$$\delta S = \sum_{j=1}^{P} \delta S^{(j)} = 0$$

$$\delta n_i = \sum_{j=1}^{P} \delta n_i^{(j)} = \delta n_i^{(1)} + \delta n_i^{(2)} = 0$$

and

$$\mu_i^{(1)}\,\delta n_i^{(1)} + \mu_i^{(2)}\,\delta n_i^{(2)} \geqslant 0$$

Elimination of $\delta n_i^{(2)}$ from these relations yields

$$[\mu_i^{(1)} - \mu_i^{(2)}]\,\delta n_i^{(1)} \geqslant 0$$

If the amount of component i in phase 1 increases, $\delta n_i^{(1)}$ is greater than zero and $\mu_i^{(1)} \geqslant \mu_i^{(2)}$; if the amount of i in phase 1 decreases, $\mu_i^{(1)} \leqslant \mu_i^{(2)}$. Hence, at equilibrium $\mu_i^{(1)} = \mu_i^{(2)}$, which is like (5.73) but more general. In other words, the Clapeyron equation founded as it is on equality of chemical potentials, is true for one component of two solutions as well as for one component of two pure phases.

If it happens that phase 1 does not initially contain component i, it could gain some i from phase 2 so that $\mu_i^{(1)} \geqslant \mu_i^{(2)}$ at equilibrium. But phase 1 could not lose component i if it initially had none, so that the chemical potential of i in a phase in which it is not actually present may be greater than it is in other phases that actually contain component i.

For a spontaneous flow of component i from any phase labeled 2, which initially contains i, to another phase labeled 1, the relation is, in contrast to that above, $[\mu_i^{(1)} - \mu_i^{(2)}]\,\delta n_i^{(1)} < 0$. If $\delta n_i^{(1)}$ is greater than zero as supposed, $\mu_i^{(1)} < \mu_i^{(2)}$. That is, spontaneous transfer of matter to phase 1 is from a region of high chemical potential $\mu_i^{(2)}$ to a region of low chemical potential $\mu_i^{(1)}$. Chemical potential is to the transfer of matter as pressure is to a change of volume or as temperature is to heat.

These necessary conditions of equilibrium, namely, equality of temperature, pressure, and chemical potential of each component, are also sufficient conditions for equilibrium, for with them (6.56) is satisfied thus:

$$T \sum_{j=1}^{\mathsf{P}} \delta S^{(j)} - P \sum_{j=1}^{\mathsf{P}} \delta V^{(j)} + \sum_{i=1}^{\mathsf{C}} \mu_i \sum_{j=1}^{\mathsf{P}} \delta n_i^{(j)} \geqslant 0$$

$$T(0) - P(0) + \sum_{i=1}^{\mathsf{C}} \mu_i(0) = 0$$

The necessary and sufficient conditions for equilibrium in a system of P phases and C components, subject to the conditions specified above, are

$$\left.\begin{array}{l}
T^{(1)} = T^{(2)} = \cdots = T^{(j)} = \cdots = T^{(\mathsf{P})} \\
P^{(1)} = P^{(2)} = \cdots = P^{(j)} = \cdots = P^{(\mathsf{P})} \\
\mu_1^{(1)} = \mu_1^{(2)} = \cdots = \mu_1^{(j)} = \cdots = \mu_1^{(\mathsf{P})} \\
\mu_2^{(1)} = \mu_2^{(2)} = \cdots = \mu_2^{(j)} = \cdots = \mu_2^{(\mathsf{P})} \\
\cdots \qquad\qquad\qquad\qquad \cdots \\
\mu_i^{(1)} = \mu_i^{(2)} = \cdots = \mu_i^{(j)} = \cdots = \mu_i^{(\mathsf{P})} \\
\cdots \qquad\qquad\qquad\qquad \cdots \\
\mu_{\mathsf{C}}^{(1)} = \mu_{\mathsf{C}}^{(2)} = \cdots = \mu_{\mathsf{C}}^{(j)} = \cdots = \mu_{\mathsf{C}}^{(\mathsf{P})}
\end{array}\right\} \qquad (6.57)$$

Verbally, these conditions are that the temperature and pressure of a system at equilibrium must be the same throughout all phases of the system and that the chemical potential of each species must be the same in every phase where it is found to exist. These conditions on μ_i are really the basis of the derivations of the Clapeyron equation (6.3) and the Poynting equation (6.1) that describes how vapor pressure depends on total pressure.

6.9 SURFACE FREE ENERGY

Condensed phases cohere because of various intermolecular forces. In liquid hydrocarbons, these forces are mainly dispersion (van der Waals) attractions and the interaction of electric dipoles. In water, they are dispersion forces, dipolar interaction, and attractions of hydrogen bonds. In molecular solids, these kinds of force influence the nature of the packing, but in ionic or covalent solids they are generally subordinate to electrostatic or covalent bonding.

The action of these various forces of attraction between molecules in liquids and solids tends to minimize their surface area, for the molecules in a surface are in an unsymmetrical environment. Even if the boundary of the phase is not defined within a distance about the size of an atom, the number of atoms or molecules of a given kind changes rapidly in a direction perpendicular to the surface. Attractive forces of the van der Waals type or stronger tend to increase the number of favorable contacts within a substance. Quite naturally, this leads to a stable state in which there is a minimum of exposed surface area. Thus, spilled mercury collects in droplets that appear from above to be round, and droplets of water on an oily surface are round and tend to unite as mercury droplets do. In field-free space, mercury, water, and all fluids would agglomerate in a spherical shape because a sphere has a minimum exposed surface area for a given volume. It is just as though a confining membrane composed of surface atoms and molecules were stretched taut about the droplets. Like fluids, which cannot support a shear stress, solids also tend to minimize their exposed area, but their rigidity prevents their taking a spherical shape.

The work that is done on a pure substance to subdivide it is proportional to the increase $d\mathscr{A}$ in its surface area. That is, as in (2.2), $dw = \gamma d\mathscr{A}$, wherein the proportionality constant γ is called the *surface tension* or *surface energy* of the substance. By (5.68), because it is non-expansion work,

$$dw_0 = \gamma d\mathscr{A} = dG \tag{6.58}$$

The value of γ depends on the nature not only of the substance whose area increases but also of the other phase. The value of γ for a liquid-air interface even depends slightly upon whether the air is saturated or not with the vapor of the volatile liquid.

If a drop of a liquid of surface tension γ_{A1} relative to air is placed on a large surface of another liquid with surface tension γ_{A2} relative to air, the liquid may spread out over the surface of the second liquid or it may collect into a droplet or lens. What happens depends on the surface tension γ_{12} of the liquid-liquid interface. In terms of Figure 6.3, if the droplet spreads, an increase in its area $\mathscr{A}_{A1}$ relative to air is equal to the increase in its area $\mathscr{A}_{12}$ in contact with liquid 2, but both occur at the expense of the area $\mathscr{A}_{A2}$ of the air interface of liquid 2; hence, $d\mathscr{A}_{A1} = d\mathscr{A}_{12} = -d\mathscr{A}_{A2}$. The net increase in free energy as $\mathscr{A}_{A1} = \mathscr{A}$

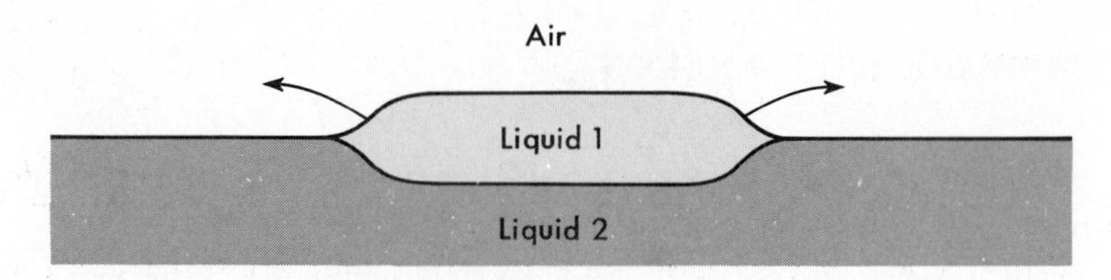

Figure 6.3. Spreading of a Droplet

increases is, therefore,

$$dG = \gamma_{A1}\, d\mathscr{A}_{A1} + \gamma_{12}\, d\mathscr{A}_{12} + \gamma_{A2}\, d\mathscr{A}_{A2}$$
$$= (\gamma_{A1} + \gamma_{12} - \gamma_{A2})\, d\mathscr{A} \qquad (6.59)$$

At constant T and P, (5.58) requires $dG < 0$ so that for $d\mathscr{A} > 0$ it is necessary that $\gamma_{A1} + \gamma_{12} - \gamma_{A2} < 0$, or

$$\gamma_{12} < \gamma_{A2} - \gamma_{A1} \qquad \text{(spreading)} \qquad (6.60)$$

for a spontaneous increase in $\mathscr{A}$. On the other hand, if the final state is a lens of minimum $\mathscr{A}$, (5.58) requires

$$\gamma_{12} > \gamma_{A2} - \gamma_{A1} \qquad \text{(contracting)} \qquad (6.61)$$

In general, γ_{12} for liquids each saturated with the other is roughly equal to $\gamma_{A2} - \gamma_{A1}$ so that it is difficult to predict whether spreading or contracting will occur. In fact, sometimes spreading occurs until, as the liquids become mutually saturated with each other, γ_{12} becomes large enough to cause contraction once again.

Table 6.4 lists values of γ for several liquids relative to air at 20°C. Any manifestation of γ can be used as a method of measuring or comparing γ's.

Table 6.4 Surface Free Energies of Liquids at Various Temperatures (*Handbook of Chemistry*, [10th Edition], ed. by N. A. Lange and G. M. Forker, New York: McGraw-Hill Book Co., Inc., 1967, pp. 1660–63.)

Substance		Temperature (°C)	γ (ergs cm^{-2})	Substance		Temperature (°C)	γ (ergs cm^{-2})
Acetic Acid	(air)	20	27.6	Ag	(air)	970	800
Acetone	(air)	20	23.7	AgCl	(air)	452	125.5
Ammonia	(air)	20	21.	Cd	(H_2)	450	621.5
Benzene	(air)	20	28.9	Cu	(H_2)	1131	1103.
Bromine	(air)	20	41.5	Hg	(air)	15	487.
CCl_4	(air)	20	26.8	Na	(vac)	100	222.
Chlorobenzene	(air)	20	33.2	NaCl	(N_2)	803	113.8
Ethanol	(air)	20	22.27	Pb	(H_2)	350	453.
Glycerol	(air)	20	63.	Pb	(H_2)	750	423.
n-Hexane	(air)	20	18.4	Pt	(air)	2000	1819.
Toluene	(air)	20	28.43	Sn	(H_2)	253	526.
Water	(air)	20	72.75	$SnCl_2$	(N_2)	307	97.
Water	(air)	100	58.85	Zn	(H_2)	477	753.

As a result, many devices are used. Figure 6.4 illustrates a very simple slide-wire device for increasing the area of a thin film of liquid. As the slide is moved a distance dx by a force F, the area of the two-sided film increases by $2l\,dx$; the work done on the film is thus $F\,dx = \gamma 2l\,dx$. Hence, $\gamma = F/2l$. With the dimensions of force per unit length, γ is appropriately called a surface tension, the

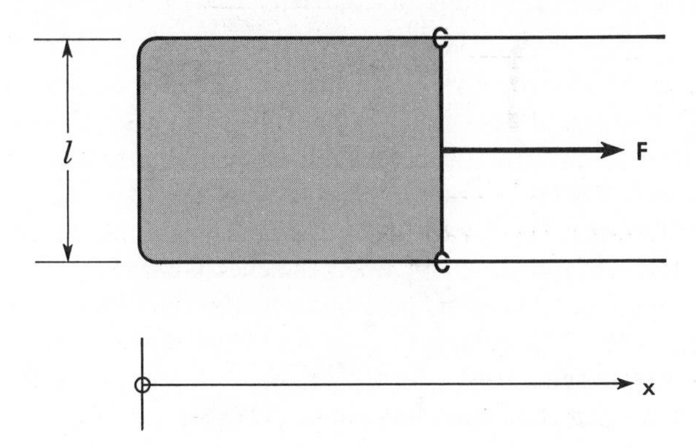

Figure 6.4. Why Surface Free Energy is Called Surface Tension

force required to prevent unit length of a one-sided film from contracting. Other ways of observing γ are similar. The extra apparent weight of a thin glass plate of length l as it is pulled vertically from the surface of a liquid is $2l\gamma$, where the factor 2 comes from the two sides of the plate. Similarly, in the du Nuoy method, the extra apparent weight of a wire ring of radius r is measured by a torsion method as the ring is pulled from the surface of the liquid with a force that is approximately $2(2\pi r)\gamma$. Or again, the weight of a drop of liquid as it falls from a tube of radius r is $2\pi r\gamma f$, where f, a complicated function of the apparatus, can be eliminated in comparisons of two different liquids in the same apparatus.

The most widely used accurate means of measuring γ, however, is the capillary rise method, which uses a small-bore tube inserted into the free surface of the liquid and the rise or fall of the liquid in the tube as the liquid either wets or does not wet the interior of the tube. It is common experience that water may not collect on a surface as mercury does. If molecules of water are adsorbed on a surface because attractive forces between water and surface are stronger than attractive forces among water molecules, then the water is said to *wet* the surface. It tends to spread out over the surface in a thin film. Thus, water wets sugar, cotton, clean glass, or a clean metallic surface. The degree to which a surface is wetted is shown by the angle between the surface and the pseudomembrane that seems to surround a droplet on the surface. This angle θ is shown for wetting and nonwetting in Figure 6.5. Figure 6.5(a) is typical of water on clean glass, while (b) is typical of mercury on glass or water on Teflon. Attraction between unlike phases decreases as θ increases.

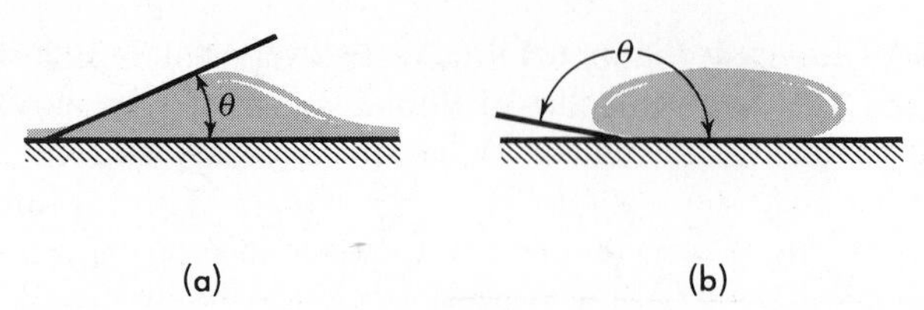

Figure 6.5. Contact Angle θ: Wetting (a) and Non-Wetting (b)

Figure 6.6 illustrates what happens when tubes of differing material are inserted into a liquid. If the liquid does not wet the tube (e.g., Hg in glass or H_2O in Teflon), the level in the tube is below the level of the free surface. However, if the liquid wets the tube's interior, it rises into the tube, as water does in clean glass. The force that at equilibrium supports the column of liquid is equal to the circumference of the tube, $2\pi r$, times the effective surface tension in the vertical direction, $\gamma \cos \theta$, where θ is the angle between the liquid surface and the vertical interior wall as shown in Figure 6.6. This upward force of magnitude $2\pi r\gamma \cos \theta$ is opposed to the downward force of gravity, which is $\pi r^2 z\rho\, g$ for a liquid of density ρ at a height z when the acceleration of gravity is g. Hence, at equilibrium, $2\pi r\gamma \cos \theta = \pi r^2 z\rho g$ and

$$\gamma = \frac{r\rho g z}{2 \cos \theta} \tag{6.62}$$

Frequently for H_2O and clean glass, $\theta \approx 0$ so that $\cos \theta = 1$.

Although (6.62) was derived for $z > 0$ and $\theta < \pi/2$, it holds equally well when $\theta > \pi/2$, for then $z < 0$. A small correction to the volume of liquid be-

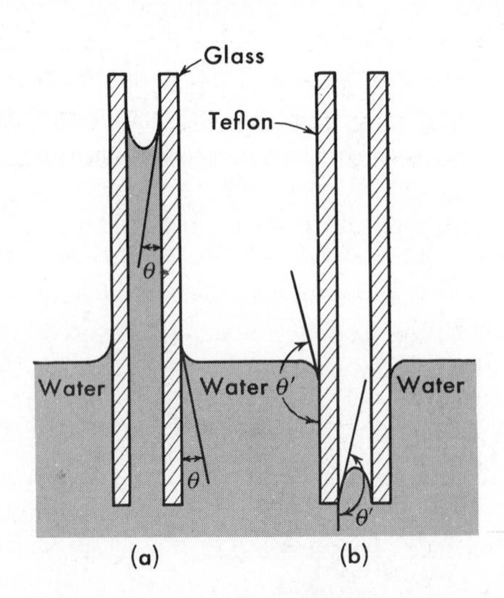

Figure 6.6. Capillary Rise Method of Determining Surface Free Energy. Wetting (a) and Non-Wetting (b)

cause its free surface is not a plane has been neglected. Moreover, ρ represents the density of the liquid relative to the phase above. If ρ_1 is the true density of liquid and ρ_0 is the density of the phase above, ρ should be replaced by $(\rho_1 - \rho_0)$.

Example 6.8. Distilled water rose to a height of 4.96 cm at 20°C in a certain capillary tube. The density of water at 20°C is 0.9982 g cm^{-3}. The same tube, when filled with mercury of density 13.55 g cm^{-3}, contained 38.3 mg cm^{-1} of tube length. Calculate the surface tension of water if the angle of contact is zero.

Since the volume of a tube of length 1.000 cm is πr^2, it follows that

$$38.3 \times 10^{-3} = 13.55 \times \pi r^2$$

$$r = 0.0300 \text{ cm}$$

Then, by (6.62), since $\cos\theta = 1$,

$$\gamma = \frac{3.00 \times 10^{-2} \times 0.9982 \times 980.7 \times 4.96}{2} = 72.8 \text{ ergs cm}^{-2}$$

The surface tension of a liquid decreases continuously as the temperature rises until, at the critical point, the liquid and gaseous phases no longer differ. The surface energy of a mole of liquid is expected to be proportional to $\gamma(M/\rho)^{2/3}$, for (M/ρ) is the volume of a mole and $(M/\rho)^{2/3}$ is thus proportional to its surface area. It has been found that the rate of change of the function $\gamma(M/\rho)^{2/3}$ with respect to temperature is constant. That is, with a negative sign to indicate that the function decreases with temperature,

$$\frac{d\left[\gamma\left(\frac{M}{\rho}\right)^{2/3}\right]}{dT} = -k \tag{6.63}$$

Definite integration of (6.63) between a state at temperature T with surface tension γ and the critical state at temperature T_c where $\gamma = 0$ relative to gas yields

$$\int_{\gamma'=0}^{\gamma'=\gamma} d\left[\gamma'\left(\frac{M}{\rho}\right)^{2/3}\right] = -\int_{T_c}^{T} k\,dT'$$

$$\gamma\left(\frac{M}{\rho}\right)^{2/3} = k(T_c - T) \tag{6.64}$$

Observed data for unassociated liquids fit (6.65), the Ramsay-Shields equation, better than (6.64).

$$\gamma\left(\frac{M}{\rho}\right)^{2/3} = 2.1(T_c - T - 6) \tag{6.65}$$

The value $k = 2.1$ is for the cgs system and is accurate generally within 10% for liquids like hydrocarbons and their halogen derivatives, ethers, and esters.

Values of k for liquids containing hydrogen bonds are generally much less than 2.1 and vary with the temperature.

6.10 VAPOR PRESSURE OF SMALL DROPS

Small droplets have a greater vapor pressure than large ones at the same T because within tiny drops the hydrostatic pressure is greater than in the surrounding vapor. The size of this extraordinary pressure within a droplet is found by considering a reversible, infinitesimal expansion of a droplet. At equilibrium at constant T, by (2.2), (2.3), and (5.61), $0 = dA = -P\,dV + \gamma d\mathscr{A}$, or

$$P\,dV = \gamma d\mathscr{A} \tag{6.66}$$

This result says that whatever reversible expansion work the droplet might do at constant T is used to increase its surface energy. This kind of frustrated work is like the interplay of expansion and gravitational work in Example 5.14.

If the drop is spherical, $dV = 4\pi r^2\,dr$ and $d\mathscr{A} = 8\pi r\,dr$; hence, (6.66) yields

$$P = \frac{2\gamma}{r} \tag{6.67}$$

This value of P is the pressure difference between the interior of the drop and its surroundings. A similar difference in pressure because of surface energy exists across any curved surface. When the surface is not spherical,

$$P = \gamma\left(\frac{1}{r_1} + \frac{1}{r_2}\right) \tag{6.68}$$

where r_1 and r_2 are the two radii of curvature at the point where P is observed.

Equation (6.67) also leads to the capillary rise equation (6.62). If r' is the radius of curvature of the liquid's free surface in a capillary of internal radius r, it is easy to show that $r = r' \cos\theta$, where θ is the angle of contact of Figure 6.6. The pressure difference $2\gamma/r'$ across the interface at equilibrium supports the hydrostatic pressure $\rho g z$ if the liquid of density ρ is at a height z. Equating $\rho g z$ and $2\gamma/r'$ with the use of $r = r'\cos\theta$ yields, as before,

$$\frac{2\gamma}{r'} = \rho g z$$

$$\gamma = \frac{\rho g z r'}{2} = \frac{\rho g z r}{2\cos\theta} \tag{6.62}$$

Example 6.9 What is the extraordinary pressure at 20°C within a spherical drop of water if its radius is 2000 A?

Since $r = 2.000 \times 10^3 \times 10^{-8}$ cm, and since at 20°C $\gamma = 72.75$ dynes cm^{-1} (ergs cm^{-2})(Table 6.4), it follows from (6.67) that

$$P = \frac{2 \times 72.75}{2.000 \times 10^{-5}} = 7.275 \times 10^6 \text{ dynes cm}^{-2} = 7.179 \text{ atm (!!)}$$

A system containing free droplets, spherical because this gives each droplet a minimum area and surface energy, has matter at pressures that differ by $2\gamma/r$. The equilibrium condition $P^{(1)} = P^{(2)} = \cdots = P^{(j)} = \cdots = P^{(\mathrm{P})}$ of (6.57) is clearly violated, for surface effects are not negligible here as they were supposed to be in deriving (6.57). It is now proper to consider the surface of each drop at equilibrium to be a rigid mechanical membrane that allows all species and heat to pass. With all $\delta V^{(j)} = 0$ at the droplets' surfaces, the condition on $P^{(j)}$ is relaxed. However, since heat (entropy) and matter can pass this boundary, the other conditions of (6.57) apply at equilibrium. The absolute pressure within a droplet of radius r surrounded by pure vapor at a pressure p is $p + P = p + 2\gamma/r$. The conditions of equilibrium between vapor and finely divided liquid require that the chemical potential $\mu_i^{(g)}(T, p)$ of the vapor equal that of the liquid inside the droplet; that is, $\mu_i^{(g)}(T, p) = \mu_i^{(1)}(T, p + P)$. If p_0 is the vapor pressure above an uncurved surface of the liquid so that direct reference can be made to the standard state of i, then by (6.48) for the liquid

$$\int_{\mu_i^{(1)}(T,p_0)}^{\mu_i^{(1)}(T,p+P)} d\mu_i = \int_{p_0}^{p+P} \bar{V}_i \, dP' \tag{6.69}$$

where $\mu_i^{(1)}(T, p_0)$ is the chemical potential of drops of i so large that further increases in size leave μ_i unaffected. If the liquid is incompressible so that $\bar{V}_i$ is independent of pressure, the right side of (6.69) is approximately $\bar{V}_i P$ since p and p_0 are nearly equal and ordinarily much smaller than P. The droplet equilibrium condition $\mu_i^{(1)}(T, p + P) = \mu_i^{(g)}(T, p)$ and the corresponding large-drop equilibrium condition $\mu_i^{(1)}(T, p_0) = \mu_i^{(g)}(T, p_0)$ then bring (6.69) to the form

$$\mu_i^{(g)}(T, p) - \mu_i^{(g)}(T, p_0) = \bar{V}_i P \tag{6.70}$$

But by (6.50) with the approximation that the vapor is a perfect gas ($f = p$), (6.70) is

$$\ln\left(\frac{p}{p_0}\right) = \frac{\bar{V}_i P}{RT} \tag{6.71}$$

where p is the vapor pressure of a droplet with extraordinary pressure $P = 2\gamma/r$ and where p_0 is the usual vapor pressure of flat surfaces at T.

Example 6.10. What is the vapor pressure of spherical droplets of water at 20°C if their radii are 2000 A?

With $r = 2.00 \times 10^{-5}$ cm, $\gamma = 72.75$ ergs cm^{-2} (Table 6.4), and $\bar{V}_i = 18.05$ cm^3 mole^{-1}, (6.71) and (6.67) give

$$\ln\left(\frac{p}{p_0}\right) = P\left(\frac{\bar{V}_i}{RT}\right) = \left(\frac{2 \times 72.75}{2.00 \times 10^{-5}}\right)\left(\frac{18.05}{8.314 \times 10^7 \times 293.2}\right) = 0.00538$$

Since $\ln(1 + x) \approx x$ when $x \ll 1$, $p = 1.00538\, p_0$. With $p_0 = 17.535$ mm Hg from Table 6.1, it follows that the vapor pressure of the droplets is $p = 17.630$ mm Hg.

6.11 MONOLAYERS

A *monolayer* is a layer that is one molecule thick. Straight-chain alkanoic acids typically form monolayers on water; the acid end of each molecule wets the water and thus dips into the aqueous phase, while the hydrocarbon ends of the molecules avoid the water and, when the monolayer is dense, pack together like a bunch of pencils. Such a monolayer is conveniently formed by placing a few drops of a dilute solution of the acid in a volatile solvent on the surface of water; the solution spreads and the solvent evaporates leaving the non-volatile acid arrayed as a monolayer. As T rises, the rather orderly packing of the hydrocarbon ends of the molecules is destroyed in favor of random gas-like positions of the acid molecules, each still having the acid group in the aqueous phase. Solids, especially catalysts, also adsorb molecules of various kinds as monolayers.

The thermodynamics of monolayers begins with the fundamental equation (6.37) after addition of non-expansion work $dw_0 = \gamma d\mathscr{A}$ to give

$$dE = T\,dS - P\,dV + \gamma d\mathscr{A} + \sum_i \mu_i\,dn_i \tag{6.72}$$

In the usual way, if $G' = E - TS + PV - \gamma\mathscr{A}$, then there results the exact differential

$$dG' = -S\,dT + V\,dP - \mathscr{A}\,d\gamma + \sum_i \mu_i\,dn_i \tag{6.73}$$

According to (6.73), $G' = G'(T, P, \gamma, n_1, n_2, \ldots, n_i, \ldots n_C)$. Euler's theorem (6.24) for G' considered as an extensive property requires, as in (6.44), that

$$G' = \sum_i n_i\mu_i(T, P, \gamma) \tag{6.74}$$

and

$$dG' = \sum_i n_i d\mu_i + \sum_i \mu_i dn_i \tag{6.75}$$

Equating (6.73) and (6.75) then requires

$$S\,dT - V\,dP + \mathscr{A}\,d\gamma + \sum_i n_i\,d\mu_i = 0 \tag{6.76}$$

If surface effects are negligible so that $\mathscr{A} = 0$, (6.76) reduces to the very useful Gibbs-Duhem equation

$$S\,dT - V\,dP + \sum_i n_i\,d\mu_i = 0 \tag{6.77}$$

which can be derived without any reference to surface effects by substituting $V = G$ into (6.34) with account of (5.19), (5.20), and (6.26).

Ordinarily (6.76) applies to each phase of a system in which surface effects are of interest, while (6.77) applies to the other ordinary bulk phases in which surface effects are negligible. Without surface effects, the energy $E^{(j)}$, entropy $S^{(j)}$, volume $V^{(j)}$, and numbers of moles $n_i^{(j)}$ of each component in the phases j would be summed to give the total values of E, S, V, and n_i for the whole system, as in (6.53) and (6.54). Every surface phase, however, also contributes to these quantities according to its size and nature so that in general

$$E = \sum_j E^{(j)} + \sum_\sigma E^{(\sigma)} \tag{6.78}$$

and so on for S, V, and n_i, where $E^{(\sigma)}$, $S^{(\sigma)}$, $V^{(\sigma)}$, and $n_i^{(\sigma)}$ are the (positive or negative) *excess surface energy*, entropy, volume, and moles of component i.

In 1886, Stefan suggested that the energy required to vaporize a molecule from a surface is about half that required to vaporize it from the interior of a phase. If so, $E^{(\sigma)}$, the energy (or perhaps enthalpy) of molecules in a surface, would be half ΔH, their heat of vaporization or sublimation. Actually, $E^{(\sigma)}/\Delta H$ decreases with rising T. Near the boiling point, molecules having the unsymmetrical and disordered environment that is theirs in a surface act as though they have somewhat more than half as many attracting neighbors as in the interior of a phase; hence, $E^{(\sigma)}$ is less than $\frac{1}{2}\Delta H$. Naturally, the entropy $S^{(\sigma)}$ is intermediate between $S^{(\text{liq})}$ and $S^{(\text{gas})}$.

The Gibbs-Duhem equation of a surface phase is commonly simplified by assuming that the volume $V^{(\sigma)}$ of the surface phase is negligible. If the temperature is also constant, (6.76) is then

$$d\gamma = -\sum_i \Gamma_i \, d\mu_i \tag{6.79}$$

where the surface concentration Γ_i of species i is defined as

$$\Gamma_i = \frac{n_i^{(\sigma)}}{\mathscr{A}} \tag{6.80}$$

Further simplification results when there are just two components, perhaps water and an organic species, for then

$$d\gamma = -\Gamma_1 d\mu_1 - \Gamma_2 \, d\mu_2 \tag{6.81}$$

Still further simplification of (6.79) or (6.81) is possible by choosing the position of the surface so that one of the Γ_i's is zero. This choice usually places the defined surface near the region where the physical and chemical properties of the contacting bulk phases change rapidly with position. Figure 6.7 illustrates a typical variation in the concentration of the major (solvent) species 1 and any other minor species i as a function of one position coordinate x taken perpendicular to the surface. The total amount of i in a cylinder with unit base and altitude z is

$$\int_0^z C_i\,dx = \Gamma_i + \int_0^s C_i^{(j)}\,dx + \int_s^z C_i^{(k)}\,dx \tag{6.82}$$

where C_i is the actual continuously varying concentration of i and where $C_i^{(j)}$ and $C_i^{(k)}$ are the constant bulk concentrations of i far from the surface. Rewritten for species 1, (6.82) is

$$\Gamma_1 = -\int_0^s (C_1^{(j)} - C_1)\,dx + \int_s^z (C_1 - C_1^{(k)})\,dx$$

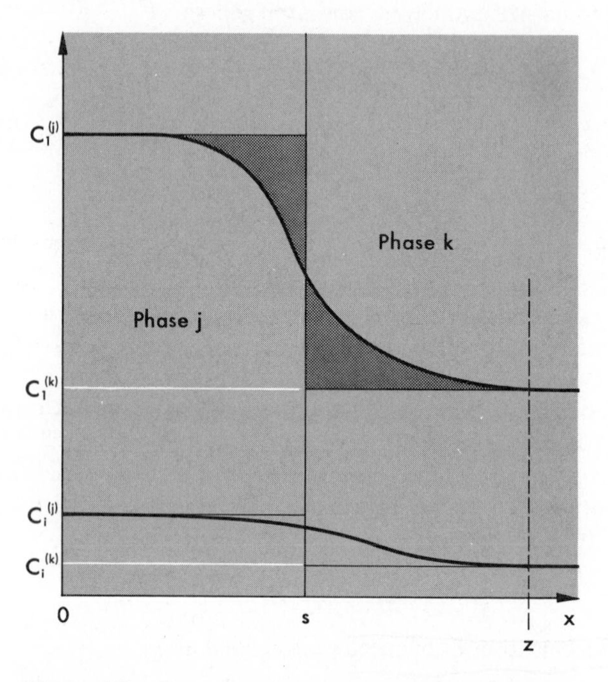

Figure 6.7. Concentrations Near a Defined Surface

where the integrals are the areas of the shaded regions of Figure 6.7. The position $x = s$ of the defined surface can be chosen so that the shaded areas are equal and $\Gamma_1 = 0$, but then for any other species Γ_i is not generally zero since the corresponding areas along the C_i curve are not equal. As drawn in Figure 6.7, $\Gamma_i > 0$.

With $\Gamma_1 = 0$, (6.81) is simply $d\gamma = -\Gamma_2\,d\mu_2$. If, as in (6.51), $d\mu_2 = RT\,d\ln a_2$, then there results the Gibbs adsorption isotherm

$$d\gamma = -\Gamma_2 RT d\ln a_2 \qquad (dT = 0) \tag{6.83}$$

$$\left(\frac{\partial \gamma}{\partial a_2}\right)_T = -\frac{\Gamma_2 RT}{a_2} \tag{6.84}$$

If species 2 is abundant in the surface so that $\Gamma_2 > 0$, then γ decreases as the activity a_2 (i.e., effective concentration) of 2 in either phase increases, for $a_2 >$

0. On the other hand, if γ increases with increasing a_2, then $\Gamma_2 < 0$ and there is a region of the interface where species 2 is rare. The thickness of this region is roughly

$$z_2 = -\frac{\Gamma_2}{a_2} = \frac{1}{RT}\left(\frac{\partial \gamma}{\partial a_2}\right)_T \tag{6.85}$$

The reason for the existence of this solute-free layer is that γ increases with a_2 for certain solutions, notably ionic solutes in water. In these, ions avoid the surface because there they do not find enough other ions to neutralize their own charges. Equations (6.83) and (6.84) have been verified directly by observing the surface energies γ of solutions of known a_2 at T and by measuring Γ_2, the excess solute or its deficiency, at the liquid-vapor interface either by direct analysis of a thin layer microtomed from a large surface or by counting radioactively tagged species 2 in the surface.

Example 6.11. Calculate the excess surface concentration of *n*-butyl alcohol in a 0.1000 molal aqueous solution at 25°C if molalities and surface tensions of such solutions are (W. D. Harkins and R. W. Wampler, *J. Am. Chem. Soc.* **53,** 850 (1931)):

m	0.00329	0.00658	0.01320	0.0264	0.0536	0.1050	0.2110	0.4330
γ	72.80	72.26	70.82	68.00	63.14	56.31	48.08	38.87

According to (6.84), the surface concentration Γ_2 depends on the slope of γ vs concentration at the concentration of interest. At $m = 0.1000$ in Figure

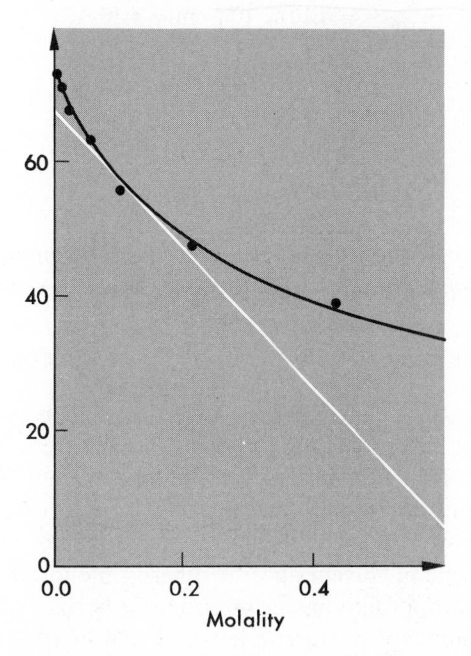

Figure 6.8. Surface Tension of Aqueous *n*-Butanol Solutions at 25°C

6.8, which gives γ as a function of m, the slope is $-$ 103 dynes cm^{-1} molal^{-1}; hence, by a modified (6.84),

$$\Gamma_2 = -\frac{m_2}{RT}\left(\frac{\partial \gamma}{\partial m_2}\right)_T = -\frac{0.100}{8.314 \times 10^7 \times 298}(-103) = 4.16 \times 10^{-10} \text{ moles cm}^{-2}$$

Since there are $N_0 = 6.023 \times 10^{23}$ molecules mole^{-1}, the area per molecule is

$$\frac{1}{N_0\Gamma_2} = \frac{1}{6.023 \times 10^{23} \times 4.16 \times 10^{-10}} = 3.99 \times 10^{-15} \text{ cm}^2 = 39.9 \text{ A}^2$$

This result is based on the excess butanol molecules in the surface; some butanol molecules belong in the surface region as solute molecules; hence, this area is a bit too high.

Example 6.12. At 20°C the surface tension of aqueous solutions of NH_4NO_3 of molality m are approximately $72.75 + 1.00\,m$ for $m < 2$. For a one-molal solution, calculate Γ_2 and the approximate thickness of the surface layer that is essentially free of NH_4NO_3.

By (6.84) with the derivative equal to 1.00

$$\Gamma_2 = -\frac{m_2}{RT}\left(\frac{\partial \gamma}{\partial m}\right)_T = -\frac{1.00(1.00)}{8.314 \times 10^7 \times 293} = -0.410 \times 10^{-10} \text{ mole cm}^{-2}$$

Since molality and molarity are about equal in dilute aqueous solution, the number of gram-formula-weights of NH_4NO_3 per cm^3 is about $m_2 \times 10^{-3}$ and thus, by (6.85), the effective vacant layer of solution has a thickness of about

$$z_2 = -\frac{\Gamma_2}{m_2 \times 10^{-3}} = \frac{0.410 \times 10^{-10}}{1.00 \times 10^{-3}} = 4.10 \times 10^{-8} \text{ cm} = 4.10 \text{ A}$$

While $(\partial\gamma/\partial m)_T$ is constant, z_2 is independent of concentration.

6.12 FILM PRESSURE

The difference between the surface tension γ of a solution with a monolayer and the surface tension γ_0 of a pure solvent is called the film (or surface) pressure π, where

$$\pi = \gamma_0 - \gamma \tag{6.86}$$

Film pressure is measured directly in a film balance. A vertical film balance observes the difference in apparent weight of a thin glass or metal plate in the pure solvent and then in the monolayered solution. This is done by replacing solvent with solution, by generating the monolayer on the solvent, or simultaneously by noting the deflection of a balanced beam supporting plates both first in the pure solvent and then one in solvent and the other in monolayered solution. Another more complex form of film balance measures π horizontally; the torque required to hold in a standard position a lever the end of which is attached to a floating barrier between solvent and monolayered solution is a measure of π. In the horizontal film balance, π is the force per unit length of the barrier acting to minimize the exposed area of the phase having the higher surface tension. For most organic monolayers on water, $\gamma_0 > \gamma$ so that $\pi > 0$ and a force must be exerted to keep the monolayer's area from increasing.

In 1891, Traube found that π is often proportional to the bulk concentration C_2 of the solute; that is,

$$\pi = \gamma_0 - \gamma = KC_2 \tag{6.87}$$

Many monolayers follow (6.87), especially at low C_2. In (6.84), with $a_2 = C_2$, (6.87) yields

$$\left(\frac{\partial \gamma}{\partial C_2}\right)_T = -K = -\frac{\pi}{C_2} = -\frac{\Gamma_2 RT}{C_2}$$

$$\pi = \Gamma_2 RT \tag{6.88}$$

If the surface concentration of species 2 is $\Gamma_2 = n_2^{(\sigma)}/\mathscr{A}$, then (6.88) is

$$\pi\mathscr{A} = n_2^{(\sigma)} RT \tag{6.89}$$

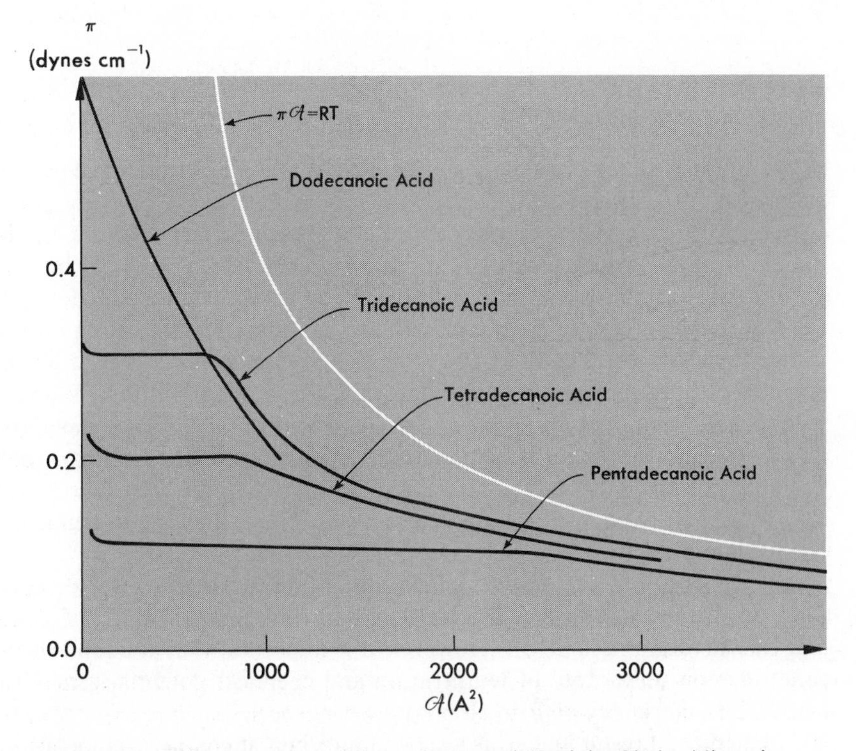

Figure 6.9. Film Pressures of Some Saturated Straight-Chain Alkanoic Acids on Water at 15°C As Functions of Area Per Molecule†

†N. K. Adam and G. Jessup, *Proc. Roy. Soc.* **A110**, 423 [1926], Fig. 1.

which suggests that the molecules of the monolayer behave as a two-dimensional gas. Figure 6.9, which shows how π depends on $\mathscr{A}$ at constant T for monolayers of straight-chain alkanoic acids, is very much like Figure 1.8, which shows how P of a gas varies with V at constant T. In Figure 6.9, three of the monolayered acids attain a state where π is independent of $\mathscr{A}$ at 0.31, 0.20, and about 0.11 dyne cm^{-1}. This behavior is analogous to a vapor pressure. It is likewise possible to write for such monolayers equations of state like those of real gases. Besides showing gas-like and liquid-like states, this kind of monolayer may also show colloid-like and solid-like states in two dimensions. In the solid-like state, these acids all occupy 21 to 25 A^2 per molecule.

Example 6.13. A monolayer containing 0.100 mg of a protein per m^2 has a film pressure of 0.0100 dyne cm^{-1} at 25°C. What is its apparent molecular weight if it is a two-dimensional gas under these conditions?

By analogy with the perfect gas in three dimensions, (6.89) becomes

$$M = \frac{WRT}{\pi\mathscr{A}} = \frac{0.100 \times 10^{-3} \times 8.314 \times 10^{7} \times 298}{0.0100 \times 10^{4}} = 2.48 \times 10^{4}$$

6.13 SUMMARY

In this chapter, vapor pressure has been cited as an index of chemical potential, the driving force of thermodynamic change. The dependence of vapor pressure on temperature, as well as on mechanical and curved-surface pressure, has been studied in detail. A special case of equilibrium, when there is only one independent intensive variable like P or T, is described by the Clapeyron equation.

The temperatures of all phases of a system must be alike at equilibrium. If every phase is open to a species so that it may enter or leave, its chemical potential must be the same in every phase of a system at equilibrium. When only a uniform normal pressure exists and there are no surface effects, membranes, torques, shear stresses, or other unusual forces that might accompany solids, this fluid pressure must be the same in all phases at equilibrium. Furthermore, if T, μ_i, and P are not uniform under these conditions, then the system is not at equilibrium.

The presence of significant surface effects introduces a new set of equilibrium conditions whose specification could involve many angles of contact, radii of curvature, and so on. However, it is important that at equilibrium the conditions on uniformity of temperature and chemical potential generally remain. Thus, constancy of μ_i in all phases where species i is free to enter or leave is a fundamental result and criterion of equilibrium at constant temperature.

The Gibbs-Duhem equation shows that within a phase, reversible changes in temperature, pressure, surface energy, and concentration (i.e., chemical potential) are not independent of each other. The Gibbs adsorption isotherm describes a special case of this interdependence: how surface energy varies with bulk and surface concentrations. The phase rule of the next chapter is a way of counting the number of independent intensive variables in a three-dimensional system of many components and many phases at equilibrium when surface effects, the nature of which is now known, can be neglected.

PROBLEMS

(Vapor pressure and solution data from *Handbook of Chemistry* [10th Edition], ed. by N. A. Lange and G. M. Forker. New York: McGraw-Hill Book Co., Inc., 1967 unless noted otherwise.)

1. Trouton's rule says that the molar entropy of vaporization of liquids is about 21 cal mole^{-1} deg^{-1} at the normal boiling point T_b. From this show that boiling points at pressure P can be corrected to 760 mm Hg by the relation $\Delta T_b = 0.00012 T_b (760 - P)$.

2. The vapor pressure of diethyl ether at 0°C is 185 mm Hg and its normal boiling point is 35°C. What vapor pressure of ether is expected at −75°C, the temperature of a dry-ice trap?
Answer: 1.68 mm Hg.

3. What is the heat of sublimation of Pt if its vapor pressures at various temperatures are (R. F. Hampson, Jr. and R. F. Walker, *J. Res. Nat. Bur. Std.* **65A,** 289 (1961)):

P (mm Hg) $\times 10^5$	6.85	3.41	7.39	17.3	11.5
T (°K)	1990	1955	2000	2047	2023

Answer: 134.9 kcal mole^{-1}.

4. If the heat of vaporization of methanol is 8850 cal mole^{-1}, and if it boils at one atm at 64.7°C, what is ΔG at 25°C for the vaporization of one mole of methanol?
Answer: 1040 cal mole^{-1}.

5. Calculate the increase in entropy of one mole of acetone as it changes from liquid at one atm at its normal boiling point of 56.1°C to gas at 56.1°C at 0.200 atm if its vapor pressure at 70.0°C is 1.58 atm.
Answer: 25.59 cal deg^{-1}.

6. Calculate (analytically in terms of grams instead of moles) the partial molar volumes of H_2O and H_2SO_4 in 1.000 molal H_2SO_4 and in 50.00% wt H_2SO_4 from these data (15.5°C):

% H_2SO_4 by wt	8.50	9.50	49.50	50.50
Density (g cm^{-3})	1.0571	1.0641	1.3931	1.4028

Answer: In 1.000 m, 18.00 and 37.11 cm^3 mole^{-1}; in 50%, 17.39 and 45.64 cm^{3}mole^{-1}.

7. Derive the equation for the effect of total pressure on vapor pressure by use of the chemical potential.

8. If, at 20°C, γ_{12} for toluene and Hg is about 360 ergs cm^{-2}, will a drop of toluene spread over the surface of Hg?
Answer: Yes.

9. Show that

$$\left(\frac{\partial \gamma}{\partial P}\right)_{\mathscr{A},T} = \left(\frac{\partial V}{\partial \mathscr{A}}\right)_{P,T}$$

10. What is the thickness of the surface layer that is effectively free of solute in 0.750 molar $CdCl_2$ if at 20°C the rate at which surface energy changes with respect to concentration at constant T is 1.60×10^3 erg cm mole^{-1} for aqueous solutions of $CdCl_2$?
Answer: 6.57 A.

11. Show by a dimensional and order-of-magnitude argument that feeble film pressures really correspond to pressures of the order of tens of atmospheres in a three-dimensional world.

12. At the air-liquid interface of a 0.1000 molar aqueous solution at 25°C, one molecule of an amine occupies 60 A^2. If this is the concentration range in which film pressure is a linear function of bulk concentration, what is the film pressure of the solution?
Answer: 6.85 dynes cm^{-1}.

13. Explain qualitatively the nature of the surface of aqueous sucrose solutions given the fact that the surface energy of these solutions in contact with air increases slightly with increasing sucrose content.
Answer: Sucrose molecules are big and avoid sticking out of the surface; they are also hydrated and hydrogen-bonded to the water.

---

14. Is there any pure substance the vapor pressure of which decreases as the total pressure increases? Is it conceivable that the partial pressure of a substance dissolved in a solvent may decrease as the total pressure increases?
Answer: If pure, no; if impure, $\bar{V}_i$ may be negative in (6.1).

15. The number of milligrams of water vapor in one liter of the actual gaseous volume under various total pressures of a gaseous mixture consisting of 3 H_2 + N_2 at 25°C are (E. P. Bartlett, *J. Am. Chem. Soc.* **49,** 65 (1927)):

mg H_2O	23.03	26.73	31.02	34.05	35.23	39.99	42.29	44.18
P (atm)	ca. 0	100	200	300	400	600	800	1000

Above what total pressure P does equation (6.2) clearly fail?
Answer: At and above 300 atm.

16. The vapor pressure of xenon at −60°C is 8.570 atm, while at −40°C it is 15.85 atm. Estimate the normal (one atm) boiling point of xenon and its molar heat of vaporization.
Answer: 164°K; 3030 cal mole^{-1}.

17. Which is more volatile at 25°C, diamond or graphite, if the species in the equilibrium vapor of each are the same? Does this result say anything *directly* about their sublimation temperatures at 1 atm?
Answer: Diamond; no.

18. From whatever is useful in the following data find the standard molar heat of formation of gaseous iodine atoms if the standard state of I_2 is solid at 25°C at 1 atm.
(a) By spectroscopic means it is known that at absolute zero at any pressure $\Delta H = +35.6$ kcal for the reaction $I_{2(g)} \rightarrow 2\,I_{(g)}$.

(b) At 25°C the molar heat of sublimation of I_2 is 14.9 kcal.
(c) At 25°C the vapor pressure of solid I_2 is 0.31 mm Hg.
Answer: $\Delta H^{\ominus} = 25{,}700$ cal.

19. What is the increase in the vapor pressure of ice at -10°C due to the presence of air at atmospheric pressure? The density of ice is 0.92 g cm^{-3} and its vapor pressure at -10°C is 1.95 mm Hg.
Answer: $\Delta p = 1.8 \times 10^{-3}$ mm Hg.

20. The melting point of benzene increases by about 0.03°C per atmosphere. If the specific gravities of solid and liquid benzene are 1.02 and 0.89 at the melting point of 5.5°C at 1 atm, what is the heat of fusion of benzene?
Answer: 2.5 kcal $mole^{-1}$.

21. Estimate the vapor pressure of ice at -20°C if the heat of fusion of ice is 80 cal g^{-1}, if the heat of vaporization of water is 600 cal g^{-1}, and if the vapor pressure of ice at 0°C is 4.59 mm Hg.
Answer: 0.773 mm Hg.

22. Table 6.5 below lists the heat of formation of $NaOH_{(s)}$ at 25°C at one atm and that of one mole of NaOH as it exists dissolved in various numbers of moles of water at 25°C at one atm. By treating enthalpy (ΔH) as an extensive property, calculate the heat evolved at 25°C at one atm when
(a) One mole $NaOH_{(s)}$ is dissolved in eight moles $H_2O_{(l)}$, the temperature rises to 52°C and then returns to the initial temperature of NaOH and H_2O, 25°C.
(b) One mole $NaOH_{(s)}$ dissolves in four moles $H_2O_{(l)}$.
(c) One mole $NaOH_{(s)}$ dissolves in the solution from (b).
(d) One mole $NaOH_{(s)}$ dissolves in a huge amount of the final solution of (b).
(e) One mole $H_2O_{(l)}$ dissolves in the final solution of (b).

Table 6.5 Heats of Formation of Sodium Hydroxide in n H_2O and Heats of Solution of Solid Sodium Hydroxide in n H_2O (25°C). (Rossini, F. D. *et al.*, *Selected Values of Chemical Thermodynamic Properties*. Washington, D. C.: Circular 500 of the National Bureau of Standards, U. S. Government Printing Office, 1952.)

Moles $H_2O_{(l)}$ n H_2O	$\Delta H^{\ominus}_f$(*KCAL*) Na^+OH^- in n $H_2O_{(l)}$	$\Delta H^{\ominus}_{sol}$(*KCAL*) $NaOH_{(s)} + n\, H_2O_{(l)} \rightarrow Na^+OH^-$ in n $H_2O_{(l)}$
0	−101.99	0.00
3	−108.894	−6.90
4	−110.219	−8.23
5	−111.015	−9.02
6	−111.520	−9.53
7	−111.836	−9.85
8	−112.011	−10.02
10	−112.148	−10.16
15	−112.228	−10.24
20	−112.235	−10.24
30	−112.203	−10.21
40	−112.175	−10.18
50	−112.154	−10.16
75	−112.123	−10.13
100	−112.108	−10.12
1000	−112.139	−10.15
10000	−112.201	−10.21
50000	−112.220	−10.23
∞	−112.236	−10.25

(f) One mole $H_2O_{(l)}$ dissolves in a huge amount of the final solution of (b).
(g) One mole $NaOH_{(s)}$ is dissolved in ten moles $H_2O_{(l)}$.
(h) Ten moles $H_2O_{(l)}$ are added to a solution containing two moles $NaOH_{(s)}$ in ten moles $H_2O_{(l)}$.
(i) Ten moles $H_2O_{(l)}$ are added to a huge amount of solution containing five moles $H_2O_{(l)}$ for every mole of $NaOH_{(s)}$.
(j) One mole $NaOH_{(s)}$ is added to a huge amount of solution containing five moles $H_2O_{(l)}$ for every mole of $NaOH_{(s)}$.
(k) Ten g pure $Na_{(s)}$ metal dissolve in an open beaker containing 4.785 moles pure water to yield H_2 at one atm and a solution of NaOH.
(l) Very dilute H_2SO_4 is added to one mole NaOH dissolved in four moles $H_2O_{(l)}$ until the base is just neutralized.
Answer: (Cal) (a) 10020; (b) 8230; (c) 1200; (d) 4190; (e) 796; (f) 1000; (g) 10160; (h) 2266; (i) 6400; (j) 5820; (k) 19100; (l) 15377.

23. One mole $NaOH_{(s)}$ at 25°C is dissolved adiabatically in an open beaker in ten moles water at 25°C. What is the temperature of the solution that results if its heat capacity is 0.95 cal g^{-1}? See Table 6.5 for data.
Answer: 74°C.

24. At 20°C, γ_{12} for toluene and water is 37 ergs cm^{-2}. A drop of which of these will spread on the surface of the other?
Answer: Toluene spreads on water.

25. A metal with a liquid molar volume of 10 cm^3 $mole^{-1}$ must achieve a gaseous pressure that is 1.050 times as great as its vapor pressure (plane surface) if it is to condense in the absence of nucleating agents at 2000°K. What is the radius of the smallest droplets that will be able to grow if its liquid has a surface energy of 500 ergs cm^{-2}?
Answer: 125 A.

26. At 19°C aqueous solutions of *n*-hexanoic acid have these surface energies (*Handbook of Chemistry*, [10th Edition] ed. by N. A. Lange and G. M. Forker. New York: McGraw-Hill Book Co., Inc., 1967, pp. 1666–67):

Molarity	0.00212	0.0064	0.0128	0.0212	0.0425	0.068	0.085
γ (ergs cm^{-2})	70	63	56	49	40	34	31

At what molarity does each acid molecule in the monolayer seem to occupy an area of about 30 A?
Answer: 0.03 *M*.

---

27. The density of ice II is 1.21 g ml^{-1}; that of ice III is 1.10 g ml^{-1}. Calculate ΔH for the transformation of one mole of ice II into ice III if these two phases are in equilibrium at 3260 atm at −25.0°C and at 2450 atm at −31.0°C (*International Critical Tables of Numerical Data, Physics, Chemistry, and Technology*, National Academy of Sciences—National Research Council, Washington, D.C. 1926–1933, *IV*, p. 11).
Answer: $\Delta H = 1200$ cal $mole^{-1}$.

28. What is the minimum value of the molar heat of vaporization of bromine at 25°C if the stable state is liquid at 25°C and if the standard entropies of liquid and gas are those of Table 4.3?
Answer: 6620 cal $mole^{-1}$.

29. The vapor pressure of bromine at 25°C is 0.298 atm, and it boils at one atm at 59°C. Find $\Delta E^{\ominus}$, $\Delta H^{\ominus}$, $\Delta S^{\ominus}$, $\Delta A^{\ominus}$, and $\Delta G^{\ominus}$ at 25°C for the vaporization of one mole of bromine.
Answer: $\Delta E^{\ominus} = 6430$ cal; $\Delta H^{\ominus} = 7020$ cal; $\Delta S^{\ominus} = 21.1$ cal deg^{-1}; $\Delta A^{\ominus} = 124$ cal; $\Delta G^{\ominus} = 716$ cal.

30. What value of the isothermal coefficient of compressibility of a condensed phase will cause the approximate expression $\Delta G = V\,\Delta P$ to be in error by one joule if $V = 50$ ml and $\Delta P = 100$ atm?
Answer: 39×10^{-6} atm^{-1}.

31. Two crystalline species of an element are in equilibrium at 1500°C at one atm. At 25°C, their standard entropies differ by 0.100 cal mole^{-1} deg^{-1}. If their molar heat capacities are equal above 25°C, what is the molar heat of formation of the form which is metastable at 25°C?
Answer: 177 cal mole^{-1}.

32. The vapor pressure of ammonia at 25°C is 9.90 atm. Calculate the absolute entropy of liquid ammonia at ten atm pressure at 25°C. The normal boiling point of ammonia is −33°C and $S^{\ominus} = 46.01$ cal mole^{-1} deg^{-1} at 25°C (Rossini, F. D., *et al.*, Circular 500 N.B.S., 1952).
Answer: 22.48 cal mole^{-1} deg^{-1}.

33. The boiling point of zinc at one atm is 1180°K where its heat of vaporization at constant pressure is 27.43 kcal mole^{-1} (F. D. Rossini et al., NBS Circular 500, 1952). If $Zn_{(g)}$ has $C_P = 5.0$ cal mole^{-1} deg^{-1}, and if $Zn_{(l)}$ has $C_P = 8.0$ cal mole^{-1} deg^{-1}, what is the vapor pressure of liquid Zn at its melting point of 693°K?
Answer: 0.158 mm Hg.

34. Benzene boils at one atm at 80.10°C; at this temperature its heat of vaporization at one atm is 7353 cal mole^{-1}; its standard entropy as liquid at 25°C at one atm is 41.30 cal mole^{-1} deg^{-1} (F. D. Rossini et al., NBS Circular C461, 1947). Over the temperature range of interest here, the average C_P may be taken to be 23.20 cal mole^{-1} deg^{-1} as gas and 34.70 cal mole^{-1} deg^{-1} as liquid. If the vapor is ideal, find ΔG, ΔH, and ΔS for the transformation of one mole of liquid benzene at one atm at 25°C into one mole of gas at 2.00 atm at 120°C.
Answer: $\Delta G = -4582$ cal; $\Delta H = 10190$ cal; $\Delta S = 27.79$ cal deg^{-1}.

35. In the preceding problem, what error results in ΔG from treating the vapor as a perfect gas? At 120°C, the second virial coefficient of benzene is $B = -461$ cm^3 mole^{-1}, where $PV = nRT + nBP$.
Answer: 11 cal mole^{-1}.

36. When the pressure on a liquid is constant (because another insoluble gas like air is present or because of curvature of certain surfaces), show that its vapor pressure P varies with temperature T exactly by the formula

$$\frac{dP}{dT} = \frac{\Delta H}{TV_g}$$

where V_g is the volume of the vapor phase and ΔH is not quite equal to the usual heat of vaporization. Then compare this result to (5.74) and (5.75).

37. If the isothermal rate of change of surface energy with respect to chemical potential for a two-component system is independent of the choice of the surface, show that the quantity $\Gamma_2 C_1 - C_2 \Gamma_1$ is constant.

38. When the surface energies of aqueous solutions of resorcinol (*m*-dihydroxybenzene) are plotted as a function of the decadic logarithm of the molarity of the solution, the graph is linear from $0.1 = M$ to $M = 10.0$ at 20°C. The constant slope of this plot is -8.0 ergs cm^{-1}. Describe the surface of these solutions.
Answer: The area per molecule is constant at 117 A^2; molecules seem to be lying flat and in some sort of order that keeps the area per molecule constant.

7

THE PHASE RULE

7.1 INTRODUCTION

The chemical potential and the phase rule were both discovered by the eminent American physicist J. W. Gibbs, of Yale University. Among the first scientists to appreciate the importance of the phase rule were Maxwell, van der Waals, and Roozeboom. Wide appreciation of its value came in about 1900, more than twenty years after it was first described in the little-read *Transactions of the Connecticut Academy of Sciences* of 1875–1878, largely through translation into German by Ostwald, into French by Le Chatelier, and into simple terms by Bancroft. Before his knowledge of Gibbs's work, Le Chatelier had formulated a few of the special situations described by the more general and powerful phase rule.

Much of the detailed verification by experiment of the very general predictions of the rule was accomplished by Roozeboom and his associates. The phase rule sets certain limits on the kind and number of thermodynamic variables in a system at equilibrium, but it does not predict specific solubilities, melting points, or other observable data. These must be found by experiment.

If even pure gases require the moderately complex mathematical discussion of fugacity and equations of state for careful description, it is understandable that accurate and thorough description of solids, liquids, and solutions, in which intermolecular interactions are much more powerful, may require very complicated mathematics. In fact, it is much safer at present merely to summarize observations on such complicated systems by graphs called *phase diagrams*.

The phase rule provides an indispensable guide to the preparation and interpretation of these phase diagrams. This chapter is concerned mainly with such diagrams.

7.2 DERIVATION OF THE PHASE RULE

The state of a system and all its properties at equilibrium can be fixed by specifying only a certain few extensive properties out of the multitude of its properties of all kinds. For example, according to (6.35), the state of a system (and its energy) is specified by its entropy, volume, and the numbers of moles of certain species, the components, out of which the system is or could be prepared. It is usually more convenient, however, to fix the equilibrium state of a system by specifying several intensive properties and one extensive one like volume or mass or energy so as to set the size or scale of the system. For example, with (6.43) as a guide, the state (and free energy, which, if given, implies that the state is given) of a system of C components can be fixed by the temperature, pressure, and $\mathsf{C} - 1$ mole fractions, the last mole fraction being fixed by (6.19), namely: $1 = \sum X_i$. There is no need to consider properties that are neither extensive nor intensive.

The phase rule is a way of determining the number of intensive properties that can be varied at will by an experimenter who has before him a system of P phases at equilibrium. A *phase* is a macroscopically homogeneous portion of matter of a certain kind. A phase may be a pure substance or a solution; it is a solid, liquid, or gas. There is in a system always only one gaseous phase, but there may be several liquid and solid phases. Several pieces of ice of the same composition and crystalline order are just one phase.

Since there is no discontinuity between chemical and physical change, it is appropriate to derive the phase rule for both situations here, for it must apply to both. This simple derivation is limited, however, to equilibrium attained in the absence of surface effects, fields, semipermeable membranes, torques, shear stresses, and other nonuniform pressures. This is tantamount to forbidding situations that would not allow an extensive property to be defined as homogeneous of first degree in mass or moles. In other words, concentrations, temperature, chemical potential, partial molar volume, a uniform normal (fluid) pressure, and simple variables like them are the only intensive variables to be considered here. Moreover, it is assumed that some changes reach equilibrium rapidly while other possible changes are so slow as to be negligible. Although the decision may be somewhat arbitrary and even subjective, it is necessary to decide exactly what changes are to reach equilibrium and what changes are to be frozen or ignored. Clearly, choices of this kind must involve good judgment by the experimenter if his predictions or descriptions are to mirror reality in suitable approximation. Without such a simplification, a discussion of a substance like

NO would be at once complicated by the possibility of its decomposition to N_2, O_2, NO_2, N_2O_4, N_2O_3, and so on. Whether or not such possibilities are to be considered depends somewhat subjectively on the completeness of the discussion, on the keenness of the observer's analytical methods, on his criteria of purity, and on the extent of his knowledge and purpose. At the very start, to avoid confusion, the observer must state clearly what he neglects and what processes he recognizes as achieving equilibrium in the real system before him.

The salient result of Chapter 6 is that the chemical potential μ_i of a species i is the same in all phases of a system at equilibrium. If it were not so, a spontaneous transfer of matter could occur from a phase where μ_i is high to one where it is lower. At equilibrium in a system of the kind considered, the temperatures and pressures of the several phases are alike. The total number of independent variables or properties whose values are thus specified is $\mathsf{C} + 2$, where C is the minimum number of chemical species out of which all P phases can each be prepared. The number $\mathsf{C} + 2$ can be counted in any of several ways; some examples are:

(a) $S, V, n_1, n_2, \ldots n_i, \ldots n_{\mathsf{C}}$, as in (6.35);
(b) $T, P, n_1, n_2, \ldots n_i, \ldots n_{\mathsf{C}}$, as in (6.43); or
(c) One extensive variable like V to fix the size of the system, T, P, and $\mathsf{C} - 1$ independent mole fractions, the last being set by $1 = \sum X_i$.

There may actually be more than C species present, and the observer may recognize this fact. If so, he will also rightly note that certain chemical reactions are possible so that all species recognized as present can be made in arbitrary proportions from the C components of minimum number.

Because phases are usually well defined and easily counted, and since each phase is made separately, the number of independent extensive variables is P, namely the mass or volume or energy of each phase. For any physically realizable system properly described, $\mathsf{P} \leqslant \mathsf{C} + 2$. The difference between P and $\mathsf{C} + 2$ is F, the number of intensive variables free to be specified arbitrarily by the experimenter. In other words, the phase rule separates the total number of independent variables into two classes, F intensive ones and P extensive ones. Hence, the phase rule in its usual form is

$$\mathsf{F} + \mathsf{P} = \mathsf{C} + 2 \tag{7.1}$$

If temperature or pressure is constant, $\mathsf{F} + \mathsf{P} = \mathsf{C} + 1$; if both are constant, $\mathsf{F} + \mathsf{P} = \mathsf{C}$. In a uniform gravitational field, $\mathsf{F} + \mathsf{P} = \mathsf{C} + 3$; the extra independent variable is, of course, the intensity of the field.

Generally the most difficult matter to decide is the value of C, the number of components. One way to determine C is to read the recipe of the system, for the method of preparation frequently says clearly what value C has. For example, the recipe may say to prepare the system from pure H_2O. This system has one component ($\mathsf{C} = 1$). Vapor, liquid, and any of the various forms of ice consist of H_2O. This kind of treatment ignores isotopes, impurities, and decomposition to H_2, O_2, OH, $H_9O_4^+$, OH^-, and other species. If $C = 1$, then $F = C - P + 2 = 3 - P$. Up to three phases can coexist in a one-component system at equilibrium, for by its nature F is zero or a real positive integer.

If the observer for some reason considers the possible chemical change $2H_2O \longrightarrow 2H_2 + O_2$, then the system may be considered to have one or two components. This chemical change really occurs at all temperatures and pressures, but the observer may be willing to ignore it because it occurs so slowly that his observations are unaffected, or because his analytical technique is so poor that he could not observe H_2 and O_2 if he tried, or because he is ignorant, or for some other reason. The system is then properly treated as a system of one component.

However, a careful observer working at elevated temperatures can detect H_2, O_2, OH, O, and other species. If he prepares his system from pure H_2O, he may still rightly consider his system to consist of just one component. However, there are then certain restraints imposed on his system. If the only new species are H_2 and O_2, the ratio of moles of H_2 to moles of O_2 will always be exactly two, as specified by the chemical equation above. This ratio of two is a particular value of an intensive variable; it is a dimensionless ratio of moles. If the observer changes this ratio by adding or withdrawing H_2 or O_2, the number of components rises to two. Then, F increases by unity because this ratio of H_2 to O_2 must somehow be specified since it is no longer exactly two. The recipe is changed; it now calls for two components.

A second way to find C is to count the number S of different chemical species and the number E of independent chemical equations. The value of C is then

$$C = S - E \tag{7.2}$$

because each independent chemical equation is the means of preparing one of the chemically distinct species involved in its chemical equilibrium. For the system consisting of H_2O, H_2, and O_2 there are three species ($S = 3$) and one equation ($E = 1$) so that, without special stoichiometric restraints, $C = S - E = 3 - 1 = 2$.

Each independent chemical reaction that attains equilibrium places one restriction of its own on the intensive variables of a system. The reason is that the mole fractions of the species listed in the reaction must satisfy the equilibrium constant; thus, each equilibrated reaction causes one of the mole fractions or concentrations to be specified by the others. An equivalent way of explaining this new condition per equation on the intensive variables is to note that ΔG is zero for any process or change at equilibrium at constant temperature and pressure. If the reaction $2\,H_2O = 2\,H_2 + O_2$ is written in the conventionalized form $0 = 2\,H_2 + O_2 - 2\,H_2O$, then the equilibrium condition at T and P is

$$0 = \Delta G = G_2 - G_1 = 2\,\mu(H_2) + \mu(O_2) - 2\,\mu(H_2O) \tag{7.3}$$

where, by (6.44), the free energy of the products is $G_2 = 2\,\mu(H_2) + \mu(O_2)$ while that of the reactants is $G_1 = 2\,\mu(H_2O)$. In general, if A reacts with B to give D, E, . . . , then the conventional reaction is

$$0 = \nu_D D + \nu_E E + \cdots + \nu_A A + \nu_B B$$
$$0 = \sum_i \nu_i \Omega_i \tag{7.4}$$

where Ω_i is a species and the stoichiometric coefficients ν_i are positive for products and negative for reactants. The equilibrium condition is then

$$0 = \sum_i \nu_i \mu_i(T, P) \tag{7.5}$$

where, as in (7.3), (6.44) gives the Gibbs free energy of initial and final states. Each reaction places on the μ_i's one algebraic restriction (7.5) that specifies one of the μ_i's in terms of the others. This is the source of the equation $\mathsf{C} = \mathsf{S} - \mathsf{E}$, for a decrease in C is tantamount to a decrease in F when P is constant.[1]

In general, then, a system of S chemically different species has a total of $\mathsf{S} + 2$ variables that describe the state of equilibrium. Of these, P extensive variables specify the size of each of the P phases, and E intensive variables are specified by the E different conditions of chemical equilibrium. If F is the number of intensive variables free to be specified at will by the experimenter, then the total number of variables, is, by this count, $\mathsf{P} + \mathsf{E} + \mathsf{F} = \mathsf{S} + 2$. But by (7.2) this is

$$\mathsf{P} + \mathsf{F} = \mathsf{C} + 2 \tag{7.1}$$

which is the phase rule. This proof emphasizes the division of the independent variables into two kinds: extensive and intensive.

A second proof of the phase rule is terse but more mathematical. The Gibbs-Duhem equation

$$S\,dT - V\,dP + \sum_{i=1}^{\mathsf{C}} n_i\,d\mu_i = 0 \tag{6.77}$$

places one restriction on the $\mathsf{C} + 2$ intensive variables T, P, and μ_i for each phase. Since (6.57) requires T, P, and μ_i to be uniform throughout all phases of a system at equilibrium, the number of independent variables in a system of P phases and C components is

$$\mathsf{F} + \mathsf{P} = \mathsf{C} + 2 \tag{7.1}$$

which is the phase rule if P is the number of independent extensive variables. This proof emphasizes the fact that F decreases by unity whenever a new phase is generated in a system of fixed C.

[1] For a detailed account of chemical equilibria in terms of the phase rule, see pp. 476–488 of W.F. Sheehan, *Chemistry, A Physical Approach*, Boston: Allyn and Bacon, Inc., 1964.

7.3 SYSTEMS OF ONE COMPONENT

When $C = 1$, as it does in one-component systems, the phase rule says that the degrees of freedom F depend upon the number of phases P that coexist. By (7.1), when temperature and pressure are variable,

$$F = C - P + 2 = 1 - P + 2 = 3 - P$$

In order that the system be something more than a vacuum, P must be greater than zero. Since the maximum value of F is then 2, these two degrees of freedom are readily expressed graphically as the two independent variables of a plane area. One degree of freedom is a curve, and no degree of freedom is a fixed point.

Figure 7.1 is the phase diagram of water with nonlinear scales of pressure and temperature because of the great range of variables to be shown. A diagram such as this cannot be predicted by the phase rule. Such a diagram is a summary of experimental data systematized and coordinated by use of the phase rule. The phase rule does not predict the existence of certain states of matter at certain temperatures and pressures, but it does tell what is possible and impossible at equilibrium. For example, it is impossible to have four phases coexisting at

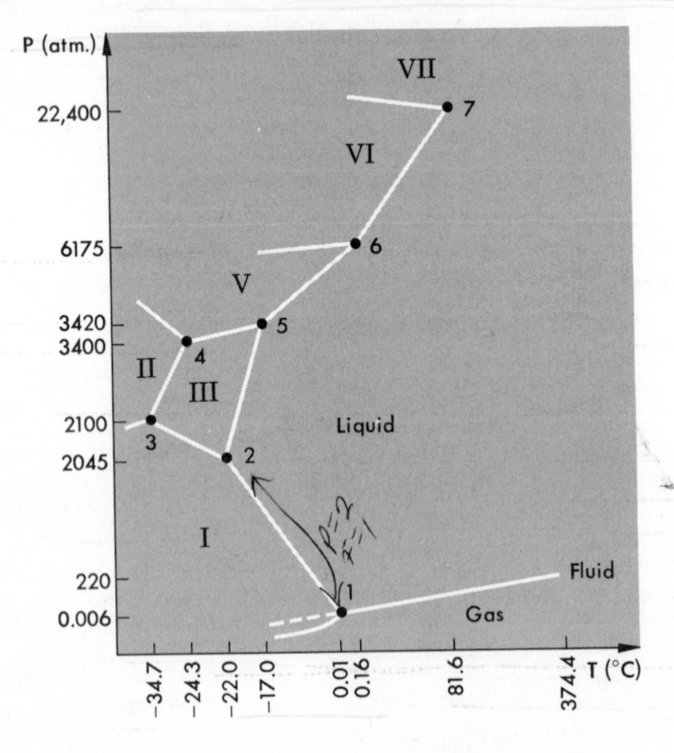

Figure 7.1. A Caricature of the Phase Diagram of H_2O

equilibrium, for if $P = 4$ then $F = 3 - 4 = -1$, which is ridiculous because it implies that the system by its nature fixes more independent variables than exist to be fixed.

In a one-component system it is possible to have three phases coexisting. Then $P = 3$ and $F = 0$ so that there are no intensive variables that can be set at will. The thermodynamic state of a one-component system containing three coexisting phases at equilibrium is completely specified by the nature of that one component. In Figure 7.1, there are seven numbered points, called *triple points* because at each there coexist three phases at equilibrium. Each triple point is a manifestation of the nature of water. Table 7.1 lists the three phases that can coexist at these fixed conditions. There is only one gaseous and one liquid phase, but there are six or seven different solid phases. At each of these points of no degree of freedom there meet three curves and three areas.

Table 7.1 Triple Points in H_2O System.

Point (Fig. 7.1)	Fixed Intensive Properties†		The Three Phases Coexistent at Equilibrium		
	Pressure (ATM)	Temperature (°C)			
1	0.00602	0.01 (defined)	Steam	Water	Ice I
2	2,045	−22.0	Water	Ice I	Ice III
3	2,100	−34.7	Ice I	Ice II	Ice III
4	3,400	−24.3	Ice II	Ice III	Ice V
5	3,420	−17.0	Water	Ice III	Ice V
6	6,175	0.16	Water	Ice V	Ice VI
7	22,400	81.6	Water	Ice VI	Ice VII

† Bridgman, P. W., *Journal of Chemical Physics*, **3**, 597 (1935), and *Journal of Chemical Physics*, **5**, 964 (1937).

When two phases ($P = 2$) exist together at equilibrium in a one-component ($C = 1$) system, the phase rule requires one degree of freedom, either temperature or pressure. That is, $F = C - P + 2 = 1 - 2 + 2 = 1$. When either temperature or pressure is specified, the state of the system is fixed. There is, then, a functional dependence of one of these variables on the other, and the curves of a figure like Figure 7.1 define this functional dependence and exhibit in their property of linear extension the one degree of freedom. Along each such curve two phases coexist at equilibrium. The curve that begins at 1 and proceeds to 219.5 atm and 374.4°C separates regions labeled *liquid* and *gas*. It is the vapor pressure curve of pure H_2O, and along it gas and liquid are in equilibrium. The curve that proceeds upward to the left from point 1 describes the variation in the freezing point of water with pressure. The solid curve that proceeds downward to the left from 1 describes the sublimation of ice, and the dashed curve from 1 describes the vaporization of supercooled water. Supercooled water is not in an equilibrium state, and the line is dashed. Relative to immediately adjacent states it is stable, but ice I is the most stable form of H_2O at these pressures and temperature.

If the scales of pressure and temperature in Figure 7.1 were true, the slopes of the curves would yield values of the derivative of P with respect to T. By the Clapeyron equation (6.4), this derivative is related to the discontinuities in enthalpy ΔH and volume ΔV on crossing the curve (i.e., on changing phases). If the slope of a curve that describes the equilibrium of one component in two phases is known or can be found from a phase diagram, either ΔH or ΔV can be calculated from the Clapeyron equation.

Example 7.1. The volume decrease when ice I becomes ice II at $-40.0°C$ is 217.4 $cm^3\ kg^{-1}$ of ice. At this temperature, the rate of change of pressure with respect to temperature is 8.8 atm deg^{-1} (*International Critical Tables of Numerical Data, Physics, Chemistry, and Technology*, National Academy of Sciences—National Research Council, Washington, D.C., 1926–1933, *IV*, p. 11). What is the increase in enthalpy at $-40.0°C$ of the reaction $H_2O_{(s)}(I) \longrightarrow H_2O_{(s)}(II)$?

By (6.4),

$$\Delta H = T \times \Delta V \times \frac{dP}{dT} = 233 \times \left(-217.4 \times \frac{18}{1000}\right) \times 8.8 \times \left(\frac{1.987}{82.05}\right)$$

$$= -195 \text{ cal mole}^{-1}$$

When only one phase ($P = 1$) is present in a one-component system ($C = 1$), there are two degrees of freedom, for $F = C - P + 2 = 1 - 1 + 2 = 2$. The temperature and pressure may be varied independently, and at equilibrium any of the points in an area can be achieved continuously from any other point in the same area. At the boundaries of such areas—that is, along the curves of one degree of freedom—two phases exist. At the boundaries there is a discontinuous change in volume, enthalpy, and some other properties.

Isothermal changes in phase diagrams like Figure 7.1 are described by vertical paths. Suppose that 1 mole gaseous H_2O at a very low pressure is compressed isothermally and reversibly at $-10.0°C$. At 1.95 mm Hg the pressure remains constant as gaseous H_2O is condensed by compression to form ice I, for the pressure is dependent upon the specification of temperature at $-10.0°C$ along a curve ($F = 1$) that separates two areas. Once all the H_2O is solidified as ice I, the pressure may rise once again during the compression, for in the area labeled I there are two degrees of freedom ($F = 2$). At 1090 atm, isothermal reversible compression causes the ice to melt; the line joining 1 and 2 is crossed and the pressure and temperature remain constant as the reversible compression converts ice I into liquid water. When the system is all liquid, the pressure once again rises continuously as the water is compressed until a pressure of 4360 atm is reached. Once again a boundary of the area labeled *liquid* is crossed and the pressure remains fixed as the water becomes ice V at $-10.0°C$. Continued isothermal compression of ice V would lead eventually to ice VI at 6169 atm and perhaps eventually to ice VII. (Data from *International Critical Tables, ibid.*)

Isobaric changes are described by horizontal lines in Figure 7.1. If ice I is heated at one atm pressure, it begins to melt at $0.0024°C$. If the melting is performed reversibly the temperature is constant until all the ice I has disappeared, for along the curve 1-2 there is one degree of freedom that is fixed by fixing the pressure. Both temperature and pressure may be varied independently within the are labeled liquid; hence, at one atm the temperature rises until bubbles form and the water boils at 100.0°C. Further reversible heating merely boils away the liquid at 100.0°C. When the last trace of liquid has vaporized, further isobaric heating increases the temperature of the gas continuously.

It is possible reversibly to transform liquid water at 25°C into water vapor at 25°C without ever having two phases present. This is accomplished by circling around the critical point at 219.5 atm at 374.4°C instead of proceeding directly along a vertical isotherm. The critical point terminates the vapor pressure curve of water, for at the critical state the two fluid phases become so much alike that their densities, enthalpies, and other properties are indistinguishable. Another way of considering the route by which liquid water at 25°C can be transformed reversibly and continuously (without a phase change) into water vapor at 25°C is to circle around the dome-shaped region of interest with regard to van der Waals' equation when pressure and volume are ordinate and abscissa as in Figure 1.8.

In real processes that approach equilibrium spontaneously, the free energy or chemical potential of a system tends to a minimum just as entropy tends to a maximum. By methods already developed it is possible to calculate the chemical potential of a phase at any temperature and pressure. The equations to be used are

$$\left(\frac{\partial \mu_i}{\partial T}\right)_P = -\bar{S}_i \tag{6.47}$$

$$\left(\frac{\partial \mu_i}{\partial P}\right)_T = \bar{V}_i \tag{6.48}$$

Since it is evident from Table 4.1 and the third law that $\bar{S}_i$ of a pure substance is greater than zero and that ordinarily the partial molar entropy $\bar{S}_i$ of any species is greater than zero, (6.47) gives

$$\left(\frac{\partial \mu_i}{\partial T}\right)_P < 0$$

That is, the chemical potential of a component of a phase ordinarily decreases as the temperature rises isobarically. Similarly, since the partial molar volume is almost always greater than zero, (6.48) gives

$$\left(\frac{\partial \mu_i}{\partial P}\right)_T > 0$$

That is, an isothermal increase in the pressure of a system leads to an increase in its chemical potential. For each component of each phase, then, there is a surface $\mu_i = \mu_i(T, P)$ of the sort shown in Figure 7.2. When two phases coexist at some pressure and temperature, as along a curve in Figure 7.1, the chemical potentials of their components are equal by (6.57). If the three surfaces that describe the chemical potentials of solid, liquid, and gas are given simultaneously

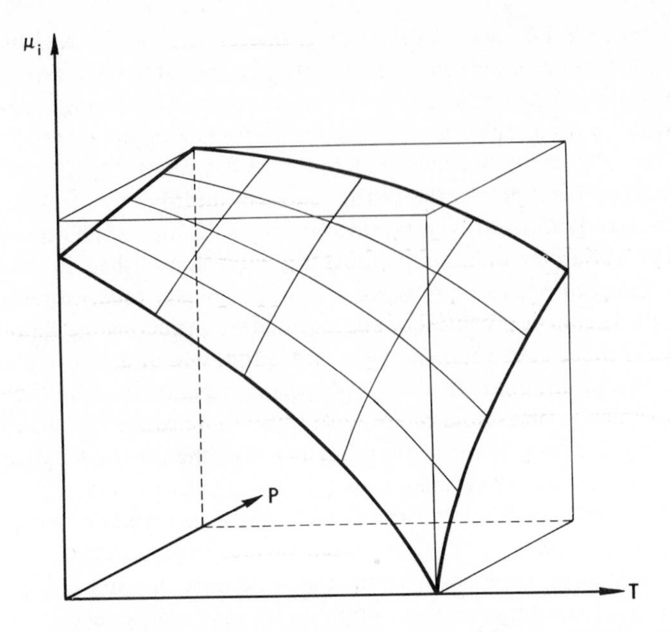

Figure 7.2. Chemical Potential μ_i as a Function of Pressure P and Temperature T

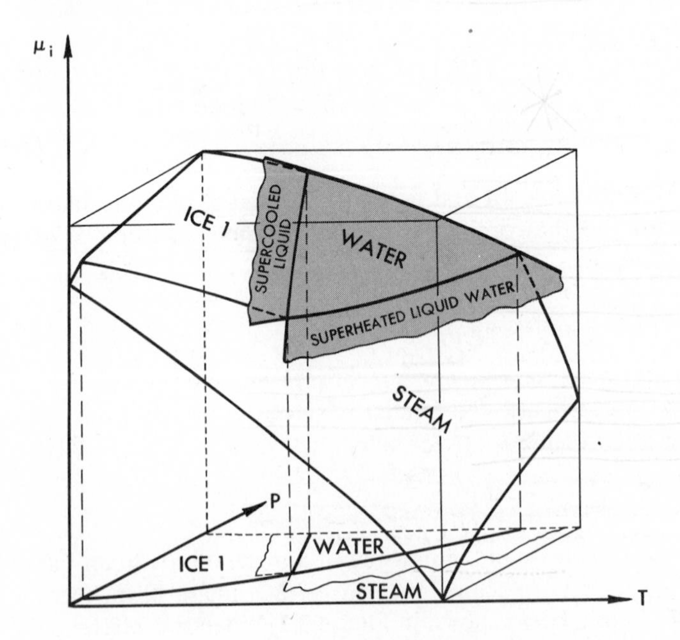

Figure 7.3. Chemical Potential Surfaces of H_2O Near the Low-Pressure Triple Point. (Figures like this near this triple point and near the critical point are given by S. H. Bauer, *J. Chem. Ed.* **35**, 289 [1958].)

as functions of P and T, Figure 7.3 is generated. The intersection of two surfaces yields a curve along which two phases have equal chemical potentials. When such curves are projected on the P-T plane the curves of Figure 7.1 are generated. The chemical potential manifested at equilibrium is the lowest of the three surfaces at any value of P and T, and only the lowest surface has been shown in most of Figure 7.3. At the triple point, all three surfaces meet because all three chemical potentials are equal at the triple point.

The chemical potential of a metastable phase is greater than that of another phase at the same temperature and pressure. It is appropriate, then, that the surface describing the chemical potential of supercooled and superheated liquid in Figure 7.3 be above those of the solid and gas. Since the solid or gas is absent in these metastable situations, equilibrium is not established and the metastable liquid phase may exist as a metastable phase until crystal nucleation or bubble formation occurs. Superheating of solids that can melt or supercooling of gases that can crystallize has not been observed.

The phase diagrams of water (Fig. 7.1) and carbon (Fig. 7.4) involve extremes of pressure and the conditions under which various kinds of solid exist.

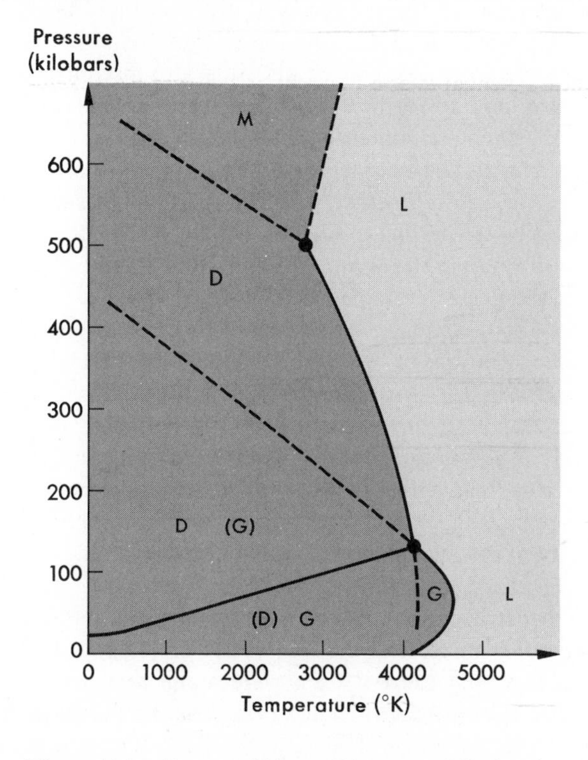

Figure 7.4. Proposed Phase Diagram of Carbon†

†F. P. Bundy, *J. Chem. Phys.* **41,** 3809 (1964) and *Science* **137,** p. 1057; 28 September, 1962.
Copyright 1962 by the American Association for the Advancement of Science.

The solid curves of Figure 7.4 indicate the conditions under which two phases coexist at equilibrium in this one-component system; along such solid curves, $F = C - P + 2 = 1 - 2 + 2 = 1$ and either P or T is independent. The dashed curves to the triple point above 600 kbars are of uncertain slope; if real, they describe two-phase equilibria like the solid curves. Liquid carbon exists in the region of Figure 7.4 labeled L; graphite, in G; diamond, in D; a metallic form of carbon is expected in the region labeled M. Diamonds are metastable in the region (D) as is graphite in (G). The dashed curves to the DGL triple point are continuations of the G-L and D-L curves; they specify limits of P and T within which diamond or graphite are metastable and may thus exist alone for limited times.

START

7.4 GASEOUS SOLUTIONS

Gaseous mixtures have never been observed to form more than one phase. A gravitational or electric field may cause a preferential distribution of the various components (e.g., in a gravitational field, the heaviest species prefer the bottom), but in the gaseous phase there are never at equilibrium any discontinuities in density, index of refraction, and so forth. With $P = 1$ for one-phase systems, $F = C - P + 2 = C + 1$. One-component gaseous systems ($C = 1$) were described at length in Chapter 1. The two degrees of freedom ($F = 2$)—namely, any two of the three: P, V/n or T—together with the equation of state of the one component that constitutes the phase and system are sufficient to fix the state of the system at equilibrium in the absence of fields and special constraints like a barrier that confines the gas to an unexpectedly small volume.

In order to specify the state of a gaseous system of more than one component, all but one of the concentrations of the several components must be specified in addition to the values of T and P. For example, dry air is a mixture mainly of nitrogen, oxygen, and argon. With three components ($C = 3$), the state of air is not completely specified until four independent intensive variables are specified ($F = 3 + 1$). The four most convenient ones would probably be pressure, temperature, and volume percentage of oxygen and argon. But density or index of refraction could have been specified instead of any of those chosen.

Dalton's law of partial pressures is a statement of the fact that there are huge voids available for interpenetration of molecules in the gaseous state. It says: the total pressure of a gaseous mixture is the sum of the pressures that each of the species of the mixture would exert if each were alone at the same temperature T in the same vessel of volume V. Let $p_i(V, T)$ be the partial pressure that component i would exert if alone. Then, by this law, the total pressure $P(V, T)$ is

$$P(V, T) = \sum_{i=1}^{S} p_i(V, T) \tag{7.6}$$

This law assumes that chemical or physical interactions among the several species can be neglected and that all gases are ideal in behavior. Deviations from ideal behavior are realized through combinations of second virial coefficients into one second virial coefficient in the equation of state of the mixture.

The mole fraction of a species i in a gaseous solution is very simply related to the partial pressure if Dalton's law obtains. By (1.29) for each species i,

$$p_i = \frac{n_i RT}{V} \tag{7.7}$$

For the mixture, by (7.6) and (7.7),

$$P = \sum_{i=1}^{S} p_i = \frac{RT}{V} \sum_{i=1}^{S} n_i \tag{7.8}$$

By the definition of mole fraction in (6.18) it follows from (7.7) and (7.8) that

$$Y_i = \frac{W_i/M_i}{\sum_{j=1}^{S} (W_j/M_j)} = \frac{n_i}{\sum_{j=1}^{S} n_j} = \frac{p_i}{P} \tag{7.9}$$

That is, the mole fraction Y_i of any species in a gaseous mixture is equal to its partial pressure divided by the total pressure of the solution.

Example 7.2. If dry air is an ideal solution of 78.0% (molar) N_2, 21.0% (molar) O_2, and 1.0% (molar) Ar, calculate the density of air at 27°C at 1.0000 atm pressure if its relative humidity is 80.0%. The vapor pressure of water at 27°C is 26.7 mm Hg.

The partial pressure of H_2O in the humid air is $0.800 \times 26.7/760 = 0.0281$ atm. If the air were dried at constant temperature and volume, its pressure dry would be less than one atm by just 0.0281 atm. Hence,

$$p_{N_2} = 0.9719 \times 0.780 = 0.758_1 \text{ atm}$$

$$p_{O_2} = 0.9719 \times 0.210 = 0.204_1 \text{ atm}$$

$$p_{Ar} = 0.9719 \times 0.010 = 0.009_7 \text{ atm}$$

By the perfect gas law as expressed in (7.7),

$$\frac{W_i}{V} = \frac{M_i p_i}{RT}$$

Accordingly, since the density ρ of the mixture is the sum of the masses of the several species divided by their common volume V,

$$\rho = \frac{\sum_i W_i}{V} = \sum_i \frac{W_i}{V} = \frac{1}{RT} \sum_i M_i p_i$$

Hence,

$$\rho = \frac{(28.01 \times 0.758_1 + 32.00 \times 0.204_1 + 39.94 \times 0.009_7 + 18.02 \times 0.0281)}{0.08205 \times 300.2}$$

$$= \frac{28.66}{0.08205 \times 300.2} = 1.164 \text{ g l}^{-1}$$

7.5 ENTROPY OF MIXING

Why are gaseous solutions homogeneous? Or why is it unlikely that all the molecules of a gas should at some time gather in one small part of their container? On the molecular level, the explanation is that the number of different ways of arranging the myriads of particles is much greater in the homogeneous situation. On the basis of probabilities alone, it is clear that the random and disordered state is more likely to occur out of all possible states than is an orderly spatial arrangement in a small region just because there are more places to put the molecules if their arrangement is random. The thermodynamic explanation, as expected, is based upon the relative entropies of unmixed and mixed states. Both questions and others related to them are answered in essence by a study of a two-component system. The second question is a special case of the first if one component is an uncomponent.

Equations (6.50) and (6.47) provide a convenient expression for the partial molar entropy $\bar{S}_i$ of component i.

$$\mu_i = RT \ln f_i + \mu_i^\ominus(T) \tag{6.50}$$

$$\bar{S}_i = -\left(\frac{\partial \mu_i}{\partial T}\right)_P \tag{6.47}$$

$$\bar{S}_i = -R \ln f_i - \frac{d\mu_i^\ominus}{dT} = -R \ln f_i + \bar{S}_i^\ominus \tag{7.10}$$

where $\bar{S}_i^\ominus = -d\mu_i^\ominus/dT$. That is, for an ideal gas i, with $p_i = f_i$,

$$\bar{S}_i = -R \ln p_i + \bar{S}_i^\ominus \tag{7.11}$$

The total entropy S of a system containing just components A and B is by (7.11) and (6.27),

$$\begin{aligned} S &= n_A \bar{S}_A + n_B \bar{S}_B \\ &= -n_A R \ln p_A - n_B R \ln p_B + n_A \bar{S}_A^\ominus + n_B \bar{S}_B^\ominus \end{aligned} \tag{7.12}$$

where p_A and p_B are the partial pressures of the two components A and B.

Toward the preparation of gaseous solution of A and B, into one of the two chambers of a thermostated vessel are put n_A moles of gas A, and into the other chamber are put n_B moles of gas B. The chambers are separated by a very thin planar barrier that can be slipped out without disturbing either gas. The pressures on the two gases are equalized and the initial state of the system is shown in Figure 7.5. Since $p_A^{\cdot} = p_B^{\cdot}$, the entropy S_1 of the unmixed gases is, by (7.12),

$$S_1 = -n_A R \ln p_A^{\cdot} - n_B R \ln p_A^{\cdot} + n_A \bar{S}_A^\ominus + n_B \bar{S}_B^\ominus \tag{7.13}$$

Slipping the very thin barrier vertically out of the way does not stir the gases.

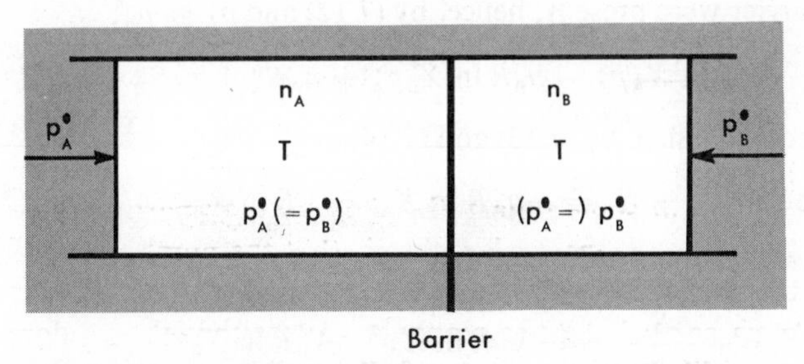

Figure 7.5. Unmixed Gases

Since their pressures are equal and there is no nonideal interaction, no change in pressure or volume is noted externally when equilibrium has been reached. Nor has removing the barrier involved heat, since ideal gases mix without heat effects. There would, of course, be heat associated with mixing if a chemical reaction or physical interaction with nonzero potential energy occurred, a nonideal physical interaction being considered a very weak chemical reaction. In other words, if the barrier were replaced after complete mixing, an observer outside the system would not be aware of a change in the system if he did not analyze the gases in the chambers. To such an ignorant observer, $\Delta S = 0$ because he is not aware of a change on removing and replacing the barrier, and (7.13) gives the value of S_2 the entropy of the system after mixing.

To an observer who can distinguish gas A from B, however, by some physical or chemical test, the final state of the system is shown in Figure 7.6, where (7.9) has been used to calculate the partial pressures. The partial pressures of A and B are the same in each compartment and the left-hand compartment has the fraction $n_A/(n_A + n_B)$ of the molecules in both chambers. The entropy S_2 of the final state of the system is the sum of the entropies of the two parts and is

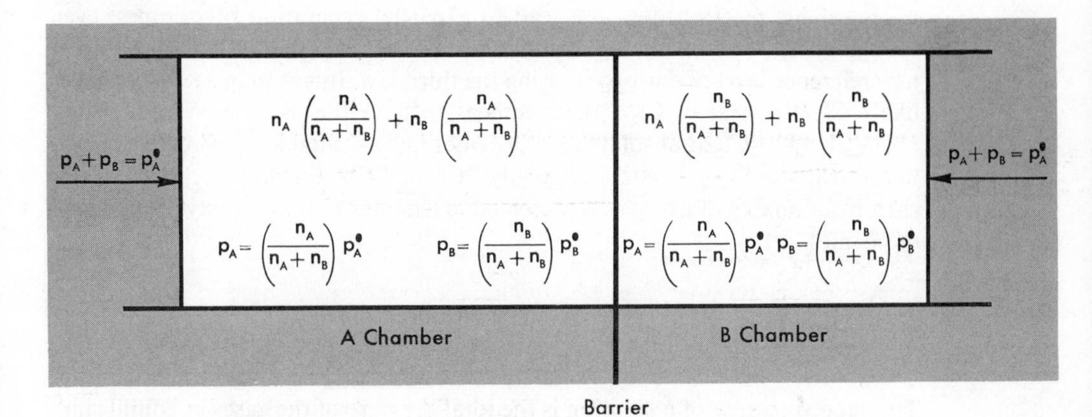

Figure 7.6. Mixed Gases

the same as if no barrier were present; hence, by (7.12) and $p_A^{\cdot} = p_B^{\cdot}$,

$$S_2 = -n_A R \ln X_A p_A^{\cdot} - n_B R \ln X_B p_A^{\cdot} + n_A \bar{S}_A^{\circ} + n_B \bar{S}_B^{\circ} \tag{7.14}$$

The increase in entropy is, then, by (7.13) and (7.14),

$$\Delta S = S_2 - S_1 = -n_A R \ln X_A - n_B R \ln X_B \tag{7.15}$$

The increase in entropy per mole of A and B is

$$\overline{\Delta S} = \frac{\Delta S}{n_A + n_B} = -X_A R \ln X_A - X_B R \ln X_B \tag{7.16}$$

If s pure species had been present in s chambers, $\overline{\Delta S}$ would have been

$$\overline{\Delta S} = -R \sum_{i=1}^{s} X_i \ln X_i \tag{7.17}$$

Mole fractions have here been noted as X_i rather than Y_i because these formulas have wide use beyond gaseous solutions.

Since $\ln X_i$ is less than zero because X_i ranges from almost zero to unity, the value of $\overline{\Delta S}$ in (7.16) or (7.17) is greater than zero. This fits the concept that in a spontaneous adiabatic process like this there should be an increase in entropy because of the increase in disorder. The value of $\overline{\Delta S}$ is zero when A and B are *indistinguishable to the experimenter*. If A were O_2 and B were N_2 and if the analyses were performed by noting the pressure or color in the chambers beforehand and afterward, $\overline{\Delta S}$ would be zero. If A were O_2 and B were N_2 and if the analyses were performed by noting the chemical properties of O_2 and N_2 before and after the mixing, then $\overline{\Delta S}$ would be greater than zero. If A were $^{16}O^{16}O$ and B were $^{18}O^{18}O$ and if the analyses were performed by noting the chemical properties of O_2 before and after mixing, $\overline{\Delta S}$ would be zero. If A were $^{16}O^{16}O$ and B were $^{18}O^{18}O$ and if the analyses were performed by a mass spectrometer, $\overline{\Delta S}$ would be greater than zero. Similarly, as along as a chemist performs reactions with the natural mixture of isotopes, he is unconcerned by this entropy of mixing if his reaction does not lead to a partial separation of isotopes, even though an entropy of mixing would exist at absolute zero and could require a new reference level of entropy in using the third law. But as long as ^{35}Cl behaves like ^{37}Cl, a crystal of $Cl_{2(s)}$ that happens to have the usual mixture of $^{35}Cl_2$, $^{35}Cl^{37}Cl$, and $^{37}Cl_2$ at absolute zero provides just as suitable a reference of absolute entropy as crystals containing only $^{35}Cl_2$ or $^{37}Cl_2$. Further discussion of this entropy of mixing of isotopes is presented in Chapter 17 in the study of statistical mechanics.

7.6 IDEAL SOLUTIONS

The vapor pressure of a solution is the total pressure of the gases in equilibrium with the liquid or solid solution. When the gases are ideal, the vapor pressure is the sum of the vapor pressures of the several volatile components as they exist in their diluted states in the solution. The interactions of mixed species in a condensed phase are so diverse, and subtle interactions often have so marked an influence upon vapor pressures, that vapor pressures of solutions can seldom be predicted. Mere tabulation of the observed values often enough is tacit admission that little more can be done with regard to most solutions.

There are, however, certain solutions the behavior of which can be described rather well by simple mathematical expressions. Although any really observed solution may behave as predicted only over a limited range of composition, and even then only as a limiting case never quite achieved, the mathematical expression may be simple enough to warrant a little relaxation from rigor especially when little else is available as a description. One of the oldest (1887) and simplest of such mathematical abstractions is *Raoult's law*: at constant temperature, the partial pressure p_i of species i in the gas phase in equilibrium with an ideal solution of mole fraction X_i in the condensed phase is

$$p_i = X_i p_i^{\cdot} \tag{7.18}$$

where $p_i^{\cdot}$ is the vapor pressure of the pure species i at the constant temperature. Species i may be either solute or solvent. Indeed, when the pure components exist in the same state of aggregation as the solution, the distinction between solvent and solute is more a matter of convenience than sense. Whether toluene or benzene is solvent in a solution of the two depends upon the viewpoint of the experimenter. The prejudice that the solvent be unchanged in phase whether pure or in solution or that it be present in excess is, however, quite general.

If the gas phase behaves ideally, the total pressure P is given by Dalton's law (7.6), $P = \sum p_i$. Since the mole fraction Y_i of species i in the gas phase is given by (7.9), $Y_i = p_i/P$, the compositions of both phases are quite simply related when both behave ideally. Ideal behavior for gaseous solutions means behavior in accord with Dalton's law; ideal behavior for nongaseous solutions means behavior in accord with Raoult's law. The phase rule is, of course, applicable whether behavior is ideal or not.

A solution is defined to be ideal with respect to species i if the chemical potential of species i at a mole fraction X_i is

$$\mu_i(T, P, X_i) = \mu_i^{\ominus}(T, P) + RT \ln X_i \tag{7.19}$$

Here, and ordinarily, $\mu_i^{\ominus}(T, P)$ is equal to the chemical potential of pure i ($X_i = 1$) at T and P. (When a solution is very dilute, the preponderant species 1 may be given preference in defining the standard state such that $\mu_1^{\ominus}(T, P)$ is its chemical potential when pure, while $\mu_i^{\ominus}(T, P)$ for each solute is the limit, as $X_1 \rightarrow 1$, of $\mu_i - RT \ln X_i$. This distinction is important in defining and using standard states.) In a mixture of perfect gases ($f_i = p_i$), the chemical potential of species i in the gaseous phase, as in (6.50), is

$$\mu_i(T, p_i) = \mu_i^{\ominus}(T) + RT \ln p_i \tag{7.20}$$

But if each species in an ideal solution is in equilibrium with such a gaseous mixture, then $\mu_i(T, P, X_i) = \mu_i(T, p_i)$ and

$$\mu_i^\circ(T, P) + RT \ln X_i = \mu_i^\circ(T) + RT \ln p_i$$

However, $\mu_i^\circ(T) - \mu_i^\circ(T, P)$ is ΔG for the transfer of one mole of i from pure liquid to pure vapor. By the methods of Sections 5.11 and 6.4, this ΔG is essentially $-RT \ln p_i^\cdot$, where $p_i^\cdot$ is the vapor pressure of pure i; hence, $RT \ln X_i = RT \ln p_i - RT \ln p_i^\cdot$ which yields Raoult's law (7.18). It is impossible to deduce (7.19) for all liquid states from (7.18) because not all ideal solutions are liquids in observable equilibrium with vapor. Moreover, (7.19) is a very convenient definition for establishing the following facts about ideal solutions.

If a solution is ideal with respect to all but one species, then it is ideal with respect to the last. The reason is that at constant T and P, (6.77) divided by the total number of moles present requires

$$0 = \sum_i X_i d\mu_i \tag{7.21}$$

But since (7.19) at constant T and P gives $d\mu_i = RTd \ln X_i$ for all but the last species j, (7.21) becomes

$$0 = \sum_{i \neq j} X_i RT\, d(\ln X_i) + X_j\, d\mu_j = \sum_{i \neq j} RT\, dX_i + X_j\, d\mu_j \tag{7.22}$$

However, (6.19) at constant T and P yields $dX_j = -\sum_{i \neq j} dX_i$; hence, (7.22) becomes $X_j\, d\mu_j = RT\, dX_j$, which upon integration gives (7.19) for the last species j. Thus j also is ideal.

For an ideal solution, the heat of solution ΔH and the volume change ΔV upon mixing are both zero. This proof begins with the fact that $\mu_i^\circ(T, P)$, the standard state of i in solution, is equal to $\mu_i^\cdot(T, P)$, the chemical potential of pure i. In (7.19), this gives for the increment in free energy ΔG upon addition of a mole of pure i to a large amount of solution

$$\Delta G = \mu_i(T, P, X_i) - \mu_i^\cdot(T, P) = RT \ln X_i$$

By (5.76), ΔH for this same process is

$$\Delta H = -T^2 \left[\frac{\partial}{\partial T}\left(\frac{\Delta G}{T}\right)\right]_P = -RT^2 \left(\frac{\partial \ln X_i}{\partial T}\right)_P = 0 \tag{7.23}$$

Similarly, by (6.48), which holds at constant composition,

$$\Delta V = \left[\frac{\partial}{\partial P}(\mu_i - \mu_i^\cdot)\right]_{T,n} = RT \left[\frac{\partial \ln X_i}{\partial P}\right]_{T,n} = 0 \tag{7.24}$$

In other words, the enthalpy and volume of a pure species are unchanged upon entry into an ideal solution. These conclusions obviously hold for an ideal mixture of perfect gases, provided the volume is $n_i RT/P$.

7.7 TWO VOLATILE COMPONENTS

Since a solution is by definition physically homogeneous, it is one phase (P = 1). If it is made by mixing arbitrary amounts of two pure substances, it is a two-component or binary system (C = 2). The number of degrees of freedom F that must be specified to fix the state of such a system or solution is three, for F = C − P + 2 = 3. These three independent intensive variables are ordinarily chosen to be temperature, pressure, and mole fraction of one of the components in the solution. These three independent variables could be graphed in a three-dimensional figure, but the simplification attendant upon transforming to two independent variables by holding either temperature or pressure constant is usually worth the sacrifice in generality. Maintaining isothermal or isobaric conditions is equivalent to taking a planar section of the three-dimensional figure. For such a section, for a two-component solution, F = C − P + 1 = 2 − 1 + 1 = 2. One composition variable and either pressure or temperature are the two degrees of freedom commonly chosen.

If the system should consist of two phases (P = 2), say, a gaseous solution and a liquid solution, then at equilibrium the phase rule F = C − P + 1 says that there is only one degree of freedom. At constant temperature, either composition or pressure is independent; at constant pressure, either composition or temperature. And if three phases (P = 3) should be present, by F = C − P + 1, there should be no degree of freedom in a two-component system. The mere presence of three phases would specify the state of the system through the natures of its two components. But if the temperature or pressure is not held constant, the state of a two-component system is completely fixed (F = 0) only if four phases coexist at equilibrium, for F = C − P + 2; 0 = 2 − P + 2; P = 4.

Figure 7.7 contains the two phase diagrams that are plane sections at constant temperature or pressure of the three-dimensional figure relating composition, temperature, and pressure variables for a two-component system in which gaseous, liquid, and solid solutions are homogeneous and ideal. The abscissas are the mole fraction of component B in one of the phases. When X_B is zero as it is at the left, none of B is present: when X_B is unity, only B is present. The upper diagram shows how pressure and composition are related at constant temperature, while the lower diagram shows how temperature and composition are related at constant pressure. The qualitative symmetry of *mirror images* between the diagrams is worthy of note. Two phases coexist at equilibrium when the independent variables have the values within the closed regions bounded

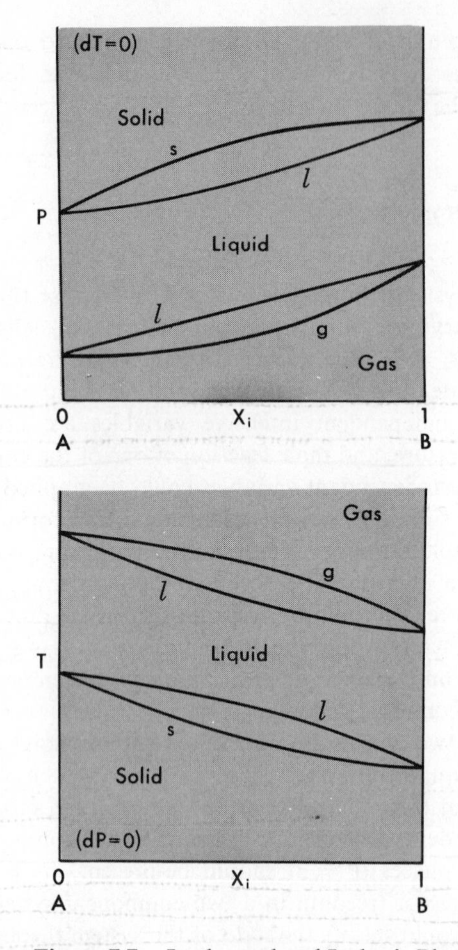

Figure 7.7. Isothermal and Isobaric Phase Diagrams of Ideal System

by two curves. One of the curves gives the values of the independent variables in one phase, and the other in the second phase.

The forms of the lower pair of curves in the upper diagram of Figure 7.7 can be derived from Dalton's and Raoult's laws. For the gas, by Dalton's law

$$P = p_A + p_B \tag{7.25}$$

By Raoult's law (7.18), however,

$$p_A = p_A^{\cdot} X_A, \qquad \text{and} \qquad p_B = p_B^{\cdot} X_B \tag{7.26}$$

where X_i is the mole fraction of species i in the liquid. Substitution of (7.26) into (7.25) with account of (6.19) yields a straight line with slope $(p_B^{\cdot} - p_A^{\cdot})$.

$$P = p_A^{\cdot} X_A + p_B^{\cdot} X_B = p_A^{\cdot}(1 - X_B) + p_B^{\cdot} X_B = (p_B^{\cdot} - p_A^{\cdot})X_B + p_A^{\cdot} \tag{7.27}$$

Since the vapor is richer and the liquid is poorer in the more volatile component B at equilibrium, the vapor curve falls below the straight line (7.27). The proof follows. By (7.6) and (7.9), the mole fraction of B in the gas is

$$Y_B = \frac{p_B}{p_A + p_B}$$

On continuation with Raoult's law (7.18)

$$Y_B = \frac{X_B p_B^{\cdot}}{X_A p_A^{\cdot} + X_B p_B^{\cdot}} = \frac{X_B}{X_B + X_A \epsilon} \tag{7.28}$$

where $\epsilon = p_A^{\cdot}/p_B^{\cdot} < 1$. The denominator of (7.28) is less than unity since it would be unity by (6.19) if ϵ were unity. Hence, for a more volatile species B,

$$Y_B > X_B \tag{7.29}$$

The forms of the other pairs of curves in Figure 7.7 can be calculated tediously. It is perhaps simplest to regard these curves as summaries of experimental data. It is quite possible, for example, that the imposition of pressure would never lead to solidification at constant temperature as implied by the upper diagram of Figure 7.7. Only if the liquid contracts on solidification would increased pressure convert liquid to solid at constant temperature. Or if the pressure were low enough, the solid might sublime and the liquid region in the lower diagram might be absent. The reason for combining diagrams in this way is to show the analogous behavior of gas-liquid and liquid-solid equilibriums.[2]

It is much more common to find only two-phase equilibriums presented in one diagram of these kinds. Figure 7.8 has been prepared for gas-liquid solutions, but isomorphous diagrams exist for liquid-solid and gas-solid solutions. For these diagrams $\mathsf{C} = 2$, and $\mathsf{F} = 2 - \mathsf{P} + 1 = 3 - \mathsf{P}$.

In regions outside those bounded and closed by two curves, one solution phase ($\mathsf{P} = 1$) is present and the two independent variables ($\mathsf{F} = 2$) are composition and either temperature or pressure. Within the gray regions bounded by two curves, two solution phases ($\mathsf{P} = 2$) are present and the independent variable ($\mathsf{F} = 1$) is composition or one of the other variables, P or T. When X_B or Y_B is zero or unity, the system contains only one component and the values of P and T are independent of each other except when two phases coexist at equilibrium.

Although the compositions that correspond to the maxima and minima of the four right-hand diagrams of Figure 7.8 do not correspond to pure substances or stoichiometric formulas, the compositions of liquid and vapor are alike. That is, upon vaporization or condensation at these maxima or minima,

[2] N.O. Smith, *J. Chem. Ed.* **35**, 125 (1958).

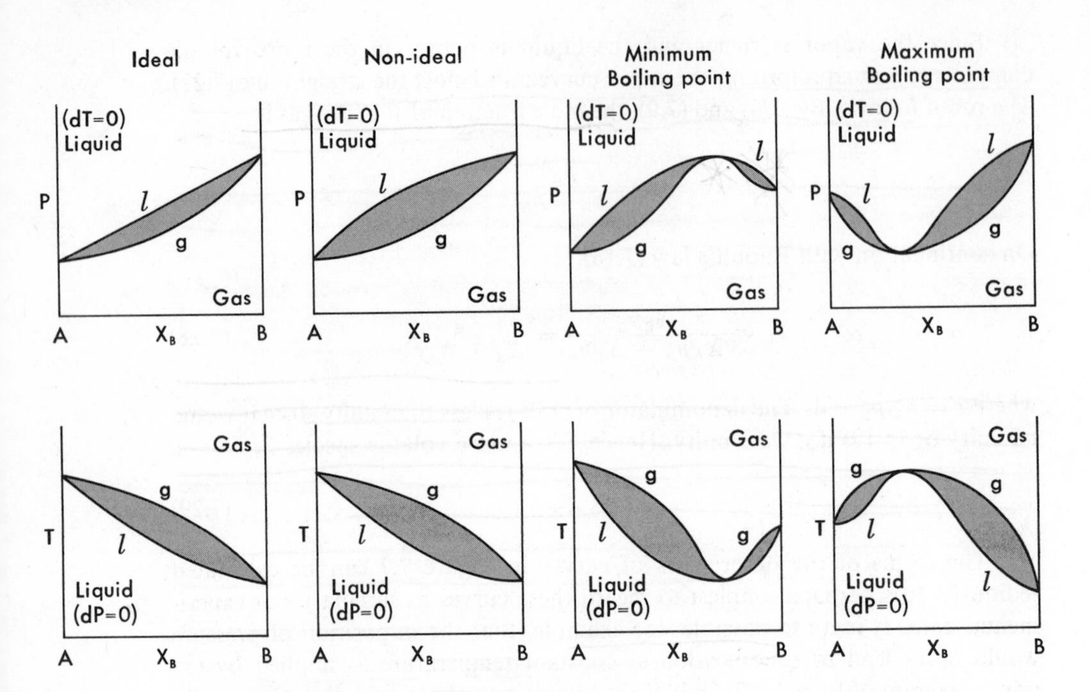

Figure 7.8. Related Phase Diagrams

the solutions behave like pure substances at the specified temperatures and pressures in that such physical changes cause no change in composition of either solution. At maxima in T or P, it is thermodynamically necessary that $X_i = Y_i$. The behavior of solutions during distillation is discussed in the next section.

Table 7.2 lists some pairs of volatile liquids that form systems of three of the four types of Figure 7.8. Components that form ideal solutions are similar in physical and chemical properties. Chemical species containing isotopic substitutions probably approach ideal behavior most closely, although there are a few pairs like CCl_4-$SnCl_4$, chlorobenzene-bromobenzene, *n*-hexane-*n*-heptane, or ethylene dibromide-propylene dibromide that behave almost ideally. Non-ideal solutions contain species not quite different enough to have minimum or maximum boiling points. A minimum boiling point or maximum vapor pressure originates in repulsive forces between species quite unlike each other. Maximum boiling points and minimum vapor pressures occur in mixtures in which the components interact strongly by the formation of hydrogen bonds or by ionization or neutralization. Hydrogen chloride and diethly ether interact strongly as acid and base to form a loose complex with an unusually low vapor pressure. Acetone and chloroform also attract each other strongly in their liquid mixtures and exhibit a maximum boiling point.

The transition from a nonideal system to one having a maximum or minimum boiling point can be though of as a continuous variation in intermolecular

Table 7.2 Behavior of Some Volatile Two-Component Systems.

A Component	B Component		
	Nonideal	Minimum Boiling Point	Maximum Boiling Point
Water	Ammonia Hydrogen peroxide Ethylene glycol Glycerol	Ethanol Isobutyl alcohol Secondary butyl alcohol Tertiary butyl alcohol	Hydrogen fluoride Hydrogen chloride Perchloric acid Nitric acid
Carbon tetrachloride	Cyclohexane Benzene	Ethanol Methyl ethyl ketone	Rare
Methanol	Water Ethanol Dioxane	Carbon tetrachloride Acetone *n*-Heptane	Rare
Acetic acid	Water Ethylene chloride Acetone	Ethanol Toluene Chlorobenzene	Pyridine
Toluene	Benzene Carbon tetrachloride	Ethanol Stannic chloride	Rare

forces. A binary system with vapor pressures larger than expected but intermediate between those of two pure components is described in Figure 7.9a. As intermolecular repulsions increase, a maximum in vapor pressure appears as in Figure 7.9b. The upper curves in Figure 7.9 are the liquid curves of Figure 7.8 and describe the composition of liquid in equilibrium with vapor at the various pressures. Their ordinates are, by Dalton's law or something akin to it, the sum of the ordinates of the other solid curves, which describe the pressure of each component as a function of liquid composition.

The dotted lines in Figure 7.9 are predicted by Raoult's law for ideal solutions. Although the observed solid curves obviously deviate from linearity, in the region of pure components solid lines of this kind are often almost straight. This empirically observed linearity when one species is present in great excess is expressed mathematically by *Henry's law*

$$p_i = X_i K(T) \tag{7.30}$$

Henry's law says that the mole fraction X_i of species i that dissolves in a solvent at a temperature T is proportional to the partial pressure exerted by i. The empirical proportionality factor $K(T)$ depends mainly on temperature.

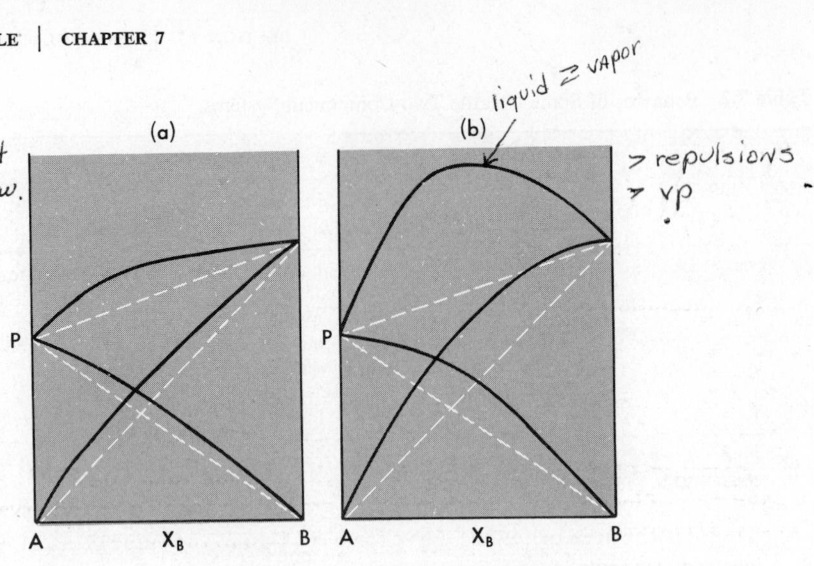

Figure 7.9. Continuity of Forms of Phase Diagrams

It is possible to calculate one of the vapor-pressure curves of Figure 7.9 from the other. At constant T, the Gibbs-Duhem equation (6.77) for the liquid phase of volume V is

$$V\,dP = n_A\,d\mu_A + n_B\,d\mu_B \tag{7.31}$$

Since μ_i is the same in the liquid and vapor, $d\mu_A$ and $d\mu_B$ can be found by (6.50), which applies to the vapor. Hence, with $d\mu_i = RT\,d(\ln f_i)$ for A and B in (7.31), there results

$$V\,dP = n_A\,RT\,d(\ln f_A) + n_B\,RT\,d(\ln f_B) \tag{7.32}$$

With two phases and two components, $\mathsf{F} = 2 - 2 + 2 = 2$; (7.32) thus fixes P, f_A, or f_B.

Generally $V \ll RT$ and after division by $(n_A + n_B)RT$ (7.32) becomes, in good approximation,

$$0 = X_A\,d(\ln f_A) + X_B\,d(\ln f_B) \tag{7.33}$$

If the vapor is ideal, $f_i = p_i$ and (7.33) is

$$0 = X_A\,d(\ln p_A) + X_B\,d(\ln p_B) \tag{7.34}$$

where X_A and X_B are mole fractions of A and B in the liquid phase. Calculations are made convenient if (7.34) is transformed by subtracting

$$0 = X_A\,d(\ln X_A) + X_B\,d(\ln X_B) = dX_A + dX_B = d(X_A + X_B)$$

and $\quad 0 = X_A\,d(\ln p_A) + X_B\,d(\ln p_B)$

The former results because $X_A + X_B$ is constant, and the latter is true because the vapor pressures $p_i^{\cdot}$ of the pure species depend primarily only on T, which is fixed. Thus, (7.34) becomes

$$0 = X_A \, d\left(\ln \frac{p_A}{p_A^{\cdot} X_A}\right) + X_B \, d\left(\ln \frac{p_B}{p_B^{\cdot} X_B}\right) \tag{7.35}$$

Definite integration of (7.35) from $X_B = 0$ (where $X_A = 1$ and $p_A = p_A^{\cdot}$) to X_B where p_B is known yields

$$* \ln\left(\frac{p_A}{p_A^{\cdot} X_A}\right) = -\int_{(X_B=0)}^{(X_B=X_B)} \frac{X_B}{1 - X_B} \, d\left(\ln \frac{p_B}{p_B^{\cdot} X_B}\right) \tag{7.36}$$

The integral in (7.36) is found graphically by plotting values of $X_B/(1 - X_B)$ as a function of $\ln(p_B/p_B^{\cdot} X_B)$, both of which are known for all X_B by observation. The integral is the area below the curve from $X_B = 0$ to the value of X_B at which p_A is desired. Henry's law assures that the integral is bound at the lower limit, for with $p_B = K(T)X_B$ by (7.30)

$$* \lim_{X_B \to 0} \ln\left(\frac{p_B}{p_B^{\cdot} X_B}\right) = \lim_{X_B \to 0} \ln\left(\frac{K(T)}{p_B^{\cdot}}\right)$$

which is finite.

It is also possible to derive the approximate result (7.33), the Duhem-Margolis equation, at constant P, and to show, if p_A exceeds (or falls below) the value predicted for an ideal solution for all X_A, that p_B also exceeds (or, conversely, falls below) its ideal value for all X_B. If p_A sometimes exceeds and sometimes falls below the value of an ideal solution, then p_B may or may not do likewise.

Addition of vapor composition curves to a plot of liquid composition curves as functions of T or P would generate phase diagrams like those of Figures 7.7 and 7.8, in which the abscissa is both X_B and Y_B. It is generally sufficient at low P to use (7.9) for the vapor curves.

Example 7.3. Predict the composition and total pressure of the gas in equilibrium with a solution of *n*-hexane and *n*-heptane in which the mole fraction of *n*-hexane is 0.400 at 50.0°C. At 50.0°C the vapor pressures of pure *n*-hexane and *n*-heptane are 408 mm Hg and 141 mm Hg. (*Handbook of Chemistry* [10th Edition] ed. by N. A. Lange and G. M. Forker. New York: McGraw-Hill Book Co., Inc., 1967, p. 1442.)

By Raoult's law (7.18),

$$p(\text{hexane}) = 0.400 \times 408 = 163 \text{ mm Hg}$$

$$p(\text{heptane}) = 0.600 \times 141 = 85 \text{ mm Hg}$$

By (7.9), the mole fraction of hexane in the gas phase is

$$Y = \frac{163}{163 + 85} = 0.657$$

The vapor is far richer in the more volatile component than is the liquid, in accord with (7.29). The total pressure is 248 mm Hg.

Example 7.4. At 0°C, 23.5 ml deoxygenated air and 48.9 ml O_2 (at standard conditions) dissolve in one 1 water when the partial pressure of such air or O_2 is 1.000 atm. (*Handbook of Chemistry* [10th Edition] ed. by N. A. Lange and G. M. Forker. New York: McGraw-Hill Book Co., Inc., 1967, pp. 1099, 1101.) Calculate the molality of air dissolved in water at 0°C and the Henry's law constants $K(T)$ for O_2 and the other gases at 0°C.

By definitions (6.16) and (6.18) for molality m_i and mole fraction X_i, if $i = 2$ in a dilute two-component solution,

$$m_2 = \frac{W_2}{M_2} \times \frac{1000}{W_1}$$

and

$$X_2 = \frac{W_2/M_2}{(W_1/M_1) + (W_2/M_2)} \approx \frac{W_2}{M_2} \times \frac{M_1}{W_1}$$

Since $M_1 = 18.02$ for water, for dilute aqueous solutions,

$$\frac{m_2}{X_2} = \frac{1000}{M_1} = \frac{1000}{18.02} = 55.5$$

Since 1 mole O_2 would occupy about 22.4 l, m_2 is $48.9/(22.4 \times 10^3) = 2.18 \times 10^{-3}$. However, by (7.30), $p_2 = X_2K(T) = (m_2/55.5)K(T)$. If p_2 is expressed in millimeters of Hg, for O_2

$$K(T) = \frac{p_2 \times 55.5}{m_2} = \frac{760 \times 55.5}{2.18 \times 10^{-2}} = 1.93 \times 10^7 \text{ mm Hg}$$

Similarly, for the other gases of air,

$$K(T) = \frac{760 \times 55.5 \times 22.4 \times 10^3}{23.5} = 4.02 \times 10^7 \text{ mm Hg}$$

Since air is 21.0% mol O_2 and 79.0% mol others, for all gases

$$m_2 = 55.5\left(\frac{0.210 \times 760}{1.93 \times 10^7}\right) + 55.5\left(\frac{0.790 \times 760}{4.02 \times 10^7}\right) = 1.29 \times 10^{-3}$$

7.8 FRACTIONAL SEPARATIONS

The two-component system acetone-water exhibits nonideal behavior at pressures less than 2.5 atm and a minimum boiling point at pressures greater than 2.5 atm. Figures 7.10 and 7.11 for this system have been drawn from the values of Table 7.3, which contains equilibrium data for this system at 1.00 and 13.5 atm total pressure.

The normal boiling points of water and acetone are 100.0°C and 56.5°C. The lower curve of Figure 7.10 describes the temperatures at which liquid solu-

Table 7.3 Equilibrium Data for Acetone-Water System (Othmer, D. F. and F. R. Morley, *Industrial and Engineering Chemistry*, **38,** 751 [1946].)

	1.00 Atmosphere		13.5 Atmospheres	
Mole Percentage Acetone In Liquid	Temperature (°C)	Mole Percentage Acetone In Vapor	Temperature (°C)	Mole Percentage Acetone In Vapor
0.0	100.0	0.0	194.3	0.0
1.0	92.0	27.9	184.9	19.5
2.5	84.2	47.0	176.4	33.4
5.0	75.6	63.0	168.8	44.4
10.0	66.9	75.4	163.1	52.8
20.0	62.4	81.3	159.8	58.7
30.0	61.1	83.2	158.2	61.8
40.0	60.3	84.2	157.2	64.4
50.0	59.8	85.1	156.6	66.9
60.0	59.2	86.3	156.2	69.7
70.0	58.8	87.5	156.0	73.4
80.0	58.2	89.7	156.0	79.6
90.0	57.4	93.5	157.6	88.5
95.0	56.9	96.2	158.2	93.4
97.5	56.7	97.9	158.5	96.4
100.0	56.5	100.0	158.7	100.0

tions of water and acetone first begin to boil at one atm. The upper curve describes the temperatures at which gaseous solutions of water and acetone first begin to condense at one atm. These two curves naturally meet at 100.0°C and 56.5°C. The temperatures at which a mixture of acetone and water first begins to vaporize or first begins to condense are not the same. A mixture of 0.500 moles acetone and 0.500 moles water would show first signs of boiling at 59.8°C at one atm. If none of the vapor were withdrawn from the system, the last drop to vaporize would disappear at 82.7°C. The composition of this last drop that vaporizes would be that of the liquid in equilibrium with a gaseous solution with a mole fraction of acetone of 0.500. This last drop would have a mole fraction of acetone of 0.028, and this would also be the composition of the first drop to condense from a gaseous solution with mole fraction of 0.500. Just as the last drop to vaporize is poor in acetone, the first drop to vaporize is rich in acetone, the more volatile component. The first vapor to come from a liquid with mole fraction of 0.500 has a mole fraction of acetone of 0.851 and would be vaporized at 59.8°C.

At temperatures between 59.8°C and 82.7°C, two phases are present in a system with an overall mole fraction of 0.500. The two curves labeled 1 and g of Figure 7.10 give the compositions of the liquid and gaseous solutions at the intermediate temperatures. For example, at 80.0°C, the mole fraction of acetone in the gas is 0.550, and in the liquid it is 0.035. The process of fractional distillation takes advantage of this disparity in concentration in order to separate a solution into its components. For example, if a liquid solution containing 1

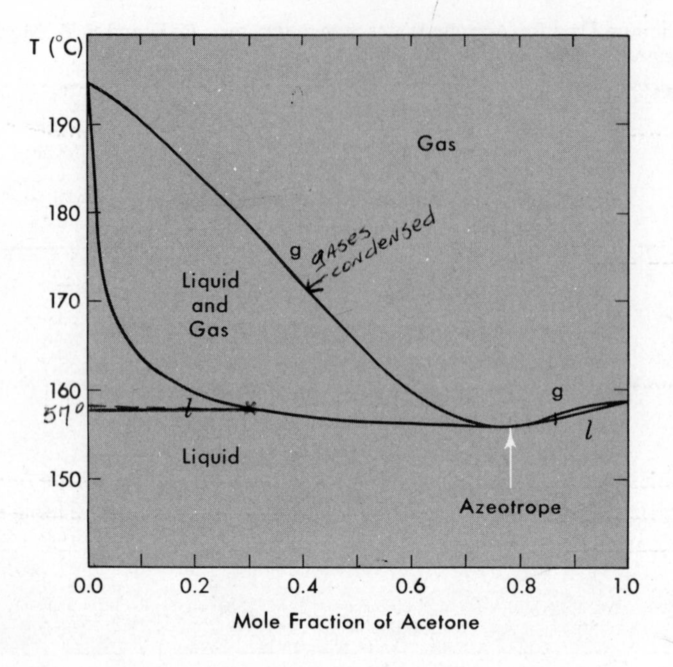

Figure 7.10. Acetone-Water System at One Atmosphere

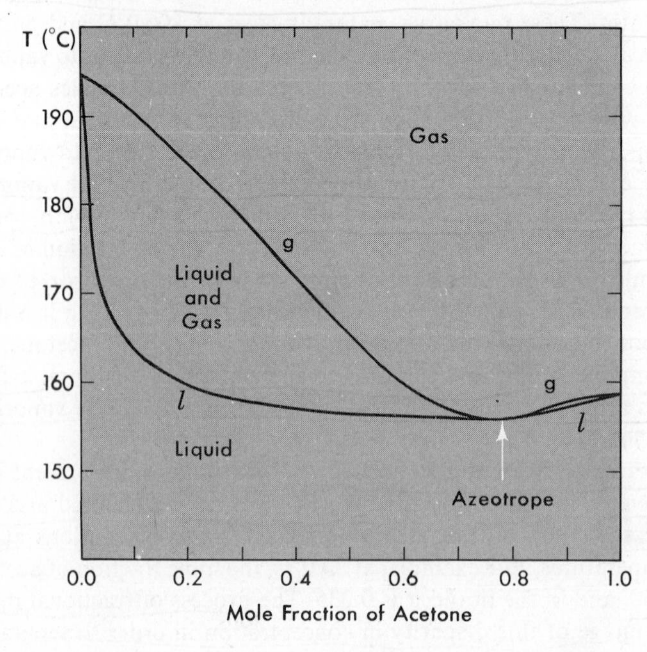

Figure 7.11. Acetone-Water System at 13.5 Atmospheres

mole acetone for every 9 moles water was heated until a little vapor was formed, the first vapor would be formed at 66.9°C and would have a mole fraction of acetone of 0.754. Total condensation of this little bit of vapor would yield a liquid solution with a mole fraction of acetone of 0.754. The first vapors from this newly condensed solution would be generated at 58.3°C and would have a mole fraction of acetone of 0.890. This vapor could be condensed totally to yield a little liquid with mole fraction of acetone equal to 0.890. Repeated partial vaporization and total condensation enriches the distillate in the more volatile component and leaves behind a solution richer and richer in the less volatile component. Thus, a partial separation is effected by the stepwise process, as shown in Figure 7.10. Continuation of this stepwise process in the two-phase region of the phase diagram would lead eventually to a little acetone that was almost pure.

Similarly, a little pure water could be separated from the original solution containing 9 moles water and 1 mole acetone by vaporizing all but a little of it at 98°C. The little liquid left unvaporized would contain only about 0.2 mole percent acetone. Repetition of the stepwise process would yield eventually a little water that was almost pure.

The composition data of Table 7.3 for the acetone-water binary system are plotted in another way in Figure 7.12. The ordinate Y_B is the mole fraction

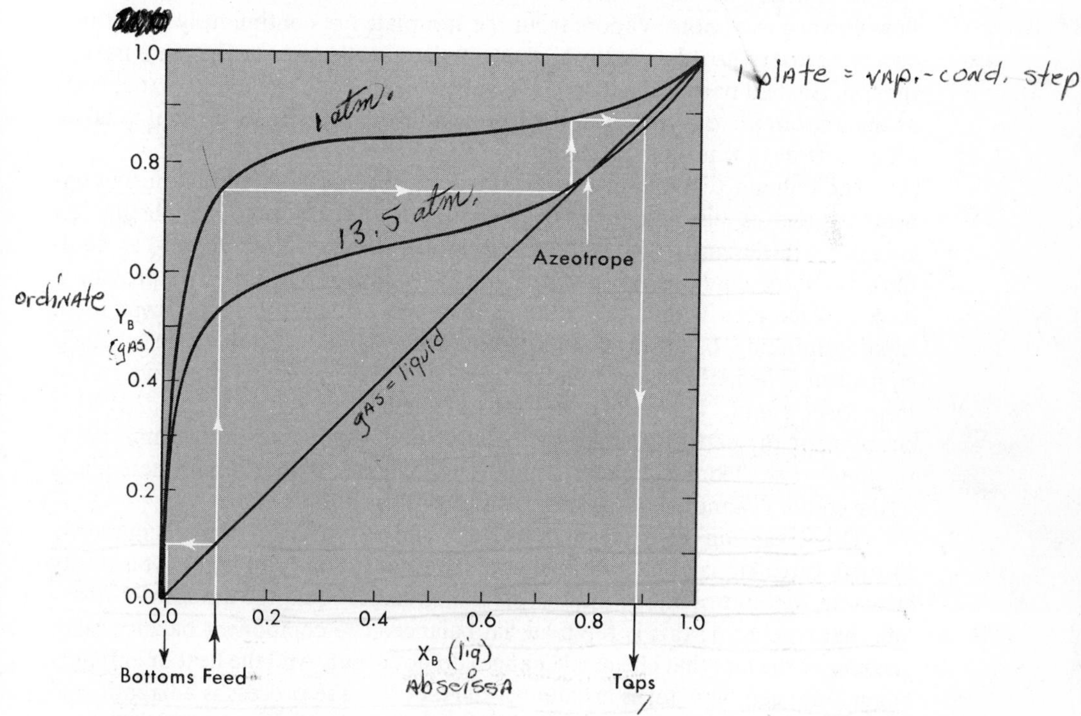

Figure 7.12. Acetone Composition of Vapor and Liquid

of acetone in the gaseous solution; the abscissa X_B is the mole fraction of acetone in the liquid solution in equilibrium with the gaseous solution of composition Y_B. Gas and liquid would be equal in concentration along the diagonal. The stepwise process of Figure 7.10 is shown also in Figure 7.12. The number of completed steps in Figure 7.10 or 7.12 is the number of complete vaporization-condensation operations. In the jargon of distillers, each step is called a *plate*. A plate represents one two-phase equilibrium of the sort that occurs in a simple distillation. The *feed* is the solution to be separated; the *tops* is the distillate; the *bottoms* is the highest boiling fraction obtained.

A fractional distillation is never performed by placing the condensed distillate from a one-plate distillation into another one-plate still. Rather, continuously bringing two phases into intimate contact so as to establish equilibriums at several temperatures is done in a fractionating column. Figure 7.13 is a schematic diagram of a three-plate column of the kind that might separate acetone-water mixtures in the way of the example. Preheated feed enters at one of the plates of the column. Hot vapors from below bubble under the bubble caps of a plate and come to equilibrium with the liquid of that plate. Condensation yields the heat of vaporization to maintain the temperature of each plate and to cause vaporization of vapors richer in the more volatile component. As liquid collects at a plate it overflows to the plate below. Thus, the less volatile species tend to flow downward as liquids and the more volatile species tend to flow upward as vapors. Vapors from the top plate are continuously condensed and most are returned as reflux to the top plate, or perhaps to the plate next to the top. A small part of the distillate is taken off as tops. The liquid that collects at the bottom plate is richest in the less volatile component. A bit of it is taken off as bottoms from time to time.

The column diagrammed in Figure 7.13 appears as a continuously connected series of distinct one-plate distillations. Actual fractional distillation columns are designed merely to facilitate the attainment of liquid-gas equilibrium. Some columns are packed with glass balls or helices that provide a large surface area within the column. Some columns are empty except for a rapidly spinning band along their axes. Some contain bubble-caps or their equivalent. The performance of a fractional distilling column is given in terms of *theoretical plates*. The number of steps of the sort shown in Figure 7.12 that account for the performance of the column as it separates a known mixture is the number of theoretical plates, even though the precise location of these plates in the column cannot be identified as simply as for bubble-caps.

The operation of a fractionating column is formulated mathematically through three kinds of balance: material, component, and enthalpy. At a steady state, the amount of vapor that leaves a plate must equal the amount of distillate that reaches it; this is the material balance. The component balance takes account of the fact that chemical changes do not occur. And the heat or enthalpy balance at each plate takes account of the fact that the process is adiabatic and

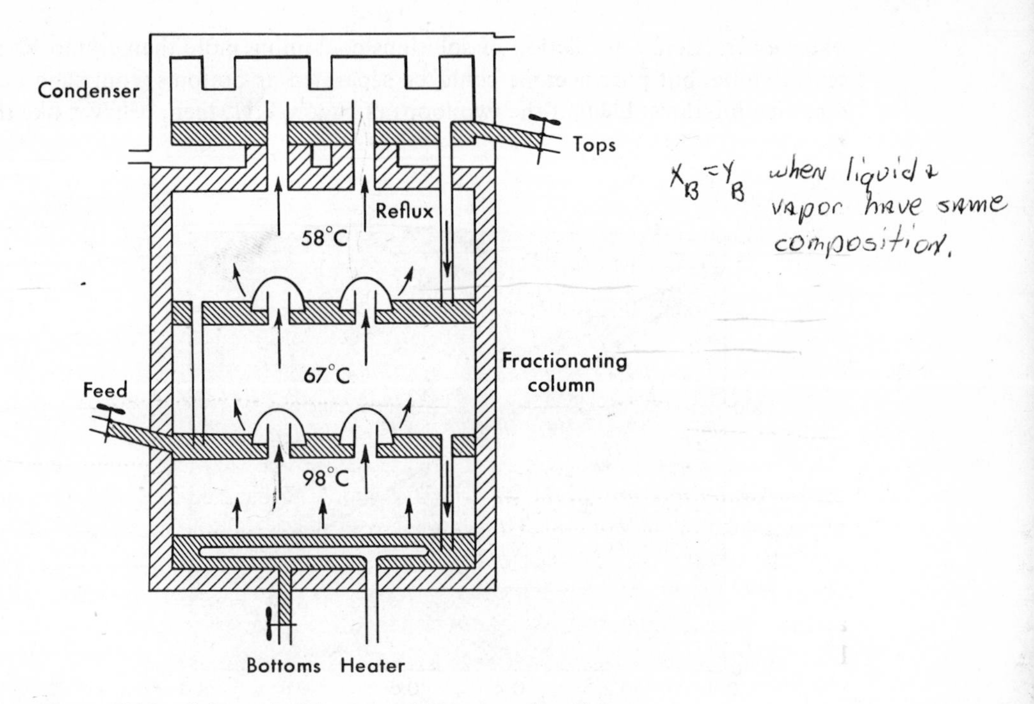

Figure 7.13. Schematic Diagram of Fractionating Column

almost isobaric, and that each plate receives heat from below and passes it on to the plate above. In other words, matter is conserved, no chemical reactions occur, and heat from the heater eventually leaves by the condenser. The ratio of reflux to distillate is called the *reflux ratio;* it provides a convenient parameter in terms of which the operation of a column is described. When no tops are taken off, the reflux ratio is infinity for there is no distillate and the idealized example for the three-plate separation of acetone and water is as stated. When some distillate (almost pure acetone) is withdrawn, then the steps in Figure 7.12 are to be constructed between the curve and a line of slope less than unity in the upper left-hand half of the figure. This construction, then, shows the need of more plates for a given separation as the amount of distillate taken off increases.

It is impossible to obtain almost pure acetone by fractionating a mixture of acetone and water with mole fraction of acetone less than 0.780 at 13.5 atm. The stepwise construction and the process it describes lead inexorably to the azeotropic mixture that boils at 156°C at 13.5 atm. This mixture, with its maximum vapor pressure and minimum boiling point, behaves under these conditions like a pure substance in that liquid and vapor have the same composition ($X_B = Y_B$ in Figure 7.12). Azeotropes can be broken by varying the pressure, as here, or by adding a third substance, which modifies the phase relations. Similarly, at 13.5 atm it would be impossible to obtain pure or almost pure water by fractional distillation of solutions containing more than 78 mole percent acetone, but pure acetone could be separated as bottoms from such acetone-rich mixtures. Each of the two loops of Figure 7.11, then, behaves like the

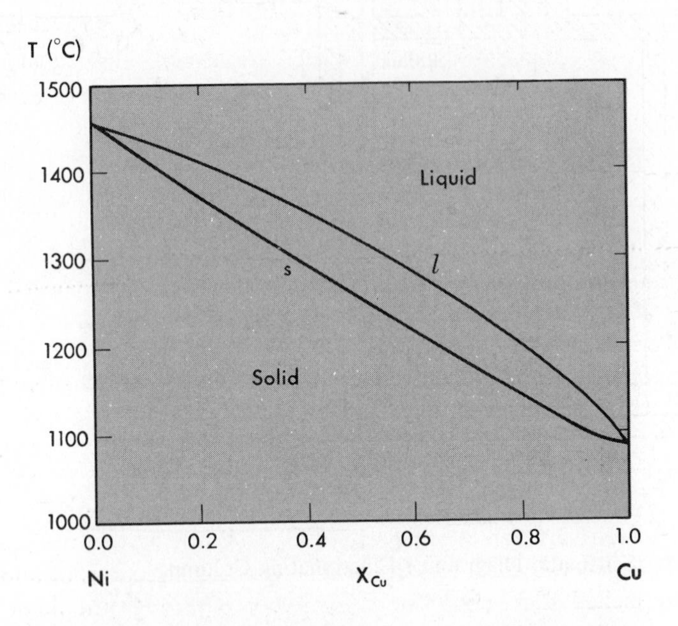

Figure 7.14. Nickel-Copper System at Constant Pressure

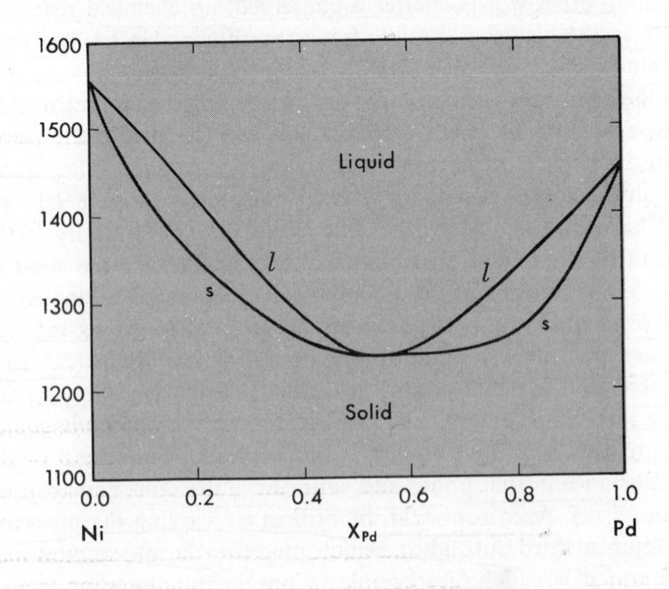

Figure 7.15. Nickel-Palladium System at Constant Pressure

single loop of Figure 7.10, even though the azeotrope is not a pure substance. At the stated pressure of 13.5 atm, Figure 7.11 behaves as two simple figures like Figure 7.10 in juxtaposition.

What has been said of fractionation of gas-liquid systems applies detail by detail to gas-solid and liquid-solid systems. Two examples of liquid-solid systems that form only one liquid and one solid phase are those of Ni-Cu and Ni-Pd, shown in Figures 7.14 and 7.15 (*Metals Handbook*, American Society for Metals, Cleveland, O., 1948). For example, cooling a homogeneous melt containing Cu with a mole fraction of 0.40 leads to crystals with mole fraction of 0.27 at 1350°C. Crystals with gradually increasing mole fraction continue to form until at 1290°C at equilibrium all the melt has crystallized. Since diffusion is a slow process in the solid state, it is unlikely that crystals formed in a real cooling would be homogeneous. Nor would the last bit have crystallized at 1290°C, for the last of the melt would be richer than 0.40 in Cu because some crystals would be rich in Ni.

The reason that fractional distillation separates a liquid mixture is that the less volatile species concentrates in the liquid, while the more volatile one concentrates in the vapor. The key to its efficiency is the speed with which equilibrium can be approached all along the length of the column as liquid and vapor *flow in opposite directions.* Effecting the same kind of countercurrent flow of liquid and solid phases of different composition leads, similarly, to purification by the process of *zone-refining.* In this process, several small sections of a long impure ingot are melted and each liquid zone is moved through the ingot. If the impurity tends to concentrate in the liquid, as Cu or Pd would from nearly pure Ni according to Figures 7.14 and 7.15, then each time a liquid region sweeps slowly through the solid it carries along more of the impurity and leaves behind new crystals containing less impurity. On the other hand, if the impurity concentrates in the solid, thorough mixing of the liquid zone will allow the impurity to cross the molten zone to the newly forming solid phase. After many passes of liquid zones to the left, the impurity would be found in the solid at the right. Like shoveling sand against a wall, however, the impurity's concentration at either end of the ingot increases until, because of back-diffusion in liquid zones of finite size, passing further zones causes no significant motion of the impurity.

Many ingenious devices exist for effecting efficient mixing and countercurrent flow, sometimes even in continuous processes. The liquid zone in ingots of high melting point is often generated by radiation; cooling of the adjacent solid zones is then also by radiation. At low T, steam heaters and coils cooled by water may carry solid and liquid in opposite directions. The length of the molten zone relative to ingot length, which with the number of passes is an important parameter in the efficiency of a separation, is controlled easily when the difference in temperatures of solid and liquid is great. Surface tension may be used to hold a liquid zone in place between solids if contamination from a container must be avoided.

7.9 IMMISCIBLE LIQUIDS

Complete miscibility generally occurs only in the gaseous phase. No one has ever observed two gas phases at equilibrium, but to have more than one liquid or solid phase coexistent is quite common. When two liquids like bromobenzene and water coexist and yet do not dissolve in each other to a significant extent, each behaves as though the other were not present. Provided both condensed phases are present, the total vapor pressure of the system at any temperature is merely the sum, by Dalton's law, of the vapor pressures of each. Figure 7.16 shows how the vapor pressures of two immiscible liquids add at various temperatures. Curve *A* is for water, curve *B* is for bromobenzene, nitrobenzene, or other volatile substance, and curve *C* is their sum. Note that the sum becomes one atm somewhat below 100°C. BP H_2O

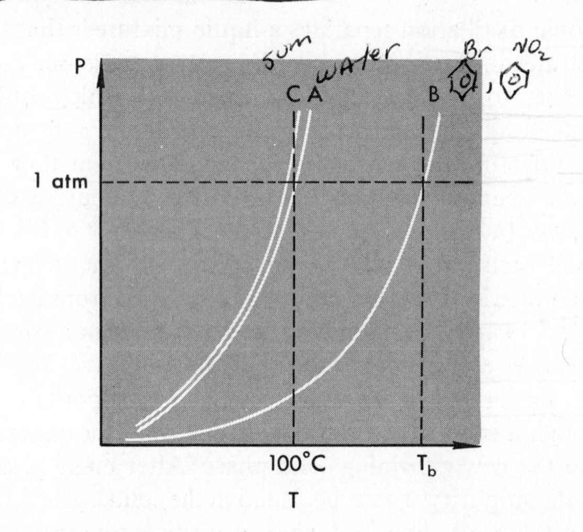

Figure 7.16. Total Vapor Pressure Above Immiscible Liquids

In the absence of its pure condensed phase a component may assume any gaseous pressure less than its vapor pressure at a given temperature. That is, its concentration in the vapor may range from a certain maximum value to zero at a fixed temperature. The regions labeled "gas" in Figure 7.17 have pressures or concentrations less than the maximum for either component. As the temperature of the gas decreases or as its pressure rises, one or both liquids may appear. One pure liquid coexists at equilibrium with gaseous solution in the regions labeled "gas" and "liquid"; in them, there is one degree of freedom (at constant *T* or *P*) since there are two phases (P = 2) and two components (C = 2). This one degree of freedom is vapor composition, or either pressure or temperature. The pressure at which both liquids coexist with vapor at a given temperature is shown by Figure 7.16 to be fixed. In the upper diagram of Figure 7.17, where the horizontal isobar and the two curves that describe the maximum pressure attained by the gas phase meet, there are three phases ($\mathsf{P} = 3$), namely, two pure immiscible liquids and one gaseous solution. For this two-component ($\mathsf{C} = 2$) system, $\mathsf{F} = \mathsf{C} - \mathsf{P} + 1 = 2 - 3 + 1 = 0$. The lower phase diagram of Figure 7.17 is drawn for the constant pressure of the fixed point ($\mathsf{F} = 0$) of the upper diagram. Once again the mirror-image symmetry is evident.[3]

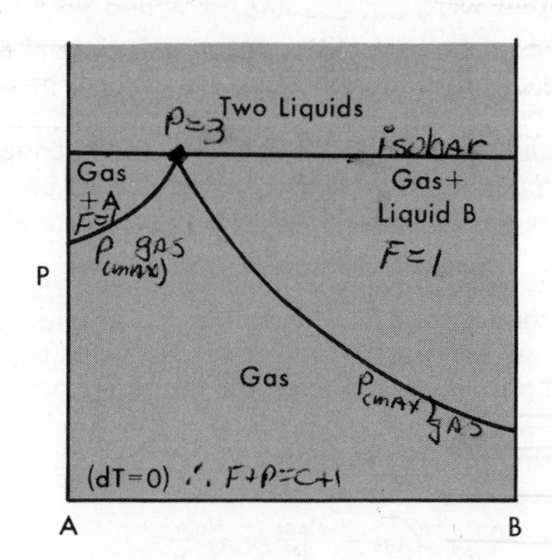

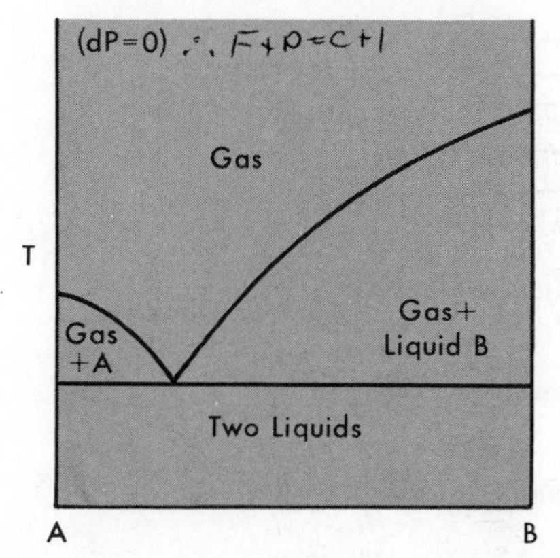

Figure 7.17. Immiscible Liquids

Steam distillation is the artifice by which a low-pressure distillation is performed without vacuum apparatus. Perhaps a substance decomposes at its normal boiling point. If it is volatile, immiscible with water as a liquid, and stable in steam, it can be steam-distilled at a temperature less than 100°C at one atm.

[3] N.O. Smith, *loc. cit.*

The composition of the gas phase is readily calculated from (7.9) and the condition that the sum of the vapor pressures must equal the atmospheric pressure P of the laboratory.

$$Y_i = \frac{p_i}{P} \tag{7.9}$$

$$P = p_A + p_B \tag{7.37}$$

Example 7.5. The vapor pressures of bromobenzene (ϕBr) and water at 80°C are 66.2 and 355.1 mmHg. (*Handbook of Chemistry* [10th Edition] ed. by N.A. Lange and G. M. Forker. New York: McGraw-Hill Book Co., Inc., 1967, pp. 1437, 1473.) The normal boiling point of ϕBr is 156°C. Calculate: (a) the temperature at which ϕBr steam-distills in a laboratory where the barometric pressure is 760 mmHg; (b) the weight percentage of ϕBr in the vapors in such a steam distillation.

(a) The pair of vapor pressures at the pair of temperatures for each component fix a straight line of the form of (6.9) when $\log p$ is graphed as a function of $1/T$. From these two straight lines, trial and error establishes that the sum of the vapor pressures is 760 mmHg at 95.4°C where the vapor pressures are 643 and 117 mmHg.

(b) By (7.9) and the definition of mole fraction,

$$Y_{H_2O} = \frac{p_{H_2O}}{P} = \frac{n_{H_2O}}{\sum_i n_i}; \quad Y_{\phi Br} = \frac{p_{\phi Br}}{P} = \frac{n_{\phi Br}}{\sum_i n_i}$$

Division of one equation by the other yields

$$\frac{n_{H_2O}}{n_{\phi Br}} = \frac{p_{H_2O}}{p_{\phi Br}} = \frac{(W_{H_2O}/M_{H_2O})}{(W_{\phi Br}/M_{\phi Br})}$$

Since the molecular weights are 18.0 and 157,

$$\frac{W_{H_2O}}{W_{\phi Br}} = \frac{p_{H_2O}M_{H_2O}}{p_{\phi Br}M_{\phi Br}} = \frac{643 \times 18.0}{117 \times 157} = 0.630$$

The weight percentage of bromobenzene is, then,

$$100 \times \left(\frac{1.000}{1.000 + 0.630}\right) = 61.4\%$$

7.10 IMMISCIBLE SOLIDS

Phase diagrams like the lower one of Figure 7.17 are common for liquid-solid equilibria in two-component systems. Some of the binary systems in which solubility of pure solid in pure solid is negligible and in which there is only one liquid phase are Al-Sn, Bi-Cd, Bi-Cu, Cu-Li, KCl-AgCl, C_6H_6-CH_3Cl, and

C_6H_6-CH_3COOH. Figure 7.18 is drawn for the Bi-Cd system at constant pressure. Pure Cd melts at 321°C, and pure Bi melts at 271°C. There is only one liquid phase ($P = 1$) at all compositions in this two-component ($C = 2$) system; hence, when only liquid is present, $F = C - P + 1 = 2 - 1 + 1 = 2$. Composition and temperature are independently variable in the area labeled "liquid." As a Bi-rich liquid is cooled, it eventually reaches a temperature at which pure solid Bi comes out of solution. While solid Bi and liquid coexist at equilibrium, there are two phases ($P = 2$) and two components ($C = 2$) so that, $F = C - P + 1 = 1$ and either temperature or composition is independent. The slanted curve that begins at 271°C in Figure 7.18 describes the temperature-dependence of the composition of liquid solutions in equilibrium with solid Bi. Any system with values of temperature and overall composition such that it is in the triangular area at the left consists of solid Bi in equilibrium with liquid solution. The composition of the liquid is given by the slanted line and the com-

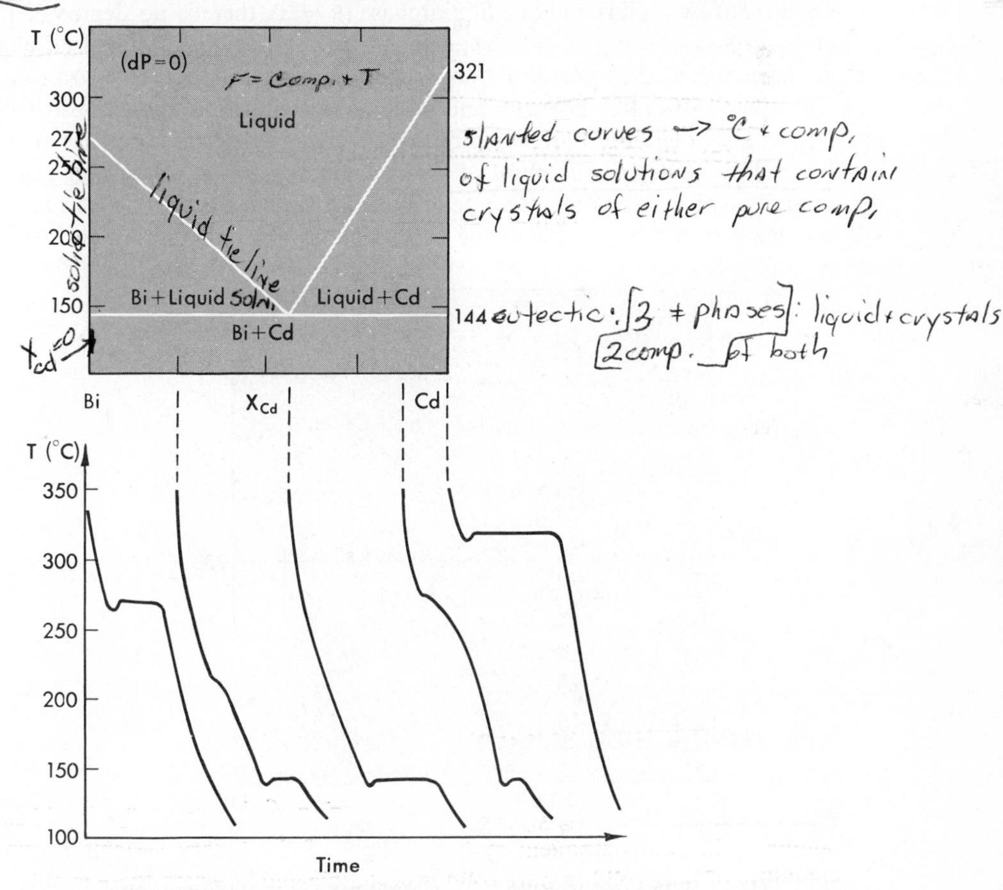

Figure 7.18. Bismuth-Cadmium System at Constant Pressure

position of the solid is given by $X_{Cd} = 0$, the vertical side of the area. Similarly, systems whose temperatures and overall composition locate them in the right-hand triangular area consist of pure Cd crystals and liquid solution. These slanted curves may be considered as the limit of the solubility of Bi or Cd in the liquid or they may be thought of as the observed freezing points of Bi or Cd in the presence of a solute that lowers the freezing point of the pure substances. The slanted curves, then, give the temperature and composition of liquid solutions that contain crystals of either pure component.

At 144°C, a liquid solution of Bi and Cd deposits both pure crystalline components at the same time. The mixture of crystals that results is called a *eutectic mixture* and contains two different phases. The eutectic mixture forms from a solution saturated with respect to both pure components; or, the eutectic mixture forms when the freezing point of the liquid has been lowered as far as possible by adjustments in composition. At the eutectic temperature, in the presence of two solids and one liquid phase ($P = 3$), there is no degree of freedom, for $F = C - P + 1 = 0$. The temperature and compositions of all phases are fixed, just as they were in Figure 7.18.

When things like viscosity and rates of crystallization do not obstruct the attainment of equilibrium, it is common practice to determine a phase diagram by cooling homogeneous melts of various composition at a constant rate. As crystalline phases separate, the rate of decrease in temperature changes, and can become zero if $F = 0$, because the formation of a crystalline lattice furnishes

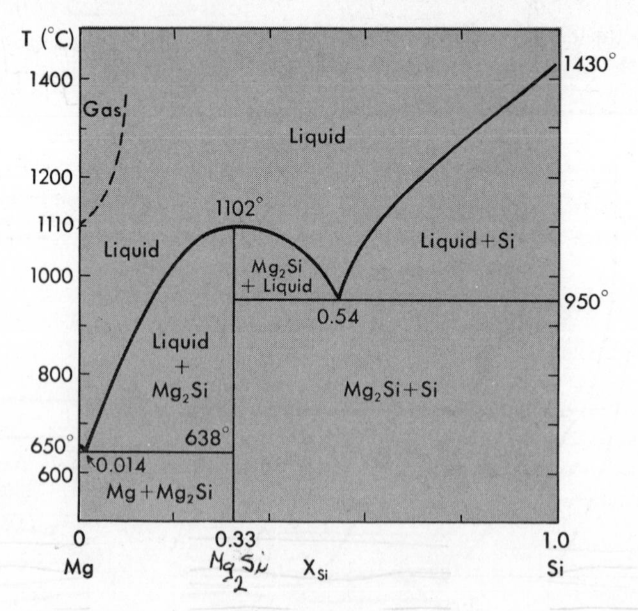

Figure 7.19. Magnesium-Silicon System at Constant Pressure†

†*Metals Handbook*, American Society for Metals, Cleveland, O.: 1948, p. 1226.

thermal energy equal to the heat of fusion. Cooling curves for several mixtures of Bi and Cd are drawn below the phase diagram of Figure 7.18. When $F = 0$, as it does at 144°C for the eutectic mixture or when a pure component freezes, the temperature remains constant. However, when $F = 1$, as it does when the liquid changes continuously in composition as the pure crystals of either component form, the temperature falls, but at a different rate.

Figure 7.19 is the phase diagram of the Mg-Si system. Magnesium forms a compound Mg_2Si with silicon. This compound is a pure substance and is just as eligible to be considered a component as is Mg or Si. If Mg and Mg_2Si were chosen as components, their phase diagram would be the left third of Figure 7.19. This left third is exactly analogous to the phase diagram of the Bi-Cd system in Figure 7.18, just as the right two-thirds is. Here Mg_2Si, if pure, is a one-component system. At 1102°C it melts to form a liquid that will again solidify as Mg_2Si if cooled. At 1102°C for this system there is no degree of freedom when crystalline Mg_2Si is in equilibrium with its melt.

Other systems forming one compound are CCl_4-dioxane (Problem 29), AgCN-KCN, acetic acid-urea, and CaO-ZrO_2. These examples suggest acid-base neutralization or complex formation. As the maximum at the melting point of a compound becomes broader and flatter, the compound is found to be more and more dissociated in the liquid.

When the melting points of two elements differ greatly, as in the Cu-Li system, the eutectic mixture generally contains very little of the high-melting component. However, when there exists a great disparity in melting points of a compound and an element, it is possible for their eutectic mixture to occur at a composition that does not lie at an intermediate value. The eutectic is then called a *peritectic*. The continuous transformation from eutectic E to peritectic P, conceived as a continuous increase in the melting point of B, is shown in Figure 7.20. The system Bi-Au, which exhibits a peritectic like that in Figure 7.20, is shown in Figure 7.21. As the temperature of pure $BiAu_2$ is increased, it decomposes to pure solid Au and liquid with $X_{Au} = 0.36$ at 373°C, and at

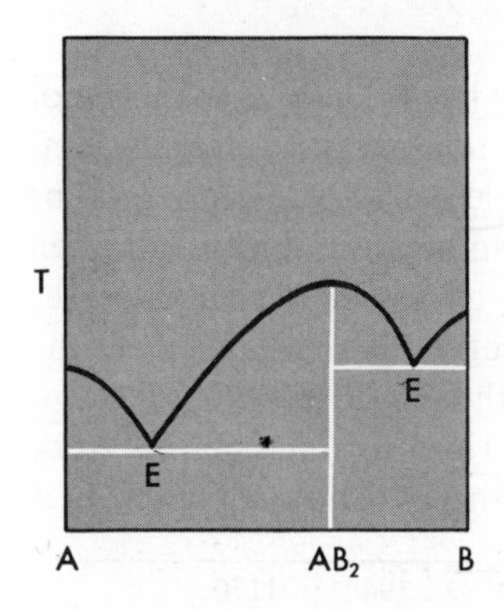

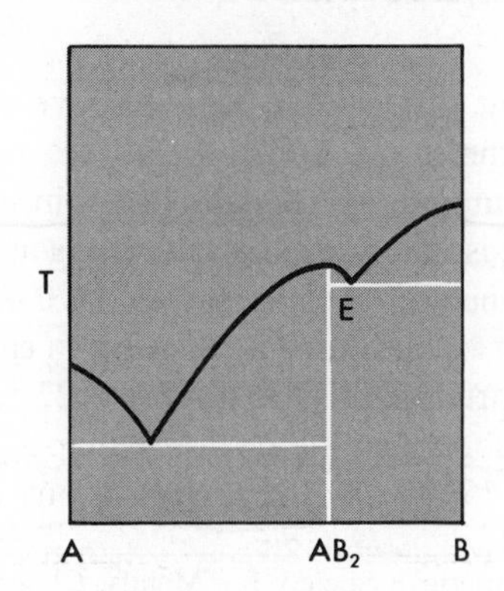

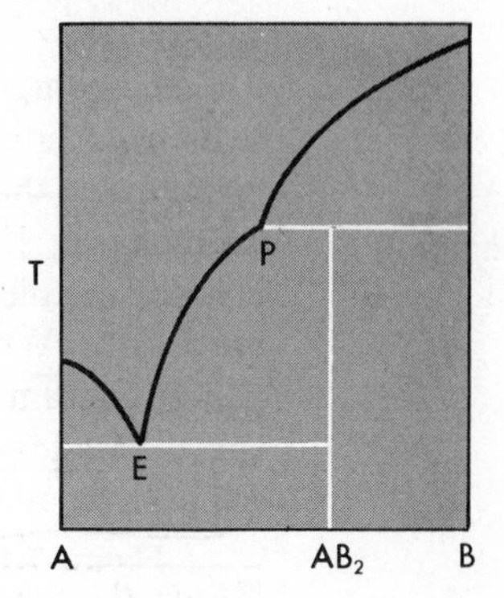

Figure 7.20. The Source of a Peritectic Point *P*

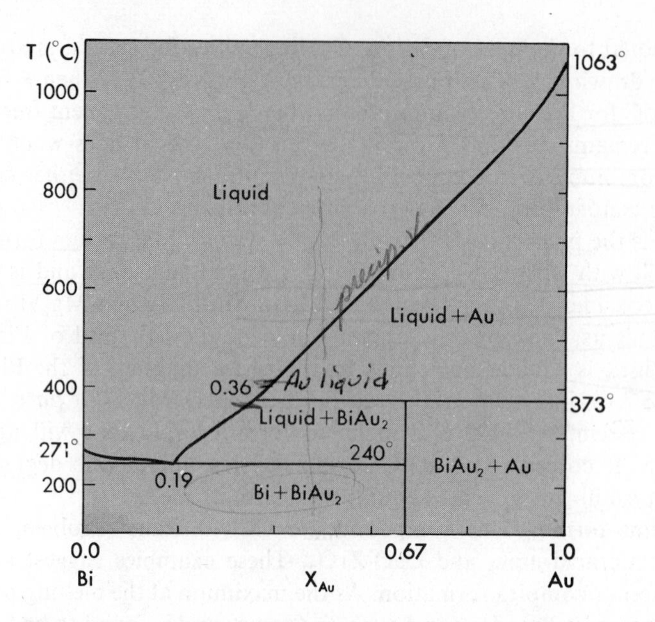

Figure 7.21. Bismuth-Gold System at Constant Pressure†

675°C the Au dissolves in the liquid phase with $X_{\mathrm{Au}} = 0.67$. Cooling a liquid with $X_{\mathrm{Au}} = 0.50$ leads to the precipitation of pure Au at 510°C, to transformation of the Au into $BiAu_2$ at 373°C with some excess liquid, to continued formation of $BiAu_2$ from the liquid, and finally at 240°C to precipitation of $BiAu_2$ and Bi from the liquid, which has become so concentrated in Bi through the formation of $BiAu_2$ that Bi also precipitates.

7.11 PARTIAL MISCIBILITY

The two-component systems considered above have been remarkable in one of two ways: either the liquid and solid phases were homogeneous for all compositions or the components were altogether insoluble in each other in liquid or solid phases. There is, of course, no such thing as absolute insolubility, but often it is reasonable to neglect such things as the 0.05% or less of Bi that dissolves in solid Cd. When two components dissolve in each other to a limited extent the phase diagram is often similar to Figure 7.22 for the Zn-Pb system. The two values of composition given by the dome-shaped curve at any temperature from 417.8°C to about 750°C are the compositions of the two liquid phases that

†*Metals Handbook*, American Society for Metals, Cleveland, O.: 1948, p. 1170.

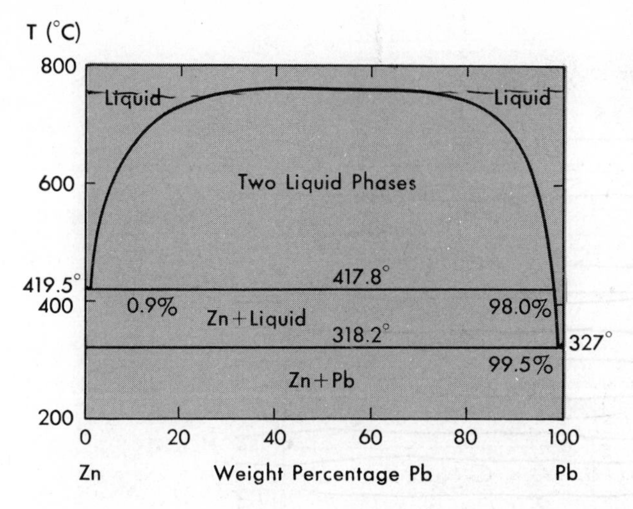

Figure 7.22. Partial Miscibility in the Zinc-Lead System at Constant Pressure†

coexist for overall compositions and temperatures in the region labeled "two liquid phases." Above about 750°C, the *consolute* or *critical solution temperature*, there is only one homogeneous liquid phase for any composition; that is, the two solutions have achieved a common composition and have thus become one phase at about 750°C. This dome-shaped curve thus describes the limited solubility of liquid Zn in liquid Pb or of liquid Pb in liquid Zn at the constant pressure for which the phase diagram is drawn.

Many metals dissolve in their salts and at high T may become miscible in all proportions. As Figure 7.23 shows, this occurs for Bi in $BiCl_3$ above 780°C. If the melting point of Bi were greater, Figure 7.23 would be like Figure 7.21.

The extent of the region exhibiting two liquid phases is readily determined in either of two ways. The composition of the liquid layers that coexist at some temperature can be determined directly, or indirectly since the overall composition of the two-phase system and the amount and composition of each phase are interrelated. Also, the temperature at which a second liquid phase just appears or just disappears in a mixture of known composition may be observed. Sometimes such measurements must be made at elevated pressures to prevent the vaporization of one of the components near the consolute temperature. Like liquids, two solid solutions can achieve a common composition at a consolute temperature.

Figure 7.24 illustrates typical ways in which regions of immiscibility develop from homogeneous solid and liquid solutions as properties of the com-

†*Metals Handbook*, American Society for Metals, Cleveland, O.: 1948, p. 1239.

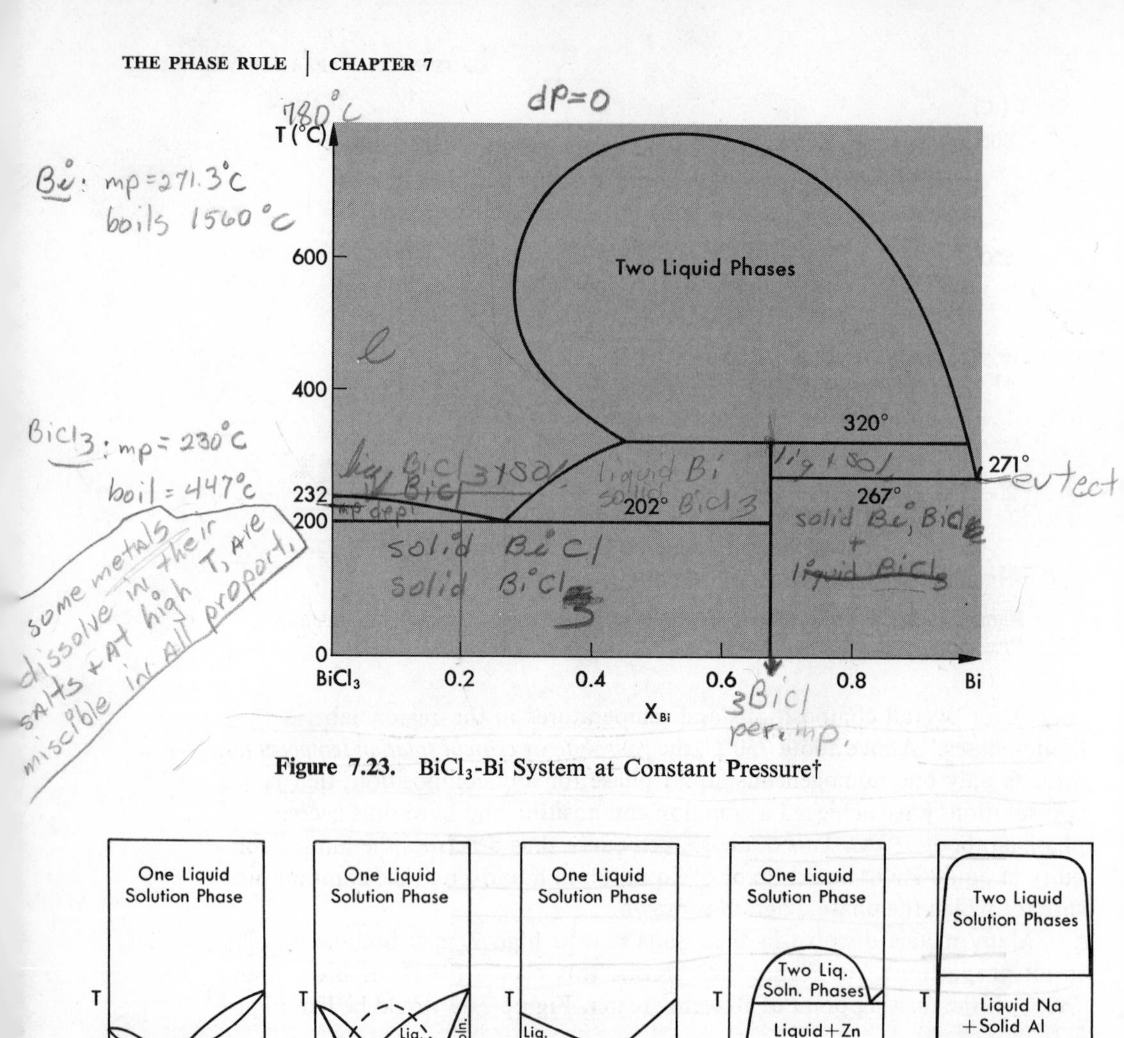

Figure 7.23. $BiCl_3$-Bi System at Constant Pressure†

Figure 7.24. Development of Regions of Immiscibility. (The temperature scales of the diagrams differ.)‡

ponents change. Since absolute insolubility does not occur, the Bi-Cd system is an extreme form of the Ag-Cu system in which solid solutions contain of the order of 10% solute rather than 0.1%. Similarly, the Na-Al system is an extreme version of the Pb-Zn system.

†S. J. Yosim, A. J. Darnell, W. G. Gehman, and S. W. Mayer, *J. Phys. Chem.* **63**, 230 (1959).
‡Data from *Metals Handbook*, American Society for Metals, Cleveland, O.: 1948.

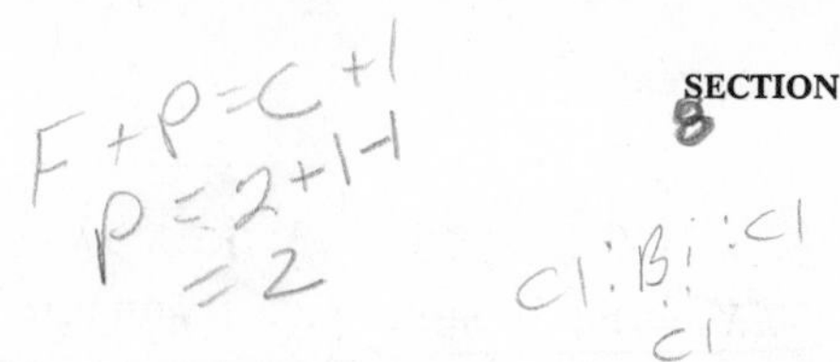

7.12 LEVER LAW

Phase diagrams not only provide quantitative data about temperatures and pressures and qualitative data about the kind and number of phases present, but also provide quantitative information about activities and the amounts of two coexistent phases when the overall composition of the system is known. Serveral typical circumstances of interest are shown in Figure 7.25 and are labeled equivalently so that each is correctly described by the following mathematical development of the so-called *lever law*.

Let X_B be the mole fraction of B in the two-phase binary system; let $X_B^{(1)}$ be the mole fraction of B in phase 1 and let $X_B^{(2)}$ be its mole fraction in phase 2, which coexists with phase 1; let n be the total number of moles of A and B in both phases; and let $n_i^{(j)}$ be the number of moles of component i in phase j. Then,

$$n = n_A^{(1)} + n_A^{(2)} + n_B^{(1)} + n_B^{(2)} \tag{7.38}$$

By (6.18),

$$X_B = \frac{n_B^{(1)} + n_B^{(2)}}{n}; \; X_B^{(1)} = \frac{n_B^{(1)}}{n_A^{(1)} + n_B^{(1)}}; \; X_B^{(2)} = \frac{n_B^{(2)}}{n_A^{(2)} + n_B^{(2)}}$$

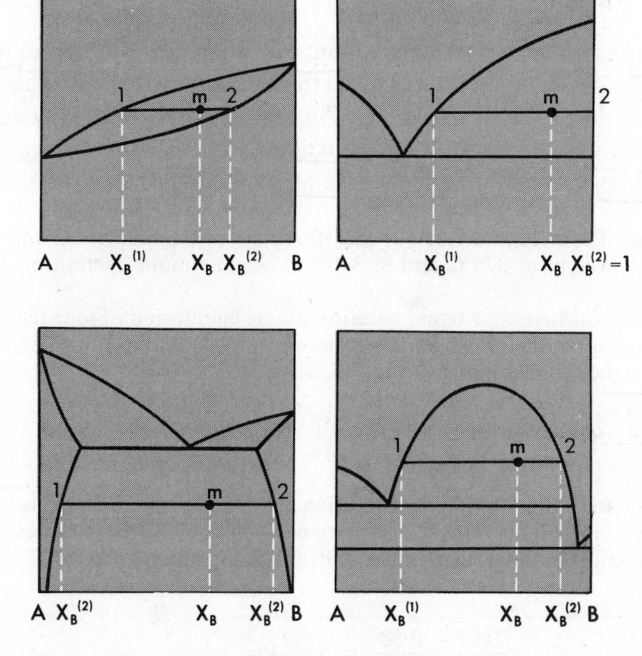

Figure 7.25. Quantitative Interpretation of Phase Diagrams

Whence

$$nX_B = n_B^{(1)} + n_B^{(2)} = [n_A^{(1)} + n_B^{(1)}]X_B^{(1)} + [n_A^{(2)} + n_B^{(2)}]X_B^{(2)}$$

But by (7.38)

$$nX_B = [n_A^{(1)} + n_B^{(1)}]X_B + [n_A^{(2)} + n_B^{(2)}]X_B$$

Equating the expressions for nX_B yields

$$[n_A^{(1)} + n_B^{(1)}]X_B + [n_A^{(2)} + n_B^{(2)}]X_B = [n_A^{(1)} + n_B^{(1)}]X_B^{(1)} + [n_A^{(2)} + n_B^{(2)}]X_B^{(2)} \tag{7.39}$$

Since the moles of A and B in phase 1 are $[n_A^{(1)} + n_B^{(1)}]$ and in phase 2 are $[n_A^{(2)} + n_B^{(2)}]$, it follows from (7.39) that

$$\frac{\text{TOTAL MOLES IN PHASE (1)}}{\text{TOTAL MOLES IN PHASE (2)}} = \frac{n_A^{(1)} + n_B^{(1)}}{n_A^{(2)} + n_B^{(2)}} = \frac{X_B^{(2)} - X_B}{X_B - X_B^{(1)}} \tag{7.40}$$

But $X_B^{(2)} - X_B$ is the length of the line joining points m and 2, while $X_B - X_B^{(1)}$ is the length of the line joining points 1 and m. Hence, if $n^{(1)}$ is the total number of moles in phase 1 and if $n^{(2)}$ is the total number of moles in phase 2, by (7.40),

$$(\overline{m2}) \times n^{(2)} = (\overline{1\,m}) \times n^{(1)} \tag{7.41}$$

As the point m approaches point 2, the amount of phase 1 decreases until, at point 2, only phase 2 exists. Equation (7.41) is the lever law, so called because of its similarity to the lever law of mechanics. An analogous law is readily developed in a similar way when X_B is a weight fraction and the n's refer to weights. The ordinate may be temperature, pressure, or any noncomposition variable.

Example 7.6. From Figure 7.21 for the Bi-Au system, estimate the amounts of the phases present at 375°C and at 370°C when the mole fraction of Au is 0.50.

At 375°C, solid Au and liquid solution are at equilibrium. Since the mole fraction of Au in the liquid is 0.36, the ratio of moles of Au and Bi in liquid to moles of Au (and Bi) in solid is

$$\frac{1.00 - 0.50}{0.50 - 0.36} = \frac{50}{14} = 3.6$$

At 370°C, solid $BiAu_2$ and liquid solution are at equilibrium. Since the mole fraction of Au in the liquid is 0.34 and since each mole of $BiAu_2$ involves three "moles" of Bi and Au, the ratio of moles of Bi and Au in liquid to moles of $BiAu_2$ in solid is

$$\frac{0.67 - 0.50}{\frac{1}{3}(0.50 - 0.34)} = 3\left(\frac{17}{16}\right) = 3.2$$

7.13 THREE-COMPONENT SYSTEMS

In a system of three components ($C = 3$), there may be up to four degrees of freedom, for, by (7.1), when only one phase is present ($P = 1$), $F = C - P + 2 = 3 - 1 + 2 = 4$. If either temperature or pressure is held constant, three or fewer degrees of freedom may occur. Three and four degrees of freedom are awkward for graphing; hence, it is customary to prepare phase diagrams of three-component systems in two dimensions by fixing both temperature and pressure. Then, $F = C - P = 3 - P \leqslant 2$. The two degrees of freedom that remain under these circumstances when $P = 1$ are two composition variables. These two independent variables may conveniently be thought of as two of the three mole fractions, where the third is fixed by

$$\sum_{i=1}^{i=C=3} X_i = 1 \tag{6.19}$$

This condition (6.19) is automatically satisfied by graphing on a set of coordinates fixed by an equilateral triangle. For, in an equilateral triangle, the sum of the three distances drawn from a point within the triangle parallel to each of the three sides is equal to the side of the equilateral triangle. Let *D* be an arbitrary point in an equilateral triangle, as in Figure 7.26. The three dis-

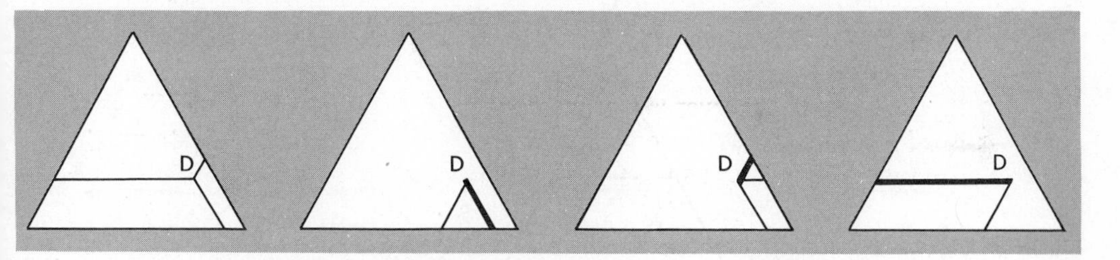

Figure 7.26. A Geometrical Property of an Equilateral Triangle

tances drawn parallel to each of the sides of the triangle are shown at the left. In view of the equality of all sides in any size equilateral triangle and the equality of opposite sides of parallelograms, the sum theorem stated above is obvious from Figure 7.26. A system of coordinates that utilizes this geometrical property is described in Figure 7.27. A point such as *D* represents a system containing 25% A, 10% B, and 65% C. Superposition of these coordinates yields Figure 7.28, wherein the percentages may be by weight, volume, mole, ...

When a diagram like Figure 7.28 contains no curves, the system is homogeneous and contains only one phase. Three-component gaseous mixtures or mixtures of ethanol-methanol-water at room temperature and pressure are

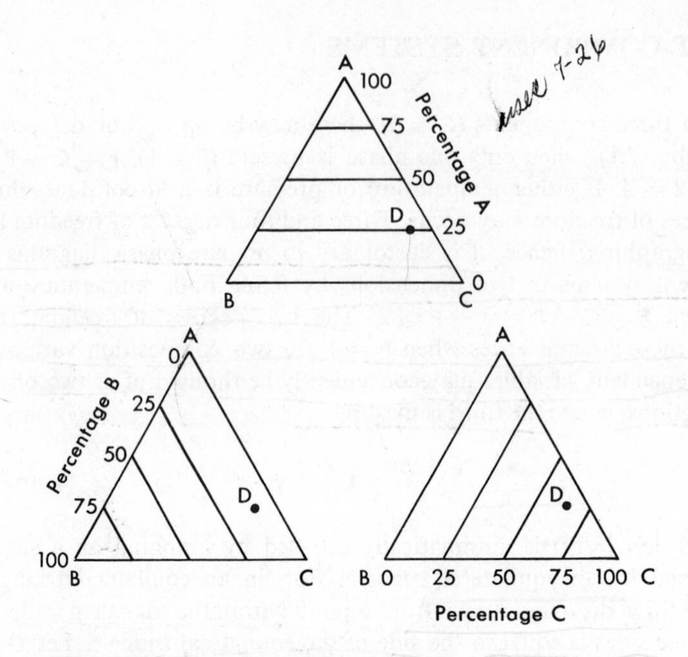

Figure 7.27. A System of Coordinates

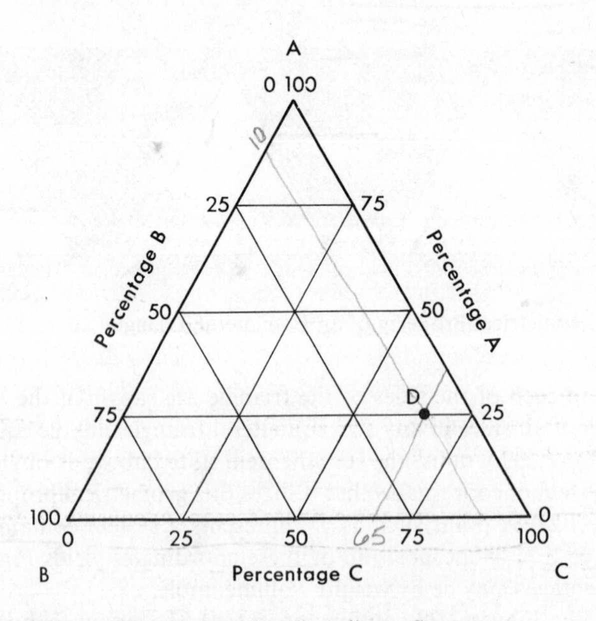

Figure 7.28. Triangular Coordinate System

examples of systems of only one phase. When two phases coexist at equilibrium for certain compositions, a curve with one degree of freedom ($\mathsf{F} = \mathsf{C} - \mathsf{P} = 3 - 2 = 1$) cuts the diagram, as in Figure 7.29. At the temperature and pressure for which this figure is drawn, B and C are only partly miscible in each other; but as component A is added, they become more and more miscible until at point *E*, called a *plait point* or *isothermal critical point*, the system becomes one homogeneous phase. In order to indicate the compositions of coexistent phases, *tie lines* like *FG* are added to the figure. Properly, all two-phase regions should be shown with tie lines. In the region crossed by tie lines there coexist two phases with the compositions given by the ends of the tie lines. The system acetic acid-water-chloroform is like Figure 7.29.

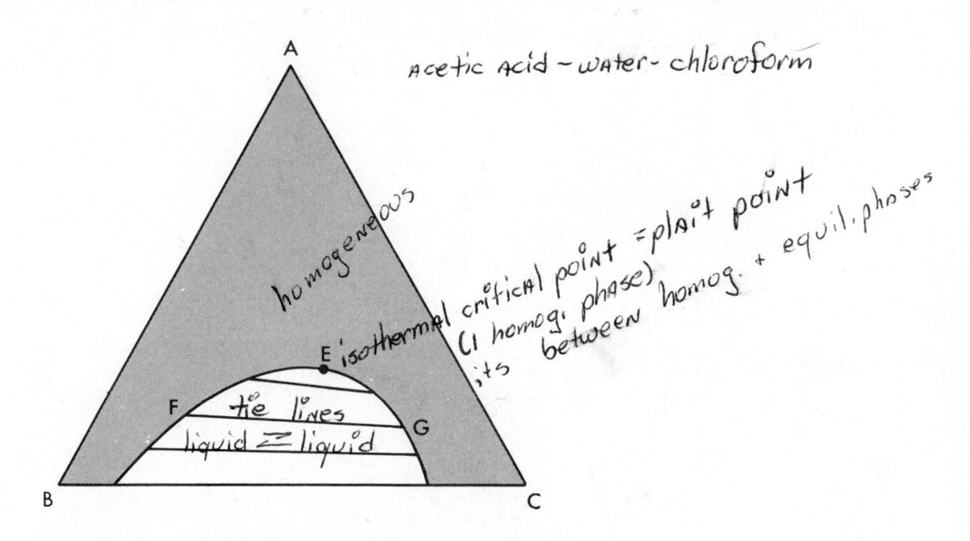

Figure 7.29. Three Components, One Pair Partly Miscible

When two or three pairs of partly miscible components become part of a three-component system, somewhat more complicated diagrams are possible. Figure 7.30 shows the transition in which immiscible regions are pictured as growing in area through changes in the natures of the components or in the temperature. In the regions crossed by tie lines there are two phases, and in the triangular region in the lower right-hand diagram, there coexist three phases with compositions given by the vertices of the triangle. In this latter case, $\mathsf{P} = 3$ and $\mathsf{F} = 0$. Tie lines are absent from both one- and three-phase regions at constant T and P; however, the sides of three-phase regions are always straight.

When the pure components A, B, and C are of different states of aggregation, for example when A is H_2O and B and C are salts or when A and B are liquids and C is a solid, a somewhat different phase diagram is drawn. In the three-component system of Figure 7.31, B is a salt that forms a crystalline hy-

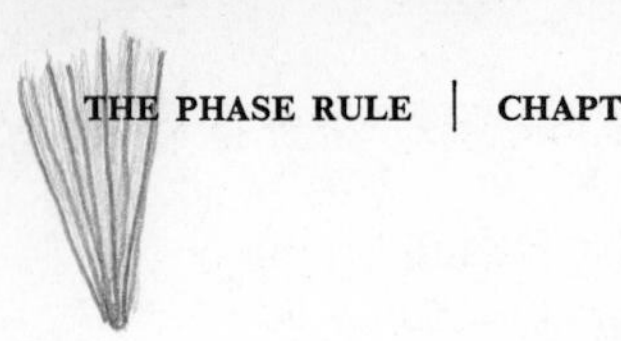

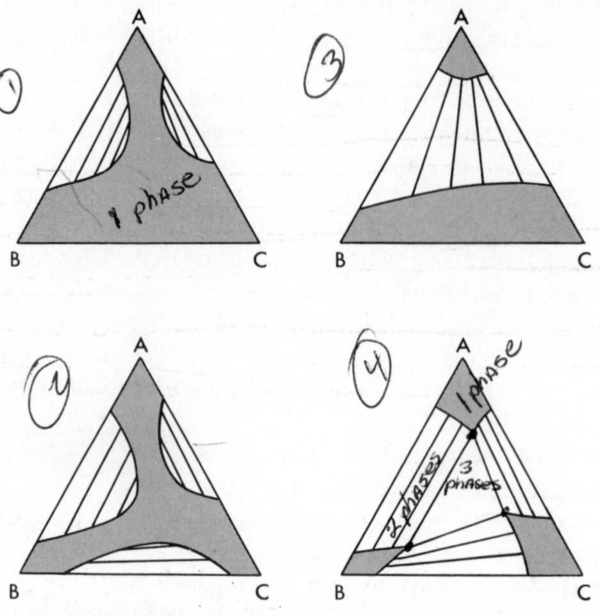

Figure 7.30. Encroachment of Immiscible Regions at Constant Pressure and Temperature

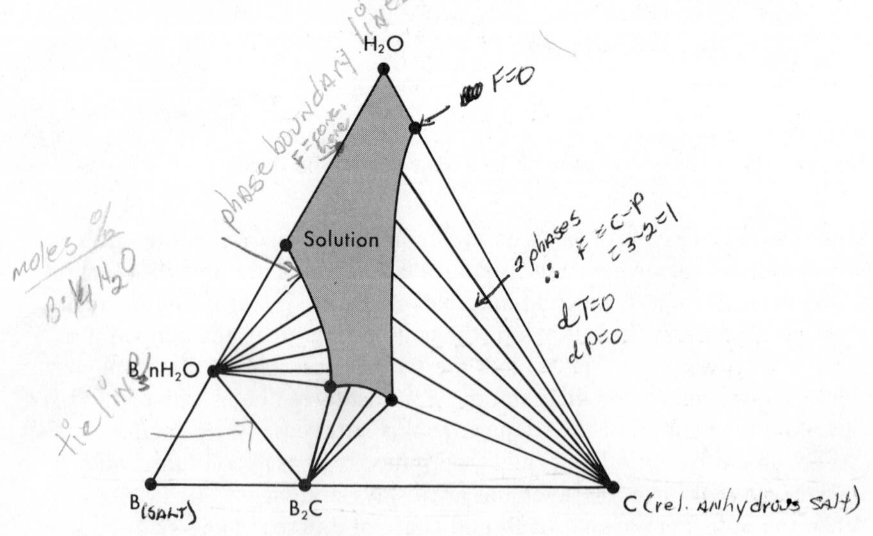

Figure 7.31. Solubilities of $B \cdot nH_2O$, B_2C, and C in H_2O

drate B·n H_2O; C is anhydrous as a salt and is less soluble in H_2O than B; and C and B form a compound B_2C. Tie lines cover regions of one degree of freedom at fixed temperature and pressure ($F = C - P = 3 - 2$), and in the unmarked regions three phases coexist with compositions given by the corners of the triangular area in which the overall composition of the system falls. Points of no degree of freedom are indicated with large dots.

Figure 7.32 represents a system consisting of water W, a salt S, and an organic compound O that is miscible in all proportions with water at the fixed temperature and pressure. The salt S dissolves more in water W than in the liquid organic component O. With a diagram of this sort[4] it is possible to discuss accurately the processes of "salting out" and precipitation of a salt by addition of another solvent. A consideration of the similar triangles involved will verify that any point on a line like SM contains W and O in the same relative proportions. If pure salt S is added to a mixture of composition M, the overall composition will vary along the line MS. When the overall composition corresponds to points within the triangular region, three phases coexist, one of them rich in O. Thus, O has been salted out of M.

When O is added to an aqueous solution of composition N, nothing happens until S begins to precipitate at Q. And when enough O has been added to give compositions within the triangular region, the solid salt S and two liquid layers coexist. Further addition of O would lead to the disappearance of the water-rich liquid layer and eventually to the solution of the salt in a layer very rich in O.

Three-dimensional triangular phase diagrams, in which the third dimension is temperature plotted vertically above a planar diagram like those above, are

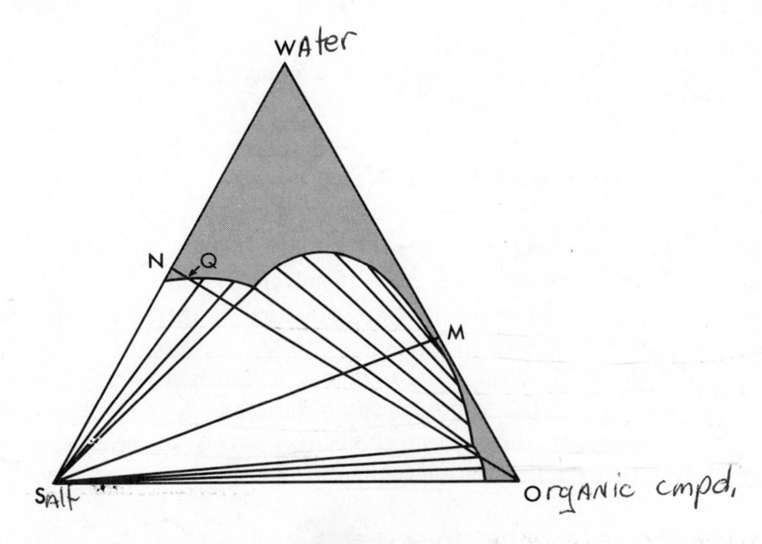

Figure 7.32. Water-Salt-Organic Liquid System

[4] N.O. Smith, *loc. cit.*

valuable in the study of alloys and ceramics. Each of the three vertical faces then represents a temperature-composition phase diagram of a two-component system. Figure 7.33 describes an organic system with two eutectics at 18.8°C and 16.6°C at which three solids and one liquid coexist ($F = C - P + 1 = 3 - 4 + 1 = 0$). One of the solids is the compound $(C_6H_5)_2NH \cdot (C_6H_5)_2CO$ melting at 40.2°C.

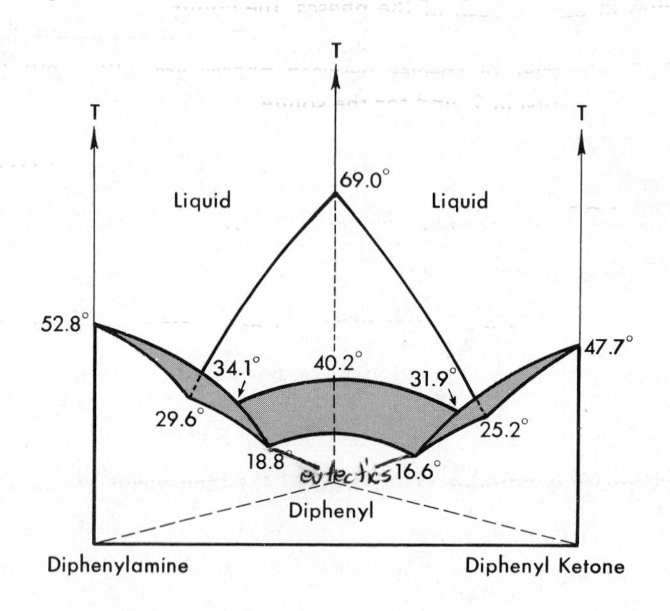

Figure 7.33. Diphenyl-Diphenylamine-Diphenylketone System at Constant Pressure (Fixed temperatures are noted on diagram.)†

WILL DISCUSS FRIDAY

7.14 DISTRIBUTION COEFFICIENT

In a system of three components (solvent 1, solvent 2, and solute; $C = 3$) and two phases (solution 1 consisting largely of solvent 1, solution 2 consisting largely of solvent 2; $P = 2$) at constant pressure and temperature, the phase rule says that there is only one independent intensive variable ($F = C - P = 3 - 2 = 1$). The thermodynamic state of such a system is fixed by specifying just one concentration. If the solute A exists mainly as A in solution 2 and mainly as A_n in solution 1, the concentrations of A and A_n in these phases are related to each other by a distribution coefficient

dependence on Temp. *

$$K = \frac{[A]^n}{[A_n]} \tag{7.42}$$

†H. H. Lee and J. C. Warner, *J. Am. Chem. Soc.* **55,** 209, 4474 (1933).

where the brackets indicate some appropriate units of concentration. The value of K depends mainly on T; its dependence on P is slight. Because A and A_n can both be made out of A if the reaction

$$A_n \longrightarrow nA \tag{7.43}$$

reaches equilibrium in one or both of the phases, the complex or polymer A_n is not a fourth component. At uniform and constant T and P, the equilibrium conditions (6.57) for transfer of species between phases are $\mu_1^{(1)} = \mu_1^{(2)}$ for solvent 1, $\mu_2^{(1)} = \mu_2^{(2)}$ for solvent 2, and for the solute

$$\mu_A^{(1)} = \mu_A^{(2)} \quad \text{or} \quad \mu_{A_n}^{(2)} = \mu_{A_n}^{(1)} \tag{7.44}$$

In solution phase 1, ΔG for (7.43) is, by (6.27) and (6.51),

$$\begin{aligned} \Delta G = G_2 - G_1 &= n\mu_A^{(1)} - \mu_{A_n}^{(1)} \\ &= n\mu_A^{\ominus(1)} + nRT \ln a_A - \mu_{A_n}^{\ominus(1)} - RT \ln a_{A_n} \end{aligned} \tag{7.45}$$

The equilibrium (7.43) in phase 1 requires ΔG to be zero; hence, by (7.45)

$$\Delta G^{\ominus(1)} = \mu_{A_n}^{\ominus(1)} - n\mu_A^{\ominus(1)} = RT\,(n \ln a_A^{(1)} - \ln a_{A_n}^{(1)}) \tag{7.46}$$

Either of the interphase conditions (7.44) with (7.46) then yields (7.42). For example,

$$\begin{aligned} \mu_A^{\ominus(1)} + RT \ln a_A^{(1)} &= \mu_A^{\ominus(2)} + RT \ln a_A^{(2)} \\ \Delta G_A^{\ominus} = \mu_A^{\ominus(2)} - \mu_A^{\ominus(1)} &= RT\,(\ln a_A^{(2)} - \ln a_A^{(1)}) \end{aligned} \tag{7.47}$$

The sum of (7.46) and n times (7.47) is

$$\Delta G^{\ominus(1)} + n\Delta G_A^{\ominus} = RT\,[\ln (a_A^{(2)})^n - \ln a_{A_n}^{(1)}] \tag{7.48}$$

As in (5.83), $\Delta G^{\ominus(1)}$ and $\Delta G_A^{\ominus}$ change very little with pressure if neither phase is a gas; hence, with $a_{A_n}^{(1)} = [A_n]$ and $a_A^{(2)} = [A]$, (7.48) is (7.42). If phase 1 is a gas, $\Delta G^{\ominus(1)}$ is a function only of T and f's replace the $a^{(1)}$'s in (7.46) and (7.47). If phase 2 is a gas, (7.48) yields Henry's law (7.30) for each gaseous species, but in the slightly modified form

$$f_A^n = Ka_{A_n} \tag{7.49}$$

Extraction with solvents is a means of purification that depends upon distribution of a component between phases. An organic chemist may wish to remove a substance from a reaction medium or an analytical chemist may wish to remove impurities from a precipitate. Addition of a solvent immiscible with the impure material permits by filtration, decantation, or use of separatory funnel the separation of immiscible phases, one of which is the desired product or contains it in a volatile solvent.

It is often necessary to minimize the amount of extracting liquor because of its cost or because of difficulty in recovering the product from it. Repeated extraction with several portions of extracting liquor dissolves more product or removes more impurity than one extraction with the same amount of liquor. Let V_2 be the total amount of extracting liquor used, and let the solvents be insoluble in each other. Each of the n extractions uses a volume V_2/n to remove y moles of soluble component from a solution that initially contained n_0 moles dissolved in a volume V_1. As in (7.42), let the distribution coefficient for this extraction be

$$K = \frac{C_1}{C_2} \tag{7.50}$$

For the first of the n extractions, (7.50) reads

$$K = \frac{(n_0 - y_1)/V_1}{y_1/(V_2/n)} \tag{7.51}$$

whence $Ky_1V_1 = (V_2/n)(n_0 - y_1)$ or

$$y_1 = \frac{V_2/n}{KV_1 + (V_2/n)} n_0$$

The moles remaining behind are then, by (7.51),

$$n_0 - y_1 = \frac{KV_1y_1}{(V_2/n)} = \frac{KV_1}{V_2/n}\left[\frac{V_2/n}{KV_1 + (V_2/n)}\right] n_0 = \left[\frac{KV_1}{KV_1 + (V_2/n)}\right] n_0 \tag{7.52}$$

Similarly, after a second extration of y_2 moles from a solution containing $(n_0 - y_1)$ moles in the volume V_1, by (7.52),

$$\begin{aligned}(n_0 - y_1) - y_2 &= \left[\frac{KV_1}{KV_1 + (V_2/n)}\right](n_0 - y_1)\\ &= \left[\frac{KV_1}{KV_1 + (V_2/n)}\right]^2 n_0\end{aligned}$$

After n similar extractions, the amount remaining behind in V_1 is

$$n_0 - \sum_{i=1}^{n} y_i = \left[\frac{KV_1}{KV_1 + (V_2/n)}\right]^n n_0 \tag{7.53}$$

If only one extraction were performed with the total volume V_2, $n = 1$ in (7.53); hence, the amount left behind is

$$n_0 - y_1 = \left(\frac{KV_1}{KV_1 + V_2}\right) n_0 \tag{7.54}$$

In order to show that repeated extractions leave less behind it is necessary to show that in (7.53) and (7.54)

$$n_0 - \sum_{i=1}^{n} y_i < n_0 - y_1$$

That is,

$$\left[\frac{KV_1}{KV_1 + (V_2/n)}\right]^n < \left(\frac{KV_1}{KV_1 + V_2}\right)$$

$$\left[\frac{1}{1 + (V_2/KV_1n)}\right]^n < \left[\frac{1}{1 + (V_2/KV_1)}\right]$$

$$1 + \frac{V_2}{KV_1} < \left(1 + \frac{V_2}{KV_1n}\right)^n$$

By the binomial expansion, the right side becomes

$$1 + \frac{V_2}{KV_1} < 1 + n\left(\frac{V_2}{KV_1n}\right) + \frac{n(n-1)}{2}\left(\frac{V_2}{KV_1n}\right)^2 + \cdots$$

$$0 < \frac{n(n-1)}{2}\left(\frac{V_2}{KV_1n}\right)^2 + \cdots \qquad \text{Q.E.D.}$$

Example 7.7. A solution that occupies a volume of 100 ml and contains 1.0 mole percentage of impurity is to be purified by extraction with a total volume of 1000 ml of extracting solvent that dissolves only the impurity. If the ratio of concentration of impurity in solution to its concentration in extract is 2.00, what mole percentage purity can be obtained by ten and by 100 extractions of equal size?

In the symbols of Equations (7.50) to (7.53), $K = 2.00$, $V_1 = 100$, $V_2 = 1000$, and $n = 10$ or 100. If $n = 10$, the fraction of the impurity that remains unextracted is, by (7.53),

$$\frac{n_0 - \sum_{i=1}^{10} y_i}{n_0} = \left[\frac{KV_1}{KV_1 + (V_2/10)}\right]^{10} = \left[\frac{2.00 \times 100}{2.00 \times 100 + (1000/10)}\right]^{10}$$

$$= \left(\frac{200}{300}\right)^{10} = 0.0173$$

If $n = 100$,

$$\frac{n_0 - \sum_{i=1}^{100} y_i}{n_0} = \left[\frac{2.00 \times 100}{2.00 \times 100 + (1000/100)}\right]^{100} = \left(\frac{200}{210}\right)^{100} = 0.0076$$

Ten extractions yield a purity of 99.983%, while 100 yield a purity of 99.992%, despite the somewhat unfavorable value of distribution coefficient K.

7.15 GAS CHROMATOGRAPHY

Chromatography is any one of several semicontinuous techniques for separating and purifying species from solution by causing the extracting and solution phases to flow past each other in opposite directions. As the phases pass, near-equilibrium is achieved as one or several species distribute themselves between the phases. The name *chromatography* originated with Tswett in 1903–1906; he separated variously colored plant pigments by passing their solution in petroleum ether or CS_2 over a column filled with powdered $CaCO_3$; colored bands of pigments differently adsorbed on the $CaCO_3$ were formed in the tube. The method was first used by Day, who in 1897 separated petroleum into fractions of different color by running it through clay. Many investigators have since contributed to the field.

Partition between liquids usually takes one of two forms. In paper chromatography, an ancient art of qualitative analysis, one liquid phase is held essentially stationary relative to another liquid phase by being absorbed into paper. In the second, a liquid is held in place by adsorption on the surface of a finely divided stationary solid phase. In gas chromatography, however, a gaseous solution passes over a liquid fixed to the wall of a capillary tube or to the surfaces of finely powdered solids packed into a column. As the gas passes, its constitutents enter and leave the liquid. If the gas flow were very slow, the gasous species would be partitioned between liquid and vapor according to Henry's law (7.30) or (7.49). Gases with small K's tend to be left behind in the fixed liquid phase, while those with large K's tend to move along with the gas. As in fractional distillation or zone refining, continued countercurrent flow accentuates the separation. The first published account of gas chromatography as an analytical tool by Martin in 1951 was very soon followed by commercial apparatus in 1955.

Two kinds of gas chromatograph are in common use. For fine resolution of microgram samples, a capillary tube up to about 30 meters long with an internal diameter of about 0.2 mm is coated on the inside with a nonvolatile liquid like a diester of phthalic acid. For routine analysis or even actual separation of macroscopic amounts of material, a five- to fifty-millimeter column packed with liquid-coated particles of fire-brick 0.2 mm in diameter is used. An inert, unabsorbed carrier gas like H_2, He, Ar, N_2, or CO_2 is used to flush the sample through the column after it is injected all at once into the flowing carrier gas. Eventually the whole sample is eluted from the column, slightly absorbed species of high volatility coming forth first, highly absorbed species of low volatility coming forth last. A species is characterized by the time it takes to be eluted or by the volume of carrier gas required to elute it. It is frequently advantageous to increase the column temperature in a calibrated way during a run in order to elute slow species in a reasonable time.

The two most common means of detecting the species eluted in the carrier gas are to note the sudden decreases in thermal conductivity of the effluent gas (H_2 and He are excellent conductors) or to observe the sudden increases in electrical conductivity of a H_2-O_2 flame (uncontaminated, such a flame has few ions). These changes are automatically plotted by a recording potentiometer as functions of time. The time a peak appears after sample injection indicates the kind of species and the area of a peak indicates its amount.

Because the column reduces the flow essentially to one dimension, the diameter of a packed column does not significantly alter the resolution or sharpness of separation. For equal flow rates, a capillary column effects a sharper separation than a packed column because it may have effectively up to a million plates, more than ten times the number of an efficient packed column. On the other hand, a capillary column accommodates only a small sample and thus requires a sensitive, rapid, and efficient detector like the flame-ionization detector.

A measure of the distance over which a sample spreads along a column is the height-equivalent-to-a-theoretical-plate $\bar{H}$. Figure 7.34 lists three factors that affect $\bar{H}$. The first, which is zero in empty capillary columns, is due to the differences in path-lengths among the particles; nonuniform packing and particle size increase the magnitude of this so-called eddy diffusion. The second depends on the diffusion of the carrier gas; it is great for H_2 and He and small for gases of higher molecular weight. The third factor, called the nonequilibrium effect, increases with the thickness of the liquid layer and with the size of the Henry's law constant K; it originates largely from the spread in average velocity v of the gas stream because a molecule is essentially stopped as it takes its turn in the liquid layer. The van Deemter equation (7.55) lists these additive lengths as A, eddy diffusion, as B/v, gaseous diffusion, and as Cv, nonequilibrium of partition.

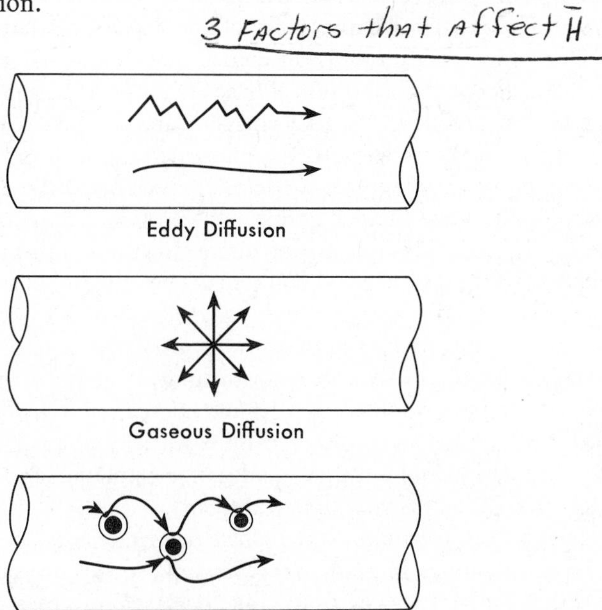

Figure 7.34. Factors Affecting Resolution and Uniformity of Flow Rate in a Packed Column of a Gas Chromatograph

$$\bar{H} = A + \frac{B}{v} + Cv \tag{7.55}$$

A typical $\bar{H}$ for a capillary or packed column of small diameter is 0.5 mm. For a column of fixed length, the greatest number of effective plates occurs when $\bar{H}$ is a minimum, where the gas velocity is

$$v = \left(\frac{B}{C}\right)^{1/2} \tag{7.56}$$

Effects like these and many others are often corrected or accounted for empirically for particular instruments and samples because theoretical treatment is too complicated.

7.16 SUMMARY

The phase rule is one of the difficult subjects of physical chemistry, surely not because of the mathematical operations, but rather because it requires (and gives) a peculiar and uncommonly perspicacious understanding of the essential features of a system at equilibrium. There is no substitute for practice in its use and probably restudy if its power is to be appreciated. It is often the first useful theoretical tool worth trying on a new situation.

Phase diagrams are geometrical expressions of the results of the phase rule for small values of **F**. The phase rule is, of course, not limited to small **F** or to physical rather than chemical equilibrium. Phase diagrams can yield quantitative data that is built into them because they correlate and summarize observations accurately and succinctly. Apparatus for full-scale industrial processes has been designed from one phase diagram; conversely, much industrial experience can be neatly presented in one phase diagram.

Besides explaining the meaning and use of phase diagrams, this chapter has presented the elementary theory of ideal solutions. The entropy of mixing is fundamental to an understanding of entropy as a measure of disorder and to solutions as examples of disorder. The entropy of mixing is, moreover, a perplexing thing that, in Chapter 14, can lead to an understanding of microscopic events beyond the domain of classical mechanics. Fractional distillation and zone refining were compared and found to be essentially alike. Henry's law has been used to keep an integral finite and to describe extraction and chromatography. All in all, this chapter is very practical theory.

Some of the many interesting articles on the phase rule in *Journal of Chemical Education* are: H. G. Deming, **16**, 215, 260 (1939); T. Y. Briggs, **20**, 484 (1943); O. Redlich, **22**, 265 (1945); I. Levin, **23**, 183 (1946); W. Swietoslawski, **24**, 606 (1947); C. A. Hollingsworth, **29**, 464 (1952); F. H. C. Kelly, **31**, 637 (1954); N. O. Smith, **35**, 125, 367 (1958); G. N. Copley, **36**, 596 (1959); J. Mindel, **39**, 512 (1962); G. L. Jones, Jr., **40**, 38 (1963); R. P. Rastogi, **41**, 443 (1964); R. H. Petrucci, **42**, 323 (1965); E. A. Peretti, **43**, 253 (1966).

PROBLEMS

(Vapor pressure and solution data from *Handbook of Chemistry* [10th Edition] ed. by N. A. Lange and G. M. Forker, New York: McGraw-Hill Book Co., Inc., 1967, unless noted otherwise.)

1. An aqueous solution of HCl has 2.00% by weight HCl and a density of 1.016 g ml^{-1}. Calculate its molality and molarity. At constant T and P, as implied here, why are two other intensive variables given?
   Answer: 0.560; 0.557 moles liter^{-1}; for convenience, and because the phase rule does not predict numerical data.

2. Is there any pure substance that can decompose to give more than two phases if the temperature is arbitrarily specified? Explain.
   Answer: Yes, in a field or not at equilibrium.

3. Calculate the number of degrees of freedom at equilibrium:
   (a) Liquid and vapor of a pure substance.
   (b) Oxygen, steam, oxygen dissolved in water at 25°C.
   (c) Ice I; dilute aqueous HCl; N_2, HCl, and H_2O in vapor.
   Give particular reasonable values of the proper number of intensive variables for each situation to fix its state.
   Answer: (a) 1; (b) 1; (c) 2.

4. If the densities of the various kinds of H_2O increase in the order gas, I, Liq., III, II, V, VI, VII, then find the signs of the various ΔH's for the several possible transformations.
   Answer: All $\Delta H > 0$: I $\longrightarrow$ L; I $\longrightarrow$ III; II $\longrightarrow$ III; II $\longrightarrow$ V; III $\longrightarrow$ L; VI $\longrightarrow$ L; V $\longrightarrow$ L; VII $\longrightarrow$ L; L $\longrightarrow$ g; I $\longrightarrow$ g; II $\longrightarrow$ I; V $\longrightarrow$ III; VI $\longrightarrow$ V.

5. Discuss the phase diagram of H_2O and the application of the phase rule by the use of "chemical" equations like $H_2O_{(s)} \longrightarrow H_2O_{(l)}$ with (7.2).

6. A mixture of 30% vol Ne and 70% vol Ar has a total pressure of 650 mm Hg at 70°C in a volume of 3.42 l.
   (a) How many moles of Ar are present?
   (b) What is the density of the mixture?
   Answer: 0.07295 moles; 1.035 g l^{-1}.

7. Explain (as in Section 7.5) why all the molecules of a gas probably will not gather in one small region of their container.

8. The mole fraction of n-hexane in the vapor above a solution of n-hexane and n-heptane is 0.750 at 50°C. What is the composition of the liquid solution? See Example 7.3 for data.
   Answer: Mole fraction of hexane = 0.509.

9. When the total pressure above a certain ideal solution of two volatile components is 400 mm Hg, the mole fraction of one of the components in the vapor is 0.400, while in the liquid it is 0.500. What are the vapor pressures of each of the pure components?
   Answer: 320 and 480 mm Hg.

10. How many grams O_2 dissolve in 600 ml water at 0°C when the partial pressure is 400 mm Hg? See Example 7.5 for data.
   Answer: 0.0220 g.

11. Describe the fractional distillation of an acetone-water solution at 1 atm if the liquid feed, with H_2O mole fraction 0.70, is fed preheated into the next-to-the-bottom plate of a fractional distilling column of six plates.
Answer: Tops at 56.9°C has $Y_A = 0.964$; bottoms at 91.5°C has $X_A = 0.011$.

12. When an organic compound immiscible with water was steam-distilled at 750 mm Hg at 98°C, the vapor contained 50% by weight water. Estimate its molecular weight.
Answer: 296.

13. If the vapor pressure of water at 90°C is 526 mm Hg, how many grams chlorobenzene will be distilled per gram of water collected in the distillate if chlorobenzene is steam-distilled at 90°C at a total pressure of 734 mm Hg?
Answer: 2.47 g.

14. Sketch the temperature-composition phase diagram of the pyridine-formamide system from these data [S. Stephanou, C. A. Vander Werf, and H. H. Sisler, *J. Am. Chem. Soc.*, **70,** 264 (1948)]:
(a) Only one liquid phase exists; no solid solutions or compounds exist, except of course pyridine and formamide.
(b) There is a simple eutectic at 32.3% mole formamide at −56.7°C.
(c) Pure pyridine melts at −41.5°C; pure formamide, at 2.2°C.
(d) Crystals first form from cooling melts thus: at −50°C from 20% mole formamide; −42°C at 40% mole formamide; −22°C at 60% mole formamide; −10°C at 80% mole formamide.
With this sketch, describe what happens when a melt with composition 50% mole formamide cools and what happens when pyridine is added to formamide at −45°C until the system is eventually almost all pyridine.
Answer: F ppt. < -30.5°C; F dissolves at $X_F = 0.38$; P ppt. at $X_F = 0.09$.

15. Sketch qualitatively the phase diagram of the water-ethanol-ethyl acetate system at 0°C and 25°C if water and ethyl acetate are not miscible in all proportions but other pairs are, and if ethyl acetate and water become more soluble in each other (with or without ethanol) as the temperature rises.

16. Show that decreasing the thickness of the liquid film in a packing of a gas chromatograph would probably require an increase in flow rate for most efficient use of the modified column.
Answer: C in (7.56) is decreased.

---

17. Calculate the degrees of freedom at equilibrium, and (if the system exists) give particular examples of observable values of enough intensive variables to specify the state of the system:
(a) At constant pressure, gaseous NH_3 and H_2O, pure ice I, and NH_3 dissolved in liquid water.
(b) Air and its aqueous solution.
(c) At arbitrary constant T and P, liquid O_2 and N_2 (one phase), $O_{2(s)}$, $N_{2(s)}$.
Answer: (a) 0; (b) C; (c) −1 (impossible).

18. At 25°C, the vapor pressure of solid iodine is 0.31 mm Hg and the standard entropies of solid and gaseous iodine are 27.9 and 62.3 cal mole^{-1} deg^{-1} [F. D. Rossini *et al.*, Circular of the National Bureau of Standards 500 (1952)]. If C_p for the solid is 13 cal mole^{-1} deg^{-1} and if I_2 is a rigid diatomic molecule, sketch the chemical potentials of solid and gaseous I_2 as functions of temperature at 1 atm. Then find the temperature at which the solid would sublime at one atm.
Answer: 164°C.

19. What is the minimum amount of isothermal work required to sort out a mixture of distinguishable ideal gases into pure species?
Answer: $-RT \sum n_i \ln X_i$.

20. Calculate the entropy of unmixing of 100 g air considered as 21% vol O_2, 78% vol N_2, and 1% vol Ar.
Answer: $\Delta S = -3.94$ cal deg^{-1}.

21. Calculate the composition of the vapor at 0°C above a solution containing 3 moles $SiCl_4$ and 4 moles CCl_4. At 0°C, the vapor pressures of $SiCl_4$ and CCl_4 are 77.4 and 34.2 mm Hg.
Answer: $Y(SiCl_4) = 0.630$.

22. The vapor pressures of *n*-hexane and *n*-heptane at 0°C are 45.5 and 11.4 mm Hg. What is the composition of a solution of these two substances if its total vapor pressure at 0°C is 37.3 mm Hg?
Answer: $X_6 = 0.760$.

23. At 25°C, 500 ml H_2O dissolve 15.03 ml CH_4 (S.T.P.) under a partial pressure of methane of one atm. If Henry's law holds, what pressure is required to cause 0.00100 mole methane to dissolve in 300 ml water?
Answer: 2.48 atm.

24. At 25°C the total pressure over an ideal two-component solution is 0.360 atm. If the vapor pressure of pure A at 25°C is 0.200 atm while that of B is 0.600 atm, what are the mole fractions of A in this liquid and in the vapor in equilibrium with it?
Answer: $X_A = 0.600$; $Y_A = 0.333$.

25. An ideal solution of two components with vapor pressures of 400 mm Hg and 300 mm Hg when pure contains two moles of the more volatile component and five moles of the less volatile one. Calculate:
(a) The total vapor pressure of the solution.
(b) The composition of the vapor in equilibrium with a solution of this composition.
(c) The composition of the last drop to vaporize from such a solution when none of the vapor is withdrawn from contact with the unvaporized mixture.
(d) The composition of the last drop to vaporize when the distillate from such a solution is continuously condensed elsewhere and is thus withdrawn from contact with the unvaporized mixture.
Answer: (a) 329 mm Hg; (b) $Y_{vol} = 0.347$; (c) $X_{vol} = 0.231$; (d) 0 to 0.231.

26. Aniline ($C_6H_5NH_2$) has a vapor pressure of 18.3 mm Hg at 80°C and 45.5 mm Hg at 100°C. Predict the temperature and vapor composition during steam distillation of aniline at 755.0 mm Hg total pressure. At 98.0°C, the vapor pressure of H_2O is 707.3 mm Hg.
Answer: 98.11°C; $Y_A = 0.0555$.

27. Sketch the temperature-composition phase diagram of the Au-Pb system given [*Metals Handbook*, American Society for Metals, Cleveland, O., 1948, p. 1173]:
(a) Only one liquid phase and no solid solutions exist.
(b) Compounds: Au_2Pb and $AuPb_2$.
(c) Peritectics: 418° at 45% wt Pb; 254° at 72% wt Pb.
(d) Eutectic: 215° at 85% wt Pb.
(e) Melting points: Au at 1063°C; Pb at 327°C.
Label areas of sketch with phases present and describe quantitatively the constitution of these systems:
(f) 40% wt Pb at 418°C, if this *T* is approached from high *T*;

(g) 70% wt Pb at 230°C.
(h) 50% wt Pb at 200°C.
Answer: (f) wt Au = ($\frac{1}{8}$) wt liq.; (g) wt liq. = (0.22) wt $AuPb_2$; (h) wt $AuPb_2$ = (0.88) wt Au_2Pb.

28. Construct the phase diagram of the liquid system aniline-hexane given [D. B. Keyes and J. H. Hildebrand, *J. Am. Chem. Soc.*, **39**, 2126 (1917)] the following temperatures of complete miscibility:

% wt Hexane	T(°C)	% wt Hexane	(T°C)
9.6	26.1°	35.9	59.2
14.8	43.9	41.6	59.4
16.3	45.9	48.0	59.6
20.0	49.9	62.9	57.9
21.0	51.4	73.1	53.9
27.2	56.0	80.6	47.2
31.0	58.2	88.1	35.6
34.6	58.2	93.8	16.5

If 150 g of a mixture containing 80.0% hexane were at 40°C, how much aniline would be in the hexane-rich layer?
Answer: 19.8 g.

29. Construct the constant-pressure phase diagram of CCl_4 (A) and dioxane-1,4 (B) from these melting points [S. M. S. Kennard and P. A. McCusker, *J. Am. Chem. Soc.* **70**, 3375 (1948)]:

X_B	0.000	0.035	0.049	0.060	0.090	0.109	0.141	0.205	0.250	0.284
T(°C)	−22.7	−24.0	−24.6	−24.2	−23.0	−22.4	−21.2	−19.2	−18.6	−18.4

X_B	0.312	0.331	0.349	0.370	0.411	0.472	0.489	0.514	0.556	0.604
T(°C)	−18.4	−18.3	−18.3	−18.4	−18.8	−19.8	−20.0	−17.6	−13.1	−9.9

X_B	0.645	0.713	0.755	0.802	0.846	0.912	0.967	1.000
T(°C)	−7.3	−3.7	−1.6	+0.9	+3.4	+7.0	+10.1	+11.8

What are the compositions and melting temperatures of any eutectics and compounds?
Answer: Eutectics at $X_B = 0.052$ (−24.7°C) and 0.495 (−20.2°C); compound at $X_B = 0.333$ (−18.2°C).

30. Sketch the constant-pressure phase diagram of an alkali metal and its halide if
(a) they form two immiscible liquids up to a consolute temperature of 1100°C;
(b) the metal is almost insoluble in the salt;
(c) a modest amount of the salt dissolves in the metal;
(d) no compounds of metal and salt exist;
(e) the metal melts at 100°C and the salt melts at 1000°C
(f) simple eutectics exist at 90°C and 950°C.

31. From Figures 7.11 and 7.12, calculate the amounts of acetone and water in gaseous and liquid phases when a system consisting of 3 moles acetone and 2 moles water is held at equilibrium:
(a) At 1 atm at 70°C.
(b) At 1 atm at 65°C.
(c) At 13.5 atm at 160°C.
(d) At 13.5 atm at 158°C.
Answer: (a) 71.5% A (gas), 7.7% A (liq).; (b) 78.0% A (gas), 13.0% A (liq.);

(c) all gas; (d) 62.5% A (gas), 32.0% A (liq.); moles gas to moles liq: (a) 4.55; (b) 2.61; (c) ∞; (d) 11.2.

32. From your qualitative knowledge of solubilities, sketch the three-component phase diagram of H_2O, CCl_4, and I_2 at 25°C at one atm, and from it calculate the distribution coefficient of I_2 in two liquid phases.

33. If a volume V of carrier gas at standard conditions (S. T. P.) is required to elute "all" of a species from a gas chromatograph column with a gaseous volume (S. T. P.) of size v, show that (approximately)

$$K = \frac{\text{conc. in liquid phase}}{\text{conc. in gaseous phase}} = \frac{V - v}{V_1}$$

where V_1 is the volume of liquid in the column.

34. State the phase rule for a system simultaneously in gravitational and uniform electrostatic fields. Give concrete examples with a mixture of $He_{(g)}$ and $HCl_{(g)}$ as system.
Answer: F = 5.

35. If $\Delta V = -1.8$ cm³ mole⁻¹ for graphite $\longrightarrow$ diamond at all T and P, calculate ΔH for this change at 2000°K. Compare to $\Delta H^\ominus$ at 25°C and explain the difference.
Answer: $\Delta H \approx -2000$ cal mole^{-1}; $\Delta H^\ominus$ decreases slightly with increasing T, but the nearly constant positive value of dP/dT suggests that $(\partial \Delta H/\partial P)_T < 0$ at all T.

36. What is the density at 37°C and 0.950 atm of air (21% vol O_2; 79% vol N_2) to which have been added: (1) CO_2 so that the final mixture has 3% vol CO_2; or (2) enough H_2O to saturate the gases at 37°C? The vapor pressure of H_2O at 37°C is 47.07 mm Hg.
Answer: (1) 1.095 g l^{-1}; (2) 1.051 g l^{-1}.

37. Calculate the increase in entropy suffered by one l dry air at 1.0000 atm at 25°C as it becomes saturated with H_2O vapor at 25°C by addition of $H_2O_{(g)}$ at its vapor pressure of 23.76 mm Hg:
(a) If the gaseous volume remains constant.
(b) If the total pressure remains constant at 1.0000 atm.
Answer: (a) $\Delta S = 0$; (b) $\Delta S = 0.002737$ cal deg^{-1}.

38. Estimate by a graphical method the temperature at which an equimolar liquid solution of chlorobenzene and bromobenzene will have a total vapor pressure of 1.000 atm. At 110°C the vapor pressure of C_6H_5Cl is 418 mm Hg; at 130°C, 724 mm Hg. At 110°C, the vapor pressure of C_6H_5Br is 198 mm Hg; at 130°C, 373 mm Hg. What will be the composition of vapor?
Answer: 415°K; 64.6% mol C_6H_5Cl.

39. At 37°C, 12.2 ml N_2 (S.T.P.) dissolve in one l water at one atm N_2. What volume of N_2, measured at 37°C at 1.000 atm, will be released by 1 l water as the partial pressure of N_2 falls from 5.00 atm to 0.80 atm? If the Henry's law constant $K(T)$ for He is twice that of N_2, what volume of He will be released under similar conditions? The difference in volumes finds application in deep-sea diving.
Answer: 58.2 ml N_2; 29.1 ml He.

40. Zone-leveling is a technique akin to zone-refining. In it a pellet of a desired solute is added to a short molten zone that eventually passes through a long ingot. If the final concentration of this added solute is to be constant in all but the final end of the ingot, what are the practical conditions on solid-liquid concentrations and on the size of the pellet?

Answer: Solute must greatly prefer liquid phase, and its concentration in liquid must be great enough that it is not appreciably changed during passage along ingot.

41. The normal boiling points of H_2O and D_2O are 100.00°C and 101.42°C. Throughout this problem assume that no HDO is formed and that all solutions are ideal.
(a) Calculate the vapor pressure of D_2O at 100.00°C if its molar heat of vaporization is 9.96 kcal $mole^{-1}$.
(b) Construct a pressure-composition diagram for the H_2O-D_2O system at 100.00°C with liquid and vapor curves.
(c) What would be the composition of the first drop of liquid to form upon condensing a gaseous mixture with mole fraction of D_2O of 0.200 at 100.00°C?
(d) What would be the composition of the first vapor to form upon vaporization of a liquid mixture with mole fraction of D_2O of 0.200 at 100.00°C?
(e) About how many theoretical plates would be required to separate a mixture of D_2O and H_2O into solutions that contain each species 95% mole pure?
Answer: (a) 721.3 mmHg; (c) 20.87% mol D_2O; (d) 80.81% mol D_2O; (e) ~100.

42. How much steam must be *furnished* to steam-distill one mole of a substance with a normal boiling point of 200°C and a molar heat of vaporization of 10.0 kcal $mole^{-1}$? The steam-distillation is done at a total pressure of 760 mm Hg and the vaporization is adiabatic, all thermal energy coming from steam at 100°C at one atm. Assume that the liquids are perfectly immiscible.
Answer: 18.33 moles $H_2O_{(g)}$.

43. The normal boiling point of cymene ($C_{10}H_{14}$) is 175.0°C. On a day when the atmospheric pressure was somewhat less than 760 mm Hg, an ideal solution of several nonvolatile substances in cymene boiled at 176.8°C. On the same day at the same total pressure, steam distillation of the same solution at 96.4°C, where the vapor pressure of water is 667.3 mmHg, gave a distillate containing 44.7% by weight cymene and 55.3% by weight H_2O. What was the vapor pressure of cymene above the same solution at 50°C? What was the mole fraction of cymene in the same solution?
Answer: 11.2 mmHg; 0.932.

44. Sketch the phase diagram of the HF-KF system from these facts [G. H. Cady, *J. Am. Chem. Soc.*, **56**, 1431 (1934)]:
(a) The transition temperature for α-KHF_2 to β-KHF_2 occurs at 195°C.
(b) α-KHF_2, β-KHF_2, and liquid HF are in equilibrium at 195°C when the overall mole percentage of HF is 53.82.
(c) Compounds and melting points: KF, 880°C; β-KF·HF, 239.0°C; KF·2 HF, 71.7°C; 2 KF·5 HF, 64.3°C; KF·3 HF, 65.8°C; KF·4 HF, 72.0°C; HF, −83.7°C.
(d) Eutectic temperatures and mole percentages of HF: −97°C at 93.11%; 63.6°C at 77.1%; 62.4°C at 72.7%; 61.8°C at 69.69%; 68.3°C at 64.9%; 229.5°C at 48.60%. Describe what happens at 65.0°C as KF is gradually added to liquid HF until the mixture is mostly KF.

45. From the phase diagram of the Al-Zn system as compiled by The American Society for Metals, explain in detail what happens as a melt containing:
(a) Three moles Zn to 7 moles Al is cooled reversibly to 100°C.
(b) 90% by weight Zn is cooled reversibly to 100°C.
(c) Pure zinc at 500°C has Al added to it until the weight percentage of Al is 80%.

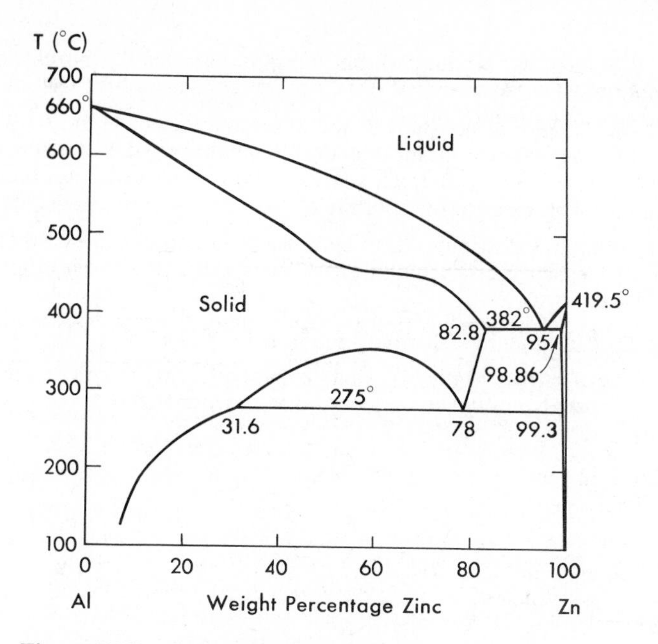

Figure 7.35. Aluminum-Zinc System†

46. What compounds of Nb and Sn exist at 0°C at one atm according to Figure 7.36? At 700°C in a system with $X_{Sn} = 0.500$ at equilibrium at one atm, what phases are present?

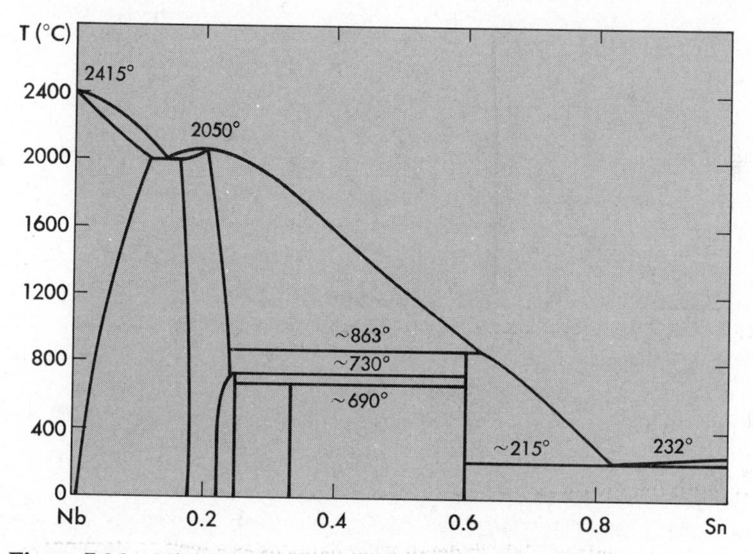

Figure 7.36. Niobium-Tin System at Constant Pressure‡

†*Metals Handbook*, American Society for Metals, Cleveland, O.: 1948, p. 1167.
‡L. L. Wyman, J. R. Cuthill, G. A. Moore, J. J. Park, and H. Yakowitz, *J. Res. Nat. Bur. Stds.* **66A,** 351 (1962).

Answer: At 0°C, Nb_4Sn, Nb_3Sn, Nb_2Sn, Nb_2Sn_3; at 700°C, Nb_3Sn and Nb_2Sn_3.

47. Sketch the phase diagram at constant T and P for the system H_2O, A, B, at 20°C if these hydrates dissolve in and remain in equilibrium with the aqueous solution: $A \cdot H_2O$; $A \cdot 3\,H_2O$; $A \cdot B \cdot H_2O$; $2\,B \cdot H_2O$. Pure A and B cannot remain at equilibrium in the presence of the solution.

48. At 25°C at one atm, H_2S distributes itself between water and benzene so that its concentration in the benzene-rich liquid phase is six times its concentration in the aqueous phase.
(a) Besides T and P, how many independent intensive variables are there in this two-phase system?
(b) If ionization of H_2S is negligible, what volume of benzene will extract in one step 95.0% of the H_2S in 100 ml of 0.100 molar aqueous H_2S?
Answer: (a) $F = 1$; (b) 317 ml C_6H_6.

8

COLLIGATIVE PROPERTIES

8.1 INTRODUCTION

This chapter explains why and how ionized and unionized solutes affect the vapor pressure, boiling point, freezing point, and osmotic pressure of a solution. The explanation is thermodynamic, and thus deals with average properties as though matter were a continuum. However, there is an obvious correlation of these effects with the number of solute particles, and thus there exists a microscopic or molecular explanation of these phenomena.

A *colligative property* is one that varies according to the number of particles without regard to their kind. The pressure of a pure perfect gas or of an ideal mixture of pure perfect gases is such a colligative property when volume and temperature are constant.

The molecular weight of a perfect gas is a number-average molecular weight defined by the equation

$$\bar{M}_N = \frac{\sum_i (m_i N_0) N_i}{\sum_i N_i} \tag{8.1}$$

where m_i is the mass of one of the N_i particles, and where $\sum_i N_i$ is the total number of particles in the system. If $m = m_i$ is the same for all particles, clearly $\bar{M}_N = m\, N_0$; however, if the substance is a mixture, then $\bar{M}_N$ depends on how many of each kind are present. Equation (8.1) is merely the standard formula for an average, namely, the sum of the items $m_i N_0$ to be averaged divided by the total number of items. It is sometimes convenient to write (8.1) in the equivalent integral form

$$\bar{M}_N = \frac{\int_0^\infty (mN_0)\phi_N(m)\,dm}{\int_0^\infty \phi_N(m)\,dm} \tag{8.2}$$

The function $\phi_N(m)$ in (8.2) is the distribution function for masses of molecules, and its meaning is that $\phi_N(m)\,dm$ is the number (like N_i) with mass between m and $m + dm$.

Sometimes a property like viscosity of a polymer solution or the amount of polymer eluted from a chromatographic column by a certain amount of solvent is used as a measure of molecular weight. It is then possible and often very instructive to calculate a molecular weight that may differ from a number-average one. For example, the weight-average molecular weight is defined as

$$\bar{M}_W = \frac{\sum_i (m_i N_0) W_i}{\sum_i W_i} \tag{8.3}$$

or, if the distribution is considered continuous, as

$$\bar{M}_W = \frac{\int_0^\infty (mN_0)\phi_W(m)\,dm}{\int_0^\infty \phi_W(m)\,dm} \tag{8.4}$$

In (8.3), W_i is the mass of material with molecules each of mass m_i. (A separate experiment on samples of uniform and known mass per molecule is used to establish the correlation of W_i with m_i through a third variable like the volume of solvent needed to elute the species from a certain chromatographic column.) Similarly, in (8.4), $\phi_W(m)\,dm$ is the mass of material with molecules each of mass from m to $m + dm$. Since $W_i = N_i m_i$, it follows from (8.3) that

$$\bar{M}_W = \frac{\sum_i (m_i N_0) N_i m_i}{\sum_i N_i m_i} = \frac{\sum_i (m_i N_0)^2 N_i}{\sum_i (m_i N_0) N_i}$$

which differs from $\bar{M}_N$ when the m's are not all alike for every particle. The ratio of $\bar{M}_W$ to $\bar{M}_N$ is a measure of the extent to which the values of m_i differ within a system.

A gaseous molecular weight is a number-average molecular weight because at fixed T and V the pressure of a perfect gas is proportional to the number of molecules. Since a colligative property also counts independent particles one by one, a molecular weight found from any colligative property is a number-average molecular weight.

Example 8.1. Calculate and compare the number-average and weight-average molecular weights of a polymer solute if, by previous calibration with samples of uniform molecular weight, the masses W_i of polymer now eluted by certain volumes of solvent are known to have these molecular weights $M_i = N_0\, m_i$:

W_i (grams)	1.00	2.00	3.00	5.00	3.00	2.00	1.00
$M_i \times 10^{-6}$	2.00	1.50	1.20	1.00	0.80	0.50	0.20

The weight-average molecular weight is, by (8.3) with $M_i = m_i\, N_0$ and $\sum W_i = 17.00$,

$$\bar{M}_W = \left(\frac{2.00 + 3.00 + 3.60 + 5.00 + 2.40 + 1.00 + 0.20}{17.00}\right) \times 10^6$$

$$= 1.01 \times 10^6$$

On the other hand, since the number of polymer molecules of molecular weight M_i is $N_i = N_0 W_i / M_i$, it follows from (8.1) with $M_i = m_i\, N_0$ that

$$\bar{M}_N = \frac{\sum_i W_i}{\sum_i W_i/M_i}$$

$$= \left(\frac{17.00}{0.50 + 1.33 + 2.50 + 5.00 + 3.75 + 4.00 + 5.00}\right) \times 10^6$$

$$= 0.770 \times 10^6$$

It is clear from (8.1) and (8.3) and this example that a number-average molecular weight stresses species of low molecular weight while weight-average molecular weight emphasizes species of high molecular weight.

8.2 VAPOR PRESSURE LOWERING

Because of the discrete nature of matter, when the vapor pressure of a substance becomes small enough, it becomes less a pressure and more a measure of the probability that a molecule will or can escape. It is often verified experimentally that the influence of the vapor of a certain compound appears to be negligible. If so, for all practical purposes, its vapor pressure $p_i^{\cdot}$ is effectively zero. The vapors above many solutions are essentially only those of the liquid solvent so that, if species 1 is the solvent, Raoult's law degenerates thus:

$$p_i = X_i p_i^{\cdot} = 0, \quad (i \neq 1) \tag{8.5}$$

$$p_1 = P = X_1 p_1^{\cdot} \tag{8.6}$$

In other words, if only species 1 is volatile, p_1 is the total pressure P. Let X_2 be the sum of the mole fractions of the nonvolatile species. Then, by (6.19), $X_1 = 1 - X_2$, where X_1 is the mole fraction of the volatile species 1. By (8.6)

$$p_1 = (1 - X_2)p_1^{\cdot} = p_1^{\cdot} - X_2 p_1^{\cdot}$$

Whence,

$$X_2 = \frac{(p_1^{\bullet} - p_1)}{p_1^{\bullet}} \tag{8.7}$$

Since X_2 measures the numbers of nonvolatile molecules relative to all molecules present, (8.7) says that the vapor pressure lowering $(p_1^{\bullet} - p_1)$ is proportional to the fraction of nonvolatile molecules. A property like this that varies according to the number of particles without regard to their kind is a *colligative property*.

Example 8.2. Exactly 100 g water contain 1.000 g urea and 2.000 g sucrose at 25°C. At 25°C, the vapor pressure of water is 23.756 mm Hg. (*Handbook of Chemistry* [10th Edition], ed. by N. A. Lange and G. M. Forker. New York: McGraw-Hill Book Co., Inc., 1967, p. 1471.) Predict the vapor pressure of the solution.

If X_2 is the summation of mole fractions of all nonvolatile components then

$$X_2 = \frac{(1.000/60.06) + (2.000/342.3)}{(100.0/18.02) + (1.000/60.06) + (2.000/342.3)}$$

$$= \frac{0.01665 + 0.00584}{5.5508 + 0.017 + 0.006} = \frac{0.02249}{5.574} = 0.00404$$

By (8.7), $p_1^{\bullet} - p_1 = 0.00404 \times 23.756 = 0.096$ mm Hg and

$$p_1 = p_1^{\bullet} - 0.096 = 23.660 \text{ mm Hg}$$

Note that use of (8.6) to obtain this result requires great calculational accuracy.

8.3 BOILING POINT ELEVATION

A solution of one volatile component boils when its vapor pressure, namely, that of its volatile component, equals the pressure of the surrounding atmosphere. The vapor pressure p_1 of an ideal solution of one volatile component is less than $p_1^{\bullet}$, that of the pure volatile component, because in (8.7) $p_1^{\bullet}$ and X_2 are positive quantities. Figure 8.1 shows that the boiling point T_b of such a solution is greater than the boiling point T_0 of the pure solvent species 1. Although pressure and fugacity may differ in real gases, the approximations to follow in this derivation justify assuming ideal behavior of gas and liquid solution despite the deviations expected from ideal behavior. For an ideal gas, $p_1 = f_1$ and (6.50) becomes

$$\mu_1^{(g)} = RT \ln p_1 + \mu_1^{\ominus(g)} \tag{8.8}$$

For the volatile solvent 1, if the solution is ideal,

$$\mu_1^{(l)} = RT \ln X_1 + \mu_1^{\ominus(l)} \tag{8.9}$$

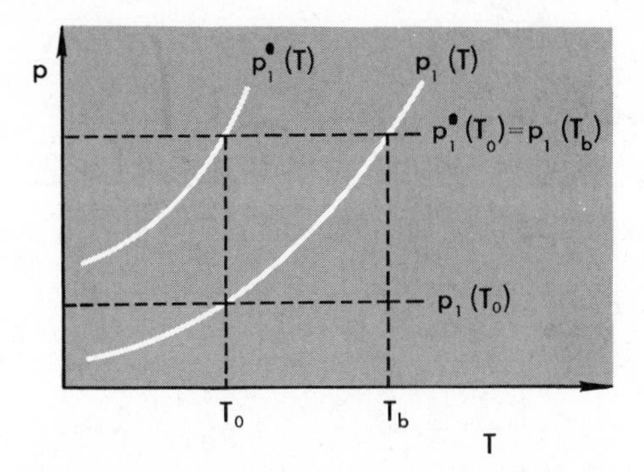

Figure 8.1. Boiling Point of a Solution

When vapor and liquid solution are in equilibrium at the boiling point, the chemical potentials of the volatile solvent, which is really present in both phases, are equal. Hence, by (8.8) and (8.9),

$$RT \ln p_1 + \mu_1^{\ominus(g)} = RT \ln X_1 + \mu_1^{\ominus(l)}$$

Since $p_1 = 1$ atm at the boiling point,

$$\mu_1^{\ominus(g)} - \mu_1^{\ominus(l)} = RT \ln X_1 \tag{8.10}$$

As in (5.76),

$$\frac{\bar{H}_i}{T^2} = -\left[\frac{\partial}{\partial T}\left(\frac{\mu_i}{T}\right)\right]_P \tag{8.11}$$

Hence, by (8.10) in (8.11),

$$-\left\{\frac{\partial}{\partial T}\left[\frac{\mu_1^{\ominus(g)}}{T} - \frac{\mu_1^{\ominus(l)}}{T}\right]\right\}_P = \frac{\bar{H}_1^{\ominus(g)}}{T^2} - \frac{\bar{H}_1^{\ominus(l)}}{T^2}$$

$$= -\left[\frac{\partial}{\partial T}(R \ln X_1)\right]_P = -R\left(\frac{\partial \ln X_1}{\partial T}\right)_P$$

But $\bar{H}_1^{\ominus(g)} - \bar{H}_1^{\ominus(l)}$ is just the molar heat of vaporization of the standard-state solvent from the solution. For ideal solutions and approximately for dilute nonideal solutions, this heat of vaporization is just ΔH_v for the pure solvent. Hence,

$$-R\left(\frac{\partial \ln X_1}{\partial T}\right)_P = \frac{\Delta H_v}{T^2} \tag{8.12}$$

Equation (8.12) is readily integrated, for $X_1 = 1$ when the boiling point is T_0; that is,

$$-\int_0^{\ln X_1} d(\ln X_1)' = \int_{T_0}^{T_b} \frac{\Delta H_v}{RT^2}\, dT$$

If ΔH_v is independent of temperature,

$$-\ln X_1 = \frac{\Delta H_v}{R}\left(-\frac{1}{T_b} + \frac{1}{T_0}\right) = \frac{\Delta H_v(T_b - T_0)}{RT_bT_0} \tag{8.13}$$

Since, as in Section 8.2, the mole fraction of all solutes is $X_2 = 1 - X_1$, (8.13) yields

$$-\ln(1 - X_2) = \frac{\Delta H_v(T_b - T_0)}{RT_bT_0} \tag{8.14}$$

When $-1 < x < 1$, $-\ln(1 - x) = x + x^2/2 + \cdots$. Since $0 < X_2 \ll 1$, the first term of this series expansion is sufficient. And since T_b is approximately equal to T_0 for common solvents, (8.14) becomes

$$X_2 \approx \frac{\Delta H_v(T_b - T_0)}{RT_bT_0} \approx \frac{\Delta H_v(T_b - T_0)}{RT_0^2} \tag{8.15}$$

Since the molality m_2 of nonvolatile solutes is related to their mole fraction X_2 by the approximate relation

$$X_2 = \frac{n_2}{n_1 + n_2} \approx \frac{1}{n_1}\left(\frac{W_2}{M_2}\right) = \frac{M_1}{W_1}\left(m_2 \times \frac{W_1}{1000}\right) = \frac{M_1 m_2}{1000}$$

it follows that the boiling point elevation $\delta T_b = T_b - T_0$ is

$$\left.\begin{aligned} \delta T_b &= K_b m_2 \\ K_b &= \frac{RT_0^2 M_1}{1000\,\Delta H_v} \end{aligned}\right\} \tag{8.16}$$

Table 8.1 Calculated Values of Ebullioscopic Constants K_b.

Solvent	ΔH_v(Pure)† (Cal Mole^{-1})	T_0† (°K)	M_1	K_b
H_2O	9720	373.16	18.02	0.514
SO_2	5960	263.14	64.07	1.480
NH_3	5580	239.73	17.03	0.348
CCl_4	7170	349.9	153.84	5.22
$CHCl_3$	7020	334.4	119.39	3.78
CH_3OH	8430	337.9	32.04	0.862
C_2H_5OH	9220	351.7	46.07	1.227
C_6H_6	7350	353.3	78.11	2.642
$C_6H_5CH_3$	8000	383.8	92.13	3.370
n-C_8H_{18}	8360	398.8	114.22	4.318

† Data taken from: Rossini, F. D., D. D. Wagman, W. H. Evans, S. Levine, and I. Jaffe, *Selected Values of Chemical Thermodynamic Properties*. Washington, D. C.: Circular of the National Bureau of Standards 500 (1952); Rossini, F. D., K. S. Pitzer, W. J. Taylor, J. P. Ebert, J. E. Kilpatrick, C. W. Beckett, M. G. Williams, and H. G. Werner, *Selected Values of Properties of Hydrocarbons*. Washington, D. C.: Circular of the National Bureau of Standards C461 (1947).

The value of the ebullioscopic constant K_b depends only on the properties of the solvent: T_0 its normal boiling point; M_1, its molecular weight; and ΔH_v, its molar heat of vaporization. Table 8.1 contains calculated values of ebullioscopic constants for several common solvents. The value for water is a matter of memory for students of general chemistry.

Example 8.3. Calculate the boiling point of the solution of Example 8.2 at 1.000 atm.

The molality of nonvolatiles is 0.2249. By Table 8.1 and (8.16), $\delta T_b = 0.514 \times 0.225 = 0.115°C$. The boiling point is predicted to be 100.115°C.

The elevation δT_b in the boiling point is a colligative property because it depends through (8.16) on the number of independent particles of solute. When a substance dissolves without association or dissociation, as urea and sucrose do in water, the value of δT_b is predicted correctly. However, when the molecular weight of solute used to calculate its molality does not correspond to the weight of the solute species that actually exist in the solution, (8.16) leads to a false prediction. For example, a substance that ionizes when dissolved produces more than one solute particle per formula weight; its δT_b is observed to be greater than predicted. Carboxylic acids generally dimerize through the formation of hydrogen bonds when dissolved in nonpolar solvents; for such solutions, δT_b is observed to be less than predicted.

Observation of δT_b for a solution permits the calculation of a number-average molecular weight of solute as it exists in solution. Equation (8.16) provides an estimate of m_2, and (6.16) yields M_2, the effective number-average molecular weight of solute. In order to avoid changes in boiling temperature due to changes in atmospheric pressure or to impurities in the solvent, it is common to determine simultaneously the boiling points of solvent and solution with accurately compared thermometers.

Example 8.4. When 764 mg of a nonvolatile solute were dissolved in 120 g benzene, its boiling point was raised by 0.083°C. What is the molecular weight of the solute?

By (8.16), $m_2 = (\delta T_b/K_b) = (0.083/2.64) = 0.0314$. By (6.16),

$$M_2 = \frac{W_2 \times 1000}{m_2 \times W_1} = \frac{0.764 \times 1000}{0.0314 \times 120} = 203$$

8.4 FREEZING POINT DEPRESSION

If two phases coexist at equilibrium in a two-component system, there are two degrees of freedom ($F = C - P + 2 = 2 - 2 + 2$). One of these, the pressure, is commonly taken to be about one atm because of the way experiments are ordinarily performed. The other independent variable is either temperature or composition. Equations (8.16) for boiling point elevation assert that at equilibrium both temperature and composition cannot be independent as a solution boils. An equation of the same sort links the freezing point of a solution and its composition.

When a pure solid component is deposited from a solution because the solution begins to freeze or because the solution is saturated with respect to that component at the temperature of the solution, the chemical potential of that pure solid is its reference value at that temperature; that is,

$$\mu_1^{(s)} = \mu_1^{\ominus(s)} \tag{8.17}$$

The chemical potential of this component 1 as it exists in solution, either as a solvent or solute, is

$$\mu_1^{(l)} = RT \ln X_1 + \mu_1^{\ominus(l)} \tag{8.18}$$

At equilibrium, the chemical potentials of components really present in two phases are equal by (6.57); hence by (8.17) and (8.18), $\mu_1^{(s)} = \mu_1^{(l)}$ and

$$\mu_1^{\ominus(s)} - \mu_1^{\ominus(l)} = RT \ln X_1 \tag{8.19}$$

When $X_1 = 1$ in (8.18), the chemical potential of the liquid is its value in the pure state. Accordingly, the value of $\mu_1^{\ominus(l)} - \mu_1^{\ominus(s)}$ is just the molar free energy of fusion at the freezing point T_f of the solution. When $X_1 = 1$ in (8.19) this molar free energy increment is of course zero and the temperature is the normal freezing point T_0. By (8.11) and (8.19),

$$-\left[\frac{\partial}{\partial T}\left(\frac{\mu_1^{\ominus(s)} - \mu_1^{\ominus(l)}}{T}\right)\right]_P = \frac{\bar{H}_1^{\ominus(s)} - \bar{H}_1^{\ominus(l)}}{T^2} = -\left[\frac{\partial}{\partial T}(R \ln X_1)\right]_P$$

But $\bar{H}_1^{\ominus(l)} - \bar{H}_1^{\ominus(s)}$ is the molar heat of fusion of the component that crystallizes so that

$$R\left(\frac{\partial \ln X_1}{\partial T}\right)_P = \frac{\Delta H_f}{T^2} \tag{8.20}$$

Definite integration at constant pressure from the freezing point T_0 of pure component 1 ($X_1 = 1$) to the state when $T = T_f$ at $X_1 < 1$ yields

$$\int_0^{\ln X_1} d(\ln X_1)' = \int_{T_0}^{T_f} \frac{\Delta H_f}{RT^2}\, dT$$

If ΔH_f is independent of temperature,

$$\ln X_1 = \frac{\Delta H_f}{R}\left(-\frac{1}{T_f} + \frac{1}{T_0}\right) = \frac{\Delta H_f(T_f - T_0)}{RT_fT_0} \tag{8.21}$$

By the same methods used in proceeding from (8.13) to (8.16) it follows that

$$\left.\begin{aligned} \delta T_f &= K_f m_2 \\ K_f &= \frac{RT_0^2 M_1}{1000\,\Delta H_f} \end{aligned}\right\} \tag{8.22}$$

Here δT_f is the freezing point depression caused by the presence of solute. If the solution is ideal at all concentrations, (8.21) describes the solubility of component 1 in any solvent at the temperature T_f if T_0 is the melting point of pure component 1.

Table 8.2 Values of Some Cryoscopic Constants K_f

Component That Crystallizes	ΔH_f (Pure)† (Cal Mole^{-1})	T_0† (°K)	M_1	K_f
Water	1436.3	273.16	18.02	1.862
Benzene	2350	278.7	78.11	5.12
Cyclohexane	637	279.7	84.16	20.5
Acetic acid	2800	289.8	60.05	3.58

† See Table 8.1 for references.

Table 8.2 lists values of the cryoscopic constant K_f as calculated by (8.22). Once again the value for water is the empirical value memorized by freshmen.

Like the elevation in boiling point, the depression of freezing point is a colligative property in that it depends only upon the number of particles through the molality m_2. A measurement of δT_f with a solvent of known K_f yields an experimental value of molality m_2 through (8.22). With known masses of solute and solvent, an average molecular weight of noncrystallizing components can then be calculated through (6.16). When K_f is large, as it is for camphor and cyclopentadecanone, even a dilute solution provides a great δT_f and ultimately an accurate molecular weight M_2. However, for solvents with large cryoscopic constants K_f, it is advisable to determine the melting point of the solvent before adding solute lest the presence of impurities give a falsely large δT_f.

Measurements of freezing point depressions are preferred to measurements of boiling point elevations because the effect of pressure variations on condensed phases is negligible. When multijunction thermocouples are used to record directly the difference in freezing points of pure solvent and solution by using the solution as cold junction and pure solvent as hot junction, values of δT_f may be reported to within about 0.00002°C. Mercury thermometers record temperatures within about 0.001°C. In order to make such measurements meaningful, it is necessary to analyze the solution that exists in equilibrium with pure crystalline solvent. Spontaneous crystallization withdraws solvent, concentrates the solution, and leads ultimately to too low a value of solution freezing point or unknown molecular weight of solute. If a solution tends to supercool, this change in concentration can be serious, since the first seed crystal leads at once to many crystals if supercooling is appreciable. When it is not possible to analyze the solution in equilibrium with crystalline solvent, the freezing point of the solution is taken as the temperature at which crystals first appear or just dissolve.

Previous discussions of phase diagrams have mentioned some of the situations in which liquids and solids can coexist at equilibrium. In view of the several kinds of behavior noted in the examples given in those previous sections, it should be clear that the freezing point of a pure substance is not always greater than its solution. Nonideal behavior is most simply treated by recourse to a phase diagram, which after all is merely an orderly record of experiments. The fortunate set of circumstances that make crystals of ice almost incapable of forming solid solutions do not apply in general to most solids. One of the very few substances enough like ice in bonding and unit cell size to form solid solutions with ice is NH_4F; up to 6.5% mol NH_4F dissolves in ice at 244.5°K.[1]

Example 8.5. A sample of camphor used in the Rast method of determining molecular weights had a melting point of 176.5°C. The melting point of a solution containing 0.522 g camphor and 0.0386 g of an unknown was 158.8°C. If the unknown compound was a hydrocarbon containing 7.7% H, what was its molecular formula? The K_f of camphor is 37.7.

By (8.22) and the value of K_f of camphor,

$$m_2 = \frac{\delta T_f}{K_f} = \frac{176.5 - 158.8}{37.7} = 0.470$$

By (6.16),

$$M_2 = \frac{W_2}{m_2} \times \frac{1000}{W_1} = \frac{0.0386 \times 1000}{0.470 \times 0.522} = 157$$

The empirical formula is found to be CH thus:

$$\frac{0.077/1.008}{0.923/12.01} = \frac{\text{H}}{\text{C}} = 0.995 \approx 1.0$$

Since 157/13 is about 12, the molecular formula is $C_{12}H_{12}$.

Example 8.6. Verify that the triple point of pure water, pure ice I, and pure water vapor is +0.01°C. Exactly zero degrees Celsius is defined as the temperature achieved by a mixture of pure ice and water in equilibrium with air at one atm.

Exactly zero degrees is lower than this triple point because of the effect of dissolved gases on the freezing point and because of the influence of pressure on the melting point of ice. The former effect is calculated by (8.22) and the result of Example 7.4, which found the molality of dissolved gases to be 1.29 $\times 10^{-3}$; hence,

$$\delta T_f = 1.862 \times 1.29 \times 10^{-3} = 0.0024°\text{C}$$

[1] L. C. Labowitz and E. F. Westrum, Jr., *J. Phys. Chem.* **65**, 408 (1961).

The latter effect is calculated by the Clapeyron equation (6.5) as in Example 6.2; hence,

$$\delta T = \left(\frac{T\Delta V}{\Delta H}\right)\delta P = \frac{273.2 \times (-0.0907)}{3290}(0.0060 - 1.0000) = 0.0075°\mathrm{C}$$

Since these effects are independent and additive, the triple point in the system of pure H_2O is calculated to be 0.0075°C + 0.0024°C, or +0.0099°C.

Example 8.7. The atomic heats of fusion of Bi and Cd are 2630 cal and 1460 cal, respectively. The melting point of pure Bi is 271°C and that of pure Cd is 321°C. [F. D. Rossini *et al.*, National Bureau of Standards Circular 500 (1952)] Calculate the eutectic temperature and its composition in the Bi-Cd system. (See Figure 7.18.)

At the eutectic temperature, one liquid solution is in equilibrium with pure solid Bi and pure solid Cd. Let X_{Cd} be the mole fraction of Cd in the ideal liquid solution, and let T be the eutectic temperature. Then, by (8.21),

$$-\ln X_{Cd} = \frac{1460 \times (594 - T)}{1.987 \times 594 \times T}$$

Similarly, for the ideal solution considered as saturated with Bi,

$$-\ln(1 - X_{Cd}) = \frac{2630 \times (544 - T)}{1.987 \times 544 \times T}$$

Solution of these simultaneous equations for N_{Cd} and T yields the result, which can be verified by substitution:

$$X_{Cd} = 0.564$$

$$T = 406°\mathrm{K}, \quad \text{or} \quad 133°\mathrm{C}$$

The value of Figure 7.18 is 144°C.

8.5 OSMOSIS

Osmosis is the process by which a solvent or some species of a solution passes through a membrane that is not permeable to other species of the solution. At equilibrium, the chemical potentials of the components that can penetrate the membrane are equal on the two sides of the membrane just as the chemical potential of a species in two coexisting phases is the same in both. There is, however, no restriction on the chemical potentials of components that cannot pass through the membrane. When the phases in contact with the membrane are at the same temperature and yet differ in concentration, equilibrium can be achieved by the imposition of pressure on one of the phases. The membrane must be mechanically strong enough to support this difference in pressure. It also conducts heat so that T can be uniform across the membrane.

The extraordinary pressure that must be exerted upon a solution to increase the chemical potential of that component which penetrates the membrane to the chemical potential of the pure component at a fixed temperature is the *osmotic pressure* of the solution. The osmotic pressure equalizes the chemical potentials on both sides of the membrane and thus establishes equilibrium with respect to the permeating species. Without a difference in pressure, this species would pass spontaneously through the membrane from the phase of high chemical potential to the solution where its chemical potential is lower. Osmotic pressure is a property of the solution and does not depend upon the nature of a membrane that is truly semipermeable or upon the theory or mechanism of operation of that membrane.

The chemical potential $\mu_1(T, P, X_1)$ of species 1 in a solution where its mole fraction is X_1 at some temperature T at any pressure P can be found from the isothermal diagram

ONE MOLE 1 (STANDARD STATE) $\mu_1^\ominus(T, P^\ominus)$	$\xrightarrow{(a)}$	ONE MOLE 1 (SOLUTION) $\mu_1(T, P^\ominus, X_1)$	$\xrightarrow{(b)}$	ONE MOLE 1 (SOLUTION) $\mu_1(T, P, X_1)$

For reversible isothermal compression of the solution in process (b), (6.48) yields

$$\mu_1(T, P, X_1) - \mu_1(T, P^\ominus, X_1) = \int_{\mu_1(T, P^\ominus, X_1)}^{\mu_1(T, P, X_1)} d\mu_1 = \int_{P^\ominus}^{P} \bar{V}_1 dP' \tag{8.23}$$

If the solution is ideal, (7.19) for process (a) requires

$$\mu_1(T, P^\ominus, X_1) - \mu_1^\ominus(T, P^\ominus) = RT \ln X_1 \tag{8.24}$$

Relative to species 1 in its standard state at $P^\ominus$ and T, its chemical potential in an ideal solution at P and T is, by (8.23) and (8.24),

$$\mu_1(T, P, X_1) = \mu_1^\ominus(T, P^\ominus) + \int_{P^\ominus}^{P} \bar{V}_1\, dP' + RT \ln X_1 \tag{8.25}$$

The conditions for equilibrium across a semipermeable membrane that passes species 1 between solution phases (1) and (2) are $T^{(1)} = T^{(2)} = T$ and $\mu_1^{(1)} = \mu_1^{(2)}$. Because of (8.25) in each phase, this condition on μ_1 is

$$\int_{P^\ominus}^{P^{(2)}} \bar{V}_1^{(2)}\, dP' + RT \ln X_1^{(2)} = \int_{P^\ominus}^{P^{(1)}} \bar{V}_1^{(1)}\, dP' + RT \ln X_1^{(1)} \tag{8.26}$$

If the ideal solutions touching the membrane are incompressible and sufficiently alike, $\bar{V}_1 = \bar{V}_1^{(1)} = \bar{V}_1^{(2)}$ is independent of pressure and (8.26) becomes simply

$$\bar{V}_1(P^{(2)} - P^{(1)}) = RT \ln \frac{X_1^{(1)}}{X_1^{(2)}} \tag{8.27}$$

The pressure difference $(P^{(2)} - P^{(1)})$ is the osmotic pressure Π of solution phase (2) provided phase (1) is pure species 1; hence, with $X_1^{(1)} = 1$ and $P^{(1)} = P^{\ominus}$, the osmotic pressure of solution phase (2) is

$$\Pi = -\frac{RT}{\bar{V}_1} \ln X_1 \tag{8.28}$$

where X_1 and $\bar{V}_1$ are the mole fraction and partial molar volume of species 1 in the solution. The pressure Π is the mechanical pressures in excess of $P^{\ominus}$ that must be exerted on the solution at T to make the chemical potential of the permeating species 1 in the solution equal to that in the pure species 1 beyond the membrane. With Raoult's law (7.18), it follows from (8.28) that

$$\Pi = \frac{RT}{\bar{V}_1} \ln \frac{p_1^{\cdot}}{p_1} \tag{8.29}$$

where p_1 is the observed vapor pressure of the solution at T at a pressure of about $p_1^{\cdot}$. Equation (8.29) is often accurate when the solution is not ideal because p_1 is an observed value.

The approximate methods of Sections 8.3 and 8.4 yield for dilute solutions an approximate equation for Π found empirically, in part by Dutrochet in 1826, and fully by van't Hoff in 1885. From (8.28),

$$\frac{\Pi \bar{V}_1}{RT} = -\ln X_1 \approx X_2 \approx \frac{n_2}{n_1} \quad (n_2 \ll n_1)$$

If $n_1 \bar{V}_1 = V$, the volume of solvent or approximately the volume of solution, then

$$\Pi V = n_2 RT \tag{8.30}$$

Since Π is proportional to n_2, osmotic pressure is classed as a colligative property because it depends on the number of dissolved particles and not on their kind.

The magnitudes of the osmotic pressures produced by even dilute solutions are great. Some of the earliest experiments performed by Abbé Nollet in 1748 involved the passage of so much water through an animal membrane into a solution of ethanol, sugar, and water that the membrane sometimes burst. The preparation of a strong membrane that was truly semipermeable to water was last at achieved by the botanist Pfeffer in 1877. He formed membranes of colloidal cupric ferrocyanide as Traube had already done, but he did so in porous ceramic pots by soaking them in cupric sulfate and then in potassium ferrocyanide. Such membranes supported by a ceramic are able to support a few hundred atmospheres pressure without damage and were used by the modern experimenters H. N. Morse and J. C. W. Frazer (1901–1923) and the Earl of Berkeley and E. G. J. Hartley (1906–1909).

The technique of Berkeley and Hartley was elegant. In Figure 8.2, which is a diagram of their apparatus, M is a ceramic tube that supports the membrane of $Cu_2Fe(CN)_6$. The annular space between M and the outer tube was filled with solution, the apparatus was placed in a thermostat, and the ceramic tube M was filled with solvent from a reservoir R until its level in the capillary stood at a fixed mark C. Pressure was then exerted on the solution through a piston in order to prevent osmosis. When the solvent level remained at the mark C, indicating no loss or gain of solvent by osmosis, the pressure exerted on the solution was its osmotic pressure Π. Thus the solution was not diluted by osmosis and equilibrium was achieved swifty. In modern commercial osmometers,

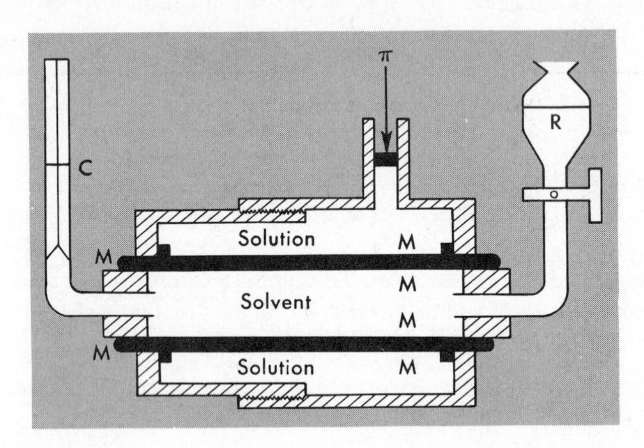

Figure 8.2. Diagram of Osmotic Pressure Apparatus of Berkeley and Hartley

an osmotic pressure can be observed in about ten minutes. Some of the Berkeley-Hartley measurements of osmotic pressure of solutions of sucrose and α-methylglucoside at 0°C are presented in Table 8.3. Also tabulated are values of Π

Table 8.3 Observed and Calculated Values of Osmotic Pressure at 0°C for Aqueous Solutions of Sucrose and α-Methylglucoside. (*International Critical Tables of Numerical Data, Physics, Chemistry, and Technology*, National Academy of Sciences–National Research Council, Washington, D.C., 1926–1933. *III*, *p*. 293; *IV*, *p*. 430.)

	Sucrose				α-Methylglucoside			
	p_1	Π	Π	Π	p_1	Π	Π	Π
Molality	(obs.) (mm Hg)	(obs.) (atm)	(8.29) (atm)	(8.30) (atm)	(obs.) (mm Hg)	(obs.) (atm)	(8.29) (atm)	(8.30) (atm)
1.0	4.489	24.76	24.76	22.4	—	25.0	—	22.4
2.0	4.381	54.9	55.0	44.8	4.384	53.8	54.2	44.8
3.0	4.257	90.0	90.6	67.2	4.273	86.4	86.1	67.2
4.0	4.132	129.7	128.8	89.6	4.159	120.2	119.7	89.6

predicted by (8.29) and (8.30). The exact thermodynamic equation (8.29) is well verified when $\bar{V}_1$ is assumed to be that for pure water, 0.01802 l.

The cause of osmosis is the difference in chemical potentials of the component that can penetrate the semipermeable membrane. The mechanism by which this component passes through the semipermeable membrane is an unsettled theoretical matter. The solute bombardment theory proposed by van't Hoff is not satisfactory. Although the form of (8.30) suggests an analogy with an ideal gas, it is necessary to picture the solute molecules as pushing the membrane against the solvent during osmosis and thus forcing solvent to enter the solution. But the solute particles are not free like gas molecules and, if solute molecules bombard the membrane, so also must solvent molecules. The three main theories of the mechanism of osmosis consider the solvent as distilling through pores in the membrane, as dissolving in the membrane, or as proceeding through the membrane as through a sieve. This last theory, the molecular sieve theory, is particularly appealing for solutions of polymers. It is quite likely that all these theoretical aspects of the mechanism are true in part and that any particular example of osmosis is described most suitably by emphasis on one of the three.

Osmosis is of paramount importance in biology. The walls of plant and animal cells are membranes permeable to water and to some of the solutes that occur in the fluids surrounding cells. If the surrounding fluid is more concentrated in solutes that do not penetrate the cell membrane than is the fluid within the cell, the cell loses fluid by osmosis. Such a surrounding solution is termed *hypertonic*, and, as it shrinks, the cell undergoes *plasmolysis*. If the surrounding fluid is *hypotonic* (more dilute), the cells accumulate fluid and may burst. *Hemolysis* is the term for the loss of red hemoglobin by burst blood cells; it occurs when the osmotic pressure of blood falls to about half the normal value of 7.65 atm at 37°C. Cells will not change in an isotonic solution such as the normal saline solution containing about 0.9% NaCl.. Intravenous feeding or injections must be done with solutions isotonic with blood.

Osmosis together with diffusion and selective absorpton is responsible for the transfer of solutes and water through many cells' membranes. Blood absorbs nutrients through villi in the small intestine and distributes them to body tissues. A fetus receives nourishment, excretes wastes, and "breathes" partly by osmosis through the placenta of the uterus. The normal absorption of water through the large intestine can be modified by a dose of epsom salts. Ductless glands secrete their products into the bloodstream partly by osmosis because their fluids are hypotonic relative to blood. The flow of water in such glands is due in part to osmosis caused by a difference in concentration between ends of the gland. The osmotic pressure of the blood tends to counter the flow of water out through blood vessels because of the hydrostatic blood pressure. The kidneys regulate the salt concentration of the blood, and the formation and concentration of urine in the kidneys is linked closely to the osmotic pressure of the blood. The kidneys remove, in part by osmosis, the nitrogenous cell wastes that the blood carries from the cells. Fresh or very salty water sensitizes exposed pain nerves because of osmotic pressure differences. Physiological saline solutions are used to bathe exposed tissues in surgery and to preserve tissues alive outside the body for a day or two. The sensation of thirst is stimulated by changes in osmotic pressure.

Outside the human body, osmosis is also of universal biological import. Cells of plant leaves take water and food from the veins and plant roots take water from the soil largely by osmosis. Foliage unfolds as the sun generates sugars in cells that then swell upon gaining volume by osmosis. Salted steaks sizzle as osmosis brings juices to the surface. Canned and salted foods are preserved from attack by bacteria because the syrup or salt is hypertonic relative to bacterial fluids, and the bacteria are thus killed or inactivated through plasmolysis. The theories for the mechanism of osmosis suggest that the distinction between osmosis and other processes like diffusion, which may influence some of these biological processes described above, is perhaps not definite.

Example 8.8. A solution of 0.635 g of a protein in 100 ml water has an osmotic pressure due to the protein of 2.35 cm H_2O at 27°C. What is the molecular weight of the protein?

By (8.30),

$$\Pi = \frac{n_2 RT}{V} = \frac{2.35}{13.6 \times 76.0} = \frac{0.635}{M_2} \times \frac{0.08205 \times 300}{0.100}$$

$$M_2 = 69{,}000$$

Example 8.9. With the aid of Raoult's law, predict the osmotic pressure of a one-molal aqueous solution at 0°C.

The mole fraction of water in a 1.00-molal solution is

$$X_1 = \frac{1000/18.02}{(10000/18.02) + 1.00} = 0.9820$$

By Raoult's law (7.18), $X_1 = (p_1/p_1^{\cdot}) = 0.9820$. Substitution in (8.29) yields the answer.

$$\Pi = \frac{RT}{\bar{V}_1}(-\ln X_1) = \frac{0.08205 \times 273.2}{0.0180} \times (-\ln 0.9820) = 22.6 \text{ atm}$$

The observed values in Table 8.3 for sucrose and α-methylglucoside are about 2 atm greater, the difference being due to failure of Raoult's law.

8.6 OSMOTIC AND ACTIVITY COEFFICIENTS

Few, if any, solutions are ideal, yet the equations of the preceding sections are often as tantalizingly close to reality as the perfect gas law is to real equations of state. The necessary small corrections of ideal to real behavior of solutes and solvent are made in two ways by adding empirical correction factors to the ideal expression (7.19). The osmotic coefficient g_i for species i is defined by

$$\mu_i(T, P, X_i) = \mu_i^{\ominus}(T, P) + g_i\, RT \ln X_i \tag{8.31}$$

where μ_i is the actual value of the chemical potential of i in the solution where its mole fraction is X_i. The second kind of correction, done in the spirit of correcting pressures to fugacities, is to correct X_i by a factor f_i. Named the activity coefficient for mole fractions, it is defined by

$$\mu_i(T, P, X_i) = \mu_i^{\ominus}(T, P) + RT \ln f_i X_i \tag{8.32}$$

where again μ_i is the observed value of the chemical potential of i in the solution. The osmotic coefficient g_i is often simpler to observe and use in equations, but the activity coefficient f_i is defined in such a way that solutions can be treated ideally until the last moment, when every X_i can then be corrected by its f_i.

Using g_i or f_i is no real simplification, for it is always necessary to determine their values by observation of some property, perhaps a vapor pressure or an osmotic pressure, from which μ_i can be found. Both g_i and f_i depend on T and P. Their values for dilute solution are taken so as to bring (8.31) and (8.32) to the ideal form (7.19). If the standard state is such that for all species

$$\mu_i^{\ominus} = \lim_{X_i \to 1} [\mu_i - RT \ln X_i] \tag{8.33}$$

then for all i (solvent and each solute)

$$RT \lim_{X_i \to 1} \ln f_i = \lim_{X_i \to 1} [\mu_i - RT \ln X_i - \mu_i^{\ominus}] = 0$$

and

$$\lim_{X_i \to 1} f_i = 1 \tag{8.34}$$

On the other hand, if the standard state is defined so that (8.33) holds only for solvent ($i = 1$) while for each solute

$$\mu_i^{\ominus} = \lim_{X_1 \to 1} [\mu_i - RT \ln X_i] \tag{8.35}$$

then $\mu_i^{\ominus}$ differs from the value for pure i when $i \neq 1$, but still

$$\lim_{X_1 \to 1} f_i = 1 \tag{8.36}$$

Equating μ_i's from (8.31) and (8.32) yields $g_i \ln X_i = \ln X_i + \ln f_i$, or

$$g_i = 1 + \frac{\ln f_i}{\ln X_i} \tag{8.37}$$

which is always true for all X_i. As all species but i become dilute,

$$\lim_{X_i\to 1} g_i = 1 + \lim_{X_i\to 1}\left(\frac{\ln \not{f}_i}{\ln X_i}\right) = 1 + \lim_{X_i\to 1}\left(\frac{\not{f}_i^{-1}}{X_i^{-1}}\right) = 1 + 1 = 2$$

where l'Hospital's rule was used to evaluate the indeterminate form. However, direct comparison of (8.31) and (7.19) strongly recommends that $g_i = 1$ if the almost pure species i behaves ideally, as generally is true. In order to get this desirable result for g_1, the osmotic coefficient of the solvent in a two-component system, it is necessary to suppose that

$$g_1 RT \ln X_1 = RT \ln X_1 + BX_2^2 + CX_2^3 + \cdots \tag{8.38}$$

Then, since $X_1 + X_2 = 1$,

$$\begin{aligned}\lim_{X_1\to 1} g_1 &= 1 + \lim_{X_2\to 0}\left(\frac{BX_2^2 + CX_2^3}{RT\ln(1 - X_2)}\right)\\ &= 1 + \left(\frac{B}{RT}\right)\lim_{X_2\to 0}\left(\frac{2X_2}{-(1 - X_2)^{-1}}\right)\\ &= 1\end{aligned} \tag{8.39}$$

Terms of the form A_0 and A_1X_2 cannot occur in (8.38) if (8.39) is to be true. With (8.38) it is also possible to calculate $\not{f}_2$ from g_1 by the Gibbs-Duhem equation. Of course, $\not{f}_1$ is related to g_1 by the identity (8.37).

Although g_1 exists for each species in any solution, generally only g_1 for the solvent is widely used in dilute solutions. There experimental values of $\not{f}_1$ and g_1 can be found directly from boiling points or freezing points. When (8.31) or (8.32) replaces (8.9) or (8.18) in the derivation of (8.12) or (8.20), the result is

$$\frac{\Delta H}{RT^2} = -\left[\frac{\partial}{\partial T}(g_1 \ln X_1)\right]_P = -\left[\frac{\partial}{\partial T}(\ln \not{f}_1 X_1)\right]_P \tag{8.40}$$

Since $g_1 = X_1 = \not{f}_1 = 1$ at T_0, definite integration of (8.40) from $X_1 = 1$ to X_1 gives

$$g_1 \ln X_1 = \ln \not{f}_1 X_1 = -\int_{T_0}^{T} \frac{\Delta H}{RT'^2}\, dT' \tag{8.41}$$

If ΔH is independent of T,

$$g_1 \ln X_1 = \ln \not{f}_1 X_1 = \frac{\Delta H}{R}\left(\frac{1}{T} - \frac{1}{T_0}\right) \tag{8.42}$$

Observation of ΔH, T, T_0, and X_1 thus yields g_1 and $\not{f}_1$. If (8.42) describes boiling point elevation ($T > T_0$), its right side must be negative when $g_1 = \not{f}_1 = 1$; hence, $\Delta H = \Delta H_v$. Since the right side must also be negative when $g_1 = \not{f}_1 = 1$ for freezing point depression ($T < T_0$) because again $\ln X < 0$, $\Delta H = -\Delta H_f$.

The reason for naming g the osmotic coefficient stems from the osmotic equation

$$\Pi \bar{V}_1 = -g_1 RT \ln X_1 \tag{8.43}$$

which results when (8.31) replaces (8.24) in the derivation of (8.28). By the usual approximation when $n_2 \ll n_1$,

$$\frac{\Pi \bar{V}_1}{g_1 RT} = -\ln X_1 = -\ln(1 - X_2) \approx X_2 \approx \frac{n_2}{n_1}$$

With $V = n_1 \bar{V}_1$, this becomes simply

$$\Pi V = g_1 n_2 RT \tag{8.44}$$

Although the derivation of (8.44) clearly differentiates the mechanism of osmosis from the activity of a gas, the similarity of the van't Hoff equations (8.30) and (8.44) to that of a perfect gas suggests a mnemonic kinship of g_1 to a compressibility factor. It is true to say that $(1 - g)$ measures the degree of departure of a species from ideal behavior.

Example 8.10. What are the mole fraction activity coefficient and osmotic coefficient of H_2O in the sucrose solutions of Table 8.3?

Since $\ln(p_1^\circ/p_1)$ in (8.29) replaces $-\ln X_1$ in (8.28), it is clear that $\ln(p_1^\circ/p_1) = -\ln f_1 X_1$; hence,

$$f_1 = \frac{p_1}{p_1^\circ X_1}$$

Equation (8.7) is the easiest route to $p_1^\circ X_1$ and (8.37) yields g_1; hence, with $p_1^\circ = 4.579$ mm Hg, the following table can be prepared in answer to the question:

m_2	X_2	$p_1^\circ X_2$	$p_1^\circ X_1$	p_1	f_1	$\ln X_1$	$\ln f_1$	g_1
1.0	0.0177	0.0810	4.498	4.489	0.9980	−0.0179	−0.0020	1.112
2.0	0.0348	0.1593	4.420	4.381	0.9912	−0.0354	−0.0088	1.249
3.0	0.0513	0.2349	4.344	4.257	0.9800	−0.0527	−0.0202	1.383
4.0	0.0672	0.3077	4.271	4.132	0.9675	−0.0696	−0.0330	1.474

8.7 IONIZATION

The values of f_i and g_i in a concentrated nonideal solution may vary rather widely from their ideal values of unity at extreme dilution. There are, however, certain solutions whose colligative properties vary more and more widely from ideal, or at least expected, behavior as they become more and more dilute. The solute in this kind of solution is called an *electrolyte*. One of the many indications that electrolytes are dissolved as electrically charged species called ions is that their solutions are good conductors of electricity.

Although he realized fully the limitations involved, van't Hoff found it convenient to compare the colligative effect (a vapor pressure lowering, a freezing or boiling point change, or an osmotic pressure) observed for a solution of an electrolyte to that expected if there were no ionization. This empirical ratio is called *van't Hoff's i* and is defined by (8.45), where the subscript zero indicates the expected value.

$$i = \frac{\Pi}{\Pi_0} = \frac{\delta T_f}{(\delta T_f)_0} = \frac{\delta T_b}{(\delta T_b)_0} = \frac{\delta p_1}{(\delta p_1)_0} \tag{8.45}$$

In (8.45), the numerators are observed values and the denominators are values calculated by (8.28) or (8.29), (8.21) or (8.22), (8.13) or (8.16) and (8.7), just as though ionization did not occur. If each ion or molecule really exerted its full influence on the colligative properties, the value of i would be the number of independent units formed by one formula weight. For sugar, i would be one; for NaCl, 2; for $MgCl_2$, 3; for $FeCl_3$, 4; for $K_4Fe(CN)_6$, 5; and so on. However, the observed values of the numerators generally are not strictly proportional to the number of ions or particles because they are not really independent or ideal in their influence. That i does approach an ideal limit for very dilute solutions is shown in Figure 8.3. Tabulations of empirically observed values of i allow the prediction of colligative properties; and (8.45) justifies the prediction of three colligative properties from a measurement of the fourth, provided i does not vary greatly with T.

The facts that X-ray determinations of crystal structure have established the existence of ions in the solid state, that solution of ionic crystals frequently involves only small energy changes, that mixing such ionic solutions yields very fast reactions or negligible heat effects in the absence of reaction, and that ionic solutions conduct an electric current well are some of the evidence for complete ionization of chemicals like the salts listed in Figure 8.3. Between these and the typically nonionic, nonconducting, slowly reacting solutions there are solutions that are intermediate in these kinds of property. There is really no discontinuity in behavior that can serve to classify a solution as ionic, slightly ionic, or nonionic. Rather, when the degree of ionization of solutions containing weak or slightly ionized electrolytes like weak organic acids is low, it is customary to give a numerical measure of the apparent degree of ionization. Sometimes a measurement of a colligative property is suitable.

Let A_aB_b be the formula of a compound that ionizes to form a cations each with charge z_+ and b anions with charge z_-. The process of ionization, considered as incomplete, is described by the equation

$$A_aB_b \rightleftharpoons aA^{z_+} + bB^{z_-}$$

 The apparent molality of solutes—dissolved A_a B_b and ions without distinction

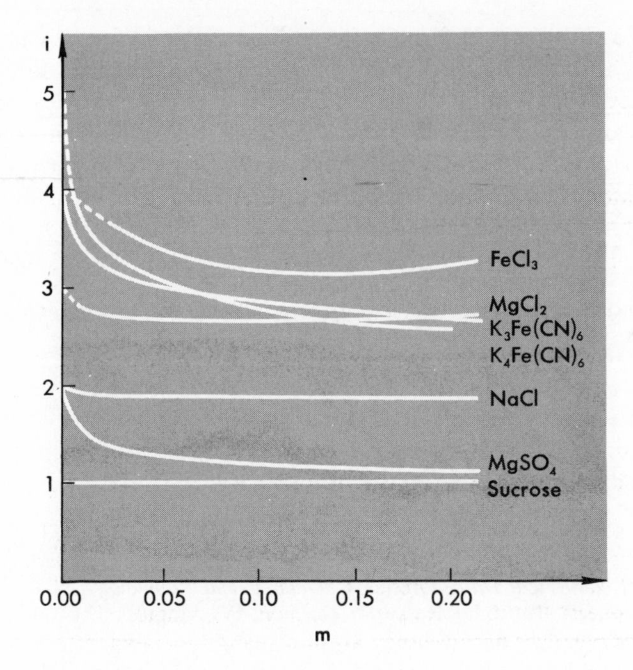

Figure 8.3. Typical Variation of i with Molality in Aqueous Solutions†

as to kind—in a solution that is m_2 molal in $A_a B_b$ before ionization is then

$$m_2(1 - \alpha) + am_2\alpha + bm_2\alpha$$

where α is the apparent degree of ionization. For dilute solutions, a colligative property like freezing point lowering is then predicted to be

$$\delta T_f = (1 - \alpha + a\alpha + b\alpha)K_f m_2$$

But by (8.22), $(\delta T_f)_0 = K_f m_2$ so that by (8.45),

$$i = \frac{\delta T_f}{(\delta T_f)_0} = \frac{K_f m_2(1 - \alpha + a\alpha + b\alpha)}{K_f m_2}$$
$$= 1 - \alpha + a\alpha + b\alpha \tag{8.46}$$

If the total number of ions produced, namely, $a + b$, is denoted by ν, it follows from (8.46) that the degree of ionization is given by

$$\alpha = \frac{i - 1}{\nu - 1} \tag{8.47}$$

†Freezing point data from *International Critical Tables of Numerical Data, Physics, Chemistry and Technology*, National Academy of Sciences–National Research Council, Washington, D.C., 1926–1933, **4,** p. 254.

A fractional value of α for a weak electrolyte has real meaning and can be found by measurement of i through a measurement of a colligative property. When ionization is complete, as it is at all concentrations for strong electrolytes like NaCl, $MgCl_2$, and many others like them, α is unity but i approaches ν in value only in very dilute solutions where solvation effects and electrostatic interactions among ions do not interfere with ideal behavior.

Example 8.11. The freezing point of a sample of abnormal blood was found to be −0.402°C. What was its osmotic pressure at 37°C?

By (8.22) and (8.45), $\delta T_f = i(\delta T_f)_0 = iK_f m_2$. Hence, the effective molality of solutes in this sample of blood was $im_2 = \delta T_f/K_f = 0.402/1.86$. By (8.45) and (8.30),

$$\Pi = i\Pi_0 = i\left(\frac{n_2RT}{V}\right) \approx im_2RT$$

$$\approx \frac{0.402}{1.86} \times 0.08205 \times 310 = 5.50 \text{ atm, lower than normal.}$$

Example 8.12. Calculate the degree of ionization of dichloroacetic acid from the freezing point depressions δT_f and molalities m listed below (*International Critical Tables of Numerical Data, Physics, Chemistry, and Technology*, National Academy of Sciences—National Research Council, Washington, D.C., 1926–1933, *IV*, p. 262).

m	δT_f(°C)	α
0.0040	0.0148	0.99
0.0100	0.0356	0.91
0.0200	0.0690	0.85
0.0500	0.1615	0.74
0.100	0.300	0.61
0.200	0.560	0.50
0.500	0.126	0.36

For the 0.100 molal solution, by (8.22) $(\delta T_f)_0 = 1.86 \times 0.100 = 0.186$°C. By (8.45), $i = 0.300/0.186 = 1.61$. Since the acid forms two ions as it ionizes, $\nu = 2$ and by (8.47),

$$\alpha = \frac{1.61 - 1}{2 - 1} = 0.61$$

The other values listed above were calculated in a similar way.

8.8 ELECTROSTATIC POTENTIAL IN DILUTE ELECTROLYTE SOLUTION

A truly random arrangement of ions has no special stability. If ions were independent of each other, each would exert its full colligative effect. The value of i differs from ν, however, because ions in solution are not independent of each other; their electrostatic interactions prevent them from exerting their full colligative effect. Besides attracting solvent molecules, each ion tends to collect oppositely charged ions around itself in a kind of ion atmosphere despite incessant thermal disordering processes. If the electrostatic forces were powerful enough relative to the continual bombardment by all the particles of the solution, dissolved ions might attain, at least at low T and high concentration, a fair degree of order as they do in ionic solids. However, the dielectric constant of a solvent that dissolves a solute as ions also reduces the electrostatic attractions to such an extent that only on the average do ions take preferred positions.

The statistically preferred positions of ions are described as an average charge density $\rho(r)$ that depends only on the distance r from an ion of charge ze; $\rho(r)$ does not depend on angles relative to axes with preferred orientation because in its disorder the solution is isotropic. In 1912, Milner offered one of the first theoretical discussions of why dilute electrolyte solutions differ fundamentally from dilute solutions of nonelectrolytes. After various contributions from Bjerrum, Brönsted, and others, in 1923 Debye and Hückel explained matters thus. When only central forces act in a medium of dielectric constant κ, the electrostatic potential $\Phi(r)$ at a point r where $\rho(r)$ is the charge density satisfies the well known Poisson equation in the form

$$-\frac{1}{r^2}\frac{d}{dr}\left(r^2\frac{d\Phi}{dr}\right) = \frac{\rho}{\kappa\epsilon_0} = \frac{\rho}{\epsilon} \tag{8.48}$$

where ϵ is the permittivity of the medium. Using (8.48) from classical physics assumes that the solution can be treated as a continuum, but it is the mark of genius to recognize what can be neglected in order to get a useful result. The coulomb potential

$$\Phi(r) = \frac{ze}{4\pi\epsilon_0 r} \tag{8.49}$$

for the effect of a charge ze at a distance r is a solution of (8.48) when there is no charge ($\rho = 0$) at r. At large r, Φ approaches zero; at small r, Φ has the sign of ze. In a solution, Φ differs from (8.49) because in their almost random motions other ions establish about any ion a nonzero average charge density. The Boltzmann distribution (4.73) describes the compromise reached between thermal disorder and the tendency of ions to surround an ion of the opposite charge. The energy of an ion of charge $z_i e$ at a place where the electrostatic potential is Φ is $z_i e\,\Phi$. If, per cubic meter, the average number of ions of charge $z_i e$ is $\bar{c}_i$, then their local concentration is

$$c_i = \bar{c}_i \exp\left(-\frac{z_i e\Phi}{kT}\right) \tag{8.50}$$

If $z_i e\Phi > 0$ because $z_i e$ and Φ are alike in sign (Φ is positive near positive ions and negative near negative ions), then $c_i < \bar{c}_i$; that is, ions of like charge avoid each other. On the other hand, if $z_i e\Phi < 0$ because $z_i e$ and Φ differ in sign, then $c_i > \bar{c}_i$ and the local concentration of ions of the opposite charge exceeds their average concentration. About the ion of charge ze that establishes the potential Φ, the average charge density is thus, from (8.50),

$$\rho = \sum_i z_i e c_i = \sum_i z_i e \bar{c}_i \exp\left(-\frac{z_i e\Phi}{kT}\right) \tag{8.51}$$

If the solution is dilute so that ions are far apart, $z_i e\Phi \ll kT$ and (8.51) expanded in a series becomes

$$\rho = \sum_i z_i e \bar{c}_i \left[1 - \frac{z_i e\Phi}{kT} + \frac{1}{2}\left(\frac{z_i e\Phi}{kT}\right)^2 - \cdots\right] \tag{8.52}$$

The solution is neutral as a whole; hence, $\sum_i z_i e \bar{c}_i = 0$ and, from (8.52) when $z_i e\Phi \ll kT$,

$$\rho \approx -\frac{e^2\Phi}{kT} \sum_i z_i^2 \bar{c}_i \tag{8.53}$$

Poisson's equation (8.48) with ρ from (8.53) is then

$$\frac{d}{dr}\left(r^2 \frac{d\Phi}{dr}\right) = \frac{r^2}{a^2}\Phi \tag{8.54}$$

where the Debye length a is defined by

$$a^2 = \frac{\epsilon kT}{e^2 \sum_i z_i^2 \bar{c}_i} \tag{8.55}$$

Stated in terms of the dimensionless parameter $q = r/a$, (8.54) is

$$\frac{d}{dq}\left(q^2 \frac{d\Phi}{dq}\right) = q^2\Phi \tag{8.56}$$

The problem now is to find a function $\Phi(q)$ that satisfies physics and (8.56).

Exceedingly dilute solutions have $\rho \longrightarrow 0$; it is thus reasonable to try a solution of the coulombic form

$$\Phi(q) = \frac{\phi(q)}{q} \tag{8.57}$$

Substitution of (8.57) into (8.56) yields the very simple equation

$$\frac{d^2\phi}{dq^2} = \phi \tag{8.58}$$

which, as substitution shows, has the solution

$$\phi(q) = Ae^{-q} + Be^{q} \tag{8.59}$$

Accordingly, the electrostatic potential is, from (8.57), (8.59) and $r = aq$,

$$\Phi(r) = \frac{Aa}{r} e^{-r/a} + \frac{Ba}{r} e^{r/a} \tag{8.60}$$

As it stands, this result is unsatisfactory at large r where Φ must vanish; hence, $B = 0$. As T rises and a increases, the local concentration tends toward the average and ρ approaches zero because complete disorder dominates the ions' behavior; hence, Coulomb's law is approached and about an ion of charge ze the value of Φ becomes

$$\frac{ze}{4\pi\epsilon r} = \frac{Aa}{r} \tag{8.61}$$

Hence, $4\pi\epsilon Aa = ze$ and (8.60) with $B = 0$ gives

$$\Phi(r) = \frac{ze}{4\pi\epsilon r} e^{-r/a} \tag{8.62}$$

The factor $e^{-r/a}$ measures the tendency of oppositely charged ions to reside about an ion having charge ze at $r = 0$. This factor enhances the reduction in potential because of the dielectric constant of the solution ($\kappa > 1$). For pure water at 25°C, $\kappa = \epsilon/\epsilon_0 = 78.54$; for pure water at 0°C, $\kappa = 88.12$; Table 8.4

Table 8.4 Dielectric Constants of Liquid Solvents. (A. A. Maryott and E. R. Smith, *Table of Dielectric Constants of Pure Liquids*, Circular of the National Bureau of Standards 514, Washington, D. C., 1951.)

Substance	Dielectric Constant	Temp. (°C)	Dielectric Constant	Temp. (°C)
HCN	158.1	0	114.9	20
$HCONH_2$			109	20
H_2O	88.12	0	78.54	25
HF	84	0		
$HCOOH$			58.5	16
CH_3OH			32.63	25
NH_3	22.4	−33.4		
CH_3COCH_3			20.70	25
SO_2			14.1	20
CH_3COOH			6.15	20
$C_2H_5OC_2H_5$			4.34	20
Br_2			3.09	20
C_6H_6			2.284	20
CCl_4			2.238	20
C_8H_{18}			1.94	20

lists other values. Generally values of κ for pure solvents are sufficient for (8.55), for the Debye-Hückel theory is accurate only for very dilute solutions. For aqueous solution, 0.001 molal is about the limit.

Example 8.13. At 25°C what is the Debye length in (a) 0.001 m NaCl; (b) 0.001 m $BaCl_2$?

Since molality is approximately equal to molarity in dilute aqueous solutions, the number of Na^+ or Cl^- per m^3 is 0.001 $N_0 \times 10^3$. Similarly, in 0.001 m $BaCl_2$, the concentration of Ba^{2+} is N_0 ions m^{-3}, while that of Cl^- is 2 N_0 ions m^{-3}. Since $4\pi\epsilon_0 c^2 = 10^7$ in mks units and since $\epsilon = \kappa\epsilon_0 = 78.54\epsilon_0$, (8.55) gives

$$a^2 = \frac{78.54 \times 10^7(1.380 \times 10^{-23})298.2}{4\pi(2.998 \times 10^8)^2(1.601 \times 10^{-19})^2(1^2 + 1^2)(6.023 \times 10^{23})}$$

$$a = 9.62 \times 10^{-9} m = 96.2 \text{ A}$$

Similarly, for 0.001 m $BaCl_2$ at 25°C, since $\sum_i z_i^2 \bar{c}_i = 2^2(N_0) + 1^2(2N_0) = 6N_0$, $a^2 = 30.9 \times 10^{-18} m^2$; $a = 55.6$ A

8.9 ACTIVITY COEFFICIENTS OF ELECTROLYTES

The activity a_i of any solute i, whether nonelectrolyte or electrolyte, is often conveniently related to its molality m_i in dilute solution where the solvent is a preferred species by an activity coefficient

$$\gamma_i = \frac{a_i}{m_i} \tag{8.63}$$

Like other activity coefficients, γ_i approaches unity upon infinite dilution. Of course, from (6.51),

$$\mu_i = \mu_i^\ominus(T, P) + RT \ln \gamma_i m_i \tag{8.64}$$

Although γ_i must be calculated tediously from observations, its advantage, especially for electrolytes, is that once it is tabulated as a function of m_i, it can on other occasions be added to equations that have been written to that point for ideal behavior ($\gamma_i = 1$).

It is impossible to measure the activity or activity coefficient of just one ion because it is impossible to obtain a solution containing just cations or just anions. It is possible, however, to measure these things for an electrolyte a mole of which yields a cations of charge z_+ and b anions of change z_-, where z_+ and $|z_-|$ are small positive integers that express the multiple of the electronic charge $\pm e$ on the ion. The chemical potential of such an electrolyte is

$$\mu_i = \mu_i^\ominus + RT \ln a_i = a\mu_+^\ominus + aRT \ln a_+ + b\mu_-^\ominus + bRT \ln a_- \tag{8.65}$$

Whence, with $\nu = a + b$,

$$a_i = a_+^a a_-^b = a_\pm^\nu \tag{8.66}$$

The quantity $a_\pm$ as defined by (8.66) is called the *mean ionic activity* of the electrolyte. To this mean activity there is attributed a mean activity coefficient $\gamma_\pm$ such that

$$a_\pm = \gamma_\pm m_\pm \tag{8.67}$$

That is, for a solution m_i molal in the electrolyte, m_+ molal in cations, and m_- molal in anions,

$$\begin{aligned} a_\pm^\nu &= \gamma_\pm^\nu m_\pm^\nu = (\gamma_+ m_+)^a (\gamma_- m_-)^b \\ &= \gamma_+^a (am_i)^a \gamma_-^b (bm_i)^b = (a\gamma_+)^a (b\gamma_-)^b m_i^\nu \\ &= a^a b^b \gamma_\pm^\nu m_i^\nu \end{aligned} \tag{8.68}$$

Analogous relations hold for solutions with compositions expressed in molarities, but it must be remembered that in dilute solutions the ratio of molarity to molality is the density of the solution.

The Debye-Hückel theory of extremely dilute solutions of electrolytes is important because it predicts the behavior of $\gamma_\pm$ at low concentrations and thus guides the extrapolation to infinitely dilute solutions of interest in standard states of solutes. In fact, the theory allows $\gamma_\pm$ to be calculated from the osmotic coefficient of the solvent, something impossible in a unique way for nonionic solutes because the energy of interaction is not known as explicitly as for ions. To relate $\gamma_\pm$ to Φ it is necessary to calculate the energy of an assembly of ions. The electric work required to bring an ion of charge $z_2 e$ from a great distance towards a charge $z_1 e$ until the distance between then is r_{12} is $w_{12} = (z_1 e)(z_2 e)/4\pi\epsilon_0 r_{12}$. To bring a third ion of charge $z_3 e$ into the potential of these two, if they remain fixed at r_{12}, the electric work is $w_{13} + w_{23} = (z_1 e)(z_3 e)/4\pi\epsilon_0 r_{13} + (z_2 e)(z_3 e)/4\pi\epsilon_0 r_{23}$. To bring many ions together from infinite separation, the work that must be done on them is

$$w_0 = \sum_i \sum_j \frac{z_i z_j e^2}{4\pi\epsilon_0 r_{ij}} \quad (i > j) \tag{8.69}$$

If the restriction $i > j$ were replaced by $i \neq j$, each r_{ij} interaction in (8.69) would be counted twice; hence,

$$w_0 = \frac{1}{2} \sum_i \sum_j \frac{z_i z_j e^2}{4\pi\epsilon_0 r_{ij}} \quad (i \neq j) \tag{8.70}$$

Since the potential experienced by i because of the other ions is

$$\Phi_i = \sum_j \frac{z_j e}{4\pi\epsilon_0 r_{ij}} \tag{8.71}$$

it follows from (8.70) and (8.71) that the total electric work done in bringing the ions together is

$$w_0 = \frac{1}{2} \sum_i z_i e \Phi_i \tag{8.72}$$

The summation in (8.72) involves every cation and every anion.

A solution that has an immense Debye length a because it has a very high T or an exceedingly dilute concentration has Φ of the coulombic form (8.49) with ϵ replacing ϵ_0; the ionic solute A_aB_b in this solution has a chemical potential of the ideal form of (8.65), namely

$$\begin{aligned} \mu_i^{(id)} &= a\mu_+^\ominus + aRT \ln am_i + b\mu_-^\ominus + bRT \ln bm_i \\ &= a\mu_+^\ominus + b\mu_-^\ominus + RT \ln (a^a b^b m_i^\nu) \end{aligned} \tag{8.73}$$

A solution with a somewhat smaller Debye length has Φ of the Debye-Hückel form (8.62) with $z = z_i$ and its ionic solute has a real chemical potential

$$\mu_i^{(r)} = a\mu_+^\ominus + b\mu_-^\ominus + RT \ln (a^a b^b \gamma_\pm^\nu m_i^\nu) \tag{8.74}$$

Since $\Delta G = w_0$ by (5.68), the hypothetical process of charging the dissolved ions of A_aB_b involves an increase in free energy of

$$\Delta G = \mu_i^{(r)} - \mu_i^{(id)} = w_0$$

which by (8.49) with $z = z_i$, (8.62) with $z = z_i$, (8.72), (8.73), and (8.74) is

$$RT \ln \gamma_\pm^\nu = \frac{1}{2} \sum_i z_i e \left[\frac{z_i e}{4\pi\epsilon r} e^{-r/a} - \frac{z_i e}{4\pi\epsilon r} \right]$$

When the real solution is quite dilute or hot, a is large and upon expanding $\exp(-r/a)$ in a series

$$\begin{aligned} \nu RT \ln \gamma_\pm &= \frac{e^2 \sum_i z_i^2}{8\pi\epsilon r} \left[1 - \left(\frac{r}{a}\right) + \frac{1}{2}\left(\frac{r}{a}\right)^2 - \cdots - 1 \right] \\ &\approx - \frac{e^2 \sum_i z_i^2}{8\pi\epsilon a} \end{aligned} \tag{8.75}$$

Since a mole of A_aB_b contains aN_0 positive ions of charge z_+e and bN_0 negative ions of charge z_-e, $\sum_i z_i^2 = aN_0 z_+^2 + bN_0 z_-^2$ and (8.75), with a given by (8.55) and $R = N_0 k$, yields

$$\begin{aligned} -\ln \gamma_\pm &= \frac{e^2(az_+^2 + bz_-^2)}{8\pi\epsilon\nu kT} \left(\frac{e^2 \sum_i z_i^2 \bar{c}_i}{\epsilon kT} \right)^{1/2} \\ &= \frac{e^3(az_+^2 + bz_-^2)}{8\pi\nu(\epsilon kT)^{3/2}} \left(\sum_i z_i^2 \bar{c}_i\right)^{1/2} \end{aligned} \tag{8.76}$$

Since A_aB_b is electrically neutral, $az_+ + bz_- = 0$; that is, $az_+ = b|z_-|$ and, therefore,

$$\frac{az_+^2 + bz_-^2}{a+b} = \frac{z_+(b\,|z_-|) + |z_-|\,(az_+)}{a+b} = z_+\,|z_-|$$

From this, with $\nu = a + b$, (8.76) becomes at last

$$-\ln \gamma_\pm = \frac{e^3 z_+\,|z_-|}{8\pi}\,(\epsilon kT)^{-3/2}\Big(\sum_i z_i^2 \bar{c}_i\Big)^{1/2} \tag{8.77}$$

Since in the mks system $e = 1.601 \times 10^{-19}$ coulomb, $k = 1.380 \times 10^{-23}$ joule deg^{-1}, $\epsilon = \kappa\epsilon_0 = \kappa\, 10^7/4\pi c^2$, and $c = 2.998 \times 10^8$ m sec^{-1}, (8.77) is

$$-\ln \gamma_\pm = 0.1209 \times 10^{-6}\, z_+\,|z_-|(\kappa T)^{-3/2}\Big(\sum_i z_i^2 \bar{c}_i\Big)^{1/2} \tag{8.78}$$

where $\bar{c}_i$ is the number of ions of kind i per m^3.

In 1921, Lewis and Randall had found empirically that it was convenient to discuss properties of electrolyte solutions in terms of the ionic strength, which is defined in terms of the molality m_i of the whole solute A_aB_b by

$$I = \frac{1}{2}\sum_i z_i^2 m_i \tag{8.79}$$

In dilute solutions, molarity (moles per liter) $C_i \approx \rho_1 m_i$ where ρ_1 is the cgs density of the solvent or solution. Furthermore, $\bar{c}_i$ (ions m^{-3}) $= C_i N_0 \times 10^3$. Hence, in view of (8.79)

$$\sum_i z_i^2 \bar{c}_i = \sum_i z_i^2 (N_0 \times 10^3)\rho_1 m_i = 2\, I N_0 \rho_1 \times 10^3 \tag{8.80}$$

With (8.80) it is possible to express (8.78) in the chemically more familiar units and variables

$$-\ln \gamma_\pm = 0.420 \times 10^7\, z_+\,|z_-|\,(\kappa T)^{-3/2}(\rho_1 I)^{1/2} \tag{8.81}$$

With the Gibbs-Duhem equation, which is a relation linking activities of species in the same solution phase, it can be tediously shown that in very dilute solutions

$$(1 - g) = -\frac{1}{3}\ln \gamma_\pm \tag{8.82}$$

where g is the osmotic coefficient of the solvent and $\gamma_\pm$ is the molal activity coefficient of its one ionic solute. Hence, (8.81) and (8.82) yield

$$(1 - g) = 0.140 \times 10^7\, z_+\,|z_-|\,(\kappa T)^{-3/2}(\rho_1 I)^{1/2} \tag{8.83}$$

Water is the solvent of preeminence. For it $\kappa = 78.54$ at 25°C and $\kappa =$

88.12 at 0°C; hence, with $\ln \gamma_{\pm} = 2.303 \log \gamma_{\pm}$, (8.81) and (8.83) give for dilute aqueous solutions ($I <$ ca. 0.01) of one electrolyte, as in Table 8.5,

Table 8.5 Debye-Hückel Constants for Dilute Aqueous Solutions. (R. G. Bates, *J. Res. Nat. Bur. Stds.* **66***A*, 179 [1962].)

Temperature (°C)	Value of Constant
0	0.4918
10	0.4988
20	0.5066
25	0.5108
30	0.5150
40	0.5242
50	0.5341
60	0.5448
70	0.5562
80	0.5685
90	0.5817

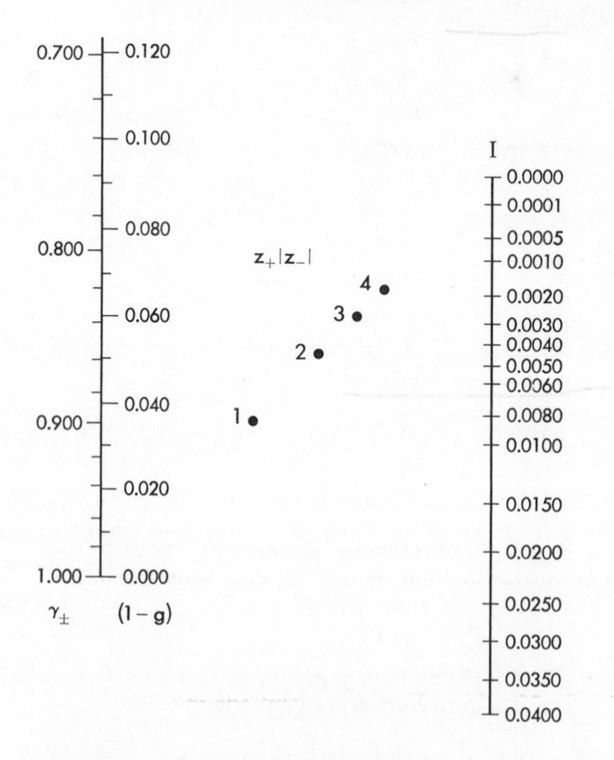

Figure 8.4. Nomograph for Osmotic Coefficient g and Mean Ionic Activity Coefficient $\gamma_{\pm}$ in Dilute Aqueous Electrolyte Solution at 25°C at One Atmosphere for Values of $z_{+}|z_{-}|$ from 1 to 4

$$-\log \gamma_{\pm} = 0.4918\, z_+ |z_-| I^{1/2} \qquad \text{(aqueous; 0°C)} \qquad (8.84)$$

$$-\log \gamma_{\pm} = 0.5108\, z_+ |z_-| I^{1/2} \qquad \text{(aqueous; 25°C)} \qquad (8.85)$$

$$(1 - g) = 0.3775\, z_+ |z_-| I^{1/2} \qquad \text{(aqueous; 0°C)} \qquad (8.86)$$

$$(1 - g) = 0.3921\, z_+ |z_-| I^{1/2} \qquad \text{(aqueous; 25°C)} \qquad (8.87)$$

Figure 8.4 is a nomograph for (8.85) and (8.87); to find $\gamma_{\pm}$ or $(1 - g)$, a straightedge is aligned by the value of I on the scale at the right and a dot for the appropriate value of $z_+ |z_-|$. The dots move very little downward to the left for 0°C. Figure 8.5 shows how actual values of $(1 - g)$ often deviate from values predicted by the limiting law (8.86) of Debye and Hückel. These deviations are accounted for by taking account of such things as ion size.

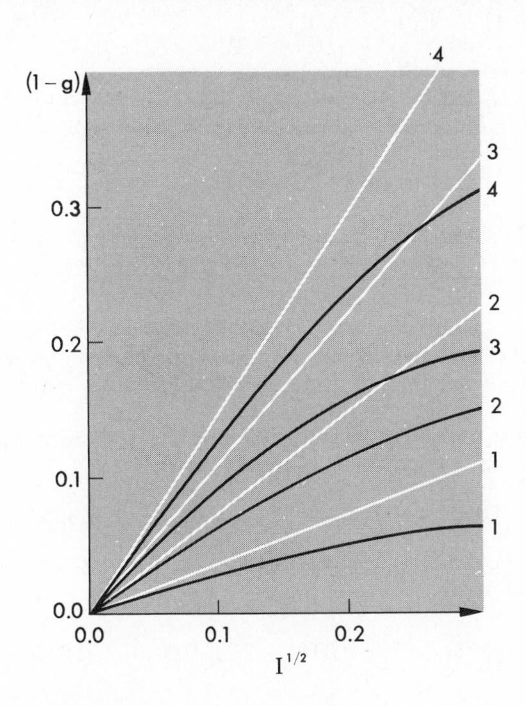

Figure 8.5. Typical Behavior of Osmotic Coefficients of Water in Dilute Aqueous Electrolyte Solution at 0°C at One Atmosphere for Values of $z_+ |z_-|$ from 1 to 4

When there are several electrolytes in a solution, I is found by (8.79) with a term for each kind of ion, and for dilute solutions in water

$$(1 - g) = 0.755 \left(\sum_i m_i\right)^{-1} I^{3/2} \qquad \text{(aqueous; 0°C)} \qquad (8.88)$$

$$(1 - g) = 0.785 \left(\sum_i m_i\right)^{-1} I^{3/2} \qquad \text{(aqueous; 25°C)} \qquad (8.89)$$

The osmotic pressure of an ideal solution of a nonelectrolyte is

$$\Pi_0 = -\frac{RT}{\bar{V}_1} \ln X_1 \tag{8.90}$$

The osmotic pressure of an ideal solution of an electrolyte so dilute that each of its ν ions per formula acts independently and thus exerts its full colligative effect is

$$\Pi = -\nu \frac{RT}{\bar{V}_1} \ln X_1 \tag{8.91}$$

The osmotic pressure of a nonideal solution of an electrolyte is

$$\Pi = -g\nu \frac{RT}{\bar{V}_1} \ln X_1 \tag{8.92}$$

where g accounts for all deviations beyond those accountable in terms of fragmentation. According to (8.45), $\Pi = i\,\Pi_0$ and thus, by (8.90) and (8.92)

$$i = g\nu \tag{8.93}$$

This simple equation with the Debye-Hückel expressions for g as a function of I offers a direct link between real colligative properties and the ionic strengths of dilute electrolyte solutions.

Example 8.14. Predict the lowering in the freezing point of a kg water in which are dissolved 0.0020 formula weights of KNO_3 and 0.0010 formula weights of $Ba(NO_3)_2$.

If these ions acted independently, the predicted lowering of freezing point would be $\delta T_f = K_f \sum m_i$. Since the molality of nitrate ions is 0.004,

$$\delta T_f = 1.86(0.0020 + 0.0010 + 0.0040) = 1.86 \times 0.0070 = 0.0130°\text{C}$$

The osmotic coefficient g takes account of the fact that the ions are really not independent. For this solution, by (8.79),

$$I = \frac{1}{2} \sum_i z_i^2 m_i = \frac{1}{2} (1^2 \times 0.0020 + 1^2 \times 0.0040 + 2^2 \times 0.0010) = 0.0050$$

By (8.88),

$$1 - g = \frac{0.755}{0.0070} (0.0050)^{3/2} = 0.0382$$

Hence, $g = 0.9618$ and $\delta T_f = 0.9618 \times 0.0130 = 0.0125°\text{C}$.

Example 8.15. By what amount is the chemical potential of Na_2SO_4 in 0.00400 molal aqueous Na_2SO_4 at 25°C changed from its ideal value if activities follow the Debye-Hückel limiting law at this concentration?

With $I = \frac{1}{2}(1^2 \times 0.00800 + 2^2 \times 0.00400) = 0.01200$, (8.85) gives $-\log \gamma_\pm = 0.511 \times 1 \times 2 \times (0.01200)^{1/2} = 0.1118$. According to (8.73) and (8.74), the ideal $\mu(Na_2SO_4)$ exceeds the nonideal value by

$-\nu RT \ln \gamma_{\pm} = 3 \times 8.314 \times 298 \times 2.303 \times 0.1118 = 1915$ joules mole^{-1}.

That is, to generate the ideal solution from the real one, about 1900 joules of nonexpansion work at 25°C at one atm would have to be done on one gram-formula-weight of Na_2SO_4 dissolved in 250 kg H_2O.

Example 8.16. Calculate from the data of Table 7.3 the activity coefficients of acetone and water in a 2.5 mole percent acetone solution at 1.00 atm at 84.2°C. At 84.2°C, the vapor pressures of pure acetone and pure water are 1820 and 420 mm Hg.

From Table 7.3, the mole fraction of acetone in the vapor is 0.470; hence, if the vapor is ideal at 1.00 atm, its fugacity is 0.470. Raoult's law would predict a vapor pressure of $p_2 = p_2^{\bullet} N_2 = (1820/760) \times 0.025 = 0.0598$ atm. By the meaning of activity coefficient in Section 8.5, the coefficient is $0.470/0.0598 = 7.9$. Similarly, for water, it is $(0.530)/(420/760) \times 0.975) = 0.98$. The magnitudes of the activity coefficients indicate that in this mixture Raoult's law greatly underestimates the fugacity of acetone and slightly overestimates that of water.

8.10 SUMMARY

As empirical corrections, activity coefficients are a bore; as tools of a practical chemist, they are indispensable; as clues to a theory of solutions, they are a challenge. Amid the profusion of mathematical detail in this chapter, probably the most important concepts are the idea of a colligative property (one that ignores kind and only counts particles), the simplest equations for colligative properties of dilute solutions and the means of mending them, and the use of chemical potential as a basic of definition and as a key to equilibrium.

PROBLEMS

(Vapor pressure and solution data from *Handbook of Chemistry* [10th Edition], ed. by N. A. Lange and G. M. Forker, New York: McGraw-Hill Book Co., Inc., 1967, unless noted otherwise.)

1. An aqueous solution of ten grams of urea in 100 g H_2O is observed at 37°C at one atm to have the same vapor pressure as an aqueous solution of 25.0 g of a sugar in 100 g H_2O. What is the molecular weight of the sugar?
   Answer: 150.

2. In 700 g water were dissolved 30.0 g sucrose ($C_{12}H_{22}O_{11}$) and 30.0 g glucose ($C_6H_{12}O_6$). What is the vapor pressure of this solution at 30°C if the vapor pressure of water is 31.82 mm Hg?
   Answer: 31.61 mm Hg.

3. The freezing point of a solution of 0.138 g of a nonvolatile solute in 15.2 g benzene is 0.53°C less than the freezing point of pure benzene. What are the molecular weight of the substance and normal boiling point of the solution?
   Answer: 88; 80.4°C.

4. Estimate the eutectic temperature and composition in the Au-Tl system if:
   (a) The melting points of pure Au and Tl are 1063°C and 304°C.
   (b) Only one liquid phase exists and no compounds or solid solutions exist.
   (c) The heats of fusion of Au and Tl are 3030 cal and 1030 cal gram-atom^{-1}.
   The thermodynamic data are from F. D. Rossini *et al.*, Circular of the National Bureau of Standards 500 (1952).
   Answer: 492°K; $X_{Au} = 0.141$.

5. Discuss the various advantages of tert-butyl alcohol as a solvent for ebullioscopic and cryoscopic determinations. It melts at 25.5°C with $\Delta H_f = 1.59$ kcal mole^{-1} and it boils at one atm at 82.8°C with $\Delta H_v = 9.66$ kcal mole^{-1}.
   Answer: Convenient temperatures; good solvent for organic and inorganic solutes; reasonably high K_f and K_b; may not crystallize pure.

6. Show that osmotic pressure, of the four usual colligative properties of solutions, is best suited to the determination of molecular weights greater than about 10^4.

7. How much dextrose ($C_6H_{12}O_6$) must be dissolved in one 1 water to yield a solution with an osmotic pressure of 7.65 atm at 37°C?
   Answer: 54.4 g.

8. Show that g_i and f_i are independent of T if $\bar{H}_i = \bar{H}_i^{\circ}$.

9. The freezing point of a 0.20 molal aqueous solution of a weak electrolyte that ionizes into two ions is -0.416°C. Calculate the degree of ionization.
   Answer: $\alpha = 0.117$.

10. If van't Hoff's i is independent of temperature, at what temperature will 2.00 molal aqueous solution of an electrolyte boil if it freezes at -6.90°C?
    Answer: 101.91°C.

11. Why it is incorrect to calculate the number of anions within $r = a$ of a cation by dividing the difference between Φ of (8.62) and Φ of Coulomb's law by the charge per anion?
    Answer: Some cations are also in the region $r < a$; the proposed method would give the difference between charge populations of anions and cations for $r \leqslant a$.

12. Predict the osmotic pressure really expected of 0.01000 m K_2SO_4 in H_2O at 25°C.
    Answer: 0.635 atm.

13. Show that
    (a) $m_{\pm}^{\nu} = a^a b^b m_i^{\nu}$ for electrolyte A_aB_b.
    (b) (8.86) is a special case of (8.88).

14. Calculate the freezing point of 0.00152 m $CoCl_2$ under air at one atm.
    Answer: -0.00806°C.

---

15. When 0.0321 g of a compound containing 68% wt C, 10% wt H, and 22% wt O was dissolved in 0.722 g cyclohexane, the solution had a freezing point of 0.15°C. What is the molecular weight and true formula of the compound?
    Answer: $C_8H_{14}O_2$.

16. Estimate the eutectic temperature and composition in the Al-Ge system if:
    (a) The melting points of pure Al and Ge are 660°C and 960°C.
    (b) Only one liquid phase exists and no compounds or solid solutions exist.
    (c) The heats of fusion of Al and Ge are 2.6 and 8.3 kcal gram-atom^{-1}.
    The numerical data are from F. D. Rossini *et al.*, Circular of the National Bureau of Standards 500 (1952).
    Answer: 822°K; $X_{Al} = 0.83$.

17. Calculate the heats of fusion of A and B and the maximum amount of pure A that can be recovered by one crystallization of a melt containing 15% mole B. Pure A melts at 100°C, forms a eutectic with B at 70% mole B at 30°C, and pure B melts at 120°C. Only one liquid phase exists, and no solid solutions or compounds exist.
Answer: $\Delta H_A = 3870$ cal; $\Delta H_B = 9400$ cal; 92.4% mole of A present.

18. The osmotic pressure of an aqueous solution containing exactly 1 g nonvolatile substances in 100.0 ml water is exactly 1 atm at 27°C. What is the average weight of the solute particles? Why was the qualification "average" made?
Answer: 246.

19. How tall a column of solution with density 1.010 g ml^{-1} can be supported at equilibrium by the osmotic pressure developed by 0.532 molar nonelectrolyte in water at 20°C? At 0°C?
Answer: 131 m (20°C); 122 m (0°C).

20. What should be the vapor pressure of an aqueous solution that is to have an osmotic pressure of 7.65 atm at 37°C? The vapor pressure of H_2O at 37°C is 47.07 mm Hg.
Answer: 46.82 mm Hg.

21. What is the vapor pressure of 1.000 molal aqueous solution of an electrolyte at 0°C if its freezing point is −3.37°C? The vapor pressure of H_2O at 0°C is 4.58 mm Hg.
Answer: 4.43 mm Hg.

22. A solution of one gram-mole of a nonelectrolyte in 500 g H_2O has a vapor pressure of 25.639 mm Hg at 27°C, while pure H_2O at 27°C under its own vapor has a vapor pressure of 26.739 mm Hg. For this dilute solution, calculate its
(a) osmotic pressure at 27°C;
(b) osmotic coefficient of H_2O at 27°C;
(c) freezing point if activity coefficients are independent of T.
Answer: (a) 57.4 atm; (b) 1.1858; (c) −4.41°C.

23. Calculate the activity of NaCl, the mean activity of NaCl, and the vapor pressure of 0.004 molal NaCl at 25°C. The vapor pressure of pure water at 25°C is 23.756 mm Hg.
Answer: 1.38×10^{-5}; 3.71×10^{-3}; 23.753 mm Hg.

24. What is the osmotic pressure of 0.00250 molal KNO_3 at 0°C? What is van't Hoff's i and the freezing point of this solution?
Answer: 0.110 atm; −0.00914°C.

25. At 20°C the vapor pressure of 5.55 m KOH is 16.4 mm Hg, while that of pure H_2O, the solvent, is 17.5 mm Hg. What are the osmotic pressure and osmotic coefficient (H_2O) of this solution?
Answer: 86 atm; 0.69.

26. What is the osmotic pressure of 0.0300 m $Ca(ClO_4)_2$ at 20°C if $\kappa = 80.4$?
Answer: 0.554 atm.

27. The number of molecules with molecular weight M in a polymer solution containing molecules of various sizes is often proportional to e^{-M}. By the use of samples of uniform M it is possible to show that the viscosity of certain polymer solutions is proportional to a power of M; that is, $\eta = kM^n$, where k and n are

empirical constants. If the viscosity-average molecular weight $\bar{M}_\eta$ is defined by

$$(\bar{M}_\eta)^n = \frac{\eta}{k} = \frac{\int_0^\infty m\left(\frac{\eta}{k}\right)\phi_N(m)\,dm}{\int_0^\infty m\phi_N(m)\,dm}$$

show that

$$\left(\frac{\bar{M}_\eta}{\bar{M}_N}\right)^n = \Gamma(n+2)$$

28. Urea (H_2NCONH_2) is soluble in alcohol (CH_3CH_2OH) but is not volatile from the solution. With data from Table 8.1, for a solution of 5.00 g urea in 800 g alcohol, find:
(a) The diminution in the vapor pressure of alcohol at 70.0°C due to the presence of the urea.
(b) The increase in boiling point of the solution at one atm.
Answer: (a) 2.62 mm Hg; (b) 0.128°C.

29. Find the compositions and temperatures of the three simple binary eutectics and the one simple ternary eutectic in the system LiF-NaF-KF and sketch the phase diagram at constant pressure with isotherms if:
(a) No compounds or solid solutions are formed.
(b) Only one liquid phase exists.
(c) The melting points are: LiF, 845°C; NaF, 995°C; and KF, 856°C.
(d) The heats of fusion are: LiF, 2400 cal mole^{-1}; NaF, 7800 cal mole^{-1}; KF, 6800 cal mole^{-1}.
The numerical data are from F. D. Rossini *et al.*, Circular of the National Bureau of Standards 500, Washington, D. C. (1952). Assume the solutions are ideal.
Answer: Ternary eutectic; calc. 500°C; obs, 454°C.

30. Why can solutions of equal osmotic pressures differ in tonicity?
Answer: A solute may permeate membrane like solvent.

31. What would be the osmotic pressure of 5.0% acetone in water solution at one atm at 75.6°C? See Table 5.3 for data and assume the vapor pressures of pure acetone and water are 1430 mm Hg and 290 mm Hg.
Answer: 50.1 atm.

32. By applying the Gibbs-Duhem equation to a two-component solution at constant T and P, show that the activity coefficients f_1 and f_2 are related by the equation

$$\left(\frac{\partial \ln f_2}{\partial \ln f_1}\right)_{TP} = -\frac{1 - X_2}{X_2}$$

33. What is wrong with these data?

X_2	0.300	0.400	0.500	0.600	0.700	0.800	0.900	1.000
f_1	0.925	0.950	0.960	0.970	0.980	0.990	0.995	1.000
f_2	1.964	1.370	1.206	1.105	1.046	1.012	1.002	1.000

Answer: f_2 is too small for $X_2 = 0.300$ and $X_2 = 0.400$.

34. Calculate the chemical potentials of Na^+, Br^-, and NaBr in 0.0030 molal NaBr at 25°C if $\mu^\ominus_{Na^+} = -62{,}589$ cal mole^{-1} and $\mu^\ominus_{Br^-} = -24{,}574$ cal mole^{-1} [Rossini, F. D., *et al.*, Circular of the National Bureau of Standards 500 (1952)].
Answer: −66,069 cal mole^{-1} −28,054 cal mole^{-1}; −94,123 cal mole^{-1}.

35. The freezing point of 0.01000 molal $CaCl_2$ is $-0.05112°C$ under air at one atm. What freezing point is predicted by the Debye-Hückel theory? What is the osmotic pressure of 0.01000 molal $CaCl_2$ at 0°C? (Data from *International Critical Tables of Numerical Data, Physics, Chemistry, and Technology*, National Academy of Sciences–National Research Council, Washington, D.C., 1926–1933, *IV*, p. 254.)
Answer: $-0.0486°C$; 0.615 atm.

36. Calculate ΔH for the change at 25°C: NaBr ($0.0025m$) $\longrightarrow$ NaBr ($0.0010m$).
Answer: $\Delta H = 0$ if $\gamma_\pm$ is independent of T; actually $\Delta H = -10$ cal.

37. Compare the ionic strengths at which $(1 - g)/z_+|z_-|$ is 0.0200 in H_2O at 25°C, in NH_3 at $-33.4°C$ where $\rho_1 = 0.670$ g cm^{-3}, and in SO_2 at 20°C where $\rho_1 = 1.39$ g cm^{-3}. See Table 8.4 for dielectric constants.
Answer: $I \times 10^4 = 26.2$ (H_2O), 0.475 (NH_3), and 0.104 (SO_2).

38. What further information, if any, is needed to calculate the activity coefficients of sucrose in the solutions of Table 8.3?
Answer: $\mu^\ominus$(sucrose) or, impractically, $g(H_2O)$ up to pure sucrose.

39. Let the ion of charge ze that establishes the potential $\Phi(r)$ in an electrolyte solution have a size r_0 such that other ions are forbidden in the region $r < r_0$. Since the whole electrolyte is neutral, the ion's charge of ze is exactly countered by the charge

$$-ze = \int_{r_0}^{\infty} 4\pi r^2 \rho(r)\, dr$$

From this size effect, show that (8.62) is to be replaced by

$$\Phi(r) = \frac{ze}{4\pi\epsilon r}\left(\frac{e^{r_0/a}}{1 + (r_0/a)}\right)e^{-r/a}$$

9
CHEMICAL EQUILIBRIUM

9.1 INTRODUCTION

As soon as a pure substance decomposes or as soon as pure substances react, a solution forms. Equilibrium thermodynamics offers a powerful and systematic description of the seemingly static but really dynamic equilibrium that is attained after reaction. Chapter 10 explains how rapidly chemical reactions occur; this chapter describes the conditions that exist at equilibrium and the innate tendency of chemicals to react without regard to time. The concepts of speed and reactivity must be distinguished in a discussion based on equilibrium thermodynamics, which ignores time. Historically, however, these concepts have been closely associated and somewhat confusing to early chemists. Some of the following remarks serve also as introduction to Chapter 10.

Perhaps the first really influential theory of chemical reactivity was Bergman's idea of elective affinity, presented in 1775. He proposed that reactions occurred because of the various chemical natures of the reactants and, as had been done for hundreds of years, offered a table of relative reactivities. He also suggested that displacement reactions should determine the order of affinities. In 1777, Wenzel noted that the rate of solution of metals depended not only on the kind of metal and acid but also on the concentration of the acid. Berthollet in 1799 examined the final states of various reactions and concluded that increasing the concentration of a 'weak' reactant could enhance its reactivity or relative position in the table of affinities. Reaction was thus related to concentration as well as affinity.

Quantitative experiments on rates of reaction were first performed in the 1850's and early 1860's. Wilhelmy observed how the rate of hydrolysis of sucrose depends on concentration; Williamson studied the production of ether from alchohol; Berthelot and St. Giles examined the esterification of acetic acid. These investigations culminated in 1863 in the law of mass action of Guldberg and Waage. Before their proposal was widely known, however, Harcourt and Esson in 1865–66 were reaching similar conclusions about the dependence of rate on concentration from their studies of the reaction of HI with H_2O_2 and of $KMnO_4$ with oxalic acid. The confusing effects of catalysts and impurities were also being explained by van't Hoff. In 1877 Ostwald noticed that the so-called active masses (that is, concentrations) of reactants and products were related at equilibrium by a constant called the equilibrium constant K. Finally, in 1884, van't Hoff explained how K depends on free energy, how it varies with T, and how it is related to nonexpansion work. Of course, Gibbs's phase rule eventually offered a different and less specific description of chemical and physical equilibrium. The very widely used thermodynamic textbook of Lewis and Randall, first published in 1923, has tended to base all calculations of chemical equilibrium on $\Delta G^{\ominus}$ even though other thermodynamic functions could be used. For example, since about 1930 de Donder's affinity, which is essentially $-\Delta G$, has come into wide use for discussing chemical equilibrium and the rate of approach to it.

The purpose of this chapter is to apply known principles in new ways, namely, in situations in which chemical rather than physical equilibria occur. Although it may be somewhat difficult to distinguish between chemical and physical changes when the process is the breaking of hydrogen bonds in vaporizing water or the solvation of ions in solution processes, nevertheless the restraint forbidding so-called chemical changes is now to be removed. No longer is it customary to choose a minimum number of independent components of a system. Rather, with each really existing species recognized explicitly, one or more relations among these various species are to be found. The relations so found will impose one or more conditions on these species and will leave unspecified a number of variables just equal to the number of degrees of freedom predicted by the phase rule if dependent species had first been eliminated from the list. These relations are, of course, the equilibrium constants. The bulk of this chapter explains how the K's can be calculated, how they vary with T, and, briefly, how they are to be used.

9.2 THE EQUILIBRIUM CONSTANT

A very simple example of an equilibrium constant is the distribution or partition coefficient of Section 7.14. There a system consisting of a solute distributed between immiscible solutions was considered a three-component ($\mathsf{C} = 3$) system of two phases ($P = 2$). As such, the degrees of freedom at constant pressure and temperature were $F = C - P = 3 - 2 = 1$. The single degree of freedom is the mole fraction of one component in one of the phases. The partion coefficient relates the compositions of the immiscible solutions at equilibrium; it relates the concentrations of solute in each solution when these two concentrations are each of interest; it relates the equilibrium concentrations of A and A_n for the reaction $A_n \longrightarrow nA$ just as though A_n and A were different components; it places a restriction upon the dissociation process in which n fragments A are generated from A_n by a physicochemical process. The reaction above could describe the extraction of acetic acid from benzene, where it exists mainly as dimer, by water, where it exists mainly as monomer. This same reaction could represent the vaporization of water from hydrogen-bonded liquid $(H_2O)_n$ to molecular gas H_2O.

For any change in which a formula weights of A, b of B, and so on become d formula weights of D, e of E, and so on, the general reaction is

$$aA + bB + \cdots \longrightarrow dD + eE + \cdots \tag{9.1}$$

A, B, . . . D, E, . . . are recognized as species that are generally not as simply related as A_n is to A. It is assumed that (9.1) is a balanced equation so that mass, kinds of atom, and charge are conserved in this closed system. It is sometimes convenient to rewrite (9.1) in the conventional form

$$0 = dD + eE + \cdots - aA - bB - \cdots = \sum_i \nu_i \Omega_i \tag{9.2}$$

where Ω_i represents the formula of a reactant or product and where the stoichiometric coefficients ν_i are positive for products and negative for reactants. Because of (6.44), the Gibbs free energy G_2 of the products D, E, . . . is $G_2 = d\mu_D + e\mu_E + \cdots$. Similarly, the Gibbs free energy G_1 of the reactants A, B, . . . is $G_1 = a\mu_A + b\mu_B + \cdots$. The increase in free energy for (9.1) or (9.2) is thus

$$\Delta G = G_2 - G_1 = d\mu_D + e\mu_E + \cdots - a\mu_A - b\mu_B - \cdots = \sum_i \nu_i \mu_i \tag{9.3}$$

A chemical transformation generally begins and ends with the species in arbitrary states. Let the reaction be: a moles of A at any fugacity f'_A and b of B at f'_B become d moles of D at any fugacity f'_D and e of E at f'_E. That is,

$$\begin{matrix} aA + bB \rightarrow dD + eE \\ f'_A \quad f'_B \quad f'_D \quad f'_E \end{matrix} \tag{9.4}$$

By (6.44) and (6.50) the Gibbs free energy of the final state is

$$G_2 = d\mu_D + e\mu_E = dRT \ln f'_D + d\mu_D^\ominus + eRT \ln f'_E + e\mu_E^\ominus$$

Similarly, for the initial state,

$$G_1 = a\mu_A + b\mu_B = aRT\ln f'_A + a\mu^{\ominus}_A + bRT\ln f'_B + b\mu^{\ominus}_B$$

Whence, for the overall change of the gaseous reaction (9.4),

$$\Delta G = G_2 - G_1 = RT\ln\left(\frac{f'^d_D f'^e_E}{f'^a_A f'^b_B}\right) + \Delta G^{\ominus}$$

$$= \Delta G^{\ominus} + RT\ln \prod_i (f'_i)^{\nu_i} \tag{9.5}$$

where $\Delta G^{\ominus} = (d\mu^{\ominus}_D + e\mu^{\ominus}_E) - (a\mu^{\ominus}_A + b\mu^{\ominus}_B)$. It is convenient to let

$$Q_e = \frac{f'^d_D f'^e_E}{f'^a_A f'^b_B} = \prod_i (f'_i)^{\nu_i} \tag{9.6}$$

On substitution of (9.6) into (9.5), the latter becomes

$$\Delta G = \Delta G^{\ominus} + \text{RT ln } Q_e \tag{9.7}$$

The same result is obtained when each reactant is brought individually to the standard state and is allowed to react to give products in their standard state, each product then being brought individually to its real final state. By the methods of Section 5.13 for the state diagram

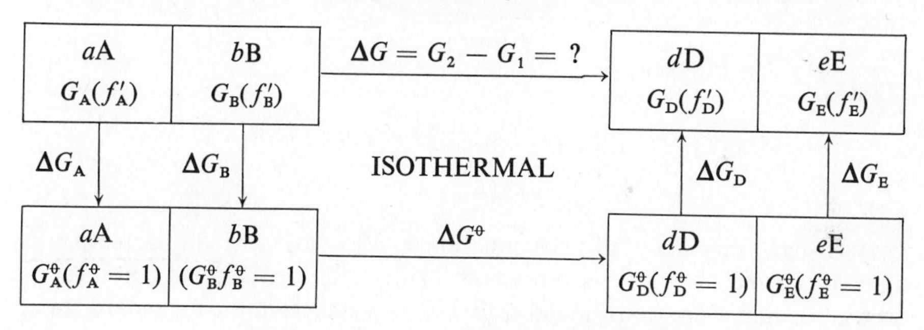

$$\left.\begin{aligned} \Delta G_A &= aG^{\ominus}_A - aG_A = aRT\ln\left(\frac{1}{f'_A}\right) \\ \Delta G_B &= bG^{\ominus}_B - bG_B = bRT\ln\left(\frac{1}{f'_B}\right) \\ \Delta G_D &= dG_D - dG^{\ominus}_D = dRT\ln\left(\frac{f'_D}{1}\right) \\ \text{and} \quad \Delta G_E &= eG_E - eG^{\ominus}_E = eRT\ln\left(\frac{f'_E}{1}\right) \end{aligned}\right\} \quad * \tag{9.8}$$

But

$$\left.\begin{aligned} \Delta G &= (dG_D + eG_E) - (aG_A + bG_B) \\ \Delta G^{\ominus} &= (dG^{\ominus}_D + eG^{\ominus}_E) - (aG^{\ominus}_A + bG^{\ominus}_B) \end{aligned}\right\} \tag{9.9}$$

Substitution of (9.9) into the summation of Equations (9.8) yields Equation (9.7). With this equation ΔG can be calculated for any isothermal change for which ΔG° and the fugacities f'_i of reactants and products are known. When reactants and products are in their standard states, f'_i is unity for all i and $\Delta G = \Delta G^{\circ}$.

If the initial and final states of (9.1) or (9.2) are at equilibrium with fugacities f_i at constant T and total pressure P, the general condition $\Delta G = 0$ as applied to G_2 for products and G_1 for reactants requires that

$$a\mu_A + b\mu_B + \cdots = d\mu_D + e\mu_E + \cdots \tag{9.10}$$

Equation (9.10) is the desired relation that imposes a condition upon the several species of (9.1) because at equilibrium all these species are not independent and classifiable as components. From the list of the reactants and products one species may be omitted in counting the minimum number of species out of which the system can be made, for the reaction considered is the means of generating this last species, which is not a component or independent intensive variable. There is one relation like (9.10) for each chemical equation like (9.1); hence, C = S − E.

Equation (9.10) is transformed into the more familiar form of an equilibrium constant thus. By (6.50)

$$\begin{aligned} aRT\ln f_A + a\mu_A^{\circ}(T) + bRT\ln f_B + b\mu_B^{\circ}(T) + \cdots \\ = dRT\ln f_D + d\mu_D^{\circ}(T) + eRT\ln f_E + e\mu_E^{\circ}(T) + \cdots \end{aligned}$$

That is,

$$\begin{aligned} -\{[d\mu_D^{\circ}(T) + e\mu_E^{\circ}(T) + \cdots] - [a\mu_A^{\circ}(T) + b\mu_B^{\circ}(T) + \cdots]\} \\ = RT[\ln f_D^d + \ln f_E^e + \cdots) - (\ln f_A^a + \ln f_B^b + \cdots)] \end{aligned}$$

The left-hand member of this last equation is just $-\Delta G^{\circ}$, the Gibbs free energy decrease for reaction (9.1) when reactants in their standard states of unit fugacity at temperature T are transformed *entirely* into products in their standard states of unit fugacity at the same temperature T. On continuation,

$$-\Delta G^{\circ} = RT\ln\left(\frac{f_D^d f_E^e \cdots}{f_A^a f_B^b \cdots}\right)$$

$$\exp\left(-\frac{\Delta G^{\circ}}{RT}\right) = \frac{f_D^d f_E^e \cdots}{f_A^a f_B^b \cdots}$$

The left-hand member of this last equation depends only upon the temperature (and, of course, the natures of the given species A, B, . . . D, E, . . .); hence, it may be represented by the function $K_e(T)$, which is known as the *equilibrium constant at the temperature T*. Then, by definition,

$$K_e(T) = \frac{f_D^d f_E^e \cdots}{f_A^a f_B^b \cdots} \tag{9.11}$$

This same conclusion that an equilibrium constant is a thermodynamic necessity can be reached for the more general reaction (9.2) of conventional form when equilibrium is reached, for by (9.3) at equilibrium

$$0 = \sum_i \nu_i \mu_i = \sum_i \nu_i \mu_i^\ominus + RT \ln \prod_i (f_i)^{\nu_i} \tag{9.12}$$

where

$$\left.\begin{aligned} \Delta G^\ominus &= \sum_i \nu_i \mu_i^\ominus \\ K_e(T) &= \prod_i (f_i)^{\nu_i} \end{aligned}\right\} \tag{9.13}$$

If the initial and final states are in equilibrium, ΔG in (9.7) is zero if only expansion work is involved; hence, f_i' becomes f_i, Q_e becomes K_e, and $0 = \Delta G^\ominus + RT \ln K_e$ so that

$$\Delta G^\ominus = -RT \ln K_e \tag{9.14}$$

Equation (9.14), which results also from (9.12) and (9.13), is extremely important because it relates $\Delta G^\ominus$ and K_e.

For the reverse reaction $dD + eE + \cdots \rightleftharpoons a\text{A} + b\text{B} + \cdots$ it follows similarly that

$$K_e'(T) = \frac{f_\text{A}^a f_\text{B}^b \cdots}{f_\text{D}^d f_\text{E}^e \cdots} \tag{9.15}$$

By (9.11) and (9.15), however,

$$K_e(T) = [K_e'(T)]^{-1} \tag{9.16}$$

That is, reversal of a reaction changes the sign of $\Delta G^\ominus$ (but not its absolute value) and changes the equilibrium constant K_e into its reciprocal. The convention that the fugacities of products be placed in the numerator is universal. It is foolhardy to attempt to use or calculate a K_e without specifying the reaction because of the many possible errors in sign or magnitude of $\Delta G^\ominus$ and ν_i.

Equations analogous to the important (9.5), (9.7), (9.13), and (9.14) can be derived in a similar way for the reaction

$$\begin{matrix} a\text{A} & + & b\text{B} & \longrightarrow & dD & + & e\text{E} \\ a_\text{A}' & & a_\text{B}' & & a_\text{D}' & & a_\text{E}' \end{matrix} \tag{9.17}$$

where a_i' is the arbitrary activity of species i. By the same methods as above, with a_i' in place of f_i', for (9.17)

$$\Delta G = \Delta G^\ominus + RT \ln \left(\frac{a_\text{D}'^d a_\text{E}'^e}{a_\text{A}'^a a_\text{B}'^b} \right) \tag{9.18}$$

and in general

$$\Delta G = \sum \nu_i \mu_i^\ominus + RT \ln \prod_i (a_i')^{\nu_i} \tag{9.19}$$

If

$$Q_a = \frac{a_D'^d a_E'^e}{a_A'^a a_B'^b} = \prod_i (a_i')^{\nu_i} \tag{9.20}$$

then

$$\Delta G = \Delta G^\ominus + RT \ln Q_a \tag{9.21}$$

At equilibrium when $\Delta G = 0$,

$$\Delta G^\ominus = -RT \ln K_a \tag{9.22}$$

where in general

$$K_a = \prod_i (a_i)^{\nu_i} \tag{9.23}$$

and where the activities a_i are the equilibrium values. When it reaches equilibrium, the forward reaction (9.17) has

$$K_a = \frac{a_D^d a_E^e}{a_A^a a_B^b} \tag{9.24}$$

When reaction (9.17) is reversed, there is again an equilibrium constant K_a',

$$K_a' = \frac{a_A^a a_B^b}{a_D^d a_E^e} \tag{9.25}$$

where

$$K_a = (K_a')^{-1} \tag{9.26}$$

A few remarks about K_e and K_a are appropriate here. Since K_e refers to a gaseous reaction, the $\mu_i^\ominus$ and $\Delta G^\ominus$ depend only on T; hence, K_e depends only on T. However, K_a refers to reaction in condensed phases where $\mu_i^\ominus$ and $\Delta G^\ominus$ depend on T and P; hence, K_a depends on both T and P. Nevertheless, K_a is almost independent of pressure because $\Delta G^\ominus$ for a chemical change is generally much greater than free energies of the form $\int \bar{V}_i \, dP$. When a reaction involves both gases and condensed phases, its equilibrium constant is a product of fugacities and activities that correspond to the choice of standard state. Again, K is a weak function of P. At fixed T, the product of fugacities, activities, or other concentrations to the powers specified by the ν_i's of the balanced chemical reaction is a number that is independent of the arbitrary values of these concentrations before equilibrium is attained.

Really each phase of a system at equilibrium is a solution containing every species of the chemical equation. Since the chemical potential of each species is the same in every phase, as required by (6.57), a detailed and thorough examination of even one phase of a system at equilibrium is sufficient to fix every μ_i, a_i, and f_i for every species of the system. It is generally expedient, however, to use the fugacity or pressure of a species in the gaseous phase rather than its activity when dissolved in a liquid or solid, to use the standard activity of an almost pure solid rather than its saturated concentration in a liquid or its vapor pressure, and so on. Hence, the activity or fugacity of a species is taken in any phase where its μ_i can be conveniently observed or calculated. Some of the ramifications of the one-phase attack are evident in Section 7.14. If a phase can be approximated as pure, then its chemical potential is $\mu_i^\ominus$ and its activity is unity if this is compatible with the standard state. Table 9.1 is a summary of the common standard states.

Table 9.1 Summary of Standard States.

Kind of Solution Phase	Standard State	Effective Concentration: Accurate Expression	Effective Concentration: Approximate Expression	Reference Sections
Gas	Unit fugacity	f_i	p_i	3.3; 3.4; 5.13
Liquid	Pure Substance	$\gamma_i X_i$	X_i	3.3; 3.4; 4.17; 7.6; 8.6
Liquid	Pure Solvent	(Use g_1.)	($\mu_1 = \mu_1^\ominus$)	3.3; 3.4; 4.17; 7.6; 8.6; 8.9
	Nonionic Solute A	$a_A = \gamma_A m_A$	m_A	
	Ionic Solute A_aB_b	$a_i = a^a b^b \gamma_\pm^v m_i^v$	$a^a b^b m_i^v$	
	Ion	$a_\pm = \gamma_\pm m_\pm$	$m_\pm$	
Solid	Pure Substance	$\gamma_i X_i$	X_i	3.3; 3.4; 4.17; 7.6; 8.6

Activity coefficients are known for very few multicomponent phases. It is generally convenient to use near-constant expressions that are of the same functional form as K but that avoid the tedium of obtaining fugacities and activities from pressures and concentrations. For example, when gases are ideal and form an ideal solution, fugacities equal partial pressures and (9.11) becomes

$$K_p = \frac{p_D^d p_E^e \cdots}{p_A^a p_B^b \cdots} \tag{9.27}$$

The value of K_p as defined by (9.27) is almost independent of everything except temperature for systems that are nearly ideal. Because K_p is much more readily determined, it is used much more often than K_e.

When activity coefficients approach unity, as they really do in dilute solutions, it is convenient to define a quasi constant K_c by

$$K_c = \frac{C_D^d C_E^e \cdots}{C_A^a C_B^b \cdots} \tag{9.28}$$

Equation (9.28) is analogous to (9.24) and the value of K_c is almost independent of everything except T.

There is a simple relation between K_p and K_c for gases. Since C_i is the number of moles of kind i per liter of solution, by the perfect gas law, $p_i = n_i RT/V = C_i RT$. By (9.27) and (9.28), however,

$$K_p = \frac{(C_D RT)^d (C_E RT)^e \cdots}{(C_A RT)^a (C_B RT)^b \cdots} = K_c (RT)^{(d+e+\cdots)-(a+b+\cdots)}$$

As in (3.1), if $\Delta n_{(g)}$ is the increase in the number of moles of gaseous species for the reaction considered,

$$K_p = K_c (RT)^{\Delta n_{(g)}} \tag{9.29}$$

9.3 DISSOCIATION

It is often relatively easy to evaluate K and ΔG° for a reaction of the form $AB_b \rightarrow A + bB$ by observing or inferring partial pressures of the gaseous products. If only one component (pure AB_b) is present at the start and if the dissociation occurs by only one definite reaction, stoichiometry provides a condition on the amounts of A and B or on their partial pressures in a rigid vessel at constant T. If α is the fraction of gaseous AB_b dissociated, then out of one mole AB_b the number intact at equilibrium is $1 - \alpha$, the number of moles of A is α, and the number of moles of B is $b\alpha$. The total number of moles is then $(1 - \alpha) + \alpha + b\alpha = 1 + b\alpha$. In a rigid vessel at constant T, the initial pressure ($\alpha = 0$) of P_0 thus rises to $P = (1 + b\alpha)P_0$, while the partial pressures at equilibrium are

$$p_A = Y_A P = \frac{\alpha}{1 + b\alpha} P$$

$$p_B = Y_B P = \frac{b\alpha}{1 + b\alpha} P$$

$$p_{AB_b} = Y_{AB_b} P = \frac{1 - \alpha}{1 + b\alpha} P$$

Substitution of these values into the expression for K_p as given by (9.27) yields K_p as a function of P, b, and α.

$$K_p = \frac{p_A p_B^b}{p_{AB_b}} = \left(\frac{\alpha P}{1 + b\alpha}\right)\left(\frac{b\alpha P}{1 + b\alpha}\right)^b \left[\frac{1 + b\alpha}{(1 - \alpha)P}\right]$$

$$= \frac{\alpha(\alpha b P)^b}{(1 - \alpha)(1 + b\alpha)^b} \tag{9.30}$$

An important case of (6.18) occurs when $b = 1$; then, $AB \rightarrow A + B$ and

$$* \quad K_p = \frac{\alpha^2 P}{1 - \alpha^2} \tag{9.31}$$

An example is $PCl_5 \rightarrow PCl_3 + Cl_2$.

When the products of dissociation A and B are indistinguishable to the experimenter who uses K_p or K_c, the forms of (9.30) and (9.31) are somewhat different. The reaction is now $A_{b+1} \rightleftharpoons (b + 1)A$, with

$$p_A = \frac{(b + 1)\alpha}{1 + b\alpha} P$$

and

$$p_{A_{b+1}} = \frac{1 - \alpha}{1 + b\alpha} P$$

Then, by (9.27),

$$K_p = \left[\frac{(b + 1)\alpha P}{(1 + b\alpha)}\right]^{b+1} \left[\frac{(1 + b\alpha)}{(1 - \alpha)P}\right]$$

$$= \frac{[(b + 1)\alpha]^{b+1} P^b}{(1 + b\alpha)^b (1 - \alpha)} \tag{9.32}$$

When $b = 1$, as it does for diatomic molecule A_2, the reaction is $A_2 \rightleftharpoons 2A$ and

$$K_p = \frac{4\alpha^2 P}{1 - \alpha^2} \tag{9.33}$$

Example 9.1. At elevated temperatures, gaseous iodine dissociates to atoms to such an extent that observed pressures P deviate measurably from expected pressures P_o. If the total pressure difference is due to dissociation, calculate K_p for the process $I_{2(g)} \rightleftharpoons 2\,I_{(g)}$ at 800°C if $P_o = 0.3153$ atm and if $P = 0.3429$ atm. (M. L. Perlman and G. K. Rollefson, *J. Chem. Phys.*, **9**, 362 (1941).)

The increase in pressure $P - P_o$ is a direct measure of the number of molecules dissociated; for, when α is the fraction dissociated, the total number of moles of all kinds is $(1 - \alpha)$ of I_2 plus 2α of I, or $(1 + \alpha)$. Since pressure is proportional to the number of free particles at constant volume and temperature,

$$\frac{P}{P_o} = \frac{1 + \alpha}{1}; \qquad \alpha = \frac{P - P_o}{P_o}$$

By (7.9),

$$p_I = \left(\frac{2\alpha}{1 + \alpha}\right) P = \frac{2(P - P_o)}{P_o} \times \frac{P_o}{P} \times P = 2(P - P_o)$$

$$p_{I_2} = \left(\frac{1 - \alpha}{1 + \alpha}\right) P = \frac{P_o}{P} \times P - \left(\frac{P - P_o}{P_o}\right)\left(\frac{P_o}{P}\right) P = 2P_o - P$$

Hence,

$$K_p = \frac{p_I^2}{p_{I_2}} = \frac{[2(P - P_o)]^2}{2P_o - P} = \frac{(2 \times 0.0276)^2}{0.2877} = 1.060 \times 10^{-2} \text{ atm}$$

Example 9.2. At what pressure is only 1.0% I_2 not dissociated to atoms at 800°C if $K_p = 1.060 \times 10^{-2}$ atm for the reaction $I_{2(g)} \rightleftharpoons 2\,I_{(g)}$?

If 1.0% is not dissociated, $\alpha = 0.990$; by (9.33),

$$P = K_p \left(\frac{1 - \alpha^2}{4\alpha^2}\right) = 1.060 \times 10^{-2} \left(\frac{1 - 0.9801}{4 \times 0.9801}\right) = 5.38 \times 10^{-6} \text{ atm}$$

Example 9.3. Account for the factor of four by which Equations (9.31) and (9.33) differ.

$$AB \rightleftharpoons A + B, \qquad K_p = \frac{\alpha^2 P}{1 - \alpha^2} \tag{9.31}$$

$$A_2 \rightleftharpoons 2A, \qquad K_p = \frac{4\alpha^2 P}{1 - \alpha^2} \tag{9.33}$$

The difference between these two situations may be real or it may arise from the attitude of the experimenter. A chemist would ordinarily recognize the difference between PCl_3 and Cl_2 as generated from PCl_5, but would ordinarily classify all iodine atoms from I_2 as indistinguishable. On the other hand, a physicist may wish to distinguish between radioactive ^{129}I and stable ^{127}I as they come from $^{129}I\ ^{127}I$ and, on the other hand, care very little, when he makes measurements of the anomalous pressures exhibited by pure gaseous PCl_5 at elevated temperatures, whether PCl_3 differs chemically from Cl_2.

Although the experimental value of K_e may come from a system containing reactants and products, the value of $\Delta G^{\ominus} = -RT \ln K_e$ is the increase in Gibbs free energy when pure reactants at unit fugacity are transformed entirely into pure products each at unit fugacity. For the experimenter who distinguishes B from A,

$$\Delta G^{\ominus}_{AB} = -RT \ln \left(\frac{\alpha^2 P}{1 - \alpha^2}\right)$$

For the one who does not distinguish B from A,

$$\Delta G^{\ominus}_{A_2} = -RT \ln \left(\frac{\alpha^2 P}{1 - \alpha^2}\right) - RT \ln 4$$

When the latter experimenter decides that B is to be distinguished from A, he must sort out the mixture of A and B that he once regarded as pure A because of ignorance or an established convention.

The entropy of mixing 1 mole A and 1 mole of similar but distinguishable B is $2\overline{\Delta S}$, where

$$\overline{\Delta S} = -R \sum_{i=1}^{C} X_i \ln X_i \tag{7.17}$$

Since the mole fraction of each is $\frac{1}{2}$, $2\overline{\Delta S} = -2R[\frac{1}{2} \ln \frac{1}{2} + \frac{1}{2} \ln \frac{1}{2}] = -2R \ln \frac{1}{2} = R \ln 4$. The entropy of purifying A and B is then $-R \ln 4$. Since the enthalpy of mixing or separating species of an ideal solution is zero, the free energy of purification at the temperature T is just $-T\,\Delta S$, or $RT \ln 4$. Both experimenters reach the same value of $\Delta G^{\ominus}_{AB}$ when both distinguish B from A, for $\Delta G^{\ominus}_{AB} = \Delta G^{\ominus}_{A_2} + RT \ln 4$.

Example 9.4. If the reaction $3\ MoO_{2(s)} = 2\ MoO_{3(g)} + Mo_{(s)}$ reaches equilibrium at one atm at 2050°K, what is $\Delta G^{\ominus}$ for this dissociation at 2050°K?

For the reaction as written, $K_p = p^2_{MoO_3} = 1^2$ at 2050°K. By (9.14), $\Delta G^{\ominus} = -RT \ln 1^2 = 0$ at this temperature.

Example 9.5. What is $\Delta G^{\ominus}$ at 1170°K for the dissociation $2\ CdSe_{(s)} = 2Cd_{(g)} + Se_{2(g)}$ if the partial pressure of Cd above initially pure CdSe is 1.84×10^{-3} atm at this T?

Since one molecule of Se_2 is generated with every two of Cd, the partial pressure of Se_2 is 0.92×10^{-3} atm at 1170°K. Hence, $K_p = p_{Cd}^2 p_{Se} = (1.84 \times 10^{-3})^2(0.92 \times 10^{-3}) = 3.11 \times 10^{-9}$ and, by (9.14), $\Delta G^\ominus = -RT \ln K_p = -1.987 \times 1170 \times 2.303\,(0.493 - 9.000) = 45{,}600$ cal.

It is instructive to consider the free energy change of an isothermal isobaric system (e.g., gases in a thermostatted cylinder with a piston) wherein the gaseous reaction $AB \longrightarrow A + B$ can be advanced or halted at will by addition or withdrawal of a catalyst. If the system is one mole of pure perfect gas AB at a pressure $p_{AB} = P$, by (6.44) its free energy is

$$G_{AB} = \mu_{AB} = \mu_{AB}^\ominus + RT \ln P \tag{9.34}$$

Decomposition of α mole of AB into the perfect gases A and B changes the free energy of the system to

$$G = \alpha\mu_A + \alpha\mu_B + (1-\alpha)\mu_{AB} \tag{9.35}$$

$$= \alpha\mu_A^\ominus + \alpha RT \ln p_A + \alpha\mu_B^\ominus + \alpha RT \ln p_B + (1-\alpha)\mu_{AB}^\ominus + (1-\alpha)RT \ln p_{AB} \tag{9.36}$$

The disappearance of each molecule of AB yields one each of A and B; since P and T are constant, (7.9) requires $p_{AB}/P = (1-\alpha)/(1+\alpha)$ and $p_A/P = p_B/P = \alpha/(1+\alpha)$. Thus (9.36) with $\Delta G^\ominus = \mu_A^\ominus + \mu_B^\ominus - \mu_{AB}^\ominus$ becomes

$$G = \alpha\Delta G^\ominus + \mu_{AB}^\ominus + 2\alpha RT \ln\left[\left(\frac{\alpha}{1+\alpha}\right)P\right] + (1-\alpha)\,RT \ln\left[\left(\frac{1-\alpha}{1+\alpha}\right)P\right] \tag{9.37}$$

As $\alpha \longrightarrow 1$ and dissociation of AB becomes complete,

$$\lim_{\alpha\to 1} G = \Delta G^\ominus + \mu_{AB}^\ominus + 2RT \ln\left(\frac{P}{2}\right) + \lim_{\alpha\to 1}(1-\alpha)\,RT \ln\left(\frac{P}{1+\alpha}\right) + \lim_{\alpha\to 1}(1-\alpha)\,RT \ln(1-\alpha) \tag{9.38}$$

The next-to-last term vanishes in the limit, but the last term approaches the indeterminate form $0 \ln 0$. However, l'Hospital's rule with $\beta = 1 - \alpha$ gives

$$\lim_{\beta\to 0} \beta \ln \beta = \lim_{\beta\to 0} \frac{\ln \beta}{\beta^{-1}} = \lim_{\beta\to 0} \frac{\beta^{-1}}{-\beta^{-2}} = 0$$

Hence, with both of the final terms of (9.38) vanishing in the limit, for the mixture of A and B

$$G_{A,B} = \lim_{\alpha\to 1} G = \Delta G^\ominus + \mu_{AB}^\ominus + 2RT \ln\left(\frac{P}{2}\right) \tag{9.39}$$

This result, with $\mu_A = \mu_A^\ominus + RT \ln(P/2)$ and $\mu_B = \mu_B^\ominus + RT \ln(P/2)$ when $\alpha = 1$ and $p_A = p_B = P/2$ in the mixture of A and B, is the same as what would result from (9.35), namely

$$\lim_{\alpha \to 1} G = G_{A,B} = \mu_A + \mu_B \tag{9.40}$$

just as $G_{AB} = \mu_{AB}$ in (9.34) when $\alpha = 0$. For any degree α of advancement, then, from (9.37) and (9.34),

$$\Delta G = G - G_{AB} = \alpha \Delta G^{\circ} + 2\alpha RT \ln\left[\left(\frac{\alpha}{1+\alpha}\right)P\right] + (1-\alpha)RT\ln\left[\left(\frac{1-\alpha}{1+\alpha}\right)P\right] - RT\ln P \tag{9.41}$$

If $\alpha = 0$, $\Delta G = 0$; if $\alpha = 1$, by (9.41), $\Delta G = \Delta G^{\circ} + 2RT\ln(P/2) - RT\ln P = \Delta G^{\circ} + RT\ln(P/4)$.

Figure 9.1 illustrates (9.41) when $P = 1$ and when ΔG° is zero and $RT \ln 10$. Since $K = \alpha^2 P/(1-\alpha^2)$ by (9.31), it follows from $\Delta G^{\circ} = RT \ln K$ that $\alpha = 0.707$ when $\Delta G^{\circ} = 0$ and $\alpha = 0.301$ when $\Delta G^{\circ} = RT \ln 10$. These values of α correspond to the minima of Figure 9.1 when G and ΔG have fallen to their lowest possible values at T and P as required by (5.54).

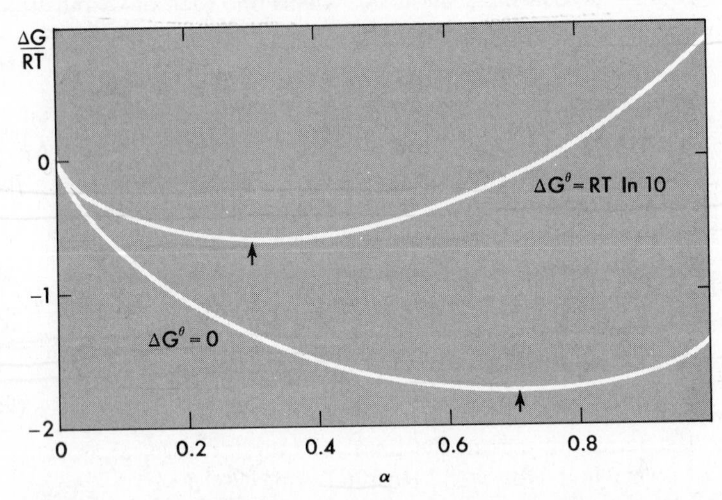

Figure 9.1. Free Energy of the System AB = A + B at Constant P and T as a Function of the Degree of Dissociation of AB When ΔG° is Zero and When $\Delta G^{\circ} = RT \ln 10$.

9.4 STANDARD FREE ENERGY

Just as it was convenient to establish for compounds and ions a table of enthalpies of formation from elements, it is also convenient to establish a table of free energies of formation. Again the elements in their stable states at 1 atm are the standards of reference with zero free energy of formation. The value of ΔG_f°, the free energy of formation or the standard free energy of a substance, is the free energy increase of the reaction in which the substance in its standard state at any T is formed from the elements in their standard states at the same T. Free energies of formation of aqueous ionic solutes are conventionally partitioned into additive contributions for each ion, as is done for their standard enthalpies of formation, with ΔG_f° of H_{aq}^+ in its standard state of unit activity at one atm being zero at any T.

The values of ΔG_f° of Table 9.2 at 25°C were determined by several experimental methods and the best value has been listed. One such method is to measure the equilibrium constant K_c or K_a and calculate ΔG° by (9.14) or (9.22). Another method is to measure heats of reaction and absolute entropies calorimetrically, as was done in preparing Table 3.1 and 4.3, and from such values to calculate ΔG° as in examples below. If a few of the values of ΔG° found in these ways are themselves free energies of formation, then the many other values of

Table 9.2 Standard Free Energies ΔG_f° at 25°C. (F. D. Rossini *et al.*, *Selected Values of Chemical Thermodynamic Properties*, N. B. S. Circular 500, Washington, D. C.: 1952; F. D. Rossini et al. *Selected Values of Properties of Hydrocarbons*, N. B. S. Circular C461, Washington, D. C.: 1947.)

		(kilocalories per gram formula weight)			
Substance	ΔG_f°	Substance	ΔG_f°	Substance	ΔG_f°
$O_{3(g)}$	39.06	C (diamond)	0.6850	$AgBr_{(s)}$	−22.930
$H^+_{(aq)}$	0.000	$CO_{(g)}$	−32.8079	$Ag_2CO_{3(s)}$	−104.48
$OH^-_{(aq)}$	−37.595	$CO_{2(g)}$	−94.2598	$Fe_2O_{3(s)}$	−177.1
$H_2O_{(g)}$	−54.6357	$CO^{-2}_{3(aq)}$	−126.22	$Fe_3O_{4(s)}$	−242.4
$H_2O_{(l)}$	−56.6902	$CH_{4(g)}$	−12.140	$CrO^{2-}_{4(aq)}$	−168.8
$F^-_{(aq)}$	−66.08	$HCO^-_{3(aq)}$	−140.31	$Cr_2O^{2-}_{7(aq)}$	−300.5
$HF_{(g)}$	−64.7	$CH_3OH_{(g)}$	−38.69	$HCrO^-_{4(aq)}$	−177.5
$Cl^-_{(aq)}$	−31.350	$CH_3NO_{2(l)}$	2.26	$H_2CrO_{4(aq)}$	−178.5
$HCl_{(g)}$	−22.769	$C_2H_{2(g)}$	50.000	$Ag_2CrO_{4(s)}$	−148.57
$Br^-_{(aq)}$	−24.574	$C_2H_{4(g)}$	16.282	$TiO_{2(s)}$ (rut)	−203.8
$Br_{2(g)}$	0.751	$C_2H_{6(g)}$	−7.860	$TiCl_{4(l)}$	−161.2
$HBr_{(g)}$	−12.72	$C_3H_{8(g)}$	−5.614	$Al_2O_{3(s)}$ (α)	−376.77
$I_{2(g)}$	4.63	n-$C_6H_{14(g)}$	0.05	$MgCl_{2(s)}$	−141.57
$HI_{(g)}$	0.31	$C_6H_{6(g)}$	30.989	$Ca^{2+}_{(aq)}$	−132.18
$S_{(g)}$	43.57	cyclo-$C_6H_{12(g)}$	7.59	$CaF_{2(s)}$	−277.7
$S^{2-}_{(aq)}$	20.0	$Pb^{2+}_{(aq)}$	−5.81	$Ba^{2+}_{(aq)}$	−134.0
$SO_{2(g)}$	−71.79	$PbS_{(s)}$	−22.15	$BaCl_{2(s)}$	−193.8
$SO_{3(g)}$	−88.52	$PbSO_{4(s)}$	−193.89	$BaCl_2 \cdot H_2O_{(s)}$	−253.1
$SO^{2-}_{4(aq)}$	−177.34	$Zn^{+2}_{(aq)}$	−35.184	$BaCl_2 \cdot 2H_2O_{(s)}$	−309.7
$H_2S_{(g)}$	−7.892	$ZnSO_{4(s)}$	−208.31	$BaSO_{4(s)}$	−323.4
$NO_{(g)}$	20.719	$ZnSO_4 \cdot H_2O_{(s)}$	−269.9	$Na^+_{(aq)}$	−62.589
$NO_{2(g)}$	12.390	$ZnSO_4 \cdot 6H_2O_{(s)}$	−555.0	$NaCl_{(s)}$	−91.785
$NO^-_{3(aq)}$	−26.41	$ZnSO_4 \cdot 7H_2O_{(s)}$	−611.9	$Na_2SO_{4(s)}$	−302.78
$NH_{3(g)}$	−3.976	$Ag^+_{(aq)}$	18.430	$Na_2SO_4 \cdot 10H_2O_{(s)}$	−870.93
$NH_{3(aq)}$	−6.37	$Ag_2O_{(s)}$	−2.586	$Na_2CO_{3(s)}$	−250.4
$NH^+_{4(aq)}$	−19.00	$AgCl_{(s)}$	−26.224	$NaHCO_{3(s)}$	−203.6

$\Delta G^{\ominus}$ for reactions that do not involve elements can be analyzed into parts attributable to the compounds that partake in the reactions. The values of Table 9.2 are a consistent set of so-called best values chosen from among several differing values determined by various methods. With Table 9.2 it is possible to calculate the increase in Gibbs free energy or the equilibrium constant of any reaction that involves the substances listed and their elements. An important goal of equilibrium chemistry is a table containing entries of $\Delta H_f^{\ominus}$, $S^{\ominus}$, and $\Delta G_f^{\ominus}$ for every conceivable substance. Such a table would be most useful in predicting possible reactions and the extent to which they could go. Whether or not the predicted possible change will occur slowly or rapidly is, however, a matter for chemical kinetics, for equilibrium thermodynamics is not concerned with time. Like $\Delta H_f^{\ominus}$'s, the $\Delta G_f^{\ominus}$'s of Table 9.2 are not to be used in calculating $\Delta G_f^{\ominus}$ for reactions that involve a transport of charge between phases or that involve explicit mention of electrons in a condensed phase (e.g., half-reactions).

Example 9.6. Calculate the free energy of formation $\Delta G_f^{\ominus}$ of NO from Tables 3.1 and 4.3.

The reaction of interest is

$$N_{2(g)} + O_{2(g)} \longrightarrow 2NO_{(g)}$$

	$N_{2(g)}$	$O_{2(g)}$	$2NO_{(g)}$
$\Delta H_f^{\ominus}$(kcal)	0.000	0.000	2(21.600)
$S^{\ominus}$(cal deg^{-1})	45.767	49.003	2(50.339)

$$\Delta H^{\ominus} = 2(21{,}600) = 43{,}200 \text{ cal}$$

$$\Delta S^{\ominus} = 2(50.339) - (49.003 + 45.767) = 5.908 \text{ cal deg}^{-1}$$

$$\Delta G^{\ominus} = 43{,}200 - 298.2(5.908) = 41{,}438 \text{ cal.}$$

For 1 mole $NO_{(g)}$, $\Delta G_f^{\ominus} = 20.719$ kcal, which is the entry in Table 9.2.

Example 9.7. Over what range of humidity is $BaCl_2 \cdot H_2O_{(s)}$ stable at 25°C?

At a constant temperature of 25°C in a two-component system ($C = 2$) of $BaCl_2$ and H_2O, $F = C - P + 1$. If only one solid phase is present with the gaseous phase ($P = 2$), there is one degree of freedom ($F = 1$), the partial pressure of water vapor. If two solid phases were present, the partial pressure of H_2O would be fixed ($F = 0$). The extreme pressures that limit the range of stability of $BaCl_2 \cdot H_2O_{(s)}$ are those established at equilibrium by the reactions

$$BaCl_2 \cdot H_2O_{(s)} \rightleftharpoons BaCl_{2(s)} + H_2O_{(g)}$$

and

$$BaCl_2 \cdot 2H_2O_{(s)} \rightleftharpoons BaCl_2 \cdot H_2O_{(s)} + H_2O_{(g)}$$

For the former reaction, by Table 9.2, $\Delta G^{\ominus} = (-193.8 - 54.6) - (-253.1) = 4.7$ kcal. The equilibrium constant is merely p_{H_2O} since the activities of the pure condensed phases are unity. By (9.14),

$$\log p_{H_2O} = -\frac{\Delta G^{\ominus}}{2.303RT} = -\frac{4.7 \times 10^3}{2.303 \times 1.987 \times 298.2} = -3.4 = 0.6 - 4.0$$

$$p_{H_2O} = 4 \times 10^{-4} \text{ atm}$$

Similarly, for the latter reaction,

$$\Delta G^{\ominus} = (-253.1 - 54.6) - (-309.7) = 2.0 \text{ kcal}$$

$$\log p_{H_2O} = -\frac{2.0 \times 10^3}{2.303 \times 1.987 \times 298.2} = -1.5 = 0.5 - 2.0$$

$$p_{H_2O} = 3 \times 10^{-2} \text{ atm}$$

Since the vapor pressure of water is 3.1×10^{-2} atm, the limits on relative humidity are almost 100% and $100 \times [(4 \times 10^{-4})/(3.1 \times 10^{-2})] = 1.3\%$.

Example 9.8. Calculate the increase in free energy at 25°C for the reaction

	$Zn_{(s)}$	$+\ 2\,H^+_{(aq)}$	$\rightarrow$	$H_{2(g)}$	$+\ Zn^{++}_{(aq)}$
Activity:	1.00	0.100		0.200	0.100
$\Delta H^{\ominus}_f$(kcal)	0.00	0.00		0.00	−36.43
$S^{\ominus}$(cal deg^{-1})	9.95	2(15.606)		31.21	5.76

[The thermodynamic data are from F. D. Rossini *et al.*, Circular of the National Bureau of Standards 500 (1952).]
As in (5.71), with $\Delta H^{\ominus} = -36{,}430$ cal and $\Delta S^{\ominus} = -4.19$ cal deg^{-1},

$$\Delta G^{\ominus} = \Delta H^{\ominus} - T\Delta S^{\ominus}$$
$$= -36{,}430 - 298.2(-4.19) = -35{,}180 \text{ cal},$$

which is essentially the value of $\Delta G^{\ominus}_f$ of $Zn^{2+}_{(aq)}$ in Table 9.2.
As in (9.6) and (9.20),

$$Q = \frac{a'_{Zn^{++}} f'_{H_2}}{a'_{Zn} a'^{2}_{H^+}} = \frac{0.100 \times 0.200}{1 \times 0.100^2} = 2$$

As in (9.7) and (9.21),

$$\Delta G = \Delta G^{\ominus} + RT \ln Q$$
$$= -35{,}180 + 1.987 \times 298.2 \times 0.6932$$
$$= -35{,}180 + 411 = -34{,}770 \text{ cal}$$

Example 9.9. Calculate the solubility product constant of AgCl at 25°C.
From the data of Tables 3.1 and 4.3, for the reaction

$$AgCl_{(s)} \rightleftharpoons Ag^+_{(aq)} + Cl^-_{(aq)}$$
$$\Delta G^{\ominus} = \Delta H^{\ominus} - T\Delta S^{\ominus}$$
$$\Delta H^{\ominus} = 25.31 + (-40.02) - (-30.36) = 15{,}650 \text{ cal}$$
$$\Delta S^{\ominus} = 33.28 + (-2.44) - 22.97 = 7.87 \text{ cal deg}^{-1}$$
$$\Delta G^{\ominus} = 15{,}650 - 298.2 \times 7.87 = 13{,}300 \text{ cal}$$

On the other hand, from Table 9.2,

$$\Delta G^{\ominus} = [18.430 + (-31.350)] - [-26.224] = 13.304 \text{ kcal}$$

Hence, $\ln K_a = -\Delta G^{\ominus}/RT$ and

$$\log K_a = -\frac{13{,}300}{2.303 \times 1.987 \times 298.2} = -9.75 = 0.25 - 10$$

$$K_a = 1.8 \times 10^{-10}$$

Example 9.10. Can PbS precipitate from an aqueous solution in which the lead ion molality is 1.0×10^{-2} and the sulfide ion molality is fixed at 1.0×10^{-22} by saturating the solution with H_2S in the presence of a suitable buffer?

The reaction of interest is $Pb^{++}_{(aq)} + S^{--}_{(aq)} \rightarrow PbS_{(s)}$. By (9.9), for this reaction $\Delta G^{\ominus} = -22.15 - (-5.81 + 20.0) = -36.3$ kcal. By (9.18),

$$\Delta G = -36{,}300 + 1.987 \times 298.2 \times 2.303 \times \log\left(\frac{1}{1.0 \times 10^{-2} \times 1.0 \times 10^{-22}}\right)$$

$$= -36{,}300 + 32{,}800 = -3500 \text{ cal}$$

Since ΔG is less than zero, the reaction is spontaneous and $PbS_{(s)}$ can precipitate. This result can be confirmed by showing that the product of the initial ionic concentrations exceeds the solubility product constant K_{sp}, which can be calculated from $\Delta G^{\ominus}$ for the reaction $PbS_{(s)} \rightleftharpoons Pb^{++}_{(aq)} + S^{--}_{(aq)}$. By (9.22),

$$\log K_{sp} = -\frac{\Delta G^{\ominus}}{2.303RT} = -\frac{+36.3 \times 10^3}{2.303 \times 1.987 \times 298.2}$$

$$= -26.6 = 0.4 - 27.0$$

$$K_{sp} = 2.5 \times 10^{-27}$$

But the product of the initial concentrations is 1.0×10^{-24}, about 1000 times in excess of K_{sp}. Precipitation is possible.

9.5 FREE ENERGY CHANGES AT ANY TEMPERATURE

When $\Delta G^{\ominus}$ has been found at some T, it is possible to calculate it at another temperature by any of the methods of Section 5.11, for the very general thermodynamic developments there make no distinction between physical and chemical processes. The most common method of finding $\Delta G^{\ominus}$ at another T when $\Delta G_1^{\ominus}$ is known at T_1 is to use (5.76) in the form

$$-\frac{\Delta G^{\ominus}}{T} + \frac{\Delta G_1^{\ominus}}{T_1} = \int_{T_1}^{T} \frac{\Delta H^{\ominus}}{T'^2}\, dT' \tag{9.42}$$

By Kirchhoff's law (3.21), $\Delta H^{\ominus}$ may be known as a function of T in a form like

$$\Delta H^{\ominus} = \Delta H_1^{\ominus} + \int_{T_1}^{T} \Delta C_P dT'$$

$$= \Delta H_1^{\ominus} + \int_{T_1}^{T} [\Delta C_P^{(0)} + \Delta C_P^{(1)} T' + \Delta C_P^{(2)} T'^2 + \cdots]\, dT'$$

$$= \Delta H_1^{\ominus} + \Delta C_P^{(0)}(T - T_1) + \tfrac{1}{2}\Delta C_P^{(1)}(T^2 - T_1^2) + \tfrac{1}{3}\Delta C_P^{(2)}(T^3 - T_1^3) + \cdots$$

That is,

$$\Delta H^{\ominus} = \Delta H_0^{\ominus} + \Delta C_P^{(0)}T + \tfrac{1}{2}\Delta C_P^{(1)}T^2 + \tfrac{1}{3}\Delta C_P^{(2)}T^3 + \cdots \tag{9.43}$$

where $\Delta H_0^{\ominus}$ is an integration constant of the form

$$\Delta H^{\ominus} = \Delta H_1^{\ominus} - \Delta C_P^{(0)}T_1 - \tfrac{1}{2}\Delta C_P^{(1)}T_1^2 - \tfrac{1}{3}\Delta C_P^{(2)}T_1^3 - \cdots \tag{9.44}$$

If so, then (9.42) and (9.43) yield

$$-\frac{\Delta G^{\ominus}}{T} + \frac{\Delta G_1^{\ominus}}{T_1} = \int_{T_1}^{T} \frac{[\Delta H_0^{\ominus} + \Delta C_P^{(0)}T' + \tfrac{1}{2}\Delta C_P^{(1)}T'^2 + \tfrac{1}{3}\Delta C_P^{(2)}T'^3 + \cdots]}{T'^2}\,dT'$$

$$= \Delta H_0^{\ominus}\left(\frac{T - T_1}{TT_1}\right) + C_P^{(0)} \ln\left(\frac{T}{T_1}\right) + \frac{\Delta C_P^{(1)}}{2}(T - T_1)$$

$$+ \frac{\Delta C_P^{(2)}}{6}(T^2 - T_1^2) + \cdots \tag{9.45}$$

Over small temperature ranges ΔT, it is often sufficient to assume that a large $\Delta H^{\ominus}$ is essentially constant since chemical energies are commonly great relative to the integral of a small ΔC_P over the small temperature range ΔT. Then, from (9.42) or with $\Delta C_P^{(i)} = 0$ in (9.45),

$$-\frac{\Delta G^{\ominus}}{T} + \frac{\Delta G_1^{\ominus}}{T_1} = -\Delta H_1^{\ominus}\left(\frac{1}{T} - \frac{1}{T_1}\right) = \frac{\Delta H_1^{\ominus}(T - T_1)}{TT_1} \tag{9.46}$$

where $\Delta H_1^{\ominus}$ is the increase in enthalpy at T_1, T and all intermediate temperatures.

The sign of $\Delta S^{\ominus}$ is the key to the way $\Delta G^{\ominus}$ changes with T, for, as in (5.74),

$$\left(\frac{\partial \Delta G^{\ominus}}{\partial T}\right)_P = -\Delta S^{\ominus} \tag{9.47}$$

If $\Delta C_P = 0$ so that $\Delta H^{\ominus} = \Delta H_1^{\ominus}$ and $\Delta S^{\ominus} = \Delta S_1^{\ominus}$ are constant between T and T_1 by (3.21) and (5.78), then, as in the second method of Section 5.11, integration of (9.47) yields $\Delta G^{\ominus} - \Delta G_1^{\ominus} = -\Delta S_1^{\ominus}(T - T_1)$. With $\Delta G_1^{\ominus} = \Delta H_1^{\ominus} - T_1\Delta S_1^{\ominus}$, it follows that at any T

$$\Delta G^{\ominus} = \Delta H_1^{\ominus} - T\Delta S_1^{\ominus} \tag{9.48}$$

When $\Delta S_1^{\ominus}$ and $\Delta H_1^{\ominus}$ exceed zero, a sufficiently high T will make $\Delta G^{\ominus}$ negative.

Like $\Delta G^{\ominus}$, the equilibrium constant K is a function of temperature. At any temperature T, for a perfect gas $-\Delta G^{\ominus}/T = \mathrm{R} \ln K_P$. Then, by (5.76)

$$\left[\frac{\partial}{\partial T}\left(-\frac{\Delta G^{\ominus}}{T}\right)\right]_P = \frac{\Delta H^{\ominus}}{T^2} = \left[\frac{\partial}{\partial T}(R \ln K_p)\right]_P$$

That is,

$$\left[\frac{\partial}{\partial T}(\ln K_p)\right]_P = \frac{\Delta H^{\ominus}}{RT^2} \tag{9.49}$$

$$\int_{\ln K_{p_1}}^{\ln K_{p_2}} d(\ln K_p) = \ln\left(\frac{K_{p_2}}{K_{p_1}}\right) = \int_{T_1}^{T_2} \frac{\Delta H^{\ominus}}{RT^2}\,dT \tag{9.50}$$

$$\ln\left(\frac{K_{p_2}}{K_{p_1}}\right) = \frac{\Delta H^\circ(T_2 - T_1)}{RT_2T_1} \tag{9.51}$$

Equation (9.51) permits the calculation of K_p at T_2 when K_p is known at T_1 and when ΔH° is constant between T_1 and T_2 or can be approximated suitably by an effective average value. Or, if K_p has been measured at two or more temperatures, an average value of ΔH° can be found just as heats of vaporization are found from vapor pressures at several temperatures.

Analogous equations involving K_c are slightly different. By (9.29)

$$\ln K_p = \ln K_c + \Delta n_{(g)} \ln RT$$

Whence

$$\frac{\partial \ln K_p}{\partial T} = \frac{\partial \ln K_c}{\partial T} + \frac{\Delta n_{(g)}}{T}$$

By (9.49),

$$\frac{\Delta H^\circ}{RT^2} = \frac{\partial \ln K_c}{\partial T} + \frac{\Delta n_{(g)}}{T}$$

$$\frac{\partial \ln K_c}{\partial T} = \frac{\Delta H^\circ - \Delta n_{(g)}RT}{RT^2}$$

But by (3.1), $\Delta H^\circ - \Delta n_{(g)}RT = \Delta E^\circ$; hence,

$$\frac{\partial \ln K_c}{\partial T} = \frac{\Delta E^\circ}{RT^2} \tag{9.52}$$

On definite integration with ΔE° constant,

$$\int_{\ln K_{c_1}}^{\ln K_{c_2}} d(\ln K_c) = \ln\left(\frac{K_{c_2}}{K_{c_1}}\right) = \int_{T_1}^{T_2} \frac{\Delta E^\circ}{RT^2}\, dT \tag{9.53}$$

$$\ln\left(\frac{K_{c_2}}{K_{c_1}}\right) = \frac{\Delta E^\circ(T_2 - T_1)}{RT_1T_2} \tag{9.54}$$

Equations like (9.52) and (9.54) are true even for changes that do not involve gases. When K_c applies to condensed phases, even at constant pressure the volume is almost constant and $\Delta E^\circ \approx \Delta H^\circ$.

Example 9.11. Gaseous iodine dissociates to atoms at high temperatures to such an extent that measurable deviations from the expected pressures are observed [M. L. Perlman and G. K. Rollefson, *J. Chem. Phys.*, **9**, 362 (1941)]. Observed pressures P and expected pressures P_o if there were no dissociation are listed below for several absolute temperatures. If the total pressure differences are due to dissociation, from these data calculate (a) the heat of dissociation of I_2, and (b) the standard free energy of an iodine atom at 25°C.

Absolute Temperature (°K)	Expected P_o (atm)	Observed P (atm)	K_p (atm)
973	0.0576	0.0624	0.175×10^{-2}
1073	0.0631	0.0750	1.108×10^{-2}
1173	0.0684	0.0918	4.87×10^{-2}
1274	0.0736	0.1122	17.05×10^{-2}

(a) The values of K_p in the table above have been calculated by the method of Example 9.1. Figure 9.2 is the plot of the logarithm of K_p vs. the reciprocal of T. The slope of the line is -8200. Since the equation of the line is of the form

$$\log K_p = -\frac{\Delta H}{2.303RT} + \frac{C_o}{2.303}$$

it follows that near 1000°K

$$\Delta H^{\ominus} = -2.303R \text{ (slope)} = 37{,}500 \text{ cal}$$

for the reaction that corresponds to K_p, namely, $I_{2(g)} \rightleftharpoons 2\, I_{(g)}$. The true value at absolute zero as derived spectroscopically is 35.55 kcal (A. G. Gaydon, *Dissociation Energies and Spectra of Diatomic Molecules*. London: Chapman & Hall, Ltd., 1953, p. 226).

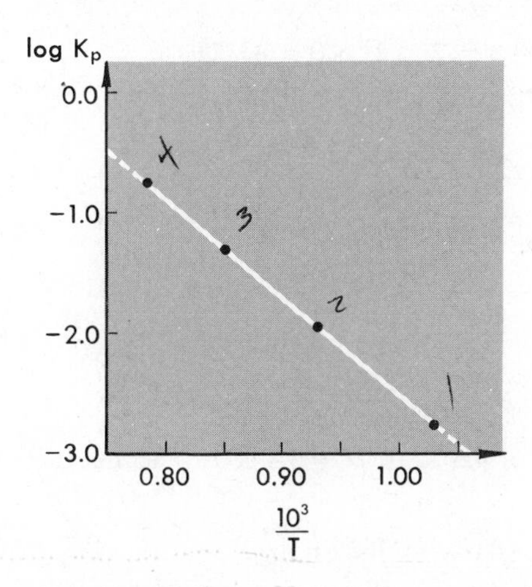

Figure 9.2. Logarithm of K_p for Dissociation of Iodine as a Function of Reciprocal Temperature

(b) ΔC_p for this reaction is about $\frac{3}{2}R$, since C_p of a perfect monatomic gas is $\frac{5}{2}R$ and is $\frac{7}{2}R$ for a perfect diatomic gas that is rigid. By (9.43)

$$\Delta H^{\ominus} = \Delta H_0^{\ominus} + \Delta C_P T$$

$$37{,}500 = \Delta H_0^{\ominus} + \tfrac{3}{2}R \times 1000$$

$$\Delta H_0^{\ominus} = 34{,}500$$

where an average temperature of 1000°K has been assumed to correspond to the graphical $\Delta H^{\ominus}$. At $T_1 = 1000$°K, $\log K_{p_1} = -2.52$ and

$$\Delta G_1^{\ominus} = -RT_1 \ln K_{p_1} = -1.987 \times 1000 \times 2.303 \times (-2.52) = +11{,}500 \text{ cal.}$$

By (9.45), with $\Delta C_P^{(1)} = \Delta C_P^{(2)} = 0$ and $T = 298.2$,

$$\Delta G^{\ominus} = \frac{298.2 \times 11{,}500}{1000} - \frac{34{,}500(298.2 - 1000)}{1000}$$

$$- \frac{3}{2} R \times 298.2 \times 2.303 \times \log\left(\frac{298.2}{1000}\right)$$

$$= 3440 + 24{,}200 + 1080 = 28{,}720 \text{ cal.}$$

Since the standard free energy of $I_{2(g)}$ at 25°C is 4.63 kcal,

$$\Delta G^{\ominus} = 2\Delta G_f^{\ominus}[I_{(g)}] - \Delta G_f^{\ominus}[I_{2(g)}]$$

$$28.72 = 2\Delta G_f^{\ominus}[I_{(g)}] - 4.63$$

$$\Delta G_f^{\ominus}[I_{(g)}] = 16.68 \text{ kcal mole}^{-1}$$

The value reported in NBS Circular 500 is 16.766 kcal mole^{-1}.

Example 9.12. What partial pressure of NO is expected in air at equilibrium at one atm at 2000°K? Assume that ΔC_P is zero.

For the reaction of interest at 25°C,

$$N_{2(g)} + O_{2(g)} \rightleftharpoons 2\,NO_{(g)}$$

$$\Delta H^{\ominus} = 2\,\Delta H_f^{\ominus}(NO) = 2 \times 21{,}600 = 43{,}200 \text{ cal}$$

and

$$\Delta G^{\ominus} = 2\,\Delta G_f^{\ominus}(NO) = 2 \times 20{,}719 = 41{,}438 \text{ cal}$$

Hence, at 25°C,

$$\log K_p = -\frac{\Delta G^{\ominus}}{2.303RT} = -\frac{41{,}438}{2.303 \times 1.987 \times 298.2} = 0.63 - 31.00$$

$$K_p = 4.3 \times 10^{-31}$$

By (9.51),

$$\log\left(\frac{K_p}{4.3 \times 10^{-31}}\right) = \frac{43{,}200(2000 - 298)}{2.303 \times 1.987 \times 2000 \times 298.2} = 26.95$$

$$K_p = 8.9 \times 10^{26} \times 4.3 \times 10^{-31} = 3.8 \times 10^{-4} \text{ at } 2000°\text{K}$$

Alternately,

$$\Delta S^{\ominus} = \frac{\Delta H^{\ominus} - \Delta G^{\ominus}}{T} = \frac{1762}{298.2} = 5.91$$

By (9.48) and (9.14) at $T = 2000°$,

$$\Delta G^{\ominus} = -RT \ln K_p = \Delta H^{\ominus} - T\Delta S^{\ominus}$$

$$2.303 \log K_p = \frac{\Delta S^{\ominus}}{R} - \frac{\Delta H^{\ominus}}{RT} = \frac{5.91}{1.987} - \frac{43200}{1.987 \times 2000} = -7.90$$

$$K_p = 3.8 \times 10^{-4}$$

Let p_{NO} be the equilibrium partial pressure of NO at 2000°K. Then since 2 NO are formed for every N_2 or O_2 that reacts, the partial pressure of N_2 is

$0.800 - (\frac{1}{2})p_{NO}$ and that of O_2 is $0.200 - (\frac{1}{2})p_{NO}$. The equilibrium constant relation serves to fix p_{NO} thus:

$$K_p = 3.8 \times 10^{-4} = \frac{p_{NO}^2}{\left(0.800 - \frac{p_{NO}}{2}\right)\left(0.200 - \frac{p_{NO}}{2}\right)}$$

Since $p_{NO} \ll 0.4$, an approximate solution is readily found.

$$p_{NO}^2 \approx 3.8 \times 10^{-4} \times 0.80 \times 0.20 = 61 \times 10^{-6}$$

$$p_{NO} \approx 7.8 \times 10^{-3} (\ll 400 \times 10^{-3} = 0.4)$$

The partial pressure of NO is only 7.8×10^{-3} atm. A more accurate value is 7.837×10^{-3} atm (E. van Beek-Visser, *J. Chem. Phys.*, **29**, 1358 (1958).)

Example 9.13. An excess of crystals of both pure ammonium thiohydroxide and pure ammonium carbamate are introduced into a vessel containing only pure gaseous hydrogen sulfide and pure gaseous carbon dioxide. These solids are completely dissociated in the gas phase thus:

$$NH_4SH_{(s)} \rightleftharpoons NH_{3(g)} + H_2S_{(g)}$$

$$NH_4OCONH_{2(s)} \rightleftharpoons 2\,NH_{3(g)} + CO_{2(g)}$$

If no solid solutions are formed and if H_2S and CO_2 do not react chemically with each other, (a) calculate the smallest number of independent variables that must be specified at 25°C in order to define completely the thermodynamic state of the system; and (b) what is the partial pressure of NH_3 at 25°C if reasonable values of the required number of variables are specified? The standard molar free energies of $NH_4SH_{(s)}$ and $NH_4OCONH_{2(s)}$ may be assumed to be -13.181 kcal and -105.80 kcal at 25°C.

(a) The system consists of three phases ($P = 3$), namely two solids and gas. Each solid can be made from NH_3 and either H_2S or CO_2; hence, NH_3, H_2S, and CO_2 are the three components ($C = 3$). At 25°C, $F = C - P + 1 = 1$. One intensive variable must be specified to fix the state of the system at 25°C.

(b) From $\Delta G^{\ominus} = -RT \ln K_p$, the usual calculation yields a value of K_p for each reaction, namely

$$K_p = p_{NH_3} \times p_{H_2S} = 0.109$$

$$K_p = p_{NH_3}^2 \times p_{CO_2} = 0.00238$$

Specification of any one of these three equilibrium partial pressures fixes the others at 25°C while both solids remain. If p_{NH_3} is itself specified, the solids will dissociate until this specified value is attained provided the initial pressures of CO_2 and H_2S are small enough that the values of K_p can be satisfied at equilibrium. A more suitable intensive variable is the ratio of p_{H_2S} to p_{CO_2} at equilibrium. Then

$$p_{NH_3} = \left(\frac{0.00238}{0.109}\right)\left(\frac{p_{H_2S}}{p_{CO_2}}\right)$$

Example 9.14. At what temperature can metallic iron be generated from $Fe_2O_{3(s)}$ by reduction with hydrogen, as suggested in Example 5.10?

If the reaction is

$$3H_{2(g)} + Fe_2O_{3(s)} = 2Fe_{(s)} + 3H_2O_{(g)}$$

then it was shown in Example 5.10 that $\Delta G_1^\ominus = 13.2$ kcal and $\Delta H_1^\ominus = 23.1$ kcal at $T_1 = 298.2°K$.

As a start, let the reaction be called possible if $\Delta G^\ominus = 0$ and $K_p = 1$ at the temperature T. If $\Delta C_P = 0$, then $\Delta H^\ominus = \Delta H_1^\ominus = 23.1$ kcal at all T and

$$-\frac{\Delta G^\ominus}{T} + \frac{\Delta G_1^\ominus}{T_1} = \frac{\Delta H_1^\ominus(T - T_1)}{TT_1}$$

$$0 + \frac{13{,}200}{298.2} = \frac{23{,}100(T - 298.2)}{298.2T}$$

$$T = 696°K$$

The reason why high temperatures favor this reaction is that $\Delta S^\ominus$ is greater than zero. At $T_1 = 298.2°K$, $\Delta S^\ominus = 33.2$ cal deg^{-1}, greater than zero mainly because oxygen atoms are transferred from a condensed phase to the gaseous phase while H and Fe atoms do not change their kind of phase. Since $\Delta S^\ominus > 0$, the term $-T\Delta S^\ominus$ decreases $\Delta G^\ominus$ more and more as T increases.

If $\Delta C_P = 0$, it follows that $\Delta S^\ominus$ is independent of T by (5.78). In other words, since $\Delta G^\ominus = \Delta H_1^\ominus - T\Delta S_1^\ominus$ at all T when $\Delta C_P = 0$, $\Delta G^\ominus = 0$ when

$$0 = 23{,}100 - T \times 33.2$$

$$T = \frac{23.100}{33.2} = 696°K$$

Actually, ΔC_P is approximately -10 cal mole^{-1} deg^{-1} so that $\Delta S^\ominus$ decreases as T increases. The term $-T\,\Delta S^\ominus$ is accordingly less effective in decreasing $\Delta G^\ominus$ than supposed above.

The condition that $\Delta G^\ominus$ be zero is rather severe. Maintaining a high pressure of H_2 and a low pressure of H_2O, perhaps by passing dry H_2 over heated Fe_2O_3, favors reduction. If p'_{H_2} equals rp'_{H_2O}, then for the change

$$3H_{2(g)}(p'_{H_2}) + Fe_2O_{3(s)} = 2Fe_{(s)} + 3H_2O_{(g)}(p'_{H_2O})$$

it follows from (9.7) that

$$\Delta G = \Delta G^\ominus + RT\ln\frac{(p'_{H_2O})^3}{(p'_{H_2})^3} = \Delta G^\ominus - 3RT\ln r$$

As r increases, ΔG decreases, just as $\Delta G^\ominus$ decreases because of $-T\Delta S^\ominus$. When $\Delta G = 0$, $\Delta G^\ominus = 3RT\ln r$. If $\Delta C_P = -10$ cal deg^{-1}, by (9.44)

$$\Delta H_0^\ominus = \Delta H_1^\ominus - \Delta C_P T_1 = 23{,}100 + 10 \times 298 = 26{,}100 \text{ cal}$$

Then, by (9.45), with $\Delta G^\ominus = 3RT\ln r$,

$$3RT\ln r = \frac{13{,}200T}{298.2} - \frac{26{,}100(T - 298.2)}{298.2} + 10T\ln\left(\frac{T}{298.2}\right)$$

That is, in this system of three components and three phases, $\mathsf{F} = 1$ at one atm and thus the operating temperature T and r are not both independent. Simplification yields

$$\log r = -3.15 + \frac{1900}{T} + 1.676\log\left(\frac{T}{298.2}\right)$$

If $T = 696°K$, $\log r = 0.20$ and $r = 1.6$. If $T = 500°K$, $\log r = 1.03$ and $r = 10.7$.

Although these calculations indicate that the reaction is possible at modest temperatures, they do not indicate its rate.

Example 9.15. Integration of C_P/T with respect to T from very low T (with the usual T^3-Debye approximation for extrapolating observed C_P's to 0°K) to 500°K at one atm for $KF_{(s)}$ yields $S^\circ = 22.26$ cal mole^{-1} deg^{-1}. Similarly, from observed and calculated C_P's and the third law, S° of α-$KHF_{2(s)}$ at 469.2°K is found to be 34.03 cal mole^{-1} deg^{-1}; for the reversible change α-$KHF_{2(s)}$ to β-$KHF_{2(s)}$ at 469.2°K at one atm, $\Delta H^\circ = 2659$ cal mole^{-1}; heating β-$KHF_{2(s)}$ from 469.2°K to 500°K has $\Delta S^\circ = 1.52$ cal mole^{-1} deg^{-1}. Near 500°K the partial pressure (in mm Hg) of HF established by the equilibrium

$$\beta\text{-KFH}_{2\,(s)} = \text{KF}_{(s)} + \text{HF}_{(g)}$$

is given by $\log_{10} P_{mm} = 8.574 - 4000/T$. (The preceding data are from E. F. Westrum, Jr. and K. S. Pitzer, *J. Am. Chem. Soc.* **71,** 1940 (1949).) For this dissociation of β-KHF_2 at 500°K, calculate ΔS° by the use of

(a) the third law if S° of $HF_{(g)}$ at 500°K is 45.13 cal mole^{-1} deg^{-1}.

(b) the expression for $\log P_{mm}$.

Then compare these two values of ΔS° at 500°K and remark on the symmetry of FHF^- as it exists in α-KHF_2 near 0°K.

The two calculations of ΔS° follow.

(a) The absolute entropy of β-$KHF_{2(s)}$ at 500°K, calculated by (4.52) and (4.114) along a reversible path in which α is heated to 469.2° and changed reversibly at this T at one atm into β, which is then heated to 500°K at one atm, is

$$S^\circ = 34.03 + \frac{2659}{469.2} + 1.52 = 41.22 \text{ cal mole}^{-1} \text{ deg}^{-1}$$

if $S^\circ = 0$ at 0°K because α-$KHF_{2(s)}$ approaches one ordered state at 0°K. Hence, at 500°K

$$\begin{array}{lcccc} & \beta\text{-KHF}_{2\,(s)} & = \text{KF}_{(s)} & + & \text{HF}_{(g)} \\ S^\circ & 41.22 & 22.26 & & 45.13 \end{array}$$

and thus $\Delta S^\circ = 45.13 + 22.26 - 41.22 = 26.17$ cal deg^{-1}.

(b) When $K_p = P$ is expressed in atm to correspond to a standard state at one atm

$$\begin{aligned} -\Delta G^\circ = RT \ln K_p &= 2.303\, RT \log (P_{mm}/760) \\ &= 2.303\, RT\left(8.574 - \frac{4000}{T} - \log 760\right) \\ &= 2.303\, R\,(5.693\, T - 4000) \end{aligned}$$

But this result in (9.47) yields

$$\Delta S^\circ = -\left(\frac{\partial \Delta G^\circ}{\partial T}\right)_P = 2.303\, R\,(5.693) = 26.05 \text{ cal deg}^{-1}$$

If the hydrogen bond in FHF^- rendered the ion unsymmetrical and if each such unsymmetrical ion could be oriented at random in either of two positions (e.g., $FH\cdots F^-$ or $F\cdots HF^-$), the zero-point entropy of α-KHF_2 predicted by (4.93) would be $R \ln 2 = 1.38$ cal mole^{-1} deg^{-1}. This size of discrepancy is much greater than the difference in the ΔS°'s, which in fact agree within experimental error. Since these values of ΔS° agree closely, there is essentially no zero-point entropy in α-KHF_2 at low T. That is, as KHF_2 is cooled, FHF^-

behaves at low T as though it is symmetrical, with H^+ equidistant from each F^- in FHF^-; there is no chemical hump in C_P that lies unobserved below the lowest T's at which C_P has been observed.

9.6 FREE ENERGY FROM CALORIMETRIC DATA

A very simple and powerful method of performing thermodynamic calculations at arbitrary temperatures most expeditiously utilizes the free energy function and the heat content function.[1] To the Gibbs free energy, to the entropy, and to the enthalpy are assigned absolute values $G_T^\ominus$, $S_T^\ominus$, and $H_T^\ominus$ for the standard states at the temperature T. At absolute zero, the value of the enthalpy is $H_o^\ominus$ and the value of the entropy $S_o^\ominus$ is, by the third law, zero. The free energy function is defined as $(G_T^\ominus - H_o^\ominus)/T$ and the heat content function as $(H_T^\ominus - H_o^\ominus)/T$. These functions can be calculated from observed heat capacities C_P and enthalpies of transition $\Delta H_{tr}^\ominus$ thus. By the definition of G in (5.3), $G_T^\ominus = H_T^\ominus - TS_T^\ominus$. Hence,

$$G_T^\ominus - H_o^\ominus = H_T^\ominus - H_o^\ominus - TS_T^\ominus$$

$$\frac{G_T^\ominus - H_o^\ominus}{T} = \frac{H_T^\ominus - H_o^\ominus}{T} - S_T^\ominus \tag{9.55}$$

The quantity $S_T^\ominus$ is the absolute standard entropy of the substance at the temperature T. Values of $S_T^\ominus$ at $T = 298.16$ have been given in Table 4.1, and at any temperature, as in (4.114),

$$S_T^\ominus = \int_0^{T_{tr}} \frac{C_P^{(\alpha)}}{T}\,dT + \frac{\Delta H_{tr}^\ominus}{T_{tr}} + \int_{T_{tr}}^{T_f} \frac{C_P^{(\beta)}}{T}\,dT + \frac{\Delta H_f^\ominus}{T_f} + \int_{T_f}^{T_v} \frac{C_P^{(l)}}{T}\,dT + \frac{\Delta H_v^\ominus}{T_v} + \int_{T_v}^{T} \frac{C_P^{(g)}}{T'}\,dT' \tag{9.56}$$

Similarly, since $H_T^\ominus - H_o^\ominus$ represents the increase in enthalpy suffered by a system as its temperature rises from the reference temperature at $T = 0$ to the temperature T at 1 atm, the second term of (9.55) is

$$\frac{H_T^\ominus - H_o^\ominus}{T} = \frac{1}{T}\left[\int_0^{T_{tr}} C_P^{(\alpha)}\,dT + \Delta H_{tr}^\ominus + \int_{T_{tr}}^{T_f} C_P^{(\beta)}\,dT + \Delta H_f^\ominus + \int_{T_f}^{T_v} C_P^{(l)}\,dT + \Delta H_v^\ominus + \int_{T_v}^{T} C_P^{(g)}\,dT'\right] \tag{9.57}$$

When the substance is not a gas at T, some of the last terms of (9.56) and (9.57) are not evaluated. Values of the free energy function are then evaluated by (9.55) with known values of C_P, ΔH_{tr}, and so on. The selected values of the free energy function of Table 9.3 have been derived in this and other ways. Table 9.4 contains

[1] J. L. Margrave, *J. Chem. Ed.* **32**, 520 (1955).

Table 9.3 Selected Values of Free Energy Function at Various Temperatures†
[Tabulated values of $-(G_T^\ominus - H_o^\ominus)/T$ (cal mole^{-1} deg^{-1})]

	Absolute Temperature					
Substance	0°K	298.16°K	500°K	1000°K	1500°K	2000°K
$O_{(g)}$	0	33.078	35.840	39.460	41.539	43.002
$H_{(g)}$	0	22.425	24.993	28.436	30.451	31.880
$N_{(g)}$	0	31.646	34.215	37.658	39.673	41.102
$C_{(g)}$	0	32.533	35.207	38.730	40.772	42.215
$O_{2(g)}$	0	42.016	45.675	50.697	53.808	56.103
$H_{2(g)}$	0	24.423	27.950	32.738	35.590	37.669
$H_2O_{(g)}$	0	37.172	41.295	47.018	50.622	53.38
$N_{2(g)}$	0	38.817	42.415	47.306	50.284	52.478
$NO_{(g)}$	0	42.980	46.760	51.864	54.964	57.239
C(graphite)	0	0.517	1.146	2.771	4.181	—
$CO_{(g)}$	0	40.350	43.947	48.860	51.864	54.078
$CO_{2(g)}$	0	43.555	47.663	54.109	58.481	61.85
$CH_{4(g)}$	0	36.46	40.75	47.65	52.84	—
$C_2H_{6(g)}$	0	45.27	50.77	61.11	69.46	—
$C_3H_{8(g)}$	0	52.73	59.81	74.10	85.86	—
$C_2H_{4(g)}$	0	43.98	48.74	57.29	63.94	—
$C_2H_{2(g)}$	0	39.976	44.508	52.005	57.231	—
$C_6H_{6(g)}$	0	52.93	60.24	76.57	90.45	—
n-$C_6H_{14(g)}$	0	70.01	83.65	111.18	133.53	—

† Rossini, F. D., *et al.* NBS Circular C461 (1947).

Table 9.4 Selected Values of Heat Content Function at Various Temperatures and Selected Values of Heats of Formation $\Delta H_o^\ominus$ at Absolute Zero†
[Tabulated values of $\Delta H_o^\ominus$ (kcal mole^{-1}) and $(H_T^\ominus - H_o^\ominus)/T$ (cal mole^{-1} deg^{-1})]

		Absolute Temperature					
Substance	$\Delta H_o^\ominus$	0°K	298.16°K	500°K	1000°K	1500°K	2000°K
$O_{(g)}$	58.586	0	5.391	5.291	5.159	5.102	5.071
$H_{(g)}$	51.620	0	4.968	4.968	4.968	4.968	4.968
$N_{(g)}$	112.55††	0	4.968	4.968	4.968	4.968	4.968
$C_{(g)}$	170.0††	0	5.228	5.126	5.048	5.022	5.014
$O_{2(g)}$	0	0	6.942	7.048	7.497	7.850	8.109
$H_{2(g)}$	0	0	6.788	6.859	6.966	7.130	7.336
$H_2O_{(g)}$	−57.104	0	7.934	8.039	8.580	9.251	9.88
$N_{2(g)}$	0	0	6.950	6.970	7.202	7.502	7.750
$NO_{(g)}$	21.477	0	7.359	7.288	7.506	7.796	8.015
C(graphite)	0	0	0.844	1.642	3.075	3.876	—
$CO_{(g)}$	−27.202	0	6.951	6.980	7.256	7.572	7.818
$CO_{2(g)}$	−93.969	0	7.506	8.446	10.222	11.336	12.072
$CH_{4(g)}$	−15.987	0	8.039	8.730	11.56	14.09	—
$C_2H_{6(g)}$	−16.517	0	9.578	12.02	18.28	23.00	—
$C_3H_{8(g)}$	−19.482	0	11.78	16.08	25.67	32.43	—
$C_2H_{4(g)}$	14.522	0	8.47	10.23	14.76	18.07	—
$C_2H_{2(g)}$	54.329	0	8.021	9.582	12.090	13.694	—
$C_6H_{6(g)}$	24.000	0	11.41	17.50	30.16	38.24	—
n-$C_6H_{14(g)}$	−30.98	0	22.44	31.10	49.11	61.50	—

† All values taken from reference to Table 9.2 except those marked with dagger (††); those latter are from Gaydon, A. G., *Dissociation Energies and Spectra of Diatomic Molecules.* London: Chapman and Hall, Ltd., 1953, pp. 197, 228.

similar selected values of the heat content function and ΔH°_o. Since these functions vary only slowly with temperature, graphical or analytical interpolation yields accurate values of these functions at any temperature.

Figure 9.3 shows how the free energy functions of graphite and several gases depend on T. As the disorder due to vibrations increases within each molecule, S°_T and, to a lesser extent, $(H^\circ_T - H^\circ_o)/T$ increase from zero at 0°K. Clearly the entropy term dominates (9.55). From 0° to 1600°K graphite shows a very small decrease in its free energy function while every gas shows a large decrease from zero; gases are much less ordered than crystals. Similarly, the united ends of the carbon chain of n-hexane are less ordered than the ring of cyclohexane, and the flexible ring of cyclohexane is less ordered than the rigid ring of benzene.

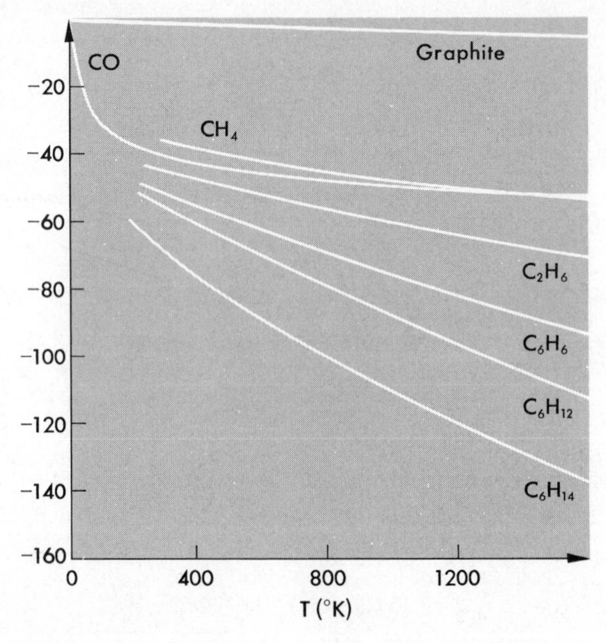

Figure 9.3. Free Energy Functions of Graphite and Gaseous Carbon Monoxide, Methane, Ethane, Benzene, Cyclohexane, and n-Hexane as Functions of Temperature†

A value of ΔG° for a reaction is calculated at some temperature T in this way from tabulated or interpolated values.

$$\Delta\left(\frac{G^\circ_T - H^\circ_o}{T}\right) = \sum_{\text{products}}\left(\frac{G^\circ_T - H^\circ_o}{T}\right) - \sum_{\text{reactants}}\left(\frac{G^\circ_T - H^\circ_o}{T}\right) \qquad (9.58)$$

†F. D. Rossini et al., *NBS Circular C461*, 1947.

But since T is fixed,

$$\Delta\left(\frac{G_T^\ominus - H_o^\ominus}{T}\right) = \frac{\Delta G^\ominus}{T} - \frac{\Delta H_o^\ominus}{T}$$

Whence
$$\Delta G^\ominus = \Delta H_o^\ominus + T\Delta\left(\frac{G_T^\ominus - H_o^\ominus}{T}\right) \tag{9.59}$$

where $\Delta H_o^\ominus$, the heat of reaction at absolute zero, is calculated from the second column of Table 9.4. These values of $\Delta H_o^\ominus$ are the real values at 0°K, for the heat capacities of (9.56) and (9.57) are the really observed values at the temperatures involved. Once $\Delta G^\ominus$ is known, (9.14) and (9.22) furnish the equilibrium constant at once. On the other hand, it is not generally recognized that only one measurement of an equilibrium constant or $\Delta G^\ominus$ at one temperature can yield through (9.59) a value of $\Delta H_o^\ominus$ that is often much more accurate than a value of $\Delta H^\ominus$ determined from a plot of log K vs. $1/T$. All that is required for this last type of calculation are $\Delta G^\ominus$ and the free energy functions of reactants and products at the temperature T. If these last are not available, they are often readily guessed with good accuracy.

The heat content functions of Table 9.4 are useful in calculating the increase in enthalpy of a change of state at any temperature without the use of equations like (3.21). Let the diagram be this.

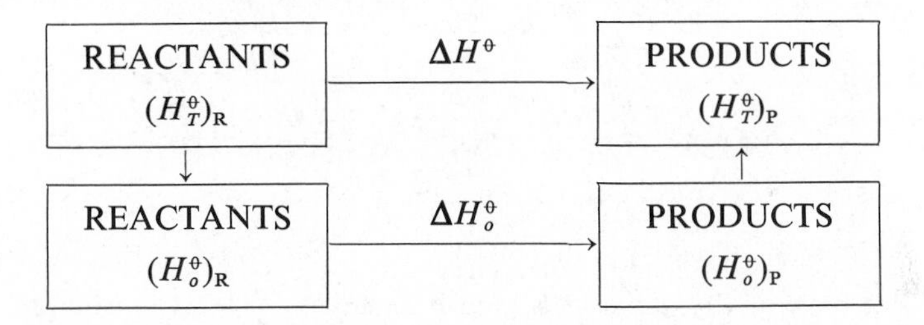

Then, for the alternate routes from reactants to products at the temperature T,

$$\begin{aligned}\Delta H^\ominus &= [(H_o^\ominus)_R - (H_T^\ominus)_R] + \Delta H_o^\ominus + [(H_T^\ominus)_P - (H_o^\ominus)_P] \\ &= \Delta H_o^\ominus + [(H_T^\ominus - H_o^\ominus)_P - (H_T^\ominus - H_o^\ominus)_R] \\ &= \Delta H_o^\ominus + \sum_P \left[T\left(\frac{H_T^\ominus - H_o^\ominus}{T}\right)\right] - \sum_R \left[T\left(\frac{H_T^\ominus - H_o^\ominus}{T}\right)\right]\end{aligned}$$

That is,

$$\Delta H^\ominus = \Delta H_o^\ominus + T\Delta\left(\frac{H_T^\ominus - H_o^\ominus}{T}\right) \tag{9.60}$$

All the quantities on the right of (9.60) are listed in Table 9.4.

Example 9.16. With the data of Tables 9.4 and 9.5, calculate the equilibrium constant at 2000°K for the reaction $N_{2(g)} + O_{2(g)} \rightleftharpoons 2NO_{(g)}$.

From Table 9.4, $\Delta H_o^\ominus = 2(21{,}477)$ cal $= 42{,}954$ cal. By (9.59) with data from Table 9.3,

$$\Delta G^\ominus = \Delta H_o^\ominus + T\Delta\left(\frac{G_T^\ominus - H_o^\ominus}{T}\right)$$

$$= 42{,}954 + 2000\,[2(-57.239) - (-52.478) - (-56.103)]$$

$$= 42{,}954 + 2000(-5.897) = 31{,}160$$

By the equivalent of (9.14),

$$\log K_p = -\frac{\Delta G^\ominus}{2.303RT} = -\frac{31{,}160}{2.303 \times 1.987 \times 2000} = -3.405 = 0.595 - 4.000$$

$$K_p = 3.94 \times 10^{-4}$$

The value calculated in Example 9.12 is 3.8×10^{-4}, and a rather accurate value is 3.770×10^{-4} [calculated from E. van Beek-Visser, *J. Chem. Phys.*, **29,** 1358 (1958)].

Example 9.17. Calculate the fraction of methane decomposed at equilibrium at one atm total pressure at 1000°K if the only reaction is $CH_{4(g)} \rightleftharpoons C_{(s)} + 2H_{2(g)}$.

By (9.59), at 1000°K,

$$\Delta G^\ominus = 15{,}987 + 1000[(-2.771) + 2(-32.738) - (-47.65)]$$

$$= 15{,}987 + 1000(-20.60) = -4610 \text{ cal}$$

By (9.14),

$$\log K_p = -\frac{\Delta G^\ominus}{2.303RT} = -\frac{-4610}{2.303 \times 1.987 \times 1000} = 1.007$$

$$K_p = 10.16 = \frac{p_{H_2}^2}{p_{CH_4}}$$

If one mole of CH_4 dissociates to give 2α moles of H_2, $(1 - \alpha)$ moles of CH_4 remain and by (7.9)

$$p_{H_2} = \left(\frac{2\alpha}{1+\alpha}\right)P \qquad p_{CH_4} = \left(\frac{1-\alpha}{1+\alpha}\right)P$$

With $P = 1$ atm,

$$K_p = \left(\frac{2\alpha}{1+\alpha}\right)^2\left(\frac{1+\alpha}{1-\alpha}\right) = \frac{4^2\alpha}{1-\alpha^2} = 10.16$$

Solution yields $\alpha = 0.847$ as the fraction of CH_4 dissociated by this reaction at 1000°K.

Example 9.18. At 2257°K at one atm total pressure, water is 1.77% dissociated at equilibrium [von Wartenberg (1906)]. With neglect of the pressure of OH that exists through the reaction $2H_2O \rightleftharpoons H_2 + 2OH$, calculate the value of $\Delta H^\ominus$ at absolute zero for the reaction $2H_{2(g)} + O_{2(g)} \rightleftharpoons 2H_2O_{(g)}$. At 2257°K, the free energy functions of $H_{2(g)}$, $O_{2(g)}$, and $H_2O_{(g)}$ are -38.56, -57.08, and -54.60 cal deg^{-1}, respectively [interpolated values from F. D. Rossini *et al.*, Circular of the National Bureau of Standards C 461 (1947)].

If $\alpha = 0.0177$ in the dissociation reaction

$$2H_2O_{(g)} \rightleftharpoons 2H_{2\,(g)} + O_{2\,(g)}$$
$$2(1-\alpha) \quad 2\alpha \quad \alpha$$

then, since the total pressure P is one atm and the total number of molecules is $2(1-\alpha) + 2\alpha + \alpha = 2 + \alpha$,

$$p_{H_2O} = \left(\frac{2-2\alpha}{2+\alpha}\right)P = \frac{2-0.0354}{2.0177} = 0.9737 \text{ atm}$$

$$p_{O_2} = \left(\frac{\alpha}{2+\alpha}\right)P = \frac{0.0177}{2.0177} = 0.00878 \text{ atm}$$

$$p_{H_2} = 2p_{O_2} = 0.0176 \text{ atm}$$

$$K_p = \frac{p_{H_2}^2 p_{O_2}}{p_{H_2O}^2} = \frac{(1.76 \times 10^{-2})^2(8.78 \times 10^{-3})}{(9.74 \times 10^{-1})^2} = 2.87 \times 10^{-6}$$

At 2257°K,

$$\begin{aligned}\Delta G^\ominus = -RT\ln K_p &= -1.987 \times 2257 \times 2.303 \times \log(2.87 \times 10^{-6}) \\ &= -1.987 \times 2257 \times 2.303 \times (0.458 - 6.000) \\ &= +57{,}240 \text{ cal}\end{aligned}$$

Hence, for the combination reaction

$$\Delta H_o^\ominus = \Delta G^\ominus - T\Delta\left(\frac{G_T^0 - H_o^\ominus}{T}\right) \tag{6.53}$$

$$\begin{aligned}&= -57{,}240 - 2257[2(-54.60) - 2(-38.56) - (-57.08)] \\ &= -57{,}240 - 2257 \times 25.00 = -113{,}660 \text{ cal}\end{aligned}$$

The value from Table 9.4 is $2(-57.104)$, or $-114{,}208$ cal.

Example 9.19. With the aid of the heat content functions of Table 9.4 and the fact that at 25°C the heat of formation of $H_2O_{(g)}$ is $-57{,}797.9$ cal mole^{-1} (Table 3.1), evaluate $\Delta H_o^\ominus$ for the reaction $2H_{2\,(g)} + O_{2\,(g)} \rightleftharpoons 2H_2O_{(g)}$.

By (9.60),

$$\Delta H_o^\ominus = \Delta H^\ominus - T\Delta\left(\frac{H_T^\ominus - H_o^\ominus}{T}\right)$$

$$\begin{aligned}&= 2(-57{,}797.9) - 298.16[2(7.934) - 2(6.788) - 6.942] \\ &= 2(-57{,}797.9) - 298.16(-4.650) = -114{,}209.4 \text{ cal}\end{aligned}$$

9.7 SUMMARY

Although thermodynamics will continue to be used as needed, this chapter is the last that deals primarily with thermodynamics. The next chapters emphasize the microscopic or structural view of physical chemistry in contrast to the macroscopic or molar view until now.

Standard molar free energies of formation ΔG_f°, which are really standard chemical potentials μ°, have been defined relative to the usual standard states. Used like standard molar enthalpies of formation, these ΔG_f°'s allow ΔG° to be calculated at one T for chemical changes. The methods of Section 5.11, which are based on the Gibbs-Helmholtz equation

$$\left(\frac{\partial \Delta G^\circ}{\partial T}\right)_P = -\Delta S^\circ$$

then can be used to calculate ΔG° at any T. With the very important equation $\Delta G^\circ = -RT \ln K$ it thus is possible to predict the equilibrium constant K of a chemical change at any T.

Calorimetric measurements of ΔH and C_P are sufficient to supply ΔH° and, by the third law, ΔS° at any T, with, of course, intent to use $\Delta G^\circ = \Delta H^\circ - T\Delta S^\circ$. Alternately, values of ΔG° can often be calculated theoretically by statistical mechanics (Chapter 17) for substances of known structure and of known energy at 0°K. At very high T where experiments are difficult and most species are simple gases, such calculated values are often superior to values based on thermodynamic observation. In contrast to the tedious calculations that may be required in these cases, the phase rule in its sophisticated elegance ignores multidigit numbers and focuses on a few essentials: the number of phases, components, and independent intensive variables at chemical or physical equilibrium. It is a boon to professors who like to state problems with a minimum of data and with assurance that a bright student will not detect an inconsistency in a superabundance of data. It is a boon also to experimenters who do not care to read extra meters or buy unnecessary apparatus.

Like the equations of state of mixtures, the activity coefficients of species in multicomponent solutions are difficult to predict or even sort out from the observed facts. For this reason, outside of aqueous solutions, K's are generally used with partial pressures or concentrations rather than the proper fugacities or activities. And when a chemical change begins and ends in nonstandard states, $\Delta G = \Delta G^\circ + RT \ln Q$, while ΔG at any T can be found by the Gibbs-Helmholtz equation as in Section 5.11.

In view of this power and breadth of thermodynamics for chemical reactions and physical changes, one is tempted to relax in the expectation that all chemistry is merely a matter of computation. This state of affairs may come eventually, but the next chapter on rates of reaction should indicate that the present modest knowledge of equilibrium chemistry is only one tiny corner of chemistry. The empirical observer still has most of chemistry to explore, for a table of ΔG°'s is powerless to describe how equilibrium is approached.

PROBLEMS

1. At 28°C the equilibrium constant for the reaction

$$BF_{3(g)} + BCl_{3(g)} \rightleftharpoons BFCl_{2(g)} + BF_2Cl_{(g)}$$

is 0.53 [T. H. S. Higgins, E. C. Leisegang, C. J. G. Raw, and A. J. Rossouw, *J. Chem. Phys.*, **23**, 1544 (1955)]. Calculate the partial pressure of $BFCl_2$ at equilibrium if the initial pressures of BF_3 and BCl_3 are 300 mm Hg and 200 mm Hg.
Answer: 102 mm Hg.

2. If pressures are known within 0.001 atm, what is the smallest value of K_p certainly known to be greater than zero at a total pressure of 1 atm for a reaction of the type $A_{2(g)} \rightleftharpoons 2A_{(g)}$?
Answer: 10^{-6}.

3. Use the phase rule to determine the number of independent intensive variables in these situations.
(a) $CO_{(g)} + 2H_{2(g)} = CH_3OH_{(g)}$
(b) $Mo(CO)_{6(s)} = Mo_{(s)} + 6CO_{(g)}$ and $Ni(CO)_{4(g)} = Ni_{(s)} + 4CO_{(g)}$
(c) $H_2O_{(g)} + C_{(s)} = CO_{(g)} + H_{2(g)}$
$H_2O_{(g)} + CO_{(g)} = CO_{2(g)} + H_{2(g)}$
$CO_{2(g)} + C_{(s)} = 2CO_{(g)}$
Answer: (a) 3; (b) 1; (c) 3 (One dependent reaction!)

4. At 3500°K, K_p for the reaction $C_2N_{2(g)} \rightleftharpoons 2\,CN_{(g)}$ is 2.50 [E. Rutner, W. H. McLain, Jr., and K. Scheller, *J. Chem. Phys.*, **24**, 173 (1956)]. What percentage by volume is not dissociated at one atm?
Answer: 38.0%.

5. For $PH_{3(g)}$ at 25°C, $\Delta G_f^{\circ} = 4360$ cal mole^{-1} [F. D. Rossini *et al.*, Circular of the National Bureau of Standards 500 (1952)]. What percentage of $PH_{3(g)}$ is dissociated into elements at one atm at 25°C at equilibrium? (Assume $P_{4(s)}$ is stable.)
Answer: 99.936%.

6. Which of these oxides can react spontaneously with gaseous hydrogen at 1.000 atm at 25°C to yield the solid metal and liquid water at 25°C? $Ag_2O_{(s)}$; $Fe_2O_{3(s)}$; $Fe_3O_{4(s)}$; $Al_2O_{3(s)}$.
Answer: Ag_2O.

7. Calculate the pressure of $H_2O_{(g)}$ in equilibrium with $ZnSO_4 \cdot H_2O_{(s)}$ and $ZnSO_4 \cdot 6H_2O_{(s)}$ at 25°C.
Answer: 13.7 mm Hg.

8. If K_{sp} of ZnS is 1.0×10^{-23} at 25°C, what is ΔG_f° of $ZnS_{(s)}$ at 25°C?
Answer: -46.6 kcal mole^{-1}.

9. What is the solubility product constant of Ag_2CrO_4 at 25°C at one atm?
Answer: 6.9×10^{-13}.

10. Equilibrium constants for the reaction $PuF_{4(s)} + F_{2(g)} = PuF_{6(g)}$ at various T are [L. E. Trevorrow, W. A. Shinn, and R. K. Steunenberg, *J. Phys. Chem.* **65**, 398 (1961)]:

T(°C)	395	336	303	251	200
$K \times 10^4$	50.5	33.5	26.5	15.1	8.18

What are ΔS° and ΔH° in this range of T?
Answer: 6.1 kcal; -1.3 cal deg^{-1}.

11. When CdSe decomposes by the reaction $CdSe_{(s)} \longrightarrow 2\,Cd_{(g)} + Se_{2(g)}$, the equilibrium partial pressures of Cd at various T are

T(°K)	1016	1081	1116	1137	1170
$p_{Cd} \times 10^5$(atm)	5.39	29.5	59.3	90.7	184

[Data from W. J. Wösten, *J. Phys. Chem.* **65**, 1949 (1961).] Calculate ΔH° and

$\Delta S^{\ominus}$ near 1100°K, and if $\Delta C_P = -6$ cal deg^{-1} for the reaction as written, find $\Delta H^{\ominus}$ at 25°C.
Answer: At 1100°K, 157.4 kcal and 95.5 cal deg^{-1}; at 25°C, 162.2 kcal.

12. Values of K_p for the reaction $C_2N_{2(g)} \rightleftharpoons 2\,CN_{(g)}$ are given for several temperatures [E. Rutner, W. H. McLain, Jr., and K. Scheller, *J. Chem. Phys.*, **24,** 173 (1956)]. Find $\Delta G^{\ominus}$, $\Delta H^{\ominus}$, and $\Delta S^{\ominus}$ for this reaction at 1500°K and 2500°K, and explain the differences in values. Estimate $\Delta H^{\ominus}$ at 0°K.

look at sign of slope

T(°K)	K_p	T(°K)	K_p
1400	2.16×10^{-10}	2400	4.28×10^{-3}
1500	3.23×10^{-9}	2500	1.08×10^{-2}
1600	3.17×10^{-8}	2600	2.56×10^{-2}

Answer: At 1500°K, $\Delta H^{\ominus} = 111.4$ kcal and $\Delta S^{\ominus} = 35.4$ cal deg^{-1}; at 2500°K, $\Delta H^{\ominus} = 110.8$ kcal and $\Delta S^{\ominus} = 35.3$ cal deg^{-1}; at 0°K, $\Delta H_0^{\ominus} = 112.3$ kcal.

13. It is common to express the dependence of $\Delta G^{\ominus}$ upon temperature in the form

$$\Delta G^{\ominus} = A + BT$$

where A and B are constants. Justify this form and identify A and B in terms of thermodynamic variables.
Answer: $A = \Delta H^{\ominus}$; $B = -\Delta S^{\ominus}$.

14. If steam at one atm is 1.77% dissociated at 2257°K and 1.18% dissociated at 2155°K, find $\Delta H^{\ominus}$ for the formation of 1 mole $H_2O_{(g)}$ at 2200°K.
Answer: -57.8 kcal mole^{-1}.

15. It is sometimes said that all gases are less soluble in water as the temperature rises. Discuss.

16. For the reaction $TiCl_{3(s)} + HCl_{(g)} \rightleftharpoons TiCl_{4(g)} + \frac{1}{2}H_{2(g)}$, $K_p = 2.74$ at 400°C and $K_p = 4.80$ at 450°C [W. F. Krieve and D. M. Mason, *J. Chem. Phys.*, **25,** 524 (1956)]. If $\Delta C_P = -6$ cal deg^{-1}, find $\Delta H^{\ominus}$ at 25°C for this reaction. What will be the partial pressure of $TiCl_{4(g)}$ if HCl at an initial pressure of one atm in a closed rigid vessel comes to equilibrium with excess $TiCl_{3(s)}$ at 500°C?
Answer: $\Delta H^{\ominus} = 13{,}240$ cal; 0.919 atm.

17. Calculate K_p at 298°K and 500°K for the reaction $C_2H_{4(g)} + H_{2(g)} \rightleftharpoons C_2H_{6(g)}$.
Answer: $K_p(298) = 4.96 \times 10^{17}$; $K_p(500) = 7.98 \times 10^{7}$.

18. Calculate the equilibrium constant at 1000°C for the reaction

$$3\,C_2H_{2(g)} \rightleftharpoons C_6H_{6(g)}$$

Answer: 1.7×10^{6}.

19. At 600°K, what is K_p for the gaseous reaction in which isobutene reacts with isobutane to yield iso-octane if (Circular C461 NBS):

Substance	$\Delta H_0^{\ominus}$(kcal mole^{-1})	$\dfrac{G^{\ominus} - H_0^{\ominus}}{T}$ (cal mole^{-1} deg^{-1})
ISOBUTENE	+ 1.68	−68.42
ISOBUTANE	−24.60	−68.95
ISOOCTANE	−40.73	−100.6

Answer: 36.4.

20. At 133°C, the density of gaseous acetic acid is 2.78 g l^{-1} at one atm [*International Critical Tables of Numerical Data, Physics, Chemistry, and Technology*, National Academy of Sciences—National Research Council, Washington, D.C. 1926–1933, *III*, p. 437]. Calculate the percentage by weight that exists as dimer and calculate K_p for the reaction $(CH_3COOH)_{2\,(g)} \rightleftharpoons 2\,CH_3COOH_{(g)}$.
Answer: 70.5%; $K_p = 0.381$.

21. Consider these equilibria in the same vessel:

$$Ag_2O_{(s)} \rightleftharpoons 2\,Ag_{(s)} + \tfrac{1}{2}O_{2\,(g)}$$
$$Ag_2CO_{3\,(s)} \rightleftharpoons Ag_2O_{(s)} + CO_{2\,(g)}$$

In what way does the presence of $Ag_2O_{(s)}$ restrict the pressures of CO_2 and O_2? Under what circumstances could Ag_2O disappear? Are the pressures of CO_2 and O_2 independent?
Answer: At one T, $K_1 = (p_{O_2})^{1/2}$ while $K_2 = p_{CO_2}$

22. Use the phase rule to determine the number of independent intensive variables when these equilibria obtain in aqueous solution in the absence of a gaseous phase.
(a) $Ag^+ + Cl^- = AgCl_{(s)}$
(b) $Ag^+ + Cl^- = AgCl_{(s)}$ and $Ag^+ + Br^- = AgBr_{(s)}$
(c) $Ca^{2+} + CO_3^{2-} = CaCO_{3\,(s)}$ and $H_2O + CO_3^{2-} = HCO_3^- + OH^-$ and $Mg^{2+} + 2\,OH^- = Mg(OH)_{2\,(s)}$
Answer: (a) 3; (b) If P = 3, F = 3; (c) 4.

23. At 502.2°K, K_p for the reaction $PCl_{3\,(g)} + Cl_{2\,(g)} \rightleftharpoons PCl_{5\,(g)}$ is 1.752 [D. P. Stevenson and D. M. Yost, *J. Chem. Phys.*, **9**, 403 (1941)]. Calculate the percentage of PCl_5 dissociated:
(a) At one atm total pressure.
(b) At ten atm total pressure.
(c) At one atm in a mixture that was made of equal numbers of moles of $Cl_{2\,(g)}$ and $PCl_{5\,(g)}$.
Answer: (a) 60.28%; (b) 23.24%; (c) 48.8%.

24. Calculate ΔG and ΔH at 25°C for the changes:
(a) $H_{2\,(g)}$ (0.10 atm) + $Cl_{2\,(g)}$ (0.90 atm) $\longrightarrow$ 2 $HCl_{(g)}$ (1.00 atm).
(b) $H_{2\,(g)}$ (0.10 atm) + $Cl_{2\,(g)}$ (0.50 atm) $\longrightarrow$ 2 $HCl_{(g)}$ (0.20 atm).
Answer: (a) $\Delta G = -44{,}111$ cal and $\Delta H = -44{,}126$ cal; (b) $\Delta G = -45{,}670$ cal and $\Delta H = -44{,}126$ cal.

25. Is 0.20 molar AgF a saturated solution at 25°C if ΔG_f^0 of $AgF_{(s)}$ is -44.2 kcal mole^{-1} (F. D. Rossini *et al.*, Circular 500 NBS.)?
Answer: No.

26. The solubility product constant of CaF_2 at 25°C is 4.0×10^{-11}. Calculate ΔG_f^0 of Ca_{aq}^{++}.
Answer: -131.3 kcal mole^{-1}.

27. Calculate K_p at 298°K for the dissociation of $HI_{(g)}$ into $H_{2\,(g)}$ and $I_{2\,(g)}$. What percentage is dissociated at 298°K?
Answer: In absence of $I_{2\,(s)}$, 6.76%.

28. What is the ionization constant of NH_4OH at 25°C and the partial pressure of $NH_{3\,(g)}$ above 0.100 molal NH_4OH at 25°C?
Answer: 1.86×10^{-5}; 1.35 mm Hg.

29. Calculate the first and second ionization constants at 25°C of H_2CrO_4.
Answer: $K_1 = 0.19$; $K_2 = 4.2 \times 10^{-7}$.

30. Calculate the equilibrium constant for the reaction $Cr_2O_{7(aq)}^{--} + H_2O_{(l)} = 2\,CrO_{4(aq)}^{--} + 2\,H_{(aq)}^{+}$ at 25°C.
Answer: 4×10^{-15}.

31. The strongest bonds in diatomic molecules like N_2 and CO require about 225 kcal mole^{-1} for dissociation to atoms at absolute zero. The temperature at which ΔG° is zero for such dissociations may be considered the upper limit of temperature for chemistry. Estimate this limit.
Answer: 7000°K.

32. By qualitative arguments based on order and disorder, explain how ΔG° and K vary with T for these reactions:
(a) $CO_{2(g)} + C_{(s)} = 2\,CO_{(g)}$
(b) $W(CO)_{6(s)} = W_{(s)} + 6\,CO_{(g)}$
(c) $ZnO_{(s)} + CO_{(g)} = Zn_{(g)} + CO_{2(g)}$
Answer: Because of increase in disorder during reaction, all have $\Delta S^{\circ} > 0$; hence, ΔG° decreases and K increases as T increases.

33. Why is care needed in deciding the sign of ΔS° for reactions like
(a) $H_2O_{(l)} + Fe(H_2O)_{n+1(aq)}^{3+} = H_3O_{(aq)}^{+} + Fe(H_2O)_nOH_{(aq)}^{2+}$
(b) $AgCl_{(s)} = Ag^{+} + Cl^{-}$
(c) $Ca(OH)_{2(s)} = Ca_{(aq)}^{2+} + 2\,OH_{(aq)}^{-}$
(d) $H_3PO_{4(aq)} + H_2O_{(l)} = H_3O_{(aq)}^{+} + H_2PO_{4(aq)}^{-}$
Answer: State of order of solvated ions is uncertain.

34. For the reaction $F_{2(g)} \longrightarrow 2\,F_{(g)}$, values of K_p at various T are [(R. N. Doescher, *J. Chem. Phys.*, **20**, 330 (1952)]:

$K_p \times 10^3$(atm)	47.7	14.	2.06	0.412	0.024
T(°K)	1084	1010	921	850	759

What is ΔH° at 25°C if $\Delta C_P = 2.4$ cal deg^{-1} for the reaction above?
Answer: 36.6 kcal.

35. The reaction $2MoS_{3(s)} = 2MoS_{2(s)} + S_{2(g)}$ reaches equilibrium at one atm at about 520°C where $\Delta H^{\circ} = 40$ kcal. If C_P's for $MoS_{3(s)}$, $MoS_{2(s)}$, and $S_{2(g)}$ are 25, 17, and 8 cal mole^{-1} deg^{-1}, what are ΔH° and ΔG° for this reaction at 25°C?
Answer: $\Delta H^{\circ} = 44$ kcal; $\Delta G^{\circ} = 22.6$ kcal.

36. At what total pressure at 400°C is ΔG zero for the gaseous reaction $2\,H_2 + CO \longrightarrow CH_3OH$ if the partial pressure of CH_3OH is to be one atm and if the partial pressure of H_2 is twice that of CO?
Answer: 62 atm.

37. What is the partial pressure of Cl_2 above excess solid $SbCl_3$ and Sb at 450°C at equilibrium if the only reaction is $2\,SbCl_{3(s)} = 2\,Sb_{(s)} + 3\,Cl_{2(g)}$? The following data are from NBS Circular 500.

Substance	ΔH_f° at 25°C (kcal mole^{-1})	S° at 25°C (cal mole^{-1} deg^{-1})	C_P (cal mole^{-1} deg^{-1})
$SbCl_{3(s)}$	−91.34	44.5	24.0
$Sb_{(s)}$	0.00	10.5	6.1
$Cl_{2(g)}$	0.00	53.3	8.1

Answer: 1.26×10^{-12} atm.

38. Equilibrium constants for the reaction $2\,NOCl_{(g)} \rightleftharpoons 2\,NO_{(g)} + Cl_{2(g)}$ were calculated from the initial pressures p^0_{NOCl}, p^0_{NO}, and $p^0_{Cl_2}$ in a rigid vessel and the final observed total pressure P [J. K. Dixon, *Zeitschrift für physikalische Chemie, Bodenstein Festband*, 679 (1931)]. Some of the data, with pressures (mm Hg), are:

T(°C)	P	p^0_{NOCl}	p^0_{NO}	$p^0_{Cl_2}$
230	539.0	208.7	0	312.4
308	648.4	241.0	0	360.6
399	781.2	278.5	0	416.9
279	676.8	441.5	163.4	0
377	867.1	519.6	192.3	0
465	1027.7	589.6	218.2	0

From these data calculate:
(a) K_p and K_c at each temperature.
(b) ΔH° for the dissociation reaction.
(c) ΔG°_f of $NOCl_{(g)}$ at 25°C if $\Delta C_P = 0$.
Answer: (a) 0.01865 and 4.52×10^{-3}; 0.2161 and 4.54×10^{-3}; 1.705 and 3.09×10^{-2}; 0.1009 and 2.23×10^{-3}; 1.179 and 2.21×10^{-2}; 5.585 and 9.22×10^{-2}; (b) 17.7 kcal; (c) 15.95 kcal mole^{-1}.

39. Which is least stable at 1000°K relative to the elements: $C_2H_{2(g)}$, $C_2H_{4(g)}$, or $C_2H_{6(g)}$?
Answer: C_2H_2.

---

40. At elevated temperatures, gaseous hydrogen reduces $CuO_{(s)}$ to $Cu_2O_{(s)}$ and/or $Cu_{(s)}$. If pure CuO and pure H_2 are heated together at equilibrium, how many intensive variables can be specified at will (and explain in terms of equilibrium constants)? If solid Cu is then added, what changes can be made?
Answer: If $\mathsf{P} = 4$, then $\mathsf{F} = 0$; if Cu is added, then $\mathsf{F} = 1$.

41. Consider a single chemical reaction linking P pure condensed phases, none of which is a solution.
(a) Show that at an arbitrarily fixed T and P such a reaction proceeds to the exhaustion of at least one phase as it achieves equilibrium.
(b) Under what circumstances could this reaction attain equilibrium with all P phases present?
Answer: (a) $\mathsf{F} = -1$; (b) Allow T or P to vary.

42. At 25°C the equilibrium constant for the reaction $2\,BrCl_{(g)} \rightleftharpoons Br_{2(g)} + Cl_{2(g)}$ is 0.15 [H. C. Mattrow, C. F. Pachucki, and N. J. Hawkins, *J. Chem. Phys.*, **22,** 1117 (1954)] and the vapor pressure of Br_2 is 0.30 atm.
(a) What is the partial pressure of BrCl in a vessel of 30.0 l containing 0.500 moles $Cl_{2(g)}$ initially and excess liquid Br_2 if Cl_2 does not dissolve in $Br_{2(l)}$ and if the reaction above is the only possible one?
(b) What is ΔG°_f of $BrCl_{(g)}$?
Answer: (a) 0.52 atm; (b) -206 cal mole^{-1}.

43. At 115.5°C, the pressure of $NO_{(g)}$ above a mixture of $Ag_{(s)}$, $AgNO_{2(s)}$, and $AgNO_{3(s)}$ is 0.395 atm, while at 142.6°C it is 1.530 atm [M. Randall, G. G. Manov, and O. L. I. Brown, *J. Am. Chem. Soc.*, **60,** 694 (1938)]. Predict the pressure of $NO_{(g)}$ above the same three solids at 100.0°C if the reaction is $2\,AgNO_{2(s)} \rightleftharpoons Ag_{(s)} + AgNO_{3(s)} + NO_{(g)}$. Can this same reaction occur if pure $AgNO_{2(s)}$ is placed in a continuously evacuated chamber at 100°C? Explain.
Answer: 0.167 atm; yes, for phase rule applies only at equilibrium.

44. Analysis of the vapors effusing from a small hole in a heated chamber containing $TiCl_{2(s)}$ yielded these results [M. Farber and A. J. Darnell, *J. Chem. Phys.*, **25**, 526 (1956)] (rounded) for equilibrium pressures above $TiCl_{2(s)}$:

T(°K)	$p(TiCl_4)$ (atm)	$p(TiCl_3)$ (atm)	$p(TiCl_2)$ (atm)
797	3.5×10^{-7}	7.5×10^{-6}	4.6×10^{-7}
828	9.4×10^{-7}	2.1×10^{-5}	1.4×10^{-6}
862	3.0×10^{-6}	5.6×10^{-5}	4.4×10^{-6}
893	9.2×10^{-6}	1.5×10^{-4}	1.2×10^{-5}

From these data find ΔH°, ΔG°, and ΔS° at 850°K for the reactions:
(a) $2\,TiCl_{2(s)} \rightleftharpoons TiCl_{4(g)} + Ti_{(s)}$.
(b) $3\,TiCl_{2(s)} \rightleftharpoons 2\,TiCl_{3(g)} + Ti_{(s)}$.
(c) $TiCl_{2(s)} \rightleftharpoons TiCl_{2(g)}$.
Calculate ΔH° and ΔG° at 850°K for the reaction $Ti_{(s)} + 3\,TiCl_{4(g)} \rightleftharpoons 4\,TiCl_{3(g)}$.
Answer: (a) 48.4 kcal, 22.0 kcal, 31.0 cal deg^{-1}; (b) 87.2 kcal, 34.1 kcal, 62.5 cal deg^{-1}; (c) 48.0 kcal, 21.5 kcal, 31.2 cal deg^{-1}.

45. As in Fig. 9.3, sketch the temperature-dependence of the free energy function of a substance that melts and vaporizes at one atm within the temperature range sketched.

46. Calculate the equilibrium constant at 850°C for the reaction

$$TiCl_{4(g)} + 2\,Mg_{(l)} \longrightarrow Ti_{(s)} + 2\,MgCl_{2(l)}$$

from these data [F. D. Rossini, P. A. Cowie, F. O. Ellison, C. C. Browne, and W. C. Arsem, *Properties of Titanium Compounds and Related Substances*, Washington, D. C.: Office of Naval Research (ONR Report ACR-17), October, 1956).]

Substance	ΔH_f° (25°C)	S° (25°C)	Average C_P (25° ⟶ ca. 1100°C)
	(kcal mole^{-1})	(cal mole^{-1} deg^{-1})	(cal mole^{-1} deg^{-1})
$TiCl_{4(g)}$	−182.4	84.4	25.4
$Mg_{(s)}$	0.0	7.78	6.6
$Ti_{(s)}$	0.0	7.334	7.0
$MgCl_{2(s)}$	−153.40	21.42	18.5

The heat of fusion of Mg at one atm at 648.7°C is 2160 cal mole^{-1}; that of $MgCl_2$ at one atm at 714°C is 10300 cal mole^{-1}. From 714°C to 850°C the average C_P of $MgCl_{2(l)}$ is 22.1 cal mole^{-1} deg^{-1}; from 648.7°C to 850°C that of $Mg_{(l)}$ is 7.40 cal mole^{-1} deg^{-1}.
Answer: 2.0×10^{14}.

47. According to data in Tables 3.1 and 9.4, at what T does pure $NaHCO_{3(s)}$ develop a total pressure of one atm by decomposition according to the reaction $2\,NaHCO_{3(s)} \longrightarrow Na_2CO_{3(s)} + CO_{2(g)} + H_2O_{(g)}$?
Answer: 387°K.

48. Magnetite (Fe_3O_4) and hematite (Fe_2O_3) form solid solutions in which the activity of each is equal to its mole fraction. From the data below, find ΔH°

and $\Delta S^{\ominus}$ near 1500°K for the reaction 6 Fe_2O_3 = 4 Fe_3O_4 + $O_{2(g)}$, where the oxides are one solid phase. [Data selected at random from O. N. Salmon, *J. Phys. Chem.* **65,** 550 (1961).]

T(°K)	$P(O_2)$ (atm)	Mole Fraction of Fe_3O_4
1422	0.00332	0.0032
1430	0.00329	0.0032
1436	0.00357	0.0048
1475	0.00501	0.0125
1486	0.00771	0.0231
1521	0.02118	0.0064
1523	0.02125	0.0068
1580	0.1195	0.0117
1598	0.1211	0.0186
1604	0.1195	0.0109

Answer: $\Delta H^{\ominus}$ = 187 kcal; $\Delta S^{\ominus}$ = 77 cal deg^{-1}.

49. From the heat content function of graphite in Table 9.5, find an expression for C_P of graphite of the form $C_P^{(0)} + C_P^{(1)}T + C_P^{(2)}T^2$ above 298°K. Then, with the aid of heat capacities from Table 2.1, find $\Delta G^{\ominus}$ as a function of temperature for the reactions $C_{(s)} + CO_{2(g)} \rightleftharpoons 2\,CO_{(g)}$ and $C_{(s)} + H_2O_{(g)} \rightleftharpoons CO_{(g)} + H_{2(g)}$.
Answer: $C_P = 1.720 + 9.524 \times 10^{-3}T - 3.79 \times 10^{-6}T^2$; for CO_2 reaction, $\Delta G^{\ominus} = 40{,}433.7 + 121.650T - 4.906T\ln T + 8.295 \times 10^{-3}T^2 - 1.257 \times 10^{-6}T^3$; for H_2 reaction, $\Delta G^{\ominus} = 30{,}499.8 + 96.737T - 4.391T\ln T + 5.178 \times 10^{-3}T^2 - 0.632 \times 10^{-6}T^3$.

50. At 2000°K, the partial pressure of $C_{(g)}$ in equilibrium with graphite is 3.3×10^{-11} atm [L. Brewer and A. W. Searcy, "High Temperature Chemistry," *Ann. Rev. Phys. Chem.*, **7,** 268 (1956)]. Calculate the heat of sublimation of graphite at absolute zero.
Answer: $\Delta H_0^{\ominus}$ = 170 kcal mole^{-1}.

10
CHEMICAL KINETICS

10.1 INTRODUCTION

Very few people need be concerned with equilibrium thermodynamics, but everyone is vitally interested in chemical kinetics, the study of the time-rates of chemical change. As viewed by the physical sciences, life itself is a complex set of coordinated and interdependent chemical reactions that sustain for a time a highly improbable system quite out of equilibrium with its surroundings. If all reactions proceeded swiftly or even at the same rate toward equilibrium, our universe would be much less varied that it is. Stability and reasonable permanence often require much effort in slowing spontaneous processes. The engineer must control corrosion, wear, and stability and strength of materials. On the other hand, a manufacturer of chemicals with many thousands of dollars invested in expensive equipment depends not only upon a favorable change of free energy. He must produce his product swiftly and efficiently to minimize his investment in equipment and labor. The many scientific publications of difficult and careful observations and controversial interpretations of these data are perhaps the surest criterion of the theoretical chemist's present interest in kinetics.

The effect of concentration and temperature on the rate of chemical reactions of fire has been known for ages, but the first really controlled observations of reaction rate were by Wenzel in 1777. In an attempt to measure chemical affinity, he observed the rates of solution of metals in various acids. In 1806, the rate of formation of H_2SO_4 in the lead chamber process was known to be accelerated and, in fact, possible because of the presence of oxides of nitrogen, and an intermediate compound of the kind $NOHSO_4$ was recognized. Platinum was found to increase the rate of the oxidation of SO_2 by Davy about 1818 and oxidation of H_2 by Dobereiner about 1822. Faraday in 1833 recognized the importance of surface area of the Pt, and about 1840 Berzelius suggested the word 'catalysis' to describe this phenomenon in which a nonreactant changes the ordinary rate of a chemical process. Berzelius and Dobereiner believed catalysis to be related to electricity.

The science of chemical kinetics is usually considered to have started in 1850 with the formulation of the first mathematical rate law by Wilhelmy, who followed the rate of hydrolysis of sucrose in aqueous acid by observing the optical activity of the solution as time passed. He found the rate to be proportional to the instantaneous concentration of sucrose at constant T and acidity in dilute solution. The 1850's and 1860's saw the development of the *law of mass action and dynamic equilibrium* by studies of rates of inorganic and organic reactions. Enough data of various kinds were at hand by 1877 that van't Hoff was able to call attention to the effect of the vessel wall on the rates of some reactions. He also sought detailed mechanisms of reactions and classified reactions by the number of reactant molecules. Every reaction was thought to be electrical (a reversal of electrolysis) by Armstrong in 1885, and he suggested that a catalyst was needed for every reaction. Catalysis was finally defined properly only in 1894 by Ostwald, who then also showed that catalysis could be described by the theoretical methods of chemical kinetics.

After van't Hoff had showed in 1884 that the logarithm of the equilibrium constant is a linear function of $\Delta H/T$, Arrhenius in 1889 showed that the logarithm of the rate constant (which specifies the rate at unit concentrations) is similarly a linear function of $\Delta H_a/T$, where the activation energy ΔH_a of the reaction is the extraordinary energy that must be achieved by those few collisions of reactants that are to be fruitful. That is, Arrhenius found that only a few of the many collisions of molecules had the necessary energy to initiate reaction. The foundations of *absolute reaction rate theory*, whereby rates are calculated from the details of molecular behavior, were laid by Marcelin and Tolman in 1915. They considered the various atomic and molecular positions and momenta involved, and formulated a reaction in terms of passage through certain critical values of position and momentum.

Light was known to start certain reactions, and in 1818 Grotthuss hypothesized that only absorbed light affected the rate. This has since become a law of photochemistry. The action of light on the combination of H_2 and Cl_2 was studied by Draper in 1843, by Bunsen and Roscoe about 1855, and by many others, often with confusing results. After the 1913 observations of Bodenstein on this reaction, and after Stark in 1908 and Einstein in 1912 had stated that in the primary step of a photochemical reaction one quantum of light excites one molecule, Nernst in 1918 explained the start of this reaction as the production of Cl atoms by Cl_2's absorption of light. The reaction of H_2 and Br_2 at constant T in the absence of light was studied carefully by Bodenstein and Lind in 1907 and its mechanism was described in 1919 by Christiansen, Herzfeld, and Polanyi. Comparison of these reactions of H_2 with Cl_2 or Br_2 was important in their eventual understanding, for each can be initiated by light that dissociates the halogen molecule to atoms and each can involve free radicals.

From 1913 to 1919, Perrin advanced the theory that all reactions begin with activation of molecules by absorption of light or other radiation. This theory did not predict correct dependence of rate on reactant concentration, but it did spur Lindemann in 1922 into advancing the very useful and long-lived theory that collisions supply a few special molecules with enough energy that they can react. Lindemann pictured such energized molecules as whirling themselves apart, while modern theory is less definite and says merely that after a time the molecule of high energy reaches a critical mode of vibration in which its parts move somewhat in phase to dissociation or other reactive configurations. Many investigators have developed the various aspects of collisional rate theory. For example, in 1926, Hinshelwood showed how the internal motions of molecules affected rates calculated by the Lindemann mechanism. Later, Kassel, Rice, and Ramsperger, together with others, developed the collisional theory still more. A very important advance came in 1935, when Eyring showed that every reaction can be described as proceeding through an unobservable species called the *activated complex*. This species is a molecule or complex of molecules in the very act of undergoing chemical change, and its thermodynamic properties can be evaluated theoretically as though it were a real, observable species. Calculation of the rate of the simple reaction $H_2 + H \longrightarrow H + H_2$ in 1932 by Pelzer and Wigner led to the Eyring theory, which in turn has dominated thinking in chemical kinetics for many years. The many recent theories for calculating rates of reaction from molecular properties often differ only in the mathematical rigor with which the fundamental ideas of the 1920's and 1930's are applied. The problems are, however, sufficiently complicated that much research continues in this wide field of physical chemistry.

The laws of thermodynamics are not directly applicable to chemical kinetics, although they do offer a set of conditions that eventually result at dynamic equilibrium. These laws of thermodynamics also recognize an order or sequence of states. The first law merely requires that the beginning and end of a change be recognized. The second law says which of two states naturally comes first, and the third law gives a microscopic explanation of the second law in terms of disorder and probability. Beyond these indirect references to time and the fact that some processes reach equilibrium while others do not, the laws of thermodynamics do not venture. All treatments of irreversible thermodynamics are, however, based on the rate of production of entropy. In brief, thermodynamics emphasizes initial and final states, while chemical kinetics is concerned with the intermediate states of a changing system.

10.2 MEASUREMENT OF RATE

To measure time quite accurately is easy but it is not always easy to decide when a chemical change began or to measure the degree to which the reaction progresses as time passes. The ideal analytical method is much swifter than the reaction of interest, yields an accurate analysis, and does not disturb the reaction. Measurement of the index of refraction, absorption spectrum, volume, or pressure of a system often fixes the progress of a reaction. Sometimes the rate of growth of crystals of a product or the loss in mass of reactants can also be followed continuously and used as a measure of the extent of a reaction. The most obvious way to analyze is, however, to withdraw typical aliquots from time to time. The withdrawal may be directly into a mass spectrometer or gas chromatograph. Chemical analysis of an aliquot ordinarily requires halting the reaction by quenching or by withdrawing a catalyst in order to allow time for the more leisurely chemical analysis.

Some of the more common methods of continuous analysis of streams of reacting chemicals are: electrical conductivity; electrode potentials; infrared, visible, and ultraviolet absorption spectroscopy; X-ray emission or fluorescence spectroscopy; density; viscosity; dielectric constant; nuclear magnetic resonance and mass spectroscopy. Instruments that continuously record process data in most of these ways are available commercially. Automation is achieved by feeding such recorded data to a computer that controls the process variables in accord with scientific and economic goals.

Frequently the measurement that is made does not of itself yield an analysis. If X_0 is the value of some physicochemical property at time $t = 0$, if X_t is its value at an intermediate time t, and if X_∞ is its final value at infinite time, then the fraction unreacted and remaining unchanged at time t is

$$\frac{X_\infty - X_t}{X_\infty - X_0}$$

while the fraction reacted or the fractional progress of the reaction is

$$\frac{X_t - X_0}{X_\infty - X_0}$$

The property X is assumed to be a linear function of the extent of the reaction. This is true of the pressure of an isothermal constant-volume reaction for which $\Delta n_{(g)}$ is not zero. It may be true also of optical activity, dielectric constant, electrical conductivity, and so on. The sum of the these two expressions is, of course, unity. In the limit at $t = 0$, the first is unity and the second is zero, while at $t = \infty$, the first is zero and the second is unity.

Precise definition of T and P by the equations

$$T = \left(\frac{\partial E}{\partial S}\right)_V \quad (5.10) \qquad \text{and} \qquad P = -\left(\frac{\partial A}{\partial V}\right)_T \quad (5.17)$$

means that T and P are not defined in systems that are not at thermodynamic equilibrium. It is common and practical, nevertheless, to extend the meanings of T and P to the records made by instruments that can observe P and T properly at equilibrium if the instruments are known to react to their environment much faster than the environment is changing.

10.3 ORDER OF REACTION

The rate of a chemical reaction can be stated in terms of the rate of disappearance of reactants or of appearance of products. These two rates may differ if, for example, reactants or products partake in more than one reaction or if varying amounts of intermediate species are generated as the reaction occurs. For the present, however, these two rates are supposed equal. Written in conventional form as in Section 9.2, the reaction $A + 2B \longrightarrow D + 3E$ is

$$
\begin{array}{ccccc}
0 = D & + \ 3E & - A & - 2B & \\
0 & 0 & C_A^0 & C_B^0 & t = 0 \\
x & 3x & C_A^0 - x & C_B^0 - 2x & t > 0
\end{array}
\tag{10.1}
$$

As the symbols below the species indicate, species A begins with a concentration C_A^0 and species B begins at C_B^0, while none of the products is present at the start. The balanced chemical equation says that 1 mole of D is generated when 1 mole of A reacts. If the change occurs at constant volume, the production of x moles of D per unit volume is accompanied by the loss of x moles of A per unit volume. This loss is indicated by a minus sign. The equation also states that 2 B react with each A; hence, the production of x moles of D per unit volume requires the loss of $2x$ moles B per unit volume so that at some time after the start the concentration of B is $C_B^0 - 2x$. Similarly, the equation says that 3 E are produced for every D so that the concentration of E is three times that of D at any instant.

The rate at which D is generated is dx/dt. In general, this derivative and others like it are taken at constant volume. If the balanced chemical equation describes the only chemical change, this is also the rate at which A is destroyed. If C_A is the instantaneous concentration of A at some time t then $C_A = C_A^0 - x$. Since C_A^0 is independent of time,

$$\frac{dC_A}{dt} = -\frac{dx}{dt} \tag{10.2}$$

Since x increases with time, dC_A/dt is less than zero. That is, C_A decreases as t increases. Moreover, changing signs in (10.2) says that the rate at which D is generated equals the rate at which A reacts, $-dC_A/dt$. Similarly,

$$\frac{dC_B}{dt} = \frac{d}{dt}(C_B^0 - 2x) = -2\frac{dx}{dt}$$

$$\frac{dx}{dt} = \frac{1}{2}\left(-\frac{dC_B}{dt}\right) \tag{10.3}$$

That is, the rate at which D is generated is one-half the rate at which B disappears. Again, the rate at which E is generated is three times the rate at which D is generated, for

$$\frac{dC_E}{dt} = \frac{d(3x)}{dt} = 3\left(\frac{dx}{dt}\right) \tag{10.4}$$

All of the facts in (10.2) to (10.4) are nicely given for a general reaction $0 = \sum_i \nu_i \Omega_i$ when its rate is taken to be

$$v = \frac{1}{\nu_i}\frac{dC_i}{dt} \tag{10.5}$$

where the stoichiometric coefficient ν_i is positive for products and negative for reactants. By (10.5), the rate of (10.1) is

$$v = \frac{dx}{dt} = \frac{dC_D}{dt} = \frac{1}{3}\frac{dC_E}{dt} = -\frac{dC_A}{dt} = -\frac{1}{2}\frac{dC_B}{dt} \tag{10.6}$$

This is the rate of (10.1) even when analysis follows the concentrations of B or E.

Every system in which reactions occur is a mixture or solution because products mix with reactants. The rate of reaction, at least at the start when only reactants have large concentrations, is proportional to a product of concentrations of reactants to various empirically observable powers. It is, in fact, incorrect to use thermodynamic activities instead of concentrations. As stated in terms of the rate of disappearance of a reactant A and the concentrations of all reactants, the rate of (10.1) is, in general,

$$v = -\frac{dC_A}{dt} = kC_A^a C_B^b \tag{10.7}$$

The overall *order of the reaction* described by this empirically observed rate law is $a + b$. The reaction is of a order with respect to A and of b order with respect to B. The proportionality constant k is a positive number independent of time and concentration of A or B but dependent upon temperature and perhaps other variables.

Equations like (10.7) are generally applicable only to fluids. Mobilities in solid solutions are low and the rates of solid-state transformations, even simple decompositions, depend in general upon formation of favorable crystal nucleuses and upon surface reactions. Even the seemingly simple process of sublimation of a molecular crystal in a vacuum involves several steps: formation of an energetically favorable arrangement, decomposition to yield molecules adsorbed on the decomposing surface, slow desorption of these physically adsorbed molecules, and diffusion of the molecules away from the surface. Thus there may be little or no meaning to the order of a heterogeneous reaction.

Frequently the products of solid-state reactions catalyze the reaction. For example, the rate of decomposition of Ag_2O after an induction period is proportional to the amount of silver produced and to the amount of oxide.[1] Once a solid-state decomposition is well under way and no new reaction sites are generated, the reaction rate is frequently proportional to the amount of decomposing substance. Although solid-state reactions are important in geology, propellants, crystallization, and semiconducting materials, their discussion is best left to advanced textbooks and Chapter 16 on solids.

If the rate of a reaction is independent of the concentrations of reactants, a and b are zero in (10.7) and the reaction is of zero order. This situation results when some factor besides concentration limits the rate or when the concentrations of reactants are artificially maintained constant. A solution may be kept saturated or the presence of a condensed volatile phase may fix the concentration of a gaseous reactant. The intensity of light may limit the rate of a photochemical reaction, or the rate at which a reactant moves between phases may limit the rate. Unless such restraints are removed, the true order of the reaction cannot be observed.

When a substance is strongly adsorbed on a catalytic surface, its rate of isomerization or decomposition is independent of time and concentration and the reaction is of zero order. As the adsorption weakens, the order rises until the rate of reaction is first-order when a single reactant is weakly adsorbed on a catalytic surface. For the zero-order reaction with strong adsorption

$$-\frac{dC}{dt} = k_0 \tag{10.8}$$

If C^0 is the initial concentration at $t = 0$, then when the concentration is C at some later time,

$$-\int_{C^0}^{C} dC' = k_0 \int_0^t dt'$$

$$C^0 - C = k_0 t \tag{10.9}$$

The time $t_{1/2}$ for half of the reactant to disappear depends upon C^0, for if $C = C^0/2$, it follows from (10.9) that

$$t_{1/2} = \frac{1}{k_0}\left(C^0 - \frac{C^0}{2}\right) = \frac{C^0}{2k_0} \tag{10.10}$$

[1] Lewis, *Zeitschrift fur physikalische Chemie*, **52**, 310 (1905).

Example 10.1. It is possible to follow the rate of decomposition of ammonia on tungsten by noting the increase in pressure of gases at constant volume and temperature. The reaction is

$$2\,NH_{3(g)} \longrightarrow N_{2(g)} + 3\,H_{2(g)}$$

At 1100°C, these half-times $t_{1/2}$ and initial pressures P_0 were observed [C. H. Kunsman, *J. Am. Chem. Soc.*, **50,** 2100 (1928)]:

P_0(mm Hg)	265	130	58
$t_{1/2}$(min)	7.6	3.7	1.7

Show that the reaction is zero order, calculate k_0 at 1100°C, and predict the total pressure 3.00 min after NH_3 at 200 mm Hg is admitted to a rigid vessel containing tungsten at 1100°C.

Since concentration is proportional to pressure at constant temperature, (10.9) requires that $t_{1/2}$ be proportional to P_0. The constancy of k_0 as given by

$$k_0 = \frac{P_0}{2t_{1/2}}$$

shows that the reaction is zero-order. Indeed, $k_0 = 17.4, 17.6, 17.0$ mm Hg min^{-1} from these data, with a mean of 17.3 mm Hg min^{-1}.

As in (10.8), after 3.00 min,

$$\begin{aligned} P_{NH_3} &= P_0 - k_0 t = 200 - 17.3 \times 3.00 \\ &= 200 - 52 = 148 \text{ mm Hg} \end{aligned}$$

Since 2 moles NH_3 yield four of products, the pressure of products is 104 mm Hg. The total pressure will therefore be 148 + 104 = 252 mm Hg.

The overall order of a reaction or its order with respect to a certain species is an empirically observed number, frequently but not always an integer or half-integer. Order is equal to the absolute value of the stoichiometric coefficient(s) ν_i only when the equation considered is the only step in the reaction. Since most reactions proceed through various intermediate species, each generated in an added step of the actual path of reaction, it is seldom possible to predict the order of an overall reaction. For example, the reaction $2NO + 2H_2 \longrightarrow N_2 + 2H_2O$ is widely known to be second-order in NO and *first*-order in H_2 at one atm at about 1000°K. Wohler's famous conversion of ammonium cyanate into urea by the net reaction $NH_4CNO \longrightarrow H_2NCONH_2$ is *second*-order in reactant when it is dissolved in water at 60°C. Indeed many pure gases decompose to the same products by a first-order reaction at high pressure and by a second-order reaction at low pressure. Only if the reaction considered is a description of what actually happens and thus leads directly from reactants to products without any observable intermediate species can the order be predicted from the stoichoiometric coefficients. When this condition is not fulfilled, the order of a reaction is merely an empirically observed exponent useful for the conditions under which it was observed.

10.4 METHOD OF INITIAL RATES

One of the main goals of chemical kinetics is to find a useful rate law. The method of initial rates is a simple, powerful, and general way of determining the order of a reaction with respect to a particular reactant. In the first stages of reaction, the rates of reaction of two or more mixtures of reactants are compared when the concentration of only one reactant differs between the mixtures. The other reactants have identical concentrations; they may perhaps be present in such excess that the fraction of these others that disappears by reaction is negligible. For example, if it is possible to measure the rate of (10.1) while $x \ll C_B^0$, then $C_B = C_B^0 - 2x \approx C_B^0$. The rate of (10.1) is essentially $v = kC_A^a C_B^b = [kC_B^{0b}]C_A^a = k'C_A^a$, where $k' = kC_B^{0b}$ is approximately constant because the reaction mixture is flooded with B. If the rate is v_1 when the concentration of A is C_A and if it is v_n when the concentration of A is nC_A, then

$$\frac{v_n}{v_1} = \frac{k'(nC_A)^a}{k'C_A^a} = n^a \tag{10.11}$$

Observing v_n and v_1 with n known or specified by the experimenter thus yields a, the order with respect to A. One by one, other reactants can be allowed to vary similarly with all others at nearly constant and perhaps relatively great concentration until the rate law is established.

Example 10.2. The amount of H_2 produced by the reaction $H_2PO_2^- + OH^- \longrightarrow HPO_3^{2-} + H_2$ was observed in a set of experiments lasting equal short times. Doubling the initial concentration of $H_2PO_2^-$ doubled the amount of H_2; doubling the initial concentration of OH^- quadrupled the amount of H_2. What is the form of the rate law?

The reaction is first-order in $H_2PO_2^-$ because, with the amount of H_2 produced in the standard time as a measure of rate, (10.11) reads $2 = 2^a$ when the initial concentration of $H_2PO_2^-$ is changed. Similarly, when the initial concentration of OH^- is doubled ($n = 2$), the ratio of rates as judged by H_2 production is $4 = 2^a$. Hence, under the conditions of the reaction as studied, the rate is $k_3[OH^-]^2[H_2PO_2^-]$, where brackets indicate concentration.

When a large amount of data is to be examined by the method of initial rates, it is convenient to proceed thus when C_A varies from experiment to experiment while C_B is effectively constant.

$$v = k' C_A^a$$

$$\log v = \log k' + \log C_A^a = a \log C_A + \log k' \tag{10.12}$$

The slope of a graph of $\log v$ as a function of $\log C_A$ is the order a. If v can be observed frequently over long periods of time for a particular reaction, (10.12) is also useful for establishing the *order with respect to concentration*, as in the following example.

Example 10.3. At 20.0°C, benzene diazonium chloride dissolved in isoamyl alcohol decomposes to yield 1 mole $N_{2(g)}$ for each mole of chloride decomposed. Some of the measurements of volume of N_2 (S.T.P.) generated at various times are [C. E. Waring and J. R. Abrams, *J. Am. Chem. Soc.*, **63,** 2757 (1941)]:

t(min)	0	40	50	90	100	140	160	200	220	300	320	∞
V(ml)	0.00	6.59	8.21	14.43	15.76	21.08	23.57	28.17	30.32	37.76	39.41	69.84

What is the order of this reaction with respect to the diazonium salt?.

The 69.84 ml N_2 at $t = \infty$ is a linear measure of the initial amount of diazonium salt. In the first 40 min the amount of salt that decomposed was proportional to 6.59 and at $t = 40$ min the amount of salt remaining was proportional to $69.84 - 6.59 = 63.25$. The amount of salt at 50 min was proportional to $69.84 - 8.21 = 61.63$ so that in the period from 40 to 50 min the average amount of salt $\bar{C}$ was proportional to $\frac{1}{2}(63.25 + 61.63) = 62.44$ and the amount that decomposed was proportional to $8.21 - 6.59 = 63.25 - 61.63 = 1.62$. In the same way the following values of rate and mean concentration are calculated.

Δt	50–40	100–90	160–140	220–200	320–300
$-\Delta C$	1.62	1.43	2.49	2.15	1.65
$-\dfrac{\Delta C}{\Delta t} = -\dfrac{dC}{dt}$	0.162	0.143	0.1245	0.1075	0.0825
$\bar{C}$	62.44	54.74	47.51	40.60	31.26

The logarithms of the rates and mean concentrations $\bar{C}$ are plotted in Figure 10.1. The slope of the line is 0.968; hence, the order is 0.968 or approximately unity.

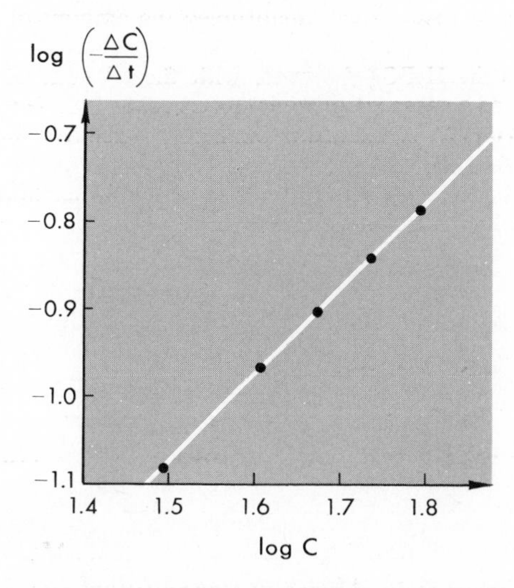

Figure 10.1. Decomposition of Benzene Diazonium Chloride

The rate constants are readily found thus:

$$k_1 = \frac{1}{C}\left(-\frac{\Delta C}{\Delta t}\right)$$

The several values of $k_1 \times 10^3$ are: 2.60, 2.61, 2.62, 2.66, and 2.64; the mean value is 2.63×10^{-3} min^{-1}.

10.5 FIRST-ORDER REACTIONS

The differential equation of a first-order reaction is

$$-\frac{dC}{dt} = k_1 C \tag{10.13}$$

Since k_1 is independent of C and t, with C^0 as initial concentration, integration yields

$$-\int_{C^0}^{C} \frac{dC'}{C'} = k_1 \int_0^t dt'$$

$$\ln\left(\frac{C^0}{C}\right) = k_1 t \tag{10.14}$$

The ratio C/C^0 is the fraction of decaying species that is unreacted at time t. Between any two times t_1 and t_2 with concentrations C_1 and C_2, (10.13) yields similarly

$$-\int_{C_1}^{C_2} \frac{dC}{C} = k_1 \int_{t_1}^{t_2} dt$$

$$\ln\left(\frac{C_1}{C_2}\right) = k_1(t_2 - t_1) \tag{10.15}$$

In terms of the rate formation of B according to the reaction $A \longrightarrow B + nD$, or

$$\begin{array}{lccc} 0 = & B + nD & & -A \\ t = 0 & 0 & 0 & C^0 \\ t & x & nx & C^0 - x \end{array}$$

the first-order rate law reads

$$v = -\frac{dC}{dt} = -\frac{d(C^0 - x)}{dt} = \frac{dx}{dt} = k_1(C^0 - x)$$

That is,

$$\int_0^x \frac{dx'}{C^0 - x'} = -\int_{C^0}^{(C^0-x)} \frac{d(C^0 - x')}{(C^0 - x')} = k_1 \int_0^t dt'$$

$$\ln\left(\frac{C^0}{C^0 - x}\right) = k_1 t \tag{10.16}$$

With $C = C^0 - x$, (10.16) is (10.14).

The half-life of a reaction is the time $t_{1/2}$ required for half a reactant to disappear. It is independent of initial concentrations for a first-order reaction and thus is a valuable index of the rate of such a reaction. If $C = \frac{1}{2}C^0$ in (10.14) or if $x = \frac{1}{2}C^0$ in (10.16)

$$\ln 2 = k_1 t_{1/2} = 0.69315 \tag{10.17}$$

Because k_1 in (10.13) has dimensions of reciprocal time, the units of concentration exactly canceling, $t_{1/2}$ is a time.

The best way to determine whether experimental data fit the first-order rate law (10.13) is to calculate values of the rate graphically or analytically and plot the logarithm of these rates as a function of the logarithm of concentration, as in Example 10.3. A very common method of establishing that a reaction is first-order is to calculate k_1 from the integrated equations (10.14), (10.15) or (10.16) for each timed observation of concentration. If the k_1's are constant, the reaction is said to be first-order *with respect to time.* It is also sometimes convenient to show experimentally that $t_{1/2}$ is independent of initial concentration. For reactions not of first order, $t_{1/2}$ depends on C^0, for in general

$$-\frac{dC}{dt} = k_n C^n$$

$$k_n \int_0^{t_{1/2}} dt = -\int_{C^0}^{C^0/2} C^{-n} dC = \frac{1}{n-1}\left[\left(\frac{C^0}{2}\right)^{1-n} - (C^0)^{1-n}\right]$$

$$t_{1/2} = \frac{2^{1-n} - 1}{2^{1-n}(1-n)k_n}(C^0)^{1-n} \tag{10.18}$$

If $n = 0$, (10.18) is (10.10); if $n = 1$, (10.17) replaces (10.18).

Some compounds that decompose by a first-order reaction are: N_2O_5, Cl_2O, NaOCl, acetone, diethyl ether, and ethylene oxide.

Example 10.4. At 298.4°C, azomethane decomposes mainly according to the reaction

$$CH_3NNCH_{3(g)} \longrightarrow C_2H_{6(g)} + N_{2(g)}$$

If this is the only reaction and if the first-order rate constant k_1 is 2.50×10^{-4} sec^{-1} [H. C. Ramsperger, *J. Am. Chem. Soc.*, **49**, 912 (1927)], what will be the partial pressures of reactant and products when azomethane initially at 200 mm Hg decomposes for 30.0 min?

With pressures replacing concentrations in (10.14), and with $P^0 = 200$,

$$2.303 \log\left(\frac{200}{P}\right) = 2.50 \times 10^{-4} \times 30.0 \times 60$$

$$\log\left(\frac{200}{P}\right) = 0.195 = \log 1.566$$

$$P = \frac{200}{1.566} = 128 \text{ mm Hg}$$

The partial pressure of azomethane is 128 mm Hg after 30.0 min. Since each mole of azomethane decomposed yields one each of ethane and nitrogen, each of the latter has a partial pressure of 200 − 128 = 72 mm Hg.

The rate of decay of a radioactive species is proportional to the number of nucleuses that can decay. That is, if N is the number of radioactive nucleuses at time t, as in (10.13),

$$-\frac{dN}{dt} = k_1 N \tag{10.19}$$

Definite integration yields

$$-\int_{N_0}^{N} \frac{dN'}{N'} = k_1 \int_0^t dt'$$

$$\ln\left(\frac{N_0}{N}\right) = k_1 t \tag{10.20}$$

Since it is customary to list half-lives rather than values of k_1, use of (10.17) yields

$$\ln\left(\frac{N_0}{N}\right) = \frac{t \ln 2}{t_{1/2}} \tag{10.21}$$

There are four disintegration series of heavy radioactive elements. One series decays to $^{209}_{83}Bi$ and has as its longest-lived radioactive member $^{237}_{93}Np$, with a half-life of 2 million years. This series was not observed to occur naturally because this half-life does not match the age of the earth, a few billion years. Three of these series are found naturally and terminate in stable isotopes of Pb. They have parents with half-lives of the order of a billion years. These long-lived parents not only preserve the series but each may produce a steady state of decay in its series of radioactive elements, just as a large mountain lake may feed a descending chain of lower lakes which retain their water for rather short times.

In such a state of radioactive equilibrium, the rates of decay of all isotopes in the series are equal. Hence,

$$-\frac{dN_1}{dt} = -\frac{dN_2}{dt} = -\frac{dN_3}{dt} = \cdots$$

Because of (10.19), $k_1 N_1 = k_2 N_2 = k_3 N_3 = \cdots$. In terms of half-lives, this becomes

$$\frac{N_1}{(t_{1/2})_1} = \frac{N_2}{(t_{1/2})_2} = \frac{N_3}{(t_{1/2})_3} \cdots \tag{10.22}$$

If one half-life is known, others in such a series can be found by a chemical analysis that fixes $N_1, N_2, N_3 \ldots$. This was once the only way to determine extremely large half-lives. The probable error in determining a decay rate is approximately equal to the square root of the number of decay events measured. For a slowly decaying species this error is relatively large, while the error in chemical analysis is small.

Radioactive tracers are useful in following the path of minute amounts of matter. Use of C^{14} has elucidated the path of carbon in and the processes of photosynthesis. Very low vapor pressures become measurable, it is possible to evaluate the completeness of precipitations and other analytical separations, slight adsorption on surfaces can be detected, and the quality of lubricants and extent of wear can be evaluated by noting the accumulation of radioactive metal in oil used to lubricate radioactive pistons and bearings. The mechanisms of chemical reactions can be determined and the rate of exchange of atoms between different species can be measured. For example, radioactive halogens rapidly react with solutions of like halide ions, for after a short time the halide ions become radioactive.

The amount of a radio-isotope is inferred through (10.19) by its rate of decay. The unit of activity is the curie, 3.7000×10^{10} disintegrations/sec. Use of (10.19) becomes suspect when the decay is so swift that the slope of $N = N_0 e^{-k_1 t}$ changes in the time of the count of events.

In order to follow the extent or mechanism of a reaction, unusual concentrations of stable isotopes are often of value. Analysis, however, must be by spectroscopy (e. g., NMR or mass spectroscopy). A famous and early use of water labeled with extraordinary amounts of stable O^{18} established that many esters are hydrolyzed without breaking the alkyl-oxygen bond. That is,

$$\mathrm{R - \overset{\overset{\displaystyle O}{\|}}{C} - O - R' + H_2O^{18} \longrightarrow R - \overset{\overset{\displaystyle O}{\|}}{C} - {}^{18}O - H + H - O - R'}$$

If the $R' - \mathrm{O}$ bond had undergone fission, the resulting alcohol would have contained ^{18}O.

Example 10.5. In the presence of perchloric acid at 27°C, the following exchange reaction occurs in H_2O containing the usual normal amount of ^{18}O:

$$\mathrm{Co(NH_3)_5H_2{}^{18}O^{+++} + H_2O \rightleftharpoons Co(NH_3)_5H_2O^{+++} + H_2{}^{18}O}$$

At the beginning of an experiment the mole fraction of ^{18}O in the complex ion was 0.006649, after 25.1 hr it was 0.004366, and at equilibrium it was 0.002192

[A.C. Rutenberg and H. Taube, *J. Chem. Phys.*, **20,** 825 (1952)]. Calculate the first-order rate constant of this exchange reaction and the half-life of the complex ion in aqueous solution.

The amount of complex ion that can be observed to react is proportional to 0.006649 − 0.002192 = 0.004457. The fraction of this that remains after 25.1 hr is

$$\frac{C}{C^0} = \frac{0.004366 - 0.002192}{0.006649 - 0.002192} = \frac{0.002174}{0.004457}$$

By (10.14),

$$k_1 = \frac{2.303}{25.1} \log\left(\frac{4.457}{2.174}\right) = 2.86 \times 10^{-2}\ \text{hr}^{-1}$$

Then, by (10.17),

$$t_{1/2} = \frac{0.693}{k_1} = \frac{0.693}{2.86 \times 10^{-2}\ \text{hr}} = 24.2\ \text{hr}$$

This calculation assumes that the reverse reaction is unimportant and that the concentration of $H_2{}^{18}O$ in the solvent is constant during the reaction.

Example 10.6. If the half-life of ^{14}C is 5800 years, how many atoms of ^{14}C are required to produce an average of five beta emissions per minute?

Since $t_{1/2} = 5800 \times 365 \times 24 \times 60$ min, it follows from (10.17) that

$$k_1 = \frac{0.693}{3.05 \times 10^9\ \text{min}} = 2.27 \times 10^{-10}\ \text{min}^{-1}$$

If $-\Delta N/\Delta t$ = five per minute, by (10.19)

$$N = \frac{-(\Delta N/\Delta t)}{k_1} = \frac{5.00}{2.27 \times 10^{-10}} = 2.20 \times 10^{10}\ \text{atoms}$$

Example 10.7. A piece of wood buried by a glacier had 25.6% as much ^{14}C as a recently grown piece of wood. If the amount of ^{14}C in the atmosphere was the same when the old wood died as it is now, when did the glacier overrun the forest?

By (10.21) with $N = 0.256N_0$,

$$t = \frac{t_{1/2}}{\ln 2} \ln\left(\frac{N_0}{N}\right) = \left(\frac{5800}{0.693}\right) 2.303 \log\left(\frac{1}{0.256}\right) = 11{,}400\ \text{years ago}$$

Radioactive decay and decomposition of species of high chemical potential are essentially irreversible. If a reverse first-order process with rate constant k_{-1} is not negligible, as may be the case in isotopic exchange, isomerization, or racemization, then the net forward velocity of a reaction A ⟶ B (that is, 0 = B − A) is

$$v = -\frac{dC_A}{dt} = \frac{dC_B}{dt} = \frac{dx}{dt} = k_1(C_A^0 - x) - k_{-1}(C_B^0 + x) \qquad (10.23)$$

At equilibrium, dx/dt is zero and

$$K = \frac{C_B^0 + x}{C_A^0 - x} = \frac{k_1}{k_{-1}} \tag{10.24}$$

Definite integration of (10.23) with $y = (k_1 + k_{-1})x$ and $\Delta = k_1 C_A^0 - k_{-1} C_B^0$ proceeds thus.

$$\int_0^t dt' = \int_0^x \frac{dx'}{k_1(C_A^0 - x') - k_{-1}(C_B^0 + x')}$$

$$t = \int_0^x \frac{dx'}{(k_1 C_A^0 - k_{-1} C_B^0) - (k_1 + k_{-1})x'}$$

$$(k_1 + k_{-1})t = \int_0^y \frac{dy'}{\Delta - y'} = \ln \frac{\Delta}{\Delta - y} \tag{10.25}$$

As equilibrium is approached at $t \longrightarrow \infty$, $y = \Delta$ because from (10.25)

$$\lim_{t \to \infty} \frac{y}{\Delta} = \lim_{t \to \infty} [1 - e^{-(k_1 + k_{-1})t}] = 1$$

When some physical or chemical property X is related linearly to the concentration of A or B as in Section 10.2 so that y/Δ or x/C^0 is the extent of reaction, $k_1 + k_{-1}$ may be mistaken for k_1, for (10.25) is isomorphous with (10.16). If, however, $K \gg 1$ in (10.24), then $k_1 \gg k_{-1}$ and (10.25) agrees with (10.16).

10.6 UNIMOLECULAR DECOMPOSITION

First-order reactions are generally of first order only in certain circumstances. Although Wilhelmy in 1850 found that the rate of hydrolysis of sugar is proportional to the concentration of unhydrolyzed sugar, the first-order rate constant really depends upon the acidity of the aqueous solution and upon the concentration of water. In dilute aqueous solutions, the concentration of water is so great that it is essentially undisturbed by the hydrolytic reaction. Even the homogeneous decomposition of a pure gaseous substance like azomethane may have a first-order rate constant that is a function of concentration or pressure of reactant. Such a functional dependence means, of course, that the process of decomposition cannot be treated like radioactive decay, as though it were a simple event. Similarly, a physicist may not treat radioactive decay as a simple event.

Chemical reactions proceed at a finite rate because not all molecules of reactants are ready to react. Some of the factors that have long been recognized as important in controlling the rate of a reaction are the number of favorable collisions, the proper orientation of colliding molecules, and a suitable excitation or activation process to overcome chemical stability and inertia. In 1922, Lindemann explained how collisions might supply the extraordinary energy required to effect reaction. From 1927 to 1932, Hinshelwood, Kassel, Rice, and Ramsperger applied the Lindemann mechanism by assuming that energy flows about an energized molecule until it eventually vibrates in a way that breaks one of its bonds. An alternate theory due to N. B. Slater in 1939 to 1948 assumes that various modes of vibration and rotation are variously excited after an energetic collision and that subsequently, without free exchange of energy among modes of vibration, a critical displacement may occur that leads to decomposition. One of the latest modifications of the Lindemann mechanism is due to R. A. Marcus.[2] It proceeds thus:

$$\left.\begin{aligned} A + M &\underset{k_{-2}}{\overset{k_2}{\rightleftharpoons}} A^* + M \\ A^* &\overset{k_1^*}{\longrightarrow} A^{\ddagger} \\ A^{\ddagger} &\overset{k_1}{\longrightarrow} \text{products} \end{aligned}\right\} \tag{10.26}$$

Species A* is an active, energized molecule of reactant A after it has collided with M, which may be A or another species. Active species A* then becomes an activated complex $A^{\ddagger}$, that crucial state of A which leads to decomposition into products. Only when the energy of activation becomes available at the reactive site in A does A* become $A^{\ddagger}$. In simple molecules A* becames $A^{\ddagger}$ rapidly, but in molecules of many atoms and many degrees of vibrational and rotational freedom, this transformation with rate constant k_1^* may proceed only slowly.

In order to express the mathematical rate law of this mechanism, it is necessary to distinguish the order of a reaction from its molecularity. The *order* of a reaction is the sum of the exponents on concentrations in the rate law like (10.7). The order of a reaction need not be integral. The *molecularity* of a reaction is, however, an integer and is equal to the number of reactant molecules that comprise the activated complex. The mechanism in (10.26) is unimolecular because $A^{\ddagger}$ consists of only one molecule of A.

The net forward rate of the first reaction of (10.26) is the rate of disappearance of A, namely,

$$-\frac{dC_A}{dt} = k_2 C_A C_M - k_{-2} C_{A^*} C_M \tag{10.27}$$

The forward rate is proportional to the concentrations of A and M as the mechanism requires, and the reverse rate $k_{-2}C_{A^*}C_M$ is likewise proportional to the number of deactivating collisions of A* and M. When the decomposition proceeds at a steady rate, generally near its initial stages, the rate of change in the concentration of the intermediate A* will be zero. According to the mechanism

[2] Marcus, R. A., *J. Chem. Phy.*, **20**, 359 (1952).

(10.26), in the steady state

$$0 = \frac{dC_{A^*}}{dt} = k_2 C_A C_M - k_{-2} C_{A^*} C_M - k_1^* C_{A^*} \tag{10.28}$$

This steady-state condition (10.28) is usually valid when the overall reaction is not unusually rapid. This condition says that the concentration of A* does not change with time. Actually it may change with time, but there is so little A* present relative to other species that its rate of change is effectively zero as stated. The value of (10.28) is that it changes a differential equation into an algebraic equation. Conditions analogous to (10.28) may be applied to several active species of very low concentration in a more complex mechanism so as to decrease the number of simultaneous differential equations that must be solved.

Solution of (10.28) for the concentration of A* yields

$$C_{A^*} = \frac{k_2 C_A C_M}{k_1^* + k_{-2} C_M} \tag{10.29}$$

With the aid of (10.28) and (10.29), (10.27) reads

$$-\frac{dC_A}{dt} = k_1^* C_{A^*} = \left[\frac{k_1^* k_2 C_M}{k_1^* + k_{-2} C_M}\right] C_A = k_1(C) C_A \tag{10.30}$$

where the unimolecular rate constant $k_1(C)$ is a function of C_M according to

$$\frac{1}{k_1(C)} = \left(\frac{k_{-2}}{k_1^* k_2}\right)\left(1 + \frac{k_1^*}{k_{-2} C_M}\right) \tag{10.31}$$

If $k_1^* \ll k_{-2} C_M$, $k_1(C)$ is independent of C_M, the decomposition is first-order, and

$$k_1^{(\infty)} = \frac{k_1^* k_2}{k_{-2}} \tag{10.32}$$

This holds when deactivation by collision predominates over activation and decomposition. High pressures and many degrees of freedom in the reactant A favor first-order decay, as in azomethane, acetone, ether, and N_2O_5 at atmospheric pressure. On the other hand, low pressures and few degrees of freedom in A favor $k_1^* \gg k_{-2} C_M$ so that (10.30) and (10.31) yield

$$-\frac{dC_A}{dt} = k_2 C_A C_M \tag{10.33}$$

If M is A, the reaction is second-order in A. The simple molecules HI, N_2O, NO, NOCl, NO_2, and CH_3CHO decompose by second-order reactions at atmospheric pressure. Great decreases in pressure frequently change the order of a decomposition reaction continuously from first to second. This happens for the dissociation of Br_2, decomposition of azomethane, N_2O, C_2H_5Cl, and O_3, isomerization of cis-butene-2 to trans-butene-2, isomerization of cyclopropane and cyclobutane to other species without rings, and many other reactions.

At the very lowest pressures at which concentrations can be followed in time, typically by gas chromatography, unimolecular decomposition may become first-order again in decomposing reactant. This has been observed[3] for the isomerization of cyclopropane below 0.001 mm Hg in an unpacked spherical one-liter vessel and below about 0.1 mm Hg in a vessel packed with glass tubing. The reason why the reaction returns to first-order is that at these low pressures the mean free path is of the order of the distance between glass surfaces; that is, the activating species M is the vessel wall and (10.33) is thus first-order with rate constant $k_2 C_M$.

Example 10.8. If cyclopropane and propylene are equally effective as M in (10.26), find the limiting values at infinite and low pressure of the first- and second-order decay rate constants at 469.6°C for the isomerization of cyclopropane to propylene. The total pressures P and apparent first-order rate constants $k_1(P)$ are [T. S. Chambers and G. B. Kistiakowsky, *J. Am. Chem. Soc.*, **56**, 399 (1934)]:

P(mm Hg)	762.7	757.0	388.1	389.1	207.6	213.7	110.2	109.0
$k_1(P) \times 10^4(\text{sec}^{-1})$	1.13	1.09	1.07	1.10	1.05	1.04	0.955	0.961

As (10.31) suggests, $[10^{-4}/k_1(P)]$ is plotted in Figure 10.2 as a linear function of $(10^3/P)$. The best straight line yields the intercept $k_1^{-1} = 0.88 \times 10^4$ at $P = \infty$; whence, $k_1(P = \infty) = 1.14 \times 10^{-4}$ sec^{-1}. The slope of the line in Figure 10.2

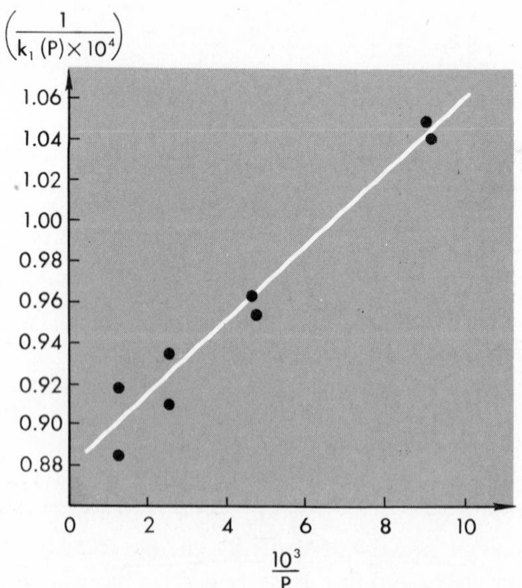

Figure 10.2. Rate Constant for Isomerization of Cyclopropane

[3] A. D. Kennedy and H. O. Pritchard, *J. Phys. Chem.* **67**, 161 (1963).

is 18.6 × 10⁴ mm Hg sec. According to (10.31), the slope is k_2^{-1} so that

$$k_2 = \frac{10^{-4}}{18.6} = 5.38 \times 10^{-6} \text{ (mm Hg)}^{-1} \text{ sec}^{-1}$$

Example 10.9. At what pressure is the isomerization of cyclopropane essentially a second-order reaction?

The reaction is second-order if $k_1^* \gg k_{-2}p_M$. According to (10.32) and Example 10.8,

$$\frac{k_1^*}{k_{-2}} = \frac{k_1(P=\infty)}{k_2} = \frac{1.14 \times 10^{-4}}{5.38 \times 10^{-6}} = 21.2 \text{ mm Hg}$$

Within 1%, $100k_{-2}p_M = k_1^*$ and $p_M = k_1^*/100k_{-2} = 0.212$ mm Hg. At pressures less than 0.212 mm Hg, the isomerization of cyclopropane would be essentially second-order.

10.7 SECOND-ORDER REACTIONS

Simple molecules like HI and CH_3CHO tend to decompose at low pressure in the absence of other substances by a second-order reaction. If C is the concentration of the species at time t and C^0 is its initial concentration, and if the reaction is irreversible, the second-order rate law is

$$-\frac{dC}{dt} = k_2 C^2 \tag{10.34}$$

$$-\int_{C^0}^{C} \frac{dC'}{C'^2} = k_2 \int_0^t dt'$$

$$\frac{1}{C} - \frac{1}{C^0} = k_2 t$$

$$\frac{C^0 - C}{CC^0} = k_2 t \tag{10.35}$$

As x moles of product are made per liter from an initial concentration C^0 by the reaction $2A \longrightarrow D + \cdots$ or, restated,

	$0 = D + \cdots$	$-\ 2A$	
$t = 0$	0	C^0	(10.36)
$t > 0$	x	$C^0 - 2x$	

it follows that, if (10.36) states the mechanism, the rate of reaction is

$$v = \frac{dx}{dt} = k_2(C^0 - 2x)^2 \tag{10.37}$$

$$\frac{1}{2}\int_0^x \frac{2dx'}{(C^0 - 2x')^2} = k_2\int_0^t dt'$$

$$\frac{1}{2}\left[\frac{1}{C^0 - 2x} - \frac{1}{C^0}\right] = k_2 t$$

$$\frac{x}{C^0(C^0 - 2x)} = k_2 t \qquad (10.38)$$

Since $C = C^0 - 2x$, $x = (C^0 - C)/2$ and (10.38) is

$$\frac{C^0 - C}{2C^0 C} = k_2 t \qquad (10.39)$$

The value of k_2 in (10.39) is half as great as k_2 in (10.35) because D forms in (10.36) at half the rate at which A disappears. By the convention of (10.5), the k_2 of (10.37) and (10.39) is preferred. Equations like (10.35) and (10.39) describe also the second-order reaction of different species if their initial concentrations are equal.

If $C_A^0 \neq C_B^0$ in the second-order reaction $A + B \longrightarrow D + \cdots$, that is,

$$0 = D + \cdots - A - B \qquad (10.40)$$

then

$$v = -\frac{dC_A}{dt} = -\frac{dC_B}{dt} = k_2 C_A C_B \qquad (10.41)$$

At any time, $dC_A = dC_B$ so that

$$\int_{C_A{}^0}^{C_A} dC'_A = \int_{C_B{}^0}^{C_B} dC'_B$$

$$C_A^0 - C_A = C_B^0 - C_B$$

Since $C_A^0 \neq C_B^0$, it follows that $C_A \neq C_B$ and

$$-\frac{dC_A}{dt} = k_2 C_A[C_A + (C_B^0 - C_A^0)]$$

$$\int_{C^0{}_A}^{C_A} \frac{dC'_A}{C'_A[C'_A + (C_B^0 - C_A^0)]} = -k_2\int_0^t dt'$$

$$\left[\frac{1}{C_B^0 - C_A^0}\right] \ln\left[\left(\frac{C_A}{C_A + (C_B^0 - C_A^0)}\right)\left(\frac{C_B^0}{C_A^0}\right)\right] = -k_2 t$$

$$k_2 t = \left(\frac{1}{C_B^0 - C_A^0}\right) \ln\left(\frac{C_B C_A^0}{C_A C_B^0}\right) \qquad (10.42)$$

The half-life $t_{1/2}$ of a second-order reaction can be found from (10.18) with $n = 2$; it is

$$t_{1/2} = \frac{1}{k_2 C^0} \qquad (10.43)$$

where k_2 in (10.43) corresponds to that in (10.35) and not that in (10.39). If the half-life of a reaction is inversely proportional to the initial concentration of a reactant, the reaction is second-order in time with respect to that species, all other concentrations being constant in k_2. If observed values of t, C, and C^0 yield a constant value of k_2 in (10.35) or (10.42), or if graphing a suitable function of concentrations against time produces a straight line with slope k_2, the reaction is termed second-order in time. The best way, however, to show that a reaction is second-order with respect to a certain species is to show that (10.34) holds for small finite increments in C and t. That is,

$$\left(-\frac{\Delta C}{\Delta t}\right) = k_2 C^2$$

$$\log\left(-\frac{\Delta C}{\Delta t}\right) = \log k_2 + 2 \log C$$

If the slope of the graph of $\log(-\Delta C/\Delta t)$ vs. $\log C$ is two, the reaction is second-order. The value of the ordinate $\log(-\Delta C/\Delta t)$ at $C = 1$ is $\log k_2$. Example 10.3 illustrated this method of determining order for a first-order reaction, and Example 10.13, which deals with a reaction of type (10.40), will illustrate how this method includes the method of initial rates as a special case.

Some well known second-order gas reactions like (10.36) are $2NO_2 \longrightarrow 2NO + O_2$, $2NOCl \longrightarrow 2NO + Cl_2$ and $2HI \longrightarrow H_2 + I_2$. Some like (10.40) are $N_2 + O_2 \longrightarrow 2NO$ and $H + Cl_2 \longrightarrow HCl + Cl$. In liquid solutions, many organic reactions (e.g., acidic or basic saponification of esters or reaction of OH^- with organic halide to yield an alcohol) and many ionic oxidation-reduction reactions are like (10.40), first-order in each reactant.

Not all second-order reactions are bimolecular. Only if the critical intermediate state, called the activated complex, contains two reactant molecules is it correct to label a reaction bimolecular. The next section describes a termolecular gas reaction that may be second-order. A unimolecular decomposition that yields just two product molecules is a bimolecular reaction if reversed. A common kind of bimolecular reaction when free radicals R cause reaction is of the type $R + AB \longrightarrow RA + B$, where B is often a free radical and where the activated complex is bimolecular $RAB^‡$. Another common type of bimolecular reaction is of type $AB + CD \longrightarrow AC + BD$; the simplest mechanism here involves energized species $AB \cdot CD$ and $AC \cdot BD$ and activated complex $ABCD^‡$, all three of about the same energy.

Example 10.10. If $k_2 = 4.00 \times 10^{-6}$ l mole^{-1} sec^{-1} at 600°K for the decomposition of HI according to the equation

$$-\frac{dC_{HI}}{dt} = k_2 C_{HI}^2$$

how many molecules of HI decompose per second at 600°K at atmospheric pressure if the reverse reaction that forms HI is negligible?

At 1 atm at 600°K,

$$C_{HI} = \frac{n}{V} = \frac{P}{RT} = \frac{1.00}{0.082 \times 600} = 2.03 \times 10^{-2} \text{mole l}^{-1}$$

According to (10.34),

$$-\frac{dC}{dt} = 4.00 \times 10^{-6}(2.03 \times 10^{-2})^2$$

$$= 16.5 \times 10^{-10} \text{ mole l}^{-1} \text{ sec}^{-1}$$

Hence,

$$-\frac{dN}{dt} = 16.5 \times 10^{-10} \times 0.602 \times 10^{24}$$

$$= 9.9 \times 10^{14} \text{ molecules l}^{-1} \text{ sec}^{-1}$$

Example 10.11. At 600°K, $k_2 = 6.3 \times 10^2$ ml mole^{-1} sec^{-1} for the reaction $2\,NO_2 \rightarrow 2\,NO + O_2$. At 600°K, how long will it take for one-tenth of a sample of NO_2 at 400 mm Hg to decompose by this reaction?

If $C = 0.900C^0$, then by (10.35),

$$t = \frac{C^0 - C}{k_2 C^0 C} = \frac{0.100C^0}{k_2 C^0(0.900C^0)} = \frac{1}{9k_2 C^0}$$

But $$C^0 = \frac{P}{RT} = \frac{(400/760)}{82.06 \times 600} = 1.07 \times 10^{-5} \text{ mole ml}^{-1}$$

hence, $$t = \frac{1}{9 \times 6.3 \times 10^2 \times 1.07 \times 10^{-5}} = 16.5 \text{ sec}$$

Example 10.12. Chloroacetic acid dissolved in dilute aqueous HCl becomes radioactive by exchange of Cl if radioactive $H^{36}_{17}Cl$ is added to the solution. From the data below [R. A. Kennedy and F. J. Johnston, *J. Phys. Chem.* **63,** 1426 (1959)], determine the order of the exchange reaction with respect to HCl and chloroacetic acid and find an approximate value of the rate constant if the half-life of $^{36}_{17}Cl$ is so long that essentially no diminution in the total counts per minute occurs in these experiments. (Hydroxyacetic acid is also formed in a competing reaction.)

Experiment Number	Time (hrs)	Concentration HCl	Concentration $HOOCCH_2Cl$	Counts Per Minute Total	Counts Per Minute $HOOCCH_2Cl$
A	0	0.0186	0.0405	876	0
B	1.00	0.0187	0.0403	876	23
C	0	0.0186	0.1214	896	0
D	1.00	0.0188	0.1212	896	68
E	0	0.0362	0.0405	1775	0
F	1.00	0.0363	0.0404	1775	48

Since 876 counts per minute (cpm) corresponds to a chloride concentration of 0.0186 mole liter^{-1} in A, a rate of 23 cpm in B is equivalent to a concentration of radioactive chloroacetic acid of $0.0186(23/876) = 0.488 \times 10^{-3}$ mole liter^{-1}.

The average rate of increase in concentration of 'hot' acid is thus 0.488×10^{-3} mole liter^{-1} hr^{-1} while the average concentration of HCl is 0.01865 mole liter^{-1} and of chloroacetic acid is 0.0404 mole liter^{-1}. Similar calculations yield rates of 1.411×10^{-3} and 0.979×10^{-3} mole liter^{-1} hr^{-1} for the initial rates of exchange for CD and EF.

Comparing experiments AB and EF shows that, at constant concentration of chloroacetic acid, doubling C_{HCl} doubles the rate of exchange. Similar comparison of AB to CD shows that, at constant C_{HCl}, tripling the concentration of chloroacetic acid triples the rate. Hence, the exchange reaction is first-order in HCl and first-order in $HOOCCH_2Cl$. Values of the second-order rate constant k_2 can be calculated from the rates v_X and concentrations by (10.41) in the form

$$k_2 = \frac{v_X}{[HCl][HOOCCH_2Cl]}$$

From AB, $k_2 = 0.488 \times 10^{-3}\ (0.01865)^{-1}(0.0404)^{-1} = 0.648$ l mole^{-1} hr^{-1}; from CD, $k_2 = 0.622$ and from EF $k_2 = 0.668$ l mole^{-1} hr^{-1}. A more sophisticated treatment of more data for longer times gave $k_2 = 0.664$ l mole^{-1} hr^{-1}.

Example 10.13. The reaction $2\,NO_2 + F_2 \rightarrow 2\,NO_2F$ is first-order with respect to F_2 and NO_2. When

$$-\frac{dC_{F_2}}{dt} = k_2 C_{F_2} C_{NO_2}$$

$k_2 = 3.40 \times 10^4$ cc mole^{-1} sec^{-1} at 25°C [Calculated from R. L. Perrine and H. S. Johnston, *J. Chem. Phys.*, **21**, 2202 (1953)]. If F_2 initially at 2.00 mm Hg reacts with NO_2 initially at 5.00 mm Hg in a rigid vessel at 25°C, what will be their pressures and the pressure of NO_2F after 30.0 sec?

The stoichiometry of the reaction requires that NO_2 disappear twice as fast as F_2. If x is the decrease in partial pressure of F_2, then $2x = 2(p^0_{F_2} - p_{F_2}) = p^0_{NO_2} - p_{NO_2}$. Since $p_i = C_i\,R\,T$, the rate law in terms of partial pressures is then

$$-\frac{dp_{F_2}}{dt} = \left(\frac{k_2}{RT}\right) p_{F_2} p_{NO_2} = \left(\frac{k_2}{RT}\right) p_{F_2}(p^0_{NO_2} - 2p^0_{F_2} + 2p_{F_2})$$

$$\left(\frac{k_2}{RT}\right)\int_0^t dt' = -\int_{p_{F_2}^0}^{p_{F_2}} \frac{dp}{p(2p + p^0_{NO_2} - 2p^0_{F_2})}$$

$$= \frac{1}{p^0_{NO_2} - 2p^0_{F_2}} \int_{p_{F_2}^0}^{p_{F_2}} \left[\frac{2}{2p + (p^0_{NO_2} - 2p^0_{F_2})} - \frac{1}{p}\right] dp$$

$$\left(\frac{k_2 t}{RT}\right) = \frac{1}{p^0_{NO_2} - 2p^0_{F_2}} \ln\left(\frac{p_{NO_2} p^0_{F_2}}{p_{F_2} p^0_{NO_2}}\right)$$

After thirty seconds at 298.2°K, since $p^0_{F_2} = 2.00$ mm Hg and $p^0_{NO_2} = 5.00$ mm Hg,

$$\frac{3.40 \times 10^4 \times 30.0}{82.06 \times 298.2} = \frac{760}{5.00 - 4.00} \ln \frac{2.00 p_{NO_2}}{5.00 p_{F_2}}$$

$$p_{NO_2} = 2.64 p_{F_2}$$

Since $p_{NO_2} = p^0_{NO_2} - 2x = 2.64\ (p^0_{F_2} - x)$ with $p^0_{NO_2} = 5.00$ and $p^0_{F_2} = 2.00$, it follows that $x = 0.44$ mm Hg and thus

$$p_{NO_2} = p^0_{NO_2} - 2x = 5.00 - 0.88 = 4.12 \text{ mm Hg}$$

$$p_{F_2} = p^0_{F_2} - x = 2.00 - 0.44 = 1.56 \text{ mm Hg}$$

$$p_{NO_2F} = 2x = 0.88 \text{ mm Hg}$$

It is worth noting that the stoichiometry of the chemical reaction affects the integrated form of (10.41).

10.8 RECOMBINATION

A third-order trimolecular gaseous reaction appears to require a triple collision. Since triple collisions are very rare, such reactions are observed only when all possible uni- and bimolecular reactions are very slow. Most known third-order gaseous reactions are of the type $2A + B \longrightarrow D + \cdots$, that is

$$\begin{array}{lcccc} & 0 = D + \cdots & - \ 2A & - \ B & \\ t = 0 & 0 & C^0_A & C^0_B \\ t > 0 & x & C^0_A - 2x & C^0_B - x \end{array} \qquad (10.44)$$

The differential equation for this reaction,

$$\frac{dx}{dt} = \frac{1}{2}\left(-\frac{dC_A}{dt}\right) = -\frac{dC_B}{dt} = k_3(C^0_A - 2x)^2(C^0_B - x) \qquad (10.45)$$

can be integrated whether or not $C^0_A = C^0_B$.

Reactions of NO with O_2, H_2 Cl_2, and Br_2 are perhaps third-order according to the mechanism

$$2\,NO + X_2 \longrightarrow 2\,NOX \qquad (10.46)$$

The reaction of H_2 with I_2, long considered bimolecular second-order, has been shown[4] to be termolecular of the form

$$2I + H_2 \longrightarrow 2HI$$

Recombination of species X is a common kind of third-order gaseous reaction.

$$2X + M \longrightarrow X_2 + M^* \qquad (10.47)$$

If the recombining species differ, the reaction is instead

$$X + Y + M \longrightarrow XY + M^* \qquad (10.48)$$

[4] Sullivan, J. H., *J. Chem. Phys.* **46**, 73 (1967).

The species X and Y in (10.47) and (10.48) may be ions, atoms, free radicals, or stable molecules, and M may be any species present in the reaction vessel. The nature of M may affect the rate; for example, Ar is only 25% and N_2 is only 40% as effective as CO_2 in causing Br or I atoms to recombine. If the third body M is not present, the hypothetical complex X_2^* or XY* of fleeting existence tends to dissociate within one vibration of the newly formed bond. For if the species X is an atom, there is no way for the species X_2^* to dissipate its vibrational energy, except perhaps by radiation within the time of one vibration. On the other hand, if the fragments X are large with many degrees of freedom, the vibrational energy of X_2^* can wander about the molecule in these other degrees of freedom until a collision withdraws enough energy to stabilize the newly formed molecule. The mechanism proposed for (10.48) is

$$\left.\begin{aligned} X + Y &\underset{k_1^*}{\overset{k_2}{\rightleftharpoons}} XY^* \\ XY^* + M &\xrightarrow{k_2^*} XY + M^* \end{aligned}\right\} \tag{10.49}$$

This mechanism may yield either second- or third-order kinetics. The rate of decay of X is

$$-\frac{dC_X}{dt} = k_2 C_X C_Y - k_1^* C^* \tag{10.50}$$

and the rate of formation of XY* is zero in the steady state so that

$$0 = \frac{dC^*}{dt} = k_2 C_X C_Y - k_1^* C^* - k_2^* C^* C_M \tag{10.51}$$

Solution of (10.51) for C^* and substitution in (10.50) yields

$$\begin{aligned} -\frac{dC_X}{dt} &= k_2 C_X C_Y - k_1^*\left[\frac{k_2 C_X C_Y}{k_1^* + k_2^* C_M}\right] \\ &= k_2 C_X C_Y\left[1 - \frac{k_1^*}{k_1^* + k_2^* C_M}\right] \\ &= \frac{k_2 k_2^* C_X C_Y C_M}{k_1^* + k_2^* C_M} \end{aligned} \tag{10.52}$$

If $k_1^* \gg k_2^* C_M$, XY* is more likely to dissociate than to suffer a stabilizing collision with M. According to (10.17), its half-life $t_{1/2}^*$ would be $t_{1/2}^* = \ln 2/k_1^*$, a time that decreases as k_1^* increases. Equation (10.52) then yields the third-order law

$$-\frac{dC_X}{dt} = \left(\frac{k_2 k_2^*}{k_1^*}\right) C_X C_Y C_M \tag{10.53}$$

The formation of a coordinate covalent bond between BF_3 and alkyl amines of low molecular weight has a mechanism like (10.49).[5] If A represents

[5] Garvin, D. and G. B. Kistiakowsky, *J. Chem. Phys.*, **20,** 105 (1952): Kistiakowsky, G. B. and R. Williams, *J. Chem. Phys.*, **23,** 334 (1955).

the amine, the mechanism is

$$\left.\begin{aligned} A + BF_3 &\underset{k_1^*}{\overset{k_2}{\rightleftharpoons}} A.BF_3^* \\ A.BF_3^* + M &\xrightarrow{k_2^*} A.BF_3 + M^* \end{aligned}\right\} \tag{10.54}$$

where M is a diluent gas that carries away energy from the excited adduct $A.BF_3^*$. The lifetime of this hot adduct is proportional to the number of its vibrational degrees of freedom. Since $A.BF_3^*$ is longer-lived than X_2^* when X is an atom, k_1^* no longer dominates $k_2^* C_M$, especially when much M is present. The analogue of (10.52) reads

$$-\frac{dC_A}{dt} = \frac{k_2 k_2^* C_A C_{BF_3} C_M}{k_1^* + k_2^* C_M} = k C_A C_{BF_3} \tag{10.55}$$

where

$$\frac{1}{k} = \frac{1}{k_2} + \frac{k_1^*}{k_2 k_2^* C_M} \tag{10.56}$$

The pseudoconstant k depends upon C_M and causes the overall order to vary from second to third. When k_1^* is small or C_M is large, k approaches k_2 and the mechanism becomes second-order.

Slight modification of the reverse of (10.54) brings it to the form of unimolecular decomposition of the species $A.BF_3$, namely by $M^* + A.BF_3 \rightleftharpoons A.BF_3^* + M$ and $A.BF_3^* \longrightarrow A.BF_3^\ddagger \longrightarrow A + BF_3$.

Example 10.14. If the second-order rate constant for the decomposition of NOCl is 0.0204 liter mole^{-1} sec^{-1} at 450°K, what is the third-order rate constant at 450°K for the elementary trimolecular gaseous reaction $2NO + Cl_2 \rightarrow 2NOCl$?

If (10.46) is the whole mechanism of the reversible reaction of 2 NO with Cl_2 as stated, then when the rate of production of NOCl is zero at equilibrium there exists the condition $0 = v = k_3 C_{NO}^2 C_{Cl_2} - k_2 C_{NOCl}^2$. From this, $K_c = C_{NOCl}^2 C_{NO}^{-2} C_{Cl_2}^{-1} = k_3 k_2^{-1}$. According the NBS Circular 500 at 25°C

	$2\,NO_{(g)}$	+ $Cl_{2(g)}$ $\longrightarrow$	$2\,NOCl_{(g)}$	
$\Delta G_f^\ominus$(cal)	2(20,719)	0	2(15,860)	$\Delta G_{298}^\ominus = -9718$ cal
$S^\ominus$(cal deg^{-1})	2(50.339)	53.286	2(63.0)	$\Delta S_{298}^\ominus = -28.0$ cal deg^{-1}

If $\Delta C_P = 0$ so that $\Delta S^\ominus$ is independent of T, by (9.47)

$$\Delta G_{450}^\ominus - \Delta G_{298}^\ominus = -\int_{298}^{450} \Delta S^\ominus \, dT = 28.0(450 - 298) = 4260 \text{ cal}$$

$$\Delta G_{450}^\ominus = -9718 + 4260 = -5460 \text{ cal}$$

By (9.14), $-\Delta G^\ominus = RT \ln K_p$; hence,

$$\log_{10} K_p = \frac{-\Delta G_{450}^\ominus}{2.303RT} = \frac{-(-5460)}{2.303(1.987)450} = 2.65$$

From this K_p is 447 and, by (9.29) with $\Delta n_g = -1$, it follows that $K_c = K_p(RT)$ $= 447\ (0.08205 \times 450) = 1.65 \times 10^4$. From above with $k_2 = 0.0204$ liter mole^{-1} sec^{-1} comes

$$k_3 = k_2 K_c = 0.0204 \times 1.65 \times 10^4 = 337 \text{ liter}^2 \text{ mole}^{-2} \text{ sec}^{-1}$$

10.9 INFLUENCE OF TEMPERATURE

Although van't Hoff had proposed that the logarithm of a rate constant k_n should depend upon absolute temperature in the way that an equilibrium constant does, it was Arrhenius in 1889 who showed with the data available to him that

$$k_n = s e^{-(\Delta H_a/RT)} \tag{10.57}$$

He found s and ΔH_a to be independent of temperature, and over modest ranges of temperature they are indeed practically constant. Accordingly, if independent of T,

$$\ln k_n = \ln s - \frac{\Delta H_a}{RT} \tag{10.58}$$

$$\frac{d \ln k_n}{dT} = \frac{\Delta H_a}{RT^2} \tag{10.59}$$

Everyone knows that reactions generally increase in rate as T increases, and therefore ΔH_a is greater than zero. Having the dimensions of energy, ΔH_a is called the *activation energy*, the energy that must be acquired by reactants in order to overcome their chemical inertia and achieve that critical intermediate state which leads to products. Equation (10.59) defines the activation energy; it is true whether or not the rate constant k_n refers to an elementary step. Equation (10.59) also shows that a given absolute error in ΔH_a has less effect on the changes in k_n at high T than at low T.

Definite integration of (10.59) between temperature T_1 at which the rate constant is $k_{n(1)}$ and temperature T_2 at which the rate constant is $k_{n(2)}$ yields (10.60) if ΔH_a is independent of T.

$$\int_{kn(1)}^{k_n(2)} d(\ln k_n) = \left(\frac{\Delta H_a}{R}\right) \int_{T_1}^{T_2} \frac{dT}{T^2}$$

$$\ln\left(\frac{k_{n(2)}}{k_{n(1)}}\right) = \frac{\Delta H_a (T_2 - T_1)}{R T_1 T_2} \tag{10.60}$$

Because the precision of observed rate constants is generally less than that of vapor pressures or equilibrium constants, (10.58) and (10.60) are quite suitable, especially over small ranges of temperature. There is no reason to expect, however, that ΔH_a is really independent of temperature. Like any increase in enthalpy, it varies with T in accord with Kirchhoff's law.

If the activation energy is ascribed to a violent bimolecular collision, the exponential factor in (10.57) represents the fraction of collisions with energy in excess of ΔH_a and s is the total number of double collisions. If so, s should vary as $\sqrt{T}$, and it often does for bimolecular reactions. Simple collision theory does not provide a suitable method of predicting rate constants from microscopic data such as molecular structure; for it cannot predict with suitable precision the efficiency of collisions, the probability that a favorable orientation is achieved at impact, or the effective collision diameter of a molecule. Collision theory does find moderate use in describing collisions of very large molecules and collisions of species that react largely because they exert attractive forces on each other. In fact, it is straightforward to show by collision theory that, in accord with experiment, the rate constant for a reaction between ions may decrease as T rises, contrary to (10.59).

A semithermodynamic approach is generally more fruitful. If H_1 is the absolute enthalpy of reactants and if H_a is the absolute enthalpy of the intermediate state of extraordinary energy that lies between reactants and products, then $\Delta H_a = H_a - H_1$. When the increase in enthalpy for the overall reaction is $\Delta H = H_2 - H_1$ where H_2 is the absolute enthalpy of products, then

$$\begin{aligned}\Delta H &= H_2 - H_a + H_a - H_1 \\ &= -\Delta H'_a + \Delta H_a \end{aligned} \tag{10.61}$$

In (10.61) the increase in enthalpy on going from products to intermediate state is $\Delta H'_a = H_a - H_2$. It therefore is the heat of activation of the reverse reaction.

This semithermodynamic approach is in accord with the results of equilibrium thermodynamics. In general, the forward and reverse rate constants k_n and k'_n are related to the equilibrium constant K of an elementary reaction by

$$K = \frac{k_n}{k'_n} \tag{10.62}$$

This, together with (10.59) and (10.61), yields the familiar thermodynamic result

$$\frac{d \ln K}{dT} = \frac{d \ln k_n}{dT} - \frac{d \ln k'_n}{dT} = \frac{\Delta H_a}{RT^2} - \frac{\Delta H'_a}{RT^2} = \frac{\Delta H}{RT^2} \tag{10.63}$$

When reactions for which k_n and k'_n have been measured are very fast, the population of reactant molecules in energy states close to the energy of the activated state may be less than the equilibrium population. If so, the kinetically observed rate constants may differ from the 'equilibrium' rate constants called for in (10.63). This possible discrepancy is seldom, if ever, observed and is ultimately related to the rather academic question of whether a thermostat that controls a reaction can have a properly defined thermodynamic temperature.

This development of K as a ratio of rate constants provides some insight into the rate constants that are products of elementary rate constants. For example, the high-pressure first-order rate constant for unimolecular decomposition is, by (10.32), $k_1^{(\infty)} = k_1^* k_2 k_{-2}^{-1}$. In view of (10.57), which holds for each of the k's, $\Delta H_a^{(\infty)} = \Delta H_a^* + \Delta H_a^{(2)} - \Delta H_a^{(-2)}$, where ΔH_a^* is the activation energy for the elementary process $A^* \longrightarrow A^\ddagger$ (it is probably always zero); where $\Delta H_a^{(2)}$ is for collisional activation by $A + M \longrightarrow A^* + M$; and where $\Delta H_a^{(-2)}$ is for deactivation by collision in $M + A^* \longrightarrow M + A$ (this also is probably zero).

Similarly, if $G_1^\ominus$, $G_a^\ominus$, and $G_2^\ominus$ represent the absolute standard free energies of initial, intermediate, and final states,

$$\begin{aligned} \Delta G^\ominus &= G_2^\ominus - G_1^\ominus = G_a^\ominus - G_1^\ominus + G_2^\ominus - G_a^\ominus \\ &= \Delta G_a^\ominus - \Delta G_a^{\ominus\prime} \end{aligned} \tag{10.64}$$

In view of (10.63) and the well-known relation $K = e^{-(\Delta G^\ominus/RT)}$ it follows that

$$\frac{k_n}{k_n'} = \frac{e^{-(\Delta G_a{}^\ominus/RT)}}{e^{-(\Delta G_a{}^{\ominus\prime}/RT)}} \tag{10.65}$$

With a factor A to adjust dimensions of concentration and time, this yields

$$\begin{aligned} k_n &= s e^{-(\Delta H_a{}^\ominus/RT)} = A e^{-(\Delta G_a{}^\ominus/RT)} \\ &= A e^{\Delta S_a{}^\ominus/R} e^{-(\Delta H_a{}^\ominus/RT)} \end{aligned} \tag{10.66}$$

and

$$s = A e^{\Delta S_a{}^\ominus/R} \tag{10.67}$$

The familiar ideas concerning entropy and disorder can often be applied in a qualitative way in interpreting trends in s for related reactions or in explaining values of s that differ greatly from the expected collision rate for simple spheres. Perhaps the intermediate state is a tightly knit complex resulting from a collision or perhaps its formation is sterically hindered, the direction and relative orientations of reactants being of critical importance. Such an intermediate state is rather organized and rather unlikely relative to reactants so that $\Delta S_a^\ominus$ would be expected to be less than zero. The effective frequency s of fruitful collisions would then be less than A, the total frequency. On the other hand, if the intermediate state greatly resembles in order and organization its reactant precursor, $\Delta S_a^\ominus$ should be near zero and $s = A$. Or, finally, if the intermediate state is loosely bound or tending toward dissociation, $\Delta S_a^\ominus$ should reflect this increase in disorder in being greater than zero. If so, s exceeds the usual collision frequency A. Such qualitative ideas are often of mnemonic but seldom of quantitiative value. The main reason that the method of collisions fails for quantitative prediction of bimolecular rate constants is that it cannot evaluate ΔS_a for collisions of polyatomic reactants. These qualitative ideas are helpful, however, in understanding why a rate constant for reaction between ions of opposite charge may actually decrease as T rises. This unusual phenomenon occurs when an attractive potential like the coulombic potential is mainly responsible for reaction at low T but may be overwhelmed by a rise in T that undoes whatever order the potential may bestow on the activated state. Thus, whatever favorable effect a low T may allow to the attraction of unlike charges is sacrificed to the randomness of a greater T.

While the collisional and semithermodynamic theories are qualitatively useful, they are not so easily refined for actual calculations of rate as is the theory of absolute reaction rates, developed by Eyring and others.[6] The intermediate state of extraordinary energy that leads from reactants to products is called the *activated complex*. It is unobservable, cannot be diverted to products other than those to which it goes, and vibrates and rotates wildly with a lifetime of the order of 10^{-12} seconds. In unimolecular reactions it consists of one reactant molecule with the energy of activation so localized that nothing more is needed for dissociation to products except time and proper movements of the parts that are to become products. In a bimolecular reaction the activated complex is the double molecule produced by the union of the two reactants. The activated complex of a trimolecular reaction is the triple molecule formed from three reactant molecules.

The activated complex stands atop the energy pass of lowest height between the energy valleys of reactants and products. With respect to all but one of its internal coordinates, it is stable; with respect to the coordinate that describes the extent of reaction, usually a bond-stretching or vibrational coordinate, but perhaps an internal rotation, it is unstable. That is, the activated complex lies at a saddle point from which all but one coordinate lead to higher energies, that one leading to the lower energies of reactants or products.

Figure 10.3 describes this one reaction coordinate for an exothermic reaction in which atom C attacks diatomic molecule AB according to the reaction $AB + C \longrightarrow A + BC$. The reaction is pictured as the movement of B away from A to form the linear activated complex $ABC^{\ddagger}$ and subsequent approach of B toward C. The dashed curves indicate the electronic energies of isolated AB and BC if each dissociated to atoms. The activated complex $ABC^{\ddagger}$ is the molecule that exists atop the energy pass that separates the stable states of $AB + C$ and $A + BC$. Figure 10.4 illustrates this same bimolecular reaction by contour lines of constant energy with the internuclear distance R_{AB} perpendicular to and independent of R_{BC}. It is clear from these figures that ΔH_a exceeds zero because the energy pass at $ABC^{\ddagger}$ is at least as high as the higher valley. Moreover, if ΔH is positive for the passage between valleys, as it is here for the reaction $A + BC \longrightarrow AB + C$, then ΔH_a is greater than ΔH because again the pass between valleys is at least as high as the higher one. When an attractive

[6] Glasstone, S., K. J. Laidler, and H. Eyring, *The Theory of Rate Processes*. New York: McGraw-Hill Book Company, Inc., 1941.

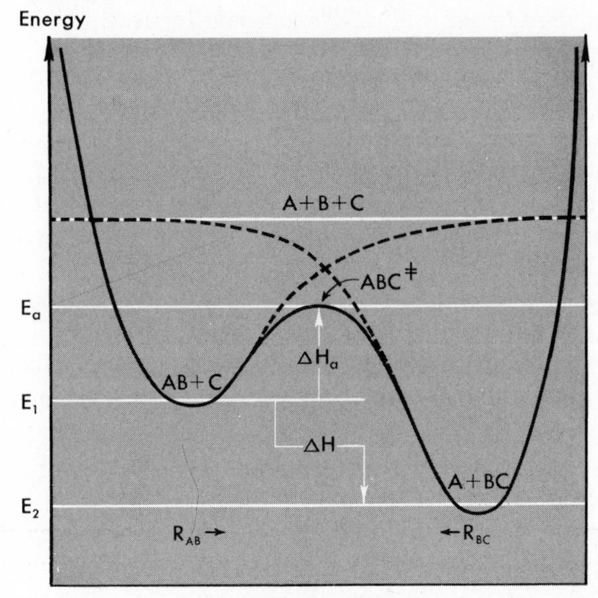

Figure 10.3. A View of the Reaction Coordinate for the Reaction $AB + C \longrightarrow ABC^{\ddagger} \longrightarrow A + BC$

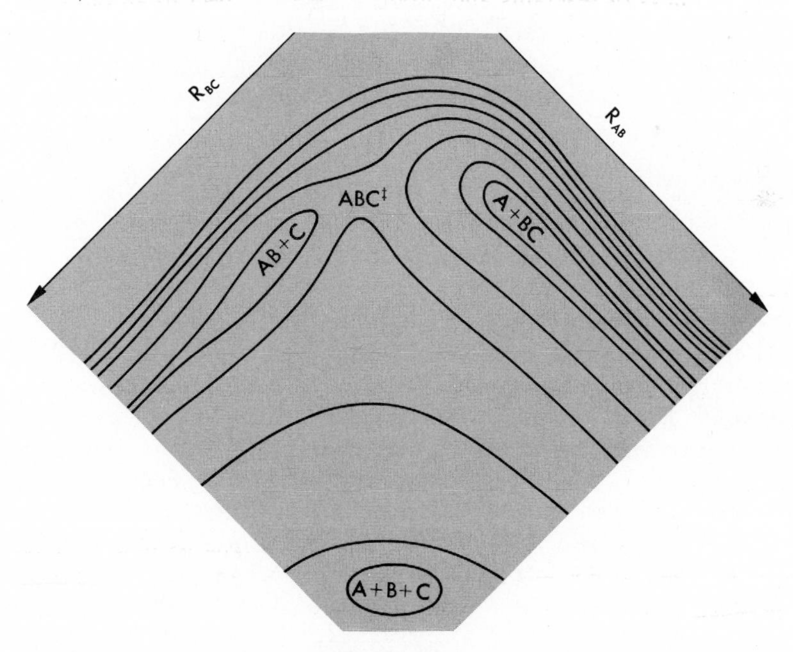

Figure 10.4. Contours of Equal Energy for the Reactions $AB + C \rightleftarrows ABC^{\ddagger} \rightleftarrows A + BC$

potential makes k decrease as T rises, as though to make ΔH_a in (10.59) less than zero, really the upper valley lacks a minimum of its own.

By definition, the activated complex cannot be observed. It is unlikely that any carbonium ion or other reasonably postulated intermediate of like reality and equal propensity for varied reaction is an activated complex, for aromatic rings can stabilize certain carbonium ions enough for observation and other less stable carbonium ions can be reasonably expected to be observed at some future time. This seems to place the activated complex as far from experience as the fine details of a collision. The great value of the Eyring theory is that it offers a way to calculate for a reaction of any molecularity the rate at which the pass is crossed and the concentration of the activated complex, which with good reason is usually assumed to be in equilibrium with reactants. These calculations by the methods of equilibrium statistical mechanics are described in Chapter 18.

Example 10.15. Calculate the activation energy ΔH_a for the decomposition of HI if k_2 is 3.95×10^{-6} l mole^{-1} sec^{-1} at 321.4°C and is 1.07×10^{-6} l mole^{-1} sec^{-1} at 300.0°C, where

$$-\frac{dC_{HI}}{dt} = k_2 C_{HI}^2$$

[Data from G. B. Kistiakowsky, *J. Am. Chem. Soc.*, **50,** 2315 (1928).]

Since $T_2 - T_1 = 594.6 - 573.2 = 21.4$°C, (10.60) yields

$$\Delta H_a = \frac{RT_1T_2}{T_2 - T_1} \ln\left(\frac{k_{2(2)}}{k_{2(1)}}\right)$$

$$= \frac{1.987 \times 573.2 \times 594.6 \times 2.303}{21.4} \log\left(\frac{3.95}{1.07}\right)$$

$$= 41{,}300 \text{ cal mole}^{-1}$$

Example 10.16. If the only reaction is decomposition of HI, how long will it take for 1% pure HI to decompose at 1 atm at 400°C? Use data from Example 10.15.

By (10.60), the rate constant k_2 at 400°C is found thus:

$$\ln\left(\frac{k_2}{3.95 \times 10^{-6}}\right) = \frac{41{,}300(673 - 595)}{1.987 \times 673 \times 595} = 4.05$$

$$k_2 = 57.2 \times 3.95 \times 10^{-6} = 2.26 \times 10^{-4}$$

After 1% decomposition, $C = 0.99C^0$ and, by (10.35),

$$\frac{C^0 - 0.99C^0}{C^0(0.99C^0)} = 2.26 \times 10^{-4}t$$

$$t = \frac{44.8}{C^0}$$

Since

$$C^0 = \frac{P}{RT} = \frac{1.00}{0.08205 \times 673}$$

$$t = 44.8 \times 0.08205 \times 673 = 2470 \text{ sec}$$

A simpler method of solution begins with (10.34) and $-\Delta C = C^0 \times 10^{-2}$ for 1% decomposition.

$$t = -\frac{\Delta C}{k_2 C^2} = \frac{C^0 \times 10^{-2}}{2.26 \times 10^{-4} \times (C^0)^2} = \frac{0.08205 \times 673 \times 10^{-2}}{2.26 \times 10^{-4}} = 2440 \text{ sec}$$

Example 10.17. With data from Example 10.15, calculate the characteristic collision diameter of HI in its decomposition at 321.4°C.

If C_{HI} is the number of moles of HI per milliliter, the number of molecules of HI that decompose per liter per second is $Nk_2(C_{HI} \times 10^3)^2$. The number that decompose per milliliter per second is therefore $Nk_2C_{HI}^2 \times 10^3$. Since two molecules of HI decompose together in one collision according to the reaction $2\text{ HI} \rightarrow H^2 + I^2$, it follows that

$$Nk_2C_{HI}^2 \times 10^3 = 2Z_2e^{-(\Delta H_a/RT)}$$

where Z_2 is the total number of bimolecular collisions of HI per milliliter per second. By (1.60),

$$Z_2 = 2\sigma^2(NC_{HI})^2\left(\frac{\pi RT}{M}\right)^{1/2}$$

Whence, with cgs units everywhere except in the exponential and k_2,

$$\sigma^2 = \frac{k_2 \times 10^3}{4N}\left(\frac{M}{\pi RT}\right)^{1/2} e^{\Delta H_a/RT}$$

$$= \frac{3.95 \times 10^{-6} \times 10^3}{4 \times 6.02 \times 10^{23}}\left(\frac{128}{\pi \times 8.314 \times 10^7 \times 595}\right)^{1/2} e^{41{,}300/(1.987 \times 595)}$$

$$= 16.4 \times 10^{-28} \times (8.24 \times 10^{-10})^{1/2} \times 1.45 \times 10^{15}$$

$$= 68.3 \times 10^{-18} \text{ cm}^2$$

$$\sigma = 0.827 \times 10^{-8} \text{ cm}$$

This cross section is considerably smaller than the value of about 3×10^{-8} cm derived from viscosities. Besides, the interatomic distance in HI is 1.60 A, also in excess of 0.83 A.

Example 10.18. Calculate the activation energies for the hydrolysis and Cl-exchange of chloroacetic acid in hydrochloric acid from these rate constants (R. A. Kennedy and F. J. Johnston, *J. Phys. Chem.* **63,** 1426 (1959)):

Temperature (°K)	353.2	363.2	373.2	383.2
Hydrolysis (hr^{-1})	0.00317	0.00859	0.0219	0.0525
Exchange (liter mole^{-1} hr^{-1})	0.235	0.664	1.60	3.67

Figure 10.5 has been prepared in accord with (10.58), which says that $\ln k = 2.303 \log_{10} k$ is a linear function of T^{-1}. Since the slope of the lines is then $-\Delta H_a/2.303R$, it follows that for hydrolysis, where the slope of the graph is -5420 deg,

$$\Delta H_a = -2.303\, R\,(-5420) = 24{,}800 \text{ cal}$$

while for exchange of Cl, where the slope is −5360 deg,

$$\Delta H_a = -2.303\,R\,(-5360) = 24{,}500 \text{ cal}$$

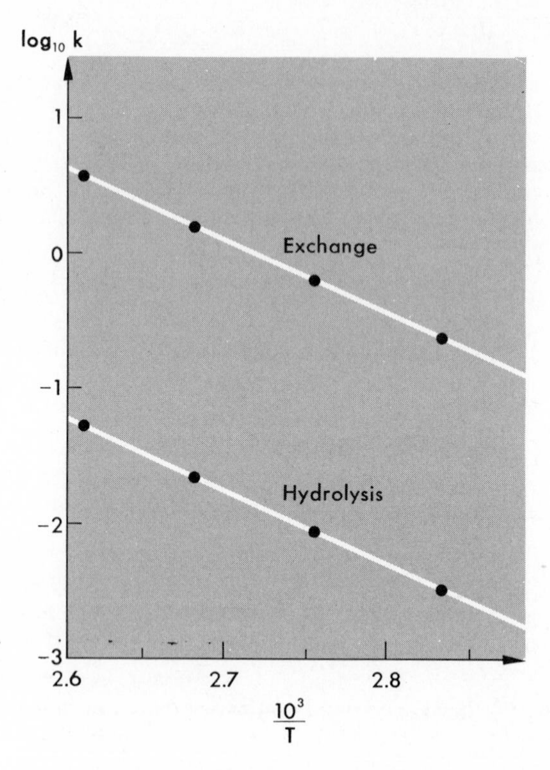

Figure 10.5. Rate Constants as Function of Temperature (Hydrolysis and Cl-Exchange of Chloroacetic Acid in Hydrochloric Acid)

10.10 CONSECUTIVE AND COMPETING REACTIONS

i.e., 2 1st order reactions

The rate of formation of a final product sometimes differs from the rate of disappearance of a reactant. Two common reasons are competing reactions that lead to more than one product or a series of consecutive reactions that generate intermediate species whose concentrations rise during the early stages of reaction and finally fall to zero. A particularly simple example of consecutive reactions is the transformation of A into C via two first-order reactions, with B as intermediate.

$$\begin{array}{ccccc} A & \xrightarrow{k_{1(1)}} & B & \xrightarrow{k_{1(2)}} & C \\ C_A^0 - x & & x - y & & y \end{array} \qquad (10.68)$$

The first-order rates for the decay of A and the growth of C are

$$\frac{dx}{dt} = k_{1(1)}(C_A^0 - x) \tag{10.69}$$

$$\frac{dy}{dt} = k_{1(2)}(x - y) \tag{10.70}$$

These simultaneous differential equations can be solved for x and y as follows. As in (10.16),

$$\int_0^x \frac{dx'}{(C_A^0 - x')} = k_{1(1)} \int_0^t dt'$$

$$\ln\left(\frac{C_A^0}{C_A^0 - x}\right) = k_{1(1)}t$$

$$\frac{x}{C_A^0} = (1 - e^{-k_{1(1)}t}) \tag{10.71}$$

Elimination of x from (10.70) with (10.71) yields

$$\frac{dy}{dt} = k_{1(2)}\{C_A^0[1 - e^{-k_{1(1)}t}] - y\}$$

$$\frac{dy}{dt} + k_{1(2)}y = C_A^0 k_{1(2)}[1 - e^{-k_{1(1)}t}] \tag{10.72}$$

Multiplication by $e^{k_{1(2)}t}$, an integrating factor, transforms the left-hand member of (10.72) into an exact derivative, namely, $(d/dt)[ye^{k_{1(2)}t}]$. Upon integration with respect to t with $y = 0$ at $t = 0$, (10.72) becomes

$$\left(\frac{y}{C_A^0}\right)e^{k_{1(2)}t} = \int_{t'=0}^{t'=t} [1 - e^{-k_{1(1)}t'}]d[e^{k_{1(2)}t'}]$$

$$= [e^{k_{1(2)}t} - 1] - \left[\frac{k_{1(2)}}{k_{1(2)} - k_{1(1)}}\right]\int_{t'=0}^{t'=t} d\{e^{[k_{1(2)} - k_{1(1)}]t'}\}$$

$$= [e^{k_{1(2)}t} - 1] - \left[\frac{k_{1(2)}}{k_{1(2)} - k_{1(1)}}\right]\{e^{[k_{1(2)} - k_{1(1)}]t} - 1\}$$

Whence,

$$\frac{y}{C_A^0} = [1 - e^{-k_{1(2)}t}] + \left(\frac{k_{1(2)}}{k_{1(2)} - k_{1(1)}}\right)[e^{-k_{1(2)}t} - e^{-k_{1(1)}t}]$$

$$= \frac{k_{1(2)}[1 - e^{-k_{1(1)}t}] - k_{1(1)}[1 - e^{-k_{1(2)}t}]}{[k_{1(2)} - k_{1(1)}]} \tag{10.73}$$

Figure 10.6 shows how the concentrations of A, B, and C vary with time if $k_{1(2)} = 2k_{1(1)}$. Although A decays according to simple first-order kinetics, the formation of B delays the formation of C. The steady-state approximation corresponds to the maximum concentration of B. If this maximum is very low, broad, and flat, as it often is in more complex reactions, the steady state is a good approximation. It is, however, preceded by an induction period similar to the one that in Figure 10.6 precedes the maximum in B. If B reaches a steady state, by (10.96) and (10.70)

$$0 = \frac{dC_B}{dt} = \frac{dx}{dt} - \frac{dy}{dt} = k_{1(1)}C_A - k_{1(2)}C_B$$

The steady-state approximation is valid only when C_B is small; hence, in this simple case, $k_{1(1)} \ll k_{1(2)}$.

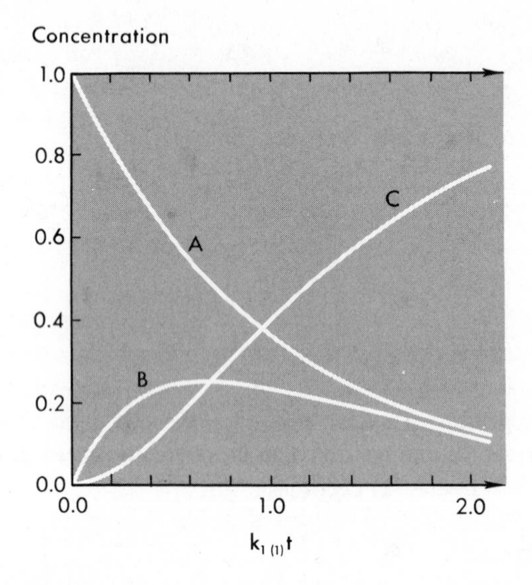

Figure 10.6. Consecutive First-Order Reactions

The steady-state approximation is valid in many different circumstances, but sometimes it does not work. To keep generality with a minimum of arbitrarily imposed restrictions, it is often possible to simplify the kinetics of a mechanism by assuming that a certain step is so slow that it alone determines the rate. Generally it is then reasonable to treat all other steps by thermodynamics, for they can be assumed to be at equilibrium via relatively swift reaction. The steady-state method is somewhat more general and less restrictive than the *method of the rate-determining step*. On the other hand, the latter proceeds directly to a simple result. For the mechanism (10.68), if the slow step is A ⟶ B, then $k_{1(2)} \gg k_{1(1)}$ and (10.73) becomes $y = C_A^0(1 - e^{-k_{1(1)}t})$, which is like (10.71). That is, C forms and A decays at the same rate because B decays almost as fast as it is formed. The steady-state approximation arrives at the same condition $k_{1(2)} \gg k_{1(1)}$ for a different reason, namely that B's rate of decay is small.

The method of the rate-determining step simplifies the mechanism of unimolecular decomposition (10.26) as follows. If the slow step of (10.26) is $A^* \longrightarrow A^\ddagger$, then the collision reaction reaches equilibrium with

$$K = \frac{k_2}{k_{-2}} = \frac{C_{A^*}C_M}{C_A C_M}$$

Hence, the rate of the slow step is $k_1^* C_{A^*} = k_1^* k_2 k_{-2}^{-1} C_A = k_1^{(\infty)} C_A$ as in (10.32). However, if $A^* \longrightarrow A^\ddagger$ is swift while activation by collision is rate-determining, then the rate is $k_2 C_A C_M$, which is (10.33). Similarly, for recombination by (10.49), if the rate-determinig step is $XY^* + M \longrightarrow XY + M^*$, then, with the condition for equilibrium for $X + Y = XY^*$ in the form $K = k_2(k_1^*)^{-1} = C^* C_X^{-1} C_Y^{-1}$, the rate of recombination is $k_2^* C^* C_M = k_2^* k_2 (k_1^*)^{-1} C_X C_Y C_M$ as in (10.53). On the other hand, if collisions are frequent while X and Y rarely meet, the rate of (10.49) is limited to $k_2 C_X C_Y$, which is (10.52) with $k_1^* \ll k_2 C_M$. Finding a rate-determining step is especially valuable when many intermediate species exist in a mechanism. Molecules adsorbed at catalyst sites of various activity form a commonly occurring set of intermediate states that are not only numerous but often ill-defined.

It is impossible to observe intermediates in any truly elementary process, and each new elementary process of a mechanism requires one more reactive intermediate if the new step is not one that destroys such reactive species by recombination or deactivation. When alternate routes are followed for an overall change, the *principle of microscopic reversibility* (or detailed balancing) requires that at equilibrium the net rate for each elementary process of a mechanism is zero. A very simple example of alternate elementary steps is the pair of reactions that precede dissociation of a diatom Y_2 in the presence of two differently acting third bodies M and N. The overall gaseous reaction is $Y_2 \longrightarrow 2Y$, but there exist the alternate routes

$$M^* + Y_2 \rightleftarrows M + Y_2^* \tag{10.74}$$

with forward and reverse rate constants k_M and k_{-M}, and

$$N^* + Y_2 \rightleftarrows N + Y_2^* \tag{10.75}$$

with forward and reverse rate constants k_N and k_{-N}. Assumed to be rate-determining is the actual dissociation

$$Y_2^* \longrightarrow Y_2^\ddagger \longrightarrow 2Y \tag{10.76}$$

with rate constant k_1^*. When (10.74) and (10.75) reach equilibrium, the net rate of change of the concentration of Y_2^* is

$$0 = \frac{dC^*}{dt} = k_M C_{Y_2} C_{M^*} + k_N C_{Y_2} C_{N^*} - k_{-M} C^* C_M - k_{-N} C^* C_N$$

whence

$$\frac{C^*}{C_{Y_2}} = \frac{k_M C_{M^*} + k_N C_{N^*}}{k_{-M} C_M + k_{-N} C_N} \tag{10.77}$$

Although C^* would seem to depend on C_M and C_N (as well as on T through the k's), the principle of microscopic reversibility requires that (10.74) and (10.75) be considered separately; hence,

$$0 = k_M C_{Y_2} C_{M^*} - k_{-M} C^* C_M \tag{10.78}$$

$$0 = k_N C_{Y_2} C_{N^*} - k_{-N} C^* C_N \tag{10.79}$$

That is, from (10.78) and (10.79),

$$\frac{C^*}{C_{Y_2}} = \frac{k_M C_{M^*}}{k_{-M} C_M} = \frac{k_N C_{N^*}}{k_{-N} C_N} \tag{10.80}$$

The concentrations of M* relative to M and of N* relative to N are fixed by the Boltzmann distribution; hence, (10.80) replaces (10.77) and C^*/C_{Y_2} depends on T but not on C_M and C_N. Thus, if (10.76) is rate-determining, the rate of dissociation of Y_2 is independent of the source of Y_2^*.

Competing reactions are common in organic systheses where isomeric products abound. Let the competing reactions be similar second-order reactions such as

$$\left.\begin{aligned} A + B &\xrightarrow{k_{2(1)}} D + \cdots \\ A + B &\xrightarrow{k_{2(2)}} E + \cdots \end{aligned}\right\} \tag{10.81}$$

If x moles of D and y moles of E have formed by time t from reactants originally at concentrations C_A^0 and C_B^0 then

$$\frac{dx}{dt} = k_{2(1)}[C_A^0 - (x + y)][C_B^0 - (x + y)]$$

$$\frac{dy}{dt} = k_{2(2)}[C_A^0 - (x + y)][C_B^0 - (x + y)]$$

If these are the only reactions to use A and B, the rate of disappearance of A or B is the sum of these rates. The ratio of D to E is

$$\frac{dx}{dy} = \frac{k_{2(1)}}{k_{2(2)}} \tag{10.82}$$

A successful synthesis often involves adjusting experimental conditions to obtain as favorable a set of rates as possible. For example, if the frequency factors s of $k_{2(1)}$ and $k_{2(2)}$ are equal, (10.82) becomes

$$\frac{dx}{dy} = \exp\left[\frac{\Delta H_{a22} - \Delta H_{a21}}{RT}\right] \tag{10.83}$$

The amount of D formed relative to E increases with T if ΔH_{a22} exceeds ΔH_{a21}. To minimize the formation of D in these circumstances, T must be kept as low as possible or practical.

10.11 ANALYSIS OF A MECHANISM

The order of a reaction is best thought of as an empirically observed exponent. The molecularity is more remote from experiment inasmuch as it involves an interpretation of observed data in terms of a mechanism or series of elementary reactions that seem plausible. The importance of a suitable mechanism is paramount, however, in really understanding reaction rates, for the mechanism lists the simple acts of chemistry by which reactants become products without detectable intermediates. On the other hand, mechanisms are so varied and sometimes appear even to be so much a matter of personal taste that any attempt at generality is gross simplification. Rather than attempt a survey here, only one mechanism is discussed in the hope that it presents typical problems and that "a picture is worth a thousand words." The particular example chosen is

$$2\,NO_2 + F_2 \longrightarrow 2\,NO_2F \tag{10.84}$$

It has been explained in detail in the literature.[7]

At low pressures, the reaction is first-order in both F_2 and NO_2. The mechanism (10.54) does not apply because at low pressures it requires third-order kinetics. The most reasonable initial reaction is then a slow, rate-limiting, bimolecular one,

$$NO_2 + F_2 \xrightarrow{k_2} NO_2F + F \tag{10.85}$$

The fluorine atoms thus generated can be removed in several ways, namely,

$$F + NO_2 + M \xrightarrow{k_3} NO_2F + M^* \tag{10.86}$$

$$F + F + M \xrightarrow{k_3'} F_2 + M^* \tag{10.87}$$

$$F + NO_2F \xrightarrow{k_2'} NO_2 + F_2 \tag{10.88}$$

or by side reactions. Species M is any third body of the reaction. The purpose of this discussion is to show that one or two of these reactions are of minor importance.

Reaction (10.88) is merely the reverse of the initial reaction (10.85), but (10.86) and (10.87) may be either second- or third-order; for each of the latter

[7] Perrine, R. L., and H. S. Johnston *J. Chem. Phys.* **21**, 2202 (1953).

is a bimolecular recombination in the presence of a third body M that removes energy. At the low pressures used to establish the second-order rate law for the overall reaction (10.84) only third-order kinetics are suitable for (10.86) or (10.87). If (10.87) is excluded, the steady-state condition for F yields

$$\frac{dC_F}{dt} = 0 = k_2 C_{NO_2} C_{F_2} - k_2' C_F C_{NO_2F} - k_3 C_F C_{NO_2} C_M$$

Solution for C_F and substitution in the equation

$$\frac{dC_{NO_2F}}{dt} = k_2 C_{NO_2} C_{F_2} - k_2' C_F C_{NO_2F} + k_3 C_F C_{NO_2} C_M$$

yields for the rate

$$\frac{1}{2}\left(\frac{dC_{NO_2F}}{dt}\right) = k_3 C_{NO_2} C_M \left[\frac{k_2 C_{NO_2} C_{F_2}}{k_2' C_{NO_2F} + k_3 C_{NO_2} C_M}\right]$$

If $k_3 C_{NO_2} C_M \gg k_2' C_{NO_2F}$, the rate is $\frac{1}{2}(dC_{NO_2F}/dt) = k_2 C_{NO_2F} C_{F_2}$, as observed. The reaction is not slowed by large values of C_{NO_2F} so that this condition means that k_2' is very small and (10.88) is negligible. That is, (10.85) and (10.86) alone are sufficient to explain the observed order of the overall reaction. If (10.87) competes with (10.86) and (10.88), there results a complex rate expression that does not fit observations.

If (10.87) is the only means of destroying F atoms, $dC_F/dt = k_2 C_{NO_2} C_{F_2} - k_3' C_F^2 C_M$ and

$$\frac{1}{2}\left(\frac{dC_{NO_2F}}{dt}\right) = \tfrac{1}{2} k_2 C_{NO_2} C_{F_2}$$

Although this last expression satisfies the rate law, the concentration of F is not observed to increase with time so that $k_3' C_F^2 C_M$ must equal $k_2 C_{NO_2} C_{F_2}$. Instead of showing that the third-order recombination is much slower than the rate of the overall reaction so that $k_3' C_F^2 C_M \neq k_2 C_{NO_2} C_{F_2}$, it is more convenient to show that (10.86) is faster than (10.87). The ratio of their rates is

$$\frac{k_3 C_F C_{NO_2} C_M}{k_3' C_F^2 C_M} \approx \frac{C_{NO_2}}{C_F}$$

for M is probably equally effective as third body in both reactions and k_3 is at least as great as k_3'. Indeed, k_3 should be greater than k_3' because NO_2F^* has more degrees of vibrational freedom than F_2^* and should therefore be longer-lived. That is, (10.86) should become second-order at lower pressures than (10.87). Since NO_2 is present in concentrations typical of a reactant, while F is a minor species generated by the reaction, this ratio greatly exceeds unity and (10.87) is of minor importance. The most reasonable mechanism is, therefore, simply

$$NO_2 + F_2 \xrightarrow{\text{slow}} NO_2F + F$$

$$F + NO_2 + M \xrightarrow{\text{fast}} NO_2F + M^*$$

10.12 CHAIN REACTIONS

Elementary reactions that depend on the same observable intermediates of high reactivity are said to be *kinetically coupled.* A sequence of kinetically coupled reactions in which certain intermediates are repeatedly regenerated is a *chain reaction.* This possibility was first noted by Bodenstein in 1913. In a way, a chain reaction offers itself a chemical bonus, for one or more of the products in the series of repeated reactions is itself a reactant in those reactions. It is often a free radical (a molecule with one or more unpaired electrons), but may also be a reactive ion or molecule.

When this reactive intermediate is destroyed, the chain of reactions is broken and the reaction sequence ceases until another reactive species is generated. A third body or a vessel wall is necessary for termination when the radicals are simple, as explained in Section 10.8. The presence of free radicals in a system can often be demonstrated by spectroscopic means (e. g. mass spectroscopy, nuclear magnetic resonance, or even infrared or ultraviolet absorption), but low concentrations may prevent detection by these means. A less direct but more sensitive method of proving the presence of free radicals is to introduce into a reacting system species that destroy free radicals or lead to ones that have reduced activity and thus recombine faster than they carry on the chains. For example, in a system containing alkyl radicals R, introducing I_2 causes $I_2 + R \longrightarrow RI + I$. If the I is less reactive than the free radical that might otherwise have been generated by R, perhaps because its reactions have a large activation energy, the reaction is at least slowed and perhaps stopped by recombination of I. Introducing NO, which has an unpaired electron, may interrupt a chain by formation of $R - N = 0$. Or again, adding negative catalysts like NH_3, O_3 O_2, ClO_2 and so on to a chain-reacting mixture of H_2 and Cl_2 greatly shortens the chains by removing the H and Cl atoms that propagate the chains. Of course, adding the proper free radicals or active intermediates can also accelerate a chain reaction that has reached a steady state, and even cause an explosion.

A chain reaction is usually initiated by dissociation of molecules thermally by energetic collision, as in unimolecular decomposition, by photolysis, when absorption of radiation causes a bond to break, or by adsorption on an active site of a catalyst, which in a way is a stabilized reactive intermediate. Thermal decomposition of dimethyl azide (CH_3–N=N–CH_3) or metal methyls like $Pb(CH_3)_4$, $As(CH_3)_3$, $Bi(CH_3)_3$, $Hg(CH_3)_2$, $Zn(CH_3)_2$, . . . yields methyl radicals, and thermal decomposition of peroxides R–O–O–R yields alkoxyl radicals by dissociation of the weak O–O bond. Similarly, absorption of light by Cl_2, Br_2, or I_2 yields atoms Cl, Br, or I, and absorption of ultraviolet light by gaseous atoms of Hg in H_2 yields H and weakly bonded HgH. Halogen atoms X can also be generated in a system containing X_2 by introduction of sodium vapor; the reaction is $Na + X_2 \longrightarrow NaX + X$. Such introduction of free radicals may increase the number of chains or it may shorten the *induction period*, the time in which no obvious reaction occurs between mixing reactants and attainment of a steady state.

Chain reactions differ from ordinary reactions in exhibiting a rate that is constant or even explosively accelerated. Ordinary reactions decrease in rate as reactants are consumed. Because an induction period is often required to generate the reactive intermediate that propagates the chain, a typical chain reaction is slow at first, swift or even explosive later, and finally slow as reactants are exhausted. If reactants could be supplied continuously, it is likely that a steady state, once realized, could endure almost indefinitely. The complicated mechanisms of reactions that depend on chains often make their rates complicated functions of concentrations and even of impurities. Finally, their rate constants are unusually great because of apparently large frequency factors.

The classic examples of chain reactions are those of H_2 with Br_2 and Cl_2. Recently[8] a similar chain reaction has been found above 600°K for the reaction of H_2 with I_2, whereas traditionally the reaction $H_2 + I_2 \longrightarrow H_2I_2^{\ddagger} \longrightarrow 2\,HI$ was considered ideally and simply bimolecular. These three overall reactions $H_2 + X_2 \longrightarrow 2\,HX$ begin with the production of halogen atoms by absorption of light and dissociation (photolysis) or, in this discussion, by thermal dissociation.

$$X_2 + M \longrightarrow X + X + M \qquad (k_D) \tag{10.89}$$

The chain-propagating reactions that advance the conversion to HX are

$$\left.\begin{aligned} X + H_2 &\longrightarrow HX + H \qquad (k_X) \\ H + X_2 &\longrightarrow HX + X \qquad (k_H) \end{aligned}\right\} \tag{10.90}$$

These two reactions can occur repeatedly, for as X generates H, it then regenerates X to complete a cycle. For HCl, this cycle may be repeated 10^6 times before interruption through depletion of H_2 or Cl_2 or by destruction of the chain carriers H and Cl. Chlorination and bromination of aliphatic hydrogens RH occur by a chain reaction like (10.90); the products are HX and RX and the chain carriers are X and R but not H. At high pressure and in large vessels, conditions that minimize recombination at the wall, the chain-carrying atoms are destroyed by the three-body collisions

(8) Sullivan, J. H., *J. Chem. Phys.* **30,** 1292, 1577 (1959); *ibid,* **36,** 1925 (1962); *ibid.* **46,** 73 (1967).

$$X + X + M \longrightarrow X_2 + M \qquad (k_{XX}) \tag{10.91}$$

$$X + H + M \longrightarrow HX + M \qquad (k_{XH}) \tag{10.92}$$

$$H + H + M \longrightarrow H_2 + M \qquad (k_{HH}) \tag{10.93}$$

Two other reactions that do not destroy the chain-carrying atoms but do slow the production of HX are the reverse of (10.90) namely,

$$X + HX \longrightarrow X_2 + H \qquad (k_{-X}) \tag{10.94}$$

$$H + HX \longrightarrow H_2 + X \qquad (k_{-H}) \tag{10.95}$$

Table 10.1 summarizes approximate values of ΔH_a for these k's.

Table 10.1 Approximate Activation Energies of Hydrogen-Halogen Reactions (kcal).

Rate Constant	Reaction	X = Cl	X = Br	X = I
k_D	10.89	58	46	36
k_X	10.90	6	18	33[a]
k_{-X}	10.94	46	42	36[a]
k_H	10.90	1	1	0[a]
k_{-H}	10.95	5	1	0[a]
k_{XX}	10.91	0	0	0
k_{XH}	10.92	0	0	0
k_{HH}	10.93	0	0	0

[a] J. H. Sullivan, *loc. cit.*

Since the heat of dissociation of H_2 is about 104 kcal mole^{-1}, while those of the halogens are only 58 for Cl_2, 46 for Br_2, and 36 kcal mole^{-1} for I_2, and since ΔS° for a diatomic dissociation is about 25 cal mole^{-1} deg^{-1} for H_2 and X_2, the value of ΔG° and the amount of H or X at equilibrium are dominated by the heat of dissociation. The activation energies for (10.89) are about equal to the dissociation energies of X_2 because in general ΔH_a is close to zero for recombination of any atoms. Thus, with comparable rates of collision with M*, dissociation of H_2 is unimportant compared to dissociation of X_2 in initiating reaction thermally.

The termolecular recombinations (10.91), (10.92), and (10.93), slow because they require essentially a triple collision, will compete with the various bimolecular reactions only when the latter are slow because of a large ΔH_a. Recombination of Cl and H seldom occurs because for (10.90) and (10.95) ΔH_a is small and their rate is rapid. In the absence of species like O_2 or NH_3 that break a chain, (10.90) may in fact be repeated 10^6 times without interruption in large vessels at high pressure where termination at a wall is unlikely. After initiation, only $Cl + HCl \longrightarrow Cl_2 + H$ is slow in this system. However, in the H_2-Br_2 system, the moderately high ΔH_a of 18 kcal for $Br + H_2 \longrightarrow HBr + H$ reduces the rate of this step (10.90) enough to allow Br to accumulate; hence, (10.91) interferes with (10.90). However, because reactions of H are swift because both ΔH_a's are low when it is a reactant in (10.90) and (10.95), the concentration of H never rises to a value that allows (10.92) or (10.93) to be significant. Thus, the important reactions for the H_2-Br_2 system are (10.89), (10.90), and (10.91), with some contribution of (10.95) when the reaction has progressed enough to yield significant amounts of HBr.

A mathematical formulation of the H_2-Br_2 reactions in terms of (10.89), (10.90), (10.91), and (10.95) yields the differential equations

$$\frac{dC_{HBr}}{dt} = k_{Br}C_{Br}C_{H_2} + k_H C_H C_{Br_2} - k_{-H}C_H C_{HBr} \tag{10.96}$$

$$\frac{dC_H}{dt} = k_{Br}C_{Br}C_{H_2} - k_H C_H C_{Br_2} - k_{-H}C_H C_{HBr} \tag{10.97}$$

$$\frac{dC_{Br}}{dt} = 2k_D C_{M^*}C_{Br_2} - k_{Br}C_{Br}C_{H_2} + k_H C_H C_{Br_2} - 2k_{BrBr}C_{Br}^2 C_M + k_{-H}C_H C_{HBr} \tag{10.98}$$

In the steady-state approximation, the concentrations of the minor species H and Br change very slowly so that (10.97) becomes the algebraic equation

$$0 = k_{Br}C_{Br}C_{H_2} - k_H C_H C_{Br_2} - k_{-H}C_H C_{HBr} \tag{10.99}$$

and, with account of (10.99), (10.98) becomes

$$0 = 2k_D C_{M^*}C_{Br_2} - 2\,k_{BrBr}C_{Br}^2 C_M \tag{10.100}$$

With C_{Br} from (10.100), it follows from (10.99) that

$$C_H = \frac{k_{Br}C_{H_2}}{k_H C_{Br_2} + k_{-H}C_{HBr}}\left(\frac{k_D C_{M^*}C_{Br_2}}{k_{BrBr}C_M}\right)^{1/2} \tag{10.101}$$

Furthermore, (10.96) and (10.99) yield

$$\frac{dC_{HBr}}{dt} = 2k_H C_H C_{Br_2} \tag{10.102}$$

Hence, by (10.101) and (10.102),

$$\frac{dC_{HBr}}{dt} = \frac{2k_H k_{Br}C_{H_2}C_{Br_2}}{k_H C_{Br_2} + k_{-H}C_{HBr}}\left(\frac{k_D C_{M^*}C_{Br_2}}{k_{BrBr}C_M}\right)^{1/2} = \frac{2k_{Br}(k_H/k_{-H})(k_D C_{M^*}/k_{BrBr}C_M)^{1/2}}{(k_H/k_{-H}) + (C_{HBr}/C_{Br_2})}\,C_{H_2}C_{Br_2}^{1/2} \tag{10.103}$$

The form of (10.103) was first found empirically by Bodenstein and Lind in 1907.

The thermal and explosive gaseous reactions of H_2 and O_2 to form H_2O have been studied experimentally and theoretically by many investigators.[9] The

[9] For a brief, readable review, see, e.g., R. N. Pease, "Kinetics of Several Oxidation Reactions," in B. Lewis, R. N. Pease, and H. S. Tayler, eds., *Combustion Processes*, Princeton, N.J.: © Princeton University Press, 1956, pp. 160–174.

reaction proceeds by means of chain reactions involving the free radicals H, O, HO, and HO_2. Between about 350°C and 600°C there are three explosion limits, the general nature of which is shown in Figure 10.7 for mixtures of $2H_2 + O_2$. The limits depend on the nature of the vessel wall and can be changed by adding other gases.

At a pressure of about 10 mm Hg ($p_{H_2} = 6.7$ and $p_{O_2} = 3.3$) at about 500°C, the main reactions of the explosion are

$$\left.\begin{aligned} H + O_2 &\longrightarrow OH + O \\ O + H_2 &\longrightarrow OH + H \\ OH + H_2 &\longrightarrow H_2O + H \end{aligned}\right\} \qquad (10.104)$$

The first two of these reactions produce twice as many free radicals as they use; hence these chain-branching steps produce ever increasing numbers of H, O, and OH as the explosion occurs. As the pressure is reduced, these species collide

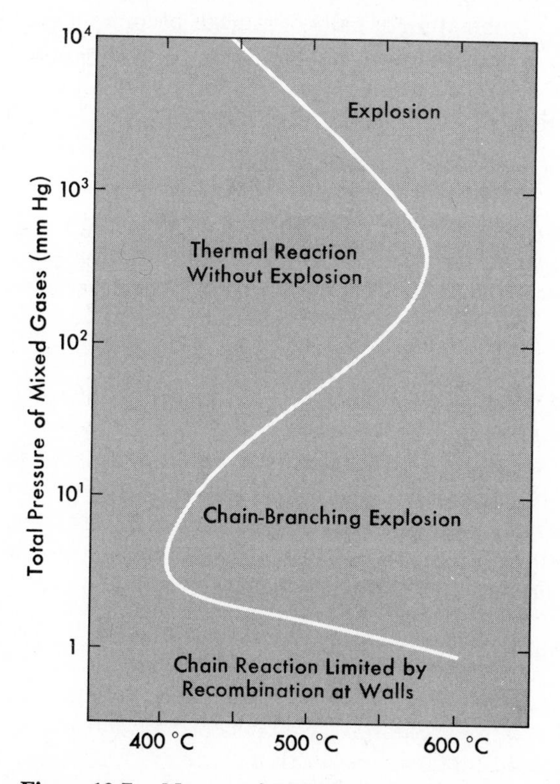

Figure 10.7. Nature of Reaction of Stoichiometric Mixtures of Hydrogen and Oxygen†

†Adapted from B. Lewis and G. von Elbe, *Combustion, Flames, and Explosions in Gases*, New York: Academic Press, 1953, p. 29.

with H_2 and O_2 less and less frequently. Finally, for mixtures with pressures less than about 1.5 mm at 500°C, the free radicals recombine at the vessel walls to yield H_2, O_2, OH, H_2O_2 and so on. This lower limit depends greatly on the nature of the surface and on the effective size of the molecules of any gas that may be added to the H_2 and O_2.

A nonexploding thermal reaction can be sustained at pressures from about 50 to 3300 mm Hg at 500°C. The explanation of this limit lies with trimolecular recombination and with a rather stable species HO_2 which is generated by the reactions

$$\left.\begin{aligned} H + O_2 &\longrightarrow HO_2^* \\ HO_2^* + M &\longrightarrow HO_2 + M^* \end{aligned}\right\} \tag{10.105}$$

As the pressure falls toward 50 mm Hg, it becomes less likely that HO_2^* will be stabilized by collision with M. As a result, when H collides with O_2 the products are OH and O, a chain-branching mechanism that causes an explosion. Above 50 mm Hg, trimolecular recombination of pairs of radicals becomes more likely and HO_2 is stable enough to reach a vessel wall and suffer recombination there. However, as the pressure rises, HO_2 may collide with H_2 to yield a free radical OH according to the reaction

$$HO_2 + H_2 \longrightarrow H_2O + OH \tag{10.106}$$

This once again serves to maintain the concentration of OH and other free radicals so that as the pressure rises chain-branching and explosion occur. Of course, during any explosion, the thermal energy liberated in the net reaction

$$2H_2 + O_2 \longrightarrow 2H_2O \tag{10.107}$$

serves also to increase the rates of all mechanisms by increasing the local temperature of the reacting mixture.

The nature of the process that produces the first few free radicals is a matter of considerable debate. Stray radiation of any kind or traces of catalytic impurity or defects in vessel walls could dissociate H_2. It is well known, for example, that the hydrogenation catalyst Pt is capable of initiating an explosion in mixtures of H_2 and O_2 at low temperature. It is also possible that thermally

$$H_2 + O_2 \longrightarrow HO_2 + H \tag{10.108}$$

Once the reaction has begun, the traces of H_2O_2 generated could yield new free radicals by

$$H_2O_2 \longrightarrow 2OH \tag{10.109}$$

Addition polymerization is another example of a chain reaction when the polymer is so large that the behavior of the active site is independent of the size of the residue R to which it is attached. If addition is by a free radical mechanism, initiation may depend on an alkoxyl radical R′–O·. Continued addition of monomer $R''CH{=}CH_2$ would involve the reactants

$$
\begin{array}{ccccc}
 & R''\ \ H & \left(\begin{array}{c} R''\ \ H \\ |\quad\ | \\ -C-C- \\ |\quad\ | \\ H\quad H \end{array}\right)_n & R''\ \ H & & R''\ \ H \\
 & |\quad\ | & & |\quad\ | & & |\quad\ | \\
R'-O- & C-C & & C-C\,\cdot & + & C=C \\
 & |\quad\ | & & |\quad\ | & & |\quad\ | \\
 & H\quad H & & H\quad H & & H\quad H
\end{array}
$$

the reaction of which might be abbreviated as

$$R_n^{\cdot} + A \longrightarrow R_{n+1}^{\cdot} \tag{10.110}$$

This chain may be ended by any one of several termination processes. If polymerization occurs by an ionic mechanism, initiation of reaction might be

$$
\begin{array}{ccccc}
 & & H\quad R'' & & H\quad R'' \\
 & & |\qquad | & & |\qquad | \\
H^+ & + & C=C & \longrightarrow & H-C-C^+ \\
 & & |\qquad | & & |\qquad | \\
 & & H\quad H & & H\quad H
\end{array}
\tag{10.111}
$$

and typical reactants of the chain might be

$$
\begin{array}{ccccc}
 & H\quad R'' & \left(\begin{array}{c} H\quad R'' \\ |\qquad | \\ -C-C- \\ |\qquad | \\ H\quad H \end{array}\right)_n & H\quad R'' & & H\quad R'' \\
 & |\qquad | & & |\qquad | & & |\qquad | \\
H- & C-C & & C-C^+ & + & C=C \\
 & |\qquad | & & |\qquad | & & |\qquad | \\
 & H\quad H & & H\quad H & & H\quad H
\end{array}
$$

the reaction of which might be abbreviated as

$$R_n^{+} + A \longrightarrow R_{n+1}^{+} \tag{10.112}$$

Anionic condensation, with initiation by an anion is also possible, with a pair of electrons in place of the + sign in the reactants above.

Copolymerization of monomers A and B offers an interesting example of a chain reaction in a steady state. If R_A is a growing polymer species with monomer A on the active end, the rate at which A or B adds to R_A depends on the rate constants k_{AA} and k_{AB} for the reactions

$$
\left.\begin{array}{ll}
R_A + A \longrightarrow R_A & (k_{AA}) \\
R_A + B \longrightarrow R_B & (k_{AB})
\end{array}\right\}
\tag{10.113}
$$

Similarly, the rate constants k_{BA} and k_{BB} tell how fast A and B add to R_B, the growing species with B on the end.

$$
\left.\begin{array}{ll}
R_B + A \longrightarrow R_A & (k_{BA}) \\
R_B + B \longrightarrow R_B & (k_{BB})
\end{array}\right\}
\tag{10.114}
$$

If (10.113) and (10.114) are the mechanism, then at a steady state wherein R_A and R_B change little in concentration

$$\begin{aligned} 0 = \frac{dC_{R_A}}{dt} &= k_{AA}C_{R_A}C_A - k_{AA}C_{R_A}C_A - k_{AB}C_{R_A}C_B + k_{BA}C_{R_B}C_A \\ &= k_{BA}C_{R_B}C_A - k_{AB}C_{R_A}C_B \end{aligned} \tag{10.115}$$

Similarly, for R_B, $0 = k_{AB}C_{R_A}C_B - k_{BA}C_{R_B}C_A$, which is like (10.115). The rates of disappearance of monomers A and B are

$$\left.\begin{aligned} -\frac{dC_A}{dt} &= k_{AA}C_{R_A}C_A + k_{BA}C_{R_B}C_A \\ -\frac{dC_B}{dt} &= k_{AB}C_{R_A}C_B + k_{BB}C_{R_B}C_B \end{aligned}\right\} \tag{10.116}$$

At any instant, the ratio of A to B entering the polymer is, by (10.116),

$$\frac{dC_A}{dC_B} = \frac{k_{AA}C_{R_A}C_A + k_{BA}C_{R_B}C_A}{k_{AB}C_{R_A}C_B + k_{BB}C_{R_B}C_B} \tag{10.117}$$

Elimination of C_R's by (10.115) yields

$$\frac{dC_A}{dC_B} = \frac{k_{AA}C_A + k_{BA}C_A\left(\dfrac{k_{AB}C_B}{k_{BA}C_A}\right)}{k_{AB}C_B + k_{BB}C_B\left(\dfrac{k_{AB}C_B}{k_{BA}C_A}\right)} = \frac{C_A\left[\left(\dfrac{k_{AA}}{k_{AB}}\right)C_A + C_B\right]}{C_B\left[\left(\dfrac{k_{BB}}{k_{BA}}\right)C_B + C_A\right]} \tag{10.118}$$

Besides concentrations, the two important parameters for the relative content of A and B in the product polymer are thus the two ratios of the rate constants in (10.118).

10.13 REACTION RATES IN SOLUTION

Every homogeneous reaction occurs in a solution as soon as products form or even before reaction if reactants differ. It is, however, difficult to apply the thermodynamics of solutions to kinetic problems because the properties of molecules and the activated complex are not always closely and clearly related to thermodynamic properties. When a reaction, such as the decomposition of N_2O_5 or Cl_2O, proceeds in some solvents at about the same rate as in the gaseous state, the mechanism and the activated state are expected to be the same in both phases. The solvent is then essentially an inert diluent.

Even an inert solvent is expected to modify any rate of reaction by limiting diffusion and by increasing the collision rate. The increase in the frequency of collision is an increase in the number of both activating and deactivating collision; hence, an inert solvent tends to speed and slow the rate to about the same extent. Similarly, collision of reactants may be slower in a solvent than in its absence, but once the reactants are close, they diffuse apart more slowly. They thus have a longer time in which they might be activated because they can rebound from solvent molecules for a second collision before they diffuse apart to the average distance between reactants throughout the solution. This *cage effect* was first noted by Franck and Rabinowitch in 1934.

A very clear proof that the cage effect is real was offered by Lyon and Levy[10] in experiments in which CH_3–N=N–CH_3 and CD_3–N=N–CD_3 were decomposed by strong illumination. The products are N_2 and methyl radicals that recombine rapidly to form ethane. When CH_3–N=N–CH_3 and CD_3–N=N–CD_3 are mixed as gases, the CH_3 and CD_3 radicals that form on photolysis yield CH_3–CH_3, CD_3–CD_3, and CH_3–CD_3 in such proportions that it is clear that CH_3 and CD_3 are randomly mixed before recombination. When, however, the CH_3–N=N–CH_3 and CD_3–N=N–CD_3 are photolyzed in the inert solvent isooctane, no CH_3–CD_3 is detected when CH_3–CH_3 and CD_3–CD_3 are formed along with N_2. It is clear that solvent molecules keep methyl radicals from the same parent molecule together until they recombine. The cage effect also prevents the formation of CH_3–CD_3 from gaseous mixtures of CH_3–N=N–CH_3 and CD_3–N=N–CD_3 at very high pressures where intact molecules act as a quasi-solvent. Besides illustrating the cage effect, this example shows that the elementary step is $CH_3\text{–N=N–}CH_3 \longrightarrow CH_3 + N_2 + CH_3$ in the gas phase and presumably in the solvent; if the reaction could be reversed, a triple collision would be required by the law of microscopic reversibility.

The rate of a gaseous reaction depends in an obvious way on pressure changes because gaseous concentrations change almost proportionally to pressure. Since pressure has little effect on concentrations in condensed phases, rates of reaction in liquids and solids do not depend greatly on P. When an appreciable P is exerted, k_0 at low pressure becomes

$$k_P = k_0 \exp\left[-\frac{P(V_\ddagger - V_R)}{RT}\right] \tag{10.119}$$

where, in the spirit of (10.65) and (5.20), $P(V_\ddagger - V_R)$ is the free energy at P beyond that at zero pressure as reactants with effective volume V_R become activated state with volume $V_\ddagger$. If $V_\ddagger$ exceeds V_R, k_P is less than k_0 and any increase in P acts to destroy the activated complex because of its large volume. However, if $V_\ddagger$ is less than V_R, then k_P exceeds k_0 because the increased pressure squeezes the reactants from a large volume V_R to a smaller volume $V_\ddagger$.

If the reactants or activated complex interact with the solvent, the rate may vary through changes in mechanism or through changes in s and ΔH_a. Essentially the same mechanism might occur because the interaction with solvent is

[10] R. K. Lyon and D. H. Levy, *J. Am. Chem. Soc.* **83**, 4290 (1961)

weak, as in solvation. Solvation of activated complex without appreciable solvation of reactants leads to a somewhat more stable intermediate and thus to smaller ΔH_a. The result is a greater rate for a mechanism essentially the same as in an inert solvent or none at all. When the reactants interact strongly with the solvent, an alternate or competing reaction path may result. The rate law then becomes a sum of terms, one for each parallel reaction route. (On the other hand, a sum of terms in the denominator of a rate law means that one or more equilibria are competing with the reaction route.)

Examples of alternate routes are the aqueous reactions of hydrated Fe^{3+} with Cl^- or SCN^-, denoted X^- in the mechanism[11]

$$Fe(H_2O)_6^{3+} + X^- \underset{k_1'}{\overset{k_1}{\rightleftharpoons}} Fe(H_2O)_5(X)^{2+} + H_2O \tag{10.120}$$

$$Fe(H_2O)_6^{3+} \overset{\text{swift}}{\rightleftharpoons} Fe(H_2O)_5(OH)^{2+} + H^+$$

$$Fe(H_2O)_5(OH)^{2+} + X^- \underset{k_3'}{\overset{k_3}{\rightleftharpoons}} Fe(H_2O)_4(OH)(X)^+ + H_2O$$

$$H^+ + Fe(H_2O)_4(OH)(X)^+ \overset{\text{swift}}{\rightleftharpoons} Fe(H_2O)_5X^{2+}$$

At the start, before $Fe(H_2O)_5X^{2+}$ or $Fe(H_2O)_4(OH)(X)^+$ are common enough to be able to cause an opposing reaction, the rate of disappearance of X^- is

$$v = k_1 C_3 C_X + k_3 C_2 C_X \tag{10.121}$$

where C_X is the concentration of X^- and C_3 and C_2 are the concentrations of $Fe(H_2O)_6^{3+}$ and $Fe(H_2O)_5(OH)^{2+}$. Because of the swift attainment of equilibrium as $Fe(H_2O)_6^{3+}$ ionizes, $K_{eq} = C_{H^+} C_2 C_3^{-1}$ and thus, by eliminating C_2 from (10.121),

$$\begin{aligned} v &= k_1 C_3 C_X + k_3 K_{eq} C_3 C_X C_{H^+}^{-1} \\ &= [k_1 + k_2 C_{H^+}^{-1}] C_3 C_X = k_H C_3 C_X \end{aligned} \tag{10.122}$$

Since only one X^- is attached to each Fe^{3+}, $v = k_H C_3 C_X$ is also the rate of $Fe^{3+} + X^- \longrightarrow FeX^{2+}$, with the state of hydration or hydrolysis unspecified. Like other reactions in solution, the order with respect to the solvent H_2O is masked by flooding. This phenomenon is as old as the science of kinetics, for in 1850 Wilhelmy found that sugar was hydrolyzed by a first-order reaction only because the concentrations of water, a reactant, and H^+, a catalyst, were almost constant during his observations. The rate of this hydrolysis is really proportional to the concentration of sugar, water, and hydronium ion.

Example 10.19. From the reference cited for (10.120), at 25°C k_H is 28.3 liter mole^{-1} sec^{-1} at $C_{H^+} = 0.90$, while at $C_{H^+} = 0.156$ k_H is 117.2 liter mole^{-1} sec^{-1}. From these selected data find k_1 and k_2.

[11] R. E. Connick and C. P. Coppel, *J. Am. Chem. Soc.* **81**, 6389 (1959)

With just these data, the simultaneous equations $28.3 = k_1 + (k_2/0.90)$ and $117.2 = k_1 + k_2/0.156)$ yield $k_1 = 9.7$ liter mole^{-1} sec^{-1} and $k_2 = 16.8$ sec^{-1}. Analysis of more data yields $k_1 = 9.4$ liter mole^{-1} sec^{-1} and $k_2 = 18.0$ sec^{-1} at 25°C.

Some reactions naturally proceed so swiftly that their rates are limited by the rate of diffusion of the reactants. When the reactants of a bimolecular diffusion-controlled reaction are electrically neutral, Smoulokowski has shown that the rate constant is

$$k_2 = \frac{4\pi\sigma\mathscr{D}N_0}{1000} \quad (\text{l mole}^{-1}\ \text{sec}^{-1}) \tag{10.123}$$

where σ is the effective collision diameter (often of the order of 5×10^{-8} cm) and where $\mathscr{D}$ is the diffusion coefficient (of the order of 10^{-5} cm^2 sec^{-1} in liquids and 10^{-1} cm^2 sec^{-1} in gases at one atm at room temperature). Typically, then, in liquid solution the greatest value of k_2 for neutral reactants is of the order of 10^9 l mole^{-1} sec^{-1}. Values of this magnitude have been observed, for example, for recombination of I generated by photolysis of I_2 dissolved in CCl_4 or hexane.

Theoretical and experimental studies agree that for electrically charged reactants in aqueous solution at room temperature, k_2 for a diffusion-controlled bimolecular reaction is of the order of 10^{10} l mole^{-1} sec^{-1} and, for neutralizations involving H^+, which appears to proceed through water by an extraordinarily fast mechanism (see Section 11.4), k_2 is of the order of 10^{11} l mole^{-1} sec^{-1} at 25°C.

Example 10.20. If $k_2 = 3 \times 10^{10}$ l mole^{-1} sec^{-1} at 25°C [M. Eigen, *Disc. Faraday Soc.* **17,** 194 (1954)] for the reaction $H_3O^+ + OH^- \rightarrow 2\,H_2O$, calculate the half-life of H_2O before ionization.

It is well known that at 25°C $K_W = C_{H_3O^+}C_{OH^-} = 1.0 \times 10^{-14}$ for the ionization equilibrium $2\,H_2O = H_3O^+ + OH^-$. Hence, since there are 55.5 moles of H_2O per liter of water,

$$K_e = \frac{C_{H_3O^+}C_{OH^-}}{C^2_{H_2O}} = \frac{1.0 \times 10^{-14}}{55.5^2} = 3.2 \times 10^{-17}$$

But at equilibrium of the reaction $2\,H_2O \underset{k_2}{\overset{k_D}{\rightleftharpoons}} H_3O^+ + OH^-$

$$0 = v = k_D C^2_{H_2O} - k_2 C_{H_3O^+}C_{OH^-}$$

$$K_e = k_D/k_2 = 3.2 \times 10^{-17}$$

With $k_2 = 3 \times 10^{10}$ it follows that k_D is 9.6×10^{-7} l mole^{-1} sec^{-1}. Hence, by (10.43),

$$t_{1/2} = \frac{1}{9.6 \times 10^{-7} \times 55} = 1.9 \times 10^4 \text{ sec}$$

Thus, whenever ionization of H_2O is a step of a mechanism, it may be slow enough to be rate-controlling or of minor importance if in competition with another path.

Apparently inert salts dissolved in a liquid solution where an ionic reaction occurs have been known since about 1890 to affect the rate of reaction. There are two kinds of influence. The secondary salt effect is due to the action of a weak electrolyte on the ionic concentrations through an ionic equilibrium and incomplete dissociation. The primary salt effect, however, deals directly with the reacting ions. With the aid of the Debye-Hückel theory and observations of rate constants as they depend on ionic strength, it is possible to show two things. First, it is possible to determine the charge of the activated complex or, what is essentially the same, the electric charge on one of the ionic reactants. Secondly, it is possible to show that the rate of a reaction is proportional to various powers of the reactants' *concentrations* and not to various powers of their activities. The reason for this second statement is that observed changes in rate constant as ionic strength is changed can be predicted theoretically if concentrations rather than activities are used in the rate law.

The rate of reaction of ion A of charge $Z_A e$ with ion B of charge $Z_B e$ is thus assumed to be, at the start of reaction before a back reaction occurs, $v = kC_A C_B$. Since the activated complex $AB^‡$ of charge $Z_A + Z_B$ is in equilibrium with A and B, thermodynamically

$$K = \frac{a_‡}{a_A a_B} = \frac{\gamma_‡ C_‡}{\gamma_A C_A \gamma_B C_B} \tag{10.124}$$

where the various γ's are activity coefficients of the various species. Accordingly, because the rate of reaction through $AB^‡$ is proportional to $C_‡$, (10.124) in the rate law yields

$$v = k_‡ C_‡ = k_‡ K\left(\frac{\gamma_A \gamma_B}{\gamma_‡}\right) C_A C_B \tag{10.125}$$

The rate constant in $v = kC_A B_B$ is thus

$$k = (k_‡ K)\left(\frac{\gamma_A \gamma_B}{\gamma_‡}\right) = k_0\left(\frac{\gamma_A \gamma_B}{\gamma_‡}\right) \tag{10.126}$$

where $k_0 = k_‡ K$ is the rate constant at infinite dilution where the γ's are unity.

The Debye-Hückel theory for sufficiently dilute solution gives as the relation for the ionic activity coefficient γ_A of ion A

$$\ln \gamma_A = -\frac{e^3 Z_A^2}{8\pi(\epsilon kT)^{3/2}} (\sum_i Z_i^2 \bar{C}_i)^{1/2} \tag{10.127}$$

This is in accord with (8.77), for by (8.69), $\gamma_A^a \gamma_B^b = \gamma_‡^\nu$ for electrolyte $A_a B_b$ and thus by (10.127)

$$\begin{aligned} \ln \gamma_‡^\nu &= a \ln \gamma_A + b \ln \gamma_B \\ &= -\frac{e^3 (\sum_i Z_i^2 \bar{C}_i)^{1/2}}{8\pi(\epsilon kT)^{3/2}} (aZ_A^2 + bZ_B^2) \end{aligned} \tag{10.128}$$

as in (8.76) Accordingly, since the charge on $AB^{\ddagger}$ is $Z_A + Z_B$, it follows from (10.126) and (10.127) that

$$\ln k = \ln k_0 + \ln \gamma_A + \ln \gamma_B - \ln \gamma_{\ddagger}$$

$$= \ln k_0 - \frac{e^3(\sum_i Z_i^2 \bar{C}_i)^{1/2}}{8\pi(\epsilon kT)^{3/2}} [Z_A^2 + Z_B^2 - (Z_A + Z_B)^2]$$

$$\ln\left(\frac{k}{k_0}\right) = \frac{Z_A Z_B e^3(\sum_i Z_i^2 \bar{C}_i)^{1/2}}{4\pi(\epsilon kT)^{3/2}} \tag{10.129}$$

As in Section 8.9, (10.129) for H_2O at 25°C yields

$$\log_{10}\left(\frac{k}{k_0}\right) = 1.017\, Z_A Z_B \sqrt{I} \tag{10.130}$$

where k is the rate constant observed at ionic strength I and where k_0 is the rate constant when $I = 0$ (or when Z_A or Z_B is zero), A and B being ionic reactants in solution with other ionic species.

Rate constants for reactions between ions of like charge ($Z_A Z_B > 0$) are accelerated by increasing I, largely because the presence of other oppositely charged ions allows A and B to approach each other. In terms of (10.126), $\gamma_{\ddagger}$ decreases faster than $\gamma_A \gamma_B$ as I increases because $AB^{\ddagger}$ is more highly charged than A or B. On the other hand, reactions between oppositely charged ions ($Z_A Z_B < 0$) are slowed according to (10.129) or (10.130) as I increases, largely because their mutual attraction is dissipated in the jumble of nonreacting ions. In terms of (10.126), $AB^{\ddagger}$ is less charged than A and B and thus $\gamma_{\ddagger}$ is closer to unity than $\gamma_A \gamma_B$. According to (10.129), k is unchanged by varying I when one or both reactants are neutral.

Observing k at various I and plotting $\log k$ vs. $\sqrt{I}$ at low I yields, according to (10.130), straight lines of slope $1.017\, Z_A Z_B$ at 25°C in aqueous solution. If Z_A or Z_B is known, the slope gives the other Z. And since charge of $AB^{\ddagger}$ is $Z_A + Z_B$, the charge of the activated complex is also known. For example, when gamma rays from ^{60}Co irradiate water containing O_2, H_2O_2, KNO_2, and acid with varying amounts of inert ionized salts to change I, the following reactions occur[12]

$$\left.\begin{aligned} &H_2O^- + H_2O_2 \longrightarrow OH + OH^- + H_2O && \text{(a)} \\ &H_2O^- + O_2 \longrightarrow HO_2 + OH^- && \text{(b)} \\ &H_2O^- + H_3O^+ \longrightarrow H + 2H_2O && \text{(c)} \\ &H_2O^- + NO_2^- \longrightarrow NO_2^{2-} + H_2O && \text{(d)} \end{aligned}\right\} \tag{10.131}$$

The rate of (a) is a convenient standard. As expected, the slope of $\log(k_b/k_a)$ vs. $\sqrt{I}$ is zero. The reducing species is H_2O^-, a hydrated electron, because

[12] G. Czapski and H. A. Schwarz, *J. Phys. Chem.* **66**, 471 (1962)

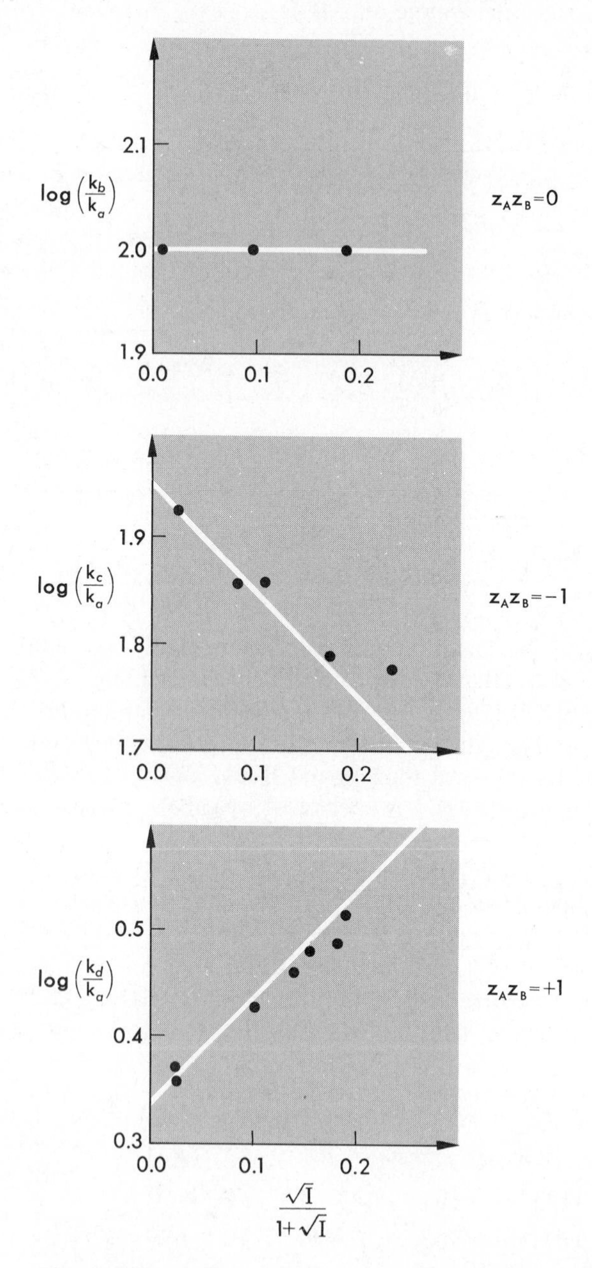

Figure 10.8. Effect of Ionic Strength on Rate Constants of Solvated Electron†

†G. Czapski and H. A. Schwarz, *J. Phys. Chem.* **66,** 471 (1962).

the slope of log (k_c/k_a) vs. $\sqrt{I}$ is -1.017, and the slope of log (k_d/k_a) vs. $\sqrt{I}$ is $+1.017$, as shown in Figure 10.8, where $\log(k/k_a)$ is plotted as a function of $\sqrt{I}/1 + \sqrt{I}$, a function that is theoretically and experimentally somewhat more accurate than $\sqrt{I}$ as I increases.

It is impossible by the usual means to mix reactants even in a rapidly flowing system in which reactant streams merge and to follow the changes in concentration upon reaction when bimolecular rate constants approach the upper limit of about 10^{10} liters mole^{-1} sec^{-1}. For such swift reactions, relaxation techniques are used. In these, the effect of a disturbance on equilibrium is followed by spectroscopic observations at frequencies high compared to the rate of reaction. The disturbance may be a sudden change in T or P, each of which shifts the equilibrium conditions slightly. The disturbance may also be a strong electric field, which may be applied suddenly and either maintained or turned off suddenly, or which may conveniently be applied as a periodic oscillation of frequency orders of magnitude slower than the frequency of radiation used in observation. Figure 10.9 shows how concentration might vary with time as a disturbance is suddenly applied and released. If the k's were infinitely great, the concentration would follow the dashed square-wave pulse.

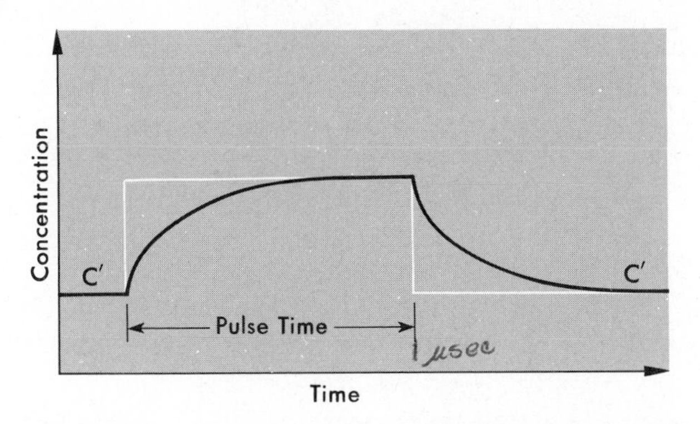

Figure 10.9. Typical Variation of Concentration in a Relaxation Experiment

A reaction AB $\longrightarrow$ A + B is at equilibrium when its rate is

$$0 = k_1' C_{AB}' - k_2' C_A' C_B' \tag{10.132}$$

Disturbed, its rate is

$$v = k_1 C_{AB} - k_2 C_A C_B = k_1(C_{AB}' + \delta) - k_2(C_A' - \delta)(C_B' - \delta)$$

where δ is the increment in concentration due to the disturbance. For small δ, so that terms of the order of δ^2 are negligible,

$$v = -\frac{d\delta}{dt} = [k_1 + k_2(C_A' + C_B')]\,\delta \tag{10.133}$$

where (10.132) and the assumption $k = k'$ have been used. Integration of (10.133) yields $-\ln \delta = t/t_L + \text{(constant)}$ in which the Langevin or relaxation time t_L is

$$t_L = [k_1 + k_2(C'_A + C'_B)]^{-1} \tag{10.134}$$

By plotting $\ln \delta$ vs. t, values of t_L can be observed for various equilibrium concentrations C'_A and C'_B. From these k_1 and k_2 are easily found.

The Bronsted-Bjerrum equation (10.125) has been verified many times via (10.130) for ionic solutions, but only recently has it been verified for the gaseous reaction $HI + HI \longrightarrow H_2 + I_2$.(13) With careful correction for nonideality of the gaseous mixture by a method due to Prausnitz, the solid curve of Figure 10.10 was calculated by Eckert and Boudart when the rate is assumed to be proportional to the concentration of the activated complex $H_2I_2^{\ddagger}$. The agree-

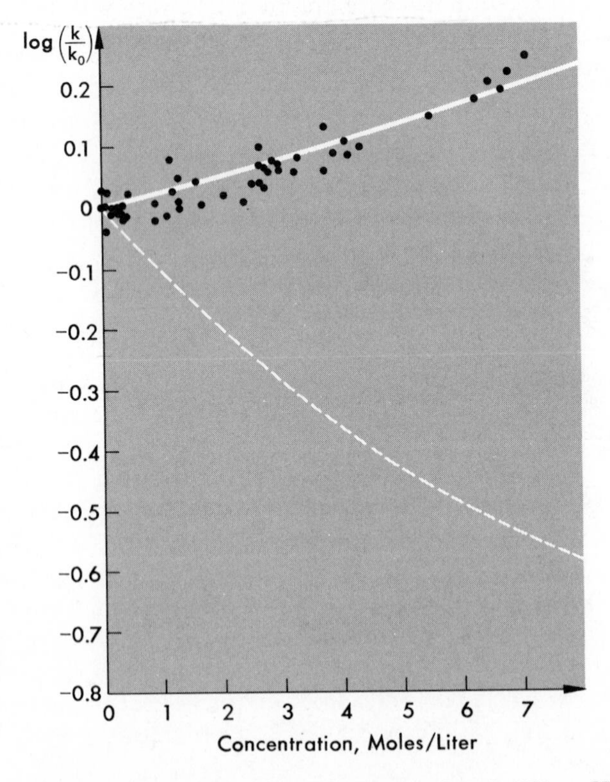

Figure 10.10. How Rate Constants for $2\ HI \longrightarrow H_2 + I_2$ at 321.4°C Depend on Pressure (Points show Kistiakowsky's observations of 1928.)†

(13) C. A. Eckert and M. Boudart, *Chem. Eng. Science* **18,** 144 (1963)

†Fig. 2 of C. A. Eckert and M. Boudart, *Chemical Eng. Science*, **18,** 144 (1963).

ment with the 1928 observations of Kistiakowsky (circles) is excellent. If, however, the rate is calculated by assuming that it is proportional to the fugacity of $H_2I_2^{\ddagger}$, the dashed curve results, obviously in very poor agreement with observations. There is thus little doubt that for ionic or gaseous reactions (and presumably for all reactions since these are so different), that rate is proportional to the concentrations (not the fugacities or activities) of the activated complex.

A few final remaks on the influence of the solution's dielectric constant κ are in order. The Gibbs free energy of an activated complex consisting of ions of charge $Z_A e$ and $Z_B e$ at a distance $r_{\ddagger}$ is greater than that of a neutral activated complex by $Z_A Z_B e^2/4\pi\epsilon_0 \kappa r_{\ddagger}$. Since the rate constants each vary with free energy according to (10.65), it follows that

$$\ln\left(\frac{k}{k_0}\right) = -\frac{Z_A Z_B e^2 N_0}{4\pi\epsilon_0 \kappa r_{\ddagger} RT} \tag{10.135}$$

where k is the rate constant relative to the value k_0 for a supposedly neutral activated complex of the same kind. By (10.135), $\log k$ is expected to be a linear function of κ^{-1} for a given reaction. In accord with (10.135), k decreases with κ when $Z_A Z_B$ is positive, and k increases with decreasing κ when $Z_A Z_B$ is negative. In fact, k can be altered by a factor of the order of 10^6 as a reaction changes solvents, part of the change being attributed to κ and part to γ as solvation of ions changes.

10.14 CATALYSIS

A *catalyst* is a substance that changes the rate of a chemical reaction without itself undergoing a net change in the overall reaction. It is a source of species of extraordinary chemical activity and it is regenerated from time to time as the reaction progresses. It partakes in the reaction as an intermediate or by modifying the concentration of reactant or activated complex. Solvation may stabilize the activated complex more than it does the reactants; if so, ΔH_a is lowered and the rate of the reaction is increased. Many organic decompositions are accelerated by I_2 because I_2 can remove a hydrogen atom as HI, combine with and stabilize molecular fragments, and later by a bimolecular reaction be regenerated as I_2, leaving the original molecule in fragments. The I_2 thus offers a reaction route of lower energy and greater speed and ease. The main action of a catalyst is its effect on ΔH_a but it can also effect favorable orientations and configurations of reactants.

The most general mechanism of catalysis is

$$A + C_1 \rightleftharpoons D + C_2 \tag{10.136}$$

$$B + C_2 \rightleftharpoons E + C_1 \tag{10.137}$$

where C_1 and C_2 are catalytic species or sites. The net reaction $A + B \longrightarrow D + E$ does not mention C_1 and C_2. If C_1 represents an active site of a solid catalyst, then C_2 may represent that site after a change or with a fragment of A adsorbed by forces that range from very specific and strong chemical bonds (chemisorption) through all intermediate forms to weak van der Waals forces. Dispersion (van der Waals or London) forces between free molecules have energies of interaction inversely proportional to the sixth power of the intervening distance. These attractive forces originate in the electrical interaction of permanent or induced dipoles. When such forces act between a plane surface and a molecule, the energy of interaction is often inversely proportional to the cube of the distance between plane and molecule. Since this energy is the nonexpansion work that must be done on an average molecule to remove it to an infinite distance from the surface, the chemical potential of a mole of species i at a distance z from a surface under these conditions is

$$\mu_i(z) = \mu_i^\ominus + RT \ln p_i^{(z)} - \frac{A}{z^3} \qquad (10.138)$$

A relatively dense layer of species i collects at a distance z from the surface where the 'vapor' pressure of i is $p_i^{(z)}$, almost as though the layer were a liquid. Equating the values of μ_i far from and near to the surface requires

$$\mu_i^\ominus + RT \ln p_i = \mu_i^\ominus + RT \ln p_i^{(z)} - \frac{A}{z^3}$$

or

$$\frac{A}{z^3} = RT \ln \left(\frac{p_i^{(z)}}{p_i} \right) \qquad (10.139)$$

Thus, even though p_i at $z \longrightarrow \infty$ is less than the vapor pressure at T, dispersion forces at the surface may cause a quasi-condensation to a pressure $p_i^{(z)}$. With increased concentration at small z, a more rapid reaction of i occurs near the surface than in the adjoining medium where z is great. Other interactions, such as those between ions and quadrupoles with energies between molecules that vary as R^{-4}, operate similarly. The entropy of species in a surface layer is, of course, unusually low because of the organization that adsorption implies.

If k_A and k_D are the forward and reverse rate constants of (10.136) and if k_B and k_E are the same for (10.137), in the steady state for catalyst sites

$$0 = \frac{dC_1}{dt} = -\frac{dC_2}{dt} = -k_A C_A C_1 + k_D C_D C_2 + k_B C_B C_2 - k_E C_E C_1$$

Whence

$$\frac{C_2}{C_1} = \frac{k_A C_A + k_E C_E}{k_B C_B + k_D C_D} \qquad (10.140)$$

But the rate of reaction is

$$v = \frac{dC_E}{dt} = k_B C_B C_2 - k_E C_E C_1 \qquad (10.141)$$

Eliminating C_2 from (10.140) and (10.141) yields

$$v = \left[\frac{k_A k_B C_A C_B - k_D k_E C_D C_E}{k_B C_B + k_D C_D}\right] C_1 \tag{10.142}$$

If (10.137) in the forward direction is so very slow that it becomes the rate-determining step, then (10.136) comes to equilibrium with $0 = k_A C_A C_1 - k_D C_D C_2$ and (10.141) gives

$$v = \left[\frac{k_A k_B C_A C_B - k_D k_E C_D C_E}{k_D C_D}\right] C_1 \tag{10.143}$$

which is much like (10.142). Both (10.142) and (10.143) state the *first law of catalysis:* the rate of a catalyzed reaction is proportional to the concentration of catalyst. (The *second law* notes what is also obvious, namely, that when catalyst concentration is constant the order of the reaction appears to be less than the true order by unity even if the order is not integral. The *third law of catalysis* says that the ΔH_a of a reaction is decreased by a catalyst.)

Although inorganic and organic decompositions, polymerizations, and syntheses often proceed well only with the aid of highly specific catalysts, biological catalysts are undoubtedly the most specialized. A biological catalyst, called an *enzyme,* may do nothing but attack a certain type of hydrogen atom. But in proper order with respect to its fellow enzymes it supports and even is life.

One common mechanism by which enzymes work is the famous Michaelis-Menten mechanism.[14]

$$\left.\begin{aligned} A + X &\underset{k_2'}{\overset{k_2}{\rightleftharpoons}} AX \\ AX &\xrightarrow{k_1} D + X \end{aligned}\right\} \tag{10.144}$$

where X is the enzyme that transforms the substrate A into the products D. As the mechanism requires,

$$\frac{dC_{AX}}{dt} = k_2 C_A C_X - k_2' C_{AX} - k_1 C_{AX} \tag{10.145}$$

and

$$\frac{dC_D}{dt} = k_1 C_{AX} \tag{10.146}$$

Since the total or initial concentration C_X^0 of enzyme is $C_X + C_{AX}$, in the steady state when the concentration of AX is effectively constant, (10.145) yields $0 = k_2 C_A (C_X^0 - C_{AX}) - (k_2' + k_1) C_{AX}$. Whence

$$C_{AX} = \frac{k_2 C_A C_X^0}{k_2 C_A + (k_2' + k_1)} \tag{10.147}$$

[14] Michaelis, L., and M. L. Menten, *Biochemische Zeitschrift*, **49**, 333 (1913).

The rate of formation of product is then

$$\frac{dC_D}{dt} = \frac{k_1 k_2 C_A C_X^0}{k_2 C_A + (k_2' + k_1)} \tag{10.148}$$

When a great excess of substrate A is present, $k_2 C_A \gg k_2' + k_1$ and

$$\frac{dC_D}{dt} \approx k_1 C_X^0 \tag{10.149}$$

first-order in enzyme concentration but zero-order in substrate concentration. However, when substrate is almost lacking, the rate is first-order in both, for $k_2 C_A \ll k_2' + k_1$ and

$$\frac{dC_D}{dt} \approx \left(\frac{k_1 k_2}{k_2' + k_1}\right) C_A C_X^0 \tag{10.150}$$

The economic importance of catalysts is great. Exothermic reactions are reversed by a temperature rise. A suitable catalyst not only decreases capital outlay in equipment by speeding a reaction, but it may also increase yields in exothermic reactions by allowing profitable operation at reduced temperatures. Examples are the production of SO_3 and NH_3 from the elements.

Industrial catalysts are usually solids of high surface area. The active species may be supported on silica or alumina with surface areas of the order of 10^2 $m^2\ g^{-1}$. Heterogeneous catalysis, usually gaseous reactants on solid catalyst, involves several steps: transport of reactants to surface, adsorption, activation, reaction, desorption, and transport away from the surface. The surface of catalyst contains inert regions, regions of high activity, strains and defects, pores and holes, and various other features to attract and activate reactants. The action may often be specific enough to favor a reaction whose competitor would in the absence of catalyst quite dominate the mode of reaction.

A true catalyst is unchanged after the reaction has been completed. Hydrogenation catalysts of Ni and Pt may approach this ideal by acting as matrices in which atomic hydrogen can dissolve preparatory to reaction. Many industrial catalysts must be regenerated from time to time because side reactions gradually deposit products that obstruct the surface. Still other reasons for loss in activity of a catalyst are gradual loss of active regions through sintering or through accumulation of trace impurities that deactivate centers of activity. Sulfur and arsenic deactivate platinum by forming such things as PtS_2 and $PtAs_2$.

A common regeneration problem concerns removal of carbon and "coke" from silica-alumina cracking catalysts. These catalysts may contain from 5-30% alumina supported on silica. The particles of catalyst are so small that they can be circulated with hot petroleum vapors in a so-called fluidized state. As cracking occurs, deposits of graphitic carbon build up. These particles of coke are removed in a regenerator by controlled burning with air. Such rough treatment inevitably causes sintering and a loss in activity. Hence, old catalyst with surface areas of about 150 $m^2\ g^{-1}$ is withdrawn from time to time and gradually replaced by new catalyst with an area of about 500 $m^2\ g^{-1}$. Although silica-alumina is not a catalyst in the strict sense because it is changed during reaction, it does speed a desired change, the production of gasoline from petroleum by decreasing the molecular weight of the hydrocarbons.

Reactions that proceed by chain reaction can be very effectively stopped by what are sometimes called *negative catalysts*. These are substances that react with and remove chain-carrying species such as free radicals. Typical examples were given in Section 10.12.

10.15 SUMMARY

The ideas developed by chemists to explain the progress of chemical reactions have been used by physicists to describe thermonuclear reactions, changes in solids, and electronic processes in semiconductors. The importance of these ideas in the theory and practice of chemistry is obvious, for most of chemistry deals with reacting systems.

While simple rate laws based on simple mechanisms can often be integrated, the matters of this chapter amply explain why even the mathematics of chemical kinetics is an art. It is necessary to be able to design and execute experiments so that nonessential features are of small importance or effectively constant, and in dealing with a possible mechanism based on such observations it is necessary to approximate real conditions by the method of the stationary state, the method of the rate-determining step, or by some other approximation tailored to the problem at hand.

This chapter describes the empirical methods of chemical kinetics and, as background, a few details of a few mechanisms so as to offer a basis for discussing the theory of reactions in chapters that follow. Some of the migration processes due to electric field as described in the next chapter are quasi-chemical; solid-state reactions are described in Chapter 16; and the final chapter, Chapter 18, focuses the ideas of valence theory, quantum mechanics, and statistical mechanics on the fundamental questions of chemistry: how, from first principles and microscopic events, to calculate the rate of any reaction and thus to predict which of all possible reactions is expected to occur under certain circumstances. This chapter in its limited detail is a success if it has somehow indicated the scope and complexity of this undertaking.

PROBLEMS

1. Formulate mathematically the rate of a zero-order reaction in terms of the rate of appearance of products and integrate the differential equation.

2. At 900°C in rigid vessel in the presence of W, pure NH_3 at 200 mm Hg initial pressure decomposes by a zero-order reaction until after 160 min the total pressure of all gases is 300 mm Hg. If in a similar experiment the initial pressure of NH_3 is to be 150 mm Hg, predict the pressure of NH_3 after 1.00 hr. [Data from C. H. Kunsman, *J. Am. Chem. Soc.*, **50,** 2100 (1928).]
Answer: 112 mm Hg.

3. At 15°C at $[H^+] = 2.0$ moles/liter, with reactants at initial concentrations of about 0.00017 molar, second-order rate constants k_2 for the reaction $Pu^{6+} + Sn^{2+} \rightarrow Pu^{4+} + Sn^{4+}$ depend on $[Cl^-]$ thus [S. W. Rabideau and B. J. Masters, *J. Phys. Chem.* **65,** 1256(1961)]:

$[Cl^-]$	1.754	1.003	0.751	0.0501	0.250
k_2 (liter mole^{-1} sec^{-1})	34520	3961	1209	332	33.6

These k_2's have been corrected for chlorocomplexing of reactants and each $[Cl^-]$ is so great that the solution is flooded with Cl^-. What is the order of this reaction with respect to Cl^-?
Answer: 3.54.

4. Calculate the average life of a substance that decomposes by a first-order reaction.
Answer: $1/k$.

5. Near atmospheric pressure at 427°C, the apparent first-order rate constant for the irreversible decomposition of cyclobutane according to the reaction $C_4H_8 \rightarrow 2C_2H_4$ is $k_1 = 1.23 \times 10^{-4}$ sec^{-1} [C. T. Genaux, F. Kern, and W. D. Walters, *J. Am. Chem. Soc.*, **75,** 6196 (1953)]. If 0.0300 mole C_4H_8 is placed in a 1-l vessel at 427°C, calculate the total pressure expected in the vessel after 2.00 hr.
Answer: 2.73 atm.

6. One curie of radiation is 3.7×10^{10} disintegrations sec^{-1}. If the half-life of Co^{60} is 5.3 yr, what mass of pure Co^{60} will provide the activity of 1.00 millicurie?
Answer: 0.890 microgram.

7. If the decomposition $AB \rightarrow A + B$ is first-order in AB with $k_1 = 2.20 \times 10^{-5}$ sec^{-1}, what pressure of B results by this gaseous reaction after one hour if pure AB is initially at 500 mm Hg?
Answer: 38 mm Hg.

8. Integrate (10.30) when M = A.
Answer: $k_1^* k_2 t = k_1^* [C^{-1} - (C^0)^{-1}] + k_{-2} \ln(C^0/C)$.

9. At 499.5°C and various total pressures P, a few of the apparent first-order rate constants for the isomerization of cyclopropane are: $k_1 = 5.94 \times 10^{-4}$ sec^{-1} at 710.4 mm Hg; 5.12×10^{-4} sec^{-1} at 99.4 mm Hg; 4.11×10^{-4} sec^{-1} at 24.4 mm Hg [T.S. Chambers and G.B. Kistiakowsky, *J. Am. Chem. Soc.* **56,** 399 (1934)]. Find the limiting value of the first-order rate constant at infinite pressure and the second-order rate constant at low pressure.
Answer: $k_1 = 5.9 \times 10^{-4}$ sec^{-1}; $k_2 = 0.57 \times 10^{-4}$ (mm Hg)$^{-1}$ sec^{-1}.

10. Describe mathematically this second-order reaction $3\,A + B \xrightarrow{k_2} D + \ldots$ in terms of the rate of formation of D if the rate is first-order in A and first-order in B.

11. At an ionic strength of 1.00 when $[OH^-] = 1.00$ molar at 25°C, the reaction $I^- + ClO^- \rightarrow IO^- + Cl^-$ is first-order in each reactant with $k_2 = 60.0$ molar^{-1} sec^{-1} [Y. Chia and R. E. Connick, *J. Phys. Chem.*, **63,** 1518 (1959)]. How long

will it take for half of the I^- to be oxidized if initially $[I^-] = 0.00200$ and $[ClO^-] = 0.00400$ molar?
Answer: 3.38 sec.

12. In an appropriate solvent, hexachlorocyclopentadiene (C_5Cl_6) couples to form bis-(pentachlorocyclopentadienyl) ($C_{10}Cl_{10}$) in the presence of the reducing agent CuCl by the free-radical mechanism [C. W. Roberts, D. H. Haigh, and W. G. Lloyd, *J. Phys. Chem.* **64,** 1887 (1960)]:

$$C_5Cl_6 + CuCl \longrightarrow C_5Cl_6\cdot CuCl \tag{1}$$
$$C_5Cl_6\cdot CuCl \longrightarrow C_5Cl_6 + CuCl \tag{2}$$
$$C_5Cl_6\cdot CuCl \longrightarrow C_5Cl_5^{\cdot} + CuCl_2 \tag{3}$$
$$2\,C_5Cl_5^{\cdot} \longrightarrow C_{10}Cl_{10} \tag{4}$$

Steps (1), (2), and (4) are rapid, while step (3) is rate-determining.
(a) Show that the rate law is first-order in C_5Cl_6 and in CuCl.
(b) Find the activation energy of step (3) if k_2 is:

Temperature (°C)	0.1	20.5	30.7	40.9	50.3
$10^3 \times k_2$ (liter mole^{-1} sec^{-1})	1.00	5.32	12.4	26.0	54.0

Answer: $\Delta H_a = 13.7$ kcal.

13. Show that the rate constant for an endothermic (ΔH positive) elementary reaction increases more rapidly with a rise in T than does the rate constant for the reverse reaction, but that in these circumstances it is seldom wise to neglect the reverse reaction as a reasonable kinetic step.

14. Gaseous oxalic acid decomposes to CO_2 and formic acid thus [G. Lapidus, D. Barton, and P. E. Yankwich, *J. Phys. Chem.* **68,** 1863 (1964)]:

Temp. (°C)	Fraction Decomposed	Time (sec)
126.6	0.403	18,000
126.6	0.516	25,200
126.6	0.669	36,600
134.1	0.288	4,200
134.1	0.679	14,400
134.1	0.825	21,600
146.4	0.286	1,800
146.4	0.515	4,200
146.4	0.698	7,200
146.4	0.854	11,400
155.6	0.585	1,715
155.6	0.634	2,015
155.6	0.817	3,350

What are the order of reaction and activation energy?
Answer: First; 30.0 kcal.

15. If isopropyl bromide decomposes to propene and HBr by a reaction first-order in isopropyl bromide with $\Delta H_a = 50.7$ kcal and the Arrhenius $s = 1.00 \times 10^{13}$ sec^{-1}, at what temperature will one-fifth of a sample of isopropyl bromide decompose thus in a time of five minutes?
Answer: 687°K.

16. In isoamyl alcohol, benzene diazonium chloride decomposes to nitrogen and other products by a first-order reaction with these rate constants:

T(°C)	20.0	30.0	40.0	50.0
$10^3 \times k_1$ (min^{-1})	2.61	11.6	47.5	192.

[C. E. Waring and J. R. Abrams, *J. Am. Chem. Soc.*, **63,** 2757 (1941).] What is the activation energy of this reaction and what is the half-life of the salt in this solution at 0°C?
Answer: $\Delta H_a = 27{,}000$ cal; 8100 min.

17. From data in Example 10.1 and Problem 2, find the activation energy for the decomposition of NH_3 on W at 1000°C.
Answer: 64.3 kcal.

18. What is the activation energy of a reaction the rate of which at 100°C is doubled by a rise in temperature of 10°C?
Answer: $\Delta H_a = 19{,}200$ cal.

19. Show that, as T rises, the ratio of products by two competing reactions (that involve the same reactants) tends to unity.

20. Find the time at which B in (10.68) reaches its maximum concentration.
Answer: $t_{max} = (k_{1(1)} - k_{1(2)})^{-1} \ln (k_{1(1)}/k_{1(2)})$.

21. When pure CH_4 is mixed with pure Br_2, the gaseous reaction $CH_4 + Br_2 \rightarrow CH_3Br + HBr$ at first follows the rate law $v = k[CH_4][Br_2]^{1/2}$. Propose a mechanism in accord with this rate law and propose a rate law for the gaseous reaction $CH_3Br + Br_2 \rightarrow CH_2Br_2 + HBr$ at $t = 0$.
Answer: Cf. $H_2 + Br_2 \rightarrow 2\ HBr$.

22. If the enthalpy or energy of the activated state increases or decreases as the enthalpy or energy of various alkyl free radicals increases or decreases, and if their order of increasing energy is tertiary-secondary-primary-methyl, then explain by a suitable free-radical chain mechanism how and why HBr in the presence of peroxides (that furnish initiating free radicals) adds to a double bond contrary to Markovnikoff's rule.

23. When acetaldehyde (CH_3CHO) and fully deuterated acetaldehyde (CD_3CDO) decompose together in a homogeneous gaseous reaction, the products at high temperature are CH_4, CH_3D, CD_3H, CD_4, and CO. Traces of ethane and hydrogen occur in the products, and at the start of reaction, CD_2H_2 is not observed [P. D. Zemany and M. Burton, *J. Phys. Chem.* **55,** 949 (1951)]. Show that these observations require the decomposition to proceed with methyl radicals and propose a reasonable chain mechanism.
Answer: $CH_3CHO \rightarrow CH_3 + HCO$; $R + CH_3CHO \rightarrow RH + CH_3CO$;
$CH_3CO \rightarrow CH_3 + CO$; $R + R' + M \rightarrow RR' + M^*$.

24. By noting the gradual change in radioactivity in M^+ and M^{+n}, the rate of the exchange reaction $^*M^+ + M^{+n} \rightarrow {}^*M^{+n} + M^+$ can be observed. Describe the activated complex of this reaction in rather dilute solutions if the second-order rate constant
a. is independent of the amount of inert salt present in the mixed solutions;
b. gradually decreases as the content of inert salt in the mixture increases, but not as noticeably as predicted by (10.130).
Answer: a. At least one reactant is neutral (e.g., M(OH) formed by hydrolysis);
b. A reaction involving oppositely charged ions (e.g., $M(OH)_2^-$ and $M(OH)_2^+$ competes with the reaction of a.

25. The rate constant for the reaction $CH_3I + OH^- \rightarrow CH_3OH + I^-$ increases continuously by almost a factor of 10^6 on going from pure solvent water to almost pure dimethylsulfoxide, which has a high dielectric constant and no tendency to form hydrogen bonds. Discuss the physical reasons for this remarkable change in k.

Answer: In water, γ_{OH^-} is much less than unity; in DMSO, γ_{OH^-} is nearly unity.

26. A cracking catalyst used in a petroleum refinery has a surface area of 300 m^2 g^{-1}. If the catalyst consists of tiny independent identical spheres with a density of 2.00 g cc^{-1}, what is the radius of one of these tiny spheres?
Answer: 50 A.

---

27. Near 225°C at about 120 mm Hg, diethyl peroxide decomposes by a first-order rate law in which $k_1 = 2 \times 10^{13} \exp [-(31.7 \times 10^3)/RT]$ sec^{-1}, where R is 1.987 cal $mole^{-1}$ deg^{-1} [R. E. Rebbert and K. J. Laidler, *J. Chem. Phys.*, **20,** 574 (1952)]. At 225°C, how long will it take for 30.0% of a sample of pure diethyl peroxide to decompose?
Answer: 1.4 sec.

28. If $t_{1/2}$ of ^{90}Sr is 28 yr, how long will it take for 95% of a sample of ^{90}Sr to decay?
Answer: 121 yrs.

29. If the half-lives of ^{238}U and ^{234}Th are 4.5×10^9 yr and 24 days, calculate the mass ratio of ^{234}Th to ^{238}U in a mineral at radioactive equilibrium.
Answer: 1.44×10^{-11}.

30. Show that (10.31) results from (10.26) only if the rate of transformation of $A^{\ddagger}$ to A^* is negligible compared to the rate with which $A^{\ddagger}$ becomes products.

31. Determine the order and rate constant of the reaction in which cis-cinnamic acid in 62.80 percent H_2SO_4 in H_2O at 45.00°C is isomerized to trans-cinnamic acid from these data [D. S. Noyce, P. A. King, F. B. Kirby, and W. L. Reed, *J. Am. Chem. Soc.* **84,** 1632 (1962)] if optical density is a linear function of composition.

Time (sec)	0	620	1200	1800	3600	4920	6000	7320
Opt. Dens.	0.219	0.236	0.248	0.263	0.302	0.326	0.345	0.367
Time (sec)	8400	9720	11400	13740	16250	17400	∞	
Opt. Dens.	0.385	0.404	0.427	0.454	0.479	0.490	0.640	

Answer: $k_1 = 5.97 \times 10^{-5}$ sec^{-1}.

32. By nuclear magnetic resonance spectroscopy, it is possible to follow ^{17}O in the reaction $M(H_2^{17}O)_n^{+x} + H_2O \rightarrow M(H_2O)(H_2O)_{n-1}^{+x} + H_2^{17}O$. Lower limits for the first-order rate constants k_1 at about 26°C for various metals are [R. E. Connick and E. D. Stover, *J. Phys. Chem.* **65,** 2075 (1961)]: 3.3×10^6 sec^{-1} (Cu^{2+}); 2.4×10^4 sec^{-1} (Fe^{3+}); 2.2×10^7 sec^{-1} (Mn^{2+}); 3.2×10^4 sec^{-1} (Ni^{2+}); 3.1×10^5 sec^{-1} (Co^{2+}). What is the half-life of a complexed water molecule on each of these ions?
Answer: 2.1×10^{-7} sec; 2.9×10^{-5} sec; 3.2×10^{-8} sec; 2.2×10^{-5} sec; 2.2×10^{-6} sec.

33. At 290°C, azomethane (CH_3NNCH_3) decomposes to ethane and nitrogen by a unimolecular process. The apparent first-order rate constants ($k_1 \times 10^5$ sec^{-1}) at various initial pressures (P mm Hg) are [H. C. Ramsperger, *J. Am. Chem. Soc.*, **49,** 1495 (1927)]: 13.5 at 707.9; 13.7 at 375.0; 13.7 at 320.0; 13.2 at 191.0; 11.8 at 44.07; 9.7 at 23.51; 9.0 at 12.03; 6.9 at 5.818; 5.8 at 2.587; 5.3 at 1.989; 4.5 at 0.879; and 3.2 at 0.309 mm Hg. From these data find the apparent first-order rate constants at 100 mm Hg and at 2000 mm Hg. How long would it take for 75% of a sample of azomethane to decompose at 290°C at these two initial pressures?
Answer: At 100 mm Hg, $k_1 = 12.8 \times 10^{-5}$ sec^{-1} and $t = 10{,}800$ sec; at 2000 mm Hg, $k_1 = 13.7 \times 10^{-5}$ sec^{-1} and $t = 10{,}100$ sec.

34. From 540°K to 727°K, the bimolecular second-order reaction $CO + NO_2 \xrightarrow{k_2} CO_2 + NO$ has $k_2 = 1.2 \times 10^{13} \exp(-31{,}600/RT)$ where $R = 1.987$ cal mole^{-1} deg^{-1} and the units of k_2 are cc mole^{-1} sec^{-1} [H. S. Johnston, W. A. Bonner, and D. J. Wilson, *J. Chem. Phys.*, **26,** 1002 (1057)]. If CO at an initial pressure of 5.00 mm Hg is mixed with NO_2 at an initial pressure of 7.00 mm Hg at 600°K, what will be the partial pressure of NO after 10.0 hr?
Answer: 1.04 mm Hg.

35. Integrate (10.45) and evaluate the integration constant.

36. Hypophosphites decompose thus:

$$H_2PO_2^- + OH^- \longrightarrow HPO_3^{--} + H_2$$

In a certain experiment, 19.5 cc H_2 (S.T.P.) were generated in 20 min when the concentration of $H_2PO_2^-$ was 0.50 and that of OH^- was 1.28. A second experiment yielded 25.0 cc H_2 (S.T.P.) in 50 min when the concentrations of $H_2PO_2^-$ and OH^- were 0.25 and 1.28. A third experiment yielded 135.0 cc H_2 (S.T.P.) in 30 min when the concentrations of $H_2PO_2^-$ and OH^- were 0.25 and 3.94. What is the order of the reaction with respect to $H_2PO_2^-$ and OH^-?
Answer: First in $H_2PO_2^-$; second in OH^-.

37. Prepare a graph like Figure 10.6 for $k_{1(1)} = 2k_{1(2)}$ and discuss the differences between it and Figure 10.6.

38. The rate constants k_2 for the reaction of Section 10.11 are 4.8×10^4 cc mole^{-1} sec^{-1} at 27.7°C, 1.35×10^5 at 50.4°C, and 3.4×10^5 at 70.2°C. Calculate s and ΔH_a. To which part of the mechanism does ΔH_a apply?
Answer: Slow step, $s = 3.9 \times 10^{11}$ cc mole^{-1} sec^{-1} and $\Delta H_a = 9.5$ kcal.

39. Show that the values of ΔH_a associated with similar reactions are proportional to the various temperatures at which the reactions achieve the same rate.

40. At 30°C in solutions of constant acidity and ionic strength without complex-forming ions, the rate of the irreversible reaction $6\,Pu^{3+} + XeO_3 + 6\,H^+ \rightarrow 6\,Pu^{4+} + Xe + 3\,H_2O$ is $-d[Pu^{3+}]/dt = 1.6 \times 10^{-2}\ [Pu^{3+}][XeO_3]$ mole liter^{-1} sec^{-1} [J. M. Cleveland, *J. Am. Chem. Soc.* **87,** 1816 (1965)]. In these circumstances, if the initial $[XeO_3]$ is 0.002000 molar, how long will it take $[Pu^{3+}]$ to fall from 0.010000 molar to 0.00732 molar?
Answer: 11,230 sec.

41. A twenty-degree rise in temperature at about 450°C increases the rate of the reaction $C_2H_5Cl \rightarrow C_2H_4 + HCl$ by a factor of three. This reaction has $\Delta H = +15$ kcal. What is the activation energy of the reverse reaction if this equation and its reverse are the mechanism of the forward and reverse reactions (that is, if the slow step of unimolecular decomposition of C_2H_5Cl is activation under the high-pressure conditions that prevail)?
Answer: 42 kcal.

42. Dissolved in benzene, methyl iodide and pyridine react by a reaction first-order in each reactant with $k_2 = 0.352 \times 10^{-4}$ l mole^{-1} sec^{-1} at 40°C and $k_2 = 1.46 \times 10^{-4}$ l mole^{-1} sec^{-1} at 60°C. What is ΔH_a and at 0°C how long does it take one-third of the pyridine to disappear by reaction in a solution initially one-molar in each reactant?
Answer: 14.7 kcal; 444,000 sec.

43. Two competing irreversible second-order reactions $A + B \rightarrow D + \ldots$ with rate constant k_{AB} and $A + C \rightarrow E + \ldots$ with rate constant k_{AC} are each first-order in each reactant. If these are the only reactions that occur, show that

at any time

$$\frac{k_{AB}}{k_{AC}} = \frac{\ln (C_D/C_D^0)}{\ln (C_E/C_E^0)} = \frac{\ln (C_B/C_B^0)}{\ln (C_E/C_E^0)}$$

Suggest uses of this equation.
Answer: Comparison of reactivities of molecules with different isotopes; determination of small differences in ΔH_a for reactions of homologues or other similar molecules.

44. The strengths of C–H bonds varies from about 100 kcal/mole for primary H to about 75 kcal for tertiary H or for H on radicals that are stabilized by resonance (e. g., benzyl). Show why free-radical chains for bromination can be made selective, whereas chlorination by the same mechanism like (10.90) yields all possible substitutions of Cl for H.
Answer: Reactions like Br + R–H → HBr + R are not slow if R–H is less than about 86 kcal (104 − 18), whereas Cl + R–H → HCl + R is fast (ΔH_a is near zero) for all C–H bonds because $(Cl\text{–}H\text{–}R)^\ddagger$ is like $(Cl\text{–}H\text{–}H)^\ddagger$ and because H–H bond energy exceeds C–H.

45. With manganate ions tagged with radioactive ^{54}Mn with a half-life of 310 days, by precipitating radioactive permanganate ions it is possible to show [J. C. Sheppard and A. C. Wahl, *J. Am. Chem. Soc.* **79,** 1020 (1957)] that the reaction $^{54}MnO_4^{2-} + MnO_4^- \rightarrow {}^{54}MnO_4^- + MnO_4^{2-}$ has a velocity $v = k_2[MnO_4^{2-}][MnO_4^-]$ in aqueous solutions containing NaOH. At 0.1°C, k_2 (1 mole^{-1} sec^{-1}) depends thus on ionic strength (mostly NaOH): 605 at $I = 0.08$; 710 at $I = 0.16$; 920 at $I = 0.32$; 1140 at $I = 0.57$; 1700 at $I = 0.99$. Moreover, at $I = 0.16$, k_2 depends thus on T: 710 at 0.1°C; 1200 at 7.8°C; 1500 at 10.8°C; 3000 at 21.9°C. Calculate ΔH_a, k_2 at 0.1°C at $I = 0.25$, and suggest reasons why $Z_A Z_B$ is not an integer.
Answer: $\Delta H_a = 10.5$ kcal; $k_2 = 817$ 1 mole^{-1} sec^{-1}; Debye-Hückel law fails and γ-radiation by ^{54}Mn yields H_2O^- that carries charge to MnO_4^-.

---

46. At 45°C, phenylmalonic acid (H_2A) and its singly charged anion (HA^-) undergo decarboxylation, but the doubly charged anion (A^{--}) is stable. Per 1 l of solution, the number of moles of CO_2 generated per hour is equal to $11.2 \times 10^{-3}\, C_{H_2A} + 35 \times 10^{-3}\, C_{HA^-}$ [E. Gelles, *J. Am. Chem. Soc.*, **75,** 6199 (1953)]. The first ionization constant of H_2A is 2.7×10^{-3}; the second is 9.4×10^{-6}. If 20.0 millimoles H_2A were dissolved in a l of buffer, how many moles of CO_2 would be evolved after 20.0 hr at 45°C if the buffer had a pH of:
(a) 0.00?
(b) 3.00?
(c) 5.00?
Answer: (a) 0.0040; (b) 0.0086; (c) 0.0101.

47. Equation (10.20) relates the number of radioactive nucleuses to time, but it is common practice to use the time rate of decay in place of N_0 and N when using this equation. Justify this use and indicate circumstances in which such practice is in error.

48. Formulate the mathematics of the unimolecular mechanism of decomposition of A when collisions of A with A differ in efficiency of energy transfer from collisions of A with M.

49. The oxidation of C_2H_2 (A) by O_3 (B) is first-order in each reactant with $k_2 = 0.0025$ mm^{-1} sec^{-1} at 30°C when $-dp_A/dt = k_2 p_A p_B$ [R. D. Cadle and C.

Schadt, *J. Chem. Phys.*, **21,** 163 (1953)]. How long will it take for 1% of an equimolar mixture of C_2H_2 and O_3 to react if the initial total pressure is 4.00 mm Hg? How long will it take for 1% of the C_2H_2 in a mixture containing it at 3.00 mm Hg and O_3 at 1.00 mm Hg to react?
Answer: 2.00 sec; 4.00 sec.

50. In the recombination mechanism for (10.47) with $X = CH_3$, $k_2 = 3.7 \times 10^{13}$ cc mole^{-1} sec^{-1} at 165°C. [G. B. Kistiakowsky and E. K. Roberts, *J. Chem. Phys.*, **21,** 1637 (1953)]. The ratio of k_1^* to k_2^* is 68×10^{16} molecules cc^{-1} for M = He and 4.0×10^{16} molecules cc^{-1} for $M = CH_3COCH_3$ [K. U. Ingold, I. H. S. Henderson, and F. P. Lossing, *J. Chem. Phys.*, **21,** 2239 (1953)]. What is the half-life of CH_3 initially at a pressure of 5×10^{-7} mm Hg:
(a) In the absence of a third body?
(b) In the presence of He at a pressure of 10 mm Hg?
(c) In the presence of CH_3COCH_3 at a pressure of 1.0 mm Hg?
Answer: (a) 1.5 sec if all $C_2H_6^* \rightarrow C_2H_6$; (b) 6.02 sec; (c) 4.15 sec.

51. From data in Problem 9 and Example 10.8 calculate the activation energies associated with the mechanism (10.26) for the isomerization of cyclopropane if $\Delta H^\circ = -5$ kcal mole^{-1} for the overall isomerization.
Answer: $\Delta H_a = 90.1$ kcal; $\Delta H_a' - \Delta H_a^* = 27.1$ kcal; probably $\Delta H_a^* \approx 0$.

52. In view of Problem 51, will the isomerization of cyclopropane tend to remain first-order to lower pressures as the temperature is increased or decreased from 500°C?
Answer: Increased.

53. Dissolved in diethyl ether, cis-2,3-dimethylbutendioic acid at concentrations of the order of 0.03 moles per liter loses water to become the cyclic anhydride with a rate second-order in acid. The second-order rate constants [J. Koskikallio, *Acta Chem. Scand.* **10,** 822 (1956)] are (liter mole^{-1} sec^{-1}) 0.000180 at 0°C, 0.00141 at 20°C, 0.0082 at 40°C, and 0.0435 at 60°C. Calculate the values of s and ΔH_a.
Answer: $\Delta H_a = 16.5$ kcal; $s = 2.8 \times 10^9$.

54. Solid or dissolved in an inert organic solvent, hexanitroethane (HNE) decomposes according to the reaction $C_2(NO_2)_6 \rightarrow 3\ NO_2 + NO + N_2O + 2\ CO_2$. At 70°C in CCl_4, the reaction is first-order in HNE with $k_1 = 2.41 \times 10^{-6}$ sec^{-1} [H. P. Marshall, F. G. Borgardt, and P. Noble, Jr., *J. Phys. Chem.* **69,** 25 (1965)]; at 100°C in CCl_4, $k_1 = 2.22 \times 10^{-4}$ sec^{-1}. If 0.100 mole HNE is dissolved in a liter of CCl_4, find the concentration of HNE and the number of moles of CO_2 produced after 1000 minutes at 70°C. Then find the value of ΔH_a.
Answer: 0.0866 molar; 0.0268 moles; $\Delta H_a = 38.3$ kcal.

55. In dilute aqueous solution, hypophosphoric acid decomposes irreversibly thus: $H_4P_2O_6 + H_2O \rightarrow H_3PO_4 + H_3PO_3$. In the first-order rate law $-d[H_4P_2O_6]/dt = k_1[H_4P_2O_6]$, k_1 is 0.000186 min^{-1} at 25°C in 2.50 molar HCl, k_1 is 0.00631 min^{-1} at 60°C in 2.50 molar HCl, and k_1 is 0.000076 min^{-1} at 60°C in 0.265 molar HCl [Van Name and Huff, *Am. J. Sci.* **45,** 91, 103 (1918)].
(a) What is the order of the reaction with respect to H^+?
(b) In 2.50 molar HCl at 60°C, how long will it take $[H_4P_2O_6]$ to fall from 0.0200 molar to 0.00200 molar?
(c) What is ΔH_a?
Answers: (a) Second; (b) 365 min; (c) 19.9 kcal.

56. In the presence of finely divided solid PuF_4 the essentially irreversible reaction $PuF_{6(g)} \rightarrow PuF_{4(s)} + F_{2(g)}$ has the rate $-dp/dt = k_0 + k_1 p$, where p is the

partial pressure of PuF_6. From the data below determine ΔH_a of each k [J. Fischer, L. Treverrow, and W. Shinn, *J. Phys. Chem.* **65,** 1843 (1961)]:

Pressures of PuF_6 in mm Hg

After 120 min at 140.1°C:

Initial	1018	995	867	763	700	640	564	485	414	140	
Final	868	856	736	622	561	522	457	374	309	71	

After 120 min at 150.3°C:

Initial	1025	498	143	140
Final	779	319	60	61

After 60 min at 173.1°C:

Initial	1087	928	755	754	689	637	530	449	312	257	222
Final	742	599	438	463	398	354	270	200	131	83	60

Answer: For k_0, 15.9 kcal; for k_1, 19.6 kcal.

57. Prepare a graph of the concentrations of A, B, and C for the mechanism of first-order reactions

$$A \xrightarrow{k_1} B \underset{k_1'}{\overset{k_1}{\rightleftharpoons}} C$$

when k_1 exceeds k_1'.

58. At what temperature is the rate of production of HI in a vessel containing H_2 and I_2 by the reaction $H_2 + I_2 \rightarrow 2\,HI$ (rate constant k_2) equal to the rate by the reaction $I + H_2 \rightarrow HI + H$ (rate constant k_2') if [J. H. Sullivan, *J. Chem. Phys.* **36,** 1925 (1962)]:
a. $k_2 = 6.60$ cc mole^{-1} sec^{-1} at 667°K and $k_2 = 1245$ cc mole^{-1} sec^{-1} at 800°K;
b. $k_2' = 1.67 \times 10^3$ cc mole^{-1} sec^{-1} at 667°K and $k_2' = 1.11 \times 10^5$ cc mole^{-1} sec^{-1} at 800°K?

Assume the the reaction $I_2 \rightarrow 2\,I$ reaches equilibrium instantaneously and that data from Example 9.11 may be extended to any T. Assume $p(I_2) = 0.500$ atm for one calculation and $p(I_2) = 0.0500$ atm for another calculation.
Answer: If $p(I_2) = 0.500$ atm, $T = 960$°K; if 0.0500, 785°K.

59. The homogeneous decomposition of H_2O_2 in basic aqueous solution follows the mechanism [F. R. Duke and T. W. Haas, *J. Phys. Chem.* **65,** 304 (1961)]:

$$H_2O_2 + OH^- = HO_2^- + H_2O \quad (1)$$
$$H_2O_2 + HO_2^- \longrightarrow H_2O + O_2 + OH^- \quad (2)$$

where the reversible step (1) is rapid and step (2) is slow. Show that the rate at which the total concentration of H_2O_2 decreases is

$$-\frac{d[H_2O_2]}{dt} - \frac{d[HO_2^-]}{dt} = k_2[H_2O_2][HO_2^-]$$

and that this rate is a maximum when half of the total peroxide is HO_2^-. Then, if k_2 (liters mole^{-1} hr^{-1}) is 0.95 at 15°C and is 2.65 at 35°C, calculate ΔH_a.
Answer: 9.0 kcal.

60. Show how the Michaelis-Menten constant $(k_2' + k_1)/k_2$ is related to the rate of formation of product when substrate is present in excess.
Answer: Maximum rate (C_A great) is $k_1C_x^0$; half the maximum rate is achieved when $(k_2' + k_1)/k_2 = C_A$.

11

MIGRATION OF CHARGED SPECIES

11.1 INTRODUCTION

Lightning and static electricity caused by friction have long been known by man, but only since the middle of the seventeenth century has he tried seriously to measure, generate, and store electricity. Leiden jars, named after the city where they were popularized, were introduced to store electric charge at about the time Benjamin Franklin made his studies of electricity in America. In 1785 Coulomb announced his very fundamental and important law of attraction and repulsion between electric charges. A few years later, Galvani found how the nerves and muscle of a frog's leg might record a flow of current. It was only in 1800, however, that chemistry clearly became involved, for it was then that Volta produced the first continuous source of direct current in meaningful amount by chemical action. Each cell of his electric pile contained two different metals and an electrolyte solution absorbed in paper or leather. Among the many early modifications of the voltaic pile, that of Zamboni in 1812 is remarkable for its use of MnO_2 mixed with honey at the positive electrode of each cell.

Cavendish and Priestley initiated various chemical reactions with electric discharges before 1800. With strong currents from Volta's electric pile, however, Nicholson and Carlisle in 1800 electrolyzed large amounts of water, and Berzelius and Hisinger in 1803 to 1807 electrolyzed salt solutions to produce solutions that were basic at the negative electrode and acidic at the positive electrode. This production of base and acid greatly impressed Berzelius and influenced his development of the dualistic theory of valence. Early chemists found it difficult to accept this theory based on electricity and charged acids and bases when it was obvious that bases like CaO and K_2O and acids like CO_2 and SO_2 were not charged, when many compounds (especially those of organic origin) reacted slowly and formed nonconducting solutions even in water. Chemists in the nineteenth century were mostly preoccupied with distillations, equivalent weights, atomic weights, and discovery of new elements and organic compounds. Thus arose the *radical theory* of valence and the various *type theories* that dominated thinking until the early 1900's.

Yet there was always ample evidence of the importance of electricity to chemical change. In 1805, Grotthuss proposed that chains of molecules carried electric charge through solutions during electrolysis. Davy very naturally thought of valence in electrical terms after being the first to prepare K, Na, Ba, Mg, Ca, and Sr from their fused salts in 1807 and thereafter. Quite by accident, Ruess in 1807 noticed the directed motion of colloidal particles in an electric field. Faraday announced his two laws of electrolysis in 1834 and proposed that electrically charged species be called ions. Twenty years later, Hittorf proved by chemical analysis that the ultimate chemical units of matter in some solutions moved during electrolysis and that each ion had a characteristic velocity in a standard electric field. Clausius described the equilibrium of ions and molecules in 1858, and in the next year Planté invented the storage battery. These chemical developments together with Dalton's atomic theory were to chemistry what the study of elementary particles is to modern physics.

The evidence for the existence of charged particles in certain aqueous solutions was gradually becoming irresistible. Kohlrausch observed in 1875 that in very dilute aqueous solutions the electric conductance was an additive property of the ions and that the ions acted independently of each other as carriers of charge and mass. Within the next ten years Arrhenius proposed his well known theory of ionization of salts, acids, and bases, and Helmholtz developed the thermodynamics of electrochemistry. The anomalous colligative properties of solutions of electrolytes had become widely known by this time, and van't Hoff defined his i and interpreted it in terms of ionization. In 1886, gaseous ions were detected in an electric discharge through a gas at low pressure. The Hall process for producing Al by electrolysis of fused oxides and fluorides was invented in 1886. Finally, in 1889, Nernst explained the common-ion effect and formulated his well known equation for the dependence of cell and electrode EMF on concentration. Unfortunately he chose a sign convention for EMF that differed both from the superior choice of Gibbs and that favored by the International Union of Pure and Applied Chemistry. The end of the nineteenth century thus saw electrochemistry in rapid development. Physics had by this time received a comprehensive basis in electricity through Maxwell's electromagnetic theory of radiation and the experimental proof of the electron's existence in the 1890's by Perrin, Thomson, Zeeman, and others.

The covalent bond, which was an unfortunate distraction to chemists in the 1800's, was given an electronic interpretation in 1916 by Lewis with the hypothesis of the electron-pair bond. Bohr and Rutherford had already done their classic work on the electron-nucleus constitution of the atom, and Moseley had found the atomic numbers through a study of X-ray spectra. Moreover, advanced theories of acid-base behavior on terms of electron transfer were being formulated. With regard to the third law of thermodynamics and quantum theory, it is interesting to note that observations of cell EMF's at low T provided excellent values of ΔH and ΔG at temperatures where ordinary reactions are very slow; these values verified the fact that ΔS for reversible processes approaches zero as T approaches zero.

The details of quantum theory, wave mechanics, and their impact on chemistry are given after Chapter 12. In Chapters 11 and 12, electrochemistry is interpreted in the restricted view of a direct continuation of developments made before 1900. Among the recent developments, the 1923 Debye-Hückel theory (Sections 8.8 and 8.9) of electrolyte solutions is outstanding for its presentation of an algebraic limiting form of the solution of a very complex mathematical problem involving ion-ion interactions in a thermally disordered solution. In 1926 Onsager made notable improvements in the Debye-Hückel theory, especially with regard to the forces acting on moving ions. A year later, Wien discovered that in fields of the order of 10^5 volts cm^{-1}, ions in aqueous solution break loose from the solvent and proceed through the solution alone more readily than expected by extrapolation of conductances at low fields. An important development for analytical chemistry came when Heyrovsky made use of the polarized dropping mercury electrode and thus invented the polarograph in 1925. There has, of course, been much subsequent work on the irreversible processes that occur at laboratory and industrial electrodes as well as on improvement of reversible electrodes and electrochemical cells for measuring thermodynamic energies, pH, and so on. The techniques of X-ray diffraction in investigating solid structures since about 1920 have dispelled any doubt about the existence of ions in solids, for the results of such experiments clearly show the presence of numbers of electrons at centers where the atomic number is different from the numbers of electrons found by the X-rays.

Electrochemistry has here been divided rather arbitrarily into two parts. Chapter 11 deals primarily with the migration of charged species by irreversible processes, while Chapter 12 tends to emphasize the use of thermodynamics for reversible electrochemical processes. In other words, Chapter 11 deals with electric currents carried by ions, while Chapter 12 deals with electromotive force. In view of Ohm's law, which links EMF and current, there is no real division of this kind.

11.2 LAWS OF ELECTRICITY

Conductors of electricity are commonly divided into two classes. In *electronic conductors*, charge is carried by electrons or their positive equivalent, holes, which are absences of electrons that should have been present. Metals and semiconductors are examples of electronic conductors. In the second class of conductor, *ionic conductors*, charge is carried by rather massive particles. Examples are electrolyte solutions like water containing Na^+ and SO_4^{2-}, fused salts like cryolite containing dissolved Al_2O_3, and certain solids in which ions, usually the smaller positive ones, can move via imperfections. This chapter is concerned mainly with liquid ionic conductors.

One of the simplest laws of electricity, *Ohm's law*, describes the time rate of transfer of electric charge. This law says that $\mathscr{I}$, the electric charge carried per second through a conductor, is proportional to the potential difference $\mathscr{E}$, which causes the flow, and is inversely proportional to the resistance $\mathscr{R}$ which opposes the flow. Mathematically, it is

$$\mathscr{I} = k\frac{\mathscr{E}}{\mathscr{R}} \tag{11.1}$$

This law is an empirical observation of the electrical behavior of steady currents in many substances. As a differential equation, (11.1) reads

$$\mathscr{R} = k\frac{d\mathscr{E}}{d\mathscr{I}} \tag{11.2}$$

If $\mathscr{R}$ is not constant as $\mathscr{E}$ and $\mathscr{I}$ vary, the conductor is said to be nonohmic. Some solids are nonohmic, and, as Wien discovered in 1927, the resistance $\mathscr{R}$ of ionic solutions may fall at high electric fields because the ions lose their associated sheath of solvent and oppositely charged ions as they move independently.

In the now outmoded international system of electrical units, the international ampere was defined as that constant current which would deposit in a standard electrolysis cell 0.00111800 g Ag sec^{-1} from an aqueous solution of silver nitrate. The international ohm was defined as the resistance of pure Hg at 0°C in a column of uniform cross section, the column containing 14.4521 g Hg in a length of 106.300 cm. The international volt was the unit of potential difference $\mathscr{E}$ and was chosen to make the proportionality factor k in (11.1) unity. That is, with $\mathscr{I}$ expressed in *amperes*, $\mathscr{E}$ in *volts*, and $\mathscr{R}$ in *ohms*, Ohm's law was

$$\mathscr{E} = \mathscr{I}\mathscr{R} \tag{11.3}$$

In 1948, the National Bureau of Standards established the absolute ampere, ohm, and volt as the legal standards. The absolute system of units is derived from electromagnetic units. The proportionality factor k in Ohm's law is unity in either the absolute or international system as the conversion factors of Table 11.1 indicate. Because exactly one international volt is 1.000330 absolute volts, it is clear that the difference in systems is noticeable only in very accurate work.

Table 11.1 Electrical Conversion Factors (National Bureau of Standards).

Unit	Absolute System	International System
Ampere ($\mathscr{I}$)	1.000000	1.000165 ± 0.000025
	0.999835	1.000000
Volt ($\mathscr{E}$)	1.000000	0.999670 ± 0.000029
	1.000330	1.000000
Ohm ($\mathscr{R}$)	1.000000	0.999505 ± 0.000015
	1.000495	1.000000

Since the current $\mathscr{I}$ is the time rate of movement of charge Q, it follows that

$$\mathscr{I} = \frac{dQ}{dt} \tag{11.4}$$

If the current $\mathscr{I}$ flows for a finite time t, the total charge Q that passes a fixed point in the circuit is

$$Q = \int_0^t \mathscr{I}\, dt' \tag{11.5}$$

When the current $\mathscr{I}$ is steady, $Q = \mathscr{I}t$. If $\mathscr{I}$ is measured in amperes and t in *seconds*, the unit that measures Q is the *coulomb*. Since the units of time are the same in the absolute and international systems, the conversion factor for charge in coulombs is the same as that for current in amperes.

The infinitesimal work dw that must be done in generating a charge dQ at a potential $\mathscr{E}$ or in moving a charge dQ through a potential difference $\mathscr{E}$ is

$$dw = +\mathscr{E}\, dQ \tag{2.4}$$

The convention on the signs of $\mathscr{E}$ and Q requires the positive sign. If the charge dQ is so small that it does not noticeably disturb the value of $\mathscr{E}$, then this electric work is independent of the path by which the charge is generated or moved, just as movement of mass in the potential of a gravitational field requires work that is independent of the path. The finite amount of work w done on a system when a finite amount of charge is generated or moved is the sum of the many infinitesimal changes.

$$w = +\int \mathscr{E}\, dQ \tag{11.6}$$

If $\mathscr{E}$ is constant for the charge Q,

$$w = +\mathscr{E} \int_0^Q dQ' = +\mathscr{E}Q \tag{11.7}$$

The unit of electric work is the *joule*; it is the product of potential difference $\mathscr{E}$ in volts and charge Q in coulombs. The *thermochemical calorie* is defined in terms of electric energy in joules. Exactly 1 cal is equivalent to 4.18400 absolute joules, and a method of comparing thermal and electric energies was discussed in Example 2.3. Since electrical measurements can be made very precisely, calorimeters are calibrated in terms of joules, and calories and kilocalories are used only because of custom.

calorie related to joules, which is a measure of work done on a system when charges are moved/generated.

11.3 ELECTROLYSIS

Electrolysis is the process by which chemical changes are caused by the flow of electric current. Ordinary metallic conductors carry electric charges as an organized movement of electrons. A metal is conceived as a kind of electron-fluid in which metallic ions are regularly arranged. The chemical changes of electrolysis are effected by these electrons as they are transferred to or from the chemicals by electrodes. The electrodes may partake in the chemical changes, or they may be inert and function merely as a source or sink of electrons. The electrode that is connected to the negative terminal of the external source of electricity furnishes electrons to the electrolytic cell and is called the *cathode*. The other electrode is the *anode*; through it the positive current enters the cell or, in other words, through it electrons leave the electrolysis cell.

Table 11.2 Chemical Changes Caused by Electrolysis of Familiar Aqueous Solutions.

Cathode	Main Cathode Reaction	Aqueous Electrolyte	Main Anode Reaction	Anode
Pt	$e^- + H^+ \rightleftharpoons \frac{1}{2} H_2$	H_2SO_4	$OH^- \rightleftharpoons \frac{1}{4} O_2 + \frac{1}{2} H_2O + e^-$	Pt
Pt	$e^- + H^+ \rightleftharpoons \frac{1}{2} H_2$	dil HCl	$OH^- \rightleftharpoons \frac{1}{4} O_2 + \frac{1}{2} H_2O + e^-$	Pt
Pt	$e^- + H^+ \rightleftharpoons \frac{1}{2} H_2$	con HCl	$Cl^- \rightleftharpoons \frac{1}{2} Cl_2 + e^-$	Pt
Ag	$e^- + H^+ \rightleftharpoons \frac{1}{2} H_2$	HCl	$Cl^- + Ag \rightleftharpoons AgCl + e^-$	Ag
Pt	$e^- + Ag^+ \rightleftharpoons Ag$	$AgNO_3$	$OH^- \rightleftharpoons \frac{1}{4} O_2 + \frac{1}{2} H_2O + e^-$	Pt
Ag	$e^- + Ag^+ \rightleftharpoons Ag$	$AgNO_3$	$Ag \rightleftharpoons Ag^+ + e^-$	Ag

Some of the typical chemical changes caused by a flow of electrons are listed in Table 11.2. The various electrolytes, the chemicals undergoing changes, conduct an electric current by virtue of the chemical changes that occur at the electrodes and by virtue of the movement of massive charge carriers called *ions* within the chemical electrolyte that separates the electrodes. Generally there is one predominant chemical change at each electrode, although concentration changes may influence the kind of change that occurs just as the natures of electrode and electrolyte do.

If the products of electrolysis are not kept apart, they will generally react and liberate heat, light, and other forms of energy. For example, mixing H_2 and Cl_2 from the third cell of Table 11.2 could yield HCl. The decrease in free energy from such a reaction could be the source of EMF of an electrochemical cell. Thus, even inert electrodes become active as products of electrolysis collect about them, for the electrical work done on the cell contents increases their free energies. In order to continue electrolyzing the electrolyte, the external source of electricity must impose a potential difference not less than that developed by the cell if it were disconnected and used as a source of electricity. These potential differences are of course opposed and exceeded during an irreversible electrolysis.

Electrolysis is a versatile means of synthesis. For example, at 0°C at Ni anodes under a potential difference of about 6 volts organic acids, ethers or amines dissolved in liquid HF are fluorinated to various degrees, even to perfluoro- compounds. The well known Kolbe synthesis of hydrocarbons begins with carboxylic acids or their salts. At the anode, acetic acid (pure or dissolved in water) becomes acetoxyl radicals $CH_3COO\cdot$ which decompose to yield CO_2 and $CH_3\cdot$; the $CH_3\cdot$'s combine swiftly to form ethane. Similarly, electrolysis can prepare glyconic acids from sugars at an anode or amines from nitro compounds at a cathode.

In 1834, Faraday stated the exact mathematical relation between the amounts of electricity and chemicals produced during electrolysis in two laws: (1) The mass of a substance generated at an electrode is proportional to the amount of electricity passed during electrolysis. (2) The masses of substances generated at several electrodes in series in a single electrolysis are directly proportional to their chemical equivalent weights. This statement of the laws assumes that only one electrode reaction occurs at each electrode.

Suppose that two electrolytic cells were connected in series as in Figure 11.1. At the cathode of the first cell, which contains aqueous $ZnBr_2$, there would be deposited metallic zinc, and at the same time elemental bromine would be generated at the inert anode. In the second cell, hydrogen would be generated at the cathode by electrolysis of dilute sulfuric acid, and oxygen would be freed at the anode. Since the only route for the transfer of electrons is around the singly connected loop that goes from external source $\mathscr{E}$ through the $ZnBr_2$ cell and then through the H_2SO_4 cell, the same amount of charge passes through each electrode. Faraday's second law then says: (a) If all the Zn and Br_2 produced were mixed and allowed to react, pure $ZnBr_2$ would be produced without any Zn or Br_2 left over. (b) Similarly, if all the H_2 produced were burned in all the O_2 produced, pure H_2O would be produced and no H_2 or O_2 would remain. (c) If all the Zn produced were dissolved in acid, it would yield exactly the same amount of H_2 as was produced in the electrolysis. (d) If all the Zn produced by electrolysis were burned in the O_2 produced by electrolysis, only pure ZnO would be made and no Zn or O_2 would remain unused. (e) If the H_2 and Br_2 produced from these cells were combined, pure HBr would be the sole product. (f) And so on.

The quantity of charge that generates exactly one gram equivalent of any chemical is the amount of charge in Avogadro's number of electrons. This amount of charge is called a *faraday*; it is 96,487.0 absolute coulombs. There is about only one chance in 400 that this value differs from the true value by more than 1.6 coulombs (see Appendix A).

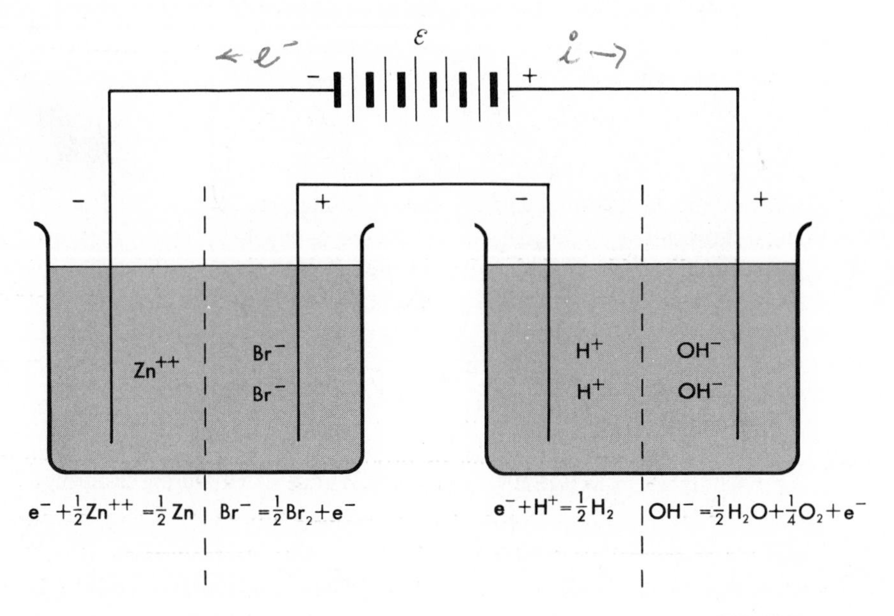

Figure 11.1. Illustration of Faraday's Laws

Example 11.1. How long will it take to deposit exactly 1 g Cu from a solution of $CuSO_4$ with a constant current of 3.000 amp if the only reaction is $2e^- + Cu^{++} \rightleftharpoons Cu$?

The meaning of this equation is that 2 faradays are required to deposit 1 atomic weight Cu or 63.54 g. That is, the equivalent weight is 31.77 g. Since charge and mass are in direct proportion by Faraday's first law and since $Q = \mathscr{I}t$,

$$\frac{1.000}{63.54} = \frac{3.000t}{2 \times 96{,}487}$$

$$t = 1012 \text{ sec}$$

Ohm's law (11.3) says that at constant current (i.e., series connections) the difference in potential $\mathscr{E}$ between two points in a conductor is proportional to its resistance $\mathscr{R}$. Figure 11.2 diagrams schematically the electrostatic potentials Φ in a cell where concentrated aqueous HCl is electrolyzed. In such a diagram, electrons and negatively charged ions, called *anions*, move upwards to higher Φ, while positively charged ions (*cations*) move downwards. The resistance of aqueous HCl is several orders of magnitude greater than that of the Pt electrodes; hence, the slope of the plot of Φ as a function of position is greater in the ionic solution region than in the metallic electrodes.

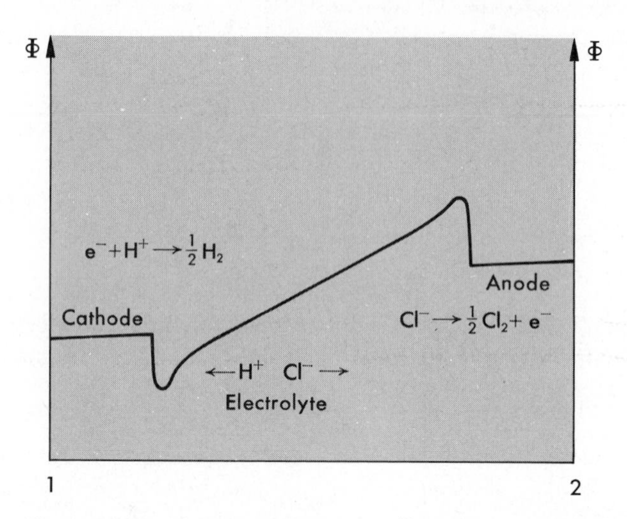

Figure 11.2. Electrostatic Potential Φ Within a Cell During Electrolysis

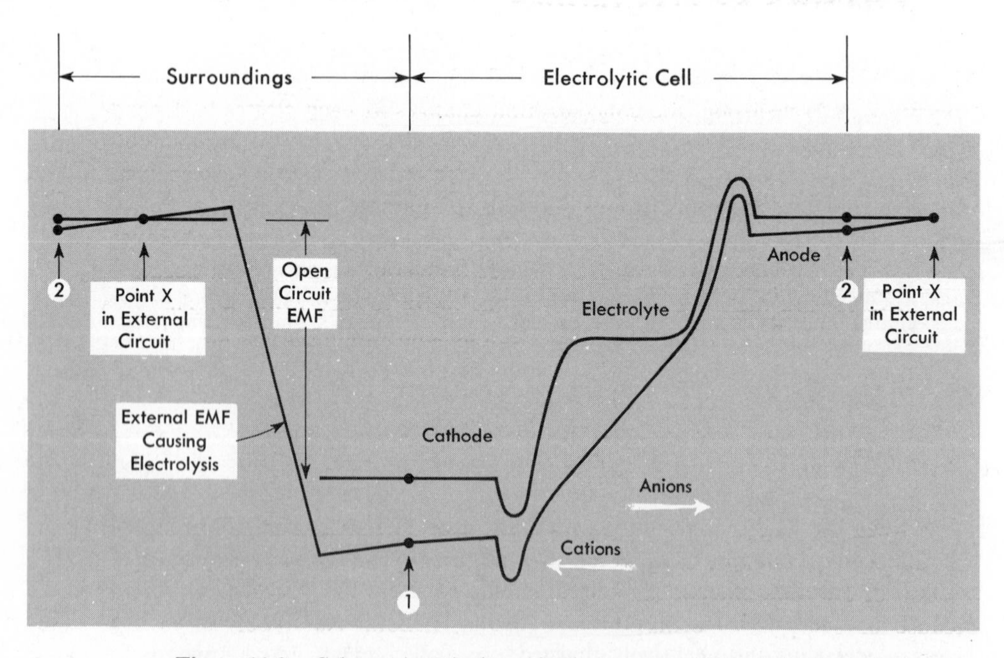

Figure 11.3. Schematic Display of Electrostatic Potential Throughout Circuit (a) With External EMF Causing Electrolysis in Electrolyte Cell; (b) With Products of Electrolysis Causing Open-Circuit EMF.

On approaching each electrode from the solution, $\mathscr{R}$ (and the slope) increases because there electrolysis is removing ions, the charge-carriers. Indeed, near both electrodes, the slope is very great and the field intense not only because of the influence of the external EMF but because the supply of positive and negative ions has been decreased by electrolysis. The abrupt and seemingly discontinuous change in Φ at each electrode surface depends on the chemical natures of the species that interact at that electrode. Really this change in Φ at the metal-electrolyte interface is a series of rapid changes associated with activated complexes that control the rates of diffusion, solvation, discharge, and adsorption and desorption of ions and atoms on the electrode.

How Φ depends on distance where electrolytic solution contacts metallic electrode is very complicated, is shown only schematically in Figures 11.2 and 11.3, and is discussed in Section 11.10. Figure 11.3 shows values of Φ throughout a typical circuit during electrolysis and after electrolysis products have converted the electrolyte-metal interfaces into active electrodes at different potentials.

11.4 TRANSFERENCE NUMBERS FROM CONCENTRATION CHANGES AT ELECTRODES

Although chemically equivalent amounts of substances are generated by electrolysis at each electrode, the concentration changes at each electrode depend upon the speeds with which ions can move through the electrolyte to maintain electroneutrality of the electrolyte near the electrode. Too rapid electrolysis may even exhaust the supply of ions and lead to alternate reactions or to cessation of electrolysis. The electrostatic field that exists in the electrolyte because of the externally imposed potential difference accelerates ions so that negative ions move toward higher Φ and positive ions move toward lower Φ. The terminal velocity reached under this acceleration depends upon the size and charge of the ion and its interactions with the solution. Within the electrolyte, part of the current is carried by positive ions and part is carried by negative ions.

The formation of complex ions or interaction with the solvent may yield unusual changes in ionic concentration. For example, in solutions of halides of zinc and cadmium, there is a net transfer of metal to the region near the *anode* when the halide ion concentration is great. The reason is that complex ions like $ZnCl_3^-$, $ZnCl_4^{--}$, CdI_3^-, and CdI_4^{--} are more plentiful and carry a larger fraction of the total current than do ions like Zn^{++}, $ZnCl^+$, Cd^{++}, and CdI^+. Because of compound formation and decomposition, Na dissolved in Hg migrates to the cathode at high T but to the anode at low T.

Or again, the speed of hydrogen ions in aqueous solutions is so great that it is obvious that hydrogen ions that appear at the cathode could not be the same ones that existed throughout the solution as electrolysis began. Since protons are indistinguishable from each other, a cooperative exchange of them among water molecules throughout the water structure could yield hydrogen at the cathode with only a very small displacement of individual protons. That is, any one proton need move only from its position near an oxygen atom to the equivalent position near the oxygen to which it had been hydrogen-bonded. A thorough comparison of theory with results of experiments in water, in mixtures of water and alcohols, and in isotopically substituted water favors the following mechanism of proton transfer.[1] At any H_3O^+ ion there exists a proton that cannot be accommodated by the usual structure of water (see Section 16.27). In particular, near H_3O^+ there are two protons along one line joining adjacent oxygen atoms, but there should be only one proton. This unfavorable configuration causes the awkwardly oriented H_2O to rotate in the field of the H_3O^+ ion. After rotation, with three adjacent oxygen atoms available to receive one of its extra protons, the H_3O^+ is free to transfer a proton to one of its neighboring H_2O molecules and thus transform it into H_3O^+. The transfer occurs swiftly by a process peculiar to individual particles of small mass like electrons and protons. The proton suddenly disappears from its position near the H_3O^+ and reappears near an H_2O. It has, by a quantum mechanical "tunneling" movement (see Section 13.10), penetrated the barrier between its twofold set of equilibrium positions without proceeding over the barrier as a mountain climber, subject to the laws of classical mechanics, must tediously and breathlessly toil up and over a mountain pass. The quantum mechanical tunneling requires only about one one-hundredth as long as the rotation of an adjacent H_2O. A rotated H_2O that has become H_3O^+ is, like the first H_3O^+, surrounded by four H_2O molecules one of which is unfavorably oriented. And so the process is repeated again and again, each time by a new proton; rotate, tunnel; rotate, tunnel; rotate, tunnel;. . . . In an electric field, the movement is given a preferred direction.

importance

Since protons move about 100 times as swiftly through ice as through water, it is clear that regular orientation of H_2O's facilitates motion of protons. It is, in fact, generally more accurate to say[2] that the acidic species in water is $H_9O_4^+$. This complex is held together by three hydrogen bonds; there is one H_2O for each H of the central H_3O^+. Somewhat like a 'hole' in a semiconductor, the extra proton, if indeed one can be preferred over the others, hovers about the central H_2O and the three closely associated waters. When it moves in the direction of a field, the proton finds that many water molecules have rotated cooperatively as already discussed.

Like a proton, any ion tends to organize the water molecules nearby in a way that does not quite fit into the structure of water. Negative ions generally cause less disturbance than positive ions because the negative ions tend to attract one of the H's of a water molecule and thus leave the rest of the molecule hang-

[1] Conway, B. E., J. O'M. Bockris, and H. Linton, *J. Chem. Phys.*, **24**, 834 (1956). See also: Eigen, M. and L. De Maeyer, *J. Chem. Phys.*, **31**, 1134 (1959).
[2] See, e.g., M. Eigen and L. DeMaeyer, *Proc. Roy Soc.* (London) **A247**, 505 (1958). On pp. 511 ff there is a concise historical account of the proton in water.

ing loose, ready to give or accept a proton in a hydrogen bond. The several molecules of water around an anion can maneuver to accommodate the usual structure of the water. Positive ions, however, tend to attract the O of water and thus present to the solvent nearby a pair of H's on a tightly held water molecule. This disrupts the local structure of the water more than the loosely held H_2O's on negative ions. Even around nonionic and nonpolar solutes, water tends to build a structure that is more rigid and regular than pure water's structure, which has short-range order but negligible long-range order. Considering properties of aqueous solutions in terms of changes in both solute and solvent has lately replaced the more traditional view that dissolved ions are as free as molecules of a dilute gas. Only in exceedingly dilute solutions is the gas analogy close to reality.

It is possibilities like these that suggest that identification and characterization of the actually existing ionic species that carry part of the current in both directions may be quite difficult. A swift nondestructive sampling technique like a spectroscopic method that does not disturb the equilibriums involving the several partially dissociated complex ions, might allow the identification of the actual charge carriers. But a chemical analysis for the total amount of Zn or Cd by precipitation of ZnS or CdS will displace equilibriums involving $ZnCl_4^{--}$ or CdI_3^- and thus yield only the total amount of metal present. Since this last kind of analysis is the only one generally available, the discussion and definition of transference numbers must allow for these awkward possibilities.

Of the several ways of defining transference numbers, the following is accurate and sufficient for this discussion.[3] The *transference number* of an *ion constituent* is the net number of equivalents of the ion constituent that crosses an imaginary plane fixed to the solvent when 1 faraday of charge passes across that plane. It is the fraction of the current carried by the ion constituent. The ion constituents of an electrolyte are those ions which can be combined in various proportions to produce the ions that really exist in the electrolyte. The ion constituents of a solution of $ZnCl_2$ and NaCl are Zn^{++}, Na^+, and Cl^-, or some other set of ions that can be mixed to yield the final solution. The ion constituents may be only minor species in the electrolyte, as Zn^{++} is in concentrated solutions of $ZnCl_2$. However, concentration changes of an ion constituent are readily determined by ordinary chemical methods.

explain transference

When the solute is completely dissociated into ions such that no partially dissociated complex ions exist, the ion constituents are the really existing charge carriers. Throughout the discussions that follow, complete dissociation into two oppositely charged ion constituents will be assumed. Simple electrolytes like NaCl, $AgClO_4$, and NH_4NO_3 behave in this way. Since the ionic molality $m_\pm$ measures the number of moles of ions per kilogram of solvent, the number of equivalents of an ion per kilogram of solvent is $z_\pm m_\pm$, where $z_\pm$ is the number of positive or negative charges per ion. Per kilogram of solvent, the number of

(3) Spiro, M., *Journal of Chemical Education*, **33**, 464 (1956).

equivalents that pass a plane fixed to the solvent is proportional to the velocity $v_\pm$ of the ions relative to the fixed solvent. The number of equivalents of cations that pass on their way to the cathode is proportional to $z_+ m_+ v_+$, while the number of equivalents of anions is proportional to $|z_-| m_- v_-$. The proportionality constants are equal because the electric field, the gradient of the potential difference, is the same for both ions at this plane. The fraction of the charge carried by the ions is just the ratio of the number of equivalents of either kind to the total number of equivalents. By the definition of the transference number $t_\pm$,

$$t_\pm = \frac{|z_\pm| m_\pm v_\pm}{z_+ m_+ v_+ + |z_-| m_- v_-} \tag{11.8}$$

However, since the solution is electrically neutral, the number of positive charges equals the number of negative charges and $z_+ m_+ = |z_-| m_-$; hence,

$$t_\pm = \frac{v_\pm}{v_+ + v_-} \tag{11.9}$$

In (11.8) and (11.9) all upper signs are used for t_+; all lower, for t_-. From this it follows at once that

$$t_+ + t_- = \frac{v_+}{v_+ + v_-} + \frac{v_-}{v_+ + v_-} = 1 \tag{11.10}$$

Equation (11.10) follows from the fact that, except for charge carried by electrons or by the solvent itself, it is the solute ions that carry all the electric charge. The ratio of transference numbers not only gives the ratio of ion velocities but also gives the ratios of charge carried and of current carried. That is,

$$\frac{t_+}{t_-} = \frac{v_+}{v_-} = \frac{Q_+}{Q_-} = \frac{\mathscr{I}_+}{\mathscr{I}_-} \tag{11.11}$$

The Hittorf method (1858) of measuring transference numbers involves analysis by ordinary chemical means of the electrolyte near each electrode and in a region between the electrodes that suffers no net change in concentration. Relative to a given mass of solvent, the number of equivalents of an ion constituent present near an electrode after electrolysis is equal to the number present initially plus those generated at the electrode minus those lost by migration to the central compartment. Since the electrode reaction may lead to a loss of equivalents while migration may lead to a partial replacement of this loss, this statement of the number of equivalents η at an electrode after electrolysis is

$$\eta = \eta_0 \pm \eta_e \mp \eta_m \tag{11.12}$$

where η_0 is the number of equivalents initially present, η_e is the total number of faradays passed through the cell (exclusive of electrons and solvent conduction), and η_m is the number of equivalents that migrate across the boundary between the region around the electrode and the unchanged region between electrodes.

The use of (11.12) is exemplified in the electrolysis of a solution of $AgNO_3$. If the cathode is Ag or Pt, the equivalents of Ag^+ near the cathode decrease due to plating of Ag on the cathode, but some of the loss is offset by migration of Ag^+ toward the cathode. If the anode is Ag, more Ag^+ dissolves in the solution because of electrolysis than is lost by migration away from the anode. If the anode is Pt, electrolysis yields oxygen gas and hydrogen ions, some of which migrate away. In other words, for this solution in these circumstances: the lower signs are used at the cathode; the upper signs are used at the anode of Ag; and at the inert anode, if the analysis is for Ag^+, $\eta = \eta_0 - \eta_m$. It is not necessary, however, that both upper or both lower signs in (11.12) be used together.

The appropriate form of (11.12) allows a calculation of η_m from a knowledge of η_e (current and time) and analyses that specify η_0 and η for a fixed amount of solvent. Since a transference number is the fraction of the total current carried by an ion, it follows that

$$t_{\pm} = \frac{\eta_m}{\eta_e} \tag{11.13}$$

During the electrolysis of aqueous LiCl the highly solvated lithium ion moves only about one-half as fast as the smaller chloride ion. Figure 11.4

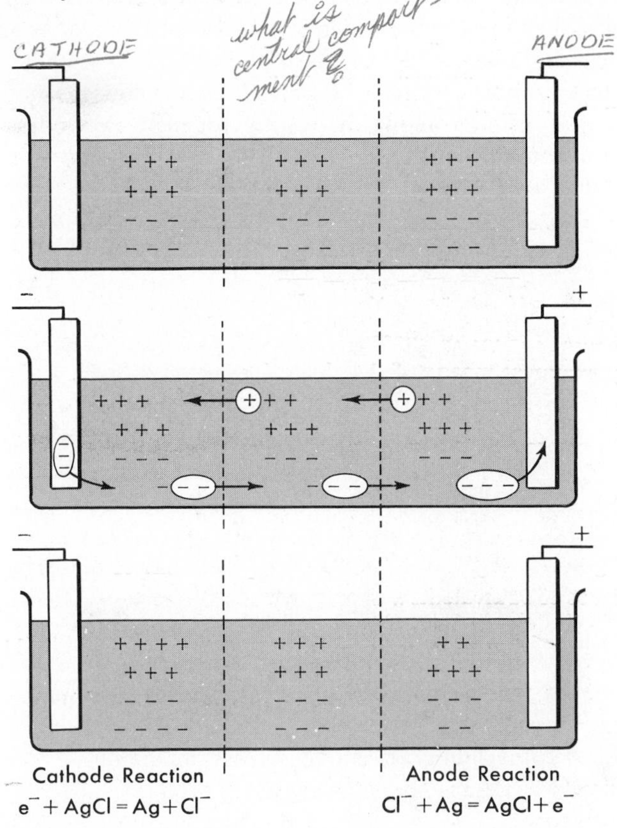

Figure 11.4. Transference in Aqueous Solution of LiCl

illustrates the situations with regard to Li^+ and Cl^- ions before and after electrolysis between Ag, AgCl electrodes. The central chamber has the same composition before and after electrolysis, but the anode and cathode chambers suffer changes even though the net reaction for the cell is nil. The passage of three faradays charge yields three equivalents of Cl^- at the cathode; two of these migrate to the central compartment while one Li^+ enters the cathode compartment from the central one. The central compartment gains one Li^+ from the anode compartment and gives it two Cl^- in an attempt to compensate for the loss of three Cl^- at the anode due to electrolysis. If the cathode had been inert, the reaction would have been

$$e^- + H^+ \rightleftharpoons \tfrac{1}{2}H_2$$

If the anode had been inert, its reaction would have been

$$OH^- \rightleftharpoons \tfrac{1}{2}H_2O + \tfrac{1}{4}O_2 + e^-$$

As long as the H^+ and OH^- ions do not reach the central compartment, the charges are carried by Li^+ and Cl^- across the compartment boundaries and the presence of H^+ near the anode and OH^- near the cathode is without effect upon the transference numbers. It may be important to know the nature of the electrodes, however, in interpreting the results, for inert electrodes give a different cell reaction from that of Figure 11.4. If only one electrode were inert,

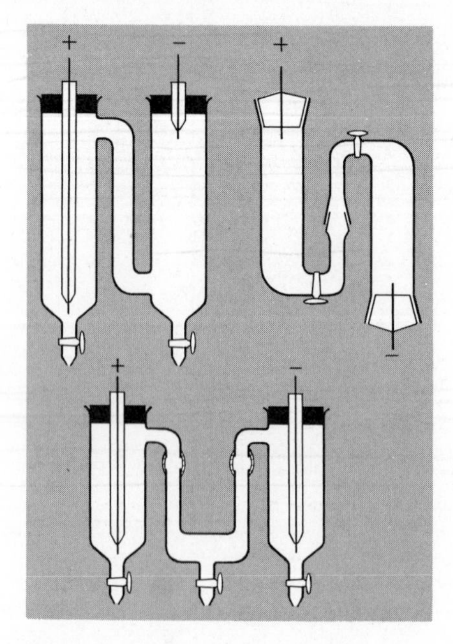

Figure 11.5. Transference Cells

the total amount of Cl^- in the three compartments would change, but the transference numbers calculated from the data would not.

Three common kinds of transference cells are shown in Figure 11.5. In series with the transference cell and the external source of electricity is a coulometer that measures accurately the amount of charge sent through the cell by the weight of silver deposited on a weighed platinum cup from an aqueous solution of $AgNO_3$. Through the years the silver coulometer's accuracy has been in doubt because of possible errors like these: loss of Ag from the cathode before weighing; inclusion of impurities in cathode during electrolysis; fractionation of isotopes of Ag during electrolysis; existence of complex ions like Ag_2^+, etc. Coulometers of the highest accuracy measure the loss of Ag from an anode of pure Ag. Although few realized it, an iodine coulometer [G. W. Vinal and S. J. Bates, *J. Am. Chem. Soc.* **36**, 916 (1914)] actually gave a more accurate value of the faraday. These investigators found one int. coulomb equivalent to 1.31502 mg I. With the latest atomic weight of I (126.9044), this yields 96,488 abs. coul eq^{-1}, in excellent agreement with the latest value of 96,487, and much more accurate than the values (e.g., 96,493) used until 1963.

Table 11.3 lists transference numbers for several electrolytes. The influence of temperature is small and more important than the influence of concentration on transference numbers.

Table 11.3 Transference Numbers of Cations by the Gravimetric Method†

Electrolyte	Temperature (°C)	Normality (equivalents per liter)					
		0.010	0.020	0.050	0.100	0.200	1.000
HCl	0	0.846	0.844	0.839			
	18	0.833	0.833	0.834	0.835	0.837	0.844
	30	0.822	0.822	0.822			
	96	0.748					
KCl	0	0.493	0.493	0.493	0.492	0.491	
	18	0.496	0.496	0.496	0.495	0.494	0.490
	30	0.498	0.498	0.498	0.497	0.496	
NaCl	0	0.387	0.387	0.386	0.385		
	18	0.397	0.396	0.393	0.390	0.385	0.365
	30	0.404	0.404	0.404	0.403		
	96			0.442	0.442	0.442	
H_2SO_4	8		0.835	0.835	0.835		
	20		0.822	0.822	0.822		0.812
	32		0.808	0.808	0.808		

† *International Critical Tables of Numerical Data, Physics, Chemistry, and Technology*, National Academy of Sciences—National Research Council, Washington, D.C., 1926–1933, **VI**, p. 310.

Example 11.2. When an aqueous solution of $CaCl_2$ was electrolyzed with Ag-AgCl electrodes, which have the reaction $AgCl + e^- \longrightarrow Ag + Cl^-$, the central compartment contained 6.374 meq of Ca per 32.40 g H_2O, while the cathode compartment had 6.793 meq Ca per 32.40 g H_2O after electrolysis. If

1.046×10^{-3} faradays of charge passed through the cell, what are the transference numbers of Ca^{2+} and Cl^- in aqueous $CaCl_2$?

Since the analyses are for Ca, which is not generated or destroyed in the reaction at the electrode, $\eta_e = 0$ for Ca in (11.12). Part of the 1.046 meq of Cl^- generated by the cathode reaction do not leave the cathode compartment; hence, to keep the solution neutral some Ca^{2+} migrate into the cathode compartment and (11.12) reads $\eta = \eta_0 + \eta_m$ when the η's refer to meq of Ca. Per 32.40 g H_2O, η is 6.793 and η_0 is 6.374; hence, for Ca

$$6.793 = \eta = \eta_0 + \eta_m = 6.374 + \eta_m$$

$$\eta_m = 0.419 \text{ meq Ca}$$

By (11.13), $t_+ = \eta_m/\eta_e = 0.419/1.046 = 0.401$.

If the analyses had found in 32.40 g H_2O that $\eta' = 6.793$ meq Cl^-, $\eta'_0 = 6.374$ meq Cl^-, then (11.12) would have been $\eta' = \eta'_0 + \eta'_e - \eta'_m$ because each faraday that goes through the cathode causes $AgCl + e^- \longrightarrow Ag + Cl^-$. That is, the Cl^- content of the cathode compartment increases by $\eta'_e = 1.046$ meq Cl^- and decreases by η'_m through emigration of Cl^-. Hence, for Cl^-

$$6.793 = \eta' = \eta'_0 + \eta'_e - \eta'_m = 6.374 + 1.046 - \eta'_m$$

$$\eta'_m = 0.627$$

By (11.13), $t_- = 0.627/1.046 = 0.599$. As expected, $t_+ + t_- = 1$.

Example 11.3. An aqueous solution of $CuSO_4$ was electrolyzed between copper electrodes. After the passage of 1.350×10^{-3} faraday charge, the 25.01 g of solution from the cathode compartment had a molality of 0.0330. The molality of the initial solution and that of the central compartment after electrolysis were 0.0500. Calculate the transference number of cupric ion in this solution.

The amount of water in the cathode compartment after electrolysis must be found in order to relate the molalities, which do not indicate the size of the experiment or the chambers, to the number of faradays charge, which measure the number of ions discharged at the cathode. Since the equivalent weight of $CuSO_4$ is 159.63/2, the grams of water x and the number of equivalents y of $CuSO_4$ in the cathode compartment are found by solving the simultaneous equations for mass and molality:

$$\left.\begin{aligned} 25.01 &= x + y\left(\frac{159.63}{2}\right) \\ 2 \times 0.0330 &= \frac{y}{x \times 10^{-3}} \end{aligned}\right\}$$

$$25.01 = x + \frac{159.63}{2} \times 6.60 \times 10^{-5} \times x$$

$$x = \frac{25.01}{1.0053} \approx 25.01(1 - 0.0053)$$

$$= 24.88 \text{ g } H_2O$$

Hence,

$$y = 0.0660 \times 24.88 \times 10^{-3}$$

$$= 1.640 \times 10^{-3} \text{ equivalent } CuSO_4$$

Initially, 24.88 g water contained 2.488×10^{-3} equivalents $CuSO_4$. Since Cu^{++} migrates into the cathode compartment while Cu^{++} ions are removed at the cathode, by (11.12),

$$1.640 = 2.488 - 1.350 + \eta_m$$
$$\eta_m = 0.502$$

Since the cathode compartment gains what the anode compartment loses by migration to the unchanged central compartment, by (11.13), $t_+ = (0.502/1.350) = 0.372$. The equivalents of solute are referred to a fixed amount of solvent, 24.88 g water, because movement relative to a plane fixed in the solvent means that the amount of water in each chamber is constant.

11.5 TRANSFERENCE NUMBERS FROM POSITION OF MOVING BOUNDARY

The Hittorf method of measuring transference numbers is tediously slow and may yield values of transference numbers precise to about 0.001. Hydration of ions may cause observed transference numbers to differ from true ones by 0.026 or less, but the addition of a nonmigrant like a sugar permits a correction for this by analysis for solvent moved by ions that are hydrated. The Hittorf method is being replaced by other methods, one of which is the very accurate moving-boundary method. Direct observation of a boundary that moves with the velocity of one of the ions permits the evaluation of the ion's transference number. Transference numbers found by the moving boundary method may differ slightly from Hittorf values because in the moving boundary method the reference position is fixed to the container and not to the solvent.

The essential feature of a moving-boundary cell is a tube of uniform cross-sectional area as diagramed in Figure 11.6. Two solutions with a common ion are placed in the cell without mixing. In order to keep the boundary between the solutions sharp during electrolysis, the denser solution is placed on the bottom and the boundary is caused to move into the solution containing the swifter noncommon ion. Since the resistance of an electrolyte increases as its ability to transfer charge decreases, the resistance of the solution containing the slower ion is greater than that containing the swifter ion. Since the current density along the tube is constant, the potential difference per unit length along the tube is greater in the solution of high resistance and slow ions. If any swift ions should lag behind the boundary, this increased field would accelerate them until they reached the boundary. Similarly, should a slow ion diffuse ahead of the boundary, the lower field in the leading solution would allow it to lag until it was once again in the boundary between the leading and indicating solutions. The boundary thus remains sharp and may be followed by noting the position of the discontinuity in index of refraction or some visible chemical change.

The time it takes the boundary to reach tiny electrodes sealed in the walls of the tube at various positions also allows a determination of velocity, for the solutions that meet at the boundary have differing resistances.

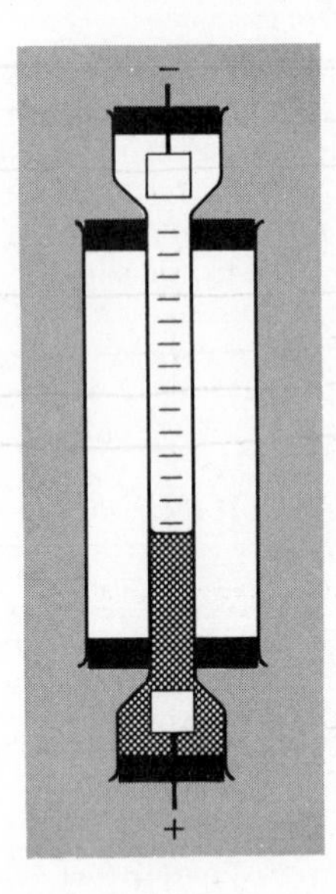

Figure 11.6. Moving Boundary Transference Cell

The boundary advances with the velocity of the noncommon ion in the leading solution. If this noncommon ion is H^+ in dilute HCl, then a suitable indicating solution is $CdCl_2$, the common chloride ion serving to conduct part of the charge downward in Figure 11.6 toward the cadmium anode. As H^+ ions proceed upward, Cd^{++} and $CdCl^+$ ions take their places and form a solution of $CdCl_2$ somewhat more dilute than the initial indicating solutions. Hydrogen gas is generated at the cathode, and cadmium dissolves at the anode to replace the lost H^+ ions. The volume ΔV generated by the boundary as it moves a distance z along the tube of constant cross section $\mathscr{A}$ is $\mathscr{A} z$. The number of gram-equivalents in a volume ΔV is $N_\pm \Delta V \times 10^{-3}$. Here $N_\pm$ is the normality of the leading solution and ΔV is measured in milliliters. The number of coulombs of charge carried by the leading ion is, then, $N_\pm \times \Delta V \times \mathscr{F} \times 10^{-3}$. For a constant current $\mathscr{I}$ that flows a time Δt, the total charge in coulombs passed through the electrolytes is $\mathscr{I} \Delta t$. Since the transference number is the fraction of the total charge carried by an ion constituent,

$$t_\pm = \frac{N_\pm \times \mathscr{F} \times \Delta V}{10^3 \times \mathscr{I} \times \Delta t} \tag{11.14}$$

 Some values of cation transference numbers determined by the moving-boundary method are listed in Table 11.4. As the table indicates, transference numbers are almost independent of concentration.

Table 11.4 Transference Numbers of Cations at 25°C by the Moving-Boundary Method†

Electrolyte	Normality (equivalents per liter)				
	0.01	0.02	0.05	0.10	0.20
HCl	0.8251	0.8266	0.8292	0.8314	0.834
KCl	0.4902	0.4901	0.4899	0.4898	0.489
NaCl	0.3918	0.3902	0.3876	0.3854	0.382
LiCl	0.3289	0.3261	0.3211	0.3168	0.311
NH_4Cl	0.4907	0.4906	0.4905	0.4907	0.491
KBr	0.4833	0.4832	0.4831	0.4833	0.484
KI	0.4884	0.4883	0.4882	0.4883	0.489
KNO_3	0.5084	0.5087	0.5093	0.5103	0.512
$AgNO_3$	0.4648	0.4652	0.4664	0.4682	—
$NaC_2H_3O_2$	0.5537	0.5550	0.5573	0.5594	0.561
$CaCl_2$	0.4264	0.4220	0.4140	0.4060	0.395
Na_2SO_4	0.3848	0.3836	0.3829	0.3828	0.383
$LaCl_3$	0.4625	0.4576	0.4482	0.4375	0.4233

† Longsworth, L. G., *J. Am. Chem. Soc.*, **54**, 2741 (1932); **57**, 1185 (1935); Longsworth, L. G. and D. A. MacInnes, *J. Am. Chem. Soc.*, **60**, 3070 (1938).

Example 11.4. The table contains some data of L. G. Longsworth [*J. Am. Chem. Soc.*, **54**, 2745 (1932)] in the determination of the transference number of Na^+ in $0.02N_\pm$ NaCl at 25°C. The anode was Cd; the following solution, $CdCl_2$; the cathode, Ag-AgCl; the regulated constant current, 0.001600 amp; the cross-sectional area of the tube, 0.1113 cm². (A small correction is to be added to the mean.) The values of the third column of this table have been calculated from (11.14).

Vertical Distance Moved (cm)	Time (Seconds)	t_+ (11.14)
0.000	0	—
2.000	689	0.3897
4.000	1380	0.3891
6.000	2070	0.3891
8.000	2757	0.3895
10.000	3453	0.3888
		Mean 0.3893

11.6 SPECIFIC CONDUCTANCE

Electrical conductance is a direct measure of ability to carry an electric current. The conductance L of a substance with a resistance $\mathscr{R}$ is conductance $$L = \frac{1}{\mathscr{R}} \tag{11.15}$$

The specific conducance L_{sp} of a conductor with a cross-sectional area $\mathscr{A}$ and length l is that proportionality factor which links L, $\mathscr{A}$, and l for a certain substance. All other things being equal, the conductance of a substance is directly proportional to its cross section $\mathscr{A}$ and inversely proportional to its length l; that is,

$$L = L_{sp}\left(\frac{\mathscr{A}}{l}\right) \tag{11.16}$$

Thus L_{sp} is numerically equal to the current that flows through a conductor 1 cm long with a cross section of 1 cm^2 under a potential difference of 1 volt. The unit of conductance is the reciprocal ohm, or mho. Substances are classified as insulators if their L_{sp}'s are less than 10^{-13} mho cm^{-1}, as semiconductors if 10^2 to 10^{-10} mho cm^{-1}, and as good conductors if about 10^5 mho cm^{-1}. Grignard reagents have L_{sp} of the order of 10^{-5} mho cm^{-1}; pure H_2SO_4 has L_{sp} of the order of 10^{-6} mho cm^{-1} at 18°C; pure NH_3, ca. 10^{-7} mho cm^{-1}.

The specific conductance of aqueous solutions of strong electrolytes like KCl, $AgNO_3$, and $CuSO_4$ in mho cm^{-1} are numerically about one-tenth of their normalities. The specific conductances of three KCl solutions at 0°C, 18°C, and 25°C are listed in Table 11.5. The conductances of many aqueous solutions

Table 11.5 Specific Conductances of Aqueous KCl† (international mho cm^{-1})

Demal Concentration	Grams KCl Per 1000 Grams Solution	Specific Conductance (L_{sp})		
		0°	18°	25°
0.01000	0.745263	0.00077364	0.00122052	0.00140877
0.10000	7.41913	0.0071379	0.0111667	0.0128560
1.00000	71.1352	0.065176	0.097838	0.111342

† Jones, G. and B. C. Bradshaw, *J. Am. Chem. Soc.*, **55**, 1799 (1933).

demal = moles KCl / 10^3 ml soln.

increase by about 2% deg^{-1} as these solutions of KCl do; hence, T must be constant within less than 0.01° for highest accuracy. The demal units of concentration measure the number of gram formula weights of KCl in exactly 1000 cc of solution at 0°C. These solutions of KCl are used as reference standards; their conductances were measured very exactly with electrodes of known area $\mathscr{A}$ and known separation l.

In order to determine the specific conductance of any solution it is necessary to measure accurately its resistance in a cell of known $\mathscr{A}$ and l. For a particular cell, an effective value of $\mathscr{A}/l$ can be found through (11.16) by measuring L for a solution of KCl of known L_{sp}. Here L can be found accurately by use of a Wheatstone bridge, diagramed in Figure 11.7. When the bridge is balanced, no current flows through the null detector, often an oscilloscope. If $\mathscr{I}_{12}$ is the cur-

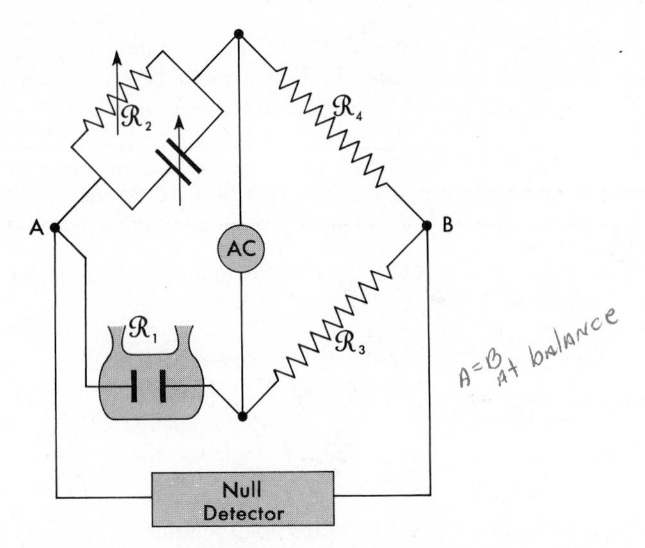

Figure 11.7. Typical Circuit for Measuring Conductance

rent through impedances $\mathscr{R}_1$ and $\mathscr{R}_2$ and if $\mathscr{I}_{34}$ is that through $\mathscr{R}_3$ and $\mathscr{R}_4$ at balance, then, because at balance there is no potential difference between A and B, $\mathscr{I}_{12}\mathscr{R}_1 = \mathscr{I}_{34}\mathscr{R}_3$ and $\mathscr{I}_{12}\mathscr{R}_2 = \mathscr{I}_{34}\mathscr{R}_4$. Division of these equations yields

$$\frac{\mathscr{R}_1}{\mathscr{R}_2} = \frac{\mathscr{R}_3}{\mathscr{R}_4} \tag{11.17}$$

Alternating current (and a layer of Pt-black on the electrodes) minimizes polarization of the electrodes in the conductance cell through accumulation of electrolysis products. The objective is to measure just the resistance of the conductance cell; at high frequencies its capacitance is great enough that it must be balanced by a capacitance in the adjustable but standardized impedance $\mathscr{R}_2$. The capacitances of $\mathscr{R}_3$ and $\mathscr{R}_4$ are either equal or so small in effect that they may be treated as simple resistances. If B is a sliding contact along a uniform resistance wire with total resistance $\mathscr{R}_3 + \mathscr{R}_4$, the ratio of lengths yields $\mathscr{R}_3/\mathscr{R}_4$. With $\mathscr{R}_2$ known, $\mathscr{R}_1$ is fixed by (11.17). If $\mathscr{R}_1$ is the impedance of a conductivity cell filled with KCl of known L_{sp}, it follows that the cell constant of that cell is, by (11.15) and (11.16),

$$\frac{\mathscr{A}}{l} = \frac{1}{\mathscr{R}_1 L_{sp}} \tag{11.18}$$

With a solution of unknown specific conductance L'_{sp} in the same cell, a second measurement of impedance $\mathscr{R}'_1$ yields

$$L'_{sp} = \frac{1}{\mathscr{R}'_1}\left(\frac{l}{\mathscr{A}}\right) = \left(\frac{\mathscr{R}_1}{\mathscr{R}'_1}\right) L_{sp} \tag{11.19}$$

Most of the electrical problems can be avoided by use of direct current; the $\mathscr{R}$'s of (11.17) are then pure resistances. However, with direct current, the electrodes must be truly reversible with respect to their reactions.

Example 11.5. At 25°C, a 0.1000 demal KCl solution had an impedance of 97.36 ohms in a certain conductivity cell. Filled with 0.100 normal NaCl, the same cell had an impedance of 117.18 ohms. Calculate the specific conductivity of the NaCl solution.

According to Table 11.1, one ohm is 0.999505 international ohm, so that the specific conductivity of 0.1000 demal KCl at 25°C is

$$L_{sp} = 0.0128560 \times 0.999505 \text{ mho cm}^{-1} = 0.0128496 \text{ mho cm}^{-1}$$

The cell constant is, by (11.18),

$$\frac{\mathscr{A}}{l} = \frac{1}{97.36 \times 0.0128496}$$

Then, by (11.19), the specific conductivity of the NaCl solution is

$$L'_{sp} = \frac{97.36 \times 0.0128496}{117.18} = 0.010676 \text{ mho cm}^{-1}$$

The conductance of ionic solutions decreases as the frequency of the accelerating field increases. At first the decrease is caused by the asymmetry of the ionic atmosphere, which cannot quite keep up with the ion as it follows the alterations of the field. As the frequency rises beyond about 10^{12} sec^{-1}, ions tend to shed their associated solvent molecules, and above about 10^{14} sec^{-1} the ions themselves cannot keep pace with the alterations of the field. This is the start of the optical range, where ionic solutions are nonconducting and transparent.

11.7 EQUIVALENT CONDUCTANCE

The equivalent conductance of a solution is the conductance of that volume of solution which contains one gram-equivalent of electrolyte when the spacing between electrodes is one cm. In a solution of normality $N_{\pm}$, the volume that contains one equivalent is $(1000/N_{\pm})$ ml. If the distance l between electrodes is one cm, the area $\mathscr{A}$ of the electrodes is $1000/N_{\pm}$. Figure 11.8 illustrates how large such electrodes would have to be to measure the equivalent conductance of a one-normal solution; the black areas would give L_{sp}. Of course, it is L that is observed and, by definition, as suggested by (11.16), the equivalent conductance is

$$\Lambda = \left(\frac{1000}{N_{\pm}}\right) L_{sp} \tag{11.20}$$

Figure 11.8. Electrodes for Measuring Equivalent Conductance of a One-Normal Solution

In terms of directly observed variables, (11.20), as transformed by (11.15) and (11.16), reads

$$\Lambda = \left(\frac{1000}{N_{\pm}}\right)\left(\frac{1}{\mathscr{R}_1}\right)\left(\frac{l}{\mathscr{A}}\right) \tag{11.21}$$

While specific conductance varies greatly with chemical concentration, the equivalent conductance of a strong electrolyte like a salt dissolved in water depends only slightly upon concentration. In the spirit of the Debye-Hückel theory, this weak dependence upon concentration is linear in the square root of the normality in dilute solutions. Because of the interference due to the other ions, equivalent conductance decreases as concentration increases; hence,

$$\Lambda = \Lambda_0 - C\sqrt{N_{\pm}} \tag{11.22}$$

where

$$\Lambda_0 = \lim_{\sqrt{N_{\pm}} \to 0} (\Lambda) \tag{11.23}$$

The limit Λ_0 at infinite dilution is conveniently found by graphical extrapolation as in Figure 11.9.

Onsager has shown theoretically that (11.22) is of the correct form. Three things oppose the movement of an ion: the viscosity of the solution, the distortion of the ion atmosphere due to movements of ions in the opposite direction, the flow of solvent and ions of opposite charge in the opposite direction. Even at infinite dilution the viscosity of the solvent would retard an ion's motion. The other two effects, however, are clearly dependent on concentration. The distortion of the ion atmosphere, called the *relaxation* or *asymmetry effect*, decreases

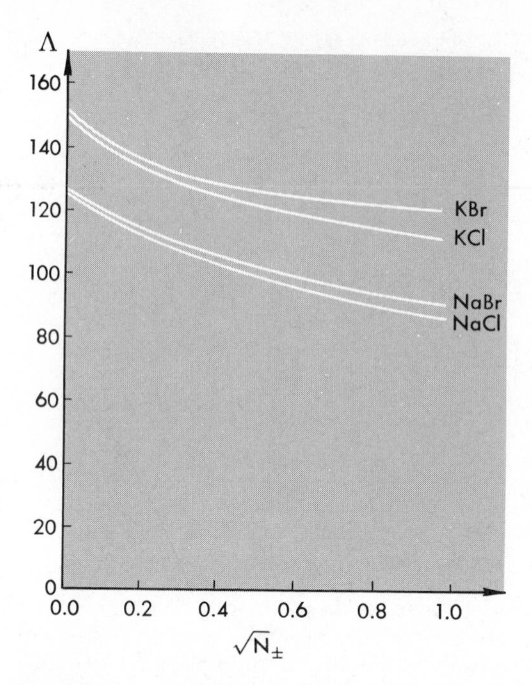

Figure 11.9. Dependence of Equivalent Conductance on Concentration (25°C)†

Λ_0 by a factor $(1 - R)$ because the ion is out of phase with its ion-cloud. The electrophoretic effect, caused by the apparently charged solution as it and its ions move in the opposite direction, decreases Λ_0 by an amount E that depends in part on the viscosity. Hence, with both effects active and with neglect of their negligible interaction,

$$\Lambda = (\Lambda_0 - E)(1 - R) \approx \Lambda_0 - E - R\Lambda_0 \tag{11.24}$$

Since E and R are each proportional to $\sqrt{I}$, it follows that

$$\Lambda = \Lambda_0 - (C_1 + C_2\Lambda_0)\sqrt{I} \tag{11.25}$$

The relaxation term $C_2\Lambda_0$ is often important for acids, for which Λ_0 is great. For 1-1 electrolytes in water at 25°C theory gives

$$\Lambda = \Lambda_0 - (60.65 + 0.2300\Lambda_0)\sqrt{I} \tag{11.26}$$

Example 11.6. Find Λ_0 for HCl at 25°C from the data [R. H. Stokes, *J. Phys. Chem.* **65**, 1242 (1961)]:

†*International Critical Tables of Numerical Data, Physics, Chemistry, and Technology*, National Academy of Sciences–National Research Council, Washington, D. C., 1926–1933, **VI,** 234–235

Λ	423.44	421.39	419.83	418.49	416.77	415.52	...
$I \times 10^4$	3.5938	10.2493	18.1756	26.749	40.733	53.061	...

Then verify (11.26).

From Figure 11.10, Λ_0 is 426.2 (Stokes gets 426.50), and near $100\sqrt{I} = 2$, $C_1 + C_2\Lambda_0 = 150$. According to (11.26), $C_1 + C_2\Lambda_0$ should be $60.65 + 0.2300(426.2) = 60.65 + 98.02 = 158.67$.

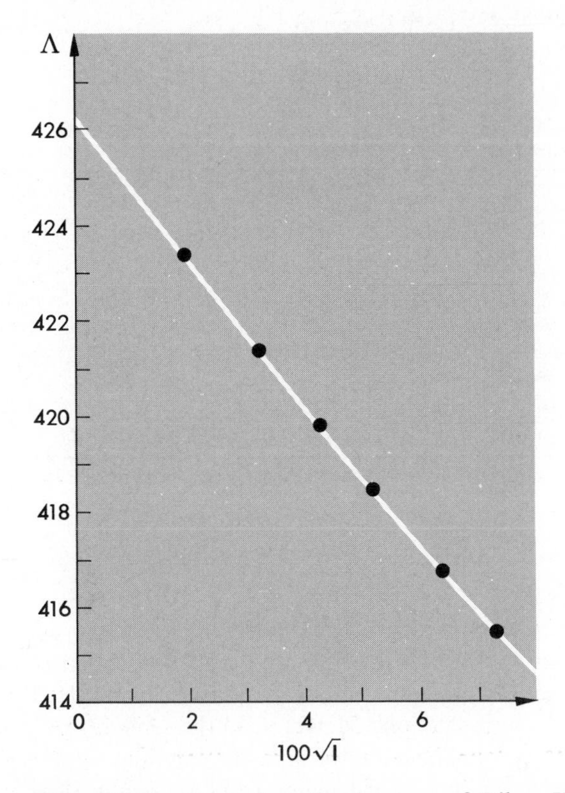

Figure 11.10. Equivalent Conductance of Dilute HCl as a Function of Concentration

About 1875, Kohlrausch advanced the hypothesis that at infinite dilution, where interionic attractions and repulsions are negligible, each ion migrates independently. The reproducible differences between Λ_0 for the chlorides and bromides of sodium and potassium of Figure 11.9 are examples in support of this hypothesis. Mathematically, if l_+^0 and l_-^0 are the equivalent conductances of cation and anion at infinite dilution,

$$\Lambda_0 = l_+^0 + l_-^0 \tag{11.27}$$

The total conductance Λ_0 is apportioned between ions according to their transference numbers; hence,

$$\Lambda_0 = t_+^0 \Lambda_0 + t_-^0 \Lambda_0 \tag{11.28}$$

where $t_\pm^0$ is the transference number at infinite dilution. A comparison of (11.27) and (11.28) yields a simple expression for ionic conductances, namely,

ionic conductances

$$l_\pm^0 = t_\pm^0 \Lambda_0 \tag{11.29}$$

Table 11.6 lists values of $l_\pm^0$ for several common ions in water.

Table 11.6 Equivalent Conductances of Ions at Infinite Dilution† (25°C)

Cation	l_+^0	Anion	l_-^0
H^+	349.82	OH^-	198.
Li^+	38.69	Cl^-	76.34
Na^+	50.11	Br^-	78.4
K^+	73.52	I^-	76.8
NH_4^+	73.4	NO_3^-	71.44
Ag^+	61.92	$C_2H_3O_2^-$	40.9
Tl^+	74.7	$C_2H_2ClO_2^-$	39.7
$\frac{1}{2}Ba^{++}$	63.64	ClO_4^-	68.0
$\frac{1}{3}La^{+++}$	69.6	$\frac{1}{2}SO_4^{--}$	79.8

† MacInnes, D. A., *Principles of Electrochemistry*. New York: Reinhold Publishing Corporation, 1939, p. 342.

11.8 WEAK AND STRONG ELECTROLYTES

The equivalent conductances of aqueous solutions of NaOH and HCl vary according to (11.22) at low concentrations. However, in the same range of low concentrations, the equivalent conductances of aqueous solutions of NH_4OH and $HC_2H_3O_2$ are far below the limit Λ_0 calculated from their equivalent ionic conductances. The reason is that NH_4OH and $HC_2H_3O_2$ are only partly ionized even at the low concentrations where the conductance of water itself begins to contribute to the conductance of the solution. Figure 11.11 illustrates the behavior typical of strong and weak electrolytes. Because extrapolation of a curve for a weak electrolyte would not yield an accurate limit at $\sqrt{N_\pm} = 0$, Λ_0 is calculated by (11.27) from ionic conductances found for salt solutions like NH_4Cl or $NaC_2H_3O_2$, which are completely ionized at all concentrations.

If C_i is the molarity of a solution of a weak electrolyte A_aB_b of which the fraction α is ionized to cations of charge z_+ and anions of charge z_-, then

$$\begin{array}{ccc} A_aB_b & \rightleftharpoons & aA^{z_+} + bB^{z_-} \\ (1-\alpha)C_i & & a\alpha C_i \quad b\alpha C_i \end{array} \tag{11.30}$$

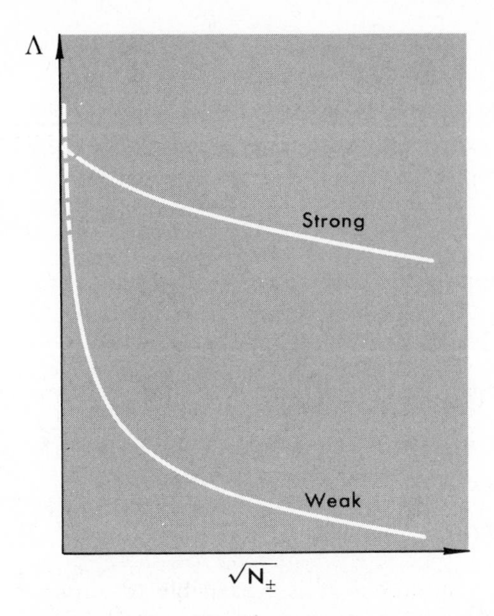

Figure 11.11. Typical Dependence of Equivalent Conductances of Strong and Weak Electrolytes

The actual molarity of cations is $a\alpha C_i$; that of anions, $b\alpha C_i$. If there is no other source of these ions, as from a salt in the same solution, then electroneutrality requires that $a\alpha C_i z_+ + b\alpha C_i z_- = 0$, where z_- is a negative integer. Also,

$$N_\pm = z_+ a C_i = |z_-| b C_i \tag{11.31}$$

For a solution with resistance $\mathscr{R}$, the time rate of transfer of charge through migration of ions is $\mathscr{I} = \mathscr{E}/\mathscr{R}$. The number of equivalents of ions per liter is $\alpha N_\pm$ and the time rate of traversal of volume by cations is $\mathscr{A} v_+$ while that by anions is $\mathscr{A} v_-$ cm^3 sec^{-1}. Accordingly, the current in amperes, or coulombs per second, is

$$\mathscr{I} = \alpha N_\pm \mathscr{F} \mathscr{A}(v_+ + v_-) \times 10^{-3} \tag{11.32}$$

But since $\mathscr{I} = \mathscr{E}/\mathscr{R}$, (11.32) yields

$$\alpha \mathscr{F}(v_+ + v_-) = \frac{\mathscr{I} \times 10^3}{N_\pm \mathscr{A}} = \frac{\mathscr{E} \times 10^3}{\mathscr{R} N_\pm \mathscr{A}} \times \left(\frac{l}{l}\right) = \left(\frac{\mathscr{E}}{l}\right)\left(\frac{1000 \times l}{N_\pm \mathscr{R} \mathscr{A}}\right) \tag{11.33}$$

In order to reduce all velocities of migration to a common basis of field intensity, the term *mobility* is used. The mobility is the velocity attained in a steady state under the influence of a potential gradient (or field) of 1 volt cm^{-1}. That is, the mobility u is

$$u = \frac{v}{(\mathscr{E}/l)} \tag{11.34}$$

where v is the velocity attained because of a potential difference $\mathscr{E}$ applied along a distance l. By (11.21) and (11.34), it follows from (11.33) that for weak electrolytes

$$\alpha\mathscr{F}(u_+ + u_-) = \Lambda \tag{11.35}$$

This is a key equation. Since α approaches unity as $\sqrt{N_\pm}$ approaches zero,

$$\lim_{\sqrt{N_\pm}\to 0} [\alpha\mathscr{F}(u_+ + u_-)] = \lim_{\sqrt{N_\pm}\to 0} [\Lambda]$$

Or,

$$\mathscr{F}(u_+^0 + u_-^0) = \Lambda_0 \tag{11.36}$$

Equation (11.36) applies to both weak and strong electrolytes. An equation like (11.36) holds for strong electrolytes even at finite concentrations; that is,

$$\mathscr{F}(u_+ + u_-) = \Lambda \tag{11.37}$$

Even at finite, nonzero concentrations it is reasonable to suppose, by analogy with (11.27) and (11.28), that for strong electrolytes

$$\Lambda = l_+ + l_- = t_+\Lambda + t_-\Lambda \tag{11.38}$$

Term-for-term comparison of (11.27), (11.28), and (11.38) with (11.35), (11.36), and (11.37) yields several relations among $l_\pm$, $t_\pm$, $u_\pm$, and Λ. For weak and strong electrolytes,

$$\mathscr{F}u_\pm^0 = l_\pm^0 \tag{11.39}$$

For weak electrolytes,

$$\alpha\mathscr{F}u_\pm = l_\pm \tag{11.40}$$

For strong electrolytes,

$$\mathscr{F}u_\pm = l_\pm = t_\pm\Lambda \tag{11.41}$$

By analogy with (11.9) and (11.29) it follows that for strong electrolytes

$$t_\pm = \frac{l_\pm}{l_+ + l_-} \tag{11.42}$$

The degree of ionization of a weak electrolyte can be estimated through measurement of a colligative property or through a measurement of conductance. If $(u_+^0 + u_-^0)$ is approximately equal to $(u_+ + u_-)$, then division of (11.35) by (11.36) yields a simple expression for α, namely,

$$\alpha = \frac{\Lambda}{\Lambda_0} \tag{11.43}$$

While (11.43) is approximately true, it is more accurate to calculate α by (11.43) when Λ and Λ_0 are measured at the same ionic strength.

Example 11.7. If the equivalent conductance of dichloroacetic acid at infinite dilution at 25°C is 388.5 (*International Critical Tables of Numerical Data, Physics, Chemistry, and Technology*, National Academy of Sciences–National Research Council, Washington, D. C., 1926–1933, *VI*, p. 262), with the aid of data in Example 8.12 estimate the conductivity of 0.100 molal chloroacetic acid. Determine also the equivalent conductance of the anion at infinite dilution.

Since l_+^0 of H^+ is 349.8 by Table 11.6, it follows from (11.27) that the equivalent conductance of chloroacetate ion at infinite dilution is $l_-^0 = \Lambda_0 - l_+^0 = 388.5 - 349.8 = 38.7$. The degree of ionization as judged from the freezing point depressions in Example 8.12 is 0.61; hence, by (11.43), $\Lambda = \alpha\Lambda_0 = 0.61 \times 388.5 = 237$. Then, by (11.20) the specific conductivity L_{sp} is

$$L_{sp} = \left(\frac{N_\pm}{1000}\right) \times \Lambda = \frac{0.100}{1000} \times 237 = 2.37 \times 10^{-2} \text{ mho cm}^{-1}$$

Example 11.8. Calculate the effective mobility of a proton in water.

From Table 11.6, the equivalent conductance of H^+ is 349.82. By (11.39), its mobility is

$$u_+ = \frac{l_+^0}{\mathscr{F}} = \frac{349.82}{96{,}487} = 36.256 \times 10^{-4} \text{ cm}^2 \text{ volt}^{-1} \text{ sec}^{-1}$$

11.9 USES OF CONDUCTIVITY

Measurements of conductivity can yield information about the degree of ionization of a weak electrolyte, as discussed in the preceding section. Simple extension of such methods furnishes information about the degree of hydrolysis of salts and the stability of complex ions. On the other hand, conductivity measurements can characterize the solvent. Figure 11.12 indicates how the equivalent conductivities of KCl, KBr, and KI depend upon concentration in water and in liquid sulfur dioxide at 0°C. In SO_2 these halides are weak electrolytes. They are only partly ionized mainly because the dielectric constant of SO_2 is only about one-sixth as large as that of water. In water, however, where the dielectric constant is great, the attraction among unlike ions is small and ionization is complete. Liquid hydrogen fluoride, which is of importance in the production of fluorine, has a dielectric constant almost equal to that of water and is similar in many ways to water.

The solvent properties of liquid ammonia are well known and have been investigated in detail.[4] Many metathetical reactions occur in NH_3 but not in

[4] Yost, Don M. and Horace Russell, Jr., *Systematic Inorganic Chemistry of the Fifth- and Sixth-Group Nonmetallic Elements*. Englewood Cliffs, N. J.: Prentice-Hall, Inc., 1944, Chapter 4. By permission.

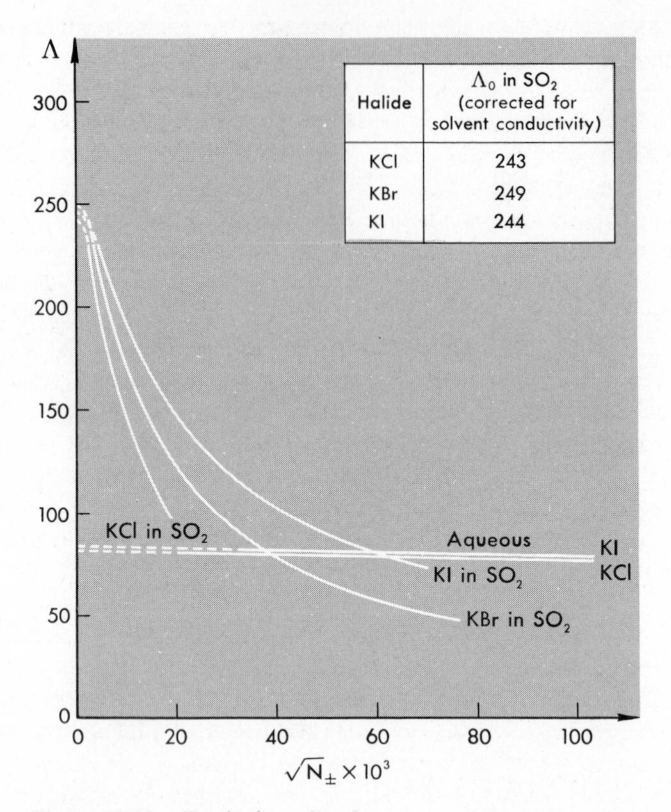

Figure 11.12. Equivalent Conductances of Potassium Halides in Water and in Liquid Sulfur Dioxide at 0°C†

water because the solubilities of salts differ. For example, AgI is quite soluble in NH_3, but MgI_2 and KCl are rather insoluble. The most remarkable solutions in liquid ammonia are, however, the solutions of alkali and alkaline earth metals. A saturated solution of Na or K in NH_3 has a mole fraction of metal of about 0.15 below 0°C. Such solutions are reddish in color and have a metallic appearance. The specific conductivity of a saturated solution of Na in NH_3 is about 0.5×10^4 mho cm^{-1}, of the same order of magnitude as metals. The transference number of the carrier of negative charge is ten to a few hundred times that of the positive carrier. Conduction is mainly by electrons that are almost free to move anywhere in the solution.

The production of Al, Mg, Na, and other metals by electrolysis of their molten salts is of great economic importance. The specific conductances of molten salts is of the order of 10^0 mho cm^{-1}. Conduction occurs by ions freed

†N. N. Lichtin and H. P. Leftin, *J. Phys. Chem.* **60,** 160 (1956); *International Critical Tables of Numerical Data, Physics, Chemistry, and Technology*, National Academy of Sciences–National Research Council, Washington, D. C., 1926–1933, **VI,** pp. 234–235

from their lattice sites by fusion, but in certain situations, especially in molten sulfides, conduction may be electronic also. The specific conductances of many solids are very sensitive to the presence of impurities and even to the intensity of light that falls on them. In these cases, electrons carry negative charge and holes (electrons that might have been) carry positive charge, but ions themselves generally remain fixed at their lattice sites. Typical metallic conduction also involves movement of electrons through an orderly array of fixed positive ions.

Since a measurement of conductivity with alternating current generally causes little electrolysis and decomposition of a sample, it is an excellent means of swift, nondestructive analysis. In determining transference numbers by a modification of the Hittorf method, the content of the electrode compartments can be found from their conductances. Rates of chemical reactions can be followed and the composition of a stream in an industrial flow process can be monitored continuously. Conductivity measurement aids in the manufacture of paper and sugar, in vat dyeing, in following the course of fractional distillation or chemical reaction, in stream pollution studies, in estimating the hardness of water, in soil studies, in detecting the adulteration of milk, in following chromatographic separations, in detecting the extent of disease in plant leaves, and in many other ways.

The end point of a chemical reaction in solution can be determined conductimetrically if there is a characteristic change in conductance at the stoichiometric point. Acid-base titrations in water can be done this way because at the equivalence point speedy H^+ and OH^- ions are few. Even though the salt produced by neutralization is present, the conductance is a minimum when chemically equivalent amounts of acid and base have reacted. In order to minimize dilution effects, the added reagent is concentrated. When a weak acid or base is titrated, a sharp change but not a minimum in conductance is produced at the equivalent point. Precipitation of a slightly soluble compound or any reaction that withdraws ions from solution can be followed in this way. The end point is found graphically.

Measurement of the specific conductance of a saturated solution of a slightly soluble substance permits calculation of its solubility product constant K_{sp}. Such a solution is usually so dilute that its equivalent conductance is almost equal to Λ_0, provided of course that the electrolyte is strong and therefore totally ionized. Then, as in (11.20),

$$N_{\pm} = \left(\frac{1000}{\Lambda_0}\right) L_{sp} \tag{11.44}$$

From $N_{\pm}$ the value of K_{sp} is readily found.

Example 11.9. At 25°C, the specific conductance of a saturated aqueous solution of TlBr is 295.2×10^{-6} mho cm^{-1} [C. R. Johnson and G. A. Hulett, *J. Am. Chem. Soc.*, **57**, 256 (1935)]. The water used had a specific conductance of 0.2×10^{-6} mho cm^{-1}. Calculate the solubility product constant of TlBr and compare with the value calculated from the following standard free energies [F. D. Rossini *et al.*, National Bureau of Standards Circular 500]: $\Delta G_f^\ominus[Tl^+_{(aq)}] = -7.8$ kcal mole^{-1}; $\Delta G_f^\ominus[Br^-_{(aq)}] = -24.6$ kcal mole^{-1}; $\Delta G_f^\ominus[TlBr_{(s)}] = -39.7$ kcal mole^{-1}.

The equivalent conductance Λ_0 of aqueous TlBr at infinite dilution is, by Table 11.6 and (11.27), $\Lambda_0 = 74.7 + 78.4 = 153.1$. The conductance of the water is due to the presence of H^+, OH^-, and impurities; hence, it is necessary to correct the specific conductance of the saturated solution by 0.2×10^{-6} mho cm^{-1}. Then, by (11.44),

$$N_\pm = \frac{1000}{153.1} \times (295.2 - 0.2) \times 10^{-6} = 1.927 \times 10^{-3}$$

Then, since $N_\pm = C_{Tl^+} = C_{Br^-}$,

$$K_{sp} = (1.927 \times 10^{-3})(1.927 \times 10^{-3}) = 3.71 \times 10^{-6}$$

Thermodynamically, as in Section 9.5, for the reaction

$$TlBr_{(s)} \rightleftharpoons Tl^+_{(aq)} + Br^-_{(aq)}$$

$$\Delta G^\ominus = -7.8 - 24.6 - (-39.7) = 7.3 \text{ kcal}$$

But $\Delta G^\ominus = -RT \ln K$; whence

$$\log K_{sp} = -\frac{\Delta G^\ominus}{2.303RT} = -\frac{7300}{2.303 \times 1.987 \times 298.2}$$

$$= -5.35 = 0.65 - 6.00$$

$$K_{sp} = 4.5 \times 10^{-6}$$

The specific conductance of water is a sensitive indication of dissolved ionic impurities. If the ion product of water at 25°C is $K_w = 1.009 \times 10^{-14}$, the concentration of H^+ or OH^- in pure water is $\sqrt{K_w} = N_\pm = 1.004 \times 10^{-7}$ mole liter^{-1}. By (11.27) and Table 11.6, for this dilute solution $\Lambda \approx \Lambda_0 = l_+^0 + l_-^0 = 350 + 198 = 548$. The specific conductance of pure water at 25°C is thus expected to be, by (11.20),

$$L_{sp} = \frac{N_\pm \Lambda}{1000} = \frac{1.004 \times 10^{-7}(548)}{1000} = 0.0550 \times 10^{-6} \text{ mho cm}^{-1}$$

In their classic work of 1894, Kohlrausch and Heydweiller achieved $L_{sp} = 0.062 \times 10^{-6}$ mho cm^{-1} by 36 distillations and use of water-cured silica containers. Slightly higher L_{sp}'s have been attained by others by distillation and ion exchange.

A significantly lower value of $L_{sp} = 0.0589 \times 10^{-6}$ mho cm^{-1} at 25°C has been attained by recirculating water in an electric field perpendicular to the direction of flow. Figure 11.13 is an exploded view of the cell, which contains two membranes, one permeable to anions and one permeable to cations. As water to be purified passes through the central compartment from F to G, the field causes cations to move through membrane D into 0.05 N NH_4OH in the

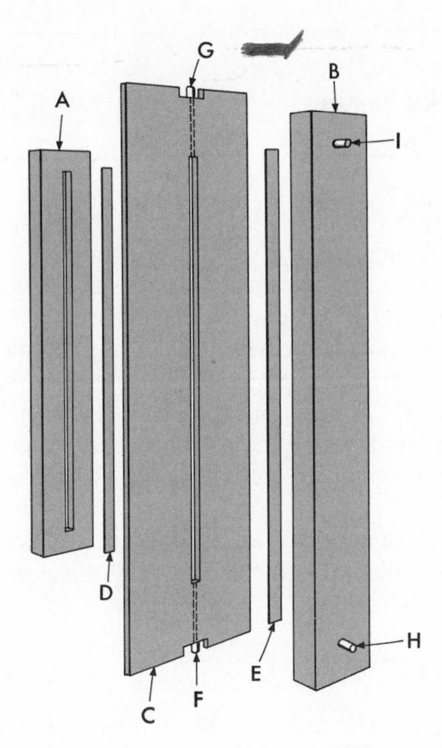

Figure 11.13. Exploded View of Cell for Purifying Water by Electrophoresis†

cathode compartment A. At the same time the field causes anions to move through membrane E into 0.02 N H_2SO_4 in the anode compartment B. The central compartment is 0.6 cm wide, 30.0 cm long, and 0.3 cm from membrane to membrane. Each electrode compartment is continuously purged of solution and gases formed at the electrodes. The main reason for this circulation through the electrode compartments is to keep their solutions homogeneous and thus lower in resistance than the central compartment; this keeps the major part of the EMF and the most intense field in the central compartment from which the ions must be drawn. The conductance of the water reaches its minimum value in less than two hours of recirculation in the field.

Example 11.10. If NaCl is the only impurity in water with $L_{sp} = 0.0589 \times 10^{-6}$ mho cm^{-1}, what is the molarity of the NaCl?

The specific conductance due to NaCl is $(0.0589 - 0.0550) \times 10^{-6} = 39 \times 10^{-10}$ mho cm^{-1}. By (11.20) with $\Lambda_0 = 126.4$ for NaCl

$$N_{\pm} = \frac{1000 \times 39 \times 10^{-10}}{126.4} = 0.309 \times 10^{-7} \text{ moles NaCl liter}^{-1}$$

†W. Haller and H. C. Duecker, *J. Res. Nat. Bur. Stds.* **64A,** 527 [1960]

11.10 DISTRIBUTION OF IONS NEAR A CHARGED SURFACE

Colloidal particles frequently adsorb (and even absorb) ions from their dispersing medium. If this sorption is much stronger than what would be expected from dispersion forces, it is called chemisorption, an interaction that lies energetically in the zone of transition between chemistry and physics. Particles of gold sol chemisorb Cl^- from watery solution, as though interactions that yield complexes like $AuCl_4^-$ were at work. Similarly, amino acids of proteins are sources of sinks of protons, and finely divided silver halide crystals may have an excess of halide or Ag^+ if precipitated in an excess of halide or Ag^+. These chemisorbed species are an integral part of the dispersed phase and are not solvated like ions in solution.

An ion in a solution tends against the urgings of randomness to produce by its electric charge a modicum of local order; the result for an ion of charge $z_i e$ is the Debye-Hückel potential

$$\Phi(r) = \frac{z_i e}{4\pi \epsilon r} \exp\left(-\frac{r}{a}\right) \tag{8.63}$$

The exponential describes the average attenuation of the Coulomb potential because of a diffuse layer of ions with charges of sign opposite to that of the ion at $r = 0$. In the same way, a surface whose potential and charge are determined by chemisorbed ions tends to organize ions in its locale. Colloidal particales are typically so large that their surfaces can be treated as if they were planar. Instead of a radial problem about an ion, the problem is to solve Poisson's equation in the one-dimensional form

$$-\frac{d^2\psi}{dx^2} = \frac{\rho}{\kappa \epsilon_0} = \frac{\rho}{\epsilon} \tag{11.45}$$

where ψ is the electrostatic potential at a distance x from a charged surface. This approach assumes that continuum physics suitably approximates the behavior of individual ions. The charge density $\rho(x)$ is the summation of the charges on the ions; if c_i is the local concentration (ions per cubic meter) of ions of charge $z_i e$, then

$$\rho = \sum_i z_i e c_i \tag{11.46}$$

The necessary compromise of electrical order with bombarding disorder is effected through the Boltzmann distribution thus:

$$c_i = \bar{c}_i \exp\left(-\frac{z_i e \psi}{kT}\right) \tag{11.47}$$

where $\bar{c}_i$ is the average concentration of i throughout the solution.

For a single ionic solute AB with ions of equal charge ($z_+ = -z_- = z$), (11.46) and (11.47) yield

$$\rho = ze\bar{c}\left[\exp\left(\frac{-ze\psi}{kT}\right) - \exp\left(\frac{+ze\psi}{kT}\right)\right]$$

$$\rho = -2ze\bar{c}\sinh\left(\frac{ze\psi}{kT}\right) \tag{11.48}$$

With the dimensionless variables

$$q = \frac{ze\psi}{kT} \tag{11.49}$$

the result of substituting (11.48) into (11.45) is

$$\frac{d^2q}{dx^2} = \frac{2z^2e^2\bar{c}}{\epsilon kT}\sinh q = \left(\frac{1}{a}\right)^2 \sinh q \tag{11.50}$$

The distance a is the Debye length of (8.55).

The problem of finding ψ as a function of x, the distance from the charged surface, can be solved approximately when $q \ll 1$ in the spirit of the Debye-Hückel method. However, for the nonradial problem (11.50) there exists the solution

$$\frac{dq}{dx} = A\sinh\frac{q}{2} + B\cosh\frac{q}{2} \tag{11.51}$$

Taking the second derivative and using the identities $\cosh^2(q/2) + \sinh^2(q/2) = \cosh q$ and $2\sinh(q/2)\cosh(q/2) = \sinh q$ yields

$$\frac{d^2q}{dx^2} = \left(\frac{AB}{2}\right)\cosh q + \left(\frac{A^2+B^2}{4}\right)\sinh q \tag{11.52}$$

which matches (11.50) if $B = 0$ and if

$$\frac{A^2}{4} = \left(\frac{1}{a}\right)^2 \tag{11.53}$$

Equations (11.51) and (11.53) then yield

$$\frac{dq}{dx} = \pm\left(\frac{2}{a}\right)\sinh\left(\frac{q}{2}\right) \tag{11.54}$$

Separation of variables and integration then gives

$$\pm\frac{x}{a} = \int\frac{dq/2}{\sinh(q/2)} = \int \operatorname{csch}\left(\frac{q}{2}\right)d\left(\frac{q}{2}\right)$$

$$= \ln\left[\tanh\left(\frac{q}{4}\right)\right] + \text{const.} \tag{11.55}$$

If the potential is ψ_0 at $x = 0$, then by (11.49) $q_0 = ze\,\psi_0/kT$ and (11.55) becomes

$$\tanh\left(\frac{ze\psi}{4kT}\right) = e^{\pm x/a} \tanh\left(\frac{ze\psi_0}{4kT}\right) \tag{11.56}$$

For small u, it happens that $\tanh u \approx u$. If thermal disorder so dominates electrical order that $ze\,\psi \ll 4kT$, (11.56) becomes

$$\frac{ze\psi}{4kT} = \frac{ze\psi_0}{4kT} e^{\pm x/a} \tag{11.57}$$

By its physical meaning ψ can only decrease as x increases; hence, with a positive, only the lower sign is acceptable and

$$\psi = \psi_0 e^{-x/a} \tag{11.58}$$

which is like (8.63). For any value of $ze\psi/4kT$, (11.56) is

$$\tanh\left(\frac{ze\psi}{4kT}\right) = e^{-x/a} \tanh\left(\frac{ze\psi_0}{4kT}\right) \tag{11.59}$$

Equations (11.58) and (11.59) are the Gouy-Chapman results for the effect ions near a charged surface have in reducing its potential ψ_0 to a value ψ that decreases as the distance x from the charged surface increases.

The charge per unit area $\sigma(x)$ that a particle appears to have at a distance x from the surface is equal in magnitude but opposite in sign to the net charge of the ions from x to $x = \infty$, for at $x = \infty$ the charged particle is so shielded by its ion atmosphere as to be electrically undetectable. Hence,

$$\sigma(x) = -\int_x^\infty \rho(x')\,dx' \tag{11.60}$$

With ρ from (11.45), the apparent surface charge density at x is

$$\begin{aligned}\sigma(x) &= +\int_x^\infty \epsilon \frac{d^2\psi}{dx'^2}\,dx' = \epsilon \int_x^\infty d\left(\frac{d\psi}{dx'}\right) \\ &= \epsilon\left[\left(\frac{d\psi}{dx}\right)_\infty - \frac{d\psi}{dx}\right]\end{aligned} \tag{11.61}$$

But at large x the rate of change of ψ becomes zero and with the aid of (11.49) and (11.54) with the minus sign, (11.61) yields for any positive x

$$\sigma(x) = -\epsilon\frac{d\psi}{dx} = -\frac{\epsilon kT}{ze}\frac{dq}{dx} = \frac{2\epsilon kT}{zea}\sinh\left(\frac{ze\psi}{2kT}\right) \tag{11.62}$$

When thermal disorder prevails over electrical order so that $ze\psi \ll 2kT$, then

$\sinh(ze\psi/2kT) \approx ze\psi/2kT$ and the surface charge density at x is, from (11.62)

$$\sigma(x) = \frac{\epsilon\psi}{a} \tag{11.63}$$

On the other hand, when electrical order dominates, $\sinh(q/2)$ can increase indefinitely except for the reasonable physical bound that $\sigma(x)$ be less than about one singly charged ion per A^2. Hence, with mks units,

$$\sigma(x) = \frac{2\epsilon kT}{zea}\sinh\left(\frac{ze\psi}{2kT}\right) \leqslant \frac{1.6 \times 10^{-19}}{(10^{-10})^2} \approx 16$$

In water at 25°C, $\epsilon = \kappa\epsilon_0 = 78.54\epsilon_0 = 78.54 \times 10^7/4\pi c^2$; since a is often of the order of 10A, it would appear that with $z = 1$

$$16 \geqslant \frac{2 \times 78.54 \times 10^7 \times 1.380 \times 10^{-23} \times 298.2}{4\pi \times (2.998 \times 10^8)^2 1.602 \times 10^{-19} \times 10 \times 10^{-10}} \times \sinh\frac{1.602 \times 10^{-19}\psi}{2(1.380 \times 10^{-23})298.2}$$

$$450 \gtrsim \sinh(20\psi)$$

$$\psi \lesssim 0.34 \text{ volt}$$

Hence, physical considerations alone limit the maximum value of ψ at any x to be of the order of a volt.

Really, ψ seldom exceeds about 0.1 volt; hence, at room T, $e\psi/4kT$ seldom exceeds unity. Figure 11.14 has been drawn for $e\psi_0 = \frac{1}{2}kT$ for 0.001 molar

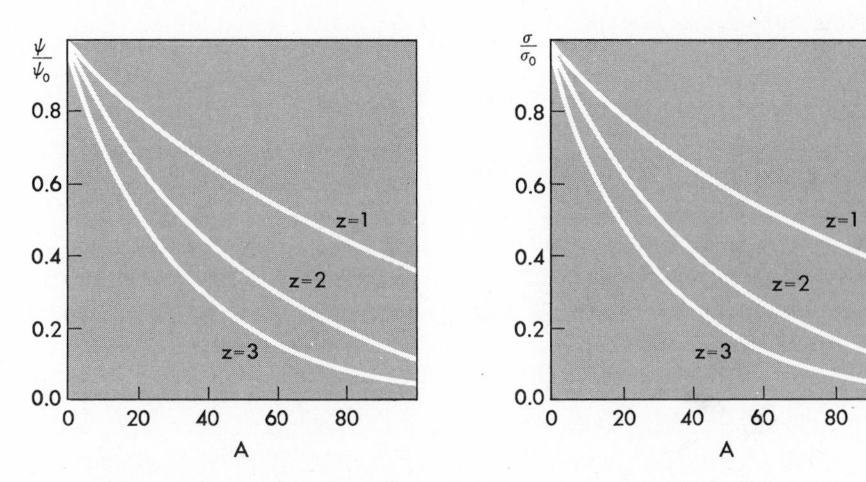

Figure 11.14. Fractional Potential (ψ/ψ_0) and Fractional Surface Charge Density (σ/σ_0) as Functions of Distance From Surface for 0.001 Molar Aqueous Solutions at 25°C

aqueous solutions at 25°C for which $z_{\pm}a = 96.2$A. Equations (11.59) and (11.62) were used to find ψ and σ as fractions of their values ψ_0 and σ_0 at $x = 0$. As Figure 11.14 shows, increasing z (the number of charges per ion) decreases the distance at which ψ or σ falls to a certain fraction of its value at $x = 0$. That is, the higher the charge per ion, the less extended and diffuse is the Gouy-Chapman cloud of ions and the closer to the surface is ψ a certain fraction of ψ_0.

The Gouy-Chapman treatment takes no account of the fact that ions are extended and thus repel each other by volume as well as by charge. In general, ignoring the ions' sizes allows curves like those of Figure 11.14 to rise too steeply at small x. To keep reasonable values of ψ and σ, Stern in 1924 proposed that ψ arbitrarily be made a linear function of x near the surface. At x_S, the linearly decreasing ψ can be matched to the Gouy-Chapman equations with $\psi = \psi_S$. The Stern layer from $x = 0$ to $x = x_S$ consists of ions held rather rigidly in place; they are not subject to thermal disordering as the ions in the more diffuse Gouy-Chapman layer are. Figure 11.15 shows how the introduction of the Stern layer affects the variation of ψ with position for surfaces with positive and negative potential-determining ions. Figure 11.16 shows how ions near such a surface with negative potential-determining ions are expected to be arranged.

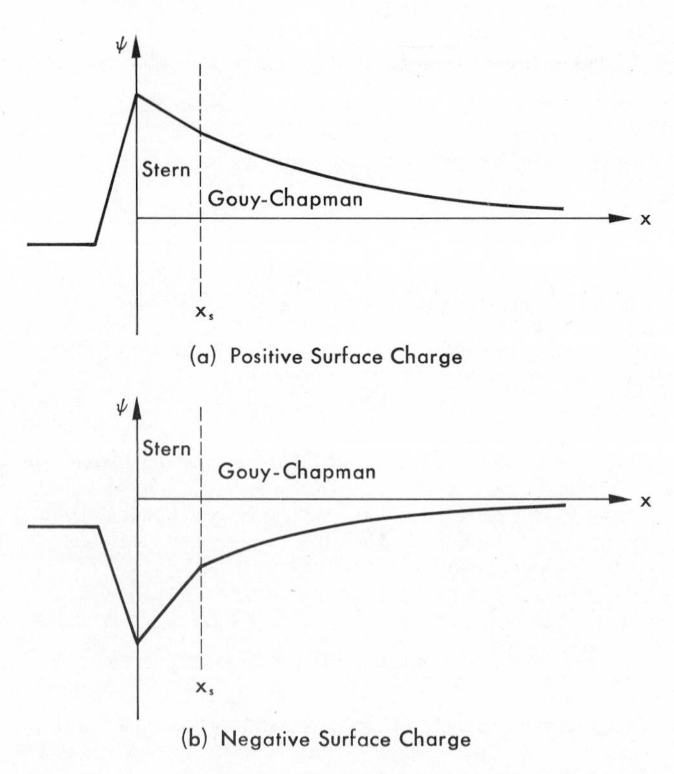

Figure 11.15. The Stern Layer of Ions at a Charged Surface

The main characterisitics of the Stern and Gouy-Chapman layers is that in both the absolute value of ψ always decreases toward zero. The sign of ψ_0 and σ is fixed by the sign of the chemisorbed ions in the potential-determining layer.

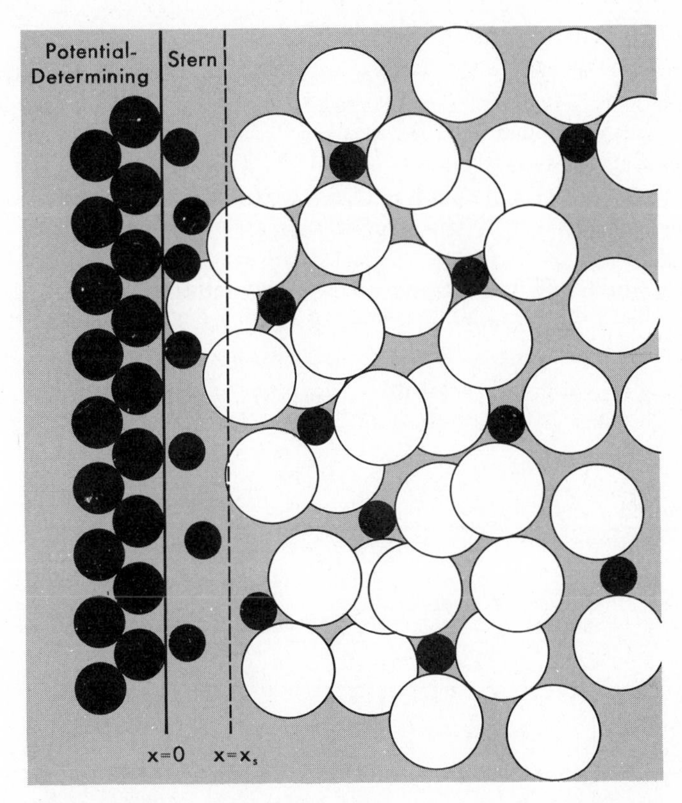

Figure 11.16. Typical Arrangement of Ions Near a Negatively Charged Surface. (Small black ions are positively charged.)

Example 11.11. According to the Gouy-Chapman model, what value of ψ_0 is required of a colloidal particle at 300°K if it is to absorb from a one-molar aqueous solution a layer of negative ions with the same concentration as that of pure crystalline AB? Assume that AB has doubly charged ions, a formula weight of 100, and a crystal density of 5.0 g cm^{-3}.

In crystals of AB the number of B ions per m^3 is

$$c_B = \frac{5.0 \times 10^6}{100} \times 6.02 \times 10^{23} = 300 \times 10^{26}\ \text{m}^{-3}$$

However, in 1.0 M AB, the average number of B ions per m^3 is

$$\bar{c}_B = 1.0 \times 10^3 \times 6.02 \times 10^{23} = 6.0 \times 10^{26}\ \text{m}^{-3}$$

By (11.47) with $z_- = -2$ for the B ions,

$$-\frac{-2e\psi_0}{kT} = \ln \frac{c_B}{\bar{c}_B} = \ln \frac{300 \times 10^{26}}{6.0 \times 10^{26}} = \ln 50 = 3.91$$

$$\psi_0 = \frac{kT \ln 50}{2e} = \frac{1.38 \times 10^{-23} \times 300 \times 3.91}{2 \times 1.602 \times 10^{-19}} = +0.0506 \text{ volt}$$

Example 11.12. If a Stern layer 10.0A thick exists on the colloidal particles of Example 11.11, what is the electrostatic potential at the outside of the Stern layer if the Gouy-Chapman layer is uncharged?

Since

$$-\frac{z_- e\psi_0}{kT} = \frac{2 \times 1.602 \times 10^{-19} \times 0.0506}{1.380 \times 10^{-23} \times 300} = \ln 50 = 3.91$$

differs widely from zero, it is necessary to use (11.59) rather than (11.58). Hence, with $x_S = 10.0 \times 10^{-10}$m and $a = 48.2 \times 10^{-10}$ m from (11.50) or (8.56), it follows from (11.59) that

$$\tanh\left(\frac{z_- e\psi_S}{4kT}\right) = \exp\left(-\frac{10.0}{48.2}\right) \tanh\left(\frac{-3.91}{4}\right) = 0.813\,(-0.752)$$

$$\frac{z_- e\psi_S}{4kT} = -0.710$$

$$\psi_S = \frac{4 \times 1.380 \times 10^{-23} \times 300(-0.710)}{(-2) \times 1.602 \times 10^{-19}} = 0.0367 \text{ volt}$$

11.11 PROPERTIES OF COLLOIDS

Colloids possess their characteristic nature because their particles lie between molecular size (ca. 10A) and the wavelength of light (ca. 5000A). Table 11.7 summarizes the ordinary properties of the two broad classes of colloid. Lyophilic (solvent-loving) colloids have ill-defined surfaces and sizes, and yet each particle generally acts as a unit because the bonds that unite the particle are much stronger than those that exist between it and the dispersing medium. Such particles tend to be impregnated with dispersing medium and would be truly soluble if the particles were of molecular size. Biological systems like milk, glue, and gelatin offer many examples of lyophilic colloids. Lyophobic (solvent-hating) colloids, on the other hand, have well defined surfaces and tend to be chemically unlike the dispersing medium in that particles of molecular size would usually be insoluble. Lyophobic colloids can be prepared by subdivision or by precipitation. For example, dropping a solution of $FeCl_3$ into a large amount of boiling water yields a brilliant red colloid of iron hydroxide through hydrolysis. An electric discharge (Bredig arc) under water may yield colloidal particles of metal torn from the electrodes.

Table 11.7. Typical Behavior of Colloids.

Lyophilic Colloids	Property	Lyophobic Colloids
Often not well defined.	Particle size.	About 50 A to about 2000 A.
Particles distinguished as individuals only with difficulty if at all.	Scattering of light (Tyndall effect).	Particles readily seen as individuals in ultramicroscope.
Direction of migration easily changed; particles may have charges of both signs or no charge at all.	Behavior in electric field.	All particles migrate in same direction and have same kind of charge.
Almost nil.	Colligative properties.	Almost nil.
Much greater than dispersing phase.	Viscosity.	Almost same as dispersing phase.
Small amounts have little effect; much may cause dispersed phase to "salt out."	Action of electrolytes.	Small amounts cause precipitation, especially when ion of high valence has charge of sign opposite to dispersed phase.
High molecular weight species: proteins; gels; glue; biological systems.	Typical examples.	Aqueous dispersions of slightly soluble species; aerosols; airborne dust.

The most obvious optical property of colloids is the scattering of light (*Tyndall effect*). An intense beam of light through water containing a little milk clearly shows this effect, which depends on a difference in index of refraction of the two phases. Scattered light is polarized and its intensity at a particular angle relative to the primary beam is inversely proportional to the fourth power of the wavelength. As a result, blue light is more intensely scattered than is red; the sky is blue because sunlight scattered by air molecules is more blue than red. Similarly, illuminated smoke, when viewed against a dark background, looks bluish, but when viewed against a source of light, it may look reddish because light from the blue range of wavelengths in the source has been preferentially scattered out of the line of sight. For this last reason, sunsets are often reddish because sunlight coming from behind the air and its dust is preferentially depleted of blue by scattering.

Accurate measurements of intensity of scattered light as a function of angle can give information about the size and general shape of colloidal particles. It is also possible to follow the path of a particular colloidal particle too small to be seen directly by noting the position from which it scatters light. The ultramicroscope accomplishes this by being fitted with a dark field that prevents the direct intense beam from passing through the lenses. The viewer sees only light scattered by each colloidal particle. Thus it is possible to follow the details of the *Brownian motion*, namely the zigzag paths of colloidal particles under bombardment by molecules of their dispersing medium.

The great surface area of a small amount of matter in the colloidal state quite naturally leads to chemisorption of any ions that may be present and the formation of a Stern-Gouy-Chapman ion atmosphere about each particle. The value of the electrostatic potential ψ and apparent surface charge density σ decreases with increasing distance from the surface, as described in the preceding section. The like charges that reside on the particles cause them to repel each other; hence, coalescence and flocculation (precipitation) are slowed. This natural stability of colloids in the presence of a meager supply of ions can, however, be effectively destroyed by an abundance of ions, especially if they are highly charged and of sign opposite to ψ and σ. For, as in Figure 11.14, ψ and σ are brought low within a short distance by highly charged ions. It is well known (Schulze-Hardy rule) that to flocculate a given positively (negatively) charged sol in a given time, the volumes of equally concentrated ionic solutions decrease by a factor of 100 as the number of negative (positive) charges per ion goes from unity to two. Thus, one drop of 1 M Na_2SO_4 is about as effective in flocculating the positive iron oxide sol as 100 drops of 1 M NaCl. A similar factor of 100 holds on going from doubly charged to triply charged ions. What is important is the effect the oppositely charged ion has on the range of the diffuse ion atmosphere. It is also well known (Hofmeister) that for ions of a given charge acting on a certain colloid, the amount needed for precipitation increases in proportion to the ionic radius. Big ions are too dilute electrically to act effectively on the diffuse layer.

11.12 ELECTROKINETIC POTENTIAL

A colloidal particle acts as though it has a charge $\sigma(x)$ per unit area at a distance x from its surface. If the external electric field has strength $\mathbf{E}$ at the distance x_E, the accelerating electric force on this charge is $F_E = \sigma\mathbf{E}$. The colloidal particle thus moves faster and faster in the field until it reaches a terminal velocity at which the electric force per unit area, $\sigma\mathbf{E}$, is exactly counterbalanced by a retarding viscous force. Per unit area, by (1.50), the viscous force is

$$F_\eta = \eta \frac{dv}{dx} \tag{11.64}$$

The shear surface of the particle at $x = x_E$ is chosen as the distance beyond which the dispersing medium can be considered effectively to move. That is, if $x > x_E$ there is relative motion, whereas if $x < x_E$ there is no motion. If F_η does not depend on x because the diffuse ion atmosphere is considered to be stationary for $x < x_E$, then (11.64) yields

$$F_\eta \int_0^{x_E} dx = \eta \int_0^{v_E} dv$$

$$F_\eta x_E = \eta v_E \tag{11.65}$$

where v_E is the velocity of the dispersing medium relative to the particle and where x_E is the distance from the surface at which this velocity exceeds zero. At the terminal velocity v_E the particle is not otherwise accelerated so that $F_E = F_\eta$, or

$$\sigma E = \eta \frac{v_E}{x_E} \tag{11.66}$$

If (11.63) holds at x_E, it follows that

$$\sigma = \frac{\epsilon \zeta}{x_E} \tag{11.67}$$

Solution of (11.66) and (11.67) for σ and substitution of u for the mobility $v_E/\mathbf{E}$ then yields

$$\zeta = \frac{\eta u}{\epsilon} \tag{11.68}$$

The electrokinetic (or zeta-) potential ζ is the value of ψ at the distance x_E where shearing of the diffuse ion atmosphere can be said to occur. Usually x_E exceeds x_S, the thickness of the Stern layer, but the difference is small.

Water has a dielectric constant of 78.54 and a viscosity of 0.000894 newton sec m^{-2} at 25°C; in (11.68) these yield

$$\zeta = \frac{(8.94 \times 10^{-4})u}{78.54[10^7/4\pi(2.998 \times 10^8)^2]} = 1.287 \times 10^6\, u \tag{11.69}$$

If the mobilities are given in the cgs units cm^2 volt^{-1} sec^{-1}, then (11.69) becomes

$$\zeta = 128.7u \qquad \text{(cgs)} \tag{11.70}$$

The magnitude and effects of the electrokinetic potential are observable in four ways: (1) by *electroosmosis*, in which a potential difference, applied to two parts of a liquid separated by a porous membrane or set of capillaries, causes a flow of liquid through the membrane because of the zeta-potential developed between membrane and liquid; (2) by the *streaming potential*, in which a potential difference between parts of a liquid on two sides of a membrane is caused by forced flow through that membrane (reverse of electroosmosis); (3) by the *Dorn effect*, in which particles falling through a fluid are stripped of part of their diffuse layer of ions by viscous forces and thus acquire a potential different from that of the surrounding fluid; and (4) by *electrophoresis*, in which colloidal particles migrate in an external electric field because they have a potential and charge different from the surrounding fluid (reverse of Dorn effect).

Example 11.13. As viewed in an ultramicroscope, particles of a silica-alumina cracking catalyst suspended in water traversed a standard distance of 0.33 mm between cross hairs toward the positive electrode in 38.2 sec in a potential gradient of 3.2 volts cm^{-1}. If the viscosity of the suspension was 0.0090 dyne sec cm^{-2} and if its dielectric constant was 78, what was the electrokinetic potential of the catalyst particles in water?

Since the velocity of the particles is $v = 0.033 \text{ cm}/38.2 \text{ sec} = 8.6 \times 10^{-4}$ cm sec^{-1} by (11.34)

$$u = \frac{8.6 \times 10^{-4}}{3.2} = 2.7 \times 10^{-4} \text{ cm}^2 \text{ volt}^{-1} \text{ sec}^{-1}$$

Then, by (11.70) with account of the direction of migration,

$$\zeta = 128.7 \times 2.7 \times 10^{-4} = -0.035 \text{ volt}$$

The negative sign on ζ indicates that the particles migrated toward the anode and had a net negative charge.

11.13 ELECTROPHORESIS

It is possible to purify and characterize pure substances and to characterize and separate complex mixtures by *electrophoresis,* the process by which dissolved or suspended colloidal particles move under the influence of an electric field. First observed by accident in 1807 by Reuss, the phenomenon became of analytical importance only in 1937 when Tiselius succeeded in building an apparatus that simplified the precise separation of colloids like proteins and other biological species.

The standard free-liquid zone electrophoresis apparatus contains an optical cell made in three pieces so that two sharp boundaries can be generated between a buffer and a buffered colloidal dispersion. By means of complex optical devices, the movements of variously charged particles are followed under the action of a potential difference by recording photographically the rate of change of the index of refraction of the solution in the direction of migration. Difficulties with stirring due to mechanical vibration and temperature gradients and the inevitable problem of diffusion, which may be very rapid for small species and thus destroy any boundary, limit the effectiveness of the Tiselius type of apparatus. It is now common to separate species by electrophoresis with the liquid somehow supported in the pores of paper or in packed columns containing gels, glass powder, and like material. The motion of a charged particle is then the net result of adsorption on the support and electrophoresis, the term *electrochromatography* sometimes being used. Instead of separating liquid regions, electrophoresis through a packed column may easily lead to well defined zones separable by removing the packing layer by layer. In some separations gravitation causes the liquid to flow downward in a piece of paper as a horizontal electric field causes horizontal motion against the forces of viscosity and adsorption. Even continuous operation is thus possible by collecting fractions at various points at the bottom of the vertical adsorber. Figure 11.17 shows a typical arrangement of this kind.

Complex organic molecules like proteins migrate because they contain ionic groups: ionized acid groups or protonated amine groups. A protein at its

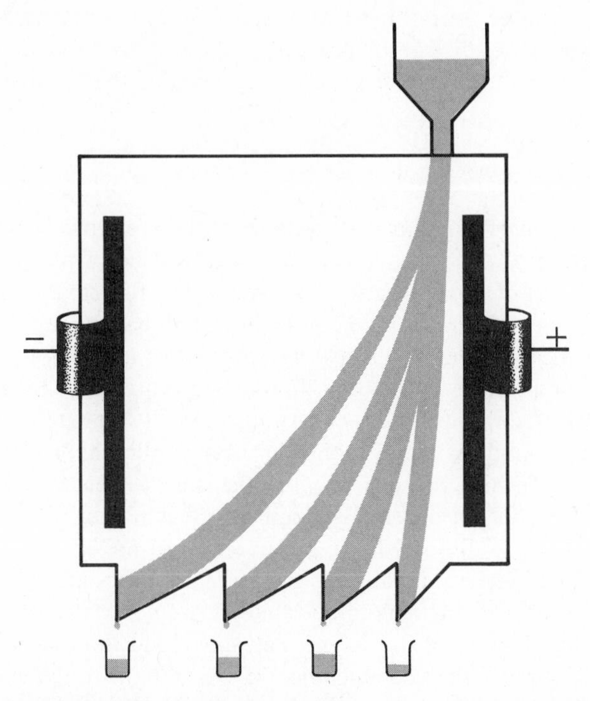

Figure 11.17. Schematic Diagram of an Electrochromatographic Apparatus

isoelectric point does not migrate because its net charge from acidic and basic sites that have lost or gained protons is zero. This acid concentration is an important characteristic of a protein.

11.14 SUMMARY

This chapter can be divided into two main parts: migration of ions and migration of colloidal particles. After Faraday's law of counting electrons, the first part on ions is largely a straightforward application of Ohm's law to various definitions (e.g., ion constituent, equivalent conductance, and mobility). Although transference is sometimes a bit confusing in the detail required to get $t_{\pm}$ from observed concentrations, nevertheless the idea that two kinds of charge-carrier with different mobilities cooperate in carrying charge to and from the electrodes is not mysterious. The confusion that may at first exist is usually easily dispelled by noting: (1) that the size of the anode and cathode compartments is not important if they are large enough to keep the central compartment unchanged; and (2) that motion relative to the solvent is found by basing the calculation on a fixed amount of water. Then everything about transference is as transparent as the many obvious corollaries of Kohlrausch's law of nearly independent migration of ions. In this half of the chapter the only key equation that is not easily derived is

$$\alpha \mathscr{F}(u_+ + u_-) = \Lambda \tag{11.35}$$

The chapter's second part explains why colloids have an electric potential and move in an electric field. The theory is a fortunate collage of physics (as though matter on this level of dimension were a continuum), Boltzmann statistics, and individual particles of various kinds. Somehow man has managed here to insist on talking in near-riddles about average properties and has left the events of a single ion or particle to the easy flow of natural events. In many regards, the mathematical developments concerning colloids are useful only as an aid in classifying the kinds of events that occur near a colloidal particle.

In solvents that can furnish protons, the proton behaves remarkably. It has in water a mobility about an order of magnitude greater than other ions (except OH^-). It is to such solutions what the electron is to metals, but on a somewhat subdued level of activity because its mass is 1840 times greater than the electron's. It is, for example, amazing to find that a proton in water has only about one percent of the mobility of one in ice. Yet, on second thought, this is expected, for it is well known that conductance of electrons through metals declines as T rises and disorder interrupts the freedom of motion allowed by regularity.

PROBLEMS

1. How many faradays are transferred when a potential difference of 3.21 volts is applied across a resistance of 1052 ohms for two hours?
Answer: 2.28×10^{-4}.

2. In three electrolytic cells connected in series, 0.473 g metallic Cu was deposited in the first cell in exactly 10 hours of operation at constant current. If the first cell contained excess aqueous $CuSO_4$:
(a) How much metallic Fe was deposited in the second cell if the only change there was $3e^- + Fe^{+++} \longrightarrow Fe$?
(b) How much metallic Tl was deposited from a solution containing excess Tl^+?
(c) What steady current flowed?
Answer: (a) 0.277 g Fe; (b) 3.05 g Tl; (c) 39.9 mamp.

3. With due regard for significant figures, determine the value of Avogadro's number from the Faraday constant and the charge of the electron in Appendix A.

4. In words and in terms of a diagram like Figure 11.2, explain why Fe^{2+}, a positive ion, may approach the anode during electrolysis when the anode reaction is $Fe^{2+} \longrightarrow Fe^{3+} + e^{-}$.

5. How many grams of KI will be in 50.00 g of the solution near the cathode if 85.3 coulombs are passed through the solution by means of electrodes reversible with respect to iodide ions? The initial molality of KI was 0.1047.
Answer: 0.925 g KI.

6. Before electrolysis, the cathode chamber of an electrolytic cell had 0.1473 mg-equivalent of $CuSO_4$ per g H_2O and after electrolysis by 1.372×10^{-3} faradays it contained 0.1183 mg-equivalent $CuSO_4$ per g H_2O. If the cathode chamber held 30.0 g H_2O before and after electrolysis, what is the transference number of cupric ion?
Answer: 0.366.

7. Calculate the final concentration of cupric ion in the anode chamber, which holds 28.0 g H_2O, for the experiment of the previous problem if:
(a) The anode was inert.
(b) The anode was copper.
Answer: (a) 0.0647 molal; (b) 0.0892 molal.

8. In a certain moving boundary experiment with 0.132 *N* HCl followed by $CdCl_2$ solution, the boundary indicated by an indicator advanced at a rate of 2.09 cm hour^{-1} with a current of 1.375 milliamperes. If the cross-sectional area of the tube was 0.153 cm^2, what was the observed transference number of H^+ in HCl?
Answer: 0.823.

9. A solution with a specific conductance of 0.0426 mho cm^{-1} had a resistance of 102.6 ohms in a certain conductance cell. A second solution in the same cell had a resistance of 82.6 ohms. What was its specific conductance?
Answer: 0.0529 mho cm^{-1}.

10. Graphically find Λ_0 of LiCl at 25°C from these data [K. A. Krieger and M. Kilpatrick, *J. Am. Chem. Soc.*, **59**, 1878 (1937)] and compare with the sum of ionic conductances:

$N_{\pm} \times 10^4$	0.52613	1.1271	1.8787	3.4888	6.5987	12.694	21.683	30.191	37.533
Λ	114.40	114.02	113.79	113.44	112.73	111.93	111.11	110.58	110.05

Answer: 114.97.

11. What speed is attained by Ag^+ in aqueous solution at 25°C in a field of 200 volts per cm?
Answer: 0.128 cm sec^{-1}.

12. At 18°C the equivalent conductances of some aqueous solutions are:

Solute	NaOH	NaCl	NH_4OH	NH_4Cl
0.00200 *N*	204.5	105.6	20.6	126.2
0.01000 *N*	203.4	102.0	9.6	122.1

If the transference number of Na^+ in very dilute NaCl is 0.397, calculate
(a) the equivalent ionic conductance of Cl^- at infinite dilution;

(b) the equivalent conductance of NH_4OH at infinite dilution;
(c) the ionization constant of NH_4OH ($NH_4OH = NH_4^+ + OH^-$);
(d) the mobility of NH_4^+ in 0.0100 N NH_4Cl.
Answer: (a) 65.4; (b) 226.4; (c) 1.82×10^{-5}; (d) 6.64×10^{-4} cm² v⁻¹ sec⁻¹.

13. At 25°C, a saturated solution of TlI in water has a specific conductivity of 36.6 $\times 10^{-6}$ mho cm⁻¹ [C. R. Johnson and G. A. Hulett, *J. Am. Chem. Soc.*, **57**, 256 (1935)] if the pure water used has a specific conductivity of 0.3×10^{-6} mho cm⁻¹. What is K_{sp} for TlI?
Answer: 5.74×10^{-8}.

14. From the free energies of formation of H^+ and OH^-, calculate the specific conductivity of water at 25°C. Then calculate the ion product of water at 37°C.
Answer: 0.552×10^{-7} mho cm⁻¹; 2.42×10^{-14}.

15. What is the charge density on the surface of a colloid with $\psi_0 = -0.050$ volt at 300°K in 0.0010 molar aqueous NaCl?
Answer: 0.00420 coul m⁻²

16. If very large ions of radius r move at a speed v through a solution like visible glass beads or other large spherical objects, then by Stokes's law the retarding force due to the solution viscosity η is $6\pi\eta rv$. When the force of this viscous deceleration equals the force of the electric field, show that
(a) $\Lambda\eta$ is a constant characteristic of the solute (Walden's rule);
(b) $l_{\pm}^{0}\eta$ is a constant of the ion.

---

17. What volume of H_2 at 25°C at 1.000 atm and how many tons of liquid chlorine are expected from ten tons NaCl if electrolysis is performed with 1000 faradays charge?
Answer: 12,230 l; 0.0391 tons.

18. How much Cu was plated out of a solution of $NaCu(CN)_2$ if 0.422 g Ag was deposited from $AgNO_3$ in a coulometer in series with the $NaCu(CN)_2$ cell?
Answer: 0.249 g Cu.

19. At 32°C, 0.0500 molal H_2SO_4 was electrolyzed by a current of 10.0 milliamperes for 1000 sec. What volume of dry H_2 was released at 32°C at 0.980 atm and what was the H^+ concentration of the cathode chamber if it held 40.0 g of solution?
Answer: 1.324 ml; 0.0994 molal.

20. During electrolysis of 0.0514 molal aqueous $AgNO_3$ between silver electrodes, 69.3 coulombs charge was carried by the solute ions. If the solution from the anode weighed 28.64 g after electrolysis and contained 1.839 mg-equivalents Ag, what was the transference number of Ag^+?
Answer: 0.467.

21. What distance will the boundary between 0.10 $N_{\pm}$ KBr and a following solution of $CdBr_2$ move in a moving-boundary experiment determining transference numbers at 25°C if a current of 2.00 milliamperes flows 843 sec through a tube of cross section 0.1372 cm²?
Answer: 0.616 cm.

22. When 0.1000 demal KCl solution at 18°C is placed in a certain conductivity cell, its resistance is 926 ohms.
(a) If the electrodes are of equal area and 5.00 cm apart, what is the area of one electrode?
(b) What resistance is expected of a solution with $L_{sp} = 0.00862$ mho cm⁻¹ in this same cell?

Answer: (a) 0.484 cm^2; (b) 1200 ohms.

23. At 25°C, the equivalent conductivities of solutions of $MgSO_4$ depend upon normality as follows (*International Critical Tables of Numerical Data, Physics, Chemistry, and Technology*, National Academy of Sciences–National Research Council, Washington, D.C., 1926–1933, **VI**, p. 234):

$N_\pm$	0.0005	0.001	0.002	0.005	0.010	0.020
Λ	123.2	117.6	110.9	98.8	88.9	79.0

What is the equivalent conductance of magnesium ion at infinite dilution?
Answer: 55.

24. The equivalent conductance of 0.03 N trichloroacetic acid is 346 at 25°C and is 387 at infinite dilution at 25°C (*International Critical Tables of Numerical Data, Physics, Chemistry, and Technology*, National Academy of Sciences–National Research Council, Washington, D.C., 1926–1933, **VI**, p. 261). What is the ionization constant of this acid?
Answer: 0.23.

25. If $BaSO_4$ is fully ionized in water at 25°C, if its saturated solution is dilute enough to make mean activity coefficients unity, find the solubility product constant of $BaSO_4$ from the fact that at 25°C its saturated solution has a specific conductance (corrected for solvent conductance) of 2943 nanomho cm^{-1} [D. R. Rosseinsky, *Trans. Faraday Soc.* **54**, 116 (1958)].
Answer: 1.05×10^{-10}.

26. If (11.58) holds, in order to cause the electrostatic potential of a colloidal particle to be halved for every additional 100A from its surface, what concentration in water at 25°C is needed when the solute is NaCl? When it is $MgSO_4$?
Answer: 0.000891 molar NaCl; 0.000223 molar $MgSO_4$.

27. At 25°C a colloidal particle in 0.001 molar NaCl has an electrostatic potential of +0.0400 volt and a Stern layer that is 10.0A thick. If the shear layer lies 20.0A from the surface of the colloid,
(a) what is the Gouy-Chapman value of ψ_0?
(b) what is the value of the Stern potential ψ_S?
(c) what is the electric field strength in the Stern layer if $\psi_0 = 0.0480$ volt?
Answer: (a) 0.0506 v; (b) 0.0450 v; (c) 3.0×10^6 vm^{-1}.

28. Explain the effect, if any, of a horizontal electric field upon the motion of glass beads falling through water.
Answer: Beads negatively charged through Dorn effect; they do not fall vertically.

29. Predict the flow of water caused by electroosmosis if a potential difference of 50 volts exists between the ends of a glass capillary tube that is 1.29 cm long and 0.083 cm in diameter. The electrokinetic potential of water and glass is −0.05 volt and for H_2O $\kappa = 80$ and $\eta = 0.010$ dyne sec cm^{-2}.
Answer: 0.0137 cm sec^{-1}; 74.2×10^{-6} ml sec^{-1}.

---

30. Electrolysis in two cells in series yielded 3.55 g Ag from $AgNO_3$ in one cell and 0.741 g Fe in the other. What fraction of the metallic iron was ferrous at the start of the electrolysis?
Answer: 0.517.

31. The freezing point of 0.500 molal $CdCl_2$ is −1.48°C. The equivalent conductivities of aqueous $CdCl_2$ depend upon normality thus (*International Critical Tables*

of Numerical Data, Physics, Chemistry, and Technology, National Academy of Sciences–National Research Council, Washington, D. C., 1926–1933, **VI,** p. 232) at 0°C:

$N_{\pm}$	0.001	0.002	0.005	0.010	0.020
Λ	64.1	60.4	54.9	50.3	45.1
$N_{\pm}$	0.050	0.070	0.100	0.200	0.500
Λ	37.5	34.8	31.8	25.9	17.9

Calculate the degree of ionization of 0.5 N $CdCl_2$ by two methods and suggest reasons for any difference noted.
Answer: 0.30 (f.p.); 0.25 (Λ).

32. At 25°C the specific conductivity of a saturated aqueous solution of $CaSO_4$ is 2211.5×10^{-6} mho cm^{-1} when water with $L_{sp} = 0.6 \times 10^{-6}$ mho cm^{-1} is used [W. D. Harkins and H. M. Paine, *J. Am. Chem. Soc.*, **41,** 1155 (1919)]. What is K_{sp} for $CaSO_4$ if the equivalent conductivities of $CaSO_4$ solutions at 25°C are:

$N_{\pm} \times 10^3$	0.099955	0.19955	0.49795	0.9959
Λ	136.63	132.88	127.38	121.57

Answer: 3.90×10^{-6}.

33. What is the most concentrated solution of NaCl that can be in contact with a colloidal particle with a Stern potential of 0.100 volt if the Stern layer is 10A thick at 300°K?
Answer: 0.0078 molar.

34. When the weak monobasic acid HA at a concentration C (moles liter^{-1}) has a fraction α in the form of ions, the ionization constant is $K_i = \alpha^2 C/(1 - \alpha)$. By eliminating α with the relation $\Lambda = \alpha\Lambda_0$, show how some function of Λ and C can be made a linear function of Λ^{-1}. With this approach, evaluate K_i and Λ_0 of n-butyric acid at 25°C from these data [D. Belcher, *J. Am. Chem. Soc.* **60,** 2744 (1938)]:

$C \times 10^3$		Λ	
0.029576	0.43277	193.29	65.335
0.055746	0.78715	154.28	49.671
0.082109	0.83817	132.99	48.242
0.10606	0.93748	120.01	45.846
0.29695	1.0096	77.368	44.319
0.33908	1.5818	72.904	35.848

Answer: Plot ΛC versus Λ^{-1} since $\Lambda C = (\Lambda_0^2 K_i)\Lambda^{-1} - (K_i\Lambda_0)$; $K_i = 1.56 \times 10^{-5}$; $\Lambda_0 = 379$.

12

ELECTROCHEMICAL CELLS

12.1 INTRODUCTION

A difference in electrostatic potential exists in a system when certain charged particles do not move freely throughout the system in the time interval of observations. If this time interval were lengthened, more processes would presumably seem to reach thermodynamic equilibrium; among them might be the transfer of charged particles through whatever shield or barrier exists until a uniform distribution of charge or only neutral species resulted. The ubiquitous electron is easily observed by metallic probes and is commonly considered to be the charged particle that is sometimes spatially inhibited. However, other charged particles can be considered. In fact, specific chemical forces between ions and the surface of a colloidal particle have already been shown in the preceding chapter to cause the electrokinetic potential and other electrostatic phenomena. Rapid changes in the permeability of biological membranes to K^+ and Na^+ likewise produce potential differences; an electrocardiogram is such a record of potential difference as a function of time.

Just as a restraint on thorough mixing of charged particles may lead to a difference of electrostatic potential from time to time and place to place, a difference in electrostatic potential conversely may lead to migration and separation of charged particles, as in electrophoresis, and even to chemical transformations, as in electrolysis. An electric potential influences and is influenced by the state of chemical equilibrium.

The gravitational potential, however, is a potential that does not influence the state of chemical equilibrium. As an open system containing various components i of formula weight M_i undergoes various thermodynamic changes and an increase in gravitational potential from $\chi_i^{(1)}$ to $\chi_i^{(2)}$, the gravitational work done on the system is

$$dw_G = \sum_i (\chi_i^{(2)} - \chi_i^{(1)}) M_i dn_i \tag{12.1}$$

and the increase in the energy of the system is

$$\begin{aligned} dE &= TdS - PdV + \sum_i \mu_i \, dn_i + \sum_i (\chi_i^{(2)} - \chi_i^{(1)}) M_i \, dn_i \\ &= TdS - PdV + \sum_i (\mu_i + \chi_i M_i) \, dn_i \end{aligned} \tag{12.2}$$

where χ_i is the gravitational potential of the final state relative to the zero reference value $\chi_i^{(1)}$. The value of χ_i, at least for small amounts of matter near the huge bulk of the earth, is independent of n_i. The symbol μ_i represents the chemical potential of i in the absence of gravity or when dw_G is negligible because $\chi_i^{(2)} = \chi_i^{(1)}$, as it is in a system at one elevation. The only true and observable chemical potential however, is

$$\left(\frac{\partial E}{\partial n_i}\right)_{S,V,n_j} = \boldsymbol{\mu}_i = \mu_i + \chi_i M_i \tag{12.3}$$

Near the surface of the earth, where the acceleration of gravity is g, $\chi_i = +gz_i$ if z_i increases with altitude. Any inertial acceleration, as in a sudden stop or in a centrifuge, has a chemical potential like (12.3) with χ_i of an appropriate form. Equations like (12.3) are to be derived in this chapter for the chemical potentials of charged particles in electrostatic potentials, while differences as well as similarities in the effects of gravitational and electric fields on chemical change are to be noted.

The usual transformations of (12.2) yield

$$dG = -SdT + VdP + \sum_i \boldsymbol{\mu}_i \, dn_i \tag{12.4}$$

where $\boldsymbol{\mu}_i$ is given by (12.3). Moreover, the usual arguments for the conditions of thermodynamic equilibrium yield, as in (6.57), common values of T, P, and $\boldsymbol{\mu}_i$ in all phases. A chemical change $a\text{A} + b\text{B} \longrightarrow d\text{D} + e\text{E}$, which in standard form is

$$0 = \sum_i \nu_i \boldsymbol{\Omega}_i \tag{12.5}$$

reaches equilibrium when $a\boldsymbol{\mu}_A + b\boldsymbol{\mu}_B = d\boldsymbol{\mu}_D + e\boldsymbol{\mu}_E$, that is, when

$$0 = \sum_i \nu_i \boldsymbol{\mu}_i \tag{12.6}$$

Since there is no way to escape gravity by a nonconducting shield or by some kind of neutralization, χ_i has the common value χ for all species i in a system at a common gravitational level, and (12.6) yields at equilibrium

$$0 = \sum_i \nu_i \mu_i^\ominus + RT \sum_i \ln f_i^{\nu_i} + \chi \sum_i \nu_i M_i \tag{12.7}$$

However, if mass is conserved in (12.5) so that $0 = \sum_i \nu_i M_i$, then (12.7) becomes the familiar equation

$$0 = \Delta G^\ominus + RT \ln K_e \tag{9.14}$$

That is, K_e and the state of chemical equilibrium are not influenced by χ when all parts of the system are at the same gravitational potential and when mass is conserved. (The same conclusion is reached through relativistic mechanics; the value of K_e is independent of position in a gravitational field provided the pertinent chemical measurements are made by a local observer at rest with respect to the chemically reacting system.)

12.2 MEASUREMENT OF POTENTIAL DIFFERENCE

Any measurement of the state of a system involves contact with the system from the surroundings, and this demands an exchange of energy. For example, the temperature of a body is measured by inserting a thermometer that can absorb heat from the system. The heat absorbed by a mercury thermometer causes the mercury to expand into the stem, and the extent of expansion is a measure of the temperature finally achieved by system and thermometer. A large mercury thermometer would absorb more heat per degree rise in the temperature of the thermometer than a tiny single-junction thermocouple, which in turn would disturb the system more than reading its temperature with an optical pyrometer. The measured temperature differs from the initial temperature of the system because of the disturbance. The measurement itself causes an uncertainty in temperature and a lower limit of precision.

The ideal method of measurement involves a null measurement. In the limit, the difference in the property of the test body and that of the system approaches zero. Thus, a temperature measurement even with a large mercury thermometer could be made quite accurate if the temperature of the thermometer were adjusted to be almost equal to that of the system before its insertion into the system.

Potential difference is readily measured by a null method. The circuit is shown in Figure 12.1 without refinements peculiar to particular instruments. A working cell W establishes a potential difference across resistors R and P. With the double switch to the left, the resistance of R is varied until the scale on

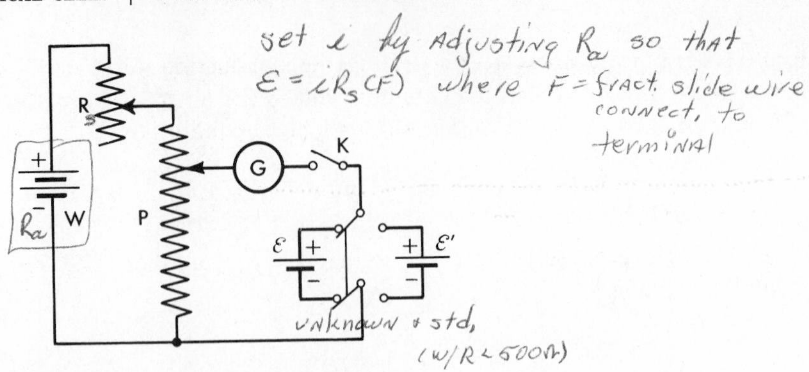

Figure 12.1. Balancing Potentiometer

P reads the standard cell potential difference $\mathscr{E}$ when the galvanometer G reads zero. When no current flows through G, $\mathscr{E}$ of the cell is undisturbed, except of course for a small discharge not noted by the galvanometer. The key K prevents more than momentary discharges in the stochastic process of attaining balance. Since the standard cell should never be subjected to a current of more than 0.0001 amp, the circuit should contain high resistances in the early stages of finding balance. Then, with the double switch in the right-hand position, the unknown potential $\mathscr{E}'$ is measured by leaving R fixed as above and varying the contact to P until the current through G is zero. If the scale of P is linear and if the potential of W has remained constant, the scale reading of P is $\mathscr{E}'$ in the units of $\mathscr{E}$. With a mechanical galvanometer, precision of the order of one part in a million is attainable, and this can be improved by taking an average of several measurements or by using an ultrasensitive galvanometer. Measurements made in this way are made essentially at equilibrium, for at thermodynamic equilibrium the flow of current is zero.

12.3 CHEMICAL POTENTIAL AND ELECTRIC WORK

The potential difference $\mathscr{E}$ measured by the experimenter in the surroundings is the difference in electrostatic potentials $\Phi^{(i)}$ of two pieces of metal connected to the electrodes of the chemical cell. These pieces of metal are commonly the copper wire used to connect the cell to the potentiometer. The two pieces of metal must be of the same substance, for only if these contacts to the potentiometer are alike chemically is the potential difference meaningful.

The value of the potential difference is

$$\mathscr{E} = \Phi^{(2)} - \Phi^{(1)} \tag{12.8}$$

If $\Phi^{(2)}$ exceeds $\Phi^{(1)}$, $\mathscr{E}$ is positive. In order to transfer a positive charge dQ from phase 1 of potential $\Phi^{(1)}$ to phase 2 of potential $\Phi^{(2)}$, a positive amount of electric work dw_E must be done on the cell. That is, as in (2.4)

$$dw_E = +\mathscr{E}\, dQ \tag{12.9}$$

The total mount of work dw done on the cell may also include expansion work dw_{PV}; hence, the first law reads

$$dE = dq + dw = dq + dw_{PV} + dw_E \tag{12.10}$$

By the usual methods of Section 5.2 (12.10) becomes

$$dG = -S\, dT + V\, dP + dw_E \tag{12.11}$$

For a reversible process at constant temperature ($dT = 0$) and constant pressure ($dP = 0$),

$$dG = dw_E \tag{12.12}$$

That is, for a reversible isothermal isobaric process that may involve only expansion and electric work, the increase in free energy dG is equal to the electric work dw_E done on the system. In general, in any reversible isothermal isobaric process, the increase in Gibbs free energy in the system is equal to all the nonexpansion work done on the system.

Electric charge is carried within and through the cell by massive chemical species called ions. The increase in energy $dE^{(j)}$ of phase j within the system is appropriately described in terms of (6.37) for an open subsystem j (or phase j), with, however, the addition of dw_E as in (12.10). If phase j is at a potential $\Phi^{(j)}$ relative to some arbitrary zero level of potential, then

$$dE^{(j)} = T\, dS^{(j)} - P\, dV^{(j)} + \Phi^{(j)}\, dQ^{(j)} + \sum_{i=1}^{C} \mu_i^{(j)}\, dn_i^{(j)} \tag{12.13}$$

Here C is the number of independently variable components, at least one of which must carry an electric charge. The condition of electroneutrality is relaxed to allow for the transfer of electric charge, but deviations from strict electroneutrality cannot be observed by chemical analysis. An excess of 10^{-10} millimole of singly charged ions per milliliter would cause a region to have a potential relative to neutral regions of the order of 10^6 volts!

If phase j contains $n_i^{(j)}$ moles of species i with charge $z_i\mathscr{F}$, then the net charge $Q^{(j)}$ on the phase is

$$Q^{(j)} = \sum_{i=1}^{C} z_i n_i^{(j)} \mathscr{F} \tag{12.14}$$

Since z_i and $\mathscr{F}$ are constants, it follows from (12.13) and (12.14) that

$$dE^{(j)} = T\, dS^{(j)} - P\, dV^{(j)} + \sum_{i=1}^{C} [\mu_i^{(j)} + z_i \mathscr{F} \Phi^{(j)}]\, dn_i^{(j)} \tag{12.15}$$

According to the definition, the chemical potential $\boldsymbol{\mu}_i^{(j)}$ of species i is

$$\boldsymbol{\mu}_i^{(j)} = \mu_i^{(j)} + z_i \mathscr{F} \Phi^{(j)} \tag{12.16}$$

which is like (12.3) in form. If the phase is at zero potential ($\Phi^{(j)} = 0$) or if species i is electrically neutral ($z_i = 0$), $\boldsymbol{\mu}_i^{(j)} = \mu_i^{(j)}$. Because $\mu_i^{(j)}$ seems experimentally to be independent of $\Phi^{(j)}$, except perhaps at potentials of the order of 10^6 volts, $\mu_i^{(j)}$ may be assumed to be the value long used in previous chapters. However, $\boldsymbol{\mu}_i^{(j)}$ is the only true and observable chemical potential.

By methods analogous to those of Section 6.8, it can be shown that at equilibrium the temperatures and pressures in all phases of an electrochemical system are equal. For any species i that exists in and can be exchanged between phases j and k, at equilibrium $\boldsymbol{\mu}_i^{(j)} = \boldsymbol{\mu}_i^{(k)}$. However, if a component cannot move between phases, its value of $\boldsymbol{\mu}_i$ need not be the same in both phases.

The difference in electrostatic potential between phases j and k is defined only when these phases are chemically alike. If in addition to chemical likeness it happens that $\mu_i^{(j)} = \mu_i^{(k)}$ as seems experimentally to be true at modest potentials, then by (12.16) and (12.8)

$$\boldsymbol{\mu}_i^{(j)} - \boldsymbol{\mu}_i^{(k)} = z_i \mathscr{F}[\Phi^{(j)} - \Phi^{(k)}] = z_i \mathscr{F} \mathscr{E} \tag{12.17}$$

If phase j differs chemically from phase k, the value of $\mathscr{E} = \Delta\Phi$ is not meaningful even though a reading could be registered on an instrument meant to measure potential difference.

12.4 AN ELECTROCHEMICAL CELL

A conglomeration of chemicals develops a finite electric potential difference between phases because one or more charged species cannot be exchanged between certain phases. This barrier to exchange may be a selective membrane, but generally it is mere physical separation in space.

A very simple cell consists of a hydrogen electrode and a silver-silver chloride electrode both immersed in the same solution of hydrochloric acid. The hydrogen electrode consists of a piece of platinum that catalyzes the equilibrium between hydrogen ions of the solution and gaseous hydrogen continuously furnished to the electrode. The other electrode is a piece of platinum connected to a piece of solid silver on which solid silver chloride is deposited. Figure 12.2 is a sketch of this cell.

The conventional cell diagram of this cell is this:

$$(\mathrm{Pt})\mathrm{H}_{2\,(g)}(f_{\mathrm{H}_2}) \,|\, \mathrm{H}^+(a_{\mathrm{H}^+}), \mathrm{Cl}^-(a_{\mathrm{Cl}^-}) \,|\, \mathrm{AgCl}_{(s)} \,|\, \mathrm{Ag}_{(s)}(\mathrm{Pt})$$

Since the platinum does not partake in the overall chemical change, it is enclosed in parentheses. A comma separates species in one phase and a single vertical

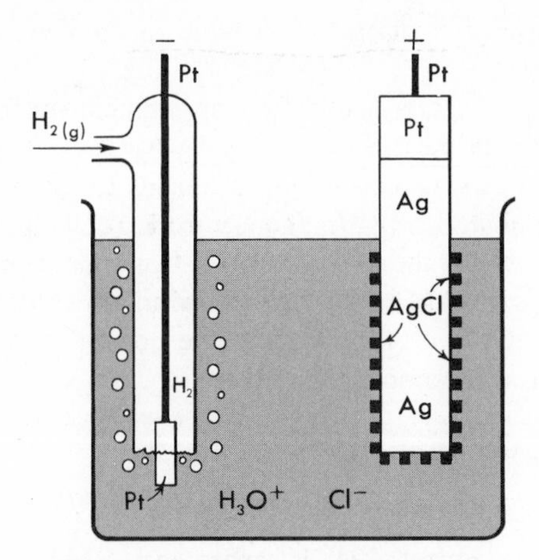

Figure 12.2. Sketch of a Simple Cell

line separates phases such as electrode and electrolyte. The activities or fugacities are enclosed in parentheses immediately after the species to which they refer.

The potential difference $\mathscr{E}$ of the cell is given the sign of the potential of the right-hand electrode relative to the left-hand one, which is at zero potential. Table 12.1 lists the observed values of $\mathscr{E}$ as a function of molality of HCl (0.001 m to 0.1 m) from 0°C to 275°C. For this cell, $\mathscr{E} > 0$ because the right-

Table 12.1 Potential Differences of the Cell

$(Pt)H_2(1\ atm) \mid HCl(m) \mid AgCl \mid Ag(Pt)$

Molality (m)	0.001	0.002	0.005	0.01	0.02	0.05	0.1
0°C[a]	0.56330	0.53131	0.48931	0.45787	0.42669	0.38588	0.35505
20°C[a]	0.57631	0.54198	0.49695	0.46323	0.42985	0.38613	0.35316
25°C[a]	0.57909	0.54418	0.49840	0.46412	0.43019	0.38579	0.35233
25°C[b]	0.57904	0.54415	0.49838	0.46411	0.43017	0.38576	0.35228
30°C[a]	0.58178	0.54628	0.49977	0.46493	0.43044	0.38533	0.35134
60°C[a]	0.59525	0.55628	0.50517	0.46694	0.42909	0.37969	0.34275
60°C[b]	0.5953	0.5565	0.5055	0.4672	0.4295	0.3802	0.3435
90°C[a]	0.6043	0.5619	0.5063	0.4648	0.4238	0.3703	0.3304
90°C[b]	0.6036	0.5617	0.5063	0.4648	0.4238	0.3705	0.3310
125°C[b]	0.6063	0.5620	0.5023	0.4571	0.4124	0.3543	0.3112
150°C[b]	0.6014	0.5571	0.4952	0.4478	0.4007	0.3396	0.2948
175°C[b]	0.5897	0.5474	0.4846	0.4354	0.3859	0.3215	0.2742
200°C[b]	0.5698	0.5308	0.4689	0.4185	0.3673	0.3002	0.2514
225°C[b]	0.5422	0.5067	0.4474	0.3970	0.3447	0.2758	0.2261
250°C[b]	0.504	0.471	0.415	0.366	0.314	0.246	0.200
275°C[b]	0.474	0.443	0.390	0.342	0.290	0.219	0.168

[a] R. G. Bates and V. E. Bower, *J. Res. Nat. Bur. Stds.* **53,** 283 (1954).

[b] R. S, Greeley, W. T. Smith, Jr., R. W. Strougton, and M. H. Lietzke, *J. Phys. Chem.* **64,** 652 (1960).

hand electrode is at a higher potential $\Phi^{(2)}$ than the left-hand one at $\Phi^{(1)}$. (At high T and m, $\mathscr{E}$ may become negative.)

If this cell were short-circuited, electrons would flow spontaneously from the hydrogen electrode through the external circuit to the Ag-AgCl electrode. At the left-hand electrode, the hydrogen would give up electrons to the platinum metal and would dissolve as ions according to the electrode (or half-cell) reaction $\frac{1}{2}H_{2(g)} \rightleftharpoons H^+ + e^-$. Upon entering the silver electrode from the external circuit, these electrons would transform AgCl into Ag according to the electrode (or half-cell) reaction $e^- + AgCl_{(s)} \rightleftharpoons Ag_{(s)} + Cl^-$. The net reaction of the entire cell is the sum of the electrode reactions, namely,

$$\tfrac{1}{2}H_{2(g)} + AgCl_{(s)} \rightleftharpoons Ag_{(s)} + H^+ + Cl^- \tag{12.18}$$

The electrons transferred from H_2 to AgCl in this reaction are forced to proceed through the external circuit because the H_2 is separated in space from the AgCl. To be sure, the trace of AgCl dissolved in the acid can contact the H_2 at the hydrogen electrode and the trace of H_2 dissolved in the acid can contact the AgCl at the Ag-AgCl electrode. But these internal short circuits are small because H_2 and AgCl dissolve only slightly. The effect is small, as is attested by the finite and reproducible potential difference developed by the cell. The aqueous phase is such a poor conductor of electrons that the Φ's of the electrons in the pieces of Pt can be observed to differ through very long periods of time.

When the electrode reactions of (12.18) are written in the standard forms

$$0 = H^+ + e^- - \tfrac{1}{2}H_{2(g)} \qquad \text{[Electrode (1)]} \tag{12.19}$$

$$0 = Cl^- + Ag_{(s)} - AgCl_{(s)} - e^- \qquad \text{[Electrode (2)]} \tag{12.20}$$

it is clear that at the left-hand electrode (1) at potential $\Phi^{(1)}$ electrons are generated ($dn_e^{(1)} > 0$) and that at the right-hand electrode (2) at $\Phi^{(2)}$ electrons are destroyed ($dn_e^{(2)} < 0$). In fact, since electrons are conserved, the infinitesimal number of e^- that pass from (1) to (2) is

$$dn = dn_e^{(1)} = -dn_e^{(2)} \tag{12.21}$$

With $z_e = -1$ because the charge of the electron is negative, the total charge passing from (1) to (2) is

$$dQ = (-1)\mathscr{F}\, dn \tag{12.22}$$

The work thus done on electrode (2) is $\Phi^{(2)}\, dQ$ and the net electric work done on the cell (the system) is, by (12.8) and (12.22)

$$dw_E = \Phi^{(2)}\, dQ - \Phi^{(1)}\, dQ = -\mathscr{E}\mathscr{F}\, dn \tag{12.23}$$

But for a reversible isothermal isobaric process like discharge through a balancing potentiometer, $dG = dw_E$ and thus

$$dG = -\mathscr{E}\mathscr{F}\,dn \tag{12.24}$$

$$\Delta G = -\mathscr{E}\mathscr{F}\int_0^n dn' = -n\,\mathscr{E}\mathscr{F} \tag{12.25}$$

The value of ΔG is for the cell reaction as written, and n is the number of faradays associated with either electrode reaction.

Example 12.1. Calculate the increase ΔG in free energy at 25°C and 1 atm for the reaction

$$H_{2(g)} + 2AgCl_{(s)} \rightleftharpoons 2Ag_{(s)} + 2H^+Cl^-$$

when the H_2 is at 1 atm and the HCl is 0.100 molal.

From Table 12.1 the average EMF is $\mathscr{E} = 0.35230$ abs. volt. The cell reaction as written in this example involves two faradays; hence, $n = 2$. By (12.25),

$$\Delta G = -2\,(0.35230)\,96487 = -67{,}985 \text{ j}$$

For (12.18), ΔG would be half as great.

12.5 ENTROPY AND ENTHALPY CHANGES FROM POTENTIAL DIFFERENCES

When the cell potential difference is measured reversibly in a balancing potentiometer, only an infinitesimal number of electrons passes through the external circuit. An infinitesimal change in potential could stop or reverse the infinitesimal flow of current at balance. The cell is at equilibrium with its surroundings. At equilibrium at constant temperature and pressure, $(\delta G)_{P,T} \geqslant 0$. But this criterion of equilibrium is derived from the condition $(\delta E)_{S,V} \geqslant 0$. Thus for the system consisting of the whole chemical cell, (12.15) requires that at constant S and V or at constant P and T

$$\sum_{j=1}^{P}\sum_{i=1}^{C}[\mu_i^{(j)} + z_i\mathscr{F}\Phi^{(j)}]\,\delta n_i^{(j)} \geqslant 0 \tag{12.26}$$

Equation (12.26) is quite general; it can be simplified in two ways. It ordinarily happens that each neutral component occurs in only one phase; hence, the summation upon j leads to only one term for each value of i and is thus superfluous. Moreover, it is customary and always possible to choose only the electron as the charged component with $z_e = -1$. All other components are chosen as neutral with $z_i = 0$. If δn moles of electrons flow through the external circuit from phase 1 with potential $\Phi^{(1)}$ to phase 2 with potential $\Phi^{(2)}$ when the reaction is $0 = \Sigma\nu_i\Omega_i$, then the increase in the number of moles of i is

$$\delta n_i = \nu_i\delta\xi \tag{12.27}$$

(where the progress of the change in the system is followed by the progress variable ξ) and the flow of electrons is at the same time

$$\delta n = \delta n_e^{(1)} = -\delta n_e^{(2)} = n\delta\xi \tag{12.28}$$

Since electrons as such are not considered to pass through the cell, $\delta n_e^{(j)} = 0$ for $1 \neq j \neq 2$. With electrodes chemically alike, $\mu_e^{(1)} = \mu_e^{(2)}$ and (12.26) (12.27), and (12.28) thus yield

$$\left[\sum_{i=1}^{C-1} \nu_i\mu_i + (-1)n\mathscr{F}\Phi^{(1)} + (-1)(-n)\mathscr{F}\Phi^{(2)}\right]\delta\xi \geqslant 0$$

For arbitrary values of $\delta\xi$,

$$\sum_{i=1}^{C=1} \nu_i\mu_i + n\mathscr{F}(\Phi^{(2)} - \Phi^{(1)}) = 0 \tag{12.29}$$

The summation proceeds over all species in the net cell reaction and by (9.3) is equal to ΔG for the cell reaction. Thus it follows from (12.29) and (12.8) that

$$\Delta G = -n\mathscr{E}\mathscr{F} \tag{12.25}$$

If reactants and products are in their usual standard states,

$$\Delta G^{\circ} = -n\mathscr{E}^{\circ}\mathscr{F} \tag{12.30}$$

The meaning of (12.25) and (12.30) is that an EMF of $\mathscr{E}$ must be maintained if the cell reaction to which ΔG or ΔG° applies is not to advance, perhaps by internal short circuit, or regress.

The Gibbs-Helmholtz equation (5.74) permits a calculation of ΔS for a change of state if ΔG is known as a function of temperature. Since $\mathscr{E}$ is the only temperature-dependent variable upon which ΔG depends in (12.25), a knowledge of $\mathscr{E}$ as a function of temperature yields ΔS, for

$$\Delta S = -\left(\frac{\partial \Delta G}{\partial T}\right)_P = n\mathscr{F}\left(\frac{\partial \mathscr{E}}{\partial T}\right)_P \tag{12.31}$$

The value of ΔH can similarly be calculated from electrical measurements, for

$$\begin{aligned}\Delta H &= \Delta G + T\Delta S \\ &= -n\mathscr{F}\mathscr{E} + T\left[n\mathscr{F}\left(\frac{\partial \mathscr{E}}{\partial T}\right)_P\right] \\ &= n\mathscr{F}\left[T\left(\frac{\partial \mathscr{E}}{\partial T}\right)_P - \mathscr{E}\right]\end{aligned} \tag{12.32}$$

Example 12.2. Calculate ΔS and ΔH for the reaction of Example 12.1.

Since (12.31) requires the isobaric temperature coefficient of cell potential difference, an average value must be found from Table 12.1. Between 20°C and 25°C,

$$\frac{\Delta\mathscr{E}}{\Delta T} = \frac{0.35233 - 0.35316}{298.12 - 293.12} = -1.66 \times 10^{-4} \text{ volt deg}^{-1}$$

Between 25°C and 30°C,

$$\frac{\Delta\mathscr{E}}{\Delta T} = \frac{0.35134 - 0.35233}{303.12 - 298.12} = -1.98 \times 10^{-4} \text{ volt deg}^{-1}$$

The average value at 25°C is -1.82×10^{-4} volt deg^{-1}; hence, by (12.31) with $n = 2$

$$\Delta S = 2(96,487)(-1.82 \times 10^{-4}) = -35.1 \text{ j deg}^{-1}$$

By (12.32)

$$\Delta H = 2(96{,}487)[298.16\,(-1.82 \times 10^{-4}) - 0.35233]$$
$$= -78{,}470 \text{ j}$$

Example 12.3. Explain in words the significance of the equation $\Delta H = \Delta G + T\Delta S$ as it applies to isothermal isobaric cell reactions.

For any isothermal reversible process, the second law requires that $q_{\text{rev}} = T\Delta S$. On the other hand, when both expansion and electric work are possible, (2.24) says $\Delta H = q_P + w_E$, whether the process is reversible or not. Since $\Delta G = w_{E\,(\text{rev})}$ = the reversible isothermal isobaric work done on the system, it follows that at constant temperature and pressure

$$q_P + w_E = w_{E\,(\text{rev})} + q_{\text{rev}}$$

That is, the heat absorbed by the system plus the electric work done on the system equals the reversible electric work done on the system plus the heat absorbed reversibly by the system. However, the isothermal isobaric electric work done on the system irreversibly exceeds that done reversibly because

$$w_E \geqslant \Delta G = w_{E\,(\text{rev})}$$

Since w_E exceeds $w_{E\,(\text{rev})}$, q_{rev} exceeds q_P. Hence, $-q_P$ exceeds $-q_{\text{rev}}$ so that an exothermic cell reaction evolves more heat irreversibly than reversibly for the same change of state at constant temperature and pressure. Most heat is evolved when no electric work is done ($w_E = 0$); least, when the electric work is reversible.

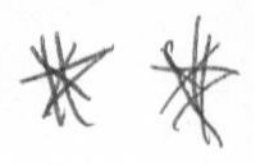

12.6 EQUILIBRIUM CONSTANTS FROM POTENTIAL DIFFERENCES

If a cell were allowed really to discharge, the concentrations of some components would change as the accompanying cell reaction occurred. In the cell of the previous sections, hydrochloric acid would be generated. But $\mathscr{E}$ decreases as acid forms in this cell as Table 12.1 shows, for there $\mathscr{E}$ decreases as m rises. Finally when $\mathscr{E}$ became zero no current would flow and ΔG would be zero. A state of equilibrium would exist with all components at the same potential. In general, at equilibrium at constant temperature and pressure, $\mathscr{E}$ is zero, as required by (12.25) when $\Delta G = 0$.

The dependence of $\mathscr{E}$ upon activities and fugacities follows at once on substituting (12.25) and (12.30) into

$$\Delta G = \Delta G^{\ominus} + RT \ln Q \qquad (9.7)\,(9.21)$$

$$-n\mathscr{F}\mathscr{E} = -n\mathscr{F}\mathscr{E}^{\ominus} + RT \ln Q \qquad (12.33)$$

$$\mathscr{E} = \mathscr{E}^{\ominus} - \frac{RT}{n\mathscr{F}} \ln Q \qquad (12.34)$$

Equation (12.34) is the well-known Nernst equation. When $\mathscr{E} = 0$ at equilibrium,

$$-n\mathscr{F}\mathscr{E}^{\ominus} = -RT \ln K \qquad (12.35)$$

This is a special form of (9.14) and (9.22), which read $\Delta G^{\ominus} = -RT \ln K$.

In (9.14), (9.22), and (12.35), K is the equilibrium constant in the absence of an electrostatic potential difference. It was concluded in Section 12.1 that a gravitational potential has no effect on the state of chemical equilibrium. However, an electrostatic potential does affect the position of chemical equilibrium, for substituting $\mu_i = \mu_i^{\ominus} + RT \ln b_i$ into (12.29) yields, as the analogue of (12.7),

$$0 = \sum_i \nu_i \mu_i^{\ominus} + RT \sum_i \ln b_i^{\nu_i} + n\mathscr{F}(\Phi^{(2)} - \Phi^{(1)}) \qquad (12.36)$$

where the summations are over neutral species (all species but the electron). Alternately, (12.36) is

$$0 = \Delta G^{\ominus} + RT \ln \left[\prod_i b_i^{\nu_i}\right] + n\mathscr{F}(\Phi^{(2)} - \Phi^{(1)}) \qquad (12.37)$$

The final term of (12.37), if it is not zero, clearly affects the value of

$$K(\Phi) = \prod_i b_i^{\nu_i} \qquad (12.38)$$

the equilibrium constant when the electrostatic potential of the electron is not the same in the pieces of metal (e.g., Pt) in contact with two of the phases of the system. These two phases are not free to exchange electrons within the cell; as a result, the activities of neutral species are b_i rather than values a_i that would have obtained in the absence of the differing Φ's. Really, $K(\Phi)$ is Q when an external agent like a potentiometer establishes a nonzero value of $\mathscr{E}$ in (12.33) or (12.34).

12.7 VARIOUS CELLS

It is customary to imagine a cell at constant T and P to consist of two electrode systems, each of which is at equilibrium within itself with respect to the electrode reaction. Here equilibrium means no spontaneous reaction and the possibility that any virtual electrode reaction can be reversed. Each electrode (half-cell) reaction explicitly acknowledges the electron as a chemically active species. The electrode consists of at least two phases (e.g., $H_{2(g)}$ and $HCl_{(aq)}$; or (Pt) in a solution of Fe^{2+} and Fe^{3+}). The minimum number of phases in a whole cell is three if each electrode involves the same phase that conducts electrons only negligibly. The cell of Figure 12.2 consists of four phases (H_2, HCl, AgCl, Ag) besides the metallic probes of like chemical nature (Pt) for observing Φ.

Examples of cells of just three phases (Pt not counted) are

$$(Pt)Zn \,|\, Zn^{2+} \,|\, Zn\text{-}Hg(Pt)$$

$$(Pt)H_2(1\text{ atm}) \,|\, H^+ \,|\, H_2(x\text{ atm})(Pt)$$

where a single vertical line indicates a change of phase. The EMF's of these cells depend on concentration differences in the electrodes. Two three-phase cells whose EMF's depend on chemical differences of the electrodes are

$$(Pt)Zn \,|\, Zn^{2+}, Cl^- \,|\, Cl_2(Pt)$$

$$(Pt)H_2 \,|\, H^+, Cl^- \,|\, Cl_2(Pt)$$

where a comma separates species in a single phase. Thus the minimum number of phases, namely three, occurs when the electrodes are reversible with respect to different species in the common electron-insulating phase or when the electrodes somehow differ and yet react with a common species of the common insulating phase.

The standard cell of known potential fixes the scale of the potentiometer by fixing R in Figure 12.1. Although several types of standard cell have been used, the most common is the unsaturated Weston cell. Its cell diagram is

$$(Pt)Cd(Hg) \,|\, Cd^{++}SO_4^{--} \,|\, Hg_2SO_{4(s)} \,|\, Hg_{(l)}(Pt)$$

The amalgam Cd(Hg) contains 12.5% by weight Cd; the aqueous solution of $CdSO_4$ is that solution which is saturated with $CdSO_3 \cdot \frac{8}{3}H_2O_{(s)}$ at 4°C; the right-hand electrode is a paste of Hg_2SO_4 and Hg in contact with $Hg_{(l)}$. The standard form of this cell is shown in Figure 12.3. The potential difference of a cell like this is about 1.01904 volts at 25°C. For highest accuracy, the value of a particular cell should be redetermined every year or two by the National Bureau of Standards. This type of cell should be kept at temperatures between 4°C and

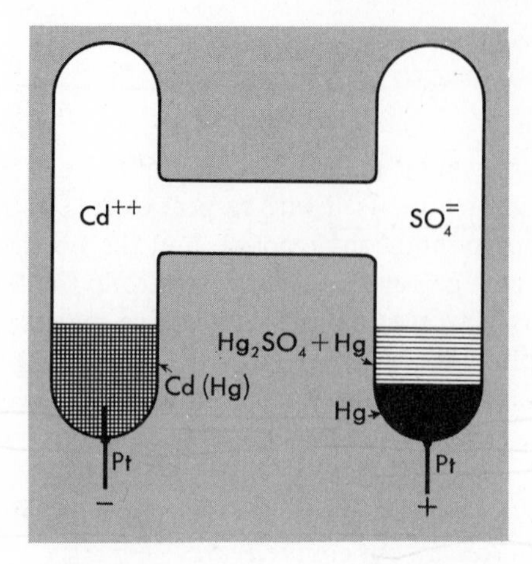

Figure 12.3. Unsaturated Weston Cell

40°C. Although its temperature coefficient is less than 10 microvolts deg^{-1}, it should be at the same temperature throughout and should never be subjected to rapid changes of temperature, for these may cause temporary changes in potential difference of a few thousandths of a volt.

The normal (or saturated) Weston cell has this cell diagram.

$$(Pt)Cd(Hg)\,|\,CdSO_4\cdot\tfrac{8}{3}H_2O_{(s)}\,|\,Cd^{++}SO_4^{--}\,|\,Hg_2SO_{4\,(s)}\,|\,Hg_{(l)}(Pt)$$

It differs from the unsaturated Weston cell in having an electrolyte saturated with respect to $CdSO_4\cdot\frac{8}{3}H_2O_{(s)}$ at the temperature of use. Its potential difference at 25°C is 1.018386 volts. It is used less often than the unsaturated Weston cell because its temperature coefficient is about −45 microvolts deg^{-1} near 25°C.

Electrode reactions may involve either anions or cations, and both oxidized and reduced forms of the active species may occur with variable activity. Pure condensed phases exhibit constant activities taken as unity. Table 12.2 lists electrode and cell reactions of various types of cells. As above, an inert electrode is within parentheses; a single vertical line indicates a change of phase; a comma separates species in one phase. If a change of phase involves solutions the cell is said to exhibit *transference*. The first cell of Table 12.2 is without transference; the second is a cell with transference. In a cell so diagramed, no correction is made for the potential due to the contact of dissimilar solutions, such as that between the solution of zinc ions and that of ferrous and ferric ions. A double vertical line indicates that this junction potential has been corrected for and that changes like diffusion of ions through the junction at different speeds and the resulting difference in electrostatic potential are to be ignored, as in the last three cells of Table 12.2. Experimentally to reduce a junction potential calls for a salt bridge (containing a solution of KCl, NH_4NO_3, or other salt).

Table 12.2 Cell Notation and Reactions of Varied Cell Types.

Cell Notation	Reactions
(Pt)Na(Hg)(0.2%) | $Na^+(a_1)$, $Cl^-(a_2)$ | Cl_2(g)(pCl_2)(Pt)	$Na(Hg) \rightleftharpoons Na^+ + e$ $e^- + \frac{1}{2}Cl_{2\,(g)} \rightleftharpoons Cl^-$ $Na(Hg) + \frac{1}{2}Cl_{2\,(g)} \rightleftharpoons Na^+ + Cl^-$
(Pt)$Zn_{(s)}$ | $Zn^{++}(a_1)$ | $Fe^{+++}(a_2)$, $Fe^{++}(a_3)$ | (Pt)	$\frac{1}{2}Zn_{(s)} \rightleftharpoons \frac{1}{2}Zn^{++} + e^-$ $e^- + Fe^{+++} \rightleftharpoons Fe^{++}$ $\frac{1}{2}Zn_{(s)} + Fe^{+++} \rightleftharpoons \frac{1}{2}Zn^{++} + Fe^{++}$
(Pt)$Hg_{(l)}$ | $Hg_2Cl_{2\,(s)}$ | $Cl^-(a_1)$ ‖ $I^-(a_2)$ | $I_{2\,(s)}$(Pt)	$Hg_{(l)} + Cl^- \rightleftharpoons \frac{1}{2}Hg_2Cl_{2\,(s)} + e^-$ $e^- + \frac{1}{2}I_{2\,(s)} \rightleftharpoons I^-$ $Hg_{(l)} + Cl^- + \frac{1}{2}I_2 \rightleftharpoons \frac{1}{2}Hg_2Cl_{2\,(s)} + I^-$
(Pt)$Zn_{(s)}$ | $ZnO_2^{--}(a_1)$ ‖ $MnO_4^{--}(a_2)$, $MnO_4^-(a_3)$ | (Pt)	$\frac{1}{2}Zn_{(s)} + 2OH^- \rightleftharpoons \frac{1}{2}ZnO_2^{--} + H_2O_{(l)} + e^-$ $e^- + MnO_4^- \rightleftharpoons MnO_4^{--}$ $\frac{1}{2}Zn_{(s)} + 2OH^- + MnO_4^- \rightleftharpoons MnO_4^{--} + H_2O_{(l)} + \frac{1}{2}ZnO_2^{--}$
(Pt) | $VO^{++}(a_1)$, $V(OH)_4^+(a_2)$ ‖ $Ce^{+++}(a_3)$, $Ce^{++++}(a_4)$ | (Pt)	$VO^{++} + 3H_2O \rightleftharpoons V(OH)_4^+ + 2H^+ + e^-$ $e^- + Ce^{++++} \rightleftharpoons Ce^{+++}$ $VO^{++} + 3H_2O + Ce^{++++} \rightleftharpoons V(OH)_4^+ + 2H^+ + Ce^{+++}$

junction potential

To eliminate its influence on $\mathscr{E}$ calls for a double cell of the type

$$(Pt)H_{2\,(g)}(p_1)|H^+(a_1), Cl^-(a_3)|AgCl_{(s)}|Ag_{(s)}|AgCl_{(s)}|Cl^-(a_4), H^+(a_2)|H_{2\,(g)}(p_2)(Pt)$$

If $a_3 = a_4$, this double cell would have the same potential difference and same cell reaction as the cell with the following seemingly simple diagram:

$$(Pt)H_{2\,(g)}(p_1)\,|\,H^+(a_1)\,\|\,H^+(a_2)\,|\,H_{2\,(g)}(p_2)(Pt)$$

This last type of cell is discussed in Section 12.11.

Example 12.4. With the aid of opposed cells like the double cell just mentioned, calculate the free energy of dilution of hydrochloric acid at 25°C from 0.1000 molal to 0.01000 molal. See Table 12.1 for data.

The cell reaction is to be

$$H^+Cl^-\ (m = 0.1000) \rightleftharpoons H^+Cl^-\ (m = 0.01000)$$

$\frac{1}{2}H_{2(g)} + AgCl_{(s)} \rightleftharpoons Ag_{(s)} + H^+ + Cl^-$

and $a_1 = a_3 \neq a_2 = a_4$. The reaction in the left-hand cell must produce the more dilute acid in view of (12.18). Since the two cells are opposed, their total potential difference is 0.46412 − 0.35233 = 0.11179 absolute volt. Hence, by (12.25)

$$\Delta G = (-1)(0.11179)(96{,}487) = -10{,}718 \text{ j}$$

A negative value of ΔG indicates that dilution is a spontaneous process. If the ratio of activities is the ratio of concentrations, ΔG° in (9.21) yields for both ions

$$\Delta G = 8.3143 \times 298.15 \times \ln \left(\frac{0.01000}{0.1000}\right)^2 = -11{,}416 \text{ j}$$

Really, of course, these ratios differ.

Example 12.5. Calculate the potential difference expected at 25°C from the cell

$$\text{(Pt)Zn}_x\text{Hg} \,|\, \text{Zn}^{++}, \text{SO}_4^{--} \,|\, \text{Zn}_y\text{Hg(Pt)}$$

if $x = 6.13 \times 10^{-3}$ and $y = 3.17 \times 10^{-6}$. The value observed by Crenshaw [*J. Phys. Chem.*, **14,** 158 (1910)] is 0.09773 volt.

If x and y were equal the electrodes would be alike and the cell reaction would be nil. Hence, $\mathscr{E}^\ominus$ is zero and, by (12.34),

$$\mathscr{E} = -\frac{RT}{n\mathscr{F}} \ln \left(\frac{X_2}{X_1}\right)$$

Here X_1 and X_2 are the mole fractions of Zn in the amalgams and are approximately equal to x and y because x and y are small compared to unity. Since the cell reaction for 2 faradays involves the transfer of 1 g formula weight of Zn from Zn_xHg to Zn_yHg, $X_1 = 6.13 \times 10^{-3}$ and $X_2 = 3.17 \times 10^{-6}$. Thus

$$\mathscr{E} = -\frac{8.3143 \times 298.15 \times 2.3026}{2 \times 96{,}487} \log \left(\frac{3.17 \times 10^{-6}}{6.13 \times 10^{-3}}\right)$$

$$= -\frac{0.059155 \times (-3.286)}{2} = +0.09719 \text{ volt}$$

Example 12.6. If $\mathscr{E}^\ominus = +0.84$ volt at 25°C for the cell (Pt) | Fe^{++}, Fe^{+++} ‖ Ce^{+++}, Ce^{++++} | (Pt) calculate the equilibrium constant of the cell reaction.

The cell reaction is $\text{Fe}^{++} + \text{Ce}^{++++} \rightleftharpoons \text{Fe}^{+++} + \text{Ce}^{+++}$. By (12.35),

$$\ln K = \frac{0.84 \times 1 \times 96{,}500}{8.314 \times 298} = 32.7$$

$$K = \frac{a_{\text{Fe}^{+++}} a_{\text{Ce}^{+++}}}{a_{\text{Fe}^{++}} a_{\text{Ce}^{++++}}} = 1.6 \times 10^{14}$$

Example 12.7. Calculate the equilibrium constant for the reaction $\text{Ag}_{(s)} + \text{Fe}^{+++} \rightleftharpoons \text{Ag}^+ + \text{Fe}^{++}$ from these facts. For the cell

$$\text{Ag}_{(s)} \,|\, \text{Ag}^+(0.100N) \,|\, \text{K}^+\text{NO}_3^-(0.1N) \,|\, \text{K}^+\text{Cl}^-(1N) \,|\, \text{Hg}_2\text{Cl}_{2\,(s)} \,|\, \text{Hg(Ag)}$$

$\mathscr{E} = -0.4523$ volt at 25°C; and, at 25°C, $\mathscr{E} = -0.4494$ volt for the cell

$$\text{(Pt)} \,|\, \text{Fe}^{++}(0.0500N), \text{Fe}^{+++}(0.0500N) \,|\, \text{K}^+\text{Cl}^-(\text{sat.}) \,|\, \text{K}^+\text{Cl}^-(1N) \,|\, \text{Hg}_2\text{Cl}_{2\,(s)} \,|\, \text{Hg(Pt)}$$

With these and other data, Noyes and Brann [*J. Am. Chem. Soc.*, **34,** 1016 (1912)] found $K = 0.100$; by analytical methods they found $K = 0.128$.

If the common normal calomel electrode at the right of each cell is removed and the remainders of the cells are joined, there results the cell

$$\text{(Pt)Ag}_{(s)} \,|\, \text{Ag}^+(0.1\ N) \,\|\, \text{Fe}^{++}(0.0500\ N), \text{Fe}^{+++}(0.0500\ N) \,|\, \text{(Pt)}$$

Since the $Ag_{(s)}$ is at a higher potential than (Pt) when compared to the calomel electrode, for this last cell $\mathscr{E} = -0.4523 - (-0.4494) = -0.0029$ volt. Its cell reaction is the one desired.

Since K can be found if $\mathscr{E}^{\ominus}$ is known, (12.34) must be used. If concentrations equal activities, (12.34) is

$$\mathscr{E} = -0.0029 = \mathscr{E}^{\ominus} - \frac{0.05916}{1} \log \left(\frac{0.100 \times 0.0500}{1 \times 0.0500}\right)$$

$$\mathscr{E}^{\ominus} = -0.0029 + 0.05916 \log (0.100)$$

$$= -0.0029 - 0.0592 = -0.0621 \text{ volt}$$

Then, by (12.35),

$$\ln K = \frac{-0.0621 \times 96{,}500}{8.314 \times 298} = -2.42$$

$$\log K = -1.05 = 0.95 - 2.00$$

$$K = 8.9 \times 10^{-2}$$

The most common portable sources of direct current are the familiar dry cell (1.5 volts) with a cell diagram of the general nature of

$$(Cu)Zn \,|\, Zn(NH_3)_4^{2+} \,|\, MnO(OH) \,|\, MnO_2 \,|\, C(Cu)$$

and the reversible lead storage cell (2.0 volts)

$$Pb \,|\, PbSO_4 \,|\, H^+, SO_4^{2-} \,|\, PbSO_4 \,|\, PbO_2 \,|\, Pb$$

Other widely used sources are the alkaline mercury cell (1.1 volts)

$$(Fe)Zn \,|\, Zn(OH)_4^{2-}, OH^- \,|\, HgO \,|\, Hg(Fe)$$

the zinc-silver oxide cell (1.4 volts)

$$(Cu)Zn \,|\, Zn(OH)_4^{2-}, OH^- \,|\, Ag_xO \,|\, Ag(Cu)$$

where $x \leqslant 2$, and the Edison cell (1.4 volts)

$$Fe_{(s)} \,|\, Fe(OH)_{2(s)} \,|\, OH^- \,|\, Ni_2O_3 \cdot yH_2O_{(s)} \,|\, Ni(OH)_{2(s)} \,|\, Ni(Fe)$$

It is even possible to generate electricity by the action of bacteria oxidizing sugar.

A cell whose reactants are supplied continuously (and whose products may be withdrawn continuously) is called a *fuel cell.* Electrodes of a fuel cell typically are not at equilibrium but exist in a steady state of chemical reaction in which catalysis and surface area are important parameters influencing the production of current and the approach toward a reversible EMF. Fuel cells meant eventually to be used as portable and economical sources of direct current usually have the net cell reactions $2CO + O_2 \longrightarrow 2CO_2$ and/or $2H_2 + O_2 \longrightarrow 2H_2O$, often at high T and P. Such cells differ widely in the nature of the electrodes and their catalytic behavior, the geometrical arrangement of electrodes and electrolyte, the nature of the electrolyte, the source of reactants (especially H_2) and disposal of products, and their operating conditions. Some diagrams of cells that yield H_2O in an aqueous electrolyte are

$$(Pt)H_2 | H^+ | O_2(Pt) \qquad \text{and} \qquad (Pt)H_2 | OH^- | O_2(Pt)$$

Because of the cost of Pt, the H_2 electrode may also be Pt-black mounted on Ta or Ni in cells that operate near room T, an alloy of Pd and Ag, or NiB, while the O_2 electrode may be mounted Pt-black, solid Ni, or solid or liquid Ag. The source of H_2 for large-scale economical operation is a gaseous reaction like $CH_3OH \longrightarrow CO + 2H_2$ at about 350°C, or $CH_4 + H_2O \longrightarrow CO + 3H_2$ at about 750°C followed by $CO + H_2O \longrightarrow CO_2 + H_2$ at about 275°C. Sometimes the CO is removed chemically or the H_2 is purified by diffusion through Pd. With a catalytic Ni electrode, however, the CO can be burned with the H_2 in a cell like

$$Ni_{(s)} | CO_{(g)}, H_{2(g)}, CO_{2(g)} | CO^{2-}_{3(l)} | O_{2(g)}, CO_{2(g)} | Ag_{(s)}(Ni) \qquad (12.39)$$

This type of cell requires CO_2 to be furnished at the Ag electrode and removed from any H_2 that is recycled to the Ni electrode. The molten carbonate electrolyte may be a mixture of Na_2CO_3 and Li_2CO_3, perhaps held in the pores of a matrix of $MgO_{(s)}$. One type of H_2–O_2 cell even uses a solid electrolyte of ZrO_2, a defect structure through which oxide ions can migrate. Other types use plastic membranes.

The ideal performance of fuel cells can be predicted by $\Delta G^\ominus = -n\mathscr{E}^\ominus\mathscr{F}$ and the Nernst equation at any T. The actual EMF at a practical power output depends strongly on the rates of the electrode reactions, the effective areas of the electrodes, and the nature of the electrolyte.

Example 12.8. Determine the net cell reaction of the fuel cell (12.39) when two faradays of charge pass through each electrode, the reversible EMF expected at 1000°K if all gases are at unit fugacity, and the change in EMF from this standard value when

(a) the temperature rises by 100°;
(b) $p(O_2)$ falls to 0.200 atm at 1000°K;
(c) $p(CO_2)$ at the negative electrode rises at 1000°K;
(d) $p(CO_2)$ at the positive electrode rises at 1000°K.

From the electrode reactions

$$CO_{(g)} + CO^{2-}_{3(l)} \longrightarrow 2CO^{(1)}_{2(g)} + 2e^-$$

$$2e^- + \tfrac{1}{2}O_{2(g)} + CO^{(2)}_{2(g)} \longrightarrow CO^{2-}_{3(l)}$$

the net cell reaction is found to be

$$CO_{(g)} + \tfrac{1}{2}O_{2(g)} + CO^{(2)}_{2(g)} \longrightarrow 2CO^{(1)}_{2(g)}$$

When all gases are at unit fugacity, Tables 9.4 and 9.5 yield $\Delta G^\ominus = -46{,}667$ cal and $\Delta H^\ominus = -67{,}550$ cal at $T = 1000$ for the reaction $CO + \frac{1}{2}O_2 \longrightarrow CO_2$. By (12.30),

$$\mathscr{E}^\ominus = -\frac{\Delta G^\ominus}{n\mathscr{F}} = -\frac{-46{,}667 \times 4.184}{2 \times 96{,}487} = 1.011 \text{ volts}$$

(a) By (5.71)

$$\Delta S^\ominus = \frac{\Delta H^\ominus - \Delta G^\ominus}{T} = \frac{-67{,}550 + 46{,}667}{1000} = -20.883 \text{ cal deg}^{-1}$$

Hence, by (12.31)

$$\left(\frac{\partial \mathscr{E}^\ominus}{\partial T}\right)_P = \frac{\Delta S^\ominus}{n\mathscr{F}} = \frac{-20.883 \times 4.184}{2 \times 96{,}487} = -0.453 \text{ millivolt/deg}$$

If $\delta T = 100°$, $\delta \mathscr{E}^\ominus = -0.0453$ volt. That is, a rise of 100° causes the EMF to fall by 0.0453 volt.

(b) With all gases except O_2 at unit fugacity, $Q = (0.200)^{-1/2}$ and (12.34) yields

$$\mathscr{E} = 1.011 - \frac{8.314 \times 1000 \times 2.303}{2 \times 96{,}487} \log_{10} (5)^{1/2}$$

$$= 1.011 - 0.0347 \text{ volt}$$

That is, using air instead of pure O_2 decreases the EMF by 0.0347v at one atm.

(c) The left-hand electrode (1) is negative because $\Delta G^\ominus$ is negative, the cell and electrode reactions being spontaneous as written. Thus, if $p(CO_2)$ at (1) rises, the net cell reaction predicts a rise in Q, which causes a decline in $\mathscr{E}$ by (12.34).

(d) A rise in $p(CO_2)$ at (2) causes Q to decrease and, as reasoned in (c), $\mathscr{E}$ to rise.

12.8 STANDARD ELECTRODE POTENTIALS

The electric potential of an electrode is the electric potential difference measurable between it and a reference electrode. As for any cell, the measurement is made between chemically identical pieces of metal joined to the electrodes. The reference electrode at zero potential is the standard hydrogen electrode. This electrode consists of a piece of platinum in contact with hydrogen gas at unit fugacity (1 atm) and an aqueous solution in which the hydronium ion activity is unity. The standard electrode potential $V^\ominus$ of this electrode is zero at all temperatures according to the convention first set forth by Nernst in 1889.

The electrical potential of an electrode is the measurable potential difference of a cell in which the left-hand electrode is a standard hydrogen electrode. This measurable potential difference is called the *electrode potential* of the right-hand electrode. It is referred to the standard hydrogen electrode at the left at zero potential [$\Phi^{(1)} = V^\ominus(H_2) = 0$]. The electrode potential of the Ag-AgCl electrode is the potential difference of the cell

$$(Pt)H_{2(g)}(f_{H_2} = 1)\,|\,H^+(a_{H^+} = 1),\ Cl^-(a_{Cl^-})\,|\,AgCl_{(s)}\,|\,Ag_{(s)}(Pt)$$

The electrode potential of the Zn-Zn^{++} electrode is the potential difference of the cell

$$(Pt)H_{2(g)}(f_{H_2} = 1)\,|\,H^+(a_{H^+} = 1)\,\|\,Zn^{++}(a_{Zn^{++}})\,|\,Zn(Pt)$$

If the species that partake in an electrode reaction are in their standard states, the electrode potential V becomes a standard electrode potential $V^\ominus$ The standard electrode potential of the Zn-Zn^{++} electrode is the measured potential difference of the cell

$$(Pt)H_{2(g)}(f_{H_2} = 1)\,|\,H^+(a_{H^+} = 1)\,\|\,Zn^{++}(a_{Zn^{++}} = 1)\,|\,Zn_{(s)}(Pt)$$

The measured value at 25°C is −0.763 volt. The standard electrode potential of the Cu-Cu^{++} electrode is +0.337 volt at 25°C, for this is the measured potential difference at 25°C of the cell

$$(Pt)H_{2(g)}(f_{H_2} = 1)\,|\,H^+(a_{H^+} = 1)\,\|\,Cu^{++}(a_{Cu^{++}} = 1)\,|\,Cu_{(s)}(Pt)$$

The potential differences of the cell

$$(Pt)H_{2(g)}\,|\,H^+,\ Cl^-\,|\,AgCl_{(s)}\,|\,Ag_{(s)}(Pt)$$

at various temperatures when all species are in standard states yield the standard electrode potentials of the Ag-AgCl electrode of Table 12.3. (The next section explains how these values of $V^\ominus$ are derived from the observed values of Table 12.1.)

Table 12.3 Standard Electrode Potential of the Silver-Silver Chloride Electrode at Various Temperatures.

T(°C)	$V^\ominus$ (volt)[a]	$V^\ominus$ (volt)[b]
0	0.23655	
25	0.22234	0.22233
60	0.19649	0.1968
90	0.1695	0.1696
125	0.1330	
150	0.1032	
175	0.0708	
200	0.0348	
225	−0.0051	
250	−0.054	
275	−0.090	

[a] R. G. Bates and V. E. Bower, *J. Res. Nat. Bur. Stds.* **53,** 283 (1954)
[b] R. S. Greeley, W. T. Smith, Jr., R. W. Stroughton, and M. H. Lietzke, *J. Phys. Chem.* **64,** 652 (1960)

Table 12.4 Standard Electrode Potentials in Acidic Aqueous Solution at 25°C†

Electrode Reaction		$V^{\ominus}$ (volts)
$e^- + \frac{1}{2} Ca^{++}$	$\rightleftharpoons \frac{1}{2} Ca_{(s)}$	−2.87
$e^- + Na^+$	$\rightleftharpoons Na_{(s)}$	−2.714
$e^- + \frac{1}{3} AlF_6^{---}$	$\rightleftharpoons \frac{1}{3} Al_{(s)} + 2F^-$	−2.07
$e^- + \frac{1}{3} Al^{+++}$	$\rightleftharpoons \frac{1}{3} Al_{(s)}$	−1.66
$e^- + \frac{1}{2} Mn^{++}$	$\rightleftharpoons \frac{1}{2} Mn_{(s)}$	−1.18
$e^- + \frac{1}{2} V^{++}$	$\rightleftharpoons \frac{1}{2} V_{(s)}$	−1.18
$e^- + \frac{1}{2} Zn^{++}$	$\rightleftharpoons \frac{1}{2} Zn_{(s)}$	−0.763
$e^- + TlI_{(s)}$	$\rightleftharpoons Tl_{(s)} + I^-$	−0.753
$e^- + TlBr_{(s)}$	$\rightleftharpoons Tl_{(s)} + Br^-$	−0.658
$e^- + \frac{1}{2} Fe^{++}$	$\rightleftharpoons \frac{1}{2} Fe_{(s)}$	−0.440
$e^- + \frac{1}{2} Cd^{++}$	$\rightleftharpoons \frac{1}{2} Cd_{(s)}$	−0.403
$e^- + Ti^{+++}$	$\rightleftharpoons Ti^{++}$	−0.37
$e^- + Tl^+$	$\rightleftharpoons Tl_{(s)}$	−0.3363
$e^- + V^{+++}$	$\rightleftharpoons V^{++}$	−0.255
$e^- + AgI_{(s)}$	$\rightleftharpoons Ag_{(s)} + I^-$	−0.151
$e^- + \frac{1}{2} Pb^{++}$	$\rightleftharpoons \frac{1}{2} Pb_{(s)}$	−0.126
$e^- + H^+$	$\rightleftharpoons \frac{1}{2} H_{2(g)}$	0.0000
$e^- + AgCl_{(s)}$	$\rightleftharpoons Ag_{(s)} + Cl^-$	0.222
$e^- + \frac{1}{2} Cu^{++}$	$\rightleftharpoons \frac{1}{2} Cu_{(s)}$	0.337
$e^- + 2H^+ + VO^{++}$	$\rightleftharpoons V^{+++} + H_2O_{(l)}$	0.361
$e^- + \frac{1}{2} Ag_2CrO_{4(s)}$	$\rightleftharpoons \frac{1}{2} CrO_4^{--} + Ag_{(s)}$	0.446
$e^- + \frac{1}{2} I_{2(s)}$	$\rightleftharpoons I^-$	0.5355
$e^- + \frac{1}{2} I_3^-$	$\rightleftharpoons \frac{3}{2} I^-$	0.536
$e^- + H^+ + \frac{1}{2} O_2$	$\rightleftharpoons \frac{1}{2} H_2O_2$	0.682
$e^- + Fe^{+++}$	$\rightleftharpoons Fe^{++}$	0.771
$e^- + Ag^+$	$\rightleftharpoons Ag_{(s)}$	0.7991
$e^- + 2H^+ + V(OH)_4^+$	$\rightleftharpoons VO^{++} + 3H_2O_{(l)}$	1.00
$e^- + \frac{1}{2} Br_{2(l)}$	$\rightleftharpoons Br^-$	1.0652
$e^- + H^+ + \frac{1}{4} O_2$	$\rightleftharpoons \frac{1}{2} H_2O_{(l)}$	1.229
$e^- + \frac{1}{2} Tl^{+++}$	$\rightleftharpoons \frac{1}{2} Tl^+$	1.25
$e^- + \frac{1}{2} Cl_{2(g)}$	$\rightleftharpoons Cl^-$	1.3595
$e^- + \frac{1}{3} Au^{+++}$	$\rightleftharpoons \frac{1}{3} Au_{(s)}$	1.50
$e^- + \frac{8}{5} H^+ + \frac{1}{5} MnO_4^-$	$\rightleftharpoons \frac{1}{5} Mn^{++} + \frac{4}{5} H_2O_{(l)}$	1.51
$e^- + Au^+$	$\rightleftharpoons Au_{(s)}$	1.68
$e^- + \frac{8}{3} H^+ + \frac{1}{3} FeO_4^{--}$	$\rightleftharpoons \frac{1}{3} Fe^{+++} + \frac{4}{3} H_2O_{(l)}$	1.9
$e^- + \frac{1}{2} F_{2(g)}$	$\rightleftharpoons F^-$	2.87

† Latimer, Wendell M., *Oxidation States of the Elements and Their Potentials in Aqueous Solutions*, 2nd ed. Englewood Cliffs, N. J.; Prentice-Hall, Inc., Copyright 1938, 1952.

Table 12.5 Standard Electrode Potentials in Basic Aqueous Solution at 25°C†

Electrode Reaction		$V^{\ominus}$ (volts)
$e^- + \frac{1}{2} ZnS_{(s)}$	$\rightleftharpoons \frac{1}{2} Zn_{(s)} + \frac{1}{2} S^{--}$	−1.44
$e^- + \frac{1}{2} CdS_{(s)}$	$\rightleftharpoons \frac{1}{2} Cd_{(s)} + \frac{1}{2} S^{--}$	−1.21
$e^- + \frac{1}{2} Tl_2S_{(s)}$	$\rightleftharpoons Tl_{(s)} + \frac{1}{2} S^{--}$	−0.96
$e^- + H_2O_{(l)}$	$\rightleftharpoons \frac{1}{2} H_{2(g)} + OH^-$	−0.828
$e^- + \frac{1}{2} Ag_2S_{(s)}$	$\rightleftharpoons Ag_{(s)} + \frac{1}{2} S^{--}$	−0.69
$e^- + \frac{1}{2} S_{(s)}$	$\rightleftharpoons \frac{1}{2} S^{--}$	−0.48
$e^- + TlOH_{(s)}$	$\rightleftharpoons Tl_{(s)} + OH^-$	−0.3445
$e^- + Ag(NH_3)_2^+$	$\rightleftharpoons Ag_{(s)} + 2NH_{3(aq)}$	0.373

† Latimer, Wendell M., *Oxidation States of the Elements and Their Potentials in Aqueous Solutions*, 2nd. ed. Englewood Cliffs, N. J.: Prentice-Hall, Inc., Copyright 1938, 1952.

Standard electrode potentials $V^{\ominus}$ in aqueous solution at 25°C are listed in Tables 12.4 and 12.5 with electrode reactions. Many of the values listed for acidic solutions can be used also in basic solutions.

Just as tables of $\Delta H_f^{\ominus}$, $S^{\ominus}$, and $\Delta G_f^{\ominus}$ tersely summarize much chemistry, these tables of $V^{\ominus}$ summarize in briefest form much electrochemistry. From them can be calculated cell potentials and free energies of cell reactions. For example, the potential expected of the cell

$$(Pt)Zn_{(s)}\,|\,Zn^{++}(a_{Zn^{++}} = 1)\,\|\,Cu^{++}(a_{Cu^{++}} = 1)\,|\,Cu_{(s)}(Pt)$$

is equal to the EMF of the double cell (with all species in standard states)

$$(Pt)Zn\,|\,Zn^{++}\,\|\,H^+\,|\,H_2(Pt) - (Pt)H_2\,|\,H^+\,\|\,Cu^{++}\,|\,Cu(Pt)$$

Because the hydrogen electrodes are alike and opposed, their effect is nil. Since the electrodes of the left part of this double cell are interchanged, the cell reaction of the left part is reversed and its potential difference is +0.763 volt. The total potential difference of the double cell is, then, +0.763 +(+0.337) = +1.100 volt. This same result is obtained from (12.8) when $V^{\ominus}$ is substituted for Φ. That is, for the cell (with all species in standard states)

$$(Pt)Zn\,|\,Zn^{++}\,\|\,Cu^{++}\,|\,Cu(Pt)$$

the electrode and cell reactions are

left electrode	$\frac{1}{2}Zn_{(s)} \rightleftharpoons \frac{1}{2}Zn^{++} + e^-$
right electrode	$e^- + \frac{1}{2}Cu^{++} \rightleftharpoons \frac{1}{2}Cu_{(s)}$
whole cell	$\frac{1}{2}Zn_{(s)} + \frac{1}{2}Cu^{++} \rightleftharpoons \frac{1}{2}Zn^{++} + \frac{1}{2}Cu_{(s)}$

By (12.8), which is always true for any cell,

$$\mathscr{E} = \Phi^{(2)} - \Phi^{(1)} = V_{(right)} - V_{(left)} \tag{12.40}$$

For this cell,

$$\begin{aligned}\mathscr{E}^{\ominus} &= \Phi^{(Cu)} - \Phi^{(Zn)} = V^{\ominus}_{(Cu)} - V^{\ominus}_{(Zn)} \\ &= +0.337 - (-0.763) = +1.100 \text{ volts}\end{aligned}$$

The positive value of $\mathscr{E}^{\ominus}$ means that the piece of Pt joined to the copper electrode is at a higher electrostatic potential (more positive) than the piece of Pt joined to the zinc electrode. If this cell were short-circuited, electrons would flow spontaneously from zinc to copper through the external circuit.

Similarly, for the cell (with all species in standard states)

$$(Pt)Cu\,|\,Cu^{++}\,\|\,Zn^{++}\,|\,Zn(Pt)$$

the electrode and cell reactions are

$$\begin{aligned}
\tfrac{1}{2}\mathrm{Cu}_{(s)} &\rightleftharpoons \tfrac{1}{2}\mathrm{Cu}^{++} + e^- \\
e^- + \tfrac{1}{2}\mathrm{Zn}^{++} &\rightleftharpoons \tfrac{1}{2}\mathrm{Zn}_{(s)} \\
\hline
\tfrac{1}{2}\mathrm{Cu}_{(s)} + \tfrac{1}{2}\mathrm{Zn}^{++} &\rightleftharpoons \tfrac{1}{2}\mathrm{Cu}^{++} + \tfrac{1}{2}\mathrm{Zn}_{(s)}
\end{aligned}$$

By (12.8)

$$\begin{aligned}
\mathscr{E}^{\ominus} &= \Phi^{(\mathrm{Zn})} - \Phi^{(\mathrm{Cu})} = \mathrm{V}^{\ominus}_{(\mathrm{Zn})} - \mathrm{V}^{\ominus}_{(\mathrm{Cu})} \\
&= -0.763 - (+0.337) = -1.100 \text{ volts}
\end{aligned}$$

The negative value of $\mathscr{E}^{\ominus}$ means that the piece of Pt joined to the zinc electrode is at a lower electrostatic potential than the piece of Pt joined to the copper electrode. It this cell were short-circuited, electrons would flow spontaneously from zinc to copper through the external circuit.

The relative potentials of the electrodes and direction of electron flow when a cell is short-circuited are specified by the nature of the chemical reaction and can be observed. In both cells just described, electrons flow spontaneously from Zn to Cu through an external short circuit. The change in sign of $\mathscr{E}^{\ominus}$ stems from the change in sign of $\Delta G^{\ominus}$ and the interchange of intial and final states of the whole cell reaction because $\Delta G^{\ominus} = -n\mathscr{E}^{\ominus}\mathscr{F}$ by (12.30). While the sign of $\mathscr{E}$ is set by the sign of ΔG, the direction assumed for the chemical reaction and the notation describing the cell are related merely by a convention which, however, is universally used.

Decomposition of a cell EMF into additive terms for each electrode system is suggested at once by the physical arrangement of the elements of a cell even though every cell is really an integral being. The electrode sign convention described above is the one originally chosen by Gibbs. It is sometimes called the *European convention* to distinguish it from the American convention popularized by Lewis. Licht and de Bethune[1] have very clearly explained and compared these two conventions concerning signs. The main advantage of the European convention used here is that the sign associated with the electrode potential is invariant. Moreover, (12.40) is always true and a negative sign is associated with electrodes that tend to donate electrons to the external circuit. The so-called European convention is that sign convention adopted in 1953 at Stockholm by the International Union of Pure and Applied Chemistry. The statement of the I.U.P.A.C. follows:[2]

The Electromotive Force of a Cell

The cells should be represented by a diagram, e.g.,

$$\mathrm{Zn}\,|\,\mathrm{Zn}^{++}\,||\,\mathrm{Cu}^{++}\,|\,\mathrm{Cu}$$

(1) Licht, T. S. and A. J. de Bethune, *J. Chem. Ed.*, **34,** 433 (1957).

(2) Christiansen, J. A., *Manual of Physico-Chemical Symbols and Terminology*. London: Butterworth's Scientific Publications 1959 pp. 4, 6. Reprinted by permission of the International Union of Pure and Applied Chemistry and Butterworth's Scientific Publications.

The electromotive force is equal in sign and magnitude to the electrical potential of the metallic conducting lead on the right when that of the similar lead on the left is taken as zero, the cell being open.

When the reaction of the cell is written as

$$\tfrac{1}{2}\mathrm{Zn} + \tfrac{1}{2}\mathrm{Cu}^{++} \longrightarrow \tfrac{1}{2}\mathrm{Zn}^{++} + \tfrac{1}{2}\mathrm{Cu}$$

this implies a diagram so drawn that this reaction takes place when positive electricity flows through the cell from left to right. If this is the direction of the current when the cell is short-circuited, as in the present example, the electromotive force will be positive (unless the ratio Cu^{++}/Zn^{++} is extremely small). If, however, the reaction is written as:

$$\tfrac{1}{2}\mathrm{Cu} + \tfrac{1}{2}\mathrm{Zn}^{++} \longrightarrow \tfrac{1}{2}\mathrm{Cu}^{++} + \tfrac{1}{2}\mathrm{Zn}$$

this implies the diagram

$$\mathrm{Cu}\,|\,\mathrm{Cu}^{++}\,\|\,\mathrm{Zn}^{++}\,|\,\mathrm{Zn}$$

and the electromotive force of the cell so specified will be negative (unless the ratio Cu^{++}/Zn^{++} is extremely small).

The Electromotive Force of a Half-Cell and the So-called 'Electrode Potential'

When we speak of the electromotive forces of the half-cells:

$$\mathrm{Zn}^{++}\,|\,\mathrm{Zn}$$
$$\mathrm{Cl}^{-}\,|\,\mathrm{Cl}_2,\ \mathrm{Pt}$$
$$\mathrm{Cl}^{-}\,|\,\mathrm{AgCl},\ \mathrm{Ag}$$
$$\mathrm{Fe}^{++},\ \mathrm{Fe}^{+++}\,|\,\mathrm{Pt}$$

we mean the electromotive forces of the cells

$\mathrm{Pt, H_2}\,|\,\mathrm{H^+}\,\|\,\mathrm{Zn^{++}}\,|\,\mathrm{Zn}$	implying the reaction	$\tfrac{1}{2}\mathrm{H_2} + \tfrac{1}{2}\mathrm{Zn^{++}} \longrightarrow \mathrm{H^+} + \tfrac{1}{2}\mathrm{Zn}$
$\mathrm{Pt, H_2}\,|\,\mathrm{H^+}\,\|\,\mathrm{Cl^-}\,|\,\mathrm{Cl_2, Pt}$		$\tfrac{1}{2}\mathrm{H_2} + \tfrac{1}{2}\mathrm{Cl_2} \longrightarrow \mathrm{H^+} + \mathrm{Cl^-}$
$\mathrm{Pt, H_2}\,|\,\mathrm{H^+}\,\|\,\mathrm{Cl^-}\,|\,\mathrm{AgCl, Ag}$		$\tfrac{1}{2}\mathrm{H_2} + \tfrac{1}{2}\mathrm{AgCl} \longrightarrow \mathrm{H^+} + \mathrm{Cl^-} + \mathrm{Ag}$
$\mathrm{Pt, H_2}\,|\,\mathrm{H^+}\,\|\,\mathrm{Fe^{++}, Fe^{+++}}\,|\,\mathrm{Pt}$		$\tfrac{1}{2}\mathrm{H_2} + \mathrm{Fe^{+++}} \longrightarrow \mathrm{H^+} + \mathrm{Fe^{++}}$

where the electrode on the left is a *standard hydrogen electrode.*

These electromotive forces may also be called *relative electrode potentials* or, in brief, *electrode potentials.*

When, on the other hand, we speak of the electromotive forces of the half-cells

$$\mathrm{Zn}\,|\,\mathrm{Zn}^{++}$$
$$\mathrm{Pt},\ \mathrm{Cl}_2\,|\,\mathrm{Cl}^{-}$$
$$\mathrm{Ag},\ \mathrm{AgCl}\,|\,\mathrm{Cl}^{-}$$
$$\mathrm{Pt}\,|\,\mathrm{Fe}^{++},\ \mathrm{Fe}^{+++}$$

we mean the electromotive forces of the cells

$Zn \mid Zn^{++} \parallel H^+ \mid H_2$, Pt	implying the reaction	$\frac{1}{2}Zn + H^+ \longrightarrow \frac{1}{2}Zn^{++} + \frac{1}{2}H_2$
Pt, $Cl_2 \mid Cl^- \parallel H^+ \mid H_2$, Pt		$Cl^- + H^+ \longrightarrow \frac{1}{2}Cl_2 + \frac{1}{2}H_2$
Ag, $AgCl \mid Cl^- \parallel H^+ \mid H_2$, Pt		$Ag + Cl^- + H^+ \longrightarrow AgCl + \frac{1}{2}H_2$
Pt $\mid Fe^{++}, Fe^{+++} \parallel H^+ \mid H_2$, Pt		$Fe^{++} + H^+ \longrightarrow Fe^{+++} + \frac{1}{2}H_2$

where the electrode on the right is a *standard hydrogen electrode*.

These electromotive forces should NOT be called electrode potentials.

Example 12.9. If the decinormal calomel electrode, with electrode reaction $e^- + \frac{1}{2}Hg_2Cl_{2\,(s)} \rightleftharpoons Hg_{(l)} + Cl^-(0.1\ N)$, has V = +0.3338 volt at 25°C, calculate the standard electrode potential of the chlorine electrode if $\mathscr{E}$ = 1.0508 volts for the cell

$$(Pt)Hg_{(l)} \mid Hg_2Cl_{2\,(s)} \mid KCl(0.1N) \parallel HCl(0.1N) \mid Cl_{2\,(g)}(0.0490 \text{ atm})(Pt)$$

[G. N. Lewis and F. F. Rupert, *J. Am. Chem. Soc.*, **33**, 299 (1911).]

The cell reaction is found thus.

$$Hg_{(l)} + Cl^-(0.1N) \longrightarrow \tfrac{1}{2}Hg_2Cl_{2\,(s)} + e^-$$

$$e^- + \tfrac{1}{2}Cl_{2\,(g)}(0.0490 \text{ atm}) \longrightarrow Cl^-(0.1N)$$

$$Hg_{(l)} + \tfrac{1}{2}Cl_{2\,(g)}(0.0490 \text{ atm}) + Cl^-(0.1N) \longrightarrow Cl^-(0.1N) + \tfrac{1}{2}Hg_2Cl_{2\,(s)}$$

If $V^\ominus$ is the standard electrode potential of the chlorine electrode, (12.40) requires that $\mathscr{E}^\ominus = V^\ominus - (+0.3338)$ volt for the cell

$$(Pt)Hg_{(l)} \mid Hg_2Cl_{2\,(s)} \mid Cl^-(0.1N) \parallel Cl^-(a_{Cl^-} = 1) \mid Cl_{2\,(g)}(1 \text{ atm})(Pt)$$

For the cell observed, (12.34) reads

$$1.0508 = V^\ominus - 0.3338 - \frac{RT}{\mathscr{F}} \ln\left(\frac{a_{Cl^-}}{f_{Cl_2}^{1/2}}\right)$$

The activity of chloride ion appears in this equation because V = +0.3338 for the decinormal calomel cell includes a term of the form $(RT/\mathscr{F}) \ln a_{Cl^-}$, for Cl^- is part of the decinormal calomel electrode reaction. The junction potential between 0.1N KCl and 0.1N HCl is ignored in this calculation. Since a_{Cl^-} = 0.0796 in 0.1 N HCl (see Section 12.9), and since the pressure is low enough to assume that fugacity and pressure are equal, it follows that

$$V^\ominus = 1.0508 + 0.3338 + 0.05916 \log\left(\frac{0.0796}{0.0490^{1/2}}\right)$$

$$= 1.0508 + 0.3338 - 0.0263 = 1.3583 \text{ volts}$$

Example 12.10. Calculate the standard molar free energy of formation of the chloride ion in aqueous solution.

For the cell

$$(Pt)H_{2\,(g)}(1 \text{ atm}) \mid H^+(a_{H^+} = 1) \parallel Cl^-(a_{Cl^-} = 1) \mid Cl_{2\,(g)}(1 \text{ atm})(Pt)$$

the cell potential is, by Table 12.4 and (12.40),

$$\mathscr{E}^{\ominus} = V^{\ominus}_{(Cl_2)} - V^{\ominus}_{(H_2)} = 1.3595 - 0 = 1.3595 \text{ volts}$$

For the cell reaction $\frac{1}{2}H_{2(g)} + \frac{1}{2}Cl_{2(g)} \longrightarrow H^+ + Cl^-$, by (12.30),

$$\Delta G^{\ominus} = -1 \times 96{,}487 \times 1.3595 = -131{,}174 \text{ joules} = -30{,}638 \text{ cal}$$

This is also the standard molar free energy of formation of $Cl^-_{(aq)}$ since all other species in the cell reaction are in standard states for which $\Delta G^{\ominus}_f = 0$. The value in Table 9.4 is $-31{,}350$ cal.

Example 12.11. Calculate the solubility product constant of TlBr at 25°C and compare the values found in Example 11.9.

Since the solubility product constant K_{sp} is the equilibrium constant of the reaction $TlBr_{(s)} \rightleftharpoons Tl^+ + Br^-$, this same reaction must be the cell reaction of the cell chosen. Two suitable electrode reactions are

$$Tl_{(s)} \rightleftharpoons Tl^+ + e^-$$

$$e^- + TlBr_{(s)} \rightleftharpoons Tl_{(s)} + Br^-$$

For the cell $Tl_{(s)} \,|\, Tl^+ \,\|\, Br^- \,|\, TlBr_{(s)} \,|\, Tl_{(s)}$ it follows from (12.40) and Table 12.4 that

$$\mathscr{E}^{\ominus} = -0.658 - (-0.3363) = -0.322 \text{ volt}$$

By (12.35),

$$\log K_{sp} = \frac{-0.322 \times 1 \times 96{,}487}{2.303 \times 8.314 \times 298.2}$$

$$= -5.44 = 0.56 - 6.00$$

$$K_{sp} = 3.6 \times 10^{-6}$$

The conductance K_{sp} was 3.71×10^{-6}, while the free-energy value was 4.5×10^{-6}. The cell used here has a nonzero EMF because Br^- at unit activity at the right-hand electrode keeps the activity of Tl^+ so low that the cell behaves like

$$Tl_{(s)} \,|\, Tl^+(a = 1) \,\|\, Tl^+(a \ll 1) \,|\, Tl_{(s)}$$

The sign of the EMF is negative because the right-hand electrode is negative (relatively) since the number of Tl^+ near that electrode is small.

Example 12.12. Calculate the cell potential of the cell (Pt)$\,|\,Ti^{++}$ $(a = 0.200)$, Ti^{+++} $(a = 0.0200) \,\|\, H^+$ $(a = 0.0100) \,|\, H_{2(g)}$(730 mm Hg)(Pt).

The cell reaction, if electrons proceed from left to right through the external circuit, is $Ti^{++} + H^+ \rightleftharpoons \frac{1}{2}H_2 + Ti^{+++}$. By (12.34) and (12.40) and Table 12.4,

$$\mathscr{E} = \mathscr{E}^{\ominus} - \frac{RT}{\mathscr{F}} \log \left(\frac{a_{Ti^{+++}} a_{H_2}^{1/2}}{a_{H^+} a_{Ti^{++}}} \right)$$

$$= [0.00 - (-0.37)] - 0.05916 \log \left[\frac{0.0200 \times (730/760)^{1/2}}{0.0100 \times 0.200} \right]$$

$$= 0.37 - 0.05916 \log 9.80 = 0.37 - 0.06 = 0.31 \text{ volt}$$

Example 12.13. Calculate the standard electrode potential at 100°C of the electrode with half-reaction

$$e^- + H^+_{(aq)} + \tfrac{1}{6}O_{3(g)} \longrightarrow \tfrac{1}{2}H_2O_{(l)}$$

According to the I. U. P. A. C. convention, the question really asks for the EMF at 100°C of the cell $(Pt)H_{2(g)} \mid H^+ \mid O_{3(g)}(Pt)$. This cell has half- and whole-cell reactions

$$\begin{array}{r}
\tfrac{1}{2}H_{2(g)} \longrightarrow H^+ + e^- \\
e^- + H^+ + \tfrac{1}{6}O_{3(g)} \longrightarrow \tfrac{1}{2}H_2O_{(l)} \\
\hline
\tfrac{1}{2}H_{2(g)} + \tfrac{1}{6}O_{3(g)} \longrightarrow \tfrac{1}{2}H_2O_{(l)}
\end{array}$$

By Tables 3.1 and 4.3, for the cell reaction at 25°C

$$\Delta H^\circ = -39.8 \text{ kcal} \qquad \Delta S^\circ = -16.72 \text{ cal deg}^{-1}$$

while $\Delta C_P = +4.0$ cal deg^{-1}; hence, by (3.21) and (5.78), at 100°C

$$\Delta H^\circ = -39{,}800 + 4.0(373.2 - 298.2) = -39{,}500 \text{ cal}$$

$$\Delta S^\circ = -16.72 + 4.0 \ln (373/298) = -15.83 \text{ cal deg}^{-1}$$

Thus, at 100°C

$$\Delta G^\circ = -39{,}500 - 373.2(-15.83) = -33{,}600 \text{ cal} = -140{,}600 \text{ j}$$

Since $\mathscr{E}^\circ = V^\circ$ by the I. U. P. A. C. convention, (12.30) yields at 100°C

$$V^\circ = \frac{-(-140{,}600)}{96{,}487} = +1.457 \text{ volts}$$

Example 12.14. Calculate V° for the Fe-Fe^{+++} electrode at 25°C.
From Table 12.4,

$$e^- + \tfrac{1}{2}Fe^{++} \rightleftharpoons \tfrac{1}{2}Fe_{(s)}, \qquad V^\circ = -0.440 \text{ volt}$$

$$e^- + Fe^{+++} \rightleftharpoons Fe^{++}, \qquad V^\circ = +0.771 \text{ volt}$$

For the reaction $2e^- + Fe^{++} \rightleftharpoons Fe_{(s)}$, by an expression analogous to (12.30),

$$\Delta G^\circ = -2 \times 96{,}500 \times (-0.440) = +84{,}900 \text{ joules}$$

For the reaction $e^- + Fe^{+++} \rightleftharpoons Fe^{++}$,

$$\Delta G^\circ = -1 \times 96{,}500 \times 0.771 = -74{,}400 \text{ joules}$$

Since G° is a function of state, for the reaction $3e^- + Fe^{+++} \rightleftharpoons Fe_{(s)}$, namely, the sum of these last two reactions,

$$\Delta G^\circ = +84{,}900 + (-74{,}400) = 10{,}500 \text{ joules}$$

Whence,

$$V^\circ = \frac{\Delta G^\circ}{-n\mathscr{F}} = \frac{10{,}500}{-3 \times 96{,}500} = -0.0363 \text{ volt}$$

Really the $\Delta G^{\ominus}$'s refer to reduction of Fe^{2+} and Fe^{3+} by H_2, while the $V^{\ominus}$'s refer to EMF's of cells with standard hydrogen electrodes at their left.

It is impossible by purely thermodynamic means to measure the absolute potential of a single electrode, for in any charge-transfer process the work attending the transfer of charge between phases consists of two parts. One part is electrical work associated with transfer of charge in the electric field; the other is nonelectrical work associated with transfer of matter. However, by measuring the angular dependence of quadrupole radiation from an electrode that is mechanically vibrated, the electrostatic potential difference between a double layer of charges at the two-phase interface can be observed.[3] This nonthermodynamic method thus may bring the absolute value of a single electrode potential within the reach of observation. Only one is needed, for then all are known, just as the arbitrary standard of the hydrogen electrode organizes all electrodes now.

12.9 ACTIVITY COEFFICIENTS FROM CELL POTENTIALS

Observed cell potentials of suitably chosen electrochemical cells provide a direct and simple means of measuring ionic activities and activity coefficients. The various kinds of activities and activity coefficients have been defined in Section 8.9. This discussion deals with mean molal activities $a_{\pm}$ and mean molal activity coefficients $\gamma_{\pm}$.

The method of calculation is readily illustrated by the cell

$$(\mathrm{Pt})\mathrm{H}_{2(\mathrm{g})}(a = 1)\,|\,\mathrm{H}^+(a_+),\ \mathrm{Cl}^-(a_-)\,|\,\mathrm{AgCl}_{(\mathrm{s})}\,|\,\mathrm{Ag}_{(\mathrm{s})}(\mathrm{Pt})$$

Since the cell reaction is $\frac{1}{2}\mathrm{H}_{2(\mathrm{g})} + \mathrm{AgCl}_{(\mathrm{s})} \rightleftharpoons \mathrm{Ag}_{(\mathrm{s})} + \mathrm{H}^+ + \mathrm{Cl}^-$ it follows at once from (12.34) that

$$\mathscr{E} = \mathscr{E}^{\ominus} - \frac{RT}{\mathscr{F}} \ln (a_+ a_-) \tag{12.41}$$

But by (8.66), $a_{\mathrm{HCl}} = a_+ a_- = a_{\pm}^2$; and by (8.67), $a_{\pm} = \gamma_{\pm} m_{\pm}$. Since $m_{\pm} = m_{\mathrm{HCl}} = m$, (12.41) reads

$$\mathscr{E} = \mathscr{E}^{\ominus} - \frac{RT}{\mathscr{F}} \ln (\gamma_{\pm} m)^2 = \mathscr{E}^{\ominus} - \frac{2RT}{\mathscr{F}} \ln \gamma_{\pm} - \frac{2RT}{\mathscr{F}} \ln m \tag{12.42}$$

where the pressure of H_2 is taken equal to its fugacity. As m approaches zero, $\gamma_{\pm}$ approaches unity and $\ln \gamma_{\pm}$ approaches zero. Hence, in the spirit of the Debye-Hückel theory,

(3) I. Oppenheim, *J. Phys. Chem.* **68**, 2959 (1964)

$$\lim_{\sqrt{m}\to 0}\left[\mathscr{E} + \frac{2RT}{\mathscr{F}}\ln m\right] = \mathscr{E}^{\ominus} \tag{12.43}$$

Inasmuch as $[\mathscr{E} + (2RT/\mathscr{F})\ln m]$ can be calculated from directly observed values of $\mathscr{E}$, m, and T, extrapolation to the limit at $\sqrt{m} = 0$ yields $\mathscr{E}^{\ominus}$. Unfortunately the extrapolation is not linear in m or $\sqrt{m}$ in this case so that an accurate value of the standard cell potential is not forthcoming.

A suitable extrapolation can be done by adding an arbitrary constant B to the limiting form of the Debye-Hückel law (8.85) so that for HCl at molality m at 25°C

$$-\log \gamma_{\pm} = 0.509\sqrt{m} + Bm \tag{12.44}$$

From (12.42) and (12.44) then come

$$\mathscr{E}^{\ominus} = \mathscr{E} - \frac{2RT}{\mathscr{F}}(2.30259)(0.509\sqrt{m} + Bm) + \frac{2RT}{\mathscr{F}}\ln m$$

$$\mathscr{E}^{\ominus} + B'm = \mathscr{E} + 2\left(\frac{2.30259\,RT}{\mathscr{F}}\right)(\log m - 0.509\sqrt{m}) \tag{12.45}$$

where B' is an empirical constant $2B(2.30259RT/\mathscr{F})$. The right-hand member of (12.45) varies slightly because the limiting form of the Debye-Hückel law is not quite correct at finite m, while the left side of (12.45) is a Maclaurin's expansion in which

$$B' = \left(\frac{\partial \mathscr{E}^{\ominus}}{\partial m}\right)_{m=0}$$

With data from Table 12.1, Table 12.6 presents the calculations required by (12.45); Figure 12.4 is the extrapolation to $m = 0$ and $\mathscr{E}^{\ominus} = 0.22230$ volts. The values of Table 12.3 were found by a more sophisticated extrapolation

Table 12.6 Calculations for Figure 12.4 With Data at 25°C from Table 12.1.

m	$\mathscr{E}$	$\log m - 0.509\sqrt{m}$	$\mathscr{E}^{\ominus} + B'm$
0.001	0.57906	−3.0161	0.22221
0.002	0.54416	−2.7217	0.22214
0.005	0.49839	−2.3370	0.22189
0.01	0.46412	−2.0509	0.22147
0.02	0.43018	−1.7709	0.22066

procedure. (If the graph in Figure 12.4 were clearly curved, an approximate value of the second derivative of $\mathscr{E}^{\ominus}$ with respect to m at $m = 0$ could be found by using the slope B' from Figure 12.4 in (12.45) to find $\mathscr{E}^{\ominus}$ as a function of m, just as B' was found from Figure 12.4.)

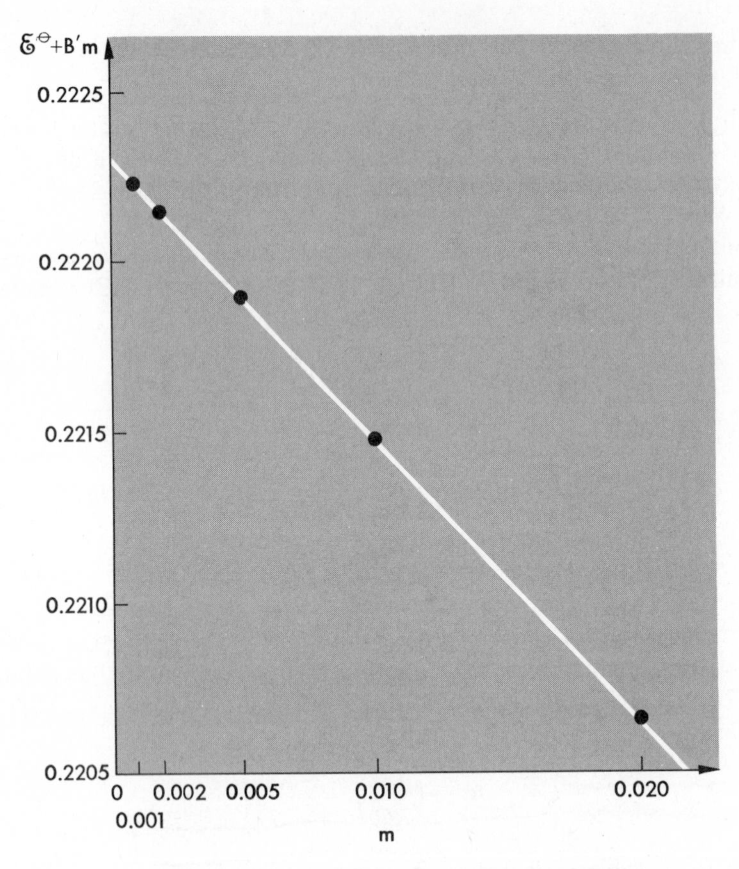

Figure 12.4. Determination of Standard Cell Potential $\mathcal{E}^{\ominus}$

With $\mathcal{E}^{\ominus}$ known, mean molal activity coefficients follow at once from (12.42) or (12.46) for each value of m.

$$\ln \gamma_{\pm} = \frac{\mathcal{F}(\mathcal{E}^{\ominus} - \mathcal{E})}{2RT} - \ln m \tag{12.46}$$

In particular, at $m = 0.1000$ where $\mathcal{E} = 0.35230$,

$$\log \gamma_{\pm} = \frac{(0.22230 - 0.35230)}{2 \times 0.059155} - \log 0.1000$$
$$= -1.0988 + 1 = 0.9012 - 1$$
$$\gamma_{\pm} = 0.7965$$

This is the value used in Example 12.9.

Figure 12.5 depicts $\gamma_\pm$ of various substances in water at 25°C. The Debye-Hückel limits for fully ionized 1–1 and 1–2 electrolytes are evidently being approached near $m = 0.1$.

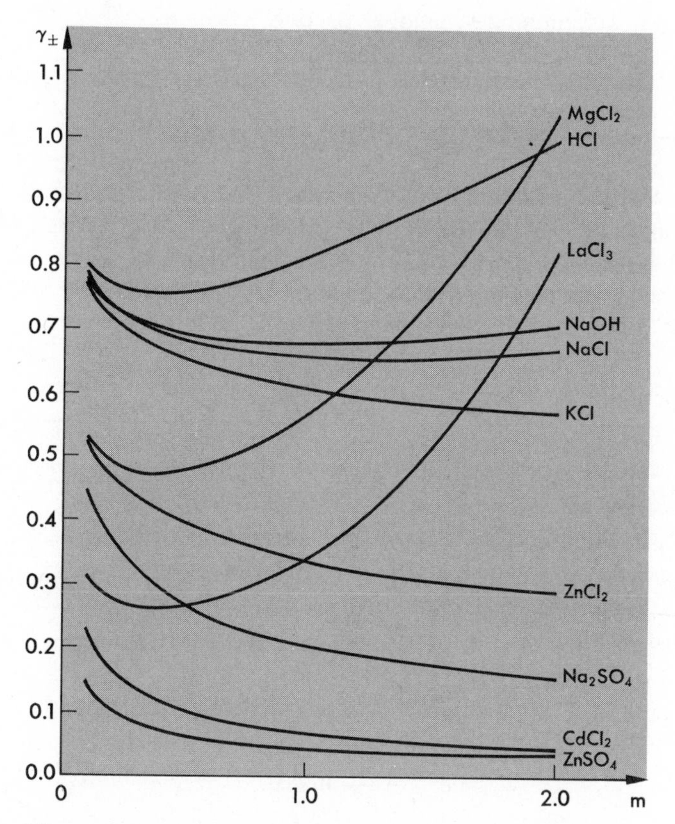

Figure 12.5. Mean Ionic Activity Coefficients at 25°C†

12.10 ION PRODUCT OF WATER AND pH

According to Table 9.4, ΔG° for the reaction $H_2O_{(l)} \longrightarrow H^+_{(aq)} + OH^-_{(aq)}$ is 19.095 kcal so that by (9.22), namely $\Delta G^\circ = -RT \ln K_a$,

$$K_w = \frac{a_{H^+} a_{OH^-}}{a_{H_2O}} = \frac{\gamma_+ \gamma_- m_+ m_-}{a_{H_2O}} = 1.007 \times 10^{-14} \qquad (12.47)$$

†R. A. Robinson and R. H. Stokes, *Electrolyte Solutions* [Second Edition], London: Butterworth's Publications Ltd., 1959, pp. 491 *ff.*

In dilute solutions, a_{H_2O} may be nearly unity while $\gamma_\pm$ still differs significantly from unity. The value of water's ion product constant K_w varies, of course, with T in a manner that can be predicted by (9.47). The chemical symbol $H^+_{(aq)}$ represents a species that is probably more complex than $H_9O_4^+$, as noted in Section 11.4.

A direct way of determining K_w involves the cells

$$(\text{Pt})\text{H}_2(1\ \text{atm})\,|\,\text{HCl}(0.01),\ \text{KCl}(m)\,|\,\text{AgCl}\,|\,\text{Ag}(\text{Pt}) \qquad \mathscr{E}' \tag{12.48}$$

$$(\text{Pt})\text{H}_2(1\ \text{atm})\,|\,\text{KOH}(0.01),\ \text{KCl}(m)\,|\,\text{AgCl}\,|\,\text{Ag}(\text{Pt}) \qquad \mathscr{E}'' \tag{12.49}$$

Table 12.7 lists EMF's of these cells at three temperatures. By (12.47), the H^+ in (12.49) is about 10^{-12} molal. Reversible with respect to H^+, the left-hand electrode of (12.48) has $\Phi'^{(1)}$ that is more positive than (12.49)'s $\Phi''^{(1)}$ because of the relatively greater number of H^+ impacts in (12.48). That is, $\Phi''^{(1)}$ is more negative than $\Phi'^{(1)}$ and thus $\mathscr{E}'' > \mathscr{E}'$, as in Table 12.7.

Table 12.7 Electromotive Force (abs. volt) of Cells (12.48) and (12.49).†

$\mathscr{E}'(0°C)$	$\mathscr{E}'(25°C)$	$\mathscr{E}'(50°C)$	m_{KCl}	$\mathscr{E}''(0°C)$	$\mathscr{E}''(25°C)$	$\mathscr{E}''(50°C)$
0.44333	0.44836	0.44975	0.01	1.04653	1.05068	1.05517
0.43487	0.43920	0.43984	0.02	1.03024	1.03294	1.03600
0.42890	0.43272	0.43294	0.03	1.02074	1.02257	1.02473
0.42058	0.42368	0.42313	0.05	1.00874	1.00955	1.01056
0.40828	0.41026	0.40886	0.10	0.99250	0.99193	0.99156

† H. S. Harned and W. J. Hamer, *J. Am. Chem. Soc.* **55**, 2194 (1933).

This difference in $\mathscr{E}''$ and $\mathscr{E}'$ yields a value of K_w, for by (12.34) and (12.18)

$$\mathscr{E}' = \mathscr{E}'^{\ominus} - \frac{RT}{\mathscr{F}} \ln a'_+ a'_- \tag{12.50}$$

$$\mathscr{E}'' = \mathscr{E}''^{\ominus} - \frac{RT}{\mathscr{F}} \ln a''_+ a''_- \tag{12.51}$$

Since $\mathscr{E}'^{\ominus} = \mathscr{E}''^{\ominus}$ because the electrode reactions are alike, and since activity coefficients are nearly equal in solutions of the same ionic strength, it follows from (12.50) and (12.51) that

$$\mathscr{E}'' - \mathscr{E}' = \frac{RT}{\mathscr{F}} \ln \frac{a'_+ a'_-}{a''_+ a''_-} \approx \frac{RT}{\mathscr{F}} \ln \frac{m'_+ m'_-}{m''_+ m''_-} \tag{12.52}$$

Using (12.47) to eliminate m''_+ then brings (12.52) to the form

$$\mathscr{E}'' - \mathscr{E}' \approx \frac{RT}{\mathscr{F}} \ln \frac{m'_+ m'_-}{m''_-} - \frac{RT}{\mathscr{F}} \ln \frac{a''_{H_2O} K_w}{\gamma''_{H^+} \gamma''_{OH^-} m''_{OH^-}}$$

from which

$$\log K_w = \frac{\mathscr{F}(\mathscr{E}' - \mathscr{E}'')}{2.30259\, RT} + \log \frac{m'_+ m'_- m''_{\mathrm{OH^-}}}{m''_-} + \log \frac{\gamma''_{\mathrm{H^+}} \gamma''_{\mathrm{OH^-}}}{a''_{\mathrm{H_2O}}} \qquad (12.53)$$

In the limit as $m_{\mathrm{KCl}} \longrightarrow 0$ the last term of (12.53) vanishes. The other terms on the right of (12.53) are specified in Table 12.7. By the simple Debye-Hückel equation (8.85) which holds approximately even in these solutions of more than one electrolyte, (12.53) with $a''_{\mathrm{H_2O}} = 1$ becomes

$$\log K_w = \frac{\mathscr{F}(\mathscr{E}' - \mathscr{E}'')}{2.30259\, RT} + \log \frac{m'_+ m'_- m''_{\mathrm{OH^-}}}{m''_-} - 0.509\sqrt{m''_{\mathrm{OH^-}}} \qquad (12.54)$$

since $m''_{\mathrm{H^+}}$ is negligible with respect to $m''_{\mathrm{OH^-}}$. As in Section 12.9, plotting the right side of (12.54) vs m_{KCl} and extrapolating to $m_{\mathrm{KCl}} = 0$ yields, as in Figure 12.6,

$$\lim_{m \to 0} \log K_w = -13.96 = 0.04 - 14.00 \qquad (25°\mathrm{C}) \qquad (12.55)$$

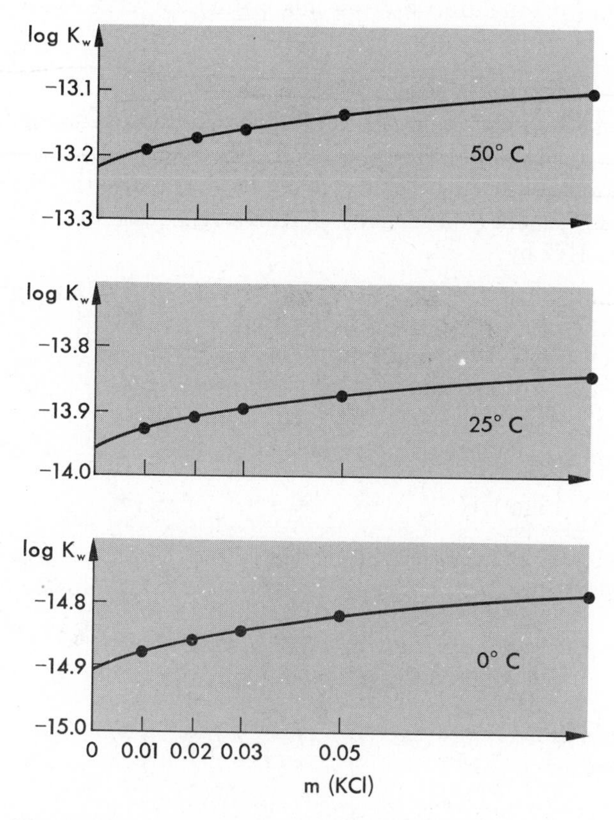

Figure 12.6. Extrapolation to Find K_w

From (12.55), K_w at infinite dilution is $1.1_0 \times 10^{-14}$ at 25°C, in close agreement with (12.47). Figure 12.6 also yields $K_w = 1.2_6 \times 10^{-15}$ at 0°C and $6.0_2 \times 10^{-14}$ at 50°C. Table 12.8 lists $\log K_w$ and K_w based on different data interpreted differently.

Table 12.8 Ionization Constants of Water.†

Temperature (0°C)	$\log K_w$	$K_w \times 10^{14}$
0	-14.943_5	0.1139
10	-14.534_9	0.2918
20	-14.166_6	0.6814
25	-13.996_5	1.008
30	-13.833_0	1.469
40	-13.534_8	2.919
50	-13.261_7	5.474
60	-13.017_1	9.614

† H. S. Harned and R. A. Robinson, *Trans. Faraday Soc.* **36,** 973 (1940).

It is mathematically straightforward to define pH by the relation

$$\text{pH} = -\log_{10} a_{\text{H}^+} \tag{12.56}$$

However, it is thermodynamically impossible by charge-transfer processes to measure just a_{H^+}, for H^+ is always in a real solution and is affected by the anions' activity. In order to remove this uncertainty caused by the anions, the National Bureau of Standards[4] defines the activity coefficiency γ_{Cl^-} of Cl^- in dilute solutions of KCl and HCl by

$$-\log \gamma_{\text{Cl}^-} = \frac{AI^{1/2}}{1 + 1.5I^{1/2}} \tag{12.57}$$

where the ionic strength I is less than about 0.1 and where A is given by Table 8.5.

This definition of γ_{Cl^-} renders pH observable in the cell

$$(\text{Pt})\text{H}_{2(g)}(1 \text{ atm}) \,|\, \text{H}^+(a_{\text{H}^+}), \text{KCl}(m) \,|\, \text{AgCl}_{(s)} \,|\, \text{Ag}_{(s)}(\text{Pt}) \tag{12.58}$$

As earlier in this section, an appropriate function of the cell observables $\mathscr{E}$, T, and m is extrapolated from about 0.01 molal to $m = 0$. In view of (12.50), for (12.58)

$$\mathscr{E} = \mathscr{E}^{\ominus} - \frac{RT}{\mathscr{F}} \ln (a_{\text{H}^+}\gamma_{\text{Cl}^-}m_{\text{Cl}^-})$$

$$\frac{\mathscr{F}(\mathscr{E} - \mathscr{E}^{\ominus})}{2.30259\, RT} = -\log a_{\text{H}^+} + \frac{AI^{1/2}}{1 + 1.5I^{1/2}} - \log m_{\text{Cl}^-} \tag{12.59}$$

[4] R. G. Bates, *J. Res. Nat. Bur. Stds.* **66A,** 179 (1962)

where (12.57) has been used. Finally, going to the limit gives

$$\mathrm{pH} = \lim_{m \to 0} \left[\frac{\mathscr{F}(\mathscr{E} - \mathscr{E}^{\ominus})}{2.30259\,RT} + \log m_{\mathrm{Cl}^-} - \frac{AI^{1/2}}{1 + 1.5I^{1/2}} \right] \tag{12.60}$$

Table 12.9 lists the pH of the standard solutions studied in this way. Although any solution could also be studied thus, Section 12.13 explains how these standards are used in a simpler procedure for analysis of unknowns.

Table 12.9 Standard Values of pH.†

Solute	Description of Aqueous Solution	Value of pH		
		0°C	25°C	50°C
$KH_3(C_2O_4)_2 \cdot 2H_2O$	0.05 molal	1.666	1.679	1.707
Potassium Hydrogen Tartrate	Saturated at 25°	—	3.557	3.549
Potassium Hydrogen Phthalate	0.05 molal	4.003	4.008	4.060
(1) KH_2PO_4 (2) Na_2HPO_4	0.025 molal in (1) 0.025 molal in (2)	6.984	6.865	6.833
(1) KH_2PO_4 (2) Na_2HPO_4	0.008695 molal in (1) 0.03043 molal in (2)	7.534	7.413	7.367
Borax	0.01 molal	9.464	9.180	9.011
$Ca(OH)_2$	Saturated at 25°C	13.423	12.454	11.705

† R. G. Bates, *J. Res. Nat. Bur. Stds.* **66A,** 179 (1962).

12.11 CONCENTRATION CELLS

Concentration cells exhibit a difference in potential through a difference in concentration and the change of free energy that occurs upon dilution or concentration of a solution. Concentration cells without transference are so made that solutions of different concentration are not in direct contact. Such cells have no salt bridges and have no need for them. Cells without transference are of two general types: (a) One electrode is reversible with respect to a cation of the common electrolyte, while the other electrode is reversible with respect to an anion of the common electrolyte. Examples are:

$$(\mathrm{Pt})\mathrm{H}_{2\,(g)} \,|\, \mathrm{H}^+, \mathrm{Cl}^- \,|\, \mathrm{AgCl}_{(s)} \,|\, \mathrm{Ag}_{(s)}(\mathrm{Pt})$$

$$(\mathrm{Pt})\mathrm{Zn}_{(s)} \,|\, \mathrm{Zn}^{2+}, \mathrm{Cl}^- \,|\, \mathrm{Cl}_{2\,(g)}(\mathrm{Pt})$$

(b) The electrodes contacting the common electrolyte have different activities of the species that can become either an anion or cation of the common electrolyte. Examples are:

$$(Pt)Zn_xHg \mid Zn^{++} \mid Zn_yHg(Pt), \qquad (x \neq y)$$

$$(Pt)Cl_2(p_1) \mid Cl^- \mid Cl_2(p_2)(Pt), \qquad (p_1 \neq p_2)$$

Even these cells are only approximations to an ideal cell, for the separation of reactive species is not perfect. The concentrations of Ag^+ and H_2, of Zn and Cl_2, of Zn and Hg, and of Cl_2 in the common electrolyte are not zero. Fortunately they are negligible. Cells of type (b) above are concentration cells without transference.

Example 12.15. Calculate the cell potential at 25°C of the cell

$$(Pt)H_{2(g)}(1.000 \text{ atm}) \mid H^+(0.1\ N) \mid H_{2(g)}(386.6 \text{ atm})(Pt)$$

Since $V^{\ominus}$ is zero for both electrodes and since the cell reaction is $H_{2(g)}$ (1.000 atm) $\rightleftharpoons H_{2(g)}$ (386.6 atm), by (12.34)

$$\mathscr{E} = -\frac{RT}{\mathscr{F}} \ln\left(\frac{386.6^{1/2}}{1.000^{1/2}}\right) = -\frac{0.05916}{2} \log 386.6 = -0.0765 \text{ volt}$$

The observed value [W. R. Hainesworth, H. J. Rowley and D. A. MacInnes, *J. Am. Chem. Soc.*, **46,** 1437 (1924)] is −0.0794 volt. The deviation is due to nonideal behavior of H_2. The fact that $\mathscr{E}$ is less than zero indicates that the cell reaction is not spontaneous, for ΔG is greater than zero.

Cells with transference have solutions of differing concentration directly in contact with each other. Ions tend to diffuse from solution to solution because ions differ in nature and mobility and concentration. The slight deviations from electroneutrality that result at the interface between solutions cause a measurable potential difference. This potential difference is called a *diffusion potential* or *junction potential.* Cells with transference are of two types: (a) Both electrodes are reversible with respect to different cations or different anions. Examples are:

w/ trans.

$$(Pt)Zn_{(s)} \mid Zn^{++} \mid Cu^{++} \mid Cu_{(s)}(Pt)$$

$$(Pt)Zn_{(s)} \mid Zn^{++} \mid Fe^{++}, Fe^{+++} \mid (Pt)$$

$$(Pt)Br_{2(l)} \mid Br^- \mid Cl^- \mid Cl_{2(g)}(Pt)$$

(b) Similar electrodes are in contact with electrolytes of different ionic activity. Examples are:

$$Zn_{(s)} \mid Zn^{++}(a_2) \mid Zn^{++}(a)_1 \mid Zn_{(s)}$$

$$(Pt)H_{2(g)} \mid H^+(a_2) \mid H^+(a_1) \mid H_{2(g)}(Pt)$$

$$(Pt)Cl_{2(g)} \mid Cl^-(a_1) \mid Cl^-(a_2) \mid Cl_{2(g)}(Pt)$$

$$Ag_{(s)} \mid AgCl_{(s)} \mid Cl^-(a_1) \mid Cl^-(a_2) \mid AgCl_{(s)} \mid Ag_{(s)}$$

Since cells of type (b) exhibit a potential difference because a_1 is not equal to a_2 they are concentration cells with transference.

The junction potential caused by the change in concentration can be decreased by connecting the solutions of differing concentration with a salt bridge. Solutions of KCl or, when K^+ or Cl^- ions would interfere with electrode reactions, NH_4NO_3 are commonly used. Although the junction potential can seldom be eliminated completely, it can be decreased sufficiently in many cases so that calculations with the Nernst equation are meaningful. An ideal salt bridge, which is considered to reduce the junction potential to zero, is indicated by two vertical lines. For example,

$$Zn_{(s)} | Zn^{++}(a_2) \| Zn^{++}(a_1) | Zn_{(s)} \tag{12.61}$$

$$(Pt)Cl_{2(g)} | Cl^-(a_1) \| Cl^-(a_2) | Cl_{2(g)}(Pt)$$

It is often possible to arrange a battery of cells without transference that has as its net reaction essentially the same change of state effected in a cell with transference. For example, for the zinc concentration cell (12.61), the cell reaction is $Zn^{++}(a_1) \rightleftharpoons Zn^{++}(a_2)$. But this is the overall reaction of the double cell

$$Ag | AgCl | Cl^-, Zn^{++}(a_1) | Zn | Zn^{++}(a_2), Cl^- | AgCl | Ag \tag{12.62}$$

provided the Cl^- activity is the same at both electrodes. The EMF of (12.62) would be zero if $a_1 = a_2$. Since ionic solutions must, however, be electrically neutral, it is clear that one or both solutions contain ions other than Zn^{2+} and Cl^- if $a_1 \neq a_2$. Hence, the cell reaction of (12.62) really takes Zn^{2+} at a_1 and brings it to a_2 in another solution that may be quite different in character. The idealized cell (12.61) makes no comment at all on the other ions while cell (12.62) notes the difference in solutions only indirectly and incompletely. The same general comments apply to the cell of Example 12.4 except that the reaction there is a simple and straightforward change of concentration by dilution or concentration since $a_1 = a_3 \neq a_2 = a_4$.

Example 12.16. Calculate the cell potential at 25°C of the cell

$$(Pt)H_{2(g)}(a = 1) | H^+(a = 10^{-7}) \| H^+(a = 1) | H_{2(g)}(a = 1)(Pt)$$

Since the cell reaction is $H^+(a = 1) \rightleftharpoons H^+(a = 10^{-7})$, by (12.34)

$$\mathscr{E} = 0.0000 - \frac{0.05916}{1} \log \left(\frac{10^{-7}}{1}\right) = +0.41412 \text{ volt}$$

Electrons tend to flow spontaneously from left to right through the external circuit in this cell because there are more protons at the right ready to accept the electrons than there are protons at the left.

12.12 JUNCTION POTENTIAL

As one faraday of electrons moves through each electrode of a cell and through the metallic conductors in the external circuit, the current through the cell's electrolyte solution is carried by oppositely charged ions moving in opposite directions. Faraday defined the *anode* (*cathode*) of an electrochemical *or* electrolytic cell as the electrode at which positive (negative) charge enters the cell. Thus, in an electrolytic cell (e. g. Figure 11.2) the negative electrode is the cathode; at it electrons enter and toward it positive ions called cations move within the cell. On the other hand, in a short-circuited electrochemical cell the negative electrode is the anode; from it electrons leave and toward it negative ions (anions) move in order to find new partners among the ions newly generated at the anode. In both cells the transference numbers of the ions of the electrolyte solution describe what fraction of the current is carried through the electrolyte by cations and anions.

With care it is possible to maintain a steady state where solutions meet in a transference cell and thus to observe a reproducible EMF. Gels or porous barriers may be used to slow the diffusion of ions, or the contact of solutions may be renewed as virgin solutions flow into or past each other. The very simple cell with liquid junction

$$\mathrm{M}\,|\,\mathrm{M}^+(a''_+),\ \mathrm{X}^-(a''_-)\,|\,\mathrm{X}^-(a'_-),\ \mathrm{M}^+(a'_+)\,|\,\mathrm{M} \tag{12.63}$$

where M is any metal has the following events occurring within it as one faraday passes through the external circuit.

$$\left.\begin{array}{ll}\text{At the left electrode (anode):} & \mathrm{M} \longrightarrow \mathrm{M}^+(a''_+) + e^- \\ \text{At the solutions' interface:} & t_+\mathrm{M}^+(a''_+) \longrightarrow t_+\mathrm{M}^+(a'_+) \\ \text{At the solutions' interface:} & t_-\mathrm{X}^-(a'_-) \longrightarrow t_-\mathrm{X}^-(a''_-) \\ \text{At the right electrode (cathode):} & e^- + \mathrm{M}^+(a'_+) \longrightarrow \mathrm{M}\end{array}\right\} \tag{12.64}$$

The transference numbers t_+ and t_- have been assumed to be the same in both solutions. The net cell reaction is the sum of (12.64), namely

$$(1 - t_+)\mathrm{M}^+(a'_+) + t_-\mathrm{X}^-(a'_-) \longrightarrow (1 - t_+)\mathrm{M}^+(a''_+) + t_-\mathrm{X}^-(a''_-) \tag{12.65}$$

If $t_+ + t_- = 1$, then (12.65) becomes

$$t_-\mathrm{M}^+(a'_+) + t_-\mathrm{X}^-(a'_-) \longrightarrow t_-\mathrm{M}^+(a''_+) + t_-\mathrm{X}^-(a''_-) \tag{12.66}$$

For the battery

$$\mathrm{Ag}\,|\,\mathrm{AgX}\,|\,\mathrm{X}^-(a'_-),\ \mathrm{M}^+(a'_+)\,|\,\mathrm{M}\,|\,\mathrm{M}^+(a''_+),\ \mathrm{X}^-(a''_-)\,|\,\mathrm{AgX}\,|\,\mathrm{Ag} \tag{12.67}$$

the net cell reaction as one faraday passes through the external circuit is very much like (12.66), namely

$$\mathrm{M}^+(a'_+) + \mathrm{X}^-(a'_-) \longrightarrow \mathrm{M}^+(a''_+) + \mathrm{X}^-(a''_-) \tag{12.68}$$

If the increase in free energy of (12.68) is $\Delta G = -\mathscr{E}\mathscr{F}$, then for (12.66) it is

$$-n\mathscr{E}_t\mathscr{F} = \Delta G_t = t_-\Delta G = t_-(-n\mathscr{E}\mathscr{F}) \tag{12.69}$$

The EMF of the cell (12.63) with transference compared to the EMF $\mathscr{E}$ of the battery (12.67) is, from (12.69)

$$\mathscr{E}_t = t_-\mathscr{E} \tag{12.70}$$

If a cell like (12.63) has electrodes reversible to negative ions, then, as in (12.70), $\mathscr{E}_t = t_+\mathscr{E}$.

When $\mathscr{E}$ and $\mathscr{E}_t$ can be observed, then (12.70) yields t. However, if t is known by Hittorff or moving boundary methods, then either $\mathscr{E}$ or $\mathscr{E}_t$ can be calculated from the other. It is sometimes possible to observe $\mathscr{E}_t$ when $\mathscr{E}$ cannot be observed because, for example, one electrode does not operate reproducibly. It could be omitted as the central ones of (12.67) are, when a cell with transference is observed. Nevertheless, for the sake of $\mathscr{E}^{\ominus}$ or $\Delta G^{\ominus}$ the electrode's properties may be quite important. In other cases, with t known, measuring $\mathscr{E}_t$ eventually gives the value of the junction potential $\mathscr{E}_j$ because by definition

$$\mathscr{E}_j = \mathscr{E}_t - \mathscr{E} \tag{12.71}$$

The sign of $\mathscr{E}_j$ is negative if the incipient interdiffusion of ions at the interface between solutions tends to make the electrostatic potential of the left-hand solution higher than that of the right. This is like the convention on potentials of electrodes of whole cells. Figure 12.7 illustrates an interface where the positively charged cations in the right-hand solution (phase 2) diffuse more rapidly (despite their greater size!) than those in the left-hand solution (phase 1) because

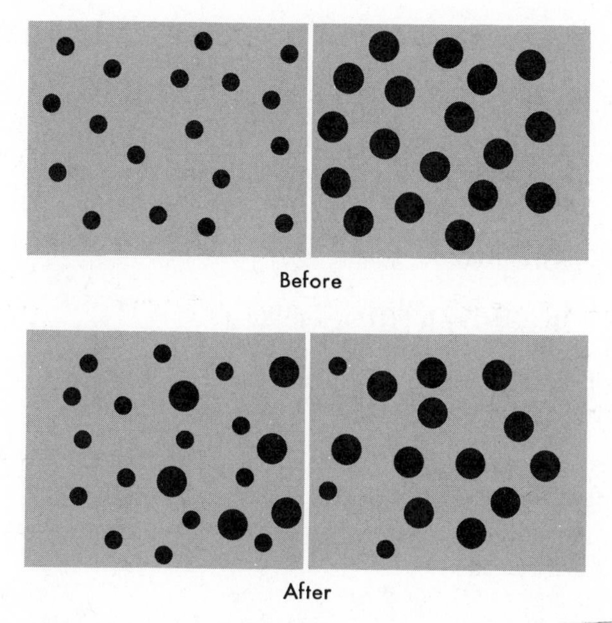

Figure 12.7. Schematic Diagram of Source of Junction Potential

of a difference in nature. The negative anions are not shown and are assumed alike in kind and concentration in both solutions. The effects of the net incipient transfer of cations to the left is transmitted throughout each solution by small displacements of all ions. A metallic probe in phase 1 would be at a higher $\boldsymbol{\Phi}$ and more positive than a like probe in phase 2; hence, $\mathscr{E}_j$ is less than zero in Figure 12.7.

Examples with $\mathscr{E}_j$ negative and $\mathscr{E}$ positive are (12.63) when M^+ is more concentrated near the right-hand electrode (phase 2) and

$$(Pt)Tl \,|\, Tl^+ \,|\, H^+ \,|\, H_2(Pt)$$

where the H^+ ions diffuse more rapidly than Tl^+.

A junction potential generally occurs in the measurement of pH for the typical cell used is essentially

$$\begin{array}{llllllll} & (Pt)H_2 \,|\, H^+, Cl^- \,|\, K^+, Cl^- \,|\, Hg_2Cl_2 \,|\, Hg(Pt) & & & & & & (12.72) \\ \text{Phase} & 1 \;\; 3 \qquad 4 \qquad\quad 5 \qquad\quad 6 \qquad\; 7 \;\; 2 \end{array}$$

Equilibrium at constant T and P obtains throughout the cell except at the liquid junction between phases 4 and 5 and except for electrons in phases 1 and 2. Since the true chemical potentials of a species are equal in phases at equilibrium, at the left-hand electrode

$$\boldsymbol{\mu}^{(3)}(H^+) = \boldsymbol{\mu}^{(4)}(H^+) \tag{12.73}$$

$$\boldsymbol{\mu}^{(3)}(e^-) = \boldsymbol{\mu}^{(1)}(e^-) \tag{12.74}$$

Similarly, since the electrode reaction $\frac{1}{2}H_2 \longrightarrow H^+ + e^-$ is at equilibrium, there exists the condition

$$\tfrac{1}{2}\boldsymbol{\mu}^{(3)}(H_2) = \boldsymbol{\mu}^{(3)}(H^+) + \boldsymbol{\mu}^{(3)}(e^-) \tag{12.75}$$

Addition of (12.73), (12.74), and (12.75) gives

$$\tfrac{1}{2}\boldsymbol{\mu}^{(3)}(H_2) = \boldsymbol{\mu}^{(4)}(H^+) + \boldsymbol{\mu}^{(1)}(e^-) \tag{12.76}$$

Similarly, at the right-hand electrode where the electrode reaction is $e^- + \frac{1}{2}Hg_2Cl_2 \longrightarrow Hg + Cl^-$, equilibrium requires

$$\boldsymbol{\mu}^{(2)}(e^-) + \tfrac{1}{2}\boldsymbol{\mu}^{(6)}(Hg_2Cl_2) = \boldsymbol{\mu}^{(7)}(Hg) + \boldsymbol{\mu}^{(5)}(Cl^-) \tag{12.77}$$

For the sake of comparisons of EMF with and without transference, the net cell reaction of (12.72) is assumed to be

$$\tfrac{1}{2}H_2^{(3)} + \tfrac{1}{2}Hg_2Cl_2^{(6)} \longrightarrow Hg^{(7)} + H^{+(4)} + Cl^{-(4)} \tag{12.78}$$

where superscripts in parentheses indicate the phase of the species. The distribution of H^+ and K^+ at the 4–5 interface is assumed to be constant in the cell because of an experimental situation; hence, its influence on ΔG is taken to be negligible. The cell will be termed one with transference if $\boldsymbol{\mu}^{(4)}(Cl^-) \neq \boldsymbol{\mu}^{(5)}(Cl^-)$. However, if the environment of Cl^- in 4 and 5 is so similar that $\boldsymbol{\mu}^{(4)}(Cl^-) = \boldsymbol{\mu}^{(5)}(Cl^-)$, then the boundary between 4 and 5 is effectively gone and the cell will be termed one without transference.

When (12.78) occurs in the cell,

$$\begin{aligned}\Delta G &= \boldsymbol{\mu}^{(7)}(\mathrm{Hg}) + \boldsymbol{\mu}^{(4)}(\mathrm{H}^+) + \boldsymbol{\mu}^{(4)}(\mathrm{Cl}^-) - \tfrac{1}{2}\boldsymbol{\mu}^{(3)}(\mathrm{H}_2) - \tfrac{1}{2}\boldsymbol{\mu}^{(6)}(\mathrm{Hg}_2\mathrm{Cl}_2)\\ &= \boldsymbol{\mu}^{(4)}(\mathrm{Cl}^-) - \boldsymbol{\mu}^{(5)}(\mathrm{Cl}^-) + \boldsymbol{\mu}^{(2)}(e^-) - \boldsymbol{\mu}^{(1)}(e^-) \end{aligned} \tag{12.79}$$

where (12.76) and (12.77) have been used. Without transference $[\boldsymbol{\mu}^{(4)}(Cl^-) = \boldsymbol{\mu}^{(5)}(Cl^-)]$, (12.17) with $z = -1$ for the electron brings (12.79) to the form

$$\Delta G = -\mathscr{F}[\Phi^{(2)} - \Phi^{(1)}] = -\mathscr{F}\mathscr{E} \tag{12.80}$$

With transference, with $z = -1$ in (12.16) for Cl^- and in (12.17) for e^- (12.79) takes the form

$$\begin{aligned}\Delta G &= \mu^{(4)}(\mathrm{Cl}^-) - \mu^{(5)}(\mathrm{Cl}^-) - \mathscr{F}[\Phi^{(4)} - \Phi^{(5)}]\\ &\qquad - \mathscr{F}[\Phi_t^{(2)} - \Phi_t^{(1)}]\\ &= \mu^{(4)}(\mathrm{Cl}^-) - \mu^{(5)}(\mathrm{Cl}^-) - \mathscr{F}[\Phi^{(4)} - \Phi^{(5)}] - \mathscr{F}\mathscr{E}_t \end{aligned} \tag{12.81}$$

where the observed EMF of the cell with transference is

$$\mathscr{E}_t = \Phi_t^{(2)} - \Phi_t^{(1)} \tag{12.82}$$

Equating ΔG in (12.80) and (12.81) because the cell reaction (12.78) has the same initial and final states yields

$$\mathscr{E} = \mathscr{E}_t - [\Phi^{(5)} - \Phi^{(4)}] + \frac{\mu^{(5)}(\mathrm{Cl}^-) - \mu^{(4)}(\mathrm{Cl}^-)}{\mathscr{F}} \tag{12.83}$$

If $\mathscr{E}_j$ is still defined by (12.71), then by (12.83)

$$\mathscr{E}_j = [\Phi^{(5)} - \Phi^{(4)}] - \frac{\mu^{(5)}(\mathrm{Cl}^-) - \mu^{(4)}(\mathrm{Cl}^-)}{\mathscr{F}} \tag{12.84}$$

In getting (12.17) from (12.16) it was noted that $\Delta\Phi$ is not a truly meaningful EMF if the phases differ chemically. To the extent that this problem can be ignored and that $\mu^{(4)}(Cl^-)$ approaches $\mu^{(5)}(Cl^-)$, it is clear that (12.84) conforms to the right-minus-left convention, the left-hand phase being at zero potential. To the extent that this problem remains, $\mathscr{E}_j$ is not the EMF that would be observed by observing $\Delta\Phi$ on chemically identical probes inserted on each side of the solutions' interface. After all, the probes of (12.72) are different whole electrodes.

Calculating the work done on the ions as they move between solutions will yield a direct estimate of $\mathscr{E}_j$. The way in which the ions' concentrations change with distance through the interface is generally important but unknown. If the concentration of each ion changes linearly with the distance parameter of integration, if the two electrolytes are uni-univalent and have a common ion such as Cl^-, if the solutions are so dilute that ionic conductances are equal to those at infinite dilution, and if the concentrations of the two solutions are equal, then for uni-univalent electrolytes it is possible to show (tediously) that

$$\mathscr{E}_j = -\frac{RT}{\mathscr{F}} \ln \left(\frac{\Lambda_0^{(2)}}{\Lambda_0^{(1)}}\right) \tag{12.85}$$

The equivalent conductance of the right-hand solution at infinite dilution is $\Lambda_0^{(2)}$. This is similar to the Lewis and Sargent formula:

$$\mathscr{E}_j = -\frac{RT}{\mathscr{F}} \ln \left(\frac{\Lambda^{(2)}}{\Lambda^{(1)}}\right) \tag{12.86}$$

Example 12.17. By means of the Lewis and Sargent formula, estimate the junction potential between 0.1 *N* HCl and 0.1 *N* KCl. The equivalent conductivities of these solutions at 25°C are 391 and 129.

By (12.86),

$$\mathscr{E}_j = -0.05915 \log \left(\frac{391}{129}\right) = -0.05915 \times 0.482 = -0.0285 \text{ volt}$$

Since the right-hand electrode was taken to be HCl, Figure 12.7 applies with $H_9O_4^+$ as the larger dots and K^+ as the smaller ones. The acid is less positive than KCl because of incipient depletion of its H^+ by diffusion into KCl.

12.13 GLASS ELECTRODE

The measurement of pH is used widely in process control, analysis of solutions, soils, biological and physiological specimens, and so on. The unwieldy hydrogen electrode of Section 12.10 is commonly replaced, at least in the less exacting routine analysis, by a glass electrode. Glass electrodes are simple to use and resist attack by species that interfere with the hydrogen electrode.

When pH is measured with a glass electrode and a calomel electrode, the complete cell diagram reads

$$Ag\,|\,AgCl\,|\,H^+(a_1^\ominus),\ Cl(a_2^\ominus)\,|\,G\,|\,H^+(a = ?)\,|\,K^+Cl^-\,|\,Hg_2Cl_2\,|\,Hg(Ag) \tag{12.87}$$

where $a_1^{\ominus}$ and $a_2^{\ominus}$ are fixed as part of the glass electrode because the HCl is enclosed by the thin glass membrane G. The liquid junction here is between the KCl solution and the solution of unknown pH. Figure 12.8 is a diagram of a typical glass electrode. The glass membrane may be made of one of several kinds of glass and it responds to the external H^+ as though it were an ion exchange membrane or in some way semipermeable to H^+. Chemisorption of ions on both sides of G with their resulting adsorption potentials is also important in the action of the electrode.

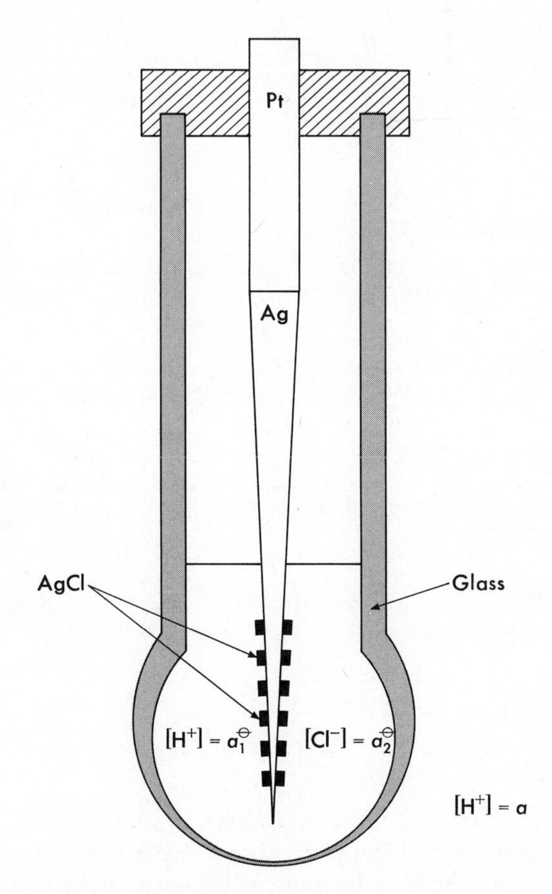

Figure 12.8. Glass Electrode

A battery with net reaction such that the Nernst equation is like that for (12.87) is

$$Ag\,|\,AgCl\,|\,H^+(a_+),\ Cl^-(a_-)\,|\,H_2\,|\,Pt\,|\,H_2\,\|\,H^+(a)\,|\,K^+,\ Cl^-\,|\,Hg_2Cl_2\,|\,Hg(Ag) \qquad (12.88)$$

wherein a is unknown and the electrode reactions are

$$Ag + Cl^-(a_-) \longrightarrow AgCl + e^-$$
$$e^- + H^+(a_+) \longrightarrow \tfrac{1}{2}H_2$$
$$\tfrac{1}{2}H_2 \longrightarrow H^+(a) + e^-$$
$$e^- + \tfrac{1}{2}Hg_2Cl_2 \longrightarrow Hg + Cl^-_{(KCl)}$$

From these equations for the battery (12.88) with equal pressures of H_2, it follows from (12.34) that

$$\begin{aligned}\mathscr{E} &= V^{\ominus}_{(\text{calomel})} - V^{\ominus}_{(\text{Ag-AgCl})} - \frac{RT}{\mathscr{F}} \ln \frac{a}{a_+ a_-} \\ &= \mathscr{E}^{\ominus} + \frac{2.30259\, RT}{\mathscr{F}}(\text{pH})\end{aligned} \qquad (12.89)$$

where (12.56) was used and where $\mathscr{E}^{\ominus}$ combines the $V^{\ominus}$'s and terms containing a_+ and a_-, for these are fixed when the glass electrode is used.

A value of $\mathscr{E}^{\ominus}$ in (12.89) is found empirically for a particular experiment by use of a standard solution with pH_s. The instrument is thus calibrated by (12.89) in the form

$$\mathscr{E}_s = \mathscr{E}^{\ominus} + \frac{2.30259\, RT}{\mathscr{F}} \text{pH}_s \qquad (12.90)$$

Then, with the unknown in place of the standard,

$$\mathscr{E} = \mathscr{E}^{\ominus} + \frac{2.30259\, RT}{\mathscr{F}} \text{pH} \qquad (12.91)$$

That is, upon elimination of the instrumental constant $\mathscr{E}^{\ominus}$, (12.90) and (12.91) yield

$$\text{pH} = \text{pH}_s + \frac{(\mathscr{E} - \mathscr{E}_s)\mathscr{F}}{2.30259\, RT} \qquad (12.92)$$

Naturally, a standard with pH and chemical nature close to that of the unknown is the best choice. The standard at $\text{pH}_s = 7.414$ at 25°C and $\text{pH}_s = 7.382$ at 38°C was developed specifically to serve the needs of physiology. Normal blood, for example, has acidity in this range. Utmost accuracy (± 0.001 pH unit) with (12.92) is achieved by a careful choice of instrument, which must respond to the tiny currents passed by the high resistance of the glass electrode, by proper conditioning of the glass electrode, and by minimizing changes in the junction potential on going from standard to unknown.

Glass electrodes work reproducibly in nonaqueous solutions and can be used to characterize their properties. Moreover, in aqueous solution, they respond to cations other than H^+. This response was once considered a limitation on the value of the glass electrode. At a pH of about 4.5, a typical glass electrode may be more sensitive to Ag^+ than to H^+, while at pH above 8 it may be useful for determining the concentration of Na^+, K^+, NH_4^+, or other ion at molalities above 0.0001. The single electrode potential in such use is of the form

$$V_{(glass)} = V^{\ominus}_{(glass)} - \frac{RT}{\mathscr{F}} \ln (a_{H^+} + ka_{M^+}) \tag{12.93}$$

where k, the *selectivity ratio*, describes the behavior of the electrode for H^+ and M^+. How low a_{H^+} must be made to allow the term ka_{M^+} to influence and even dominate changes in $V_{(glass)}$ depends on k. As in finding pH and because the response of an electrode to M^+ is a function of other ions in the solution, it is usually necessary to establish an empirical calibration curve for synthetically prepared solutions like the unknowns.

12.14 ELECTRODE PROCESSES

The single events that occur at an electrode in operation can be inferred with the aid of the usual methods of chemical kinetics. Mixing electrochemistry with kinetics introduces into an erstwhile purely equilibrium thermodynamic discussion such nonequilibrium concepts as time, diffusion rates, and catalysis by the electrode. There also exists on the surface of a reversible or irreversible electrode a double layer of ions like that on colloidal particles; this layer is a cause and result of the cell EMF.

As soon as electrolysis begins, the decomposition products formed at the electrodes convert the electrodes and electrolyte into a chemical cell. The newly created cell potential is opposed to the externally imposed potential difference that causes the electrolysis and can be calculated by methods already described. If the electrolysis is to proceed irreversibly, as it must if measurable electrolysis occurs, the externally imposed potential difference $\mathscr{E}'$ must exceed the newly created cell potential $\mathscr{E}$. Part of the irreversible work done in the cell is converted into heat. The current $\mathscr{I}$ through the cell is $\mathscr{I} = L(\mathscr{E}' - \mathscr{E})$ where L is the cell conductivity. Measurement with a balancing potentiometer is done when $\mathscr{I}$ is zero and $\mathscr{E}'$, the potential difference of the potentiometer, equals $\mathscr{E}$. A negative value of $\mathscr{I}$ would mean irreversible operation of the cell as a source of current.

The difference

$$\eta = |\mathscr{E}' - \mathscr{E}| \tag{12.94}$$

is called the *overvoltage* of the cell. Overvoltage may be attributed to just one electrode because of its small size, low surface area, chemical nature, or other design that renders it less able to carry the cell current than its partner. Figure 12.9 illustrates how η can be measured. A cathode ray oscilloscope (*CRO*) as galvanometer synchronized with the switch S permits almost instantaneous comparison of $\mathscr{E}'$ (irreversible) and $\mathscr{E}$ (reversible). By varying the switching rate, the experimenter may change the time during which side reactions of the electrode mechanism occur. Knowledge of the effects of these competing reactions frequently helps to establish the electrode reaction's mechanism, which can be as complex relative to the net electrode reaction as any net reaction is when compared with its elementary steps. Overvoltage is not simply an extraordinary value of $\mathscr{E}$ because the concentrations at the electrodes are not known; nor is it due to a decrease in conductivity due to changes in the electrolyte or bubbles of newly generated gases that adhere to the electrodes and reduce their exposed surface. Rather, η is largely a surface phenomenon, the magnitude of which depends in part upon how ions are discharged at the electrodes and in part upon the rate at which they are discharged.

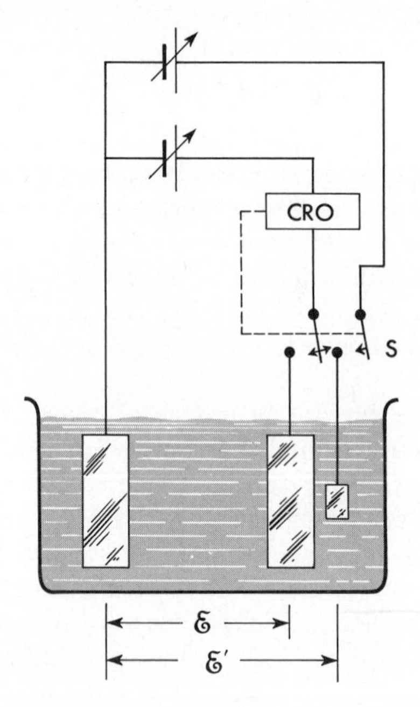

Figure 12.9. Measurement of Overvoltage

The hydrogen electrode with Pt as probe holds a unique position among electrodes as reference electrode and an important position in the exact measurement of pH. With another contact, the hydrogen electrode is important in the performance of many fuel cells, and deposition of metals by electrolysis from aqueous solution involves it indirectly. Because many metals have small or zero values of overvoltage when deposited from aqueous solution, it is possible to deposit them even though hydrogen might theoretically be expected. By decreasing the activity of H^+ and by using electrodes that exhibit large values of η for deposition of H_2, very active metals can be removed from aqueous solution.

Pure zinc can be removed from solution by electrolysis, and even metallic sodium can be generated from aqueous NaCl provided the cathode is an amalgam in which the newly generated Na can dissolve and thereby achieve a lower activity than that of the pure metal. The high overvoltage of H_2 on Hg prevents the simultaneous formation of H_2 as the Na is deposited as amalgam.

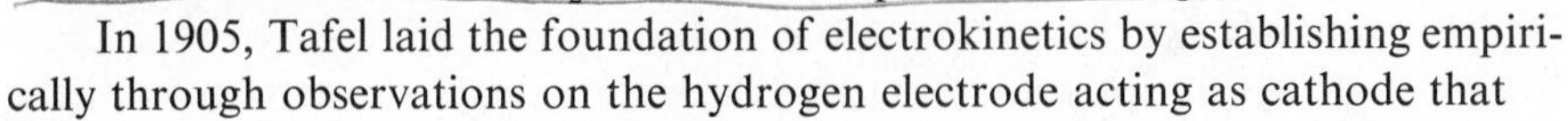

In 1905, Tafel laid the foundation of electrokinetics by establishing empirically through observations on the hydrogen electrode acting as cathode that

$$|\eta| = a + b \log i \tag{12.95}$$

where $i = \mathscr{I}/\mathscr{A}$ is the current density at the electrode. The empirical constant a varies by many orders of magnitude according to the nature and history of the electrode on which H_2 is deposited, but the empirical constant b is generally of the order of 0.1 volt. For smooth Pt, b is about 0.2 volt; for Pt-black, it is about 0.02 v; for metals like Ni and Cd, it is close to 0.17 v; for some metals it is 0.12 v.

Figure 12.10 illustrates the typical interdependence of i and η of an electrode made of Pt or other metal at which $e^- + H^+ = \frac{1}{2}H_2$ occurs in the forward

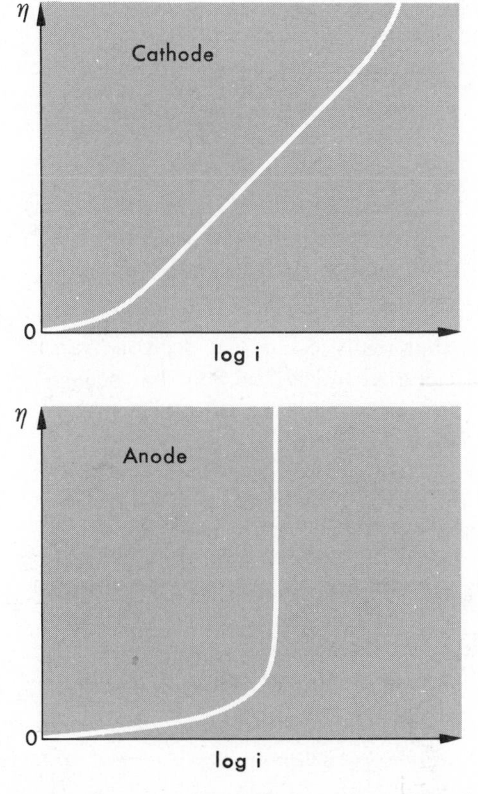

Figure 12.10. Overvoltage as a Function of Current Density at Cathode or Anode

or reverse sense. The linear part of the upper curve is (12.95). When H_2 is generated at cathodes less ideal than Pt, there may be slight curvature at high i. Such curvature is surely present even at a Pt anode (when $H_2 \longrightarrow H^+$); the limiting value of i is caused in part by adsorption of ions from the electrolyte on the anode with consequent limitation of its free surface or active sites, for the limiting value of i is sensitive to the nature of the electrolyte's anions. Moreover, transport of H_2 may also limit i, but H^+ is so speedy that it seldom causes a limit to i by 'backing up' at the electrode. In fact, there is evidence that violent bubbling of H_2 or stirring increases a limiting value of i at an anode by thinning the Helmholtz double layer of ions on the anode. A limiting value of i occurs at a Pt cathode where H_2 is generated only in basic solutions because in acidic solutions the speedy H^+ is plentiful. Of course, on typically high-overvoltage cathodes like Hg, Ag, and C, the limiting value of i is very small.

The reactions, one of which may be rate-limiting, at a hydrogen cathode are $e^- + H^+ \longrightarrow H$ followed by either

$$e^- + H + H^+ \longrightarrow H_2 \tag{12.96}$$

or

$$H + H \longrightarrow H_2 \tag{12.97}$$

where H and H_2 are adsorbed or chemisorbed on the cathode. Whether (12.96) or (12.97) dominates depends on experimental conditions. The elementary reactions are expected to include penetration of the double layer by an electron or perhaps by an ion with a critical activated state somewhere along the course of reaction.

Joining widely separated fields of kinetics is the remarkable theoretical relation[5]

$$(k_{ex}/10^{11})^{1/2} \geqslant (k_{el}/10^4) \tag{12.98}$$

where k_{ex} is the rate constant for isotope exchange (e. g., $MnO_4^- + Mn^*O_4^{2-} \longrightarrow MnO_4^{2-} + Mn^*O_4^-$) reactions that really occur via electron transfer, and where k_{el} is the rate constant of electrochemical reaction that occurs by one-electron transfer. The constants 10^{11} liters mole^{-1} sec^{-1} and 10^4 cm sec^{-1} are the usual orders of magnitude of the pre-exponential factors A in $k = A \exp(-\Delta G^*/RT)$ for these rate constants. Equation (12.98) has been nicely verified for several reactions.

12.15 ELECTROCAPILLARITY

Surface energy γ is related to chemical potential at constant T and P by (6.79) restated for electrochemical circumstances in the form

$$0 = d\gamma + \sum_i \Gamma_i \, d\boldsymbol{\mu}_i \tag{12.99}$$

[5] R. A. Marcus, *J. Phys. Chem.* **67**, 853 (1963).

For when electrostatic potential is not uniform, only $\boldsymbol{\mu}_i$ is correct as chemical potential.

A two-phase system with an interface may contain a solution of ions, but these may always be combined in stoichiometric proportions to yield neutral components, and whatever electrostatic potential may exist at the interface can then be attributed to electrons with a surface charge density $\sigma = -\mathscr{F}\boldsymbol{\Gamma}_e$. Hence, for all species except the electron, z is zero and $\boldsymbol{\mu}_i = \mu_i$. At constant T, P, and composition, $d\boldsymbol{\mu}_i$ is zero for all neutral species while for the electron $d\boldsymbol{\mu}_i = -\mathscr{F}\,d\Phi = -\mathscr{F}\,d\mathscr{E}$, where $\mathscr{E}$ varies linearly with Φ. As a result, (12.99) becomes simply $d\gamma = -\mathscr{F}\boldsymbol{\Gamma}_e d\mathscr{E} = \sigma\,d\mathscr{E}$, or

$$\left(\frac{\partial \gamma}{\partial \mathscr{E}}\right)_{T,P,\boldsymbol{\mu}_i} = \sigma \qquad (12.100)$$

The Gibbs isotherm in the form

$$\left(\frac{\partial \gamma}{\partial a_2}\right)_{T,P} = -\left(\frac{RT}{a_2}\right)\boldsymbol{\Gamma}_2 \qquad (6.84)$$

describes how the bulk activity of a solute 2 affects γ at a surface with a surface excess concentration $\boldsymbol{\Gamma}_2$. Here, the Lippmann equation (12.100) describes how an electrostatic potential difference $\mathscr{E}$ affects the surface energy γ of a surface with charge density σ when T, P, and composition are fixed.

Figure 12.11 describes how variations in the surface energy of Hg in contact with an electrolyte solution might be observed when a variable EMF is imposed

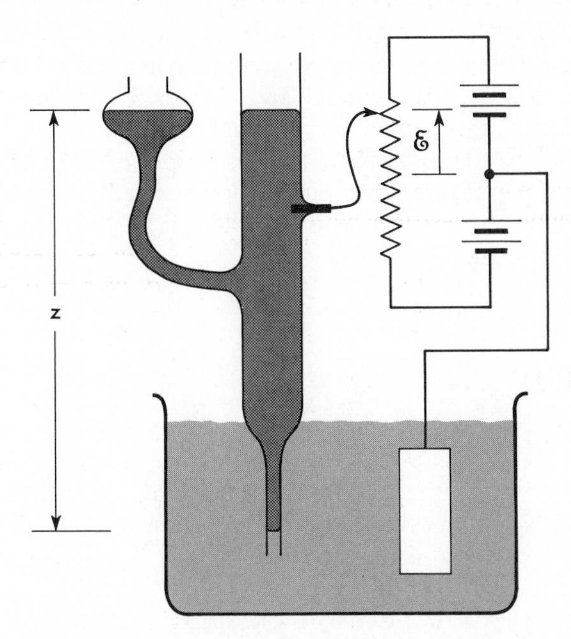

Figure 12.11. Apparatus for Observing How Surface Energy Varies with EMF

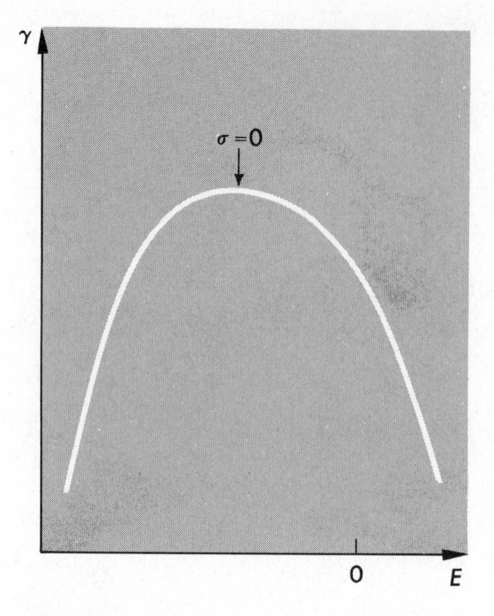

Figure 12.12. How the Surface Energy of Hg Varies with Imposed EMF

across the Hg-solution interface. The altitude z is transformed into surface energy by a variant of (6.62) in which $\Delta\rho$, the difference in density of Hg and solution, replaces ρ and where θ is assumed to be π. The Hg surface is renewed by forcing a few droplets out of the capillary by a temporary change of z.

Since a Hg electrode is easily polarized, it is possible by varying $\mathscr{E}$ to change the surface charge density σ without significant electrolysis. When $\mathscr{E}$ is zero, Hg tends to adsorb negative ions from the solution ($\sigma < 0$). As Φ is made still more negative by decreasing $\mathscr{E}$, these anions are loosened and sent off into the solution until eventually σ may become zero. At this point, by (12.100), γ reaches a maximum, as shown in Figure 12.12. Further decrease in $\mathscr{E}$ then makes σ positive and γ falls. The nature of the ions is important in determining the values of γ and $\mathscr{E}$ at which σ is zero.

12.16 POLAROGRAPHY

Analysis by electrochemical methods takes several forms. The mass deposited at an electrode can be measured quantitatively by direct weighing. In the method called *coulometry*, Faraday's laws are used directly by measuring the charge required to cause a certain chemical change whether or not the electrode is affected. The various equations of solution conductivity allow concentration to be calculated from a knowledge of L_{sp}. *Chronopotentiometry* infers a value of EMF by observing $\mathscr{R}$ as a function of time at constant current, while *chronoconductimetry* measures $\mathscr{I}$ as a function of time at constant EMF. The Nernst equation itself is also a means of observing concentrations in Q by observing $\mathscr{E}$ at equilibrium. One of the most popular methods, however, is *polarography*. In this method, the current passed by a continually renewed but always polarized electrode is measured as a function of the imposed EMF. The characteristic EMF's at which the electrolysis current is found to increase serve to identify the species undergoing electrochemical reaction at the polarized electrode. And from the magnitude of the increment in current as a new electrode process becomes possible at the polarized electrode, it is possible to infer, by comparison to a standard, how much of the newly affected species is being electrolyzed and is in the solution.

Mercury is almost always chosen as the polarized electrode. As a cathode, its high overvoltage for the reaction $e^- + H^+ \longrightarrow \frac{1}{2}H_2$ allows even Ra ($V^\circ = -2.9$ v) and Al ($V^\circ = -1.7$ v) to be deposited from aqueous solution, while Zn^{2+} and Fe^{2+} are easily reduced to the metallic state. On the other hand, as an anode, the reaction $Hg \longrightarrow \frac{1}{2}Hg_2^{2+} + e^-$ is sufficiently difficult that the Hg electrode has a total useful range of about 2.2 volts. However, certain species like Fe^{3+}, CN^-, S^{2-}, OH^-, or halide ion react with Hg_2^{2+} and must be excluded from the electrolyte when Hg is the anode so as to prevent a reaction like $Cl^- + Hg \longrightarrow \frac{1}{2}Hg_2Cl_2 + e^-$. The range for Pt is about 1.1 volts, half of Hg's because Pt catalyzes reactions of H and has a low overvoltage. Mercury is suitable also because as a liquid its surface can be continually renewed and thus purified by allowing drops of Hg to grow at the end of a capillary tube (inner diameter about 0.04 mm) immersed in the solution. The time a drop grows at a dropping mercury electrode (DME) is commonly 2 to 5 seconds, although under special circumstances a droplet lifetime may be reduced to only 0.2 seconds. To keep the capillary clear and unclogged, the Hg must be kept flowing continuously from a reservoir whenever its tip is immersed in a solution.

Figure 12.13 is a diagram of a very simple polarographic cell; many other geometrical arrangements are in use, some for use on exceedingly small samples. Nitrogen (or H_2) is bubbled through the solution to sweep and keep out O_2, which interferes with analyses by undergoing reduction to H_2O_2 and H_2O at two different potentials. Oxygen must also be excluded to prevent oxidation of Hg. The large unpolarized Hg electrode at the bottom of the flask in Figure 12.13 is usually replaced by a large calomel electrode and its salt bridge [$\ldots | K^+Cl^- | Hg_2Cl_2 | Hg(Pt)$].

Figure 12.14 illustrates a simplified polarographic circuit; the similarity to Figure 12.1 is clear. The current $\mathscr{I}_D$ through the cell with resistance $\mathscr{R}_c$ is calculated from known $\mathscr{R}'$ and the potential difference $\mathscr{E}'$ observed across $\mathscr{R}'$ by circuits not shown in Figure 12.14. A polarogram of a solution is the record of the diffusion current $\mathscr{I}_D = \mathscr{E}'/\mathscr{R}'$ as the potential difference across P is varied. If DME is the cathode, whenever $\mathscr{E}$ becomes great enough to cause an ion M^{+n} in the solution to be reduced by the reaction $ne^- + M^{+n} \longrightarrow M$, or perhaps by a reaction like $e^- + M^{+n} \longrightarrow M^{+(n-1)}$, the current $\mathscr{I}_D$ rises. If $\mathscr{E}$ is great enough, several cathode reactions may occur simultaneously when sev-

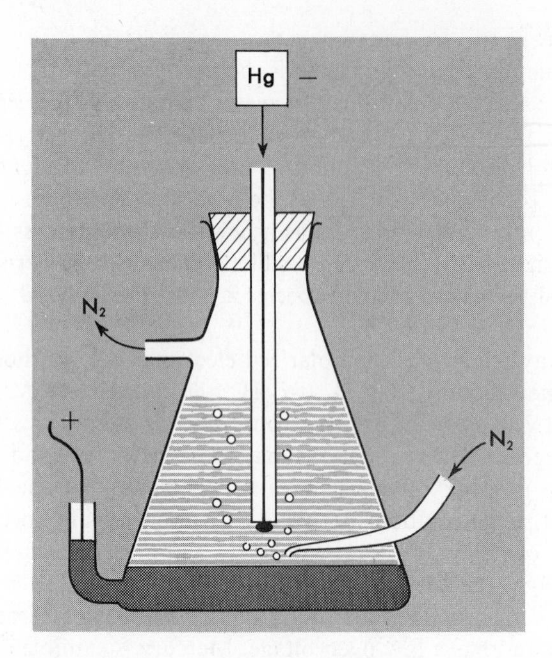

Figure 12.13. A Very Simple Polarographic Cell

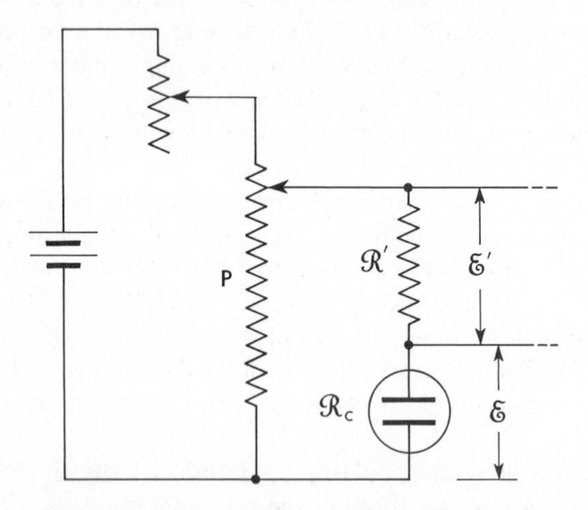

Figure 12.14. Simplified Polarographic Circuit

eral reducible ions are in the solution. Figure 12.15 illustrates the general nature of a polarogram of a solution containing three reducible species.

The range of values of $\mathcal{E}$ is spanned by varying the contact at P. If the rate of varying $\mathcal{E}$ is slow relative to the rate of formation of drops, the curve is jagged to match the growth and detachment of drops at DME. On the other hand,

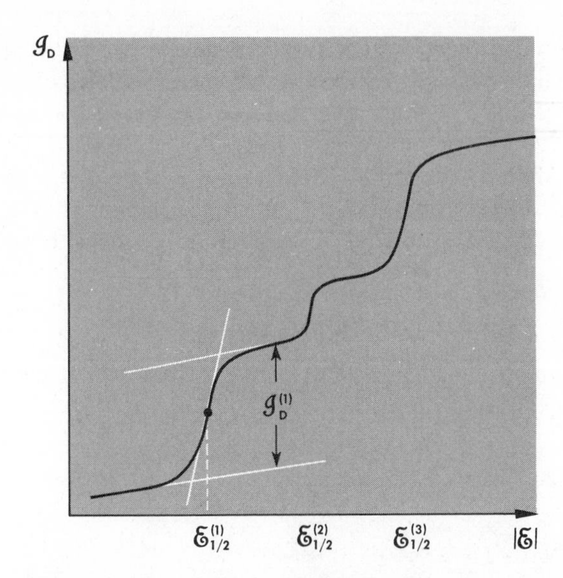

Figure 12.15. A Typical Polarogram

if the values of $\mathscr{E}$ are spanned rapidly, once or perhaps even several times during the life of any drop, then the curve, as in Figure 12.15, is smooth. This last method of recording a polarogram can be achieved by imposing a sawtooth voltage across the cell. (A *sawtooth voltage* is a periodic EMF with a rapid return to its starting value after an increase that is linear in time, as though the slide-wire P were wound into a head-near-tail circle and the contact were moved around and around at a constant angular velocity.) As a measure of $\mathscr{I}_D$, the potential difference $\mathscr{E}'$ is displayed vertically on the cathode ray oscilloscope, while the horizontal axis displays $\mathscr{E}$. The sweep rate is usually synchronized with the formation of Hg drops and the record may select only a certain part of the lifetime of each drop. It is also common to arrange for automatic spanning of $\mathscr{E}$ bit by bit when the lifetime of a drop is small relative to the time for spanning the full range of $\mathscr{E}$. In fact, this is how the first automatic polarograph was rigged by Heyrovsky in 1925. Since then, many techniques have been developed.

The first polarographic wave in Figure 12.15 has a geometric construction for finding the half-wave potential $\mathscr{E}_{1/2}^{(1)}$. This wave records the easiest reduction if the DME is cathode or the easiest oxidation if DME is anode. The low diffusion current at the left of the wave is a residual current carried by impurities or ions of no interest. The higher current to the right is the limiting current reached upon local depletion of ions changed at $\mathscr{E}_{1/2}^{(1)}$. The difference in currents is the diffusion current $\mathscr{I}_D^{(1)}$ for this first species. One way of finding $\mathscr{E}_{1/2}^{(1)}$ is to extrapolate these two values of current toward the wave, to draw the tangent to the curve at its inflection point, to bisect the segment of this tangent between the linear extrapolations, and to take the half-wave potential $\mathscr{E}_{1/2}^{(1)}$ as the abscissa of the point of bisection. This point may differ from the inflection point.

The values of $\mathscr{E}_{1/2}$ for various electrode reactions generally parallel their standard electrode potentials $\mathbf{V}^{\ominus}$, but the $\mathscr{E}_{1/2}$'s may vary by a few tenths of a volt as the electrolyte is changed. Such changes are caused by changes of the mechanism of discharge or by the formation of complex ions or partly ionized species that are not recognized in the way the electrode reaction is written. The experimental points of Figure 12.16 illustrate how $\mathscr{E}_{1/2}$ for the reduction of NH_4^+ at DME depends on pH. The curve was drawn by assuming the reactions to be

$$NH_4^+ + e^- + x\,Hg \longrightarrow NH_4(Hg)_x \qquad \text{(low pH)}$$

$$NH_4OH + e^- + x\,Hg \longrightarrow NH_4(Hg)_x + OH^- \qquad \text{(high pH)}$$

where $NH_4(Hg)_x$ is ammonium amalgam, a briefly stable species that decomposes to H_2 and NH_3 after the Hg drop has left DME.

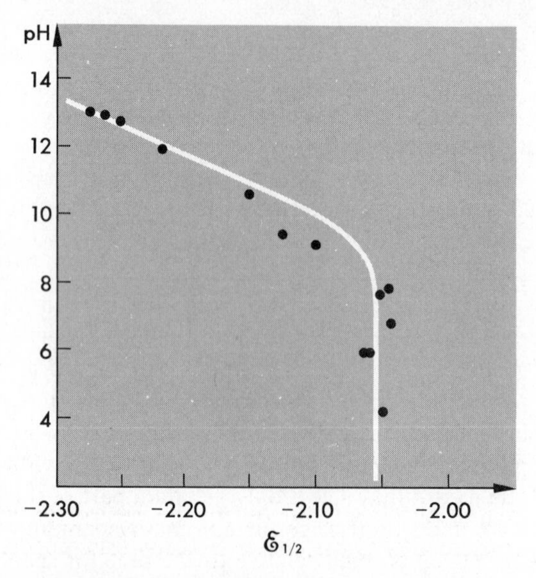

Figure 12.16. pH-Dependence of Half-Wave Potential for Reduction of NH_4^+†

At any time t, the diffusion current $\mathscr{I}_D$(μ amp) carried by affected ions with concentration C (millimoles/liter) and with $|z|$ elementary charges per ion is given by the Ilkovic equation of 1938:

$$\mathscr{I}_D = 706|z|D^{1/2}Cm^{1/2}t^{1/2} \tag{12.101}$$

where D is the ion's diffusion coefficient (cm²/sec) and m is the rate of flow of Hg (mg/sec). If t_D is the time between drops of Hg, the average current (μ amp) is

$$\overline{\mathscr{I}}_D = 606|z|D^{1/2}Cm^{2/3}t^{1/6} \tag{12.102}$$

†C. J. Nyman, J. L. Ragle, and P. F. Linde, *Anal. Chem.* **32,** 352 [1960]

If $|z|$, D, m, and t_D are constant in an experiment, it is clear the $\mathscr{I}_D$ and $\overline{\mathscr{I}}_D$ are directly proportional to C, the concentration of the reducible (or oxidizable) ions. The D's generally depend very little on concentration. A particular kind of analysis is calibrated with similar synthetic knowns or, after analysis as an unknown, a solution may have added to it a known amount of the species studied so that subsequent rerun of the doctored sample gives a larger measured $\mathscr{I}_D$.

It is found empirically that for a given DME the quantity $\mathscr{I}_D/Cm^{2/3}t^{1/6}$ is approximately constant for each of several ions; if not, it at least varies with $\mathscr{E}$ in the same way for several ions. Hence, for samples of a certain general nature, as in routine control, a new DME needs to be calibrated in terms of the old DME by study of only one ion of the several having related values of $\mathscr{I}_D/Cm^{2/3}t^{1/6}$.

A state of pure concentration-polarization is said to exist when the electrode reactions are so fast that the electrodes act reversibly even while the local concentration of ions at the surface of the electrode is in a steady state limited by diffusion. If such a state of polarization exists at the amalgam electrode, then steady discharge of the cell

$$(\mathrm{Pt})\mathrm{H}_2\,|\,\mathrm{H}^+\,\|\,\mathrm{M}^{+n}\,|\,\mathrm{M}_{\mathrm{Hg}}(\mathrm{Pt}) \tag{12.103}$$

can be used to relate $\mathscr{E}_{1/2}$ to $\mathrm{V}^{\ominus}$. If the hydrogen electrode is standard, the EMF of (12.103) is, by (12.34) with $\mathrm{V}^{\ominus}_{\text{left}} = 0$,

$$\mathscr{E} = \mathrm{V}^{\ominus}_{\text{right}} - \frac{RT}{n\mathscr{F}} \ln \left(\frac{\gamma_M C_M}{\gamma_+ C_+^{(\text{el})}}\right) \tag{12.104}$$

where the right-hand electrode reaction is $ne^- + \mathrm{M}^{+n} \longrightarrow \mathrm{M}_{\mathrm{Hg}}$. By (12.102), the current in the polarographic wave is

$$\mathscr{I}_D = k_+[C_+^{(\infty)} - C_+^{(\text{el})}] \tag{12.105}$$

where $C_+^{(\infty)}$ is the bulk concentration of M^{+n} far out in the electrolyte, where k_+ is $606\ nD_+^{1/2}m^{2/3}t_D^{1/6}$, and where $C_+^{(\text{el})}$ is the effective steady-state concentration of M^{+n} at the electrode surface. Likewise, in the amalgam

$$\mathscr{I}_D = k_M C_M \tag{12.106}$$

where k_M is for M. Upon passing well beyond the half-wave potential, the value of $\mathscr{I}_D$ rises to the limit

$$\mathscr{I}'_D = k_+ C_+^{(\infty)} \tag{12.107}$$

which is (12.105) with $C_+^{(\text{el})} = 0$, for in these circumstances the concentration of M^{+n} near the now completely concentration-polarized electrode is very small. By (12.105) to (12.107),

$$\frac{C_M}{C_+^{(\text{el})}} = \frac{\mathscr{I}_D/k_M}{C_+^{(\infty)} - (\mathscr{I}_D/k_+)} = \frac{k_+}{k_M}\left(\frac{\mathscr{I}_D}{\mathscr{I}'_D - \mathscr{I}_D}\right)$$

Hence, (12.104) becomes

$$\mathscr{E} = \mathrm{V}^{\ominus}_{\text{right}} - \frac{RT}{n\mathscr{F}} \ln\left(\frac{\gamma_M k_+}{\gamma_+ k_M}\right) - \frac{RT}{n\mathscr{F}} \ln\left(\frac{\mathscr{I}_D}{\mathscr{I}'_D - \mathscr{I}_D}\right) \tag{12.108}$$

If $\mathscr{I}_D = \mathscr{I}'_D - \mathscr{I}_D$ so that the last term of (12.108) is zero, then $\mathscr{I}_D = (1/2)\mathscr{I}'_D$ and $\mathscr{E} = \mathscr{E}_{1/2}$. In Figure 12.15 the halfwave potential was likewise chosen when the diffusion current is halfway to its limiting value $\mathscr{I}'_D$. That is, (12.108) is

$$\mathscr{E} = \mathscr{E}_{1/2} - \frac{RT}{n\mathscr{F}} \ln\left(\frac{\mathscr{I}_D}{\mathscr{I}'_D - \mathscr{I}_D}\right) \tag{12.109}$$

Equation (12.109) was first derived in 1935 by Heyrovsky and Ilkovic.

12.17 SUMMARY

As always, chemical potential is the theoretical focus of any thermodynamic discussion of equilibrium involving the states of chemicals. In a phase at an electrostatic potential $\Phi^{(j)}$, the chemical potential of species i is, as in (12.16), $\boldsymbol{\mu}_i^{(j)} = \mu_i^{(j)}(T, P, X_i) + z_i\mathscr{F}\Phi^{(j)}$. From this and $\mathscr{E} = \Phi^{(2)} - \Phi^{(1)}$ comes the fundamental result $\Delta G = -n\mathscr{E}\mathscr{F}$, which is (12.25). From this, in turn, comes the very useful Nernst equation (12.34) and, via the Gibbs-Helmholtz equation (6.46), there also comes the temperature coefficient of EMF, namely $(\partial\mathscr{E}/\partial T)_P = \Delta S/n\mathscr{F}$, which is (12.31). The emphasis is continually on ΔG and on the chemical reaction as the source of cell EMF.

Microscopic theory in the form of the Debye-Hückel theory guides the choice of (a) standard states of ions and the experimental determination of standard electrode potentials $\mathrm{V}^{\ominus}$ (Section 12.9); and (b) a theoretically sound and directly useful definition of pH (Section 12.10). The existence of ions, their mode of transport, and the methods of chemical kinetics supplement thermodynamics in formulating such useful results as:

(1) Relative to the EMF $\mathscr{E}$ of a cell without transference, certain cells with transference have an EMF that is $\mathscr{E}_t = t_\pm\mathscr{E}$, as in (12.70).

(2) In all cells with transference, the junction potential is $\mathscr{E}_j = \mathscr{E}_t - \mathscr{E}$, as in (12.71).

(3) Under certain common circumstances when different solutions of uni-univalent electrolytes meet, the junction potential is approximately $-(RT/\mathscr{F})\ln(\Lambda_0^{(2)}/\Lambda_0^{(1)})$, as in (12.85).

(4) According to the empirical Tafel equation (12.95), irreversible operation of an electrode at a current density i often occurs at an overvoltage $|\eta| = a + b \log i$, which is pleasingly noted to be of a general form reminiscent of $\Delta G^{\ominus} = -RT \ln K$ and the Arrhenius rate-constant equation. The remarkable behavior of the glass electrode and polarized dropping mercury electrode are just two of several very practical applications of electrochemistry.

The twelve chapters thus far may all reasonably be termed practical, classical, conventional, and generally macroscopically oriented. They explain chemical behavior in familiar terms; the explanation usually remains on the macroscopic level. Many reasons are indeed given for statements and in derivations, but the terse question “Why?” is seldom given a direct answer in terms more fundamental than the atoms of Dalton, the ions of Faraday and Arrhenius, the forces of van der Waals, the energy of Gibbs and others, the statistics of Boltzmann, or the theory of Debye and Hückel. In fact, the attempt to squeeze a little more information out of data leads to partial molar quantities, which tend to obscure the fundamental reasons for specific chemical attraction and repulsion. The full futility of thermodynamics alone in offering a clear and simple answer to “Why? is nicely and clearly shown by the arbitrary location of the Gibbs surface between phases, the invention of that useful monster called the activity coefficient, the ignorance of how an osmotic membrane really works, and so on. The explanation of such phenomena must be at the molecular level, for the microscopic reason for the third law of thermodynamics and the elucidation of elementary steps through kinetic studies are examples of satisfying answers to “Why?” To say that the first twelve chapters are of small value, however, is to forget their everyday practicality and their importance as the heritage which the more penetrating theory ahead is to explain. Whatever detailed microscopic explanations have been given do rather suggest and even demand that this attitude of theory, namely treatment in terms of elementary steps and single events, is what physical chemistry in general, and chemistry as a whole, need for their full development. Physical chemistry surely needs such a basis if it is to qualify as truly theoretical chemistry.

The first twelve chapters are, in a way, the raw material of the modern theoretical chemist just as observations have always been the raw material of the practical chemist. The next six chapters on quantum theory, valence, structure of solids and liquids, and statistical mechanics offer a simple account of what is happening in certain macroscopic systems in the hope that each student will himself be able, when called on, to distill something new from the known of his day and thus surpass what is given here and even what is now known at the frontier of theoretical chemistry. When these challenging and interesting chapters ahead become the proper domain of physics is uncertain; what is certain is that chemistry in physicists' terms is too complicated even for physicists. And this is why these six chapters come last even for chemists.

PROBLEMS

1. What form does χ_i in (12.3) take in a centrifuge rotating at an angular velocity of ω radians sec^{-1}, if the work done on n_i moles of species i of formula weight

M_i to increase its distance r_i from the axis of rotation by dr_i is $dw_c = -n_i M_i \omega^2 r_i \, dr_i$?
Answer: $\chi_i = -\frac{1}{2}\omega^2 r_i^2$

2. Is any realizable electrochemical cell capable of being run in a truly reversible manner? Explain with specific examples.

3. Calculate the cell potential of the cell

$$(\mathrm{Pt})\mathrm{H}_{2(g)}\ (0.127\ \mathrm{atm})\,|\,\mathrm{H}^+, \mathrm{Cl}^-\,|\,\mathrm{H}_2(6.43\ \mathrm{atm})\ (\mathrm{Pt})$$

Answer: -0.0504 volt.

4. Calculate ΔA at 25°C for the change

$$\mathrm{Cl}_{2(g)}\ (0.100\ \mathrm{atm}) + \mathrm{Ca}_{(s)} \longrightarrow \mathrm{Ca}^{++}(a = 1) + 2\,\mathrm{Cl}^-(a = 1)$$

Answer: -808 kj.

5. In what circumstances is it possible to obtain more energy from chemicals as electric work than as evolved heat?

6. Calculate an electrochemical value of ΔH for the cell reaction of the cell $\mathrm{Tl}\,|\,\mathrm{TlCl}_{(s)}\,|\,\mathrm{KCl}(1\ N)\,|\,\mathrm{Hg_2Cl}_{2(s)}\,|\,\mathrm{Hg}_{(l)}$ if $\mathscr{E} = 0.7290$ v at 25°C and if $\mathscr{E}$ increases by 0.75 millivolt per degree rise in temperature [G. Jones and W. C. Schumb, *Proceedings of the American Academy of Arts and Sciences*, **56**, 199 (1919); by permission of the American Academy of Arts and Sciences].
Answer: $-48{,}700$ joules.

7. What will be the potential at 50°C of this cell?

$$(\mathrm{Ag})\mathrm{Pb}_{(s)}\,|\,\mathrm{Pb}^{++}(a = 1.07 \times 10^{-4})\,\|\,\mathrm{Cl}^-(a = 0.100)\,|\,\mathrm{AgCl}_{(s)}\,|\,\mathrm{Ag}_{(s)}.$$

Assume entropies of dilution are ideal.
Answer: 0.534 v.

8. Two identical electrochemical cells are allowed to generate 1 mole H_2 from H_2SO_4. One does so reversibly and the other does so irreversibly. Explain qualitatively the differences noted in the final states of the cell, acid solution, H_2, and so on.

9. For the cell $(\mathrm{Pt})\mathrm{H}_{2(g)}\,|\,\mathrm{HCl}\,|\,\mathrm{AgCl}_{(s)}\,|\,\mathrm{Ag}_{(s)}(\mathrm{Pt})$, wherein the HCl is dissolved in N-methylacetamide, $\mathscr{E}^\circ$ at various temperatures has been found to be [L. R. Dawson, W. H. Zuber, Jr., and H. C. Eckstrom, *J. Phys. Chem.* **69**, 1335 (1965)]:

Temp. (°C)	40	45	50	55	60
$\mathscr{E}^\circ$ (abs. volt)	0.20573	0.20091	0.19456	0.18972	0.18357

From these data calculate ΔG°, ΔH°, and ΔS° at 50°C for the cell reaction when one faraday passes.
Answer: $\Delta G^\circ = 18.77$ kj; $\Delta H^\circ = 43.55$ kj; $\Delta S^\circ = 76.68$ j/deg.

10. At 25°C what is the EMF of the cell

$$(\mathrm{Pt})\mathrm{Ag}_{(s)}\,|\,\mathrm{Ag}^+(a = 0.0100), \mathrm{F}^-(a = 0.100)\,|\,\mathrm{F}_{2(g)}\ (0.500\ \mathrm{atm})(\mathrm{Pt})$$

Answer: 2.24 v.

11. How is the standard EMF of the cell $(\mathrm{Pt})\mathrm{Pb}\,|\,\mathrm{Pb}^{2+}, \mathrm{Cl}^-\,|\,\mathrm{Cl}_2(\mathrm{Pt})$ expected to change as T and P increase near room T?

Answer: $\mathscr{E}^{\ominus}$ rises as P rises but falls as T rises.

12. Diagram an electrochemical cell that has these equations as net cell reaction:
(a) $AgCl_{(s)} + I^{-}_{(aq)} \rightleftharpoons Ag_{(s)} + Cl^{-}_{(aq)}$.
(b) $Zn_{(s)} + H_2SO_{4(aq)} \rightleftharpoons ZnSO_{4(aq)} + H_{2(g)}$.
(c) $10\ FeSO_{4(aq)} + 2\ KMnO_{4(aq)} + 8\ H_2SO_{4(aq)} \rightleftharpoons K_2SO_{4(aq)} + 2\ MnSO_{4(aq)} + 5\ Fe_2(SO_4)_{3(aq)} + 8\ H_2O_{(l)}$.
(d) $Fe_{(s)} + Cl_{2(g)} \rightleftharpoons FeCl_{2(aq)}$.
Answer: (a) $Ag|AgI|I^-\|Cl^-|AgCl|Ag$; (b) $(Pt)Zn|Zn^{2+}\|H^+, HSO_4^-|H_2(Pt)$; (c) $(Pt)|Fe^{2+}, Fe^{3+}, SO_4^{2-}\|H^+, SO_4^{2-}, MnO_4^-, Mn^{2+}|(Pt)$; (d) $(Pt)Fe|Fe^{2+}\|Cl^-|Cl_2(Pt)$.

13. Several investigations indicate that at 25°C the absolute standard entropy of $H^+_{(aq)}$ is close to zero. What effect will an experimental result for this quantity that differs from the conventional zero have on the $S^{\ominus}$ of an ion like Cl^-?
Answer: $S^{\ominus}$ of Cl^- would decrease by the amount that $S^{\ominus}$ of H^+ should exceed zero.

14. Justify the value -0.828 volt for $V^{\ominus}$ of the half-cell in basic solution:
$e^- + H_2O_{(l)} \rightleftharpoons \frac{1}{2}H_{2(g)} + OH^-$.

15. Calculate the solubility product constant of Ag_2CrO_4 at 25°C.
Answer: 1.15×10^{-12}.

16. Calculate the solubility product constants of Ag_2S and TlOH at 25°C.
Answer: 4×10^{-51} (Ag_2S); 0.73 (TlOH).

17. What is the standard potential of the electrode reaction $e^- + \frac{1}{3}Tl^{+++} \rightleftharpoons \frac{1}{3}Tl_{(s)}$?
Answer: $+0.72$ volt.

18. Calculate $V^{\ominus}$ for the half-cell $e^- + \frac{1}{2}\,Sn^{++} \rightleftharpoons Sn_{(s)}$ if $\mathscr{E} = -0.643$ volt at 25°C for the cell $(Zn)Sn_{(s)}|Sn^{++}(a = 0.347)\|Zn^{++}(a = 0.100)|Zn_{(s)}$.
Answer: -0.136 volt.

19. With the aid of Tables 3.1 and 4.3, find $V^{\ominus}$ of $e^- + AgBr_{(s)} \rightleftharpoons Ag_{(s)} + Br^-$.
Answer: $+0.0706$ volt.

20. What is the minimum voltage necessary to electrolyze 1.00 molal $ZnBr_2$ to produce Zn and Br_2? Assume $\gamma_{\pm} = 1.000$
Answer: 1.810 volts.

21. If the electrode potential for the decinormal calomel electrode is $+0.3338$ volt at 25°C as in Example 12.9, calculate $\mathscr{E}$ for the cells:
(a) $(Pt)Hg_{(l)}|Hg_2Cl_{2(s)}|KCl(0.1\ N)\|Zn^{++}(a = 0.732)|Zn_{(s)}(Pt)$.
(b) $(Pt)Hg_{(l)}|Hg_2Cl_{2(s)}|KCl(0.1\ N)\|HCl(0.1N)|H_{2(g)}(1\ atm)(Pt)$.
Answer: (a) -1.105 v; (b) -0.3930 v.

22. Values of EMF at various molalities for the cell at 25°C

$$(Pt)Tl_{(Hg)}|Tl_2SO_4(m)|Hg_2SO_{4(s)}|Hg(Pt)$$

are [J. M. Creeth, *J. Phys. Chem.* **64,** 920 (1960)]:

Molality (m)	0.021433	0.024561	0.034212	0.042219
EMF (volts)	1.0990	1.0950	1.0862	1.0805

If $\mathscr{E}^{\ominus} = 0.9480$ volt, find $\gamma^{\pm}$ of Tl_2SO_4 at the various m's.
Answer: 0.58; 0.57; 0.51; 0.48.

23. From data of Tables 12.8 and, independently, 12.9 find $\Delta H^{\ominus}$ for the ionization

of water at room temperature and compare to values found from $\Delta H_f^{\ominus}$'s of Table 3.1.

24. Quinhydrone ($Q \cdot QH_2$), a compound of quinone ($Q = C_6H_4O_2$) and hydroquinone ($QH_2 = C_6H_4(OH)_2$) is slightly soluble in water. Because it provides equal numbers of moles of Q and QH_2, its half-cell reaction $e^- + H^+ + \frac{1}{2}Q_{(aq)} \rightleftharpoons \frac{1}{2}QH_{2(aq)}$ depends only upon the activity of H^+ in the presence of excess $Q \cdot QH_2$. If $V^{\ominus}$ of the quinhydrone electrode is +0.6996 v at 25°C, for the cell

$$(Pt)Q \cdot QH_{2(s)} | H^+(pH = ?) | K^+Cl^- | Hg_2Cl_{2(s)} | Hg_{(l)}(Pt)$$

with a normal calomel electrode ($V^{\ominus} = +0.2802$ v), find:
(a) The $\mathscr{E}$ of cell when pH = 5.00.
(b) The pH when $\mathscr{E}$ of cell is zero.
(c) Which electrode is positive when pH = 7.50.
Answer: (a) −0.1236 v; (b) 7.09; (c) calomel.

25. If activities equal concentrations, what is the potential at 25°C of (Pt)Na(0.200% in Hg) | NaCl (0.150 *m*) | $AgCl_{(s)}$ | $Ag_{(s)}$ | $AgCl_{(s)}$ | NaCl (0.0372 *m*) | Na (0.200% in Hg)(Pt)?
Answer: −0.0716 v.

26. If the potential difference of the cell

$$(Pt)H_{2(g)}\ (p\ \text{atm}) | H^+(a = 0.100) \| H^+(a = ?) | H_{2(g)}(p\ \text{atm})(Pt)$$

is 0.0861 volt, what is the pH of the solution round the right-hand electrode if:
(a) It is positive at 25°C?
(b) It is negative at 25°C?
(c) It is negative at 0°C?
Answer: (a) −0.45; (b) 2.46; (c) 2.59.

27. Calculate ideally the free energy change upon diluting 1 mole NaCl from 0.020 *m* to 0.0010 *m* at 25°C and design an electrochemical battery without transference for measuring ΔG.
Answer: −14,840 joules.

28. Diagram two batteries in which the free energy of dilution of aqueous solutions of HCl might be measured without interference from junction potentials.

29. What unnoticed change in hydrogen pressure will cause an error of 0.01 pH unit when pH is measured with a hydrogen electrode at 25°C at laboratory pressures?
Answer: 36 mm Hg.

30. Account for the fact [M. H. Lietzke and R. W. Stroughton, *J. Am. Chem. Soc.* **75,** 5226 (1953)] that for the cell

$$(Pt)Hg_{(l)} | Hg_2SO_{4(s)} | H_2SO_4(M) | Ag_2SO_{4(s)} | Ag_{(s)}(Pt)$$

the standard cell potential in 0.5 *M* H_2SO_4 is constant up to 150°C, while in 0.05 *M* H_2SO_4 it decreases gradually as *T* rises above 75°C.
Answer: Hydrolysis of Hg_2SO_4 to HgO and Hg causes $\mathscr{E}^{\ominus}$ to decrease.

31. If the cell (Ag)Zn | $Zn(OH)_4^{2-}$, OH^- | AgO | Ag is to produce one kilowatt-hour at an EMF of 1.4 volts, what is the minimum mass of Zn required as anode?
Answer: 869 g Zn.

32. Under what conditions is the half-wave potential equal to the standard electrode

potential if the polarization of an amalgam electrode is caused only by concentration effects and not by irreversibility of the electrode as it follows its local concentrations?
Answer: At a certain DME, $k_+ D_M^{1/2} = k_M D_+^{1/2}$.

33. Show how (12.101) leads to (12.102).
Answer: Integrate from $0 \longrightarrow t_D$.

---

34. Show that at hydrostatic equilibrium in a one-component fluid system at constant T the rate of change of pressure P with altitude z is

$$\frac{dP}{dz} = -\frac{M}{V}\frac{d\chi}{dz}$$

35. Theoretically how much electric energy could be obtained at 1000°K and 1 atm by burning 1 mole CH_4 to H_2O and CO?
Answer: 604,290 joules.

36. Explain how mixing distinguishable species could yield electric work, and how electric work might unmix them.

37. Predict the potential at 10°C of the cell:

$$(Pt)H_{2(g)}\ (0.800\ atm)\,|\,H^+(a = 1),\ Cl^-\ (a = 1)\,|\,Cl_{2(g)}\ (1.00\ atm)\ (Pt).$$

Answer: 1.3587 v.

38. Derive an equation for the dependence of potential difference of an electrochemical cell upon total pressure if only condensed phases take part in the cell reaction.

39. Calculate the partial equilibrium pressure of O_2 above 0.100 molal aqueous H_2O_2 at 25°C.
Answer: 10^{35} atm.

40. For dilute aqueous NaOH, the cell $(Pt)H_{2(g)}$ (1 atm)$\,|\,Na^+OH^-\,|\,HgO_{(s)}\,|\,Hg_{(l)}(Pt)$ has a potential of 0.9264 v at 25°C [Ming Chow, *J. Am. Chem. Soc.*, **42**, 488 (1920)]. What is the standard free energy of formation of $HgO_{(s)}$?
Answer: $\Delta G_f^\ominus = -13.97$ kcal mole^{-1}.

41. Diagram two electrochemical cells for each pair of reactants that could convert the chemical potential energy of these reactants into useful electric energy:
(a) H_2 and Cl_2.
(b) Ag^+ and Cl^-.

42. Calculate the cell potentials at 25°C and reactions for the cells:
(a) $(Pt)Cu_{(s)}\,|\,Cu^{++}(a = 0.0010),\ Cl^-(a = 0.30)\,|\,Cl_{2(g)}$ (0.950 atm) (Pt).
(b) $(Pt)\,|\,V^{++}(a = 0.242),\ V^{+++}(a = 0.0033)\,||\,V^{++}(a = 0.425)\,|\,V_{(s)}(Pt)$.
(c) $(Pt)Cl_{2(g)}$ (1.12 atm)$\,|\,Cl^-(a = 0.526)\,||\,I^-(a = 0.100)\,|\,AgI_{(s)}\,|\,Ag_{(s)}(Pt)$.
Answer: (a) 1.151 volts; (b) −0.82 volt; (c) −1.469 volts.

43. In this problem assume that the final concentrations of plentiful ionic species are 1 molar and that the final concentrations of rare ionic species are less than 0.001 molar. With the aid of Table 12.4, predict the final state of almost all vanadium at equilibrium if:
(a) The vanadium in solution is all reduced to V^{++} just before the solution is buffered at pH = 0.
(b) Excess metallic copper is added to a solution of V^{+++} buffered at pH = 0.
(c) A solution of Fe^{++} is added to a solution of $V(OH)_4^+$ buffered at pH = 0.

(d) A solution of Fe^{+++} is added to a solution of VO^{++} buffered at pH = 0.
(e) A solution of Cu^{++} is added to a solution of VO^{++} buffered at pH = 0.
Answer: (a) V^{3+}; (b) V^{3+}; (c) VO^{2+}; (d) VO^{2+}; (e) VO^{2+}.

44. Calculate the equilibrium constant for the reaction $AlF^{---}_{6(aq)} \rightleftharpoons Al^{+++}_{(aq)} + 6\,F^{-}_{(aq)}$.
Answer: 1.6×10^{-21}.

45. What is the concentration of triiodide ion in equilibrium with excess solid iodine at 25°C in a solution in which the molality of iodide was 0.1000 before the addition of iodine?
Answer: 0.0500 *m*.

46. Calculate the standard potential of the electrode reaction

$$e^- + \tfrac{1}{2}\,Au^{+++} \rightleftharpoons \tfrac{1}{2}\,Au^{+}.$$

Answer: $\mathbf{V}^{\ominus} = +1.41$ v.

47. Diagram a cell in which the solubility product constant of ZnS might be measured and calculate K_{sp} from standard electrode potentials.
Answer: $Zn\,|\,Zn^{2+}\,||\,S^{2-}\,|\,ZnS\,|\,Zn$ $K_{sp} = 1.0 \times 10^{-23}$.

48. Calculate the standard molar free energy of aqueous Pb^{++} and the potential of the cell $(Pt)H_{2(g)}(2.34\text{ atm})\,|\,H^+(a = 0.0022)\,||\,Pb^{++}(a = 0.377)\,|\,Pb_{(s)}(Pt)$.
Answer: $\Delta G_f^{\ominus} = -5810$ cal mole^{-1}; $\mathscr{E} = +0.030$ v.

49. If the solubility product constant of Hg_2Cl_2 is 4.2×10^{-18} for the reaction $Hg_2Cl_{2(s)} \rightleftharpoons Hg_2^{++} + 2\,Cl^-$, and if the decinormal calomel electrode with half-cell reaction $e^- + \tfrac{1}{2}\,Hg_2Cl_{2(s)} \rightleftharpoons Cl^-(0.1\,N) + Hg_{(l)}$ has electrode potential of +0.334 volt, what is $\mathbf{V}^{\ominus}$ of the half reaction $e^- + \tfrac{1}{2}\,Hg_2^{++} \rightleftharpoons Hg_{(l)}$?
Answer: $\mathbf{V}^{\ominus} = +0.789$ v.

50. For the cell $(Pt)H_{2(g)}$ (1 atm) $|\,H^+(a = 0.803)\,||\,Ce^{3+}(a_1), Ce^{4+}(a_2)(Pt)$ the EMF's at various activities a_1 and a_2 at 25°C are [A. A. Noyes and C. S. Garner, *J. Am. Chem. Soc.* **58,** 1265 (1936)]:

a_1	0.06513	0.04504	0.02768	0.01808
a_2	0.02387	0.05083	0.07413	0.08703
EMF(v)	1.5892	1.6174	1.6389	1.6546

What is the standard electrode potential of $Ce^{3+} - Ce^{4+}$ at 25°C?
Answer: 1.610 v.

51. The table lists values of EMF of the cell

$$(Pt)H_2(1\text{ atm})\,|\,KH_2PO_4(m_1),\ Na_2HPO_4(m_2),\ Cl^-(m_3)\,|\,AgCl\,|\,Ag(Pt)$$

at 25°C and 38°C [Values are averages of observations reported in V. E. Bower, M. Paabo, and R. G. Bates, *J. Res. Nat. Bur. Stds.* **65 A,** 267 (1961)] when $m_1 = 0.008695$ and $m_2 = 0.03043$.

m_3	EMF (25°C)	EMF (38°C)
0.005	0.80320 v	0.81798 v
0.010	0.78509	0.79909
0.015	0.77436	0.78788

By extrapolating a suitable function to $m_3 = 0$ find pH_s at each temperature.
Answer: 7.414 at 25°C; 7.383 at 38°C.

52. Like every electrochemical cell, the cell of Example 12.15 is not ideal. Why? Calculate ΔG and the EMF when the fugacity of H_2 is given by (5.91).
Answer: H_2 dissolves in and diffuses through the acid; $\Delta G = 15{,}410$ j; $\mathscr{E} = -0.0799$ volt.

53. Predict the potential difference of the cell (Pt)$H_{2(g)}$ (0.970 atm) | NaOH(0.332 N) | Na(0.147% mole amalgam)(Pt) at 25°C if activities equal concentrations.
Answer: -1.776 v.

54. Estimate the magnitude and determine the sign of the junction potential between two solutions having $\Lambda_0 = 101.6$ and 118.6 by the Lewis and Sargent formula.
Answer: 4.0 millivolts; lower Λ_0 positive.

55. In a cell consisting of glass electrode in solution with pH of 7.00 and a calomel electrode, the cell potential was 0.062 volt. When a solution of unknown pH replaced the standard buffer, the cell potential was 0.145 volt with the glass electrode negative. Calculate the unknown pH if, during the calibration, the glass electrode was:
(a) Negative.
(b) Positive.
Answer: (a) 8.40; (b) 10.5.

56. What is the minimum potential difference required to electrolyze 0.100 molal $ZnBr_2$ at 25°C if $\gamma_\pm = 0.550$? How much isothermal isobaric reversible electric work is done on the 0.100 m $ZnBr_2$ at 25°C to produce one mole of Br_2?
Answer: 1.920 v; 370.7 kj.

57. Show that $\partial^2\mathscr{E}/\partial\mathscr{I}_D^2$ is zero (inflection point of graph of $\mathscr{E}$ vs $\mathscr{I}_D$) when $\mathscr{I}_D = \mathscr{I}'_D/2$ if $\mathscr{E}$ is the EMF that causes the diffusion current $\mathscr{I}_D$ through a cell whose electrodes are polarized solely because of concentration effects and not because of other irreversibility. As in Section 12.16, $\mathscr{I}'_D$ is the limiting current.

---

58. Calculate the potential difference between the electrodes and determine their signs at 25°C for the cell

$$Fe_{(s)} \,|\, Fe^{++} \,|\, Fe_{(s)}\ \text{(compressed spring)} \,|\, Fe_{(s)}$$

if 10.0 cal reversible isothermal isobaric work were done in compressing the 1 lb coiled spring electrode at the right.
Answer: $\mathscr{E} = -26.6$ microvolts.

59. With the aid of Table 3.1 and 4.3, find $V^\ominus$ for each of these half cells:
(a) $e^- + \frac{1}{2}NO_{2(g)} + H^+ \rightleftharpoons \frac{1}{2}NO_{(g)} + \frac{1}{2}H_2O_{(l)}$.
(b) $e^- + \frac{1}{2}C_2H_{2(g)} + H^+ \rightleftharpoons \frac{1}{2}C_2H_{4(g)}$.
Answer: (a) 1.048 v; (b) 0.731 v.

60. Calculate $V^\ominus$ the chlorine-chloride electrode at 37°C.
Answer: 1.3444 v.

61. For the cell (Pt)$H_{2(g)}$(p atm) | HCl(0.1 N) | H_2(p atm) | $Ag_2S_{(s)}$ | $Ag_{(s)}$(Pt) $\mathscr{E} = -0.03779$ v at 10°C, -0.03670 v at 25°C, and -0.03584 v at 35°C [A. A. Noyes and E. S. Freed, *J. Am. Chem. Soc.*, **42**, 476 (1920)]. Calculate ΔG, ΔH, and ΔS for the cell reaction at 20°C and 25°C.
Answer: At 25°C, $\Delta G = 3541$ j; $\Delta H = 5810$ j; $\Delta S = 7.6_2$ j/deg. At 20°C, $\Delta G = 3578$ j; $\Delta H = 5750$ j; $\Delta S = 7.4$ j/deg.

62. Calculate $\Delta G^\ominus$ for the cell reaction at 25°C, 100°C, 200°C, and 250°C for the cell

$$\text{(Pt)}Ag \,|\, AgCl \,|\, HCl(M) \,|\, Hg_2Cl_2 \,|\, Hg\text{(Pt)}$$

when the molarity M is 1.0 and 0.1 if the EMF's of the cell are [M. H. Lietzke and J. V. Vaughen, *J. Am. Chem. Soc.* **77**, 876 (1955)]:

1.0 M	Temp. (°C)	25	50	87	110	154	166	200	235	247	254
	EMF (millivolts)	46	55	68	75	89	95	107	120	128	133
0.1 M	Temp. (°C)	25	60	110	135	143	173				
	EMF (mv)	46	57	82	92	106	128				

Plot calculated and observed values of the standard cell potentials as functions of temperature and explain any systematic trends or deviations noted.

Answer: In 0.1 M HCl hydrolysis of Hg_2Cl_2 occurs above 100°C, while in 1.0 M HCl the same occurs above 240°C.

63. By extrapolation of observations of EMF of cells containing $PuCl_3$ dissolved in liquid KCl, the EMF of the cell

$$(Pt)Pu_{(l)} \mid PuCl_{3\,(l)} \mid Cl_{2\,(g)}\ (1\ atm)(Pt)$$

was found [R. Benz, *J. Phys. Chem.* **65**, 81 (1961)] to depend on T thus between about 900°K and 1000°K:

$$\mathscr{E}(\text{volts}) = 2.980 - 0.5576 \times 10^{-3}\, T$$

At 700°C calculate $\Delta G_f^\ominus$ and $\Delta H_f^\ominus$ of $PuCl_3$ as supercooled liquid.

Answer: $\Delta G^\ominus = -169$ kcal/mole; $\Delta H^\ominus = -206$ kcal/mole.

64. Calculate the theoretical potential difference developed at 1000°K by the fuel cell

$$(Ag\text{-}Pt)H_{2\,(g)}(2.50\ atm) \mid M_2CO_{3\,(l)} \mid O_{2\,(g)}(0.50\ atm)\ (Ag).$$

Express the result as a function of H_2O pressure, and assume that p_{CO_2} is the same at both electrodes. What will the potential difference be during operation of the fuel cell?

Answer: Less than $\mathscr{E} = 1.024 - 0.0992 \log_{10} p(H_2O)$.

65. Calculate the standard EMF of a fuel cell that operates on solid sucrose ($\Delta G_f^\ominus = -371.6$ kcal/mole) and O_2 at one atm to yield liquid water and gaseous CO_2 at one atm at 25°C.

Answer: 1.250 volts.

66. At 25°C, $\mathscr{E}$ is 1.05080 volts for the cell [E. J. Roberts, *J. Am. Chem. Soc.*, **52**, 3877 (1930)]:

$$(Pt)H_{2\,(g)}(1\ atm) \mid Na^+OH^-(a_1),\ Na^+Cl^-(a_1) \mid AgCl_{(s)}Ag_{(s)}(Pt)$$

With the aid of data for the cell $(Pt)H_{2\,(g)}(1\ atm) \mid HCl(m) \mid AgCl_{(s)} \mid Ag_{(s)}(Pt)$ calculate the ion product K_w of water at 25°C. Estimate mean molal activity coefficients by $-\log \gamma_\pm = 0.509 z_+ |z_-| \sqrt{I}$.

Answer: $K_w = 0.889 \times 10^{-14}$.

67. The solubility product constants of $PbSO_4$ and $BaSO_4$ are 1.35×10^{-8} and 1.35×10^{-9}, respectively. An electrode reversible to barium can be made by depositing $PbSO_4$ and $BaSO_4$ on an electrode of Pb. Explain its operation and find its standard electrode potential.

Answer: -0.096 volt.

68. For the cell (Pt)$In_{(s)}$ | $In_2(SO_4)_3(m)$ | $Hg_2SO_{4(s)}$ | $Hg_{(l)}$(Pt) the EMF varies thus with molality m and T [E. M. Hattox and T. DeVries, *J. Am. Chem. Soc.* **58,** 2126 (1936)]:

m	0°C	15°C	25°C	35°C
0.1676	1.0627	1.0560	1.0515	1.0470
0.0526	1.0700	1.0631	1.0591	1.0551
0.0281	1.0749	1.0698	1.0658	1.0617
0.0158	1.0800	1.0742	1.0703	1.0664
0.0100	1.0838	1.0782	1.0744	1.0705

Find the standard cell EMF at each T. If the Hg-Hg_2SO_4 standard electrode potential is 0.614 at 25°C, what is $V^{\ominus}$ for the In-In^{3+} electrode? Explain how the standard entropy of $In^{3+}_{(aq)}$ might be found from these data and others readily available.

Answer: $\mathscr{E}^{\ominus}$ = 0.974, 0.962, 0.954, and 0.946 volt; $V^{\ominus}$ = −0.340 v.

69. Calculate $\Delta G^{\ominus}$, $\Delta H^{\ominus}$, and $\Delta S^{\ominus}$ at 25°C for the dissociation

$$HB^+ + H_2O = B + H_3O^+$$

where B is 4-aminopyridine from the data [R. G. Bates and H. B. Hetzer, *J. Res. Nat. Bur. Stds.* **64A,** 427 (1960)] for the cell (Pt)$H_{2(g)}$(1 atm) | $HB^+(m_1)$, $B(m_2)$, $Cl^-(m_1)$ | $AgCl_{(s)}$ | $Ag_{(s)}$(Pt).

m_1	m_2	EMF (20°C)	EMF(25°C)	EMF(30°C)
0.10066	0.09914	0.83611	0.83499	0.83384
0.08005	0.07884	0.84058	0.83958	0.83829
0.05993	0.05902	0.84651	0.84559	0.84460
0.04985	0.04923	0.85038	0.84964	0.84869
0.03986	0.03926	0.85482	0.85406	0.85325
0.02996	0.02959	0.86097	0.86041	0.85972
0.02003	0.01973	0.86964	0.86914	0.86872
0.009766	0.009646	0.88575	0.88556	0.88561

Answer: $\Delta G^{\ominus}$ = 52.013 kj/mole; $\Delta H^{\ominus}$ = 47.090 kj/mole; $\Delta S^{\ominus}$ = −16.5 j deg^{-1} mole^{-1}.

70. At 25°C at one atm, the EMF of the cell

$$(Pt)Cd_{amalgam}(4.6\%\ Cd) | CdCl_2(0.500\ M) | Cd(Pt)$$

is −0.0534 volt. At 25°C at one atm, the EMF of the cell

$$(Pt)Cd_{amalgam}(4.6\%\ Cd) | CdCl_2\ (C\ M) | AgCl | Ag(Pt)$$

varies with C thus [W. G. Horsch, *J. Am. Chem. Soc.* **41,** 1787 (1919)]:

$C \times 10^3$	0.1087	0.1269	0.2144	0.3659
EMF (volt)	0.9023	0.8978	0.8803	0.8614

If the standard electrode potential of the Ag-AgCl electrode is 0.2222 volt,

(a) what is the standard electrode potential of the Cd-Cd^{2+} electrode?
(b) what is $\Delta G_f^\ominus$ of $Cd^{2+}_{(aq)}$?
(c) what is the mean ionic activity coefficient of 0.0001269 m $CdCl_2$?
Answer: (a) −0.395 v; (b) −18.21 kcal/mole; (c) 0.863.

71. Estimate the minimum potential difference required at 800°C to produce solid metallic calcium and gaseous chlorine at 1 atm from fused $CaCl_2$ by electrolysis if for $CaCl_2$:
(a) C_P of liquid and solid = 18 cal deg^{-1} $mole^{-1}$.
(b) The molar heat of fusion is 6.78 kcal $mole^{-1}$ at 782°C at 1 atm.
(c) The molar heat of formation of the solid at 25°C is −190.0 kcal $mole^{-1}$.
(d) The standard free energy of formation of the solid at 25°C is −179.3 kcal $mole^{-1}$.
[Data from F. D. Rossini, *et al.*, Circular of the National Bureau of Standards 500 (1952)].
Answer: 3.34 volts.

72. A thermocell is a cell that has electrodes at different temperatures; if these temperatures were alike, the EMF of the simplest of such cells would be zero. A typical example of such a simple cell is $Ag_{(s)}$(cold) | $AgNO_{3(l)}$ | $Ag_{(s)}$ (hot). In this cell, list the cause of the EMF and describe some of the processes that occur upon short-circuiting the cell if the cold electrode is negative.
Answer: The cause is transfer of entropy from hot thermostat to hot electrode. [For processes, see, e.g., K. S. Pitzer, *J. Phys. Chem.* **65,** 147 (1961).]

13
QUANTA, WAVES, AND PARTICLES

13.1 INTRODUCTION

Chemistry is the art and science of dealing with electrons in molecules. It is a science because the behavior of the electron has been systematized in general terms and in certain ordinary situations. However, chemistry remains an art not only for the experimenter but also for the theoretician who must often resort to qualitative and empirical rules in describing the antics of the marvelous electron. An electron can be conceived as an ordinary ball of mass and electric charge for the purpose of Faraday's laws and the operation of electrochemical cells, but in any single event or in any study of a single electron, such a common-sense concept cannot deal adequately with a real electron's real behavior. Given the proverbial inch, an electron always takes more than the proverbial mile. It may be harder to locate than a golf ball, more elusive than a curve ball, more slippery than a muddy football, and harder to direct than a basketball, because the analogy that uses the model of a ball must be replaced by mathematical insight into an equation of motion that is less definite in describing the electron than are Newton's equations in describing a ball's motion.

The elementary training of a chemist in concepts that are mostly thermodynamic is at once penetrating and superficial. Explanations of phenomena remain generally close to the world of sense and muscle. Any chemist without this conventional macroscopic training is not well trained, for frequently all that is needed to solve a chemical problem is just such an attitude or model and just such information skillfully applied. Moreover, it is generally true that chemistry in terms of the electron is so complicated that a theoretical basis in such terms cannot in general cope with real complexities and thus fails to help the chemist through maze-like complications that can be avoided. It is, for example, pointless to spend hours attempting to predict a melting point on the basis of valence theory and intermolecular forces when a simple observation in a few minutes furnishes the desired datum.

On the other hand, such an attitude is quite superficial. Why indeed are certain melting points higher than others? When the power of the kinetic theory (even in its classical attitude of colliding spheres), when the microscopic explanation of the third law of thermodynamics, and when the seeming simplicity of the Debye-Hückel theory are really appreciated as aids to classical thermodynamics, it is clear that there are many interesting hidden aspects to familiar events. What follows in these last chapters is a tantalizing preliminary account of a universally applicable theory that may eventually give suitable answers to the vexing little question "Why?" At least for chemistry.

Why, for example, should the increase in entropy upon mixing ideal gases depend upon whether the *observer* decides that the species are alike or different? Surely the subjective attitude of the observer is an unusual aspect of a calculation as premeditated and state-determined as those of thermodynamics. Or, again, why should heat capacities of crystalline solids be observed to approach zero as absolute zero is approached? As long as infinitesimal vibrations are allowed, equipartition of energy requires that the molar heat capacity C_V equal $3R$ in a pure monatomic crystal at all temperatures, regardless of how low T may be. Conceivably C_V could decrease to $2R$, R, or even zero, but only if one, two, or all three degrees of freedom were completely lost, as if space had lost its three-dimensional character. Such discontinuous decreases in C_V are not in fact observed, nor is it reasonable to expect any body following the law of classical mechanics utterly to stop moving at a finite temperature. Or why should the heat capacities of many gases be clearly less than the values predicted by equipartition of energy? The discrepancies are less than or almost equal to what would be expected of rigid molecules, but, as for crystals, is any classical structure motionless at a temperature above absolute zero?

Furthermore, why and how can a beam of light eject electrons from a metal into an evacuated space as soon as the light hits the metal surface even though the density of energy as computed classically is too low per unit area to energize the ejected electron, a small particle, to the extent observed? And why does the maximum energy of such photoelectrons depend on the wavelength but not the intensity of the light? It was questions like these at the end of the nineteenth century that marred the apparently completed edifice of science based on thermodynamics, Maxwell's electromagnetic theory, and Newton's mechanics. The answers to these questions involve concepts that are so unusual and foreign to common experience that the usual historical comments of the introduction are deferred to the discussions that follow.

13.2 ENERGY QUANTA

The clue to answers to awkward questions like these came with the brilliant hypothesis of Planck in 1900 that matter absorbs and emits radiant energy in discrete packets called quanta. The idea of quantized matter was as old as the atomic theory, but this concept of quantized energy was quite revolutionary in an age when diffraction and interference phenomena seemed to demand that light be a pure wave. Although Newton favored corpuscles of light, his mechanics allowed mechanical energy to vary continuously in accord with everyday experience.

Before 1900 there were three important laws of radiation. The *Stephan-Boltzmann law* stated that a body at a uniform absolute temperature T radiated energy at a rate proportional to T^4. The chemical nature and surface of the body influenced the rate in general, but all substances radiated at the same rate at T if their surfaces were properly prepared. The ideal in this regard was a tiny hole in a hollow isothermal sphere of the substance. Called a *black body*, such a hole was both a perfect radiator and a perfect absorber of radiation of all wavelengths. Its rate of radiation at T was observed to be $5.67 \times 10^{-8}T^4$ joules sec^{-1} m^{-2}. This rate included radiation of all wavelengths λ.

The typical or most intense λ emitted by a body depends on T, for a red-hot body is cooler than a white-hot body. Two laws summarized the dependence of intensity on λ for a black body. At short wavelengths, *Wien's law* said that the intensity of radiation of wavelength λ was proportional to $\lambda^{-5}e^{-c_2/\lambda T}$, where the universal value of the second radiation constant c_2 was 1.44×10^{-2} m-deg. This law failed, however, at long wavelengths, where *Rayleigh's law* said that the intensity at λ was proportional to $T\lambda^{-4}$. Moreover, Rayleigh's law failed at small λ, where in fact it predicted an "ultraviolet catastrophe" involving infinite intensity at $\lambda = 0$.

What Planck did in 1900 was to show that Wien's and Rayleigh's laws were limiting forms of one radiation law, and that the one new law could be derived if the radiating oscillators of the black body absorbed and emitted radiation in elementary bits of energy. This model required that energy be quantized in bits of energy $h\nu$, where $\nu = c/\lambda$ is the frequency of the radiation and h is a universal constant that could be found by fitting Planck's radiation law to observations of intensity as a function of λ and T.

Planck assumed that all the oscillators in the walls of the black-body cavity have one fundamental frequency ν; hence, the energy of one of them is $\varepsilon_i = ih\nu$, where i is an integer. If the classical Boltzmann distribution regulates the numbers of oscillators in the various states, then the fraction in state i of energy ε_i is

$$\frac{N_i}{N} = \frac{e^{-\beta\varepsilon_i}}{\sum_j e^{-\beta\varepsilon_j}} \tag{4.73}$$

where $\beta = 1/kT$. Since N_i/N is the probability that a randomly chosen oscillator has the energy ε_i, the average energy of an oscillator is

$$\bar{\varepsilon} = \sum_i \varepsilon_i \left(\frac{N_i}{N}\right) \tag{4.75}$$

Since all oscillators are alike in ν, the average energy of the system of N oscillators at equilibrium at T under Boltzmann statistics can be calculated, as in Section 4.12, by taking N times $\bar{\varepsilon}$, the average energy of one oscillator, where

$$\bar{\varepsilon} = -\frac{\partial \ln I_\nu}{\partial \beta} \tag{13.1}$$

and

$$I_\nu = \sum_{j=0}^{\infty} e^{-\beta jh\nu} = 1 + e^{-\beta h\nu} + e^{-2\beta h\nu} + \cdots \tag{13.2}$$

A geometric series, (13.2) has a term-to-term ratio $r = e^{-\beta h\nu}$. The sum of a finite series with r_0 as its first term is

$$I = r_0 + r_0 r + r_0 r^2 + \cdots + r_0 r^n \tag{13.3}$$

Multiplication of (13.3) by r yields

$$rI = r_0 r + r_0 r^2 + r_0 r^3 + \cdots + r_0 r^{n+1} \tag{13.4}$$

Subtraction of (13.4) from (13.3) term by term yields $I(1 - r) = r_0 - r_0 r^{n+1}$. When r is less than unity, and when I involves many terms, it follows that

$$\lim I = \lim_{n\to\infty} \left[\frac{r_0(1 - r^{n+1})}{1 - r}\right] = \frac{r_0}{1 - r} \tag{13.5}$$

But $r_0 = 1$ and $r = e^{-\beta h\nu}$ so that (13.5) and (13.2) give

$$I_\nu = (1 - e^{-\beta h\nu})^{-1} \tag{13.6}$$

By (13.1) and (13.6) it follows that the average energy of an oscillator at T is

$$\bar{\varepsilon} = -\frac{\partial}{\partial\beta}[-\ln(1 - e^{-\beta h\nu})] = \frac{h\nu e^{-\beta h\nu}}{1 - e^{-\beta h\nu}} = \frac{h\nu}{e^{\beta h\nu} - 1} \tag{13.7}$$

where, as in (4.84), $\beta = 1/kT$.

The equilibrium that exists in the (barely pierced) hollow sphere of volume V is classically considered to contain standing waves of radiation. It can be shown that for such waves

$$(m^2 + n^2 + p^2) = \left(\frac{2}{\lambda}\right)^2 V^{2/3} \tag{13.8}$$

where m, n, and p are positive real integers. In one dimension, (13.8) would be simply $m(\lambda/2) = V^{1/3}$; that is, the standing waves have nodes (zero amplitude) at the container walls. The number of standing waves in V is the number of ways of giving m, n, and p values. This calculation is eased by listing values of m, n, and p as coordinates in a three-dimensional space. In this m-n-p space, (13.8) is a sphere of radius $(2/\lambda)V^{1/3}$; hence, the number of ways of choosing the real positive integers m, n, and p is the number of sites in the $+++$ octant of the sphere. The volume of this octant is

$$\frac{1}{8}\left(\frac{4}{3}\pi r^3\right) = \frac{\pi}{6}\left[\left(\frac{2}{\lambda}\right)V^{1/3}\right]^3 = \frac{4\pi V}{3\lambda^3} \tag{13.9}$$

Equation (13.9) is the number of standing waves satisfying (13.8). Since light waves are transverse and have two planes of polarization, the number of unpolarized standing transverse waves in V is twice as great as (13.9), namely, $8\pi V/3\lambda^3$. Between λ and $\lambda - d\lambda$, the number of waves is

$$N(\lambda)d\lambda = d\left(\frac{8\pi V}{3\lambda^3}\right) = \frac{8\pi V}{\lambda^4}\, d\lambda \tag{13.10}$$

Since radiation moves at a speed c, opening a unit area of the sphere would allow radiation to come out of a volume $V = c \times 1^2$ in one second; hence, in view of (13.7) and (13.10), the intensity (joules $\sec^{-1}$ per unit range of λ) at λ is expected to be

$$\begin{aligned} \bar{\varepsilon}N(\lambda) &= \frac{8\pi chv}{\lambda^4}(e^{\beta hv} - 1)^{-1} \\ &= \frac{8\pi c^2 h}{\lambda^5}(e^{hc/\lambda kT} - 1)^{-1} \end{aligned} \tag{13.11}$$

Planck's law (13.11) reduces to Wien's law if $\exp(hc/\lambda\, kT) \gg 1$; this occurs when λT is sufficiently small. When λT is sufficiently great, expansion of exp $(hc/\lambda kT)$ as a power series in $(hc/\lambda kT)$ yields, to the first term, (13.11) in the form

$$\frac{8\pi c^2 h}{\lambda^5}\left(1 + \frac{hc}{\lambda kT} + \cdots - 1\right)^{-1} = \frac{8\pi c^2 h}{\lambda^5}\left(\frac{\lambda kT}{hc}\right)$$

which is of the form of Rayleigh's law, (const.) $\times\, T\lambda^{-4}$. Figures 13.1 and 13.2 illustrate how Planck's law, which fits observations at all λ, merges at large λT with Rayleigh's law and at small λT with Wien's law. While this agreement of (13.11) with observed radiation intensities was most gratifying, the idea that the oscillators in matter absorb and radiate energy in discrete bundles was of truly transcendent importance.

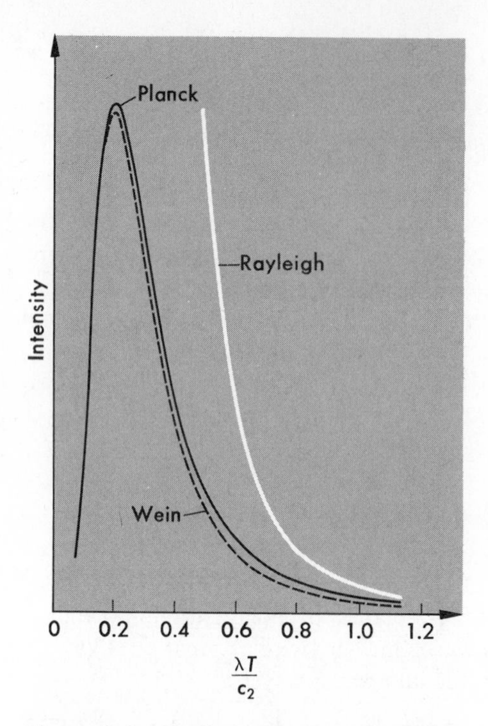

Figure 13.1. Radiation Laws at Small λT

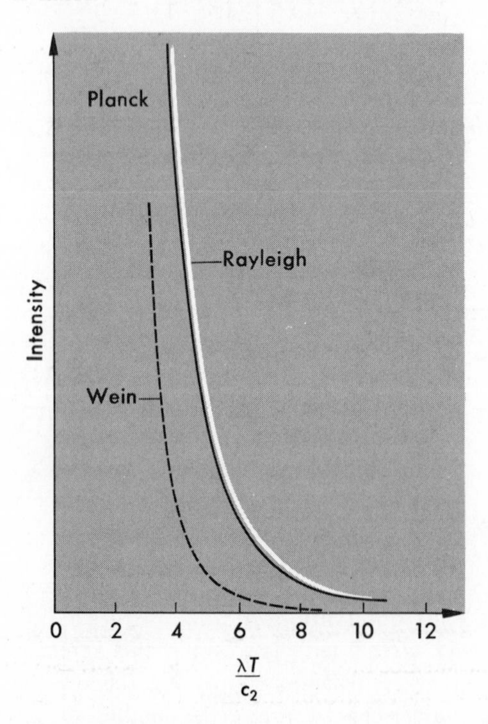

Figure 13.2. Radiation Laws at Large λT

Example 13.1. Show that Planck's radiation law yields the Stephan-Boltzmann law, namely that radiation at equilibrium with matter at T is radiated at a rate proportional to T^4.

Since (13.11) applies at only one λ, for all λ the intensity is the sum of (13.11) for all λ, namely

$$8\pi c^2 h \int_0^\infty \frac{d\lambda}{\lambda^5(e^{hc/\lambda kT} - 1)} = 8\pi c^2 h\left(\frac{kT}{hc}\right)^4 \int_\infty^0 \left(\frac{hc}{\lambda kT}\right)^3 \frac{d\left(-\dfrac{hc}{\lambda kT}\right)}{(e^{hc/\lambda kT} - 1)}$$

$$= 8\pi c^2 h\left(\frac{kT}{hc}\right)^4 \int_0^\infty \frac{x^3 dx}{(e^x - 1)}$$

Since the integral is a constant ($\pi^4/15$), it follows that the intensity is proportional to T^4, as required to fit the Stephan-Boltzmann law.

13.3 PHOTOELECTRIC EFFECT

In 1905 Einstein took the next step away from classical physics by offering an unusual model to explain certain twenty-year-old observations on electrons ejected from metals by a beam of light. The most significant experimental facts:

(1) At fixed λ or ν, the number of electrons ejected is proportional to the intensity of the light.

(2) The electrons are ejected at once without a time lag when the light is turned on, even at exceedingly low light intensity.

(3) The maximum energy of the ejected electrons is independent of the intensity of light.

(4) The maximum energy of the ejected electrons is a linear function of the frequency of the light.

The model proposed by Einstein was to treat light as a particle. As a pure classical wave, light is not localized; now as a particle called the photon, it has mass and position. If intensity measures the number of photons, then fact (1) is easily understood if photons of a given ν are all alike and if the ratio of photons to photoelectrons ejected is constant. Fact (2) is readily explained by the photon hypothesis, for a particle acts at a point; hence, there is no need for a time lag during which energy can be accumulated and concentrated from a large area. A pure wave, however, would be spread so thin over the metal surface that a time lag would be most probable at low intensity.

The last two facts about the maximum energy of the photoelectrons are best explained by use of Figure 13.3. At a distance x_D from the surface of the metal at $x = 0$ there is an electron detector at ground ($\Phi = 0$). The surface of the metal is at a positive electrostatic potential Φ_s so that the work $e\,\Phi_s$ must be done on an electron to move it from the surface of the metal to the detector. Electrons exist in a range of energies from E_0 to E_F within the metal ($x < 0$). The work function ϕ is the least work that must be done on the least tightly held electron

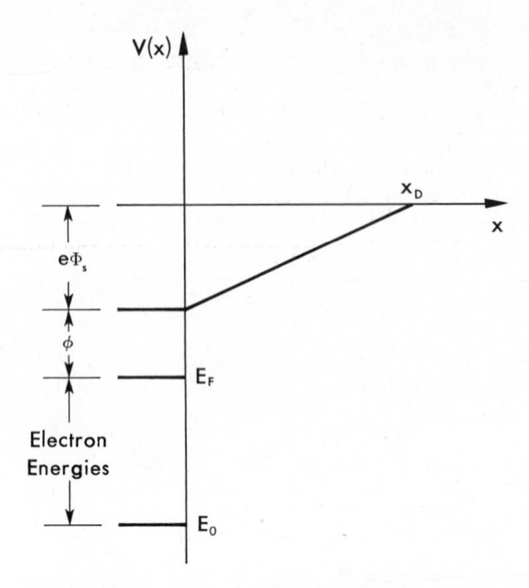

Figure 13.3. Electron Energies Inside and Outside a Metal in an Electric Field

(it has energy E_F) in order to remove it from the metal in the absence of an external field ($\Phi_s = 0$).

If the photon that gives its energy to one of the metallic electrons has an energy $h\nu$, then as the electron goes from energy E_1 within the metal to energy E_2, conservation of energy in the absorption process requires

$$E_2 = E_1 + h\nu \tag{13.12}$$

The initial energy E_1 of the electron lies between E_0 and E_F; hence, $E_0 \leqslant E_1 \leqslant E_F$. Since $E_F = -\phi - e\Phi_s$, it follows from (13.12) that $E_2 - h\nu = E_1 \leqslant -\phi - e\Phi_s$. The maximum energy of an ejected electron is, therefore,

$$E_2^{(\max)} = h\nu - \phi - e\Phi_s \tag{13.13}$$

In accord with fact 4, (13.13) states that the maximum energy $E_2^{(\max)}$ of the photoelectron is a linear function of ν for a certain metal in a fixed external field. And, in accord with fact (3), the model adequately explains why $E_2^{(\max)}$ need not depend on the intensity of the light.

In the days when physical constants were evaluated one by one instead of en masse by the method of least squares, the photoelectric effect was a convenient way to evaluate the ratio of Planck's constant h to the electronic charge e. If the experimenter gradually increases the bias voltage Φ_s while holding ν constant, he will eventually bring $E_2^{(\max)}$ so low that no electron can reach the detector. That is, even if a photon forces an electron through the work function, the electron eventually curves around outside the metal, which is positive, and returns to the surface. If Φ_0 is the critical value of Φ_s at which this return of the electron barely occurs and at which the detector no longer receives electrons ($E_2^{(\max)} = 0$), then (13.13) yields

$$\Phi_0 = \left(\frac{h}{e}\right)\nu - \left(\frac{\phi}{e}\right) \tag{13.14}$$

Thus Φ_0 becomes an indirect measure of $E_2^{(\max)}$. When Φ_0 is measured as a function of ν, a graph like Figure 13.4 results. The slope is h/e, and the intercept at $\nu = 0$ is $-(\phi/e)$. If e is known, both ϕ for the metal and the universal constant h can be evaluated. According to Appendix A, the best value of Planck's constant is $h = 6.62559 \times 10^{-34}$ joule sec.

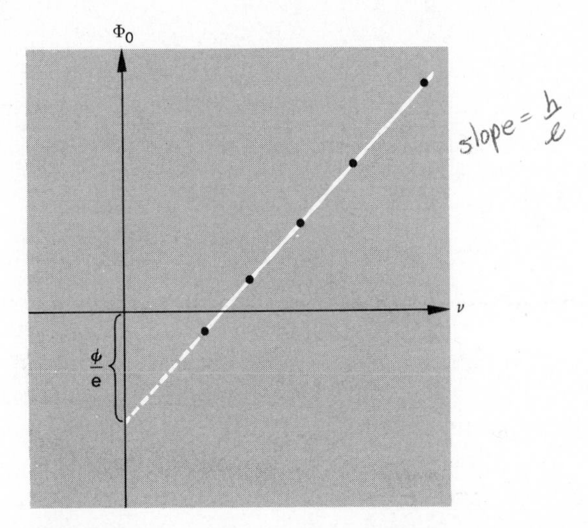

Figure 13.4. Critical Potential Difference Φ_0 as a Function of Light Frequency ν

Table 13.1 lists for several elements the average values of their work functions ϕ. These are the energies required to remove the least tightly held electron to an infinite distance from the surface and leave it there at rest. The *electron volt*, the unit of energy used in Table 13.1, is the kinetic energy acquired by one free electron as it is accelerated from rest through a potential difference of one absolute volt. Initially the electron's kinetic energy T_1 is zero while its potential energy is $V_1 = -e\,\Phi_1$, where e is unsigned. Afterwards, its kinetic energy is T_2 and its potential energy is $V_2 = -e\,\Phi_2$. Hence, in this conversion of potential energy to kinetic energy,

$$0 = \Delta E = (T_2 + V_2) - (T_1 + V_1) = (T_2 - T_1) - e(\Phi_2 - \Phi_1)$$

$$T_2 - T_1 = e(\Phi_2 - \Phi_1) = e(\Delta\Phi) \tag{13.15}$$

According to the definition and (13.15), one electron volt is the energy $T_2 - T_1$

Table 13.1 Mean Work Functions of Some Elements (1924–1949)†

Substance	ϕ (e.v.)	Substance	ϕ (e.v.)
Li	2.39	Ti	4.09
Na	2.27	V	4.11
K	2.15	Cr	4.51
Rb	2.13	Mn	3.95
Cs	1.89	Fe	4.36
Be	3.37	Co	4.18
Mg	3.46	Ni	4.84
Ca	2.76	Cu	4.47
Sr	2.35	Zn	3.74
Ba	2.29	Ga	3.96
C	4.39	Ge	4.56
Si	4.1	As	5.11
Ge	4.56	Se	4.72
Sn	4.11	W	4.50
Pb	4.02	Pt	5.29
Ce	2.7	Au	4.58
Pr	2.7	Hg	4.52

† H. B. Michaelson, *J. Appl. Phys.* **21**, 536 (1950).

when $\Delta\Phi = 1$ abs. volt; hence, with $e = 1.60210 \times 10^{-19}$ coulomb,

$$T_2 - T_1 = 1.60210 \times 10^{-19} \text{ joule} \tag{13.16}$$

$$= 1.60210 \times 10^{-12} \text{ erg} \tag{13.17}$$

The frequency ν_1 of a photon with one electron volt of energy is

$$\nu_1 = \frac{1.60210 \times 10^{-19} \text{ joule}}{h \text{ (joule-sec)}} = \frac{1.60210 \times 10^{-19}}{6.62559 \times 10^{-34}}$$

$$= 2.41804 \times 10^{14} \text{ sec}^{-1} \tag{13.18}$$

The wavelength λ_1 of such a photon is

$$\lambda_1 = \frac{c}{\nu_1} = \frac{2.997925 \times 10^{8} \text{ m sec}^{-1}}{2.41804 \times 10^{4} \text{ sec}^{-1}}$$

$$= 1.239810 \times 10^{-6} \text{ m} \tag{13.19}$$

A convenient relation between electron volts and λ originates from the relation for a photon's energy

$$h\nu = e(\Delta\Phi) = \frac{hc}{\lambda} \tag{13.20}$$

$$\lambda(\Delta\Phi) = \frac{hc}{e} = 1.239810 \times 10^{-6} \text{ m-volt} \tag{13.21}$$

where $\Delta\Phi$ is numerically equal to the number of electron volts of a photon of wavelength λ.

Equation (13.20) indicates that the energy of a photon is inversely proportional to its wavelength. Before adequate values of h and c were known, spectroscopists found it convenient to state energies to their observed accuracy in terms of reciprocal wavelengths (*in vacuo*). From (13.21), one electron volt is equivalent to reciprocal lengths thus:

$$1 \text{ ev} \asymp 0.806573 \times 10^{6} \text{ m}^{-1} \tag{13.22}$$

$$1 \text{ ev} \asymp 8065.73 \text{ cm}^{-1} \tag{13.23}$$

The electron volt is an energy of a single electron, a single photon, or, generally, a single event. If a gram mole of events (i.e., $N_0 = 6.02252 \times 10^{23}$ events) occurs, each event having an energy of one electron volt, then the total energy of the N_0 events is, by (13.16), $6.02252 \times 10^{23} \times 1.60210 \times 10^{-19} = 9.64326 \times 10^{4}$ joules mole^{-1}. Since 4.18400 j equal one calorie,

$$1 \text{ ev} \asymp 2.3061 \times 10^{4} \text{ cal mole}^{-1} \tag{13.24}$$

$$1 \text{ ev} \asymp 23.061 \text{ kcal mole}^{-1} \tag{13.25}$$

In view of (13.25) and the usual sizes of thermochemical energies, an electron volt is a convenient unit of energy for single chemical events. Figure 13.5 relates these energies to each other for quick reference.

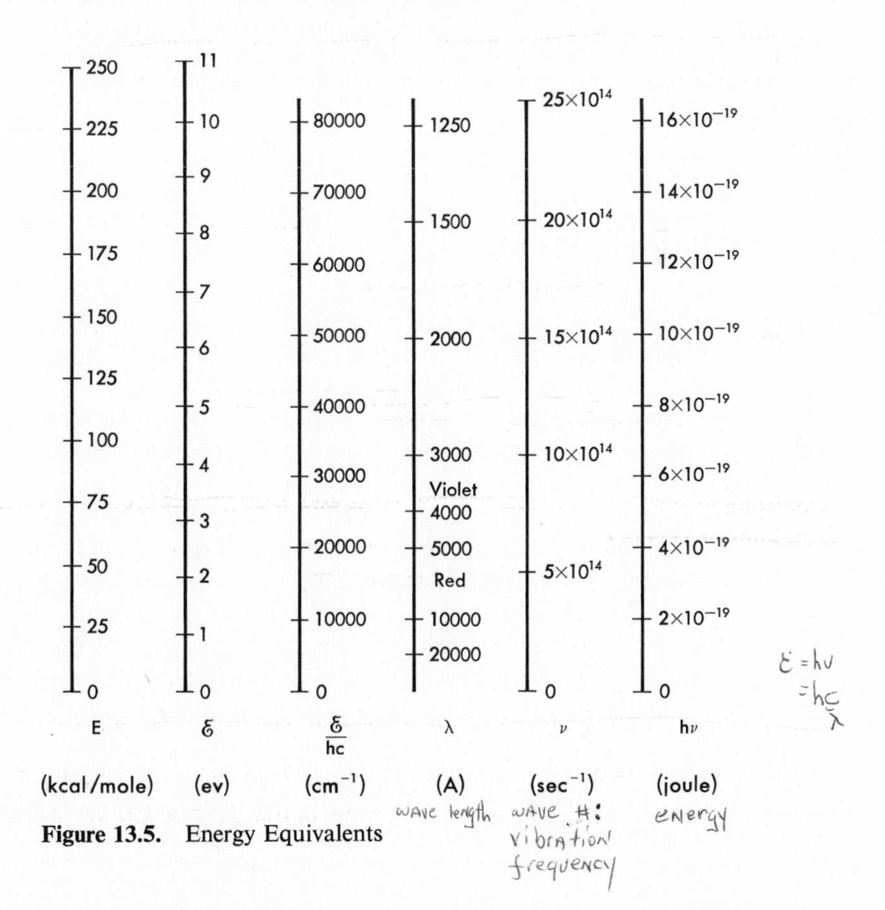

Figure 13.5. Energy Equivalents

Example 13.2. In the absence of an external field, the energy required to remove the least tightly held electron from an alkali metal is about 2.0 ev. What is the longest wavelength of light just able to eject photoelectrons from an alkali metal?

If no electric field exists between metal and detector, Φ_s in (13.13) is zero. And $E_2^{(\max)}$ is zero if the light is barely energetic enough to eject the electron. Hence, by (13.13), $0 = h\nu - \phi$ so that the longest wavelength able to eject an electron is

$$\lambda = \frac{c}{\nu} = \frac{hc}{\phi}$$

But $\phi = 2.0$ ev $\simeq 3.20 \times 10^{-19}$ j by (13.16); hence, with $c = 3.00 \times 10^8$ m sec^{-1} and $h = 6.626 \times 10^{-34}$ j sec,

$$\lambda = \frac{6.626 \times 10^{-34} \times 3.00 \times 10^8}{3.20 \times 10^{-19}} = 6.21 \times 10^{-7}\ \text{m}$$

Since 1 m $\simeq 10^{10}$ A, it follows that

$$\lambda = 6.21 \times 10^3 \times 10^{-10}\ \text{m} = 6210\ \text{A}$$

Radiation that is green ($\lambda = 5000$ A) or blue (4000 A) is more energetic than 6210 A (orange); hence, green or blue light could eject photoelectrons with excess kinetic energy while red or infrared light ($\lambda \geqslant 7000$ A) could not do so in one event.

13.4 HYDROGEN ATOM

The quantum theory became very well established by its success in explaining the photoelectric effect as well as black-body radiation. In 1906, Einstein explained the decline in heat capacities toward zero as T was reduced toward absolute zero by assuming that the atoms of a crystal had quantized mechanical energies. An atom might have any energy that is a multiple of $h\nu$, where ν is the characteristic vibration frequency of the atom in the crystal. The energy $h\nu$ is then a quantum of mechanical energy. As $T \to 0$, the Boltzmann distribution (4.73) requires that more and more atoms lose energy (in bits of $h\nu$) until, at very low T, so few atoms would have energies of $h\nu$, $2h\nu$, . . . that the energy of the crystal becomes essentially constant. For when $kT \ll h\nu$, a classically disproportionate number of atoms have the lowest possible energy because there is no other state available at an energy less than $h\nu$. With the crystal energy essentially constant at the minimum near $T = 0$, the heat capacity is nearly zero. It is the very discontinuity in available energies that distinguishes the Einstein model from the classical model. As T rises and kT exceeds $h\nu$, many atoms attain any of several states of energy $nh\nu$, where n is a positive real integer. With a seemingly continuous range of energy thus realized by most atoms, the energy rises almost continuously with T and the heat capacity approaches the classical limit. By allowing the atoms a range of vibrational frequencies, Debye in 1912 brought Einstein's theory of heat capacity into very close agreement with observation (Section 17.11).

While Einstein was thus applying the quantum theory to the photoelectric effect and low-temperature heat capacities, others were preparing the way for Bohr to apply it to the energy states of atoms. About 1903, Rutherford and Soddy formulated their rules about radioactive decay and the existence of isotopes. The ratio of the mass to the charge of the electron was first measured in 1897 by several observers, and similar ratios for ionized atoms were under study after 1900. In 1911, Millikan put these ratios on an absolute basis by observing an accurate value of the electronic charge in his famous oil-drop experiment. Also in 1911, from experiments in which alpha particles were either seldom scattered or occasionally deflected mightily on passage through a thin film of metal, Rutherford concluded that every atom consisted of a small massive nucleus with a positive charge and a much larger region containing electrons spread out somehow in space. Meanwhile, Ritz had observed that the various wavelengths of radiation absorbed or emitted by an atom of a certain kind were related by a combination principle which said that the reciprocal of any such wavelength was the sum or difference of the reciprocals of two other wavelengths absorbed or emitted by the same kind of atom. Moreover, it was possible to summarize the term values of this additive relation in a diagram like Figure 13.6, which applies to H. In view of (13.20), it is clear that the Ritz combination principle dealt with energy states of the atom.

One of the simplest spectroscopic formulas at hand was Balmer's of 1885 for the wavelengths of radiation of hydrogen atoms:

$$\lambda = 3.6456 \times 10^{-5}\left(\frac{m^2}{m^2 - 2^2}\right)(\text{cm}) \tag{13.26}$$

where m is an integer greater than 2. Nowadays, (13.62) is generally restated in the energy-like form

$$\frac{1}{\lambda} = R\left(\frac{1}{n^2} - \frac{1}{m^2}\right) \tag{13.27}$$

where $R = 2^2/3.6456 \times 10^{-5}$ and, to match (13.26), $n = 2$. The energy terms $-R/n^2$ are shown in Figure 13.6, which is called a *term diagram*. Indeed, with such a diagram the wavelengths emitted by H, as listed in Table 13.2, and many not listed there, could be calculated by the method of Ritz, who suspected the existence of the series to be discovered by Lyman in 1906. The spectra of many atoms can be thus organized with great accuracy. The term values of the alkali metals can be represented approximately by $-R/(n - \delta)^2$, where δ is an empirical constant for certain related term values.

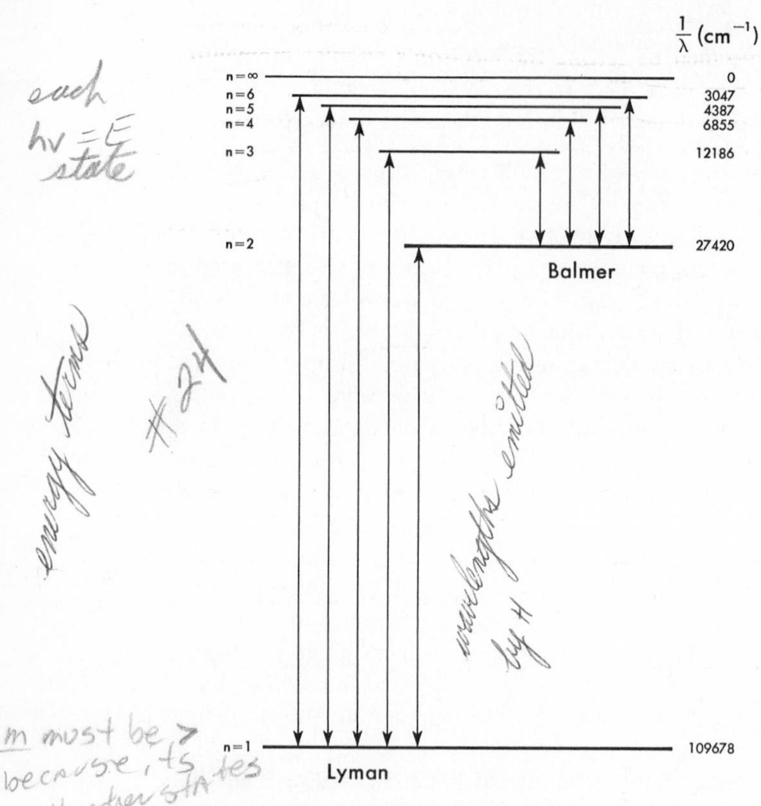

Figure 13.6. Term Values of Hydrogen Atom

Table 13.2 Some Wavelengths of Emission Spectrum of Hydrogen (A)†

m	Lyman ($n = 1$)	Balmer ($n = 2$)	Paschen ($n = 3$)	Brackett ($n = 4$)	Pfund ($n = 5$)
2	1215.68				
3	1025.83	6562.79			
4	972.54	4861.33	18,751.05		
5	949.74	4340.47	12,818.11	40,500.	
6	937.81	4101.74	10,938.	26,300.	74,000.
∞	911.76	3645.98			

† Landolt-Bornstein, *Zahlenwerte und Funktionen I Band Atom- und Molekularphysik* **1.** *Teil Atome und Ionen.* Berlin: Verlag Julius Springer, 1950, S. 51.

In this setting, Bohr in 1913 proposed a simple model of H to account for its spectra. He thought of H as a massive, positively charged proton around which sped an electron in circular orbits. The electron's energies were quantized, just as the energies of atoms in crystals were quantized by Einstein. These discrete energy states of the electron in H endured for a relatively long time, and their energies were specified by letting the electron's angular momentum be an integral multiple of $\hbar = h/2\pi$. That is, the electron's angular momentum was quantized. Moreover, he connected this hypothesis with spectroscopy by assuming that a transition from a state of energy E_1 to a state of energy E_2 was accompanied by emission or absorption of a photon of energy $h\nu$, where

$$E_2 - E_1 = \pm h\nu \tag{13.28}$$

On absorption, $E_2 > E_1$ and the positive sign obtains, while on emission, $E_2 < E_1$ and the negative sign obtains.

In amplifying this proposal in the next few years, Wilson and Sommerfeld found that the quantum condition on angular momentum could be neatly and very generally stated for periodic motion (like the revolution of an electron in a circular or elliptical orbit) in the form

$$\oint p\, dq = nh \tag{13.29}$$

where n is a quantum number, h is Planck's constant, and p is the momentum conjugate to the coordinate q. The integral proceeds over one cycle of motion.

With (13.28) and (13.29) it is possible to evaluate the Rybderg constant R in (13.27) in terms of fundamental constants. On a circular orbit the angular momentum of the electron with reduced mass μ is μvr, where v is its velocity along the arc and r is the radial distance of the electron from the center of mass. Since the angle ϕ is conjugate to μvr, and since μvr is constant on a circular orbit of fixed energy, (13.29) yields

$$nh = \oint p\, dq = \mu vr \oint_0^{2\pi} d\phi = 2\pi\mu\, vr \tag{13.30}$$

The radial acceleration is exactly equal to the coulombic attraction of proton for electron; hence,

$$\frac{\mu v^2}{r} = \frac{Ze^2}{4\pi\epsilon_0 r^2} \tag{13.31}$$

where $Z = 1$ for H, 2 for He^+, 3 for Li^{2+}, and so on. Solution of (13.30) and (13.31) for v^2 and r yields

$$v^2 = \frac{4\pi^2 Z^2 e^4}{(4\pi\epsilon_0)^2 n^2 h^2} \tag{13.32}$$

$$r = \frac{n^2 h^2 (4\pi\epsilon_0)}{4\pi^2 \mu Z e^2} \tag{13.33}$$

In center-of-mass coordinates, the energy of the system in state n is

$$E_n = \frac{\mu v^2}{2} - \frac{Ze^2}{4\pi\epsilon_0 r} = \frac{4\pi^2\mu Z^2 e^4}{2n^2h^2(4\pi\epsilon_0)^2} - \frac{4\pi^2\mu Z^2 e^4}{(4\pi\epsilon_0)^2 n^2 h^2} = -\frac{2\pi^2\mu Z^2 e^4}{(4\pi\epsilon_0)^2 n^2 h^2} \tag{13.34}$$

In (13.28), (13.34) for states m and n yields (without regard for signs, which do not matter)

$$h\nu = \frac{hc}{\lambda} = \frac{2\pi^2 \mu Z^2 e^4}{(4\pi\epsilon_0)^2 h^2}\left(\frac{1}{n^2} - \frac{1}{m^2}\right)$$

$$\frac{1}{\lambda} = \frac{2\pi^2 \mu Z^2 e^4}{(4\pi\epsilon_0)^2 h^3 c}\left(\frac{1}{n^2} - \frac{1}{m^2}\right) \tag{13.35}$$

Comparison of (13.27) and (13.35) yields for the Rydberg constant

$$R = \frac{2\pi^2 \mu Z^2 e^4}{(4\pi\epsilon_0)^2 h^3 c} \tag{13.36}$$

When R is observed for nuclei of increasing mass, μ approaches m, the mass of the electron. From Appendix A the value of R for infinite nuclear mass is

$$R_\infty = 10973731 \text{ m}^{-1} \tag{13.37}$$

This value is so exact and the formula (13.36) with $\mu = m$ has been so well substantiated by all present theories that (13.36) and (13.37) are one of the most accurate pieces of data used in the evaluation of the fundamental constants m (electron mass), e, h, and c.

Bohr's model of H was eminently successful in stimulating research; in explaining term values of one-electron atoms like H, He^+, Li^{2+}, . . . ; and in making it plausible for electrons to avoid continuous loss of energy through radiation and gradual spiral to annihilation upon collision with the nucleus. On the other hand, the model gave atoms with only two dimensions, inadequate accounts of even the simplest systems with more than one electron (e.g. He, H_2) despite almost superhuman efforts by Sommerfeld, and no results when asked certain reasonable questions. The quantum numbers, especially for elliptic orbits, were always introduced in a rather arbitrary way; some quantum numbers were even half-integers. Despite its excellence in 1913, by 1923 the Bohr theory of the atom was in serious trouble.

13.5 WAVELENGTH OF A PARTICLE

Einstein's special theory of relativity of 1905 states that mass m and energy E are interconvertible according to the equation

$$E = mc^2 \tag{13.38}$$

His explanation of the photoelectric effect suggested that, as a particle, a photon should exhibit the particle properties of momentum and mass even though a photon cannot be stopped to be weighed. In 1923, Compton showed that the lengthening of the wavelengths of X-rays scattered by matter was the result of collisions between photons and electrons. Among other things, Compton found that the momentum of a photon is $h\nu/c$. This result comes from the fact that the mass of a photon is a result of its energy, which is

$$E = h\nu \tag{13.39}$$

When (13.38) and (13.39) are equated, the momentum of the photon is found to be

$$mc = \frac{h\nu}{c} = \frac{h}{\lambda} = p_\gamma \tag{13.40}$$

The Compton effect thus confirmed the fact that a photon may behave like a particle in suffering collision with an electron (surely a particle!), and in exchanging momentum in the collision.

It occurred to de Broglie in 1924 that if a photon can behave like a particle in a collision and like a wave in an interference or diffraction experiment, then it is not unreasonable to expect a particle like the electron to behave like a wave if an attempt is made to observe its wave behavior. By analogy with (13.40), he suggested that the linear momentum p and wavelength λ of any particle are related by

$$p = \frac{h}{\lambda} \tag{13.41}$$

Despite his professors' skeptical attitude toward so radical a proposal, de Broglie's imaginative idea was fully vindicated in 1927 when Davisson and Germer detected the diffraction of electrons from Ni crystals, as though electrons were behaving like X-rays in the well known diffraction experiments first done by von Laue in 1912.

Meanwhile, de Broglie's startling proposal led Schrödinger in 1926 to propose that the electron in an atom behaves like a vibrating rubber ball after a bounce. Like a plucked string with its nodes and loops characteristic of its fundamental and harmonics, a struck ball pulsates with three-dimensional standing waves. Each bounce or blow initiates a pattern of three-dimensional standing waves that persist long after any transient waves are damped. Even the two-dimensional Bohr atom had a suggestion of such standing waves for the electron, for with $p = h/\lambda$ of (13.41) in the Wilson-Sommerfeld quantum condition (13.29) there results

$$\oint \frac{h}{\lambda}\, dq = nh \tag{13.42}$$

On a circular orbit of radius r, the quantities E, p, and λ are all constant so that upon integration around the orbit

$$\oint dq = 2\pi r = n\lambda \tag{13.43}$$

That is, the circumference of any long-lived orbit accommodated an integral number of wavelengths of the electron on the orbit; the electron was thus in phase with itself in the long-lived Bohr states.

For the electron, Schrödinger found that classical physics and de Broglie's wave-particle idea are nicely commingled for a "thing" of mass m in the three-dimensional wave equation

$$-\frac{\hbar^2}{2m}\left(\frac{\partial^2\psi}{\partial x^2}+\frac{\partial^2\psi}{\partial y^2}+\frac{\partial^2\psi}{\partial z^2}\right)+V(x, y, z)\psi=-\frac{\hbar}{i}\frac{\partial\psi}{\partial t} \tag{13.44}$$

As a legacy from classical physics, $V(x, y, z)$ is the potential energy of the particle at the position x, y, z. The Schrödinger equation in any of its forms cannot be derived; its support depends upon the fact that its predictions are observed. As in classical mechanics, (13.44) is expected to describe the position and general mechanical behavior of the particle as a function of time t. However, because ψ is a wave amplitude, the description is less definite than a solution of Newton's equations for classical behavior. The solution of (13.44) is a wave function ψ depending on time and position; hence,

$$\psi = \psi(x, y, z, t) \tag{13.45}$$

Furthermore, just as the intensity of light (number of photons) is even classically a square of an amplitude function with wavelike properties, here the density of matter at x, y, z at time t is proportional to

$$|\psi|^2 = \psi^*(x, y, z, t)\,\psi(x, y, z, t) \tag{13.46}$$

where ψ^* is the complex conjugate of ψ, which may be a complex quantity. In 1926, Born interpreted $|\psi|^2$ as a probability distribution function that tells the probability that the particle can be found at x, y, z at time t. He also explained how average values of position, momentum, and other mechanical properties of the particle can be calculated if ψ is known. These rules are given in Section 14.4, where a more general formulation of the Schrödinger equation for one or more particles is presented after a few of the marvelous features of wave mechanics are derived from (13.44).

consider c

Example 13.3. What is the wavelength of a free electron accelerated from rest by a potential difference of 40,000 absolute volts? (Neglect any relativistic increase in mass.)

By (13.15), the kinetic energy of the electron after acceleration is

$$E = e(\Delta\Phi) = (1.602 \times 10^{-19})(4.00 \times 10^4) = 6.408 \times 10^{-15}\text{ j}$$

However, in terms of its momentum p, its energy is

$$E = \frac{mv^2}{2} = \frac{(mv)^2}{2m} = \frac{p^2}{2m}$$

Hence, since the electron rest mass is $m = 9.10 \times 10^{-31}$ kg

$$p = \sqrt{2mE} = \sqrt{2 \times 9.10 \times 10^{-31} \times 6.408 \times 10^{-15}}$$
$$= 1.080 \times 10^{-22} \text{ kg m sec}^{-1}$$

By (13.41),

$$\lambda = \frac{h}{p} = \frac{6.626 \times 10^{-34}}{1.080 \times 10^{-22}} = 6.14 \times 10^{-12} \text{ m}$$
$$= 0.0614\text{A}$$

Example 13.4. What is the wavelength of a colloidal particle with a "molecular" weight of 10^5 at 300°K?

If free, the colloidal particle has energy

$$E = \frac{3}{2}kT = \frac{3}{2} \times 1.380 \times 10^{-16} \times 300$$
$$= 6.21 \times 10^{-14} \text{ erg}$$

Since its mass (in grams) is $10^5/N_0$, its momentum is

$$p = \sqrt{2mE} = \left(\frac{2 \times 10^5 \times 6.21 \times 10^{-14}}{6.02 \times 10^{23}}\right)^{1/2}$$
$$= 1.435 \times 10^{-16} \text{ g cm sec}^{-1}$$

Hence, by (13.41)

$$\lambda = \frac{6.626 \times 10^{-27}}{1.435 \times 10^{-16}} = 4.62 \times 10^{-11} \text{ cm}$$
$$= 0.00462 \text{ A}$$

A comparison of the wavelengths here and in Example 13.3 indicates that wave-like behavior is likely to be observed only for very small particles because h is small.

13.6 UNCERTAINTY PRINCIPLE

The uncertainty principle was discovered by Heisenberg in 1927. It says that system and observer interact during an observation of a mechanical property in such a way that it is impossible to make a correction or allowance for the effect of the observer on the system. The uncertainty introduced into the mechanical state of a system increases as the observation is made more accurate. If a property p_i is measured, then the observer loses knowledge of a property q_i which is said to be canonically conjugate to p_i. In classical mechanics, both p_i and q_i could be observed at once with no restriction on accuracy. Some pairs of canonically conjugate properties are: energy and time; x-coordinate and the x-component of linear momentum p_x; y and p_y; z and p_z; and so on. Since quantum mechanics deals only with observables, it is pointless from a scientific viewpoint to speculate about whether or not the disturbed system behaves within itself in a way that would correspond to exact specification of both of the paired variables, as though classical mechanics were valid between observations. The uncertainty principle merely states what everyone admits; a (second) observation of the other property of such a pair yields an unpredictable result.

Even in classical physics it is impossible to measure the frequency of a pure wave with no error. To reduce the error in ν to zero would require an indefinitely long time so that a suitably great number of oscillations could be counted. Observing such a wave for a time Δt inevitably leads to an uncertainty $\Delta\nu$ in frequency, the best possible experiment being one in which $2\pi\,\Delta\nu\,\Delta t = 1$. For any observation, this condition is

$$2\pi\,\Delta\nu\,\Delta t \geqslant 1 \tag{13.47}$$

An error of $\Delta\nu$ in the frequency of a photon means an error of $\Delta E = h\Delta\nu$ in its energy if (13.39) holds; hence, with (13.47),

$$\Delta E \cdot \Delta t \geqslant \hbar = \frac{h}{2\pi} \tag{13.48}$$

The Heisenberg uncertainty principle (13.48) says quantitatively that under the most favorable experimental conditions it is necessary to observe a system for a time longer than Δt if its energy afterwards is to be known within an uncertainty ΔE. Since $\hbar \sim 10^{-34}$ joule-sec, (13.48) is without practical effect for macroscopic systems. However, it is indeed a limitation on an experimenter's ability to observe properties of a system of atomic or subatomic size. All scientists agree that (13.48) states a natural limit upon their ability to measure E and t of a system because of an unpredictable interaction of observer and system during an observation.

The energy of a particle free to move in one dimension is

$$E = \frac{mv_x^2}{2} = \frac{(mv_x)^2}{2m} = \frac{p_x^2}{2m} \tag{13.49}$$

where p_x is the component of linear momentum along the one dimension of motion. If dp_x is the uncertainty in p_x upon measurement, then by (13.49) the uncertainty in (kinetic) energy is $dE = (p_x/m)\,dp_x$. But since (p_x/m) equals $v_x = dx/dt$, it follows from (13.48) with finite differences ΔE, Δp_x, Δx, and Δt in place of infinitesimals, that

$$\Delta p_x \cdot \Delta x = \Delta E \cdot \Delta t \geqslant \hbar \tag{13.50}$$

The uncertainty principle in the form (13.50) says that it is impossible to devise an experiment that can observe the conjugate variables p_x and x with uncertainties less than Δp_x and Δx in (13.50). A statement still more general than

(13.50) is

$$\Delta p_i \cdot \Delta q_i \geqslant \hbar \tag{13.51}$$

where p_i and q_i are any two canonically conjugate mechanical variables. (The meaning of canonically conjugate variables is given in Section 14.3.)

The Heisenberg uncertainty principle is commonly illustrated in two ways. In one, the position of a particle is to be observed with a microscope. However, microscopes are limited by the wavelength of light, just as location by ear is limited by the wavelength of sound. The minimum uncertainty Δx in position as determined by the best of microscopes is of the order of λ, the wavelength of light used; hence, $\Delta x \approx \lambda$.

It would appear, then, that X-rays or gamma rays would be ideal for locating the particle. However, the momentum of a photon is h/λ by (13.40). Although a photon with small λ could reduce the size of Δx on locating a particle by collision and scattering into a microscope, it can also transfer momentum to the particle, as in the Compton effect. It happens that the uncertainty Δp_x in the located body's momentum is of the order of h/λ regardless of the degree of optical sophistication in the microscope. As a result, (13.50) holds. With less care, of course, Δx and Δp_x may exceed their minimum.

The uncertainty principle can be illustrated by the idealized experiment of Figure 13.7, which shows apparatus for observing the x-component of position with as little disturbance as possible to the x-component of momentum. Elec-

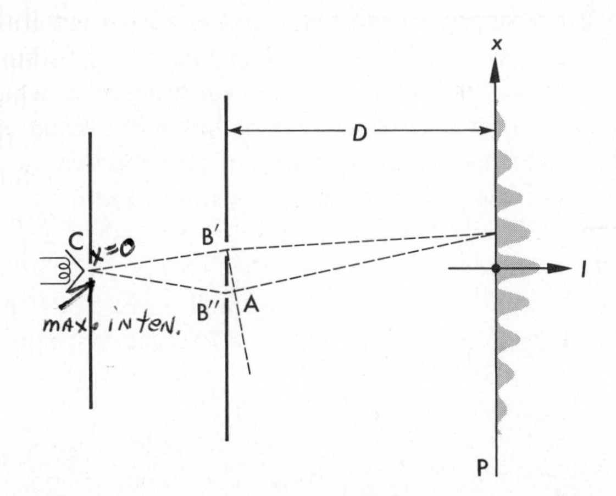

Figure 13.7. The Two-Hole Experiment

trons proceed from a cathode C through a small hole which acts as a point source, thence through a barrier having two identical small holes a distance ϵ apart, and finally on toward a photographic plate P to be recorded. The record is observed to be a diffraction pattern similar in kind to that made by electrons diffracted from Ni. The two holes in the barrier act like a grating to cause reinforcement and interference. There is a maximum of intensity at the center ($x = 0$) since the alternate routes are equal in length and what starts from C in phase is also in phase at the center of P. Alternate paths to other maxima in the record at P will differ in length by $n\lambda$, an integral number of wavelengths. If the distance between maxima is small compared to D, the distance between barrier and P, then the extra distance through, say, hole 2 is approximately B″A, where the line B′A is perpendicular to the path from B″ to P. In nearly similar triangles, when the distance x from the center of P is small relative to D,

$$\frac{n\lambda}{\epsilon} \approx \frac{x}{D}$$

On the other hand, at a minimum of recorded intensity, interference occurs since the difference in path length is $(n + \frac{1}{2})\lambda$ and

$$\frac{(n + \frac{1}{2})\lambda}{\epsilon} \approx \frac{x'}{D}$$

The change of angle required to displace a maximum at x to a minimum at x' is, then, approximately $\lambda/2\epsilon$.

The diffraction pattern remains as long as both holes are open, even if the intensity is decreased until only one particle at a time traverses the distance from C to P. As long as the experimenter does not attempt to determine which hole is or is not used by placing a counter near a hole or by closing a hole, the diffraction pattern remains. However, when the experimenter ever so carefully attempts to follow the path of the particle through one hole, the pattern is changed because the particle interacts with the device which specifies which hole is or is not used. The pattern becomes a particle pattern, with a particle record in line with the unobstructed hole. When its trajectory is known or specified, the particle behaves like a particle. When it is not, it behaves like a wave.

If a counter is placed near a hole, it will in general cause a change Δp_x in the x component of the particle's momentum such that $\Delta p_x = p_y \sin \alpha$, where α is the angle by which its erstwhile path is deflected. For small α, $\sin \alpha \approx \alpha$ and $\Delta p_x \approx p_y\alpha$. If $\alpha \ll \lambda/2\epsilon$, the diffraction pattern remains unchanged, but if $\alpha \approx \lambda/2\epsilon$, maximum falls on minimum and the diffraction pattern fades because the counter is too definite in locating the particle at the barrier.

When the particle is observed at one of the holes as distinguished from the other hole, the uncertainty or maximum error Δx in its x coordinate in space is less than the distance ϵ between holes so that $\Delta x \leqslant \epsilon$. If $p_y\lambda = h$ by (13.41) and if the diffraction pattern is to remain essentially unchanged, then

$$\Delta p_x \cdot \Delta x \leqslant p_y\alpha\epsilon \ll \left(\frac{h}{\lambda}\right)\left(\frac{\lambda}{2\epsilon}\right)\epsilon = \frac{h}{2} \tag{13.52}$$

In this hypothetical situation, accurate location at the barrier (small Δx) together with small interaction with the counter (small α and Δp_x) is supposed to maintain the diffraction pattern at P. However, it is observed that accurate location at the barrier yields a simple particle pattern rather than a diffraction pattern with several maxima and minima. The simple particle pattern is really a smeared out diffraction pattern having one main maximum in line with the particle's path through the barrier. The diffraction pattern is smeared when Δp_x is great; this happens when Δx is small. When Δx is great because both holes are open, the diffraction pattern is not smeared. Apparently Δp_x and Δx cannot both be observed to be as small as desired. The uncertainty principle $\Delta p_x \cdot \Delta x \geqslant \hbar$ is thus the antithesis of the hypothetical situation (13.52), which contradicts observation. The equality holds for the best possible simultaneous measurements of p_x and x, and the inequality of (13.50) applies to measurements which are less than the best.

Example 13.5. An excited state of a molecule is observed spectroscopically to have an uncertainty in energy of 5.0 cm^{-1}. Estimate the lifetime of this excited state.

Since $E = h\nu = hc/\lambda = hc\bar{\nu}$, $\Delta E = 6.6 \times 10^{-27} \times 3.0 \times 10^{10} \times 5.0$ erg. By (13.48)

$$\Delta t \geqslant \frac{\hbar}{\Delta E} = \frac{1}{2\pi \times 3.0 \times 10^{10} \times 5.0} = 1.0 \times 10^{-12} \text{ sec}$$

The lifetime is about 1.0×10^{-12} sec.

Example 13.6. If the excited state of Example 13.4 is observed at 27°C at 1 atm, could deactivating collisions be the reason for the limited lifetime of the excited state?

If collisions were the main cause of decay of this excited state, the time between collisions must be of the order of the lifetime, 1×10^{-12} sec. The time between collisions is about equal to the mean free path l divided by the root mean square velocity; hence, by (1.37) and (1.33),

$$\Delta t \approx \frac{l}{u} = \frac{V}{\sqrt{2}\, N\pi\sigma^2}\left(\frac{M}{3RT}\right)^{1/2}$$

For a gas of molecular weight of 30 with $\sigma^2 = 10 \times 10^{-16}$ cm^2, at the stated conditions

$$\Delta t \approx \frac{2.5 \times 10^4}{\sqrt{2} \times 0.60 \times 10^{24} \times \pi \times 10^{-15}}\left(\frac{30}{3 \times 8.3 \times 10^7 \times 300}\right)^{1/2}$$

$$= 1.9 \times 10^{-10} \text{ sec}$$

Since the time between collisions is more than 100 times the lifetime, the main cause of decay is not collisions.

13.7 STATIONARY ENERGY STATES

For convenience, and because the Schrödinger equation for systems of any complexity is based on an analogy with the Hamiltonian method of classical mechanics, the Schrödinger equation is generally written in the form

$$\mathbf{H}\psi = -\frac{\hbar}{i}\frac{\partial \psi}{\partial t} \tag{13.53}$$

The Hamiltonian operator, for the purposes of this book, is simply

$$\mathbf{H} = -\frac{\hbar^2}{2}\sum_i \frac{1}{m_i}\left(\frac{\partial^2}{\partial x_i^2} + \frac{\partial^2}{\partial y_i^2} + \frac{\partial^2}{\partial z_i^2}\right) + V \tag{13.54}$$

The summation proceeds over all particles, each of mass m_i, and V is the potential energy of the system of particles stated as a function of coordinates. In general **H** may be much more complicated and may even depend explicitly upon time.

The wave function ψ in (13.53) is a function of all coordinates of the particles and of time. It is the full and complete description of the system. It is in accord with the uncertainty principle in every way; no further knowledge of the system could be found or verified by experiment.

If $|\psi|^2$, the probability density of matter in space at time t, is in fact independent of time (and if the state is such that a net flow of matter does not occur), then the state described by ψ is called a stationary (or steady) state. In stationary states, **H** is independent of time.

Stationary states have wave functions of the form

$$\psi(x_i, y_i, z_i, t) = u(x_i, y_i, z_i)f(t) \tag{13.55}$$

The general form of $f(t)$ is found by substituting (13.55) into the wave equation (13.53). On the left,

$$\mathbf{H}\psi(x_i, y_i, z_i, t) = f(t)\mathbf{H}u(x_i, y_i, z_i)$$

and on the right,

$$-\frac{\hbar}{i}\frac{\partial \psi}{\partial t} = -\frac{\hbar}{i}u(x_i, y_i, z_i)\frac{df(t)}{dt}$$

After equating these expressions and dividing by ψ, the result is

$$\frac{1}{u}\mathbf{H}u = -\frac{\hbar}{if}\frac{df}{dt} \tag{13.56}$$

Since the left-hand member of (13.56) is independent of t while the right-hand member is independent of positional coordinates, each side must be independent of x_i, y_i, z_i, and t for neither changes when these variables change. If E is a constant independent of these variables, then the right side of (13.56) yields

$$-\frac{\hbar}{if}\frac{df}{dt} = E$$

and

$$f(t) = a \exp\left(-\frac{iEt}{\hbar}\right) \tag{13.57}$$

From (13.56) come two equations, namely,

$$-\frac{\hbar}{i}\frac{\partial f(t)}{\partial t} = Ef(t) \tag{13.58}$$

$$\mathbf{H}u(x_i, y_i, z_i) = Eu(x_i, y_i, z_i) \tag{13.59}$$

Mathematicians call equations like these *eigenvalue equations.* The constant E is a number, called an *eigenvalue*, and $f(t)$ and $u(x_i, y_i, z_i)$ are *eigenfunctions.* Often only a very special set of numbers $E_1, E_2, \cdots, E_n, \cdots$ can satisfy (13.58) and (13.59). Every observable quantity in quantum mechanics is an eigenvalue and each eigenvalue has an operator. For the energy E, the operator is $\mathbf{H}$ or $-(\hbar/i)(\partial/\partial t)$. An individual measurement of the energy of a quantum mechanical system in a stationary state would yield one of the values E_n. Each stationary state has its own wave function such that (13.53), (13.58), and (13.59) are

$$\mathbf{H}\psi_n = -\frac{\hbar}{i}\frac{\partial \psi_n}{\partial t} \tag{13.60}$$

$$-\frac{\hbar}{i}\frac{df_n(t)}{dt} = E_n f_n(t) \tag{13.61}$$

$$\mathbf{H}u_n(x_i, y_i, z_i) = E_n u_n(x_i, y_i, z_i) \tag{13.62}$$

where

$$\psi_n = a_n u_n(x_i, y_i, z_i) e^{-iE_n t/\hbar} \tag{13.63}$$

The constant a_n is adjusted so that the integral of $|\psi_n|^2$ over all space is normalized; hence, if $d\tau$ is the element of volume,

$$1 = \int \psi_n^* \psi_n \, d\tau = a_n^* a_n \int u_n^* u_n \, d\tau \tag{13.64}$$

In order to be physically meaningful, ψ and its first derivatives must be continuous, finite, and single-valued everywhere. The general normalization condition

$$1 = \int \psi^* \psi \, d\tau \tag{13.65}$$

or the interpretation of $|\psi|^2 = \psi^*\psi$ as a probability density of matter somewhere this side of infinity generally requires also that ψ approach zero asymptotically for large values of its coordinates. As can be verified by substitution into (13.53), the most general solution of the wave equation in terms of eigenfunctions of the energy is

$$\psi(x_i, y_i, z_i, t) = \sum_n a_n u_n(x_i, y_i, z_i) e^{-iE_n t/\hbar} \tag{13.66}$$

Each term of ψ describes a state of the system. If several states have the same energy E_n, then they are called *degenerate*. Stationary states that are not degenerate have all but one a_n equal to zero.

This discussion and its conclusions are quite general and, in fact, anticipate the next chapter. What is of interest here is the general possibility of removing time from a problem by considering only stationary states by (13.62). Physicists and physical chemists studying collisions or rates of reaction or situations where a field is turned on or off often need to consider t as a variable, and may make the a_n's functions of time. Chemists, however, are sometimes interested in molecules that endure for several periods of vibration. As Δt in the uncertainty principle (13.48) increases, the uncertainty in the energy of the system decreases. As a result, in dealing with species of ordinary lifetimes, chemists center their attention on energy states of molecules. These are readily observed by use of photons, for, by (13.12), a change in the energy of a chemical species is $\Delta E = h\nu$. Equation (13.62) is the important equation when the natures of stationary states of atoms and molecules are the major interest of quantum chemistry. But when rates of reaction and collisions are under study, as in Chapter 18, the important equation is (13.53).

13.8 FREE PARTICLE

A simple beginning to the solutions of (13.62) is the description of a free particle. A particle free to move throughout space has no potential energy; hence, $V(x, y, z) = 0$. On the other hand, it has no definite position so that Δx, the uncertainty in its position, can be very great. If Δx approaches infinity, then the uncertainty principle does not forbid an exact measurement of p_x, for by (13.52) the uncertainty in p_x is $\Delta p_x \geqslant \hbar/\Delta x \rightarrow 0$.

In a stationary state with $V = 0$, the Schrödinger equation (13.62) for one particle is

$$-\frac{\hbar^2}{2m}\left(\frac{\partial^2 u}{\partial x^2} + \frac{\partial^2 u}{\partial y^2} + \frac{\partial^2 u}{\partial z^2}\right) = Eu \qquad (13.67)$$

A solution is of the form

$$u = \exp\left[\pm \frac{i}{\hbar}(p_x x + p_y y + p_z z)\right] \qquad (13.68)$$

for

$$\frac{\partial u}{\partial x} = \pm \frac{i}{\hbar} p_x u, \qquad \text{and so on}$$

$$\frac{\partial^2 u}{\partial x^2} = -\frac{p_x^2}{\hbar^2} u, \qquad \text{and so on.}$$

On substitution into (13.67) the result is

$$\left(-\frac{\hbar^2}{2m}\right)\left(-\frac{p_x^2}{\hbar^2}-\frac{p_y^2}{\hbar^2}-\frac{p_z^2}{\hbar^2}\right)u = Eu$$

If the particle exists, $u \neq 0$, and, as expected of a particle with only kinetic energy, its energy is

$$E = \frac{p_x^2 + p_y^2 + p_z^2}{2m} \tag{13.69}$$

Since $\Delta p_i \longrightarrow 0$, E is as well known as p_x, p_y, and p_z. This classical looking result is possible because in a stationary state $\Delta t \longrightarrow \infty$ and $\Delta E \geqslant \hbar/\Delta t \longrightarrow 0$ by (13.48).

The wave function (13.68) is the amplitude of the wave-particle of fixed energy and no particular position. With the positive sign, u represents a particle proceeding toward $x = \infty$, $y = \infty$, $z = \infty$, while the negative sign indicates motion toward $x = -\infty$, $y = -\infty$, $z = -\infty$. Either form of u consists of factors like

$$u_x = A_{\pm x} e^{\pm i p_x x/\hbar} \tag{13.70}$$

where $A_{\pm x}$ is a constant. With the well-known Euler relation $e^{\pm iv} = \cos v \pm i \sin v$, and with no preferred direction along the x-axis, A_{+x} and A_{-x} are alike and

$$\begin{aligned} u_x &= A_+ \, e^{+ip_x x/\hbar} + A_- \, e^{-ip_x x/\hbar} \\ &= (A_+ + A_-)\cos\left(\frac{p_x x}{\hbar}\right) + i(A_+ - A_-)\sin\left(\frac{p_x x}{\hbar}\right) \\ &= 2A_{+x}\cos\left(\frac{p_x x}{\hbar}\right) \end{aligned}$$

In three dimensions, the wave function of a free particle is

$$u = A\cos\left(\frac{p_x x}{\hbar}\right)\cos\left(\frac{p_y y}{\hbar}\right)\cos\left(\frac{p_z z}{\hbar}\right) \tag{13.71}$$

as substitution would show. In fact, whenever a Hamiltonian operator $\mathbf{H}$ is a sum of terms that do not share coordinates, like $\mathbf{H} = \mathbf{H}_x + \mathbf{H}_y + \mathbf{H}_z$ as in (13.67), then the wave function is a product like (13.71). For substitution of $u = u_x u_y u_z$ in $\mathbf{H}u = Eu$ followed by division by u gives

$$\frac{\mathbf{H}_x u_x}{u_x} + \frac{\mathbf{H}_y u_y}{u_y} + \frac{\mathbf{H}_z u_z}{u_z} = E$$

in which each of the terms on the left is a function of only one variable. Thus $\mathbf{H}_x u_x/u_x = E_x$ and so on, and $E = E_x + E_y + E_z$ as in (13.69). Another form of (13.71) is

$$u = A \cos\left(\frac{2\pi x}{\lambda_x}\right) \cos\left(\frac{2\pi y}{\lambda_y}\right) \cos\left(\frac{2\pi z}{\lambda_z}\right) \tag{13.72}$$

where $p_x \lambda_x = 2\pi \hbar$ as in (13.41). In general, $2\,mE = p_x^2 + p_y^2 + p_z^2 = p^2 = (h/\lambda)^2$ so that

$$\frac{1}{\lambda^2} = \frac{1}{\lambda_x^2} + \frac{1}{\lambda_y^2} + \frac{1}{\lambda_z^2} \tag{13.73}$$

If the particle moves parallel to the x-axis, then $p_y = p_z = 0$ and $\lambda_y = \lambda_z = \infty$ while $\lambda = \lambda_x$ and

$$u = A \cos \frac{2\pi x}{\lambda} \tag{13.74}$$

The u of (13.74) is clearly a wave and the maxima in its probability $|u|^2$ occur when $x = \pm n(\lambda/2)$ as shown in Figure 13.8.

A free particle observed to be in a certain region Δx has a wave function like Figure 13.9. The uncertainty principle (13.52) says that the error in a mea-

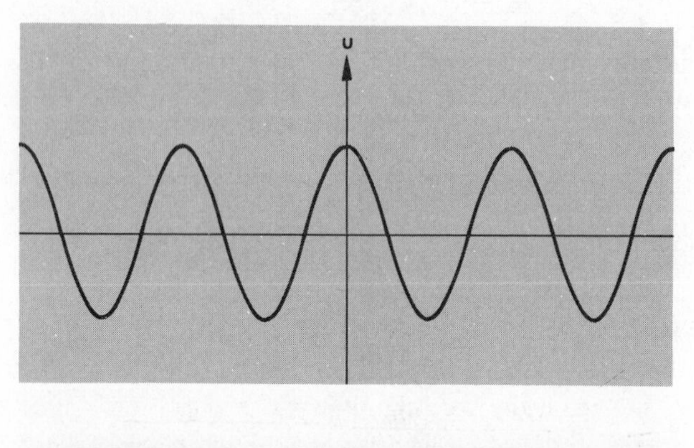

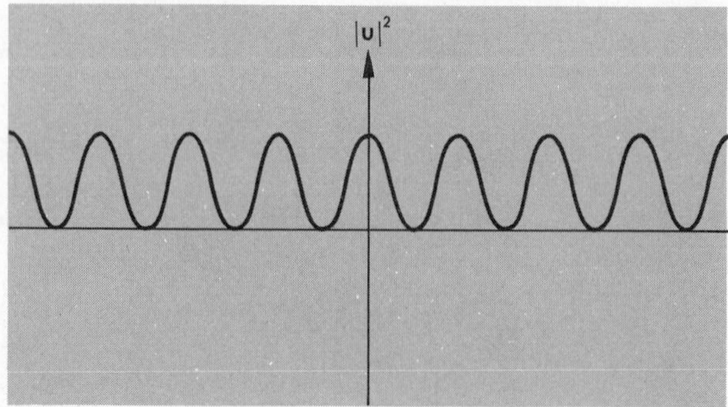

Figure 13.8. Amplitude u and Probability Density $|u|^2$ of an Infinitely Extended Free Particle

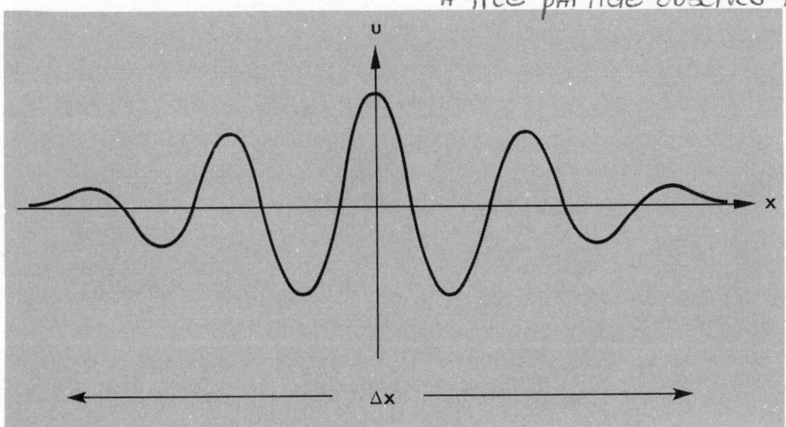

Figure 13.9. Wave Function of a Wave Packet

surement of p_x is $\Delta p_x = \hbar/\Delta x$. The corresponding uncertainty in λ is a kind of internal interference of the particle with itself in a way that restricts its activity to the region Δx. A wave that is thus restricted in space is called a *wave packet.*

13.9 PARTICLE IN BOX

A box is a potential V that is easy to handle mathematically and yet gives much qualitatively interesting information applicable to particles held by more realistic potentials. The description of a particle free to move about in a finite region of space called the *box* differs from that of the completely free particle in that the particle is not completely delocalized. That is, Δx, Δy, and Δz are restricted by the size of the box. Within the box, the potential energy $V(x, y, z)$ is zero; without, it is infinite. The stationary-state wave equation of one particle of mass m within the box is

$$-\frac{\hbar^2}{2m}\left(\frac{\partial^2 u}{\partial x^2} + \frac{\partial^2 u}{\partial y^2} + \frac{\partial^2 u}{\partial z^2}\right) = Eu \tag{13.75}$$

A solution, as for (13.67), is of the form

$$u = \exp\left[\pm\frac{i}{\hbar}(p_x x + p_y y + p_z z)\right] \tag{13.76}$$

This solution, however, is subject to certain restraints, called *boundary conditions*, at the box walls.

In order to show that the box walls cause u to be zero at and outside the box walls, it is sufficient to examine the one-dimensional equation like (13.75), namely

$$-\left(\frac{\hbar^2}{2m}\right)\frac{d^2u_x}{dx^2} + Vu_x = Eu_x \tag{13.77}$$

where $u_x = u_x(x)$ and where $V(x)$ is zero within the box ($|x| \leqslant a/2$) and infinite without ($|x| \geqslant a/2$). That is, the one-dimensional box extends from $x = -a/2$ to $x = a/2$ and x is zero at its midpoint. From (13.77)

$$\frac{d^2u_x}{dx^2} = \left[\frac{2m(V-E)}{\hbar^2}\right]u_x \tag{13.78}$$

If $|x| \geqslant a/2$, u_x and its second space derivative have the same algebraic sign since $V > E$. The fact that d^2u_x/dx^2 is positive means that, as x increases, the slope du_x/dx will eventually become positive regardless of the sign of du_x/dx if $u_x > 0$, for d^2u_x/dx^2 is the rate of change of du_x/dx with respect to x. The upper part of Figure 13.10 shows how du_x/dx eventually becomes positive for large x when $u_x > 0$. The negative slopes at points 1 and 4 eventually become positive for large x, while the positive slopes at points 2 and 3 become more positive as x increases. In fact, since V is infinite in (13.78) when $|x| \geqslant a/2$, the curves through 1 and 4 *very* quickly become like those through 2 and 3, and these in turn very quickly attain an infinite value of du_x/dx. It is this extremely rapid change in slope that prevents u_x near 2 or 4 from remaining bounded as $x \longrightarrow \pm\infty$. For, as stated in Section 13.7, the wave function and its first derivatives must be finite everywhere in order that they be physically meaningful (e.g, $|u_x|^2$ for a finite density of matter).

Similarly, when $V > E$ and $u_x < 0$, (13.78) requires d^2u_x/dx^2 to be negative; hence, regardless of its sign, du_x/dx eventually becomes negative if $u_x < 0$. And it does so vehemently when $V \longrightarrow \infty$. Hence, curves through points 5, 6, 7, and 8 of Figure 13.10 are as unacceptable as those through 1, 2, 3, and 4. If u_x is to remain finite in a region where V is infinite, it is necessary that u_x be zero throughout that region.

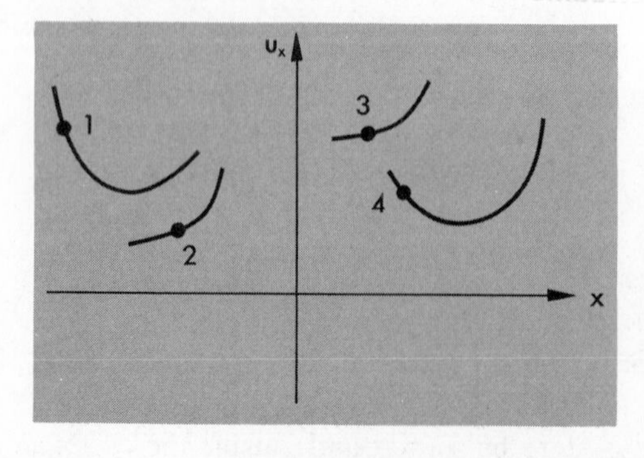

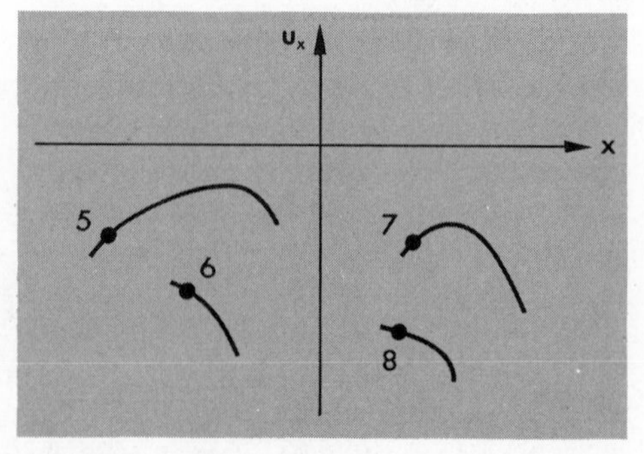

Figure 13.10. Wave Functions Where V is Infinite

If the three-dimensional box has its walls at $x = \pm a/2$, $y = \pm b/2$, and $z = \pm c/2$, then, as in one dimension, u of (13.76) must be zero when $|x| \geqslant a/2$, $|y| \geqslant b/2$, $|z| \geqslant c/2$. This means that, if the particle is in the box ($|u|^2 > 0$ within), the particle cannot escape from the box and that at the boundary of the box

$$0 = \exp\left[\pm \frac{i}{\hbar}\left(\frac{p_x a}{2} + \frac{p_y b}{2} + \frac{p_z c}{2}\right)\right] \tag{13.79}$$

Because of (13.79), only certain values of p_x, p_y, and p_z are allowed in a stationary state of the particle in the box. These values are found most easily when (13.79), after being factored, is restated in the forms

$$0 = \cos\left(\frac{p_x a}{2\hbar}\right) \pm i \sin\left(\frac{p_x a}{2\hbar}\right) \quad \text{and so on} \tag{13.80}$$

Since both real and imaginary parts of (13.80) must be zero, it follows that u is zero at the walls when

$$\frac{p_x a}{2\hbar} = \frac{\pi}{2}(2n'_x + 1) \quad n'_x = 0, 1, 2, \cdots \tag{13.81}$$

$$\frac{p_x a}{2\hbar} = \frac{\pi}{2}(2n''_x) \quad n''_x = 0, 1, 2, \cdots \tag{13.82}$$

But, together, (13.81) and (13.82) cover both even and odd integers so that (13.80) is satisfied when

$$\frac{p_x a}{2\hbar} = \frac{\pi}{2} n_x \quad n_x = 0, 1, 2, 3, \cdots \tag{13.83}$$

Hence, (13.83) in (13.69), which is true here as well as for the free particle, yields stationary state energies

$$E = \frac{\pi^2 \hbar^2}{2m}\left[\left(\frac{n_x}{a}\right)^2 + \left(\frac{n_y}{b}\right)^2 + \left(\frac{n_z}{c}\right)^2\right] \tag{13.84}$$

where n_x, n_y, and n_z are quantum numbers with values 1, 2, 3, ...

The form of u and the reason for excluding $n_x = 0$ in (13.84) are easily seen in one dimension with

$$\begin{aligned} u_x(x) &= A \exp\left(+\frac{i\pi n_x x}{a}\right) + B \exp\left(-\frac{i\pi n_x x}{a}\right) \\ &= (A + B) \cos\left(\frac{\pi n_x x}{a}\right) + i(A - B) \sin\left(\frac{\pi n_x x}{a}\right) \end{aligned} \tag{13.85}$$

where (13.83) has been used to remove p_x from $u_x(x)$, the x factor of (13.76), and where A and B are the amplitudes of waves of opposite momentum. The boundary conditions at $x = \pm a/2$ require that when n_x is even

$$0 = u_x\left(\pm \frac{a}{2}\right) = (A + B)(\pm 1) + i(A - B)(0) \tag{13.86}$$

while when n_x is odd

$$0 = u_x\left(\pm\frac{a}{2}\right) = (A + B)(0) + i(A - B)(\pm 1) \tag{13.87}$$

Because of (13.87), $A = B$ and (13.85) for odd n_x is

$$u_x(x) = 2A \cos\left(\frac{\pi n_x x}{2}\right) \qquad (n_x \text{ odd}) \tag{13.88}$$

Similarly, for the states having n_x even rather than odd, from (13.86), $A = -B$ and (13.85) for even n_x is

$$u_x(x) = 2iA \sin\left(\frac{\pi n_x x}{a}\right) \qquad (n_x \text{ even}) \tag{13.89}$$

The presence of i in (13.89) is unimportant because it is $|u|^2$ and not u that is observable. The three-dimensional wave functions like (13.88) and (13.89) are of the forms $u_x(x)\, u_y(y)\, u_z(z)$. If n_x or n_y or n_z is zero and a factor of u of the form of (13.89) vanishes, the particle is not in the box. Thus, zero is not allowed for n_x, n_y, or n_z.

While the infinite potential V and the abrupt curvature in V at the corners of the box make this situation unrealistic, the solution is nevertheless of great value in a qualitative way. Figure 13.11 shows the lowest five wave functions and energies

Eigenvalue after boundary conditions

$$E_x = \left(\frac{\pi^2\hbar^2}{2ma^2}\right) n_x^2 \tag{13.90}$$

of a particle in a one-dimensional box. The particle behaves like a standing wave with nodes at the walls and, in excited states ($n_x > 1$), with nodes at fixed points between the walls. The probability of finding the particle is zero at the nodes, where $u_x(x)$ and $|u_x|^2$ are each zero. As n_x increases by unity, one node is added to u_x It is possible, in fact, to show that for *any potential* the wave function u_2 for stationary state of energy E_2 has one (or more) nodes between the closest nodes of u_1, the wave function of the state of energy E_1, if $E_2 > E_1$. For adjacent states such that no stationary state lies between E_2 and E_1, only one new node is added on going from u_1 to u_2, but each node of u_1 lies alone between adjacent nodes of u_2. The nodes of Figure 13.11 behave thus.

There are two classes of u_x. When n_x is odd, u_x is said to be of even parity for $u_x(x) = +u_x(-x)$. That is u_x is a cosine, an even function of x. However, when n_x is even, u_x is a sine, $u_x(x) = -u_x(-x)$ and the parity of u_x is odd. Since one new node is added to u_x as n_x increases by unity, the parity of u_x changes as n_x changes by unity.

Parity is a very general kind of symmetry property. If, for example, the potential energy is an even function of x such that $V(x) = +V(-x)$, then the

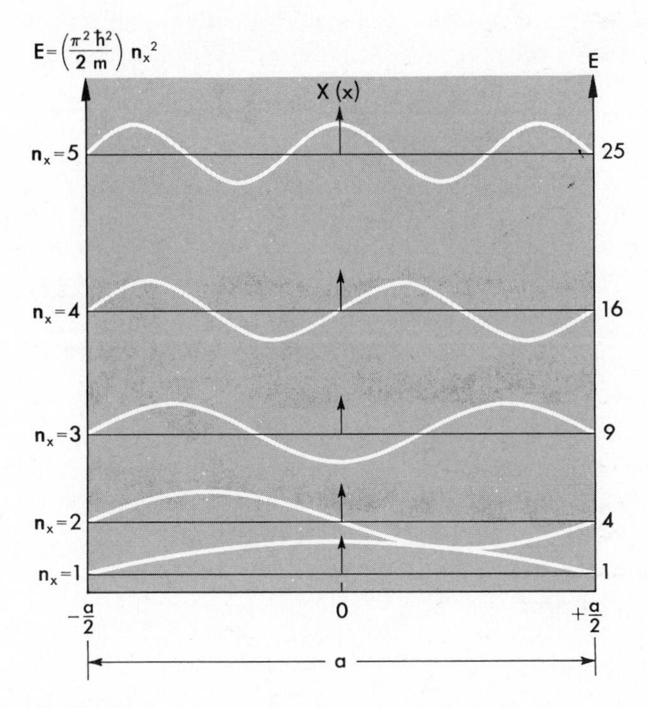

Figure 13.11. Wave Functions and Energies of Particle in One-Dimensional Box

Hamiltonian operator is also an even function of x. That is, $V(x)$ and the Hamiltonian operator are of even parity and changing the sign of x leaves $\mathbf{H}$ unchanged in sign and form. Hence, if $\mathbf{H}(x)\, u(x) = E\, u(x)$, then $\mathbf{H}(-x)\, u(x) = E\, u(x)$, which latter result, after a change in the arbitrary direction of x, yields $\mathbf{H}(x)$ $u(-x) = Eu(-x)$. From $u(x)$ and $u(-x)$ can be constructed two wave functions, one of even parity:

$$u_+ = u(x) + u(-x) \tag{13.91}$$

and one of odd parity:

$$u_- = u(x) - u(-x) \tag{13.92}$$

Equation (13.88) is an example of (13.91) with $u(x) = \exp(ip_x x/\hbar)$ and $u(-x) = \exp(-ip_x x/\hbar)$. Likewise, (13.89) is an example of (13.92). If a state must have either odd or even parity, then u_+ or u_- is zero.

If $V(x) \neq V(-x)$(and if $V(x) \neq 0$), then it is possible for u_+ and u_- each to differ from zero. In such a case, linear combinations of u_+ and u_-, corresponding to superposition of waves, yield two wave functions for the same energy. The state is then said to be degenerate, and the order of the degeneracy is two because two linearly independent wave functions have the same eigenvalue E. Degeneracy exists for a particle in a two-, three-, or multi-dimensional box if the linear dimensions of the box are equal or if their ratio is a ratio of integers. For then more than one set of n_i's can yield the same energy.

Besides parity, the solution of the particle in the box yields a very interesting state of minimum energy. A classical particle would rest on the bottom of the box with zero energy. With $n_x = 1$ in (13.90), the lowest energy is $E_x = \pi^2\hbar^2/2ma^2$, which exceeds zero! Since the wave-particle is somewhere in the box, the length a of the box edge measures roughly the uncertainty Δx in its position. If E_x is likewise a measure of its uncertainty in energy, then the uncertainty in its momentum is approximately $\Delta p_x = \sqrt{2mE_x} = \pi\hbar/a$. That is, $\Delta p_x \Delta x = \pi\hbar = h/2$, which is the uncertainty principle (13.50) within a factor of π. The energy by which the lowest quantum state of a system or particle exceeds the classically expected minimum energy is called the *zero-point energy* of the system or particle. Real systems exhibit, in one way or another, all of these remarkable features of the particle in the one-dimensional box, including such general matters as factorability of the wave function when the energy is a sum.

13.10 TUNNEL EFFECT

It is easy to remove one of the unrealistic features of the box with impenetrable sides by making $V(x)$ less than infinite when $|x| > a/2$. Figure 13.12(a) shows a potential $V(x)$ for a one-dimensional box with walls that can be surmounted classically at energies greater than V_0 when $|x| \geqslant a/2$. When $|x| \leqslant a/2$, $V(x)$ is zero and the wave equation is $-(\hbar^2/2m)(d^2u_x/dx^2) = E_x u_x$ with stationary-state solutions of the form $u_x = \exp(-ip_x x/\hbar)$. The number of such states depends upon the size of the box and on V_0. If $E > V_0$, there is a continuous range of energies and the particle ranges from $x = -\infty$ to $x = +\infty$.

Since V_0 is not infinite, the wave function need not be zero when $|x| \geqslant a/2$ even though $E < V_0$. The wave equation for $|x| > a/2$ is

$$-\left(\frac{\hbar^2}{2m}\right)\frac{d^2u_x}{dx^2} + V_0 u_x = E_x u_x \tag{13.93}$$

That is,

$$\frac{d^2u_x}{dx^2} = B^2 u_x \tag{13.94}$$

where

$$B^2 = \frac{2m(V_0 - E_x)}{\hbar^2} \tag{13.95}$$

The solution when $V_0 > E_x$ is

$$u_x = N_1 e^{Bx} + N_2 e^{-Bx} \tag{13.96}$$

as substitution will show. Since $u_x \neq 0$ for $|x| > a/2$, $|u_x|^2$ has a finite value when $|x| > a/2$ and $E_x < V_0$. That is, the particle sometimes has $E_x < V_0$, which is impossible classically. Since $u_x(x)$ goes to zero for large x, $N_1 = 0$ when $x \geqslant a/2$ and $N_2 = 0$ when $x \leqslant -a/2$. And $|u_x|^2$ varies as $e^{-2B|x|}$ in the classically forbidden region.

Figure 13.12(b) shows an analogous situation. A barrier of finite height V_0 exists for $|x| \leqslant a/2$. If a particle of energy E_x comes to this barrier from the left, it can enter and even penetrate the barrier. For when $|x| \leqslant a/2$ its wave function is again (13.96) and $|u_x|^2$ is greater than zero. When $2ma^2(V_0 - E_x) \gg \hbar^2$, the probability that a particle will be observed to tunnel through the barrier and appear at the right is proportional to e^{-2Ba}. Not only can the quantum mechanical particle penetrate the barrier, but its behavior near $x = 0$ is disturbed when $E_x > V_0$.

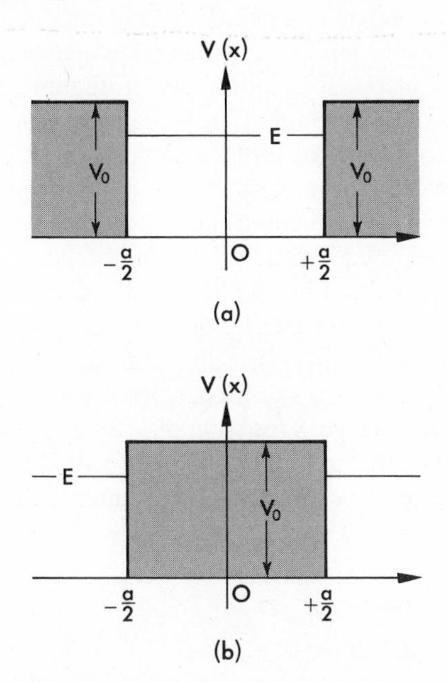

Figure 13.12. Some Simple Potentials (a) Square Well; (b) Penetrable Barrier

A classical particle would always continue past the barrier, but at a slower speed because part of its energy would be potential energy when it passes the barrier ($|x| < a/2$). A quantum mechanical particle, however, with $E_x > V_0$ is partly reflected (that is, has a chance of being either reflected or transmitted) except when the barrier thickness a is a multiple of $\lambda/2$. If $a = n(\lambda/2)$, the quantum mechanical particle does not notice the barrier and passes without reflection.

The really important feature of this section is the fact that the wave function is not zero in a region where the total energy is less than the potential energy.

If this circumstance prevails everywhere, then u_x and its second derivative always agree in sign, as required by (13.93). If $u_x > 0$, its slope always increases with increasing x or decreases with decreasing x; if $u_x < 0$, the reverse obtains. The only way to prevent u_x from increasing without bound, contrary to its postulated behavior, is to require u_x to be zero everywhere. However, if the total energy exceeds the potential energy in only a part of space, then a solution like (13.96) can be joined to the wave function for the region where $V < E$. If the condition $V > E_x$ extends to $x = \pm\infty$, then u_x has no nodes in the classically forbidden region, for the requirement that $|u_x|^2$ be finite, as in (13.65), requires that u_x approach zero exponentially and monotonically as the distance from the locality of high particle-probability increases. If the condition $V > E_x$ is surrounded by regions where $V < E_x$, then u_x may have either one node or none in the region where $V > E_x$, but its form will remain like (13.96).

The tunnel effect, in which a particle enters a classically forbidden domain, is most pronounced when B is small. The probability of penetration increases as m or $(V_0 - E_x)$ or both decrease. It also increases as a decreases in Figure 13.12 (b), for a thin barrier exerts the exponential damping of the wave over a shorter distance than a thick barrier. Radioactive decay by alpha emission can be considered to be penetration of a narrow nuclear potential barrier by an alpha particle or its equivalent in the nucleus. Certain molecular motions such as rotation of CH_3 against CH_3 in ethane, interconversion of enantiomers, and reactions involving a transfer of a proton without really passing over the energy-pass of the activated complex are well substantiated. The small mass of the electron gives it very great freedom to move nonclassically. Indeed, its small mass and its long wavelength are really related views of its delocalization. Electrons penetrate insulators and zip through the work function of a metal-vacuum surface with ease if aided by a sufficiently strong electric field. And within molecules, electrons move freely at times from atom to atom in a manner that has become known as resonance.

13.11 QUALITATIVE WAVE FUNCTIONS

It is relatively easy to write the Schrödinger wave equation but it is generally very hard to solve it. If an analytic solution is possible, the work to find it is usually excessive; and, if such a solution cannot be found, various approximate methods of solution are possible. According to their degree of sophistication and accuracy, approximate solutions may or may not aid chemical intuition for the problem at hand or related problems. Numerical solutions with the aid of a computer are sometimes attempted; with proper formulation these solutions may be of value for the next problem. What is of utmost significance, however, concerning all such valiant efforts is that the Schrödinger equation, or any mathematically equivalent formulation of quantum mechanics, is always fully vindicated for all problems in atomic and molecular physics and chemistry. (The equation is not quite satisfactory for describing all the facets of interaction of matter with light.)

Since chemical systems are generally complicated enough to prevent a reasonably compact exact solution of the Schrödinger equation for ψ and its energies, it is clearly interesting to be able to understand with as much insight as possible the general nature of a stationary state wave function. This can be done merely by use of the results for the free particle and the particle in the boxes of impenetrable and penetrable walls. It is assumed here that the problem can somehow be transformed (at least approximately) into one or more problems each involving but one dimension, just as the problem of a particle free in a three-dimensional box becomes three one-dimensional problems when E is resolved into three parts $(E_x + E_y + E_z)$ and the wave function is factored $(u_x \times u_y \times u_z)$. Thus, the one dimension of interest may be a distance between nuclei, an angle of rotation, a so-called normal coordinate (which describes the motion of several particles as they vibrate in phase at the same frequency), or perhaps even a parameter describing passage through the critical intermediate state during an elementary chemical event.

The key to this qualitative understanding is the stationary-state wave equation in the form

$$\frac{d^2u}{dx^2} = \frac{2m[V(x) - E]}{\hbar^2} u \tag{13.97}$$

As part of the process of writing (13.97) for a particular problem, $V(x)$ is presumed to be known because the kind and nature of the system are known. The problem then is to find acceptable values of E and $u(x)$. A simple way to start is to guess—perhaps on the basis of intuition, experience, or analogy to a similar system—a trial value of E and then determine whether it leads to an acceptable wave function u. A wave function is acceptable in general if it and its first derivatives are everywhere continuous, finite, and single-valued and if u and u^*u obey the appropriate boundary conditions. For example, if a system is in any way localized, then $\int u^*u \, d\tau$ for all space must be finite; hence, u must approach zero sufficiently rapidly for large values of the space coordinate. The alternative method, namely, guessing u and calculating E, has been systematized and is widely used in such methods as the variation method (Section 14.11), the perturbation method (Section 14.13), and the local energy method. In the local energy method, an average value of E is found by calculating $E = \mathbf{H}u/u$ after guessing u at several places.

When the trial value of E is less than $V(x)$ for all values of x, then u and its second derivative have the same sign by (13.97), for $m > 0$. Then u is zero, as argued in Figure 13.10, and there is no problem because $|u|^2$ vanishes. The system is nothing.

When the trial value of E exceeds $V(x)$ everywhere, then u and its second derivative always differ in sign. The free particle is an example of this kind when

$V(x)$ is constant; the solution is a sine and a cosine. Whenever $E > V(x)$, the value of u curves back toward $u = 0$, perhaps by passing through a maximum or minimum. For when u is positive, the slope of u must decrease because d^2u/dx^2 is negative by (13.97); and vice versa when the signs are reversed. The rate at which the slope changes is proportional to m, to u itself, and to $[V(x) - E]$. As for the free particle, the wavelength of the particle decreases as E rises farther and farther above $V(x)$. The wave functions of Figure 13.11 show how λ decreases as E increases, and the same kind of behavior results over any limited range of x if $V(x)$ varies below E.

When $E > V(x)$ for all values of x, there are two forms of u with the same energy. The energy state is said to have a degeneracy of order two. Its wave functions are of the form: $\exp(+ip_x x/\hbar)$ and $\exp(-ip_x x/\hbar)$, which correspond to motion to and fro. However, when $E < V(x)$ for all values of x greater than a

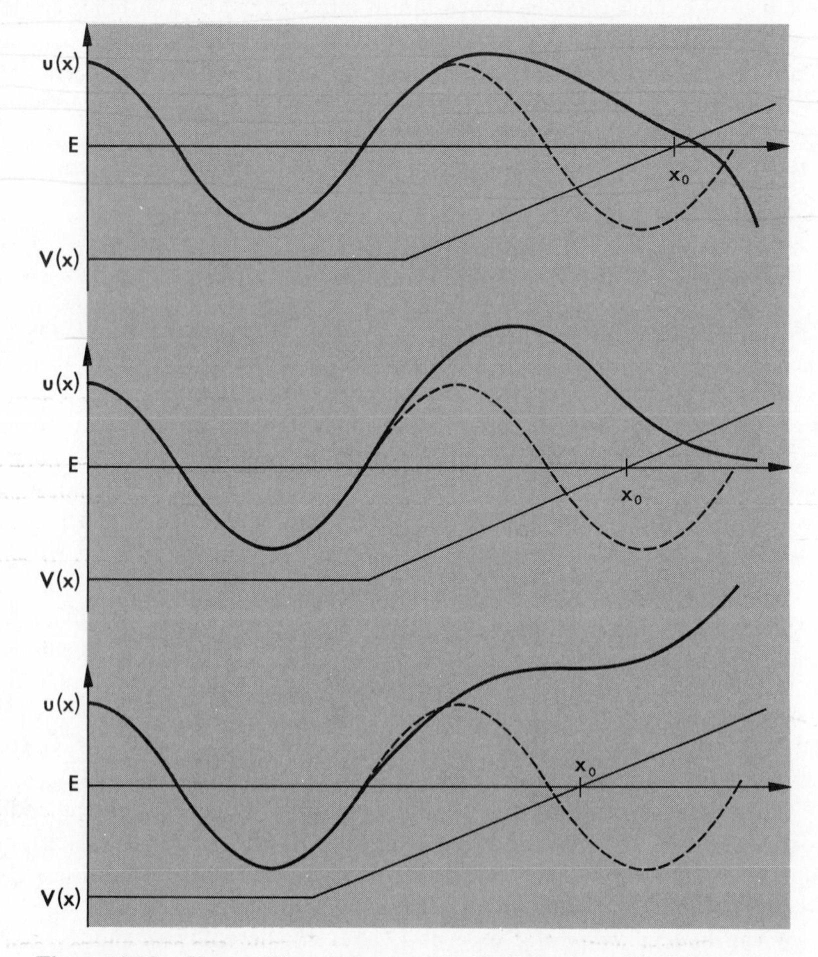

Figure 13.13. How a Wave Function Fits Its Boundary Conditions

certain value x_0 as in Figure 13.13, then the state with energy E is not degenerate. In this case, there is only one form of u because the motion is inhibited in one direction. Beyond x_0 the value of u must not "blow up" as it does (Figure 13.10) when $E < V(x)$ for all x. There must be a nice compromise such that u is brought smoothly to zero for $x > x_0$.

To show why the conditions at the point where E equals $V(x_0)$ are of critical importance, all possible signs of u and its derivative du/dx at x_0 are given in Table 13.3. Near x_0, where $E_x = V(x_0)$, the wave function is nearly linear because, by (13.97), d^2u/dx^2 is nearly zero. Thus, the sign of $u(x)$ when x is slightly

Table 13.3 Consequences of all possible combinations of signs of a wave function and its derivatives when $V(x_0) = E < V(x)$ if $x > x_0$.

Sign of $u(x_0)$	Sign of $\frac{du}{dx}$ at x_0	Sign of u $(x \gtrsim x_0)$	Sign of $\frac{d^2u}{dx^2}$ $(x \gtrsim x_0)$	Value of $u(x)$ $(x \longrightarrow \infty)$
+	+	+	+	$+\infty$
+	0	+	+	$+\infty$
+	−	{ +	+	$\pm\infty$ or 0
		{ −	−	$-\infty$
0	+	+	+	$+\infty$
0	0	0	0	0
0	−	−	−	$-\infty$
−	+	{ +	+	$+\infty$
		{ −	−	$\pm\infty$ or 0
−	0	−	−	$-\infty$
−	−	−	−	$-\infty$

greater than x_0 is easily predicted from the signs of u and du/dx at x_0; column three of Table 13.3 lists these signs of $u(x)$ when $x \gtrsim x_0$.

Since $V(x) > E_x$ when $x > x_0$, (13.97) requires the sign of d^2u/dx^2 to be the same as that of $u(x)$; column four of Table 13.3 lists the signs of d^2u/dx^2 when $x \gtrsim x_0$. If d^2u/dx^2 has the same sign as du/dx, u continues to increase or decrease as $x \longrightarrow \infty$ and thus is not properly bounded, as required by (13.65). If du/dx is zero at x_0, $u(x)$ will likewise increase without limit and without beoming zero if $u(x_0) > 0$, and $u(x)$ will similarly decrease without limit if $u(x_0) < 0$ when du/dx is zero.

If the sign of du/dx at x_0 differs from the sign of u and d^2u/dx^2 when x exceeds x_0, $u(x)$ may remain properly bounded at $x = \infty$. If d^2u/dx^2 is positive while du/dx at x_0 is negative, then du/dx may increase to zero and $u(x)$ may reach a limit at $x \longrightarrow \infty$. Too much increase in du/dx when $u(x_0) > 0$ may cause $u(x)$ to increase without limit as $x \longrightarrow \infty$. Or too little increase in du/dx when $u(x_0) > 0$ may cause $u(x)$ to pass through zero and thenceforth decrease without limit as $x \longrightarrow \infty$. Somewhere between too little and too much is the satisfactory behavior shown by the middle part of Figure 13.13. Parallel remarks hold when d^2u/dx^2 is negative while du/dx at x_0 is positive. Finally, the case where u and its slope at x_0 are both zero is of little interest because u is zero everywhere; this system is a void.

Figure 13.13 explains graphically how u "blows up" at large x when the slope or phase of $u(x)$ is not just right at x_0. The dashed curves indicate what $u(x)$ would have been if $V(x)$ had been constant. The effective wavelength of the particle increases as $V(x)$ increases because d^2u/dx^2 and the curvature of u decrease according to (13.97); a kind of "piling up" of u near x_0 thus results. When $V(x_0) = E$, the curvature in u is zero and the slope of u in Figure 13.3 is prepared to increase from a negative value toward zero slope. At the top of Figure 13.3. the slope of u slows its decrease when $V(x) > E$, as required by (13.97) when $u > 0$. However, before du/dx rises to zero the value of u is negative; hence, d^2u/dx^2 in (13.97) is negative and the slope du/dx decreases without bound. In the bottom diagram of Figure 13.3, $u(x)$ is so great when $V(x)$ begins to exceed E that the slope du/dx increases very rapidly as x increases. In fact, u and du/dx increase without limit. The middle diagram is neither too hot nor too cold; it is just right to bring $u(x)$ toward zero properly at large x. Any energy E is allowed, but each state is not degenerate because the phase or slope of $u(x)$ must fit $u(x)$ to its boundary condition at $x \longrightarrow \infty$.

The tendency of $u(x)$ to "blow up" when $V(x) > E$ becomes a major concern when $V(x)$ rises above E at two or more values of x. A very simple case of this is the particle in a box; the energy states are discrete. The continuum of energy states has become discontinuous by virtue of the added boundary conditions. When E is an eigenvalue of (13.97), $u(x)$ approaches zero asymptotically for large x where $V(x)$ exceeds E. The wave function of the *ground state*, the state

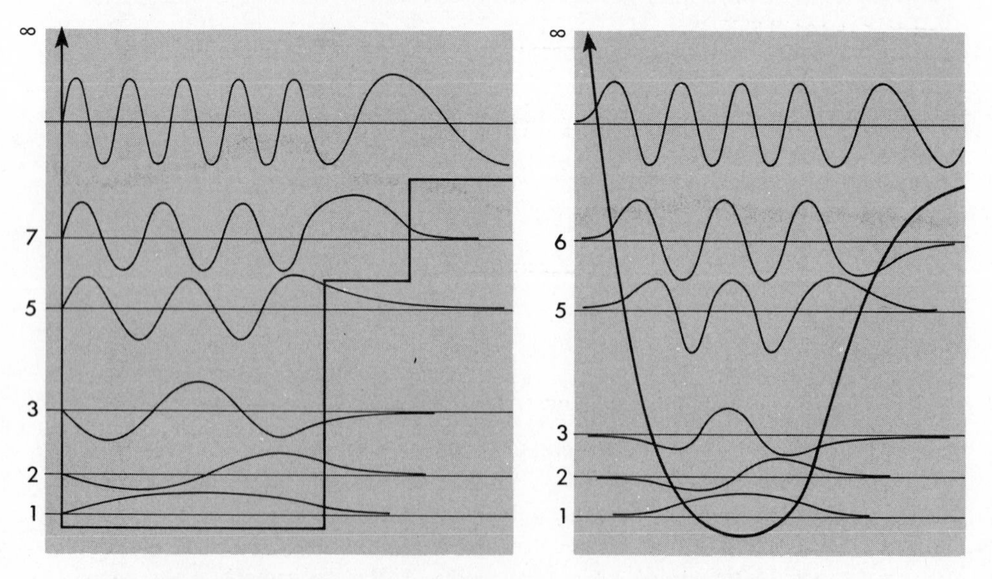

Figure 13.14. Wave Functions and Energies of Some States of Similar Potentials with One Minimum

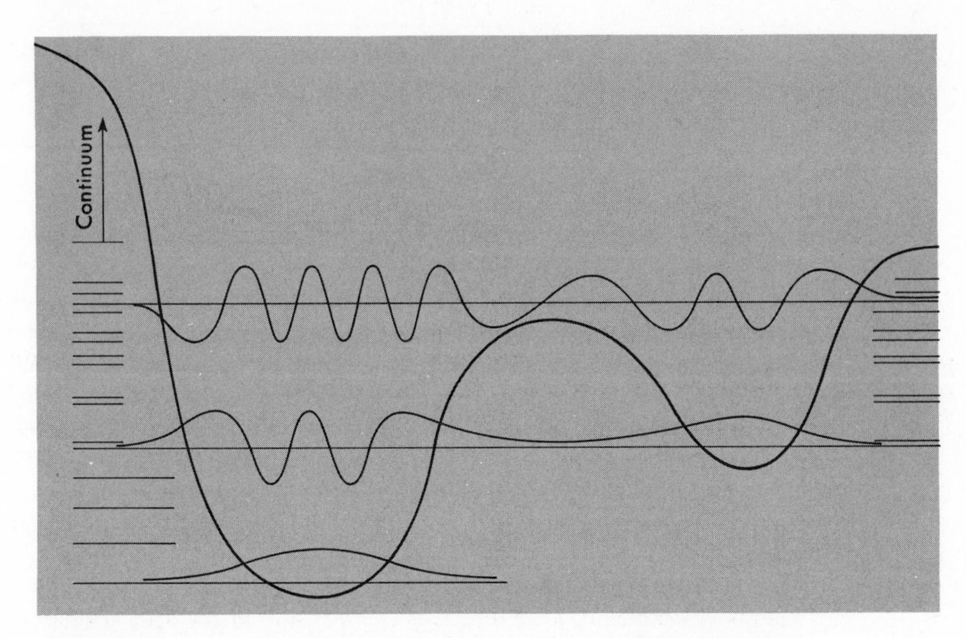

Figure 13.15. Wave Functions and Energies of a Potential with Two Minima

of lowest energy, never has a node. The wave functions of excited states, however, have nodes because $u(x)$ oscillates between positive and negative values when $E > V(x)$. These wave functions are qualitatively like those Figure 13.11, with exponential tails into regions where $[V(x) - E]$ is positive but finite.

As already stated in Section 13.9, if $E_2 > E_1$ and if there is no stationary state with energy between E_1 and E_2, the wave function for the state of energy E_2 has one more node than that of the state of energy E_1. The number of nodes increases with E and, for a given value of $E - V$, with m. Figure 13.14 shows stationary-state energies and their wave functions for a few of the most stable states of a system with a potential of the kind expected for the motion of an electron near an atom, of an atom near a free radical, or of a molecule near a surface. Figure 13.15 might refer to an electron held by two different atoms, the proton in the middle of $HHCl^{\ddagger}$, or a molecule held by lattice sites of different size and stability. The general similarity of these to Figure 13.11 is obvious. Figures 13.14 and 13.15 may profitably be studied with a rereading of this section.

13.12 SUMMARY

This chapter has confined itself to elementary quantum theory and elementary wave mechanics. It has traced the history of modern theoretical chemistry from Planck's discovery of quanta in radiation in equilibrium with matter in 1900 to Schrödinger's discovery of the wave equation in 1926. In this development, Einstein's interpretation of the photoelectric effect and his explanation of decreasing heat capacities at low T were very strong independent confirmation of the quantum theory in its infancy. Rutherford's idea of the nuclear atom and Bohr's idea of quantum states for the electron in H are perhaps the true beginning of modern theoretical chemistry, for these discoveries implemented the quantum theory. In their success, they, too, confirmed the quantum theory. In 1914, Franck and Hertz observed the existence of atomic energy states without photons by bombarding atoms with electrons. Even the very critical mechanical analyses of Sommerfeld and others were fruitful in hastening Compton, de Broglie, Schrödinger and others to the wave-particle duality of all matter. The Bohr theory was too definite a model mechanically to succeed if particles are waves. Since the Schrödinger equation seems correct in every way for chemical problems, it has fallen to the theoretical physicist and chemist to find its solutions, for there seem to be no successors to Hamilton among the pure mathematicians.

The similarity between the mathematical statements of the Heisenberg uncertainty principle and de Broglie's $p\lambda = h$ is not an accident. The seeming restrictiveness of the former is the wonder of the latter, for it is indeed fortunate for chemistry (and thus for everyone) that the electron is as elusive as it is. The freedom it has by virtue of its wavelike behavior makes molecules integrated individuals with unique properties. Strict additivity is seldom found in molecular and electronic properties when wave behavior is important. It is also fortunate for chemist and every physical scientist that the photon is such an excellent detector of stationary energies. Thus, in either of the forms $\Delta E \cdot \Delta t \geqslant \hbar$ or $\Delta p_x \cdot \Delta x \geqslant \hbar$, the uncertainty principle makes life simple for the chemist by removing half the work he might have expected on the basis of his senses and classical ideas. The velocity of light places a kind of natural limit on the usefulness of classical mechanics for big, speedy systems by leading to relativistic mechanics. Similarly, at the other extreme of the classical range, Planck's constant as a quantum of action places a natural limit on man's intuitive or everyday understanding of small, unmassive systems. Each limit calls for a mathematical appreciation of events too subtle for direct human experience.

One of the most important values to be derived from this chapter is a *qualitative* appreciation of wave mechanics. The meaning of the wave function as an amplitude and of its square as a probable intensity of matter is of fundamental importance. When calculations become more complex than those for the free particle allowed everywhere or within a box, it is often advantageous to draw upon the qualitative idea of the last few sections of this chapter for guidance. Wisdom in theoretical chemistry takes many forms. Frequently the art of approximation or the art of avoiding messy mathematics is worth more than much technical ability in mathematical analysis. There is, of course, no substitute for such ability in analysis when more than a qualitative answer is needed.

Most of the *Why's* have been answered at least qualitatively. The dilemma of the ambiguity of entropy of mixing remains as an alternate basis of the postulates of quantum mechanics in the next chapter. There, a more rigorous attitude toward wave functions and energies is awaiting study.

PROBLEMS

1. The minimum energy required to eject the least tightly bound electron in many metals is 4 ev. At what wavelengths of light would such a metal emit photoelectrons?
   Answer: $\lambda < 3100$ A.
2. What is the energy of a photon of wavelength 7000 A (red)?
   Answer: 2.84×10^{-19} j.
3. What temperature is required to make kT equal one electron volt?
   Answer: 11 605°K.
4. From the wavelengths of the Lyman series in the spectrum of monatomic hydrogen in Table 13.2, calculate the energies of the states of H in ev.
   Answer: -13.60; -3.40; -1.51; -0.85; -0.543; -0.378; etc.
5. Find the Rydberg constant of Equation (13.27) for He^+ if $H^+ = 1.00757$ and $He^{++} = 4.00281$.
   Answer: 109721 cm^{-1}.
6. Calculate the radius of the first Bohr orbit ($n = 1$).
   Answer: 0.529 A.
7. What is the minimum energy required to ionize an atom of hydrogen in its most stable state?
   Answer: 13.6 ev.
8. At what pressure can an uncertainty in energy of an excited state of 1.0 cm^{-1} be detected at room temperature in a gas with $\sigma^2 = 10 \times 10^{-16}$ cm^2 and $M = 30$?
   Answer: ~40 atm.
9. Verify by substitution that $|\psi|^2$ is independent of time for states of a definite energy.
10. What potential difference is needed to accelerate an electron so that it acts like a wave with a wavelength the size of a typical nucleus, namely, about 1.00×10^{-15} m, if relativistic corrections are ignored?
    Answer: 1.504×10^{12} volts.
11. Show that $|u|^2$ is independent of position if u is the stationary state wave function of a free particle.
12. Show that the wave function of a particle with energy greater than the classical energy V_0 of a potential barrier is influenced by the barrier, even though classically it would not be so influenced.

---

13. The quantity $e^2/\hbar c$ (cgs) or $e^2/4\pi\epsilon_0\hbar c$ (mks) (where $\hbar = h/2\pi$, where c is the

velocity of light, and where e is the charge of the electron) is called the fine-structure constant because Sommerfeld found it useful for interpreting the details of certain spectra in terms of the Bohr theory. Show that the fine-structure constant is dimensionless and find a value for its reciprocal.
Answer: 137.04.

14. The mass of a proton is 1.660×10^{-24} gram. If $E = mc^2$, to how many electron volts is the mass of one proton equivalent?
Answer: 9.383×10^8 ev.

15. The minimum energy required to emit photoelectrons from $W_{(s)}$ is 4.5 ev. What potential difference is just sufficient to prevent photoelectrons from being ejected from $W_{(s)}$ by radiation with wavelength of 2000 A?
Answer: 1.7 volts.

16. What are the electron quantum numbers n and m of the initial and final states of a hydrogen atom that account for the Fraunhofer absorption line at 4861A in the solar spectrum?
Answer: $2 \longrightarrow 4$.

17. What is the wavelength of a proton accelerated from rest by 10^7 volts if the mass of a proton is 1.660×10^{-24} gram?
Answer: 9.08×10^{-13} cm.

18. What is the zero-point energy of an electron in a three-dimensional cubic box that is 1.50 A on an edge?
Answer: 0.804×10^{-10} erg.

19. Draw the potential of a square well with sides of finite height, show how it is modified by an external electric field, and show how a particle might tunnel out of such a well when the field is not zero.
Answer: Field slants top horizontal part of potential.

20. Trace $V(x)$ and the various energy values of Figure 13.15 and for each energy state draw a wave function with proper attention to wavelength, curvature, near-symmetry, etc.

---

21. Wien's displacement law of radiation says that the most probable wavelength λ_{max} radiated by a black body at T is $\lambda_{max} = hc/4.965kT$. Prove this by maximizing (13.11).

22 When electrically accelerated electrons are suddenly stopped by a target, about one or two percent of their kinetic energy is converted into X-rays when the accelerating potential is of the order of kilovolts. This process is essentially the reverse of the photoelectric effect. If λ_x is the shortest wavelength of the continuous spectrum of X-rays thus generated at a potential V, show that $\lambda_x V = 12398$ and the accuracy possible if the work function of the target metal is neglected. Show how a measurement of λ_x and V might be used to evaluate Planck's constant.

23. Positronium is like H except that the positively charged particle has the mass of an electron (it is a positron). For positronium, calculate
(a) the Rydberg constant R;
(b) the distance between electron and positron in the stationary state with $n = 2$ according to the Bohr theory.
Answer: (a) $5.47 \times 10^6\ m^{-1}$; (b) 4.24 A.

24. Calculate the wavelength of radiation that will cause positronium, an electron-positron pair, to go from its state of lowest energy to:

(a) Its next highest energy state.
(b) Complete separation of positron and electron.
Answer: (a) 2430 A; (b) 1825 A.

25. List the several states of a particle with energy $7\pi^2\hbar^2/ma^2$ in a cubic box of edge a.
Answer: (n_x, n_y, n_z): (1, 2, 3)(1, 3, 2)(2, 1, 3)(2, 3, 1)(3, 1, 2)(3, 2, 1).

26. If the wave function and its first space derivative are continuous at $x = \pm a/2$ where the potential energy is discontinuous as in Figure 13.12 (a), find solutions of the wave equation for a particle with $E < V_0$.
Answer: $E = E(V_0, a, m)$ where

$$\sqrt{\frac{V_0 - E}{E}} = \tan\left(\frac{a\sqrt{2mE}}{2\hbar}\right) = -\text{ctn}\left(\frac{a\sqrt{2mE}}{2\hbar}\right)$$

27. If the probability of tunneling through a square one-dimensional barrier is the value of $|u|^2$ upon exit divided by the value of $|u|^2$ upon entry, what is the probability that an electron can tunnel through a barrier 100 A thick if its height above the electron energy is 500 cm^{-1}? If 5000 cm^{-1}?
Answer: 8.5×10^{-12}; 9.3×10^{-36}.

28. Draw wave functions for the four most stable states with energy E less than V_0 for the potential $V(\phi) = -V_0(1 + \cos 3\phi)$ where ϕ varies from 0 to 2π.

29. In the region of a maximum in $V(x)$, it is possible for a stationary-state wave function to have a node ($u = 0$) when $E < V(x)$. By varying $V(x)$ gradually so as to eliminate the maximum, show why this is reasonable despite what is implied in Section 13.11 that u must not become zero when $E < V(x)$.

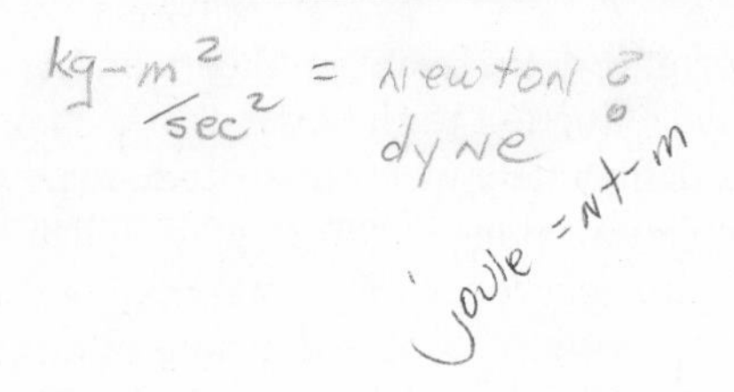

14
QUANTUM MECHANICS

14.1 INTRODUCTION

The preceding chapter on the origins of the quantum theory and on the ambivalence of all matter is itself the introduction to the more mathematical quantum mechanics of this chapter. The deliberately pictorial attitude there is now to be refined in a few important calculations done in some detail. Fidelity in descriptions of matter is based on mathematical concepts, for it is as important to realize that matter is neither a particle nor a wave as it is to acknowledge that it is the nature of the experiment that reveals the particle-like or wavelike behavior of matter. Matter is an ideal commingling of the ideal concepts of wave and particle so that the result is something whose properties are best explained by examples in the hope that such understanding will yield an intuition concerning matter akin to the "feel" of an athlete for his sport.

Significant historical details will, as before, be mentioned with the development of the subject. Since this chapter deals in large part with the wave equation of Schrödinger, it is appropriate to retrace his reasoning in 1926. When the potential energy is V, the total energy of a particle of mass m and linear momentum p is the sum of kinetic and potential energies, namely

$$E = \frac{p^2}{2m} + V \tag{14.1}$$

If the new hypothesis (13.41) of de Broglie should be right, then (14.1) yields

$$p^2 = \left(\frac{h}{\lambda}\right)^2 = 2\,m(E - V) \tag{14.2}$$

The equation of classical mechanics

$$\frac{d^2u}{dx^2} + \left(\frac{2\pi}{\lambda}\right)^2 u = 0 \tag{14.3}$$

tells how the amplitude u of a one-dimensional pure wave varies with position, for a solution of (14.3) is $u = \cos(2\pi x/\lambda)$ or $u = \sin(2\pi x/\lambda)$. Combining (14.2) and (14.3) yields

$$\frac{d^2u}{dx^2} + (2\pi)^2 \left[\frac{2m(E - V)}{h^2}\right] u = 0$$

That is,

$$-\frac{\hbar^2}{2m}\left(\frac{d^2u}{dx^2}\right) + (V - E)u = 0 \tag{14.4}$$

which is the Schrödinger equation without time for the amplitude of matter. In three dimensions, (14.4) is

$$-\left(\frac{\hbar^2}{2m}\right)\left(\frac{\partial^2u}{\partial x^2} + \frac{\partial^2u}{\partial y^2} + \frac{\partial^2u}{\partial z^2}\right) + [V(x, y, z) - E]u = 0 \tag{14.5}$$

This equation is linear and homogeneous in u and thus allows for the superposition of waves by allowing u to be expressed as a sum of terms of various importance and kind.

The classical equation

$$\mathscr{D}\left(\frac{\partial^2\psi}{\partial x^2} + \frac{\partial^2\psi}{\partial y^2} + \frac{\partial^2\psi}{\partial z^2}\right) = \frac{\partial\psi}{\partial t} \tag{14.6}$$

describes the flow of anything that must be accounted for continuously in transit. If (14.6) describes the flow of heat, ψ is the temperature as a function of time t and position and $\mathscr{D}$ depends on the body's thermal conductivity and heat capacity. If ψ is concentration, then (14.6) is *Fick's second law of diffusion* and $\mathscr{D}$ is the diffusion coefficient. In a steady state of temperature or concentration, $\partial\psi/\partial t = 0$. It was natural, therefore, for Schrödinger to expect the steady-state amplitude of matter of energy E to develop in time according to an equation like (14.6). With $\hbar$ inserted for dimensional homogeneity, he wrote as his hypothesis (other time equations were also not unreasonable)

$$-\frac{\hbar^2}{2m}\left(\frac{\partial^2\psi}{\partial x^2} + \frac{\partial^2\psi}{\partial y^2} + \frac{\partial^2\psi}{\partial z^2}\right) + V(x, y, z)\psi = -\frac{\hbar}{i}\frac{\partial\psi}{\partial t} \tag{13.44}$$

Since (13.44) is first-order in time, only $\psi(x, y, z, t)$ is needed for a full and complete description of a system. An equation second-order in time would require two facts (ψ and something else) to fix the state of a system now and at all times. There was and is no derivation of the Schrödinger equation. Its justification lies entirely in its eminent success at describing observed reality for events in which relativity can be ignored. When relativistic effects (like space-time transformations or spin) are important, then time must be treated like x, y, and z by inclusion as a second time derivative (Klein-Gordon equation) or the equation of motion can be cast in the form of simultaneous linear first-order partial differential equations for four components of the relativistic wave function (Dirac equation).

14.2 CONTINUITY OF ENTROPY[1]

Like energy or volume, entropy is an extensive property. If surface effects are negligible, slipping a thin barrier from between two identical systems A and B without work should yield a united system with exactly twice the energy, volume, and entropy of the systems initially apart. Yet molecules from A mix with those from B upon union, and the inevitable increased disorder attending mixing might be expected to more than double the entropy. Gibbs resolved all doubts by treating chemically and physically identical molecules as indistinguishable even though, in the classical mechanics of his day, it was theoretically possible to predict and follow the path of every molecule for all time and thus keep track of kinds A and B. In his view, the entropy of the double-sized system was just twice the entropy of either of the identical initial systems.

If molecules from system A were, however, somehow chemically or physically distinguishable from those from system B by virtue of some observable property, the disorder after mixing would surely exceed that before union of A and B. Hence, the entropy of the united system would surely be more than twice as great as the sum of the entropies of A alone and B alone, yet they might be mixed without a change in total energy if A and B were ideal, nonreacting gases and if the thin barrier were slipped out without macroscopic stirring (work). If an observer in the surroundings sees no difference in the initial unmixed state and the final mixed state, he must report $\Delta S = 0$ because entropy is a function of state. He is here supposed to be ignorant because he did not know that the partition separating pure A and pure B was withdrawn and replaced or because he lacks suitably refined instruments for distinguishing A from B. But if another observer in the surroundings notes a difference in the initial and final states by distinguishing A from B, he must report $\Delta S > 0$. Thus two honest observers state different results.

If A and B were really alike, the second observer would report $\Delta S = 0$. His report depends upon his decision: like or unlike. Regardless of how similar A and B may be, he is forced to decide on the basis of his analytical method

[1] The ideas of this section are drawn from these sources: Landé, A., *Foundations of Quantum Theory, a Study in Continuity and Symmetry*. New Haven, Conn.: Yale University Press, 1955. Landé, A., *American Scientist*, **41**, 439 (1953); Landé, A., *American Journal of Physics*, **20**, 353 (1952); Landé, A., *The Physical Review*, **87**, 267 (1951).

whether ΔS is zero or the full $\overline{\Delta S} = R \ln 2$ given by (7.17). There is no in-between; he is limited to two choices: zero or $R \ln 2$. What is really troublesome is that he could base his decision upon a variable that changes continuously from A to B and thus could differ only infinitesimally in A and B. If his analysis were by length of molecule, as the difference in lengths of type A and type B approaches zero as a limit, $\overline{\Delta S}$ remains fixed by (7.17). However, when the limit itself is reached (that is, when he decides that type A and type B are alike or at least indistinguishable in length), ΔS is suddenly and discontinuously zero. Since entropy is an extensive property, the presence of the partition between chambers of like gases should be without effect, for the entropy of a system is the sum of the entropies of its parts.

Faced with this obnoxious discontinuity, A. Landé postulates continuity of entropy. Complete likeness or unlikeness is replaced by a fractional degree of likeness. As type A becomes less and less distinguishable from type B, $\overline{\Delta S}$ continuously approaches zero. In other words, the observer who must measure $\overline{\Delta S}$ is not always faced with the simple alternative, like or unlike.

The familiar macroscopic world presents no fractional likenesses: everything is either like or unlike. A mixture of molecules can be separated into groups of various length, the number of groups depending upon the accuracy with which the lengths are distinguished. Even in the microscopic world of fractional likeness, long molecules can be distinguished as completely unlike short molecules and completely like other long ones. But in the same microscopic world, when long pointed molecules must be distinguished from long rounded molecules by a test for bluntness, they often lose their length characteristics. That is, it may happen that a molecule cannot be termed long *and* pointed in the world of fractional likenesses. Rather, if long molecules are tested for bluntness, some will pass the test and be labeled blunt while the remainder are termed pointed. There is no predicting the outcome for a particular molecule; the result of the test for bluntness is the history of a chance event. The test for bluntness determines what fraction of the long molecules is blunt and rejects as fractionally unlike those which are found to be pointed. The acute student has probably guessed that exact values of conjugate mechanical variables subject to the uncertainty principle are really such fractionally like states, and that a test for bluntness or length destroys information about the other property. Thus, while molecules in the abstract can be distinguished as either like or unlike by various tests (e.g., mass spectrometry for isotopic substitution or abundance), a truly complete characterization of a real molecule regards certain mechanical properties as marks of distinguishability. Identical molecules with different momenta or identical molecules with different energies are distinguishable. What Heisenberg says in his uncertainty principle, Landé merely reiterates without implying that O_2 (in the abstract) is fractionally like N_2 or continuously transformable (except perhaps by more and more ignorance) into N_2, or $^{16}O\,^{16}O$ into $^{16}O\,^{17}O$.

In the familiar world of like and unlike, the probability of a sequence of chance events is the product of the probabilities of the events of the sequence.

The probability of throwing heads with an unbiased coin is $\frac{1}{2}$ for each toss. To do so five times in a row has a probability of $(\frac{1}{2})^5$. Heads is completely unlike tails. Similarly, on a baseball team consisting of players who either strike out or hit a single, the probability that the first man at bat in an inning will get beyond first base is the sum of several terms. The first term is the product of his batting average times the probability that he can steal second. The second term is the product of his own batting average times the batting average of the batter who follows him. The third term is the product of his own batting average times that of the third batter, and so on, with every possible way contributing a term to the sum. In general, the probability q_{12} of achieving state 2 from state 1 via any one of n intermediate states i is

$$q_{12} = \sum_{i=1}^{n} q_{1i} q_{i2} \tag{14.7}$$

where q_{1i} is the probability of achieving intermediate state i from state 1 and q_{i2} is the independent probability of achieving the final state 2 from state i.

In the unfamiliar world of fractional likenesses, (14.7) often errs. The only known rule that satisfies all the properties required of fractional likenesses q is

$$q_{12} = |\phi_{12}|^2 = \phi_{12}^* \phi_{12} \tag{14.8}$$

where

$$\phi_{12} = \sum_{i=1}^{n} \phi_{1i} \phi_{i2} \tag{14.9}$$

In (14.9), the famous law of superposition of probability amplitudes, ϕ is called a *probability amplitude* because it yields a true probability when squared as in (14.8). It is generally a complex quantity, ϕ^* being the complex conjugate of ϕ. Equation (14.9) replaces (14.7) in the world of fractional likenesses. Its analogue in optics is the equation for the net amplitude of n waves; the analogue in optics of (14.8) is the equation that finds intensity (q) from amplitude (ϕ). Thus (14.9) describes a matter-wave, in accord with de Broglie's equation (13.41) and experiment.

A simple but definite example of the wave nature of matter is the well-known diffraction experiment in which a particle penetrates a barrier with two holes. The experimentally observed facts were discussed in Section 13.6. If the experimenter leaves both holes open and does not determine which hole the particle passes through (that is, if he does not determine that the particle really went through one hole), the record is a diffraction pattern characterized by intensity maxima out of line with source and holes and some intensity minima even on a direct line from source through holes to plate. This diffraction pattern is unaltered in kind even when the intensity is reduced so low that only one particle at a time passes the barrier. The recorded pattern is, however, changed in kind when the experimenter determines directly or indirectly which hole each particle uses. He can close one hole or put a very delicate counter in line with a hole and note whether or not the particle passes. However subtly he tries, a unique determination of position at the barrier by noting which hole is or is not used inevitably alters the very nature of the record. It is no longer a diffraction pattern; it becomes rather a particle pattern with just one maximum behind each open hole. The particle behaves like a particle if its exact trajectory is traced; it behaves like a wave if its path is not traced.

When only one hole is open (or known to be used), only one intermediate state i is possible. In going from source (state 1) to record (state 2), by (14.8) and (14.9), $\phi_{12} = \phi_{1i}\phi_{i2}$ and the intensity of the recorded pattern is

$$q_{12} = \phi_{12}^*\phi_{12} = \phi_{1i}^*\phi_{i2}^*\phi_{1i}\phi_{i2} = q_{1i}q_{i2} \tag{14.10}$$

However, when both holes (a and b) are open, by (14.9), $\phi_{12} = \phi_{1a}\phi_{a2} + \phi_{1b}\phi_{b2}$ and by (14.8), the intensity of the diffraction pattern is,

$$\begin{aligned} q_{12} &= (\phi_{1a}^*\phi_{a2}^* + \phi_{1b}^*\phi_{b2}^*)(\phi_{1a}\phi_{a2} + \phi_{1b}\phi_{b2}) \\ &= q_{1a}q_{a2} + q_{1b}q_{b2} + \phi_{1a}^*\phi_{a2}^*\phi_{1b}\phi_{b2} + \phi_{1b}^*\phi_{b2}^*\phi_{1a}\phi_{a2} \end{aligned} \tag{14.11}$$

Even if the holes were opened alternately (14.10) would be merely

$$q_{12} = q_{1a}q_{a2} + q_{1b}q_{b2} \tag{14.12}$$

The last two terms of (14.11) set its q_{12} apart from the particle-like behavior of (14.10) or (14.12). These are the interference terms peculiar to waves.

Although the particles that may go through the hole are identical in the abstract, they become fractionally alike or unlike when no experiment determines which hole is used. For, within the confines of the uncertainty principle, the experimenter considers hole position and momentum change as distinguishing marks of a particle and enough to fix his decision about likeness or unlikeness. Thus, by admitting continuity of entropy, which calls for fractional likenesses, Landé is forced into a description involving superposition of probability amplitudes as in (14.9) and the uncertainty principle. By further general arguments, he establishes a set of postulates for quantum mechanics.

14.3 ACTION AND ALL PATHS

Education may be defined as the perception of relation. Since it is a great advantage to see the same ideas from various viewpoints, especially when the ideas are quite unfamiliar, it is appropriate to consider the general nature of another postulatory basis of quantum mechanics. This one is tailored to describe collisions and is valuable here as a striking contrast to classical mechanics, as a source of insight into how particles really move, as an example of how quantum mechanics becomes classical, and as an example of another remarkable set of postulates of quantum mechanics.

It happens frequently that Cartesian or other widely used coordinates are not the most convenient choice for a particular dynamic problem. Regardless of the choice of coordinates, however, the classical laws of mechanics can be stated[2] in the unchanging form

$$\frac{d}{dt}\left(\frac{\partial L}{\partial \dot{q}_i}\right) = \frac{\partial L}{\partial q_i} \qquad i = 1, 2, 3, \ldots \tag{14.13}$$

where q_i is any one of the several coordinates, $\dot{q}_i$ is its first time derivative, and L is the Lagrangian function

$$L(q, \dot{q}) = T - V \tag{14.14}$$

where the potential energy V is a function only of the coordinates q_i, and where the kinetic energy T may be a function of all $\dot{q}_i$ and q_i. The momentum p_i canonically conjugate to q_i is defined as

$$p_i = \frac{\partial L}{\partial \dot{q}_i} \tag{14.15}$$

This is a very proper way to find p_i and q_i for the uncertainty principle. Thus, in terms of Cartesian coordinate x_i, (14.14) is

$$L = \frac{m\dot{x}_i^2}{2} - V(x_i)$$

and (14.13) is

$$\frac{d}{dt}(m\dot{x}_i) = \frac{dp_{xi}}{dt} = -\frac{\partial V}{\partial x_i} \tag{14.16}$$

where the last member of (14.16) is clearly a force. The great advantage of (14.13) is that it works in *any* coordinate system.

Equation (14.13) is truly remarkable in the further sense that it represents the necessary (and often sufficient) condition[3] that

$$S(q, \dot{q}) = \int_{t_1}^{t_2} L(q, \dot{q})\, dt \tag{14.17}$$

which is called the *action function*, be an extreme value (maximum, minimum, or stationary value) between times t_1 and t_2 at the beginning and end of the classical motion. In view of these things, classical mechanics is very tersely

[2] See any advanced physics textbook.
[3] See any advanced physics or calculus textbook.

stated: A system moves naturally along a path that makes the action function $S(q, \dot{q})$ an extreme value, usually a minimum. Such a statement of Newton's laws is at once simple and independent of the coordinate system chosen for the description of the path.

In his approach to quantum mechanics, Feynman[4] makes two postulates. The first is the law of superposition of probability amplitudes in a form that acknowledges the many routes open to a wave-particle that moves from state 1 to state 2. In terms of time t and one coordinate q, Figure 14.1 shows the classically expected path as a white curve and approximations to a few of the infinite

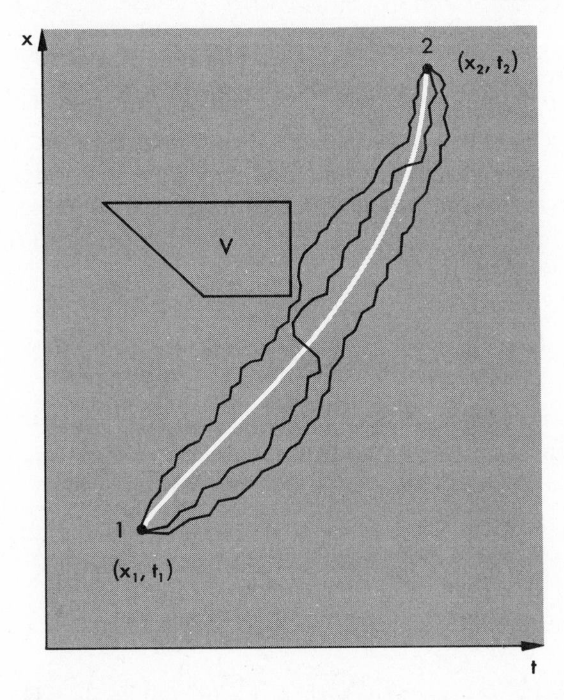

Figure 14.1. Space-Time Trajectories of a Wave-Particle Relative to Its Classically Expected Path (solid)

number of possible quantum mechanical paths as joined line segments. Only points 1 and 2 are well specified for the nonclassical paths. Along one segment, time advances from t_i to t_{i+1} while position advances from x_i to x_{i+1}. For the whole quantum mechanically possible space-time trajectory from state 1 at (x_1, t_1) to state 2 at (x_2, t_2), the amplitude is the sum of the many ways, namely

$$\phi_{12} = \lim_{\epsilon \to 0} \int_{(1)}^{(2)} \Phi(x_1, \cdots x_i, x_{i+1}, \cdots x_2)\, dx_1 \cdots dx_i \cdots dx_2 \tag{14.18}$$

[4] R. P. Feynman, *Revs. Mod. Phys.* **20,** 367 (1948)

where $\epsilon = t_{i+1} - t_i$ and where Φ is a probability amplitude functional that depends on all possible paths $x(t)$ from (x_1, t_1) to (x_2, t_2). If a region of space-time is (partially or totally) forbidden to the particle because of the operation of a potential, then the integral in (14.18) omits paths (partially or entirely) through such regions. Region V in Figure 14.1 is an example. Otherwise, the integral in (14.18) lies over all of space-time and may allow even paths that move backward in time. (An electron moving backward in time is a positron.) As in (14.8), the probability q_{12} that the particle lies in the region linking (x_1, t_1) and (x_2, t_2) is $q_{12} = |\phi_{12}|^2$.

Feynman's second postulate is that

$$\Phi(x_1, \cdots x_i, x_{i+1}, \cdots x_2) = \frac{\exp\left(\frac{iS}{\hbar}\right)}{A'} \tag{14.19}$$

where A' is a suitable factor for adjusting the amplitude. The dimensions of S are energy-time, as shown by (14.17). The action S must be an extreme value for the whole path and for each portion. For the part from (x_i, t_i) to (x_{i+1}, t_{i+1}), it is necessary that

$$S(x_{i+1}, x_i) = \int_{t_i}^{t_{i+1}} L(\dot{x}, x)\, dt \tag{14.20}$$

be an extremum. The classical path $x(t)$, along which S in (14.19) is calculated, is the limit as ϵ approaches zero of the point-to-point trajectory $(x_1, t_1), \ldots (x_i, t_i), \ldots$. For the whole classical path, S is an extremum and

$$S = \sum_i S(x_{i+1}, x_i) \tag{14.21}$$

Because (14.21) is a sum, (14.19) is a product, and (14.18) reads

$$\phi_{12} = \lim_{\epsilon \to 0} \int_{(1)}^{(2)} \exp\left[\left(\frac{i}{\hbar}\right) \sum_i S(x_{i+1}, x_i)\right]\left(\frac{dx_1}{A'}\right) \cdots \left(\frac{dx_i}{A'}\right) \cdots \left(\frac{dx_2}{A'}\right) \tag{14.22}$$

If the path from 1 to 2 is divided into two parts, the part before some intermediate state at (x_j, t_j) is, on factoring the exponential,

$$\psi(x_j, t) = \lim_{\epsilon \to 0} \int_{(1)}^{(j)} \exp\left[\left(\frac{i}{\hbar}\right) \sum_{i=-\infty}^{j-1} S(x_{i+1}, x_i)\right]\left(\frac{dx_{j-1}}{A}\right)\left(\frac{dx_{j-2}}{A}\right) \cdots \tag{14.23}$$

In (14.23), the state 1 has been moved to a past time which is conventionally indexed as $i = -\infty$. The function $\psi(x_j, t)$ describes, as completely as possible in the world of fractional likenesses, the past behavior of the system. The intermediate real or virtual state j divides past from future, and the future experiments about to be undergone by the system are described by

$$\chi^*(x_j, t) = \lim_{\epsilon \to 0} \int_{(j)}^{(2)} \exp\left[\left(\frac{i}{\hbar}\right) \sum_{i=j}^{\infty} S(x_{i+1}, x_i)\right]\left(\frac{1}{A}\right)\left(\frac{dx_{j+1}}{A}\right)\left(\frac{dx_{j+2}}{A}\right) \cdots \tag{14.24}$$

When (14.23) and (14.24) are substituted into (14.18), dropping the subscript j yields

$$\phi_{12} = \int \chi^*(x, t)\, \psi(x, t)\, dx \tag{14.25}$$

for the probability amplitude ϕ.

The function $\psi(x, t)$ is the wave function of this one-dimensional system. It is the full and complete description of the system at time t. No further knowledge could be found or verified by experiment.

As the system moves from (x_j, t_j) to (x_{j+1}, t_{i+1}), where $t_{j+1} = t_j + \epsilon$, the wave function changes, in accord with (14.22) and (14.23), to

$$\psi(x_{j+1}, t_j + \epsilon) = \int \exp\left[\left(\frac{i}{\hbar}\right) S(x_{j+1}, x_j)\right] \psi(x_j, t_j) \frac{dx_j}{A} \tag{14.26}$$

Equation (14.26) is like (14.23) except that the intermediate state-of-now is at (x_{j+1}, t_{j+1}) instead of at (x_j, t_j). Equation (14.26) tells how the state of the system changes with time. By straightforward but tedious expansion of all quantities in (14.26) in terms of rapidly converging series in ϵ and $(x_{j+1} - x_j)$, equation (14.26) can be transformed into a differential equation, which also tells how the state of the system changes with time. The resulting differential equation was historically prior to (14.26) and is more convenient mathematically. It is the famous Schrödinger wave equation:

$$\mathbf{H}\psi = -\frac{\hbar}{i}\frac{\partial \psi}{\partial t} \tag{13.53}$$

Feynman has given a very clear and detailed account of how (13.53) is derived from (14.26).

Equation (14.26) tells how a small particle really proceeds by feeling its way along a path and around potentials, which may be barriers or fields or other particles. The particle always proceeds so as to stay as much in phase with its reduced action $S/\hbar$ as possible. As a wave packet with small $S/\hbar$, it meanders. As $S/\hbar$ increases, however, its behavior becomes more and more classical, as though the classical path were the only one along which the thing might propagate itself without destructive interference. For a meandering multi-path of a high-frequency wave (massive particle or high-energy particle) leads quickly to extinction. While a classical particle takes the path of minimum action with negligible deviation therefrom, a wave-particle approximates such a path with deviations that are not negligible for it. If these excursions from the straight-and-narrow were followed by observation, then much of the wave behavior of the particle would be quenched. That is, (14.22) describes the path when the particle is not observed at the points intervening between (1) and (2).

14.4 WAVE MECHANICS

The preceding postulatory bases of Landé and Feynman are interesting, educational, and suitable for many types of problems in physics. They have a certain cultural value for an appreciation of quantum mechanics. For chemistry, however, the Schrödinger equation and similar formulations are most suitable, for they can be stated clearly in mathematical terms that are reasonably familiar. The 1925 matrix mechanics of Heisenberg anticipated Schrödinger's method; however, since it requires mathematical techniques that may not be as widely known as the methods of the calculus, the use of matrices is to be avoided here as much as possible. Moreover, what is presented here in this introduction to quantum mechanics ought to be straightforward, clear, appealing, direct, and simple, as well as immediately useful and closely related to understandable experiments. What follows is not an irreducible set of postulates, for such a minimum set is often surrounded by a pedantic fog of derivations.

Observation of a property of a physical system yields a value w_n from a spectrum of values. If the system is macroscopic or nearly so, there are generally so many states of the system with nearly equal values of the property that the quantization is not observable. However, when the system is very small, the difference in values w_n and w_m of adjacent states is generally large enough to be noticed by an observer who can "see" the small system. Every observable property of a physical system has associated with it an operator $\mathbf{w}_{op}$ such that a real value (that is not containing $i = \sqrt{-1}$)w_n of the property is the eigenvalue w_n in the equation

$$\mathbf{w}_{op}\,\psi_n = w_n\,\psi_n \tag{14.27}$$

Operators are recipes for mathematical activity on the quantities that follow them. An operator may extract roots or merely act as a coefficient. On the other hand, an operator may give directions for taking certain derivatives, as the Hamiltonian operator of (13.54) does. Table 14.1 lists several common operators based on classical functions when ψ_n is given as a function of the independent variables position and time, and when ψ_n is given as a function of the independent variables linear momentum and time. The symmetry that exists between these two classes of operator is important in some statements of the postulates.

Table 14.1 applies only to Cartesian coordinates. When other coordinate systems are used, the transformation of coordinates is effected after the operator is generated in Cartesian coordinates. The key to the transformation is the square of the element of arc, which is

$$ds^2 = dx^2 + dy^2 + dz^2 \tag{14.28}$$

$$= (a_1\,dq_1)^2 + (a_2\,dq_2)^2 + (a_3\,dq_3)^2 \tag{14.29}$$

Here a_1, a_2, and a_3 are functions of the orthogonal curvilinear coordinates q_1, q_2, q_3. For example, for spherical polar coordinates

$$ds^2 = dr^2 + r^2\,d\theta^2 + r^2 \sin^2\theta\,d\phi^2 \tag{14.30}$$

Table 14.1 Some Important Operators of Quantum Mechanics and Their Classical Analogues.

Cartesian Co-ordinates

Name of Property	Classical Function	Quantum Mechanical Operator†	
		When Time and Position Are Independent	When Time and Momentum Are Independent
Position	x	x	$i\hbar\frac{\partial}{\partial p_x}$
	y	y	$i\hbar\frac{\partial}{\partial p_y}$
	z	z	$i\hbar\frac{\partial}{\partial p_z}$
N-th Power of Position	x^n	x^n	$\left(i\hbar\frac{\partial}{\partial p_x}\right)^n$
	y^n	y^n	$\left(i\hbar\frac{\partial}{\partial p_y}\right)^n$
	z^n	z^n	$\left(i\hbar\frac{\partial}{\partial p_z}\right)^n$
Components of Linear Momentum	p_x	$-i\hbar\frac{\partial}{\partial x}$	p_x
	p_y	$-i\hbar\frac{\partial}{\partial y}$	p_y
	p_z	$-i\hbar\frac{\partial}{\partial z}$	p_z
Kinetic Energy	$\frac{p_x^2 + p_y^2 + p_z^2}{2m}$	$-\frac{\hbar^2}{2m}\left(\frac{\partial^2}{\partial x^2} + \frac{\partial^2}{\partial y^2} + \frac{\partial^2}{\partial z^2}\right)$	$\frac{p_x^2 + p_y^2 + p_z^2}{2m}$
Potential Energy‡	$V(x, y, z)$	$V(x, y, z)$	$V\left(i\hbar\frac{\partial}{\partial p_x}, i\hbar\frac{\partial}{\partial p_y}, i\hbar\frac{\partial}{\partial p_z}\right)$
Energy‡	$\mathscr{H}(p, q)$	$\mathbf{H}\left(-i\hbar\frac{\partial}{\partial q}, q\right)$ or $-\frac{\hbar}{i}\frac{\partial}{\partial t}$	$\mathbf{H}\left(p, i\hbar\frac{\partial}{\partial p}\right)$ or $-\frac{\hbar}{i}\frac{\partial}{\partial t}$
Components of Angular Momentum‡	$L_x = yp_z - zp_y$	$-i\hbar\left(y\frac{\partial}{\partial z} - z\frac{\partial}{\partial y}\right)$	$i\hbar\left(p_z\frac{\partial}{\partial p_y} - p_y\frac{\partial}{\partial p_z}\right)$
	$L_y = zp_x - xp_z$	$-i\hbar\left(z\frac{\partial}{\partial x} - x\frac{\partial}{\partial z}\right)$	$i\hbar\left(p_x\frac{\partial}{\partial p_z} - p_z\frac{\partial}{\partial p_x}\right)$
	$L_z = xp_y - yp_x$	$-i\hbar\left(x\frac{\partial}{\partial y} - y\frac{\partial}{\partial x}\right)$	$i\hbar\left(p_y\frac{\partial}{\partial p_x} - p_x\frac{\partial}{\partial p_y}\right)$
Any Function‡	$F(p, q)$	$F\left(-i\hbar\frac{\partial}{\partial q}, q\right)$	$F\left(p, i\hbar\frac{\partial}{\partial p}\right)$

† Operators in other coordinate systems must first be stated as operators in Cartesian coordinates before transformation to the other coordinates.
‡ If the order of operators is doubtful, the operator must be rendered Hermitian (see [14.40]).

The transformation of the very important kinetic energy operator involves use of the general expression

$$\frac{\partial^2}{\partial x^2}+\frac{\partial^2}{\partial y^2}+\frac{\partial^2}{\partial z^2}=\frac{1}{a_1a_2a_3}\left\{\frac{\partial}{\partial q_1}\left[\left(\frac{a_2a_3}{a_1}\right)\frac{\partial}{\partial q_1}\right]+\frac{\partial}{\partial q_2}\left[\left(\frac{a_1a_3}{a_2}\right)\frac{\partial}{\partial q_2}\right]+\frac{\partial}{\partial q_3}\left[\left(\frac{a_1a_2}{a_3}\right)\frac{\partial}{\partial q_3}\right]\right\} \tag{14.31}$$

For spherical polar coordinates, (14.29) and (14.30) prescribe $a_1 = 1$, $a_2 = r$, $a_3 = r \sin\theta$ so that (14.31) yields

$$\frac{\partial^2}{\partial x^2}+\frac{\partial^2}{\partial y^2}+\frac{\partial^2}{\partial z^2}=\frac{1}{r^2\sin\theta}\left\{\frac{\partial}{\partial r}\left[(r^2\sin\theta)\frac{\partial}{\partial r}\right]+\frac{\partial}{\partial\theta}\left[(\sin\theta)\frac{\partial}{\partial\theta}\right]+\frac{\partial}{\partial\phi}\left[\left(\frac{1}{\sin\theta}\right)\frac{\partial}{\partial\phi}\right]\right\} \tag{14.32}$$

The elementary discussions here will ordinarily choose time and position as independent variables.

The Hamiltonian operator $\mathbf{H}$ is generated from the classical Hamiltonian function

$$\mathscr{H}(p, q, t) = \sum_i p_i\dot{q}_i - L(q, \dot{q}) \tag{14.33}$$

By (14.15) in Cartesian coordinates, with $L = T - V$ from (14.14),

$$p_x = \frac{\partial L}{\partial \dot{x}} = \frac{\partial}{\partial \dot{x}}\left[\frac{m}{2}(\dot{x}^2+\dot{y}^2+\dot{z}^2) - V(x, y, z)\right] = m\dot{x}$$

Hence, with $p_x = m\dot{x}$, $p_y = m\dot{y}$, and $p_z = m\dot{z}$, (14.33) yields for one particle

$$\begin{aligned}\mathscr{H} &= m(\dot{x}^2+\dot{y}^2+\dot{z}^2) - \left[\frac{m}{2}(\dot{x}^2+\dot{y}^2+\dot{z}^2) - V\right]\\ &= \frac{m}{2}(\dot{x}^2+\dot{y}^2+\dot{z}^2) + V = T + V\end{aligned}$$

That is, $\mathscr{H}$ is the total energy of the system, a fact true in general for many particles. In general, for n particles

$$\mathscr{H} = \sum_{i=1}^{n}\frac{(p_x^2+p_y^2+p_z^2)_i}{2m_i} + V(x, y, z) \tag{14.34}$$

where m_i is the mass of particle i and where $V(x, y, z)$ is the potential energy as a function of the various coordinates of the particles.

Table 14.1 prescribes no change of space coordinates and a replacement of each canonically conjugate linear momentum coordinate by a first partial derivative; hence, by (14.34)

$$\mathbf{H} = -\frac{\hbar^2}{2}\sum_{i=1}^{n}\frac{1}{m_i}\left(\frac{\partial^2}{\partial x_i^2}+\frac{\partial^2}{\partial y_i^2}+\frac{\partial^2}{\partial z_i^2}\right) + V \tag{14.35}$$

When fields and radiation are present, $\mathbf{H}$ depends explicitly on the time, and it may even be inadequately defined through Table 14.1. Here (14.35) is adequate.

Any physical system changes with time t according to the very important Schrödinger equation

$$-\frac{\hbar}{i}\frac{\partial \psi}{\partial t} = \mathbf{H}\psi \tag{14.36}$$

In (13.66), it was shown how ψ can be expressed as a sum of stationary-state functions ψ_n. The physical interpretation of ψ_n as the amplitude of matter in state n and of $|\psi_n|^2$ as proportional to the probability density of matter in state n requires that ψ_n and its first derivatives be continuous, single-valued functions of their arguments and that they be finite almost everywhere. Moreover, the integral of $|\psi_n|^2$ over the entire range of its arguments τ must be finite. If

$$1 = \int |\psi_n|^2 \, d\tau = \int \psi_n^* \psi_n \, d\tau \tag{14.37}$$

then $|\psi_n|^2$ is equal to the probability density of matter and not merely proportional to it. Equation (14.37) adjusts the amplitude of ψ_n so that ψ_n is then said to be normalized, as baseball batting averages are normalized to 1.000.

The average value of a property of any physical system is real and equal to

$$\bar{w} = \int \psi^* \mathbf{w}_{\text{op}} \psi \, d\tau \tag{14.38}$$

If $\mathbf{w}_{\text{op}}\,\psi_n = w_n \psi_n$ and if ψ is a normalized sum of the ψ_n's then (14.38) is akin to

$$\bar{w} = \sum_i w_i P_i$$

where P_i is the normalized probability of w_i and where $w_i P_i$ is the expected value of w_i. The integration in (14.38) proceeds over all values of the space variables, and $\bar{w}$ may be a function of time. The quantity $\bar{w}$ is the value expected of one measurement of the property having eigenvalues w_n, or it is the average value of many measurements made on a statistical population of identical systems each with wave function $\psi(q, t)$. While one observation finds w_n, their average is $\bar{w}$.

Quantum mechanical operators are linear and Hermitian. The operator $\mathbf{w}_{\text{op}}$ is linear if

$$\mathbf{w}_{\text{op}}(c_1\psi_1 + c_2\psi_2) = c_1 \mathbf{w}_{\text{op}}\psi_1 + c_2 \mathbf{w}_{\text{op}}\psi_2 \tag{14.39}$$

The operator $\mathbf{w}_{\text{op}}$ is Hermitian if

$$\int \psi_1^* \mathbf{w}_{\text{op}} \psi_2 \, d\tau = \int (\mathbf{w}_{\text{op}}\psi_1)^* \psi_2 \, d\tau \tag{14.40}$$

The eigenvalues of Hermitian operators are real, for (14.27) in (14.40) requires

$$w_2 \int \psi_1^* \psi_2 \, d\tau = w_1^* \int \psi_1^* \psi_2 \, d\tau$$

$$(w_2 - w_1^*) \int \psi_1^* \psi_2 \, d\tau = 0 \tag{14.41}$$

where w_2 and w_1^* are constants because they are eigenvalues. If $w_2 \neq w_1^*$, then by (14.41)

$$\int \psi_1^* \psi_2 \, d\tau = 0 \tag{14.42}$$

By analogy to a scalar product of vectors, when (14.42) holds, ψ_1 and ψ_2 are said to be *orthogonal functions.* On the other hand, if ψ_1 and ψ_2 are equal, their eigenvalues are equal. If $\psi_1 = \psi_2$, then (14.41) yields $w = w^*$, which is a statement that w is real.

It is possible for one eigenvalue w to have more than one eigenfunction. States with the same eigenvalue are said to be *degenerate*, the order of the degeneracy being the number of linearly independent wave functions with the one eigenvalue. If ϕ_1 and ϕ_2 are nonorthogonal wave functions such that $\mathbf{w}_{op}\phi_1 = w\phi_1$ and $\mathbf{w}_{op}\phi_2 = w\phi_2$, it is possible to find orthogonal wave functions ψ_1 and ψ_2 with w as eigenvalue. This is done by proper choice of the real constant c in $\psi_2 = \phi_2 - c\phi_1$. Orthogonality of $\psi_1 = \phi_1$ and ψ_2 requires, as in (14.42),

$$0 = \int \psi_1^* \psi_2 \, d\tau = \int \phi_1^* \phi_2 \, d\tau - c \int \phi_1^* \phi_1 \, d\tau$$

$$0 = \int \psi_2^* \psi_1 \, d\tau = \int \phi_2^* \phi_1 \, d\tau - c \int \phi_1^* \phi_1 \, d\tau$$

If $1 = \int \phi_1^* \phi_1 \, d\tau = \int \phi_2^* \phi_2 \, d\tau$ because ϕ_1 and ϕ_2 are each normalized, then

$$c = \int \phi_1^* \phi_2 \, d\tau = \int \phi_2^* \phi_1 \, d\tau \tag{14.43}$$

where (14.40) with $\mathbf{w}_{op} = 1$ has been used. With (14.43), ψ_1 is orthogonal to ψ_2. While $\psi_1 = \phi_1$ is already normalized, in order to normalize ψ_2 it is necessary that a be such in $\psi_2' = a\,\psi_2$ that

$$\begin{aligned}
1 &= \int \psi_2'^* \psi_2' \, d\tau = a^*a \int \psi_2^* \psi_2 \, d\tau \\
&= a^*a\left[\int \phi_2^* \phi_2 \, d\tau + c^2 \int \phi_1^* \phi_1 \, d\tau - 2c \int \phi_1^* \phi_2 \, d\tau\right] \\
&= a^*a[1 + c^2 - 2c(c)] \\
&= a^*a(1 - c^2)
\end{aligned} \tag{14.44}$$

where (14.43) was used for (c). Hence, with c given by (14.43), the orthogonal normalized wave functions of the doubly degenerate state are

$$\left.\begin{aligned}
\psi_1' &= \psi_1 = \phi_1 \\
\psi_2' &= a\psi_2 = (1 - c^2)^{-1/2}(\phi_2 - c\phi_1)
\end{aligned}\right\} \tag{14.45}$$

The functions ψ_1' and ψ_2' are still eigenfunctions of $\mathbf{w}_{op}$ for

$$\mathbf{w}_{op}\psi_1' = \mathbf{w}_{op}\phi_1 = w\phi_1 = w\psi_1'$$

while

$$\mathbf{w}_{\text{op}}\psi'_2 = (1 - c^2)^{-1/2}(\mathbf{w}_{\text{op}}\phi_2 - c\mathbf{w}_{\text{op}}\phi_1)$$
$$= (1 - c^2)^{-1/2}w(\phi_2 - c\phi_1) = w\psi'_2$$

The convenience of working with orthogonal normalized functions will be evident in Section 14.11 and in what follows here.

It is generally assumed that the wave functions $\psi_n(q, t)$ or $u_n(q)$ form a complete set. All ψ_n's or u_n's from both the discrete spectrum of eigenvalues w_n and the continuous spectrum of eigenvalues must be included in the set. If complete, any arbitrary function v can be expanded in terms of them; for example,

$$v(q) = \sum_n a_n u_n(q) \tag{14.46}$$

The constants a_n are found easily if the $u_n(q)$ are normalized and orthogonal, for

$$u_m^*(q)v(q) = \sum_n a_n u_m^*(q)u_n(q)$$
$$\int u_m^*(q)v(q)\,dq = \sum_n a_n \int u_m^*(q)u_n(q)\,dq$$

If $m \neq n$, $\int u_m^*(q)\,u_n(q)\,dq$ is zero because the u_n's are orthogonal. If $m = n$,

$$\int u_m^*(q)v(q)\,dq = a_m \tag{14.47}$$

because the u_n's are normalized. With the a_n's known by (14.47), $v(q)$ is given by (14.46), if the expansion is valid, as supposed.

These, then, are the most useful and important properties of wave functions, the rules for calculating observable properties, and the quantum mechanical equations of matter. The postulates are not set apart and numbered because various choices of a minimum set can be made. For completeness, a final postulate about the relativistic property called *spin* and its effects on the symmetry of allowed wave functions would be required. This matter is deferred to Sections 14.7 and 14.8 in order that two extremely important applications of these abstract rules may be made at once.

14.5 HARMONIC OSCILLATOR

Simple harmonic motion in classical mechanics is the motion of an undamped vibrator whose restoring force is proportional to the displacement x from equilibrium at $x = 0$. Although few if any real systems have a force that is really linear in the displacement (Hooke's law), linearity is often a very good approximation for small amplitudes of vibration. The analytic solution of this problem is straightforward and the periodic small vibrations of very complicated systems can be resolved, by a suitable choice of so-called *normal coordinates*, into several simultaneous modes of such vibration. The motion of the harmonic oscillator has thus become a standard of comparison and reference for real motions that are much more complicated.

The harmonic oscillator is relatively more important in quantum mechanics than it is in classical mechanics. Planck's initial model of vibrators of one frequency in equilibrium with radiation is a very basic example of a system that behaves like a quantum mechanical harmonic oscillator. Einstein's explanation of the decline in heat capacities near $T = 0$ by means of a crystal having quanta of one fundamental frequency of vibration is another example. Almost all molecules vibrate at certain characteristic frequencies, each of which behaves like a simple harmonic oscillator for small vibrational energies. What is of truly paramount importance in quantum mechanics is the fact that an analytic solution is easily attained. This is remarkable because few problems in quantum mechanics can be solved in terms of well-known functions. In fact, it is remarkable to find any analytic solution for the wave function in any problem. Consequently, the harmonic oscillator in quantum mechanics not only is a standard of reference for motion in a certain kind of potential but is a basis for almost *any* approximate solution involving *any* potential with a minimum of energy. Without the harmonic oscillator, a beginning to the inevitable approximate solutions of the Schrödinger equation would be truly difficult. Finally, the harmonic oscillator exhibits zero-point energy in accord with the demands of the uncertainty principle.

It is pedagogically proper to begin this discussion with an application of the postulatory statements of Section 14.4 and their foundation in classical mechanics. If, in one dimension x, the restoring force F_x is proportional to x, is directed toward smaller values of x, and is derived from a potential $V(x)$, then

$$F_x = -\frac{\partial V}{\partial x} = -kx$$

$$V(x) = (1/2)kx^2 \tag{14.48}$$

where k is the force constant and the minimum (zero) of $V(x)$ is at $x = 0$. The Lagrangian function (14.14) is, therefore,

$$L(x, \dot{x}) = \left(\frac{m}{2}\right)\dot{x}^2 - \left(\frac{k}{2}\right)x^2 \tag{14.49}$$

And, by (14.13), the equation of classical motion is

$$\frac{d}{dt}(m\dot{x}) = -kx \tag{14.50}$$

$F = \frac{d(mv)}{dt}$

Since Newtonian force is the time rate of change of momentum, (14.50) says that the force is proportional to the displacement. Since (14.50) could have been written without the use of $L(x, \dot{x})$, using (14.13) to get (14.50) is like killing ants with a cannon—it's instructive. Without relativity, (14.50) is

$$\frac{d^2x}{dt^2} + \left(\frac{k}{m}\right)x = 0 \tag{14.51}$$

which has solutions of the form

$$x = Ae^{\pm i\omega t} \tag{14.52}$$

since

$$\frac{dx}{dt} = \pm\, i\omega A e^{\pm i\omega t}$$

$$\frac{d^2x}{dt^2} = (\pm\, i)^2 \omega^2 A e^{\pm i\omega t} = -\omega^2 x \tag{14.53}$$

With (14.53) in (14.51) it follows that

$$\omega^2 = k/m \tag{14.54}$$

Moreover, since $e^{\pm i\omega t} = \cos \omega t \pm i \sin \omega t$ it is clear that one cycle of motion occurs in a time $2\pi/\omega$. Hence, the frequency of the motion in cycles per second is, by (14.54),

$$\nu = \frac{\omega}{2\pi} = \frac{1}{2\pi}\left(\frac{k}{m}\right)^{1/2} \tag{14.55}$$

The potential energy, with (14.55) in (14.48), is thus

$$V(x) = \frac{1}{2}(2\pi\nu)^2 mx^2 = 2\pi^2 m\nu^2 x^2 \tag{14.56}$$

where ν is the fundamental frequency of the undamped vibration.

The quantum mechanical harmonic oscillator has a Schrödinger equation derived from the Hamiltonian function (14.34) in the form

$$\mathscr{H}(p, x) = \frac{p^2}{2m} + 2\pi^2 m\nu^2 x^2 \tag{14.57}$$

A description in terms of position x and time requires, as indicated in Table 14.1, that p be replaced by $-i\hbar\partial/\partial x$: hence, the Hamiltonian operator is

$$\mathbf{H} = \frac{1}{2m}\left(-i\hbar\frac{\partial}{\partial x}\right)^2 + 2\pi^2 m\nu^2 x^2$$

$$= -\frac{\hbar^2}{2m}\frac{d^2}{dx^2} + 2\pi^2 m\nu^2 x^2 \tag{14.58}$$

where the total derivative replaces the partial derivative in this one-dimensional problem. In a stationary state, the quantum mechanical harmonic oscillator obeys the wave equation

$$-\frac{\hbar^2}{2m}\frac{d^2u}{dx^2} + 2\pi^2 m\nu^2 x^2 u = Eu \tag{14.59}$$

where $u = u(x)$ and where (14.58) is the Hamiltonian (energy) operator. The values of E in (14.59) are discrete because, as noted in Section 13.11, $V(x) = (1/2)kx^2$ is not bounded at large x.

One of the stationary states described by (14.59) has the lowest energy of the spectrum of discrete energies. It is called the *ground state* of the system and by (14.56), has an energy

$$E_0 = \frac{\overline{p_0^2}}{2m} + 2\pi^2 m\nu^2 \overline{x_0^2} \tag{14.60}$$

where $\overline{p_0^2}$ and $\overline{x_0^2}$ are the average values of the squares of the minimum values of momentum and position consistent with the uncertainty principle. Because real systems act so as to allow an ideal observation at any time, this principle is here stated ideally

$$p_0 x_0 = \frac{\hbar}{2} \tag{14.61}$$

where p_0 and x_0 in (14.61) are root mean square values. Minimizing (14.60) subject to the condition (14.61) by the method of Lagrange (Section 4.12) requires

$$0 = \frac{\partial E_0}{\partial p_0} + \gamma\frac{\partial}{\partial p_0}(p_0 x_0) = \frac{p_0}{m} + \gamma x_0$$

$$0 = \frac{\partial E_0}{\partial x_0} + \gamma\frac{\partial}{\partial x_0}(p_0 x_0) = 4\pi^2 m\nu^2 x_0 + \gamma p_0$$

Eliminating the undetermined multiplier γ from these conditions yields

$$p_0^2 = (2\pi m\nu)^2 x_0^2 \tag{14.62}$$

By use of (14.62), (14.61) requires

$$\left.\begin{aligned} 2(2\pi m\nu)\overline{x_0^2} &= \hbar \\ 2\overline{p_0^2} &= \hbar(2\pi m\nu) \end{aligned}\right\} \tag{14.63}$$

Hence, (14.60) with p_0 and x_0 eliminated by use of (14.63) indicates a minimum energy E_0 of the harmonic oscillator to be

$$E_0 = \frac{(2\pi m\nu)\hbar}{2(2m)} + 2\pi^2 m\nu^2\left(\frac{\hbar}{2(2\pi m\nu)}\right) = \frac{h\nu}{4} + \frac{h\nu}{4} = \frac{h\nu}{2} \tag{14.64}$$

In (14.64), E_0 is the zero-point energy of the quantum mechanical harmonic oscillator. In its most stable state, its energy lies $(1/2)(h\nu)$ above the classical energy $V(0) = 0$. This behavior is like the particle in the box; the most stable real state has an energy greater than the minimum classical potential energy.

The analytic solution of (14.59) for all eigenvalues of E is best achieved by use of dimensionless variables $\xi = \alpha x$ and $\epsilon = \beta E$ to put (14.59) in the form

$$\frac{d^2w}{d\xi^2} + (\epsilon - \xi^2)w = 0 \tag{14.65}$$

where $u(x) \equiv w(\xi)$. With $\xi = \alpha x$ and $\epsilon = \beta E$, (14.59) is transformed thus:

$$\frac{d^2u}{dx^2} + \left(\frac{2mE}{\hbar^2} - \frac{4\pi^2m^2\nu^2x^2}{\hbar^2}\right)u = 0$$

$$\alpha^2\frac{d^2u}{d\xi^2} + \left(\frac{2m\epsilon}{\beta\hbar^2} - \frac{4\pi^2m^2\nu^2\xi^2}{\alpha^2\hbar^2}\right)u = 0$$

$$\frac{d^2u}{d\xi^2} + \left(\frac{2m\epsilon}{\alpha^2\beta\hbar^2} - \frac{4\pi^2m^2\nu^2\xi^2}{\alpha^4\hbar^2}\right)u = 0 \tag{14.66}$$

Since the dimensions of w and u cancel in (14.65) and (14.66), comparison of these two equations requires

$$1 = \frac{2m}{\alpha^2\beta\hbar^2} \quad \text{and} \quad 1 = \frac{4\pi^2m^2\nu^2}{\alpha^4\hbar^2}$$

Hence,

$$\alpha^2 = \frac{2\pi m\nu}{\hbar} = \frac{4\pi^2 m\nu}{h} = \frac{\xi^2}{x^2} \tag{14.67}$$

$$\beta = \left(\frac{2m}{\hbar^2}\right)\left(\frac{\hbar}{2\pi m\nu}\right) = \frac{2}{h\nu} = \frac{\epsilon}{E} \tag{14.68}$$

$$w(\xi) \equiv u(x) \tag{14.69}$$

Sommerfeld's method of finding $w(\xi)$ is to note that at sufficiently large ξ, (14.65) becomes

$$\frac{d^2w}{d\xi^2} = \xi^2 w \tag{14.70}$$

Furthermore, $w = \exp(\pm\xi^2/2)$ yields

$$\frac{d^2w}{d\xi^2} = (\xi^2 \pm 1)\exp(\pm\xi^2/2) = (\xi^2 \pm 1)w \tag{14.71}$$

which also reduces to (14.70) for large ξ. However, since $\int |w|^2\, d\xi$ must remain finite when ξ varies (like x) from $-\infty$ to $+\infty$, the form $e^{+\xi^2/2}$ must be discarded

Hermite ⊥ funct: wave func. for harmon. oscillator

in favor of

$$w(\xi) = e^{-\xi^2/2} \tag{14.72}$$

From (14.72), as in (14.71),

$$\frac{d^2w}{d\xi^2} + (1 - \xi^2)w = 0 \tag{14.73}$$

Comparison of (14.65) and (14.73) shows at once that (14.72) is a solution of (14.65) if $\epsilon = 1$. Hence, the state with wave function (14.72) has an eigenvalue of the energy

Hermite polynomials

$$E = \frac{\epsilon}{\beta} = \frac{h\nu}{2} \tag{14.74}$$

where (14.68) and $\epsilon = 1$ have been used. This is the same result as (14.64) for the ground state.

Sommerfeld's method continues for states of energy greater than (14.74) by assuming a power series solution

$$w(\xi) = e^{-\xi^2/2} \sum_n a_n \xi^n \tag{14.75}$$

in the hope that, as required by (14.37), the polynomial can be quenched at large ξ by the exponential. Equation (14.75) gives

$$\frac{dw}{d\xi} = [-\xi(\sum_n a_n \xi^n) + \sum_n n a_n \xi^{n-1}]e^{-\xi^2/2}$$

$$\begin{aligned}\frac{d^2w}{d\xi^2} &= -\xi[-\sum_n a_n \xi^{n+1} + \sum_n n a_n \xi^{n-1}]e^{-\xi^2/2} \\ &\quad + [-\sum_n (n+1)a_n \xi^n + \sum_n n(n-1)a_n \xi^{n-2}]e^{-\xi^2/2} \\ &= \sum_m [a_{m-2} - m a_m - (m+1)a_m + (m+2)(m+1)a_{m+2}]\xi^m e^{-\xi^2/2}\end{aligned} \tag{14.76}$$

Substitution of (14.75) and (14.76) into (14.65) yields

$$0 = \sum_m [a_{m-2} - (2m+1)a_m + (m+2)(m+1)a_{m+2} + \epsilon a_m - a_{m-2}]\xi^m e^{-\xi^2/2} \tag{14.77}$$

This is true for any value of ξ; hence, the coefficients of $\xi^m \exp(-\xi^2/2)$ must be zero. Thus (14.77) requires

$$0 = (\epsilon - 2m - 1)a_m + (m+2)(m+1)a_{m+2}$$

$$a_{m+2} = a_m \frac{2m + 1 - \epsilon}{(m+2)(m+1)} \tag{14.78}$$

Equation (14.78) is a recursion formula telling how the coefficients in the assumed solution (14.75) are related to each other. There are two series, one when m is odd, one when m is even.

If (14.75) is to be an acceptable wave function, it must converge properly for all ξ from $-\infty$ to $+\infty$. Every term of the even-m series and every term of the odd-m series has the same algebraic sign when $\epsilon < 2m + 1$. A series of terms of the same sign converges only if the absolute value of the limit of the ratio of successive terms is less than unity as the index of the terms increases without limit. Here, one of the two series will converge if

$$\left| \lim_{m\to\infty} \frac{a_{m+2}\xi^{m+2} e^{-\xi^2/2}}{a_m \xi^m e^{-\xi^2/2}} \right| < 1 \tag{14.79}$$

The factors $\xi^m \exp(-\xi^2/2)$ cancel in (14.79) so that $w(\xi)$ converges if

$$\left| \lim_{m\to\infty} \frac{a_{m+2}\xi^2}{a_m} \right| = \xi^2 \left| \lim_{m\to\infty} \left(\frac{a_{m+2}}{a_m}\right) \right| < 1 \tag{14.80}$$

But by (14.78), with recourse to l'Hospital's rule,

$$\lim_{m\to\infty} \left(\frac{a_{m+2}}{a_m}\right) = \frac{2}{2m+3}$$

Hence, the condition is

$$\xi^2 \left(\frac{2}{2m+3}\right) < 1 \tag{14.81}$$

It is clear that (14.81) is not satisfied for arbitrarily large ξ. Unless each series $\Sigma a_m \xi^m$ is somehow terminated, $w(\xi)$ becomes unacceptable at large ξ, because $\int |w|^2 \, d\xi$ must be bounded as in (14.37).

One of the two series may be annihilated by setting either a_0 or a_1 equal to zero. The other series may be terminated at the term $a_m \xi^m$ by setting $2m + 1 - \epsilon = 0$ as suggested in (14.78). If m is thus kept finite by the eigenvalue ϵ, the dominant term in $w(\xi)$ will be of the order of $\xi^m \exp(-\xi^2/2)$. But with m fixed,

$$\lim_{\xi\to\infty} \left[\frac{\xi^m}{e^{\xi^2/2}}\right] = 0$$

by l'Hospital's rule for indeterminate forms. As a result, $w(\xi)$ remains finite for all ξ if the polynomial is terminated at $\epsilon = 2m + 1$.

Termination of one series by the condition $2m + 1 - \epsilon = 0$ thus reveals the eigenvalue of the energy of state m to be

$$E_m = \frac{\epsilon}{\beta} = \frac{2m+1}{(2/h\nu)} = (m + \tfrac{1}{2})h\nu \tag{14.82}$$

The quantum number m has come in a natural way as a condition for keeping $w(\xi)$ finite for all ξ. If m is even in (14.82), recourse to (14.78) and (14.75) shows that $w_m(\xi) = +w_m(-\xi)$, while, if m is odd, $w_m(\xi) = -w_m(-\xi)$. In scientific jargon, the parity of $w(\xi)$ is even if m is even, while it is odd if m is odd.

The recursion formula (14.78) allows $w_m(\xi)$ and E_m to be found for any m. If $a_1 = 0$ and $m = 0$, then the condition

$$2m + 1 = \epsilon \tag{14.83}$$

gives, as in (14.82), $E_0 = (1/2)h\nu$. At the same time, (14.78) gives $a_n = 0$ for $n \geqslant 1$. Hence, (14.75) and (14.78) give

$$w_0(\xi) = a_0 e^{-\xi^2/2} \tag{14.84}$$

The state with the next energy has $a_0 = 0$ and $m = 1$ in (14.82), while (14.78) gives $a_n = 0$ for $n \geqslant 2$. Hence, (14.75) and (14.78) for the state with $E_1 = (3/2)h\nu$ give

$$w_1(\xi) = a_1 \xi e^{-\xi^2/2} \tag{14.85}$$

The state with the next energy has $a_1 = 0$ and, by (14.78), $a_n = 0$ for n odd. Its energy, by (14.82) with $m = 2$, is $E_2 = (5/2)h\nu$. With $m = 2$ and $\epsilon = 2m + 1 = 5$, it follows from (14.78) that $a_n = 0$ if $n \geqslant 4$. The only nonzero coefficients are, therefore, a_0 and a_2. By (14.78) with $\epsilon = 5$, $a_2 = -2\,a_0$ and so (14.75) yields

$$w_2(\xi) = (a_0\xi^0 - 2a_0\xi^2)e^{-\xi^2/2} = a_0(1 - 2\xi^2)e^{-\xi^2/2} \tag{14.86}$$

Similarly, if $\epsilon = 7$ and $E_3 = (7/2)h\nu$, $a_0 = 0$ and

$$w_3(\xi) = a_1\left[\xi - \left(\frac{2}{3}\right)\xi^3\right]e^{-\xi^2/2} \tag{14.87}$$

while if $\epsilon = 9$ and $E_4 = (9/2)h\nu$, $a_1 = 0$ and

$$w_4(\xi) = a_0\left[1 - 4\xi^2 + \left(\frac{4}{3}\right)\xi^4\right]e^{-\xi^2/2} \tag{14.88}$$

It is customary to choose a_0 or a_1 to satisfy the normalization condition

$$1 = \int_{-\infty}^{\infty} |u(x)|^2\,dx = \frac{1}{\alpha}\int_{-\infty}^{\infty} |w_m(\xi)|^2\,d\xi \tag{14.89}$$

The integration in (14.89) is over dx and not $d\xi$; hence, the factor α^{-1} from (14.67). The actual process of normalization is this for $w_3(\xi)$:

$$\begin{aligned}
1 &= \frac{1}{\alpha}\int_{-\infty}^{\infty} a_1^2\left[\xi - \left(\frac{2}{3}\right)\xi^3\right]^2 e^{-\xi^2}\,d\xi \\
&= \frac{2a_1^2}{\alpha}\int_0^{\infty}\left[\xi^2 - \frac{4}{3}\xi^4 + \frac{4}{9}\xi^6\right]e^{-\xi^2}\frac{d\xi^2}{2\xi} \\
&= \frac{a_1^2}{\alpha}\left[\Gamma\left(\frac{3}{2}\right) - \frac{4}{3}\Gamma\left(\frac{5}{2}\right) + \frac{4}{9}\Gamma\left(\frac{7}{2}\right)\right] \\
&= \frac{a_1^2}{\alpha}\left[\frac{\sqrt{\pi}}{2} - \frac{4}{3}\left(\frac{3}{2}\right)\frac{\sqrt{\pi}}{2} + \frac{4}{9}\left(\frac{5}{2}\right)\left(\frac{3}{2}\right)\frac{\sqrt{\pi}}{2}\right] \\
&= \frac{a_1^2}{\alpha}\left[\frac{1}{2} - 1 + \frac{5}{6}\right]\sqrt{\pi} = \frac{a_1^2\sqrt{\pi}}{3\alpha}
\end{aligned}$$

where $\Gamma(n)$ is explained in Appendix C. Hence, $a_1^2 = 3\alpha/\sqrt{\pi}$ and

$$w_3(\xi) = \left(\frac{3\alpha}{\sqrt{\pi}}\right)^{1/2}\left[\xi - \left(\frac{2}{3}\right)\xi^3\right]e^{-\xi^2/2}$$

Normalized wave functions for the three most stable states of the linear harmonic oscillator, with α given by (14.67), are

$$w_0(\xi) = \left(\frac{\alpha}{\sqrt{\pi}}\right)^{1/2} e^{-\xi^2/2} \tag{14.90}$$

$$w_1(\xi) = \left(\frac{2\alpha}{\sqrt{\pi}}\right)^{1/2} \xi e^{-\xi^2/2} \tag{14.91}$$

$$w_2(\xi) = \left(\frac{\alpha}{2\sqrt{\pi}}\right)^{1/2} (1 - 2\xi^2)e^{-\xi^2/2} \tag{14.92}$$

These are graphed in Figure 14.2; their similarity to Figure 13.14 is obvious.

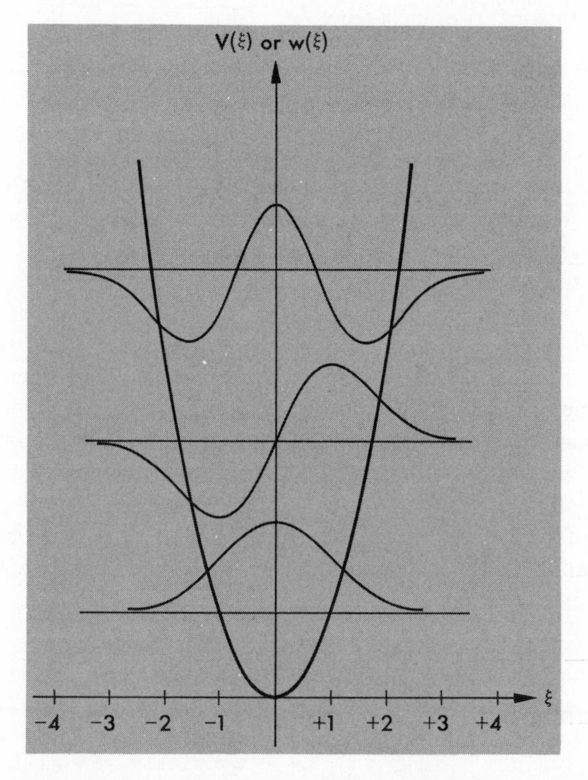

Figure 14.2. Wave Functions of the Three Most Stable States of the One-Dimensional Harmonic Oscillator

A glance at Table 14.1 and (14.57) shows that a solution of the one-dimensional harmonic oscillator in terms of momentum p (instead of position x as above) leads to an equation almost exactly like (14.65).

If a two-dimensional oscillator is described by position coordinates x and y, its Hamiltonian function is

$$\mathscr{H}(p, q) = \frac{p_x^2}{2m_x} + \frac{p_y^2}{2m_y} + \frac{k_x x^2}{2} + \frac{k_y y^2}{2} \tag{14.93}$$

and the Schrödinger equation like (14.59) is

$$-\frac{\hbar^2}{2m_x}\frac{\partial^2 u}{\partial x^2} - \frac{\hbar^2}{2m_y}\frac{\partial^2 u}{\partial y^2} + \left(\frac{k_x}{2}\right)x^2 u + \left(\frac{k_y}{2}\right)y^2 u = Eu \tag{14.94}$$

If $u = X(x)\ Y(y)$ in (14.94), then substitution and division by u gives

$$E = \left[-\frac{\hbar^2}{2m_x X}\frac{d^2 X}{dx^2} + \frac{k_x x^2}{2X}\right] + \left[-\frac{\hbar^2}{2m_y Y}\frac{d^2 Y}{dy^2} + \frac{k_y y^2}{2Y}\right]$$

Since the first brackets enclose a function of x alone and the second enclose a function of y alone, as in Section 13.7, the two-dimensional problem resolves itself into two one-dimensional problems with

$$\begin{aligned} E &= E_x + E_y \\ &= \left(n_x + \frac{1}{2}\right)h\nu_x + \left(n_y + \frac{1}{2}\right)h\nu_y \end{aligned}$$

as in (14.82). The wave functions $X(x)$ and $Y(y)$ are like (14.90), (14.91), and so on. In the same way, a multidimensional harmonic oscillator has a product wave function and an energy

$$E = \sum_i \left(n_i + \frac{1}{2}\right)h\nu_i \tag{14.95}$$

when n_i is the quantum number of the vibration with frequency ν_i. If some of the ν_i are alike, some states are degenerate because they have the same eigenvalue of E by a various choice of n_i's and one-dimensional wave functions. Equation (14.95) is the same as Planck's hypothesis of 1900 concerning the energy states of the oscillators if n_i changes by unity upon absorption or emission of radiation. This it does. Equation (14.95) likewise fits the vibrational energies of a simple crystal like Einstein's and those of real molecules with small energies of vibration.

14.6 HYDROGEN ATOM

As the simplest and most abundant atom in the universe, H easily qualifies for careful study. As an example of a two-particle system in three dimensions, it provides a natural setting for discussion of the use of center-of-mass coordinates and angular momentum. It provides a direct comparison of the theories of Bohr and Schrödinger on terms as favorable as possible to the older Bohr theory. It offers an example of how a wave function can be factored into functions of one variable and how a partial differential equation can be resolved into more than one total differential equation. The problem of finding wave functions and energies of H, where the potential energy is a function only of the distance r between particles so that $V = V(r)$, is the prototype of all atomic problems and of all central-force problems. Most and often all of the quantum numbers of the electron in H apply to the states of every electron in every atom; that is, an understanding and classification of the states of the electrons in any atom is qualitatively the same as for the electron in H. Finally, Pauli in 1925 discovered that every electron in an atom has four different quantum numbers. A thorough understanding of three electronic quantum numbers and their basis in ordinary space prepares the way for the fourth quantum number and a nonspatial quantum distribution of a particle in states specified by the spin of a particle.

The only interaction of importance here for H is the coulombic or electrostatic attraction of proton for electron and vice versa. Hence, with a reference at $r = \infty$, the potential energy for H is

$$V(r) = -\frac{\mathbf{Z}e^2}{4\pi\epsilon_0 r} \tag{14.96}$$

where $\mathbf{Z}e$ is the nuclear charge ($\mathbf{Z} = 1$ in H, $\mathbf{Z} = 2$ in He^+, etc.) and where r is the distance between the nucleus and electron. The possibility of a nuclear reaction that removes the electron from the scene is not considered in (14.96), and so-called weak interactions and gravitation are negligible. If subscripts e and n refer to electron and nucleus, the Schrödinger equation for a stationary state of a one-electron atom is

$$-\frac{\hbar^2}{2m_e}\left(\frac{\partial^2 u}{\partial x_e^2} + \frac{\partial^2 u}{\partial y_e^2} + \frac{\partial^2 u}{\partial z_e^2}\right) - \frac{\hbar^2}{2m_n}\left(\frac{\partial^2 u}{\partial x_n^2} + \frac{\partial^2 u}{\partial y_n^2} + \frac{\partial^2 u}{\partial z_n^2}\right) + V(r)u = Eu \tag{14.97}$$

where $V(r)$ is given by (14.96) and where

$$r^2 = (x_e - x_n)^2 + (y_e - y_n)^2 + (z_e - z_n)^2 \tag{14.98}$$

In terms of relative coordinates, (14.98) is

$$r^2 = x^2 + y^2 + z^2 \tag{14.99}$$

where

$$x = x_e - x_n, \quad y = y_e - y_n, \quad \text{and} \quad z = z_e - z_n \tag{14.100}$$

As for classical motions, a separation into motion of the center of mass and relative motion within the system is effected by the use of the center-of-mass coordinates

$$x_0 = \frac{m_e x_e + m_n x_n}{M}$$

$$y_0 = \frac{m_e y_e + m_n y_n}{M}$$

$$z_0 = \frac{m_e z_e + m_n z_n}{M} \tag{14.101}$$

where the sum of the masses of nucleus m_n and electron m_e is $M = m_e + m_n$. The wave function is expected to be of the form

$$u(x_e, y_e, z_e, x_n, y_n, z_n) = W(x, y, z)X(x_0)Y(y_0)Z(z_0) \tag{14.102}$$

The physical reason is that $V(r)$ is not affected by the motion of the center of mass at x_0, y_0, z_0. Thus there will be three equivalent one-dimensional free-particle problems, as in Section 13.8, and one problem involving $V(r)$.

The way these choices simplify the problem is shown by a consideration of the simplified function $u(x_e, x_n) = W(x)X(x_0)$.

$$\frac{\partial u}{\partial x_e} = \frac{\partial u}{\partial x}\frac{\partial x}{\partial x_e} + \frac{\partial u}{\partial x_0}\frac{\partial x_0}{\partial x_e} = \frac{\partial u}{\partial x} + \frac{m_e}{M}\frac{\partial u}{\partial x_0}$$

$$\frac{\partial u}{\partial x_n} = \frac{\partial u}{\partial x}\frac{\partial x}{\partial x_n} + \frac{\partial u}{\partial x_0}\frac{\partial x_0}{\partial x_n} = -\frac{\partial u}{\partial x} + \frac{m_n}{M}\frac{\partial u}{\partial x_0}$$

where (14.100) and (14.101) have been used. Furthermore

$$\begin{aligned}\frac{\partial^2 u}{\partial x_e^2} &= \frac{\partial}{\partial x_e}\left(\frac{\partial u}{\partial x_e}\right) = \left(\frac{\partial^2 u}{\partial x^2}\right)\left(\frac{\partial x}{\partial x_e}\right) + \left(\frac{\partial^2 u}{\partial x \partial x_0}\right)\left(\frac{\partial x_0}{\partial x_e}\right) \\ &\quad + \frac{m_e}{M}\left(\frac{\partial^2 u}{\partial x \partial x_0}\right)\left(\frac{\partial x}{\partial x_e}\right) + \frac{m_e}{M}\left(\frac{\partial^2 u}{\partial x_0^2}\right)\left(\frac{\partial x_0}{\partial x_e}\right) \\ &= \frac{\partial^2 u}{\partial x^2} + 2\left(\frac{m_e}{M}\right)\left(\frac{\partial^2 u}{\partial x \partial x_0}\right) + \left(\frac{m_e}{M}\right)^2 \frac{\partial^2 u}{\partial x_0^2}\end{aligned} \tag{14.103}$$

where the mixed second derivatives have been assumed to be equal. Similarly, with further use of (14.100) and (14.101),

$$\frac{\partial^2 u}{\partial x_n^2} = \frac{\partial^2 u}{\partial x^2} - 2\left(\frac{m_n}{M}\right)\left(\frac{\partial^2 u}{\partial x \partial x_0}\right) + \left(\frac{m_n}{M}\right)^2\left(\frac{\partial^2 u}{\partial x_0^2}\right) \tag{14.104}$$

Finally, with the simplified $u = W(x)X(x_0)$, (14.103) and (14.104) give

$$\begin{aligned}\frac{1}{m_e}\frac{\partial^2 u}{\partial x_e^2} + \frac{1}{m_n}\frac{\partial^2 u}{\partial x_n^2} &= \left(\frac{1}{m_e} + \frac{1}{m_n}\right)\left(\frac{\partial^2 u}{\partial x^2}\right) + \left(\frac{m_e + m_n}{M^2}\right)\left(\frac{\partial^2 u}{\partial x_0^2}\right) \\ &= \frac{X}{m}\frac{d^2 W}{dx^2} + \frac{W}{M}\frac{d^2 X}{dx_0^2}\end{aligned} \tag{14.105}$$

where the reduced mass m is defined as in classical mechanics by

$$\frac{1}{m} = \frac{1}{m_e} + \frac{1}{m_n} \tag{14.106}$$

In view of (14.105) and analogous results for the other coordinates, the real u of (14.102) in (14.97) yields

$$-\frac{\hbar^2 XYZ}{2m}\left(\frac{\partial^2 W}{\partial x^2} + \frac{\partial^2 W}{\partial y^2} + \frac{\partial^2 W}{\partial z^2}\right) + V(r)WXYZ$$

$$-\frac{\hbar^2 W}{2M}\left(YZ\frac{d^2 X}{dx_0^2} + XZ\frac{d^2 Y}{dy_0^2} + XY\frac{d^2 Z}{dz_0^2}\right) = EWXYZ$$

Division by $WXYZ$ yields a set of terms dependent only on x, y, and z and three terms, each dependent on one of the variables x_0, y_0, or z_0. As in Section 13.7, since these four groups of terms are each independent of variables in the other groups of terms, each must be a constant. Hence, it follows from above that

$$-\frac{\hbar^2}{2mW}\left(\frac{\partial^2 W}{\partial x^2} + \frac{\partial^2 W}{\partial y^2} + \frac{\partial^2 W}{\partial z^2}\right) + V(r) = E_{\mathrm{H}} \tag{14.107}$$

$$-\frac{\hbar^2}{2MX}\frac{d^2 X}{dx_0^2} = E_X \quad \text{(and so on for } Y \text{ and } Z\text{)} \tag{14.108}$$

where

$$E = E_{\mathrm{H}} + E_X + E_Y + E_Z \tag{14.109}$$

The motion of the center-of-mass at x_0, y_0, and z_0 has thus been treated like the motion of a free particle (Section 13.8) with a continuum of energies $E_X + E_Y + E_Z$ and wave functions $X(x_0)Y(y_0)Z(z_0)$. As in classical mechanics, such a separation is always possible in wave mechanics.

The internal motions of H (or any two-particle system having central forces only) in terms of the relative Cartesian coordinates x, y, and z are treated most easily by transforming (14.107) to spherical polar coordinates. By (14.32), (14.107) with

$$W(x, y, z) = R(r)\Theta(\theta)\Phi(\phi) \tag{14.110}$$

becomes, after multiplication by $-2mr^2/\hbar^2$,

$$+\frac{1}{\Theta \sin\theta}\frac{d}{d\theta}\left(\sin\theta\frac{d\Theta}{d\theta}\right) + \frac{1}{\Phi\sin^2\theta}\frac{d^2\Phi}{d\phi^2}$$

$$+\frac{1}{R}\frac{d}{dr}\left(r^2\frac{dR}{dr}\right) + \frac{2mr^2}{\hbar^2}[E_{\mathrm{H}} - V(r)] = 0 \tag{14.111}$$

Since the first two terms of (14.111) are independent of r while the last two are independent of θ and ϕ, each pair must be a constant. With $l(l+1)$ as the constant (for reasons yet to be explained), there result from (14.111) two equations:

$$\frac{1}{R}\frac{d}{dr}\left(r^2\frac{dR}{dr}\right)+\frac{2mr^2}{\hbar^2}[E_H - V(r)] = l(l+1) \tag{14.112}$$

$$\frac{\sin\theta}{\Theta}\frac{d}{d\theta}\left(\sin\theta\frac{d\Theta}{d\theta}\right)+\frac{1}{\Phi}\frac{d^2\Phi}{d\phi^2}+l(l+1)\sin^2\theta = 0 \tag{14.113}$$

A glance at (14.113) shows that the second term depends only on ϕ while the others depend only on θ; hence, as before, with m^2 as the constant, there result from (14.113) two equations:

$$\frac{d^2\Phi}{d\phi^2}+m^2\Phi = 0 \tag{14.114}$$

$$\frac{1}{\sin\theta}\frac{d}{d\theta}\left(\sin\theta\frac{d\Theta}{d\theta}\right)+\left[l(l+1)-\frac{m^2}{\sin^2\theta}\right]\Theta = 0 \tag{14.115}$$

By these maneuvers with the constants $l(l+1)$ and m^2, (14.111) has been resolved into three ordinary second-order total differential equations. Both (14.112) and (14.115) may be solved by the use of power series or by more sophisticated methods, while (14.114) obviously is solved by

$$\Phi(\phi) = N_\phi e^{\pm im\phi} = N_\phi(\cos m\phi \pm i\sin m\phi) \tag{14.116}$$

Since ϕ is an angle, the condition that Φ be single-valued requires $\Phi(0) = \Phi(2\pi) = \Phi(4\pi) = \ldots$; hence, m is zero or a positive or negative integer. If $m = 0$, (14.114) yields $\Phi(\phi) = N_\phi + N'\phi$ as a solution, wherein N' is chosen to

Table 14.2 Surface Harmonics $\Theta_{lm}(\theta)\Phi_m(\phi)$ for Use When $V = V(r)$.†

Item	$l=0$	$l=1$	$l=2$	$l=3$
$m=0$	$\frac{1}{2}$	$\frac{\sqrt{6}}{2}\cos\theta$	$\frac{\sqrt{10}}{4}(3\cos^2\theta-1)$	$\frac{\sqrt{14}}{4}(5\cos^3\theta-3\cos\theta)$
$m=\pm 1$	Impossible	$\frac{\sqrt{3}}{2}\sin\theta$	$\frac{\sqrt{15}}{2}\sin\theta\cos\theta$	$\frac{\sqrt{42}}{8}(\sin\theta)(5\cos^2\theta-1)$
$m=\pm 2$	Impossible	Impossible	$\frac{\sqrt{15}}{4}\sin^2\theta$	$\frac{\sqrt{105}}{4}\sin^2\theta\cos\theta$
$m=\pm 3$	Impossible	Impossible	Impossible	$\frac{\sqrt{70}}{8}\sin^3\theta$

Item	Complex	Real
$m=0$	$\left(\frac{1}{2\pi}\right)^{1/2}$	$\left(\frac{1}{2\pi}\right)^{1/2}$
$m>0$	$\left(\frac{1}{2\pi}\right)^{1/2}e^{im\phi}$	$\frac{\cos m\phi}{\sqrt{\pi}}$ and $\frac{\sin m\phi}{\sqrt{\pi}}$
$m<0$	$\left(\frac{1}{2\pi}\right)^{1/2}e^{-im\phi}$	

† Pauling, L. and E. B. Wilson, Jr. *Introduction to Quantum Mechanics*. New York: McGraw-Hill Book Company, 1935, pp. 133–4.

be zero to keep Φ single-valued. The normalization constant N_ϕ in (14.116) is found thus:

$$1 = N_\phi^2 \int_0^{2\pi} e^{\mp im\phi} e^{\pm im\phi} \, d\phi = 2\pi N_\phi^2$$

$$N_\phi = \left(\frac{1}{2\pi}\right)^{1/2} \tag{14.117}$$

The sign of m^2 in (14.114) cannot be negative, for solutions of $d^2\Phi/d\phi^2 = n^2\Phi$ are of the form $e^{-n\phi}$, which is not cyclic to fit the cyclic variable ϕ and thus would not give a single value to Φ.

The functions $\Theta(\theta)$ that satisfy (14.115) are called the *associated Legendre polynomials*. These are not infinite series because the requirement that $\Theta(\theta)$ be finite at $\theta = 0$ and $\theta = \pi$ requires the series to be terminated, as for the harmonic oscillator. The special values of $l(l+1)$ that terminate the potentially infinite series solution of (14.115) are the eigenvalues of (14.115). Table 14.2 contains several of the simplest solutions $\Theta_{lm}(\theta)\ \Phi_m(\phi)$ of (14.113), as substitution will show. The functions in Table 14.2 are normalized and orthogonal. Figure 14.3 shows the absolute values of some of these angular functions when the ϕ-functions are real (sines and cosines). The wave functions $\Theta_{3m}(\theta)\Phi_m(\phi)$ are very clearly explained in the literature.[5] The quantum number l corresponds to the azimuthal quantum number introduced by Sommerfeld to explain the angular momentum of the electron in elliptical Bohr orbits. For historical reasons, states with no orbital angular momentum ($l = 0$) are called s states; those with $l = 1$ are called p states; with $l = 2$, d states; with $l = 3$, f states; with $l = 4$, g states; and so on. The magnetic quantum number m indicates the component of angular momentum along the z-axis, the direction of which is specified by a uniform magnetic field external to the atom. The allowed values of m are $+l, (l-1), (l-2), \ldots, 1, 0, -1, \ldots -l$. If the external field does not exist, then $2l + 1$ states are degenerate (have the same energy).

The reasons for calling l an angular momentum quantum number are explained in Section 14.7. Here it is perhaps sufficient to note that the effective potential energy in (14.112) is

$$V' = V(r) + \frac{l(l+1)\hbar^2}{2mr^2} \tag{14.118}$$

The total effective force along the direction r is thus

$$F_r = -\frac{\partial V'}{\partial r} = -\frac{\partial V}{\partial r} + \frac{l(l+1)\hbar^2}{mr^3} \tag{14.119}$$

where the final term represents an addition to the expected force due to $V(r)$.

[5] H. G. Friedman, Jr., G. R. Choppin, and D. G. Feuerbacher, *J. Chem. Ed.* **41,** 354 (1964); C. Becker, *J. Chem. Ed.* **41,** 358 (1964); E. A. Ogryzlo, *J. Chem. Ed.* **42,** 150 (1965).

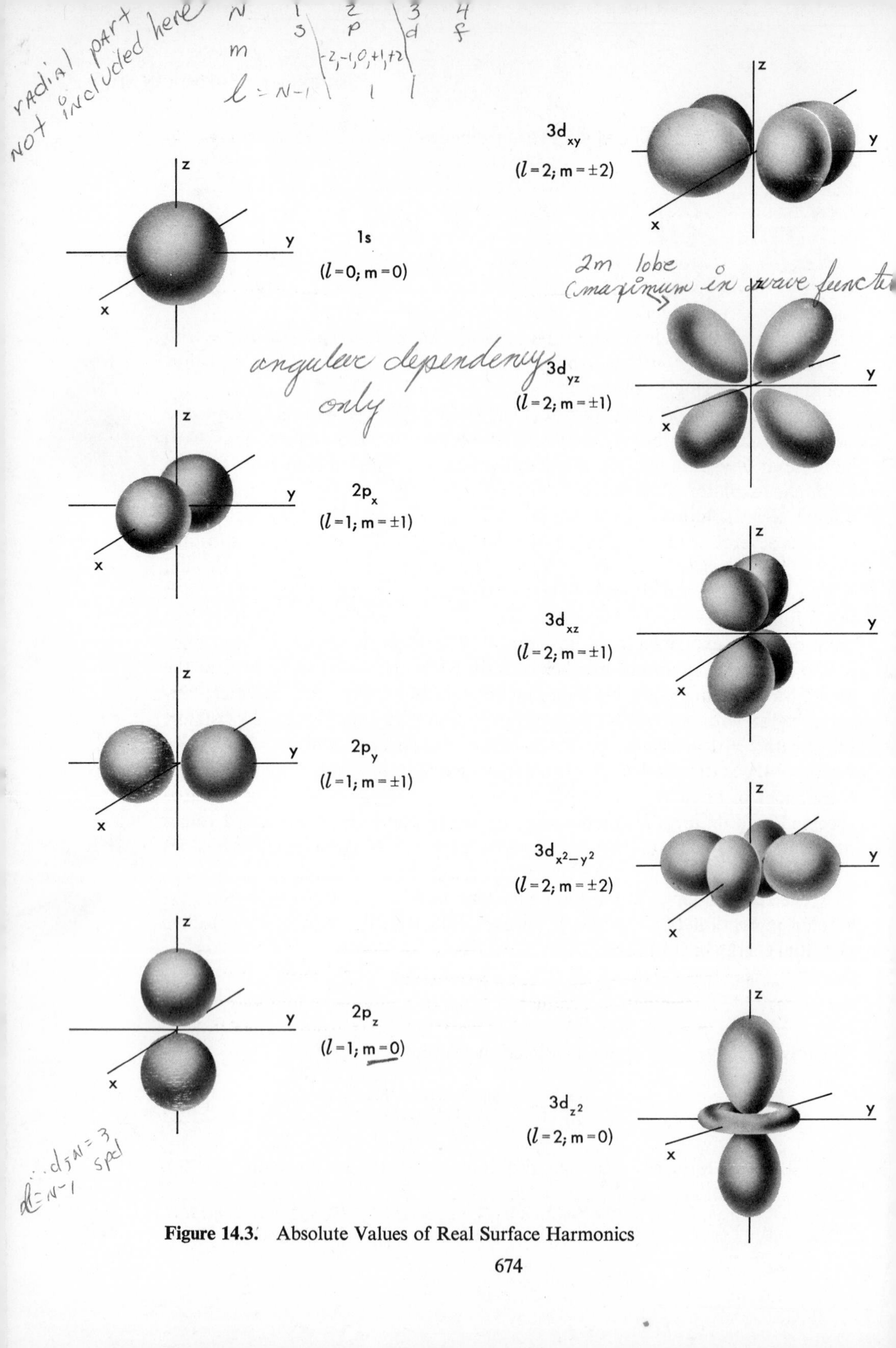

Figure 14.3. Absolute Values of Real Surface Harmonics

The Bohr theory, through (13.29), predicts the square of the angular momentum to be $n^2\hbar^2$, but spectroscopic observations required that the form be empirically adjusted to $l(l+1)\hbar^2$, a form that results naturally with the associated Legendre polynomials. Classically, the angular momentum of a mass m revolving at a distance r at an angular speed ω is $mr^2\omega$. If $(mr^2\omega)^2 = l(l+1)\hbar^2$, then the final term of (14.119) is $mr\omega^2$, which classically is the force needed to keep m at the distance r from its axis. Accordingly, the last term of (14.118) is an effective rotational potential.

The radial equation (14.112) has interesting behavior at $r = \infty$ and $r = 0$. With (14.96) and $E_{\mathrm{H}} = E_n$, (14.112) is

$$\frac{d^2R}{dr^2} + \frac{2}{r}\frac{dR}{dr} + \left[\frac{2mE_n}{\hbar^2} + \frac{2m\mathbf{Z}e^2}{\hbar^2 4\pi\epsilon_0 r} - \frac{l(l+1)}{r^2}\right]R = 0 \qquad (14.120)$$

Since dR/dr is finite, at large r (14.112) is approximately

$$\frac{d^2R}{dr^2} = -\frac{2mE_n}{\hbar^2}R = \frac{2m\,|E_n|}{\hbar^2}R \qquad (14.121)$$

for $E_n < 0$. It is clear from (14.121) that the asymptotic form of R is simply

$$R = \exp\left[-\left(\frac{2m\,|E_n|}{\hbar^2}\right)^{1/2} r\right] \qquad (14.122)$$

for a positive sign within the brackets of (14.122) would make R infinite at large r. On the other hand, near $r = 0$, the form of (14.120) approaches

$$\frac{d^2R}{dr^2} = l(l+1)R \qquad (14.123)$$

so that to fit (14.123) the form of R is

$$R = r^l f(r) \qquad (14.124)$$

The function $f(r)$ is a polynomial rather than an infinite series because, to keep R finite at large r, the series must be terminated. As for $\Theta(\theta)$ and the harmonic oscillator, termination produces a quantum number n and eigenvalues E_n of the energy in a natural mathematical way that is not arbitrary like Bohr's. In joules per atom, the energy of a bound stationary state of H is

$$E_n = -\left(\frac{m\mathbf{Z}^2e^4}{2(4\pi\epsilon_0)^2\hbar^2}\right)\left(\frac{1}{n^2}\right) \qquad (14.125)$$

where $n = 1, 2, 3, \ldots \infty$. It is also necessary that n exceed l. Amazingly, (14.125) is the same as the Bohr result in (13.34). The E_n of (14.125) is the E_{H} of (14.112) and (14.109) when H is in a stationary state with $E_n < 0$. To E_n must be added any translational energy $E_X + E_Y + E_Z$ by motion of the center of mass along x_0, y_0, and z_0.

Qualitative discussions of wave functions and the probability density of matter are often guided by the number of nodes (zeroes) in the wave function. Since the functions sin $n\phi$ and cos $n\phi$ reach zero $2n$ times in the range $0 \leqslant \phi < 2\pi$, the real forms of $\Phi_m(\phi)$ in Table 14.2 are expected to have $2m$ nodes. Projecting the wave functions of Figures 14.3 on the x-y plane shows the $2m$ nodes and the $2m$ lobes (maxima in wave function) between the $2m$ nodes. The number of nodes in $\Theta_{lm}(\theta)$ of Table 14.2 is $l - m$; that is, in the range $0 < \theta < \pi$, $\Theta_{lm}(\theta)$ reaches zero $l - |m|$ times.

The polynomials $f(r)$ in (14.124) reach zero $n - l - 1$ times in the range $0 < r < \infty$. These nodes occur rather close to $r = 0$. As a result, for many chemical problems, it is sufficient to approximate R by its leading term, the one containing r to the greatest power, which is $n - 1$. Radially nodeless wave functions of the form

$$\rho^{n^*-1} e^{-\mathbf{Z}^*\rho/n^*} \Theta_{lm}(\theta)\Phi_m(\phi) \tag{14.126}$$

are called *Slater orbitals*. The parameter ρ is

$$\rho = r\left(\frac{me^2}{4\pi\epsilon_0\hbar^2}\right) \tag{14.127}$$

The angular dependence of (14.126) is not an approximation, but n^* is an effective value of n and $\mathbf{Z}^*$ is an effective value of nuclear charge. Since Slater orbitals are used mainly for polyelectronic atoms, $\mathbf{Z}^*$ represents the nuclear charge after its effect is partially neutralized by electrons whose average position is closer to the nucleus than the electron with orbital (14.126). Empirical values of n^* and $\mathbf{Z}^*$ are available for atoms and ions.[6]

14.7 OPERATORS AND EIGENVALUES

A quantum mechanical operator acts on an eigenfunction to draw out an eigenvalue of the system. For example, the Hamiltonian operator $\mathbf{H}$ acts on the stationary-state wave function of a system to give the eigenvalue E of energy of the system in the state specified by the wave function u; the mathematical statement is $\mathbf{H}u = Eu$. Section 14.4 has stated this in more general terms for an operator $\mathbf{w}_{op}$ with eigenvalues w_n such that $w_{op}\psi_n = w_n\psi_n$ when the eigenfunction of the state is ψ_n.

One way of finding an eigenvalue is to solve for it in the form

$$w_n = \frac{\mathbf{w}_{op}\psi_n}{\psi_n} \tag{14.128}$$

[6] A. Tubis, *Phys. Rev.* **102**, 1049 (1956).

Really all that is needed is ψ_n and its derivatives at just one point. (The so-called *local energy method* uses this approach by guessing ψ_n and its derivatives in $\mathbf{H}\psi$ at many points in order to get a suitably accurate value of E. Often a million points are needed to get E within one part in 10^3. When various efficient statistical techniques are used to improve E, the calculation tends to become very much like the variational method to be described in Section 14.11.) If the correct form of ψ_n is somehow known, then (14.128) is quite correct, of course. However, wave functions are scarce because the equations like (14.128) involve *two* unknowns per equation: ψ_n and the eigenvalue w_n. Another more common method of calculating an eigenvalue is to perform the integration

$$\int \psi_n^* \mathbf{w}_{\text{op}} \psi_n \, d\tau = \int \psi_n^* w_n \psi_n \, d\tau \tag{14.129}$$

where $\mathbf{w}_{\text{op}}\psi_n = w_n\psi_n$ by supposition. Since w_n is a constant, the result of (14.129) is just w_n if ψ_n is normalized as in (14.37). When the wave function ψ of a system includes several eigenfunctions, then integration can find the expectation value of a particular eigenvalue. If the wave function of the systems is $\psi = \sum_n a_n\psi_n$ and if the eigenvalue of interest is w_m, then the expectation value of w_m is

$$\int (a_m\psi_m)^* \mathbf{w}_{\text{op}} \left(\sum_n a_n\psi_n\right) d\tau = \sum_n a_m^* a_n \int \psi_m^* w_n \psi_n \, d\tau = \sum_n a_m^* a_n w_n \int \psi_m^* \psi_n \, d\tau \tag{14.130}$$

If $w_m \neq w_n$ so that, by (14.42), $\int \psi_m^*\psi_n \, d\tau = 0$ then the value of (14.130) is $a_m^* a_m w_m$ because terms with $n \neq m$ do not contribute to the sum. The product $a_m^* a_m = |a_m|^2$ is the probability that the system is in state m and that w_m will be observed out of the spectrum of eigenvalues w_n allowed by ψ.

Whenever operators are used, a calculation like one of these above is implied. The result will always be a real quantity because all quantum mechanical operators are Hermitian and thus obey (14.40). Nevertheless, many interesting results can be stated merely in operator language without recourse to (14.128), (14.129), or (14.130). For example, if $\mathbf{v}_{\text{op}}$ and $\mathbf{w}_{\text{op}}$ are operators for a pair of canonically conjugate variables, there is the general rule (in operator language)

$$\mathbf{w}_{\text{op}}\mathbf{v}_{\text{op}} - \mathbf{v}_{\text{op}}\mathbf{w}_{\text{op}} = \pm i\hbar \tag{14.131}$$

As a pair, the variables with operators $\mathbf{v}_{\text{op}}$ and $\mathbf{w}_{\text{op}}$ are subject to the Heisenberg uncertainty principle. The operators in (14.131) are said to be noncommuting for they do not follow the usual law of multiplication: $2 \times 3 - 3 \times 2 = 0$. However, if two operators $\mathbf{H}$ and $\mathbf{w}_{\text{op}}$ do commute so that

$$\mathbf{w}_{\text{op}}\mathbf{H} - \mathbf{H}\mathbf{w}_{\text{op}} = 0 \tag{14.132}$$

then as a pair they are not subject to the uncertainty principle, and eigenvalues of $\mathbf{H}$ and $\mathbf{w}_{\text{op}}$ can be observed on the same system.

Although (14.132) is not limited to use with the Hamiltonian operator, the case when $\mathbf{H}$ is the Hamiltonian operator is especially important. For then the eigenvalues of $\mathbf{w}_{\mathrm{op}}$ are constants of the system and, like the energy E, are independent of time. It is tedious to show that there is one set of eigenfunctions for each operator $\mathbf{H}$ and $\mathbf{w}_{\mathrm{op}}$ when (14.132) is true. The converse is, however, easily illustrated. If ψ_n is one of a set of functions such that $\mathbf{H}\psi_n = E_n\psi_n$ and $\mathbf{w}_{\mathrm{op}}\psi_n = w_n\psi_n$, and if (as is commonly postulated in quantum mechanics) the full set of ψ_n's forms a complete set such that any function f can be expressed as $f = \sum_n a_n\psi_n$, then, with care concerning the order in which the operators work (e.g., imagine it to be differentiation), it follows that

$$\begin{aligned}(\mathbf{w}_{\mathrm{op}}\mathbf{H} - \mathbf{H}\mathbf{w}_{\mathrm{op}})f &= \sum_n a_n(\mathbf{w}_{\mathrm{op}}E_n - \mathbf{H}w_n)\psi_n \\ &= \sum_n a_n(E_n\mathbf{w}_{\mathrm{op}}\psi_n - w_n\mathbf{H}\psi_n) \\ &= \sum_n a_n(E_n w_n - w_n E_n)\psi_n = 0\end{aligned}$$

The result is zero because w_n and E_n are constants. Thus, if ψ_n is an eigenfunction of two operators, the operators commute [that is, (14.132) is true].

Position $\mathbf{x}$ and linear momentum $\mathbf{p}_x$ are operators that do not commute; they follow (14.131) rather than (14.132). By the rules of Table 14.1, when time and position are independent variables for the wave function,

$$\begin{aligned}(\mathbf{p}_x\mathbf{x} - \mathbf{x}\mathbf{p}_x)f &= -i\hbar\frac{\partial}{\partial x}(xf) - x\left(-i\hbar\frac{\partial f}{\partial x}\right) \\ &= -i\hbar\left(x\frac{\partial f}{\partial x} + f - x\frac{\partial f}{\partial x}\right) \\ &= -i\hbar f\end{aligned}$$

as implied by (14.131). In terms of operators alone, this is

$$\mathbf{p}_x\mathbf{x} - \mathbf{x}\mathbf{p}_x = -i\hbar \tag{14.133}$$

It is very easy to show similarly that $\mathbf{x}\mathbf{p}_x - \mathbf{p}_x\mathbf{x} = +i\hbar$.

14.8 ANGULAR MOMENTUM

Classical angular momentum is the vector

$$\boldsymbol{r} \times \boldsymbol{p} = \begin{vmatrix} \mathrm{i} & \mathrm{j} & \mathrm{k} \\ x & y & z \\ p_x & p_y & p_z \end{vmatrix} = \begin{matrix} \mathrm{i}\,(yp_z - zp_y) \\ +\,\mathrm{j}\,(zp_x - xp_z) \\ +\,\mathrm{k}\,(xp_y - yp_x) \end{matrix} \tag{14.134}$$

For circular motion at an angular speed of ω(radians/sec), p is $mr\omega$ and (14.134) yields $mr^2\omega$ as in Section 13.4. There is no difficulty about the order of factors when (14.134) is made a quantum mechanical operator, for y and p_z commute, as do other pairs. In terms of operators, the components of angular momentum are

$$\mathbf{M}_x = -i\hbar\left(y\frac{\partial}{\partial z} - z\frac{\partial}{\partial y}\right) \tag{14.135}$$

$$\mathbf{M}_y = -i\hbar\left(z\frac{\partial}{\partial x} - x\frac{\partial}{\partial z}\right) \tag{14.136}$$

$$\mathbf{M}_z = -i\hbar\left(x\frac{\partial}{\partial y} - y\frac{\partial}{\partial x}\right) = -i\hbar\frac{\partial}{\partial \phi} \tag{14.137}$$

where $\mathbf{M}_z$ has been stated in both Cartesian and spherical polar coordinates. That $\Phi_m(\phi)$ is an eigenfunction of $\mathbf{M}_z$ follows from (14.116) and (14.137), for

$$\mathbf{M}_z\Phi_m = -i\hbar\frac{\partial}{\partial\phi}(N_\phi e^{\pm im\phi}) = \pm m\hbar\Phi_m$$

That is, $\pm m\hbar$ is the eigenvalue of the z-component of angular momentum. It is also clear that $\mathbf{H}$ and $\mathbf{M}_z$ commute, for $\mathbf{M}_z$ operates only on $\Phi_m(\phi)$ to give constants that are untouched by $\mathbf{H}$, while $\mathbf{H}$ in extracting the constant E from the wave function does not alter $\Phi_m(\phi)$. It can be shown, likewise, that $\mathbf{H}$ commutes with $\mathbf{M}^2 = \mathbf{M}_x^2 + \mathbf{M}_y^2 + \mathbf{M}_z^2$ when $V = V(r)$ and that in general $\mathbf{M}_z$ commutes with $\mathbf{M}^2$. This last remark means that there is no theoretical limit to the accuracy with which the square of the total angular momentum and its component along any direction can each be observed for the same system.

The operators $\mathbf{M}_x$, $\mathbf{M}_y$, and $\mathbf{M}_z$ for the three components of angular momentum have several interrelationships that allow various eigenvalues to be calculated without a knowledge of their eigenfunctions. Moreover, various general properties of angular momentum can be established at the same time.

The first interrelationship is

$$\mathbf{M}_x\mathbf{M}_y - \mathbf{M}_y\mathbf{M}_x = i\hbar\mathbf{M}_z \tag{14.138}$$

The proof is established by reference to (14.135) to (14.137), for

$$\begin{aligned}\mathbf{M}_x\mathbf{M}_y &= (-i\hbar)^2\left(y\frac{\partial}{\partial z} - z\frac{\partial}{\partial y}\right)\left(z\frac{\partial}{\partial x} - x\frac{\partial}{\partial z}\right)\\ &= (-i\hbar)^2\left[y\frac{\partial}{\partial z}\left(z\frac{\partial}{\partial x} - x\frac{\partial}{\partial z}\right) - z\frac{\partial}{\partial y}\left(z\frac{\partial}{\partial x} - x\frac{\partial}{\partial z}\right)\right]\\ &= (-i\hbar)^2\left[y\frac{\partial}{\partial x} + yz\frac{\partial^2}{\partial z\partial x} - xy\frac{\partial^2}{\partial z^2} - z^2\frac{\partial^2}{\partial y\partial x} + xz\frac{\partial^2}{\partial y\partial z}\right]\end{aligned}$$

while

$$\mathbf{M}_y\mathbf{M}_x = (-i\hbar)^2\left(z\frac{\partial}{\partial x} - x\frac{\partial}{\partial z}\right)\left(y\frac{\partial}{\partial z} - z\frac{\partial}{\partial y}\right)$$
$$= (-i\hbar)^2\left(yz\frac{\partial^2}{\partial x\partial z} - z^2\frac{\partial^2}{\partial x\partial y} - xy\frac{\partial^2}{\partial z^2} + x\frac{\partial}{\partial y} + xz\frac{\partial^2}{\partial z\partial y}\right)$$

Hence, as already stated in (14.138),

$$\mathbf{M}_x\mathbf{M}_y - \mathbf{M}_y\mathbf{M}_x = (-i\hbar)^2\left(y\frac{\partial}{\partial x} - x\frac{\partial}{\partial y}\right) = i\hbar\mathbf{M}_z$$

It is equally straightforward to show that

$$\mathbf{M}_y\mathbf{M}_z - \mathbf{M}_z\mathbf{M}_y = i\hbar\mathbf{M}_x \tag{14.139}$$
$$\mathbf{M}_z\mathbf{M}_x - \mathbf{M}_x\mathbf{M}_z = i\hbar\mathbf{M}_y \tag{14.140}$$

Equations (14.138), (14.139), and (14.140) are alike in the sense that one leads to the next when the subscripts x, y, z are permuted cyclically (if $x \longrightarrow y$, then $y \longrightarrow z$ and $z \longrightarrow x$).

The operators

$$\mathbf{M}_+ = \mathbf{M}_x + i\mathbf{M}_y \tag{14.141}$$
$$\mathbf{M}_- = \mathbf{M}_x - i\mathbf{M}_y \tag{14.142}$$

have the interesting property that

$$\mathbf{M}_z\mathbf{M}_\pm = \mathbf{M}_\pm(\mathbf{M}_z \pm \hbar) \tag{14.143}$$

The proof of (14.143) begins with the use of (14.140) and (14.139) in

$$\begin{aligned}\mathbf{M}_z\mathbf{M}_\pm &= \mathbf{M}_z\mathbf{M}_x \pm i\mathbf{M}_z\mathbf{M}_y \\ &= (i\hbar\mathbf{M}_y + \mathbf{M}_x\mathbf{M}_z) \pm i(\mathbf{M}_y\mathbf{M}_z - i\hbar\mathbf{M}_x) \\ &= i\hbar(\mathbf{M}_y \mp i\mathbf{M}_x) + (\mathbf{M}_x \pm i\mathbf{M}_y)\mathbf{M}_z \\ &= \hbar(\pm\mathbf{M}_x + i\mathbf{M}_y) + \mathbf{M}_\pm\mathbf{M}_z \\ &= \mathbf{M}_\pm\mathbf{M}_z \pm \hbar(\mathbf{M}_x \pm i\mathbf{M}_y) \\ &= \mathbf{M}_\pm(\mathbf{M}_z \pm \hbar)\end{aligned}$$

If $\mathbf{\Phi}_m$ is the eigenfunction of $\mathbf{M}_z$, then $\mathbf{M}_z\mathbf{\Phi}_m = \pm m\hbar\mathbf{\Phi}_m$ as noted above. That is, by (14.143),

$$\begin{aligned}\mathbf{M}_z\mathbf{M}_+\mathbf{\Phi}_m &= \mathbf{M}_+(\mathbf{M}_z + \hbar)\mathbf{\Phi}_m \\ &= \mathbf{M}_+(\pm m\hbar + \hbar)\mathbf{\Phi}_m \\ &= (\pm m + 1)\hbar\mathbf{M}_+\mathbf{\Phi}_m\end{aligned} \tag{14.144}$$

But (14.144) says that $\mathbf{M}_+\mathbf{\Phi}_m$ is an eigenfunction of $\mathbf{M}_z$ with the eigenvalue

$(\pm m + 1)\hbar$. After $\mathbf{M}_+$ operates on Φ_m, the eigenvalue of the z-component of angular momentum ($\mathbf{M}_z$ extracts the z-component) is increased by $\hbar$. For this reason, $\mathbf{M}_+$ is called the *step-up operator*. The operator $\mathbf{M}_-$, for analogous reasons, is called the *step-down operator* because the z-component of angular momentum, as found by $\mathbf{M}_z$, is $(\pm m - 1)\hbar$ after $\mathbf{M}_-$ has operated on Φ_m.

It is possible to show that the square of the z-component of angular momentum is less than the square of the total angular momentum. Since the latter is bounded by the finiteness of matter, there must then be a maximum value of the z-component of angular momentum for any system. That is, for a given value of l, there is a maximum value of m. If $\mathbf{M}_+$ should operate on the eigenfunction of the state of maximum z-component of angular momentum $\Phi_{\max}$, the result would be an increase by unity in a quantity that was already at its maximum; hence $\mathbf{M}_+\Phi_{\max} = 0$ because this system with a larger z-component is impossible. For similar reasons, $\mathbf{M}_-\Phi_{\min} = 0$. These two results are needed below.

The average value of $\mathbf{M}_-\mathbf{M}_+$ establishes a connection between the square of the total angular momentum and the maximum value of the z-component. By (14.141), (14.142), and then (14.138)

$$\begin{aligned}
\mathbf{M}_-\mathbf{M}_+ &= (\mathbf{M}_x - i\mathbf{M}_y)(\mathbf{M}_x + i\mathbf{M}_y) \\
&= \mathbf{M}_x^2 + \mathbf{M}_y^2 + i(\mathbf{M}_x\mathbf{M}_y - \mathbf{M}_y\mathbf{M}_x) \\
&= \mathbf{M}_x^2 + \mathbf{M}_y^2 + i(i\hbar\mathbf{M}_z) \\
&= \mathbf{M}_x^2 + \mathbf{M}_y^2 + \mathbf{M}_z^2 - \mathbf{M}_z^2 - \hbar\mathbf{M}_z
\end{aligned}$$

But since the square of the total angular momentum is the operator

$$\mathbf{M}^2 = \mathbf{M}_x^2 + \mathbf{M}_y^2 + \mathbf{M}_z^2 \tag{14.145}$$

if follows that

$$\mathbf{M}_-\mathbf{M}_+ = \mathbf{M}^2 - \mathbf{M}_z^2 - \hbar\mathbf{M}_z \tag{14.146}$$

Since $\mathbf{M}_+\Phi_{\max} = 0$ when the z-component is its maximum, it follows from (14.146) that for a system with total value M and maximum z-component m_+,

$$\begin{aligned}
0 &= \hbar^2 M^2 - \hbar^2 m_+^2 - \hbar(\hbar m_+) \\
m_+(m_+ + 1) &= M^2
\end{aligned} \tag{14.147}$$

Similarly, for the same system with minimum z-component m_-, since $\mathbf{M}_-\Phi_{\min} = 0$ when the z-component is at a minimum, as above

$$\begin{aligned}
\mathbf{M}_+\mathbf{M}_- &= (\mathbf{M}_x + i\mathbf{M}_y)(\mathbf{M}_x - i\mathbf{M}_y) \\
&= \mathbf{M}_x^2 + \mathbf{M}_y^2 + i(\mathbf{M}_y\mathbf{M}_x - \mathbf{M}_x\mathbf{M}_y) \\
&= (\mathbf{M}_x^2 + \mathbf{M}_y^2 + \mathbf{M}_z^2) - \mathbf{M}_z^2 + i(-i\hbar\mathbf{M}_z) \\
&= \mathbf{M}^2 - \mathbf{M}_z^2 + \hbar\mathbf{M}_z
\end{aligned}$$

whence

$$0 = \hbar^2 M^2 - \hbar^2 m_-^2 + \hbar^2 m_-$$

$$m_-(m_- - 1) = M^2 \tag{14.148}$$

By (14.147) and (14.148) for this system with $\hbar^2 M^2$ as the square of its total angular momentum, $m_+(m_+ + 1) = m_-(m_- - 1)$. Solution of this quadratic for m_+ gives

$$m_+ = \frac{-1 \pm \sqrt{(1 - 2m_-)^2}}{2} = -\frac{1}{2} \pm \left(\frac{1}{2} - m_-\right)$$

The choice of lower sign yields $m_+ = -1 + m_-$, which is ridiculous since m_+ is a maximum value while m_- is a minimum value of m. The choice of upper signs gives the eminently reasonable result that

$$m_+ = -m_- \tag{14.149}$$

Because of the properties of $\mathbf{M}_+$ and $\mathbf{M}_-$ and their ability to use the eigenfunctions of $\mathbf{M}_z$, the eigenvalues of the z-component of angular momentum form a spectrum of values that progress, by steps of $\pm\hbar$, to larger or smaller values. Because of (14.149), this range of values is symmetrical about a midpoint at zero, with the number of states having m greater than zero equal to the number having m less than zero because of (14.149). The only possibilities in accord with these conclusions are (a) integral values of m, the values being m_+, $m_+ - 1$, $\ldots + 1, 0, -1, -2, \ldots -m_+$; or (b) half-integral values of m, the values being m_+, $m_+ - 1, \ldots + \frac{3}{2}, +\frac{1}{2}, -\frac{1}{2}, -\frac{3}{2}, -\frac{5}{2}, \ldots -m_+$.

This development shows that angular momentum $\mathbf{M}$ and its component $\mathbf{M}_z$ have a discrete spectrum of eigenvalues, never a continuum. What is truly remarkable is the attainment of these sets of eigenvalues without a knowledge of the eigenfunctions. These conclusions apply to any quantum mechanical system and are especially important for elementary (or fundamental) particles. *Bosons* are elementary particles with intrinsic angular momenta (spin) that are zero or integers. *Fermions*, on the other hand, are elementary particles with half-integral spin. These classes of particle behave quite differently.

The name *angular momentum* is closely related to classical ideas for the revolution of an electron around a nucleus, and the magnetic dipole or moment associated with this kind of motion is easily pictured as the magnetic field caused by a solenoid of one loop, the loop being the orbit of the electron. This is the attitude of the Bohr theory of the atom. The more general and truer attitude is merely to acknowledge the existence of certain quantized states. Just as $|u|^2$ tells a probability density of matter rather than exact location of particles, the classical concept of angular momentum has likewise suffered a revision that leaves only a number of states, each less well characterized than classical mechanics would allow. In the absence of a preferred direction specified by an external magnetic field, $2m_+ + 1$ is the order of degeneracy of a system having a maximum possible z-component of angular momentum of m_+. For integral values of m_+, the order of degeneracy is odd; for half-integral values of m_+, it is even (but not zero). The orbital angular momentum quantum number l is an integer and its various z-components are $+l$, $(l - 1), \ldots +1, 0, -1, \ldots -l$. The order of degeneracy in the absence of a magnetic field is $2l + 1$.

The name *spin* originated in 1925 when Uhlenbeck and Goudsmit were able to explain the spectra of H and more complex atoms by supposing that the electron had an intrinsic magnetic moment. This moment was attributed to rotation of the electrons as though its spherical charge density were acting like the current in a solenoid. While the name remains, there is no longer any serious attempt to find a classical analogy to explain the magnetic behavior of the electron.

The existence of the magnetic properties of the electron was inferred from the various energy states exhibited by atoms as they absorbed and emitted photons in the presence of electric and magnetic fields within the atom or imposed on it from the surroundings. The first direct evidence of the electron's magnetic moment was found by Stern and Gerlach in 1922. They reported that a beam of gaseous Ag atoms was divided into two distinct groups after passage through an inhomogeneous magnetic field. The separation was proportional to the rate of change in field intensity with respect to a direction perpendicular to the beam's direction. Classically only a broadening of the beam was expected because the magnetic moment presumably might take any angle with respect to the field and thus cause a continuously variable interaction and path. The observation of just two well resolved and distinct beams was clear evidence of a quantum of something—angle, momentum, ... With a degeneracy of order two, $2m_+ + 1$ is 2, and $m_+ = 1/2$. That is, the maximum angular momentum of Ag is $+1/2$, while its minimum is $-1/2$. These values are, of course, attributable to the odd electron on Ag. Beams of atoms of H, Li, Na, K, Rb, Cs, Cu, and Au behave just like Ag.

14.9 EXCLUSION PRINCIPLE

The half-integral spin of the electron results automatically from Dirac's relativistic wave equation for the electron (1928). This same equation also predicts the existence of a negative energy state to correspond to every positive energy state of the kind observed for a real physical electron. When such a state of negative energy is not full, it acts like a positive electron and annihilates any electron that enters it. At the same time, radiation of energy $2\,mc^2$ is generated, where m is the mass of one electron. The reason that a real electron does not generally disappear into nothingness in a negative energy state is that it cannot do so. Almost all such states are occupied. If a negative energy state could accommodate any number of electrons, annihilation of real electrons would be commonplace. In fact, without some sort of control on occupancy, it would be impossible to fill all the negative energy states. It is thus necessary to postulate that only one electron can exist in any negative energy state. Since positive energy states are of the same kind as negative ones, the Dirac view suggests that the number of electrons per positive energy state is either one or none.

Pauli in 1925 found it necessary in explaining optical spectra of atoms to assign four different quantum numbers to electrons. Besides n, l, and m (the z-component of l), he invented a hitherto unknown quantum number that distinguished states that would otherwise be doubly degenerate. His fourth quantum number of an electron in an atom is the z-component of the electron's spin. With these four quantum numbers he could account for the spectra of atoms and for the periodic table of elements by saying that every electron in an atom must have a unique set of four quantum numbers. That is, any possible electronic state can be filled by only one electron or none at all.

The *Pauli exclusion principle* has a very wide application and is stated most generally: Every wave function is antisymmetric with respect to an interchange of identical or indistinguishable fermions. If particles are indistinguishable, their Hamiltonian operator is unaffected by relabeling the particles or by interchanging their coordinates of position, momentum, spin, and so on. That is, $\mathbf{H}(1, 2) = \mathbf{H}(2, 1)$, where the interchange of 1 and 2 signifies the interchange of coordinates of identical particles. If a state is nondegenerate, it has only one wave function $\psi(1, 2)$. An interchange of particles cannot change the nature of ψ except perhaps for a factor so that $\psi(2, 1) = c\psi(1, 2)$. Another interchange gives $\psi(1, 2) = c\,\psi(2, 1) = c^2\,\psi(1, 2)$. That is, $c^2 = 1$ and $c = \pm 1$. If $\psi(2, 1) = +\psi(1, 2)$, the wave function is said to be *symmetric* with respect to the interchange of particles; if $\psi(2, 1) = -\psi(1, 2)$, it is said to be *antisymmetric*. The symmetry of ψ is always preserved, for in any small time interval δt, the change in ψ is, by the Schrödinger equation (13.53),

$$\delta\psi = -\frac{i}{\hbar}(\mathbf{H}\psi)\delta t \tag{14.150}$$

Since $\mathbf{H}(1, 2) = \mathbf{H}(2, 1)$, the symmetry of $\delta\psi$ is that of ψ, for δt is always positive when (14.150) is adequate. The antisymmetry or symmetry of a wave function tells whether it changes sign or not when the coordinates of two indistinguishable particles are interchanged, while parity (Section 13.9), odd or even, tells whether the sign of a wave function, expressed in terms of Cartesian coordinates, changes or not when all coordinates change sign. The wave function of a real system is entirely symmetric or entirely antisymmetric with respect to interchanges of identical particles; it cannot be partly symmetric and partly antisymmetric.

Although matrix methods are particularly suitable for discussing all forms of angular momentum and especially spin, it is most convenient here to develop a mathematical description of spin as a function capable of two values: $\alpha(\omega)$

for $+\frac{1}{2}\hbar$ and $\beta(\omega)$ for $-\frac{1}{2}\hbar$.[7] These spin functions are orthogonal and normalized, for

$$\left.\begin{aligned}\int \alpha(\omega)\alpha(\omega)\,d\omega = \int \beta(\omega)\beta(\omega)\,d\omega = 1\\ \text{orthogonal:} \int \alpha(\omega)\beta(\omega)\,d\omega = 0\end{aligned}\right\} \tag{14.151}$$

Here ω is a variable formally like a position coordinate. Spin and its artificial variable ω differ, however, from position in that spin can assume only discrete values. A hydrogen-like electron with quantum number n, l, m, and $s = +\frac{1}{2}$ has a wave function $R_{nl}(r)\Theta_{lm}(\theta)\Phi_m(\phi)\alpha(\omega)$. If $s = -\frac{1}{2}$, $\beta(\omega)$ replaces $\alpha(\omega)$.

The spin functions of two electrons are: $\alpha(1)\alpha(2)$ and $\beta(1)\beta(2)$ if their spins are alike; $\alpha(1)\beta(2)$ and $\beta(1)\alpha(2)$ if their spins differ. There are three symmetric spin functions for two electrons, namely,

$$\left.\begin{aligned}&\alpha(1)\alpha(2)\\ &\frac{1}{\sqrt{2}}[\alpha(1)\beta(2) + \beta(1)\alpha(2)]\\ &\beta(1)\beta(2)\end{aligned}\right\} \tag{14.152}$$

The factor $2^{-1/2}$ is a normalization factor. Interchanging coordinates in each of (14.152) yields the same spin wave function; for example: $1/\sqrt{2}[\alpha(2)\beta(1) + \beta(2)\alpha(1)]$. Only one antisymmetric spin wave function of two electrons exists:

$$\frac{1}{\sqrt{2}}[\alpha(1)\beta(2) - \beta(1)\alpha(2)] \tag{14.153}$$

Interchanging coordinates yields

$$\frac{1}{\sqrt{2}}[\alpha(2)\beta(1) - \beta(2)\alpha(1)] = -\frac{1}{\sqrt{2}}[\alpha(1)\beta(2) - \beta(1)\alpha(2)]$$

This antisymmetric function is conveniently expressed in the form of a Slater determinant

$$\frac{1}{\sqrt{2}}\begin{vmatrix}\alpha(1) & \beta(1)\\ \alpha(2) & \beta(2)\end{vmatrix} \tag{14.154}$$

The general problem of generating antisymmetric spin wave functions has been solved,[8] but is beyond this discussion in need and difficulty.

Since every electronic wave function must be antisymmetric, the spin of an electron being a half-integral value, a polyelectronic wave function is conveniently expressed in the form of a Slater determinant

---

[7] Pauling, L. and E. B. Wilson, Jr., *Introduction to Quantum Mechanics*. New York: McGraw-Hill Book Company, Inc., 1935, pp. 210, 214-15.
[8] P.O. Lowdin, *Revs. Modern Phys.* **36**, 966 (1964).

$$u(1, 2, \cdots, n) = (n!)^{-1/2} \begin{vmatrix} u_a(1) & u_b(1) & \cdots & u_n(1) \\ u_a(2) & u_b(2) & \cdots & u_n(2) \\ \cdots & \cdots & & \cdots \\ u_a(n) & u_b(n) & \cdots & u_n(n) \end{vmatrix} \tag{14.155}$$

where the wave functions $u_a, u_b, \cdots, u_n$ are functions of coordinates and spin. The wave function $u_a(1)$ might be $R_{nl}(r_1)\Theta_{lm}(\theta_1)\Phi_m(\phi_1)\alpha(1)$, the electron 1 being in state a, which is characterized by the quantum numbers n, l, m, and $s = +\frac{1}{2}$. Since interchanging rows or columns of a determinant changes its algebraic sign, $u(1, 2, \cdots, n)$ is completely antisymmetric, as required experimentally. The factor $(n!)^{-1/2}$ is a normalization factor.

The Pauli exclusion principle states that no two electrons can exist in the same quantum state. This is to say that no two columns of the determinant in (14.155) can be alike if $u(1, 2, \cdots, n)$ is not to vanish. When two rows or columns of a determinant are alike, the determinant is zero. For example, it is impossible to have three electrons with principal quantum number $n = 1$, which requires $l = 0$ and $m = 0$ because of remarks made with Table 14.2. If $u_{100}(i)$ means $R_{10}(r_i)\,\Theta_{00}(\theta_i)\,\Phi_0(\phi_i)$ for electron i, then the electronic wave function for three electrons with $n = 1$ is, in view of (14.155),

$$u(1, 2, 3) = \left(\frac{1}{3!}\right)^{1/2} \begin{vmatrix} u_{100}(1)\alpha(1) & u_{100}(1)\beta(1) & u_{100}(1)\sigma(1) \\ u_{100}(2)\alpha(2) & u_{100}(2)\beta(2) & u_{100}(2)\sigma(2) \\ u_{100}(3)\alpha(3) & u_{100}(3)\beta(3) & u_{100}(3)\sigma(3) \end{vmatrix}$$

But this $u(1, 2, 3)$ is zero because $\sigma(i)$ can be only $\alpha(i)$ or $\beta(i)$, and either choice makes two columns alike. Thus the exclusion principle, when stated in the general terms of antisymmetric ψ's for fermions, merely summarizes in an elegant way what states are never observed. At least one of three electrons must differ in something besides spin. This formulation of $u(1, 2, 3)$ has assumed that the spatial wave function of each electron is like that of one electron in H, a somewhat dubious assumption because of electron-electron repulsion.

With one or two electrons, the electronic wave function can be factored into a space part and a spin part. One of these parts can be made symmetric while the other can be made antisymmetric. For example, for He in the state $1s^2$, with $u_{100}(1)$ as the spatial wave function for electron 1 with $n = 1$, $l = 0$, $m = 0$, the electronic wave function including spin is

$$u_0(1, 2) = \frac{1}{\sqrt{2}} \begin{vmatrix} u_{100}(1)\alpha(1) & u_{100}(1)\beta(1) \\ u_{100}(2)\alpha(2) & u_{100}(2)\beta(2) \end{vmatrix}$$

$$= 2^{-1/2}[u_{100}(1)\,u_{100}(2)][\alpha(1)\beta(2) - \alpha(2)\beta(1)]$$

wherein the spatial part is symmetric while the spin part is antisymmetric. Again, the electronic wave function for He in the excited state $1s2s$, with spins alike, is

$$u_e(1, 2) = \frac{1}{\sqrt{2}} \begin{vmatrix} u_{100}(1)\alpha(1) & u_{200}(1)\alpha(1) \\ u_{100}(2)\alpha(2) & u_{200}(2)\alpha(2) \end{vmatrix}$$

$$= 2^{-1/2}[u_{100}(1)\, u_{200}(2) - u_{100}(2)\, u_{200}(1)][\alpha(1)\alpha(2)]$$

wherein the spatial part is antisymmetric while the spin part is symmetric. For excited He ($1s2s$) with unlike spins and a symmetric spin factor, the wave function is

$$u_e(1, 2) = 2^{-1/2}[u_{100}(1)\, u_{100}(2) - u_{100}(2)\, u_{200}(1)][\alpha(1)\beta(2) + \alpha(2)\beta(1)]$$

It would thus appear that an electronic wave function might be factored into a spatial part $u(q)$ of definite symmetry and a spin part $\sigma(\omega)$ of opposite symmetry such that

$$\phi(q, \omega) = u(q)\, \sigma(\omega) \tag{14.156}$$

However, it is seldom possible to factor a wave function for three or more electrons into a spin part and a spatial part, each with definite symmetry or antisymmetry.

Example 14.1. In terms of a Slater determinant, construct an electronic wave function for the most stable state of Be.

The most stable state of Be has the configuration $1\,s^2\,2\,s^2$. The $1\,s^2$ electrons have quantum numbers (n, l, m, s) with values $(1, 0, 0, +1/2)$ and $(1, 0, 0, -1/2)$. The $2s^2$ electrons have values $(2, 0, 0, +1/2)$ and $(2, 0, 0, -1/2)$. Hence, the electronic wave function of the ground state of Be is

$$u = \left(\frac{1}{4!}\right)^{1/2} \begin{vmatrix} u_{100}(1)\alpha(1) & u_{100}(1)\beta(1) & u_{200}(1)\alpha(1) & u_{200}(1)\beta(1) \\ u_{100}(2)\alpha(2) & u_{100}(2)\beta(2) & u_{200}(2)\alpha(2) & u_{200}(2)\beta(2) \\ u_{100}(3)\alpha(3) & u_{100}(3)\beta(3) & u_{200}(3)\alpha(3) & u_{200}(3)\beta(3) \\ u_{100}(4)\alpha(4) & u_{100}(4)\beta(4) & u_{200}(4)\alpha(4) & u_{200}(4)\beta(4) \end{vmatrix}$$

An interchange of any two sets of coordinates (say 1 and 3) is tantamount to an interchange of rows; hence, u changes sign and is antisymmetric. Still, every column and every row is unique so that $u \neq 0$.

14.10 ATOMIC SPECTRA

Absorption or emission of a photon of energy $h\nu$ is accompanied by a change in energy $\Delta E = h\nu$ of the system that absorbs or emits the photon. Besides energy, it is necessary that angular momentum be conserved in such an event. A photon has a spin of unity; it is a boson. While the net number of fermions is always conserved in any change, the number of bosons need not be conserved. Absorption or emission of a photon is the annihilation or generation of a photon. Since the component of its spin may be $+1$, 0, or -1, the system from which it originates suffers a net increase in angular momentum of $-1, 0$, or $+1$ for angular momentum is conserved like energy, number of fermions, and so on. It is impossible, however, for a system with no angular momentum to emit a photon and yet end in a state of no angular momentum.

These very general remarks about angular momentum can be stated (after suitable tedious mathematical transformations have been effected on certain expressions) briefly by saying that for the usual kind of radiation (electric dipolar) whereby a system with wave function ψ_m becomes one with ψ_n, one or more of the integrals $\int \psi_n^* x \psi_m \, d\tau$, $\int \psi_n^* y \, \psi_m \, d\tau$, and $\int \psi_n^* z \, \psi_m \, d\tau$ must differ from zero. Since x, y, and z range from $-\infty$ to $+\infty$, integrals like these are zero if $\psi_n^* \, \psi_m$ is an even function of x, y and/or z. For example, if $\psi_n^* \, \psi_m$ is even, then $\psi_n^* \, x \, \psi_m$ is odd, and integration from $-\infty$ to 0 gives values which exactly counter oppositely signed values from 0 to $+\infty$. These integrals differ from zero only when $\psi_n^* \, \psi_m$ is odd, for then $\psi_n^* \, x \, \psi_m$ is even and contributes equal terms from $-\infty$ to 0 and from 0 to $+\infty$.

The term *parity* (Section 13.9) describes the even-odd character of a wave function. If $\psi_n(x) = +\psi_n(-x)$, the parity of ψ_n or ψ_n^* is even; if $\psi_m(x) = -\psi_m(-x)$, the parity of ψ_m or ψ_m^* is odd. The state itself is also said to have even or odd parity with respect to inversion through the origin (x becomes $-x$, y becomes $-y$, . . . for each variable in $d\tau$). The most general and rigorous rule (the Laporte rule) for electric dipolar radiation says that the inversion parities of initial and final states differ. An even state, sometimes labeled g for the German word *gerade*, always becomes odd, or u for *ungerade*. Similarly u becomes g upon electric dipolar radiation.

The Laporte rule for radiative transitions of a one-dimensional harmonic oscillator would suggest that photon energies $h\nu$, $3h\nu$, $5h\nu$, $7h\nu$, $9h\nu$, . . . might be possible. As Figure 14.2 shows, ψ_n has even parity if n is even, while ψ_m has odd parity if m is odd. Actually, the wave functions of the harmonic oscillator are such that only $h\nu$ is allowed. That is, $\Delta n = \pm 1$ is allowed, while the changes $\Delta n = 0, \pm 2, \pm 3, \pm 4, \ldots$ are forbidden for electric dipolar radiation by a harmonic oscillator. Rules of this kind for changes of quantum number are called *selection rules*.

For the hydrogen atom, the principal quantum number may change by any amount during electric dipolar radiation. That is, there is no selection rule on n. There are, however, selection rules on l and m, namely $\Delta l = \pm 1$ and $\Delta m = 0, \pm 1$. The spin of the electron in H is not important because there is only one electron. The rule $\Delta l = \pm 1$ occurs because states with even l have even parity while states with odd l have odd parity. For example, in Figure 14.3, the sphere for the s orbital ($l = 0$) has the same sign in all directions; hence, it is even upon inversion through the origin. The p states ($l = 1$) in Figure 14.3 are odd, however, for the two lobes of ψ have different signs. In general, the signs of such lobes alternate, so that the d states ($l = 2$) are even, f states ($l = 3$) are odd, and so on. Absorption and emission of electric dipolar radiation by H involves transitions like ($1s \rightleftharpoons 2p \rightleftharpoons 3s$) or ($2p \rightleftharpoons 4d$) but ($1s \not\rightleftharpoons 2s$) or ($2p \not\rightleftharpoons 3p$) are forbidden, as the slash would suggest.

If the wave function can be factored, as in (14.156), then each set of factors may produce an approximate selection rule. A rather stringent rule of this kind is the rule that the total electron spin remains unchanged upon absorption or emission of radiation. The reason is that integration over the spin coordinates of an electron with different spin in initial and final states gives zero by the rule $\int \alpha(1)\beta(1)\,d\omega_1 = 0$, as in (14.153). If $S = \sum_i s_i$ is the total spin of a system of electrons, each of spin s_i, then this rule is $\Delta S = 0$.

To the extent that it is reasonable to extract angular momentum factors from the wave function of a system of electrons, it is reasonable to calculate their total angular momentum $J = \sum_i j_i$. Here, for each electron, $j_i = l_i + s_i$ is the sum of an orbital part l_i and a spin part s_i. The radiation selection rule is $\Delta J = 0$ or ± 1, but $J = 0 \not\leftrightarrow J = 0$. This kind of coupling of spin and orbital angular momentum for each electron to give a total j_i for each electron is common for atoms having many electrons (e.g., Pb, Tl, U) and is called *j-j coupling*. The state of the electrons in such an atom is specified by J, which cannot change by more than unity during electric dipole radiation. If J is zero in either terminal state, then $\Delta J = \pm 1$ during electric dipole radiation (or absorption).

In atoms of low atomic number, it is general to find a preliminary coupling of all electronic spins s_i to give a net value $S = \sum_i s_i$ and a preliminary coupling of all electronic orbital angular momenta l_i to give a net value $L = \sum_i l_i$ for the whole atom. This is called *Russell-Saunders coupling* of the electrons. The nearly rigorous selection rules for electric dipolar radiation are then $\Delta L = 0, \pm 1$ (but $L = 0 \not\leftrightarrow L = 0$) and $\Delta S = 0$. The state of an atom with Russell-Saunders coupling is specified by L, S, and J, where J is total angular momentum of the electrons. The maximum value of J is $L + S$. If $L \geqslant S$, J has the values $L + S$, $L + S - 1, \ldots L - S \geqslant 0$, as though L and S were one-dimensional vectors adding to give a resultant J. If $L < S$, then the "vector" S is longer than L and the possible values of J are $S + L$, $S + L - 1, \ldots S - L$. The number of states with a given L is $2L + 1$ if $L \leq S$, but it is $2S + 1$ if $S < L$.

The Russell-Saunders symbol for an electronic state of an atom consists of L preceded by a numerical superscript equal to $2S + 1$ and followed by a numerical subscript J. The superscript $2S + 1$ is called the *multiplicity* of the electronic state. The superscript and subscript are attached to the symbol S if $L = 0$, to P if $L = 1$, to D if $L = 2$, to F if $L = 3$, to G if $L = 4$, and so on. According to the selection rule $\Delta L = 0, \pm 1$, electric dipolar radiation occurs when $(S \rightleftharpoons P \rightleftharpoons D)$ or when $(P \rightleftharpoons P)$ or when $(D \rightleftharpoons D)$, and so on, but a Russell-Saunders S state does not become D by emission or absorption of a photon. The rule on spins ($\Delta S = 0$) means that the multiplicity ordinarily does not change; hence $({}^3P \rightleftharpoons {}^3S)$ but $({}^1P \not\rightleftharpoons {}^3S)$. These selection rules are not as rigorous as the even-odd rule of Laporte.

The *aufbau principle* supposes that a system of atomic electrons can be built by adding one electron at a time. The most stable state of an atom is thus found by adding each electron to the empty state of lowest energy. The order of energy increases with n in general, but important exceptions occur for systems of more than 20 electrons. When the maximum number $2(2l+1)$ of electrons has been added to states of given principal quantum number n and orbital angular momentum l(e.g. s^2, p^6, d^{10}, f^{14}, ...) a subshell is said to have been completed. In a complete subshell, all electrons are grouped in pairs in which one electron has spin $\alpha = +1/2$ while the other has spin $\beta = -1/2$; hence, $S = 0$ for the filled subshell. Moreover, two electrons exist in every possible value of $m(m = +l, +(l-1), \ldots +1, 0, -1, \ldots -l)$; hence, $L = 0$ for the complete subshell. Consequently, completed shells and subshells may be ignored in calculating S, L, J and the Russell-Saunders symbol, because their net angular momentum is zero.

Example 14.2. Calculate the Russell-Saunders symbols for atoms containing completed subshells plus

(a) one p electron (e.g. B, Al);
(b) two equivalent p electrons (e.g. C, Si);
(c) an s and a d electron.

(a) For one p electron, $L = l = 1$ and $S = s = 1/2$, the sign of S and s being unimportant since there is no other electron under study. Hence, $J = +\frac{3}{2}$ or $+\frac{1}{2}$. Since the symbol for $L = 1$ is P, and since the multiplicity is $2S + 1 = 2$, the states are $^2P_{3/2}$ ("doublet P three-halves") and $^2P_{1/2}$.

(b) The Pauli exclusion principle requires a careful account of electrons so that no two electrons have the same set of quantum numbers. Here n and l are alike for both. There is no physical significance to labeling the electrons because they are indistinguishable. However, a spin $\alpha = +1/2$ can be distinguished from $\beta = -1/2$, and an electron of spin α can be observed to have $m = +1$ rather than $m = 0$ or $m = -1$. A complete list of possibilities in accord with the Pauli principle and indistinguishability of equivalent electrons is given in Table 14.3.

Table 14.3 Quantum Numbers of Two Equivalent p Electrons.

Config.	$m = +1$	$m = 0$	$m = -1$	Σs	Σm
1	α	α		1	1
2	α		α	1	0
3		α	α	1	-1
4	$\alpha\beta$			0	2
5	α	β		0	1
6	β	α		0	1
7	α		β	0	0
8		$\alpha\beta$		0	0
9	β		α	0	0
10		α	β	0	-1
11		β	α	0	-1
12			$\alpha\beta$	0	-2
13	β	β		-1	$+1$
14	β		β	-1	0
15		β	β	-1	-1

Configurations 1, 2, 3, 13, 14, and 15 are clearly triplets with $2S + 1 = 3$. In view of (14.152), electron configurations with spins α and β may also contribute to the triplet series. In fact, configurations 5, 6, 7, 9, 10, and 11 contribute to the triplet series and to a singlet ($\Sigma\, s = 0$) series in which $\Sigma\, m$ takes the spectrum of values $+2, +1, 0, -1, -2$. This singlet series is clearly ^1D, while the triplet series is ^3P because $\Sigma\, m$ takes the values $+1, 0, -1$ three times. Configuration 8 is not yet accounted for; since for it $\Sigma\, s = 0$ and $\Sigma\, m = 0$, it is ^1S.

The complete list of Russell-Saunders states for two equivalent p electrons is, therefore,

(i) $^1S_0$ (since $J = 0 + 0$)
(ii) $^1D_2$ (since $J = L + 0 = 2$)
(iii) $^3P_2$, $^3P_1$, and $^3P_0$ (since $L = 1$ and $S = 1$ yields $J = 2$, 1, and 0).

(c) The s and d electrons act independently in the sense that each surely differs from the other in orbital angular momentum. In fact, since the s electron has no angular momentum, the value of L for both is always 2; hence, all states are D. The spins may, however, be alike, to give a triplet state as in (14.152), or different, to give a singlet as in (14.153). There are twenty configurations that yield ^3D and ^1D. Since J ranges from $L + S$ to $L - S$, the complete Russell-Saunders symbols are $^3D_3$, $^3D_2$, $^3D_1$, $^1D_2$. Note that summing $2J + 1$ gives $20 = (2 \times 3 + 1) + (2 \times 2 + 1) + (2 \times 1 + 1) + (2 \times 2 + 1)$.

The several Russell-Saunders states of a particular set of electrons having specified orbital angular momenta have different energies. *Hund's rules* are an empirical summary of what has been observed about the relative energies of such states. The first rule says that the Russell-Saunder (R-S) state with greatest multiplicity is most stable. That is, ^3D has a lower energy than ^1D, while ^3P is more stable than ^1P. The second rule says that of R-S states of the same multiplicity, the state with largest L is most stable. That is, ^2D has a lower energy than ^2P or ^2S. The third rule says that when a subshell is less than half filled, the energies of R-S states increase with increasing J, while their energies increase with decreasing J when a subshell is more than half filled. As a review of a few particular cases would easily show, the absence of x electrons from an otherwise filled subshell produces the same number and kind of R-S states as does the presence of x electrons in an otherwise empty subshell. Hence, B($1s^2$ $2s^2$ $2p$) and F ($1s^2$ $2s^2$ $2p^5$) have R-S states $^2P_{3/2}$ and $^2P_{1/2}$, while C($1s^2$ $2s^2$ $2p^2$) and O($1s^2$ $2s^2$ $2p^4$) have the R-S states $^3P_2$, $^3P_1$, $^3P_0$, $^1D_2$, $^1S_0$. Hund's rules predict the ground state of B to be $^2P_{1/2}$, while that of F is $^2P_{3/2}$. Similarly, the most stable electronic state of C is $^3P_0$, while O's is $^3P_2$.

The physical basis of the behavior summarized by Hund is the tendency for electrons to avoid each other. For three equivalent p electrons, the least repulsion exists when all three p orbitals are used. This forces $\Sigma\, m$ to be $0 = (+1) + (0) + (-1)$ and yet allows the spins complete freedom. The spins are alike in the most stable state because this makes the electrons as alike as possible, given the electrostatic arrangement in spatially separated orbitals. As the next sections show, alikeness opens more avenues for wavelike dissipation throughout space and thus allows the electrons to minimize their energy through properly coordinated reinforcement and interference. The energy differences of R-S states of different J are small for light atoms, but the differences becomes great for heavy atoms. For example, $^2P_{1/2}$ is about 7600 cm^{-1} above $^2P_{3/2}$ for I, but is only about 400 cm^{-1} above $^2P_{1/2}$ for F. Similarly, the $^3P_1$ state lies above the ground state by about 16 cm^{-1} for C, about 160 cm^{-1} for O, but is above by about 7800 cm^{-1} for Pb and about 4700 cm^{-1} for Te.

The coupling of orbital angular momenta to give a net value L and the coupling of spins to give S is modified in electric and weak magnetic fields and may be completely undone in a strong field. In a weak magnetic field (*Zeeman effect*) L and S still couple to form J, but the field removes the J-degeneracy to give $2J + 1$ states distinguished by the quantum number M_J with values J, $J - 1, \ldots -J$. For electric dipolar radiation in a weak magnetic field, $\Delta M_J = 0$ or ± 1, but $\Delta M_J \neq 0$ if $J = 0$. In a strong magnetic field (*Paschen-Back effect*), J is destroyed and the quantum numbers are $M_L = +L, +(L - 1) \ldots -L$ and $M_S = +S, +(S - 1), \ldots -S$ because L and S are uncoupled. The selection rules are then $\Delta M_L = 0$ and $\Delta M_S = 0$. In a weak electric field (*Stark effect*), the states M_J and $-M_J$ are degenerate. An intense electric field destroys J by uncoupling L and S to yield doubly degenerate states. Figure 14.4 illustrates schematically how $^2D_{5/2}$ and $^2D_{3/2}$ might be split in a weak field. The Schröd-

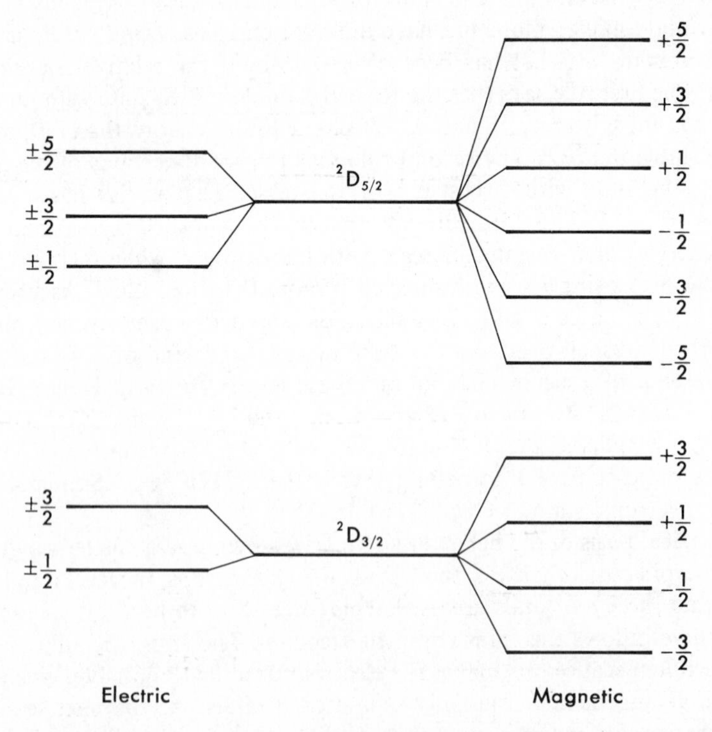

Figure 14.4. The Effect of a Weak External Field in Removing the Degeneracies of $^2D_{5/2}$ and $^2D_{3/2}$ States

inger theory of the atom found much early support through its excellent account of the Zeeman effect. These effects are of great value to astronomers interested in fields in stars or space.

14.11 VARIATION METHOD

It is almost always impossible to solve the Schrödinger equation for E or a wave function. The exceptional cases of the hydrogen atom and harmonic oscillator are particularly important because they suggest ways of attaining approximate solutions. The most important approximate method for chemists is the variation method. It applies to the most stable state of a given parity or symmetry. The most stable state of an atom or molecule is generally the one of primary chemical interest.

The basic idea of the variation method begins with the prescription (14.38) as it applies to the expectation value of the energy

$$\bar{H} = \int \psi^* \mathbf{H}\psi \, d\tau \tag{14.157}$$

The wave function ψ can be any properly behaved function because the system can be in any state. If the system were in its most stable stationary state, ψ would be u_0 and (14.157) would yield the ground state energy

$$E_0 = \int u_0^* \mathbf{H}u_0 \, d\tau \tag{14.158}$$

for $\mathbf{H}\, u_0 = E_0 u_0$ and it is presumed that $1 = \int u_0^* \, u_0 \, d\tau$. Since the energy eigenfunctions u_n form a complete set, it follows as in (14.46) that

$$\psi = \sum_n a_n \, u_n(\tau) \tag{14.159}$$

where

$$\mathbf{H}\, u_n = E_n \, u_n \tag{14.160}$$

In general, then, (14.157), (14.159), and (14.160) yield

$$\begin{aligned} \bar{H} &= \int \sum_m a_m^* u_m^* \mathbf{H}(\sum_n a_n u_n) \, d\tau \\ &= \sum_m \sum_n a_m^* E_n a_n \int u_m^* u_n \, d\tau \end{aligned}$$

Terms with $m \neq n$ are zero because $E_m \neq E_n$ and, by (14.42), $\int u_m^* u_n \, d\tau = 0$; hence,

$$\bar{H} = \sum_m a_m^* a_m E_m \tag{14.161}$$

The product $a_m^* a_m$ is the square of the absolute value of a_m; it is, therefore, positive. Moreover, since $E_m \geqslant E_0$ for all m,

$$\sum_m (E_m - E_0)\, a_m^* a_m \geqslant 0 \tag{14.162}$$

Since the u_m's are orthogonal, normalizing ψ requires

$$1 = \int \psi^* \psi \, d\tau = \sum_m a_m^* a_m \tag{14.163}$$

Combining (14.161), (14.162), and (14.163) thus yields

$$\bar{H} = \sum_m E_m a_m^* a_m \geqslant E_0 \tag{14.164}$$

Even without this proof of (14.164), it would perhaps be obvious that the expectation value $\bar{H}$ of the energy of a system in any state other than the ground state exceeds the ground state energy E_0.

Any arbitrary function $v(\tau)$ that depends on the independent variables in $u_n(\tau)$ is a conceivable state for the system. The only restrictions on $v(\tau)$ are those usual boundary conditions on any wave function: it must be finite, single-valued, continuous, capable of being normalized. Hence, by (14.164) and (14.157),

$$E_0 \leqslant \int v^*(\tau) \mathbf{H} v(\tau)\, d\tau = E' \tag{14.165}$$

Good fortune or sagacity in guessing $v(\tau)$ might hit upon the eigenfunction $u_0(\tau)$ so that (14.165) reduces to (14.158). However, in view of the complexity of wave functions, especially for the problems that cannot be solved directly, the inequality of (14.165) is expected to hold. On the other hand, if $v(\tau)$ is of the right form and embodies much flexibility, it is conceivable that the difference between the terms of (14.165) might be reduced toward zero.

The variation method is a thorough and systematic way of adjusting $v(\tau)$ by minimizing E' in (14.165) with respect to certain parameters of $v(\tau)$. As proved in (14.165), the value of E' cannot be less than E_0, the lowest energy of the system. A wise choice of $v(\tau)$ can, in fact, reduce the difference between E and E_0 to negligible size. The real system behaves in itself as an ideal analog computer by always getting a perfect wave function with the energy E_0.

Example 14.3. With a variation function of the form ce^{-ax^2}, calculate the lowest energy of even parity for the harmonic oscillator.

The constant c allows for normalization of $v(x) = ce^{-ax^2}$. Its value is found thus. By (14.37), with $v = \psi$,

$$\begin{aligned} 1 &= c^*c \int_{-\infty}^{\infty} e^{-ax^2} e^{-ax^2}\, dx \\ &= \frac{c^2}{(2a)^{1/2}} \int_0^{\infty} y^{-1/2} e^{-y}\, dy \\ &= \frac{c^2}{(2a)^{1/2}} \Gamma\left(\frac{1}{2}\right) = c^2 \sqrt{\frac{\pi}{2a}} \end{aligned}$$

where $\Gamma(\frac{1}{2})$ is explained in Appendix C. Hence,

$$c^2 = \left(\frac{2a}{\pi}\right)^{1/2} \quad \text{and} \quad v(x) = \left(\frac{2a}{\pi}\right)^{1/4} e^{-ax^2}$$

The constant a is to be varied in accord with (14.165). As a first step

$$\frac{d^2e^{-ax^2}}{dx^2} = \frac{d}{dx}(-2axe^{-ax^2})$$
$$= -2ae^{-ax^2} + 4a^2x^2e^{-ax^2}$$

Hence, by (14.158) and (14.165)

$$E' = \int v^*\mathbf{H}v\,d\tau = c^2\int_{-\infty}^{\infty} e^{-ax^2}\left[-\frac{\hbar^2}{2m}(4a^2x^2 - 2a) + 2\pi^2m\nu^2x^2\right]e^{-ax^2}\,dx$$
$$= \left(\frac{2a}{\pi}\right)^{1/2}\left[\left(\frac{a\hbar^2}{m}\right)\int_{-\infty}^{\infty} e^{-2ax^2}\,dx + \left(2\pi^2m\nu^2 - \frac{2a^2\hbar^2}{m}\right)\int_{-\infty}^{\infty} x^2e^{-2ax^2}\,dx\right]$$
$$= \frac{a\hbar^2}{m} + \left(\frac{2a}{\pi}\right)^{1/2}\left(2\pi^2m\nu^2 - \frac{2a^2\hbar^2}{m}\right)\frac{2\sqrt{2a}}{8a^2}\int_0^{\infty} y^{1/2}e^{-y}\,dy$$
$$= \frac{a\hbar^2}{m} + \left(\frac{2a}{\pi}\right)^{1/2}\left(2\pi^2m\nu^2 - \frac{2a^2\hbar^2}{m}\right)\frac{2\sqrt{2a}}{8a^2}\left(\frac{\sqrt{\pi}}{2}\right)$$
$$= \frac{a\hbar^2}{2m} + \frac{\pi^2m\nu^2}{2a}$$

Minimizing E' with respect to variations in a requires

$$0 = \frac{\partial E'}{\partial a} = \frac{\hbar^2}{2m} + \frac{\pi^2m\nu^2}{2}\left(-\frac{1}{a^2}\right)$$

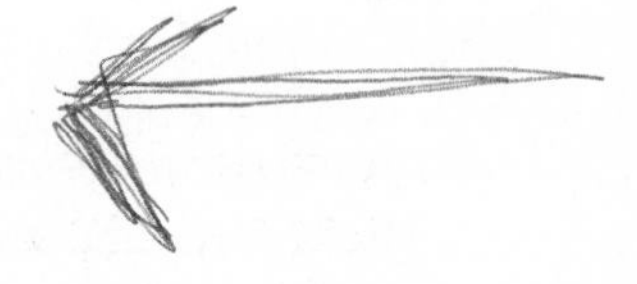

$$a = \frac{\pi m\nu}{\hbar}$$

This value of a in (14.165) or E' above yields

$$E_0 \leqslant E' = \left(\frac{\pi m\nu}{\hbar}\right)\frac{\hbar^2}{2m} + \frac{\pi^2m\nu^2}{2}\left(\frac{\hbar}{\pi m\nu}\right) = \frac{h\nu}{2}$$

But, as shown in Section 14.7, this value of E' is exactly equal to E_0! The reason is that v happened to be chosen of the proper functional form. For hydrogen, the trial function ce^{-ar^2} yields only $(8/3\pi)\,E_1$, where E_1 is given by (14.125) with $n = 1$. However, with $c'e^{-a'r}$, $E' = E_1$ because, by good luck, ce^{-ar} is of the right form.

The Bohr theory was an outstanding success for H, but for He and other atoms of more than one electron it was unable to yield reasonable energies. As early as 1930, however, Hylleraas and others had used the Schrödinger theory to calculate the electronic energy of He relative to $He^{2+} + 2e^-$. Their result was even more accurate than observations of their day. Not only did these calculations confirm the Schrödinger theory; they also provided a precise energy for H^- infinitely separated from all disturbances to its highly polarizable electrons.

The presently accepted experimental energy of He is 5.8066 E_1, where E_1 is the energy of H in the $1s$ state as given by (14.125) with $n = 1$. The nonrelativistic Schrödinger equation for He in center-of-mass coordinates yields 5.8074 E_1.[9] In fact, since calculations can be done for excited states of He with errors less than about 1 in 10^8, such theoretical results are useful together with observations to evaluate fundamental physical constants[10] in the way that (14.125) is used to evaluate m, e, and h.

The problem of the nucleus with two electrons would be tractable if the term e^2/r_{12} were not present in the potential energy. The reason for this is as follows. If ∇_i^2 is the symbol for (14.31) as it applies to electron i, the Schrödinger equation in center-of-mass coordinates for electron 1 at a distance r_1 from the nucleus of charge $\mathbf{Z}e$ and for electron 2 similarly at r_2 is

$$\mathbf{H}u = -\frac{\hbar^2}{2m}(\nabla_1^2 u + \nabla_2^2 u) + \frac{e^2 u}{4\pi\epsilon_0}\left(-\frac{\mathbf{Z}}{r_1} - \frac{\mathbf{Z}}{r_2} + \frac{1}{r_{12}}\right) = Eu \qquad (14.166)$$

In similar notation, the equation for a one-electron atom is

$$\mathbf{H}_i u(i) = -\frac{\hbar^2}{2m}\nabla_i^2 u(i) + \frac{e^2 u(i)}{4\pi\epsilon_0}\left(-\frac{\mathbf{Z}}{r_i}\right) = E_i u(i) \qquad (14.167)$$

That is, if (14.166) is compared to (14.167), the former is

$$(\mathbf{H}_1 + \mathbf{H}_2)u + \frac{e^2 u}{4\pi\epsilon_0 r_{12}} = Eu \qquad (14.168)$$

Moreover, if $u = u(1)u(2)$, multiplication of (14.168) by u^* and integration over $d\tau_1$ and $d\tau_2$ gives, after a look back at (14.167),

$$E_1 + E_2 + \frac{e^2}{4\pi\epsilon_0}\iint \frac{u^* u}{r_{12}}\, d\tau_1\, d\tau_2 = E \qquad (14.169)$$

The term with r_{12} in (14.169) prevents a simple additivity of one-electron energies E_i. This is reasonable, of course, because the electrons repel each other and prevent the nucleus from exerting its usual attractiveness on each of them. In polyelectronic atoms there are many electron-electron interactions of the form $1/r_{ij}$. Fortunately, the quantum repulsions described by the Pauli principle tend to keep the electrons apart so that rather good results are attained by treating electrons in pairs. The r_{12} term of (14.169) correlates the motion of the electrons; neglecting it in He or polyelectronic systems lends to what is called *correlation error*. Just as the energy may be divided into two parts, one of which is attributed to electron correlation, so also may a wave function ψ be resolved into a Slater-like part ψ_s and a correlation part ψ_c with

$$\psi = \psi_s + \psi_c \qquad (14.170)$$

[9] C. L. Pekeris, *Phys. Rev.* **112,** 1649 (1958)
[10] C. Schwartz, *Phys. Rev.* **134A,** 1181 (1964)

Although parameters may be introduced into a variation function in many ways, the most commonly used variation functions are of the form

$$v = \sum_i c_i v_i \tag{14.171}$$

Since the c_i's are the variational parameters, v of (14.171) is called a *linear variation function.* The starting functions v_i are any reasonable set of functions. For atoms and even for molecules, it is common to chose v_i to be Slater-type functions of (14.126) or hydrogen-like functions or even Gaussian error functions, which yield relatively easy integrals. The kind and number to be included in v are guided by experience or the accuracy hoped for. Figure 14.3 is a useful guide to where angular functions would place electrons. Substituting (14.171) into (14.165) gives

$$E' = \frac{\int (\sum_i c_i^* v_i^*)\mathbf{H}(\sum_j c_j v_j)\, d\tau}{\int (\sum_i c_i^* v_i^*)(\sum_j c_j v_j)\, d\tau} \tag{14.172}$$

The denominator of (14.172), which occurs because the v_i's need be neither orthogonal nor normalized, is the reciprocal of the square of the factor N that normalizes v of (14.171), for

$$1 = \int N^* v^* N v\, d\tau = N^* N \int (\sum_i c_i^* v_i^*)(\sum_j c_j v_j)\, d\tau \tag{14.173}$$

It is customary to simplify notation in (14.172) before minimizing E' through adjustments in the c_i's. By definition, the *overlap integral* is

$$S_{ij} = \int v_i^* v_j\, d\tau \tag{14.174}$$

Similarly, the numerator of (14.172) is abbreviated by the definition

$$H_{ij} = \int v_i^* \mathbf{H} v_j\, d\tau \tag{14.175}$$

With (14.174) and (14.175), it follows that (14.172) is

$$\sum_i \sum_j c_i^* c_j S_{ij} E' = \sum_i \sum_j c_i^* c_j H_{ij} \tag{14.176}$$

According to (14.175) and (14.40), which states the Hermitian nature of $\mathbf{H}$,

$$H_{ij} = \left[\int v_i \mathbf{H}^* v_j^*\, d\tau\right]^* = \left[\int (\mathbf{H} v_j)^* v_i\, d\tau\right]^* = H_{ji}^* \tag{14.177}$$

If the v_i's are real, it is clear from (14.174) and (14.177) that $S_{ij} = S_{ji}$ and

$H_{ij} = H_{ji}$. Thus, when the v_i's are real, (14.176) is

$$\sum_i c_i^2 S_{ii} E' + \sum_{i \neq j} \sum c_i c_j S_{ij} E' = \sum_i c_i^2 H_{ii} + \sum_{i \neq j} \sum c_i c_j H_{ij}$$

Partial differentiation with respect to c_k thus yields

$$2c_k S_{kk} E' + 2 \sum_{j \neq k} c_j S_{kj} E' = 2c_k H_{kk} + 2 \sum_{j \neq k} c_j H_{kj} \tag{14.178}$$

The integrals S_{ij} and H_{ij} are independent of c_k. And because it is E' that is being minimized, $\partial E'/\partial c_k$ is zero. Hence, (14.178) in the form

$$\sum_j c_j(H_{kj} - S_{kj}E') = 0 \tag{14.179}$$

is a set of linear algebraic equations that fix the c_j's. Since the equations (14.179) are homogeneous in the c_j's, a trivial solution is $c_1 = c_2 = \ldots = c_j = \ldots = 0$. But this yields $v = 0$, which is like $\psi = 0$, namely, a void or vacuum. In order that (14.179) have a nontrivial solution, it is necessary that

$$\begin{vmatrix} H_{11} - S_{11}E' & H_{12} - S_{12}E' & \cdots \\ H_{12} - S_{12}E' & H_{22} - S_{22}E' & \cdots \\ H_{13} - S_{13}E' & H_{23} - S_{23}E' & \cdots \\ \cdots & \cdots & \cdots \end{vmatrix} = 0 \tag{14.180}$$

where $H_{ij} = H_{ji}$ and $S_{ij} = S_{ji}$ have been used. Equation (14.180) is a polynomial in E', of order equal to the number of rows or columns of the determinant. The smallest root E' of (14.180) is greater than or equal to E_0 by (14.165). However, if not all H_{ij} are zero, this smallest root is less than the smallest H_{ii}. That is, mixing several possible amplitudes into v by use of several terms in (14.171) has freed the system of some of the artificial or unrealistic constraints imposed by v_i because it is somehow inadequate as a wave function.

If v_1 and v_2 each possess certain attributes as possible wave functions of a system that is approximately describable by v_1 from one viewpoint and by v_2 from another viewpoint, then the variation function

$$v = c_1 v_1 + c_2 v_2 \tag{14.181}$$

is better than just v_1 or v_2. It is as though the aribtrary "pure" cases v_1 and v_2 are superposed as reinforcing or interfering waves to give a net nonclassical effect. The condition (14.180) is then

$$\begin{vmatrix} H_{11} - S_{11}E' & H_{12} - S_{12}E' \\ H_{12} - S_{12}E' & H_{22} - S_{22}E' \end{vmatrix} = 0 \tag{14.182}$$

 If v_1 and v_2 are each normalized, $S_{11} = 1$ and $S_{22} = 1$. If, as sometimes happens, S_{12} can be neglected, then (14.182) becomes simply

$$\begin{vmatrix} H_{11} - E' & H_{12} \\ H_{12} & H_{22} - E' \end{vmatrix} = 0 \tag{14.183}$$

Expansion of (14.183) and solution for E' yields

$$(E')^2 - (H_{11} + H_{22})E' + H_{11}H_{22} - H_{12}^2 = 0$$

$$E' = \frac{H_{11} + H_{22} \pm \sqrt{(H_{11} + H_{22})^2 - 4H_{11}H_{22} + 4H_{12}^2}}{2}$$

$$= \frac{H_{11} + H_{22}}{2} \pm \frac{\sqrt{(H_{11} - H_{22})^2 + 4H_{12}^2}}{2} \tag{14.184}$$

If $|H_{12}| \gg |H_{11} - H_{22}|$, then the two roots of (14.183) are approximately

$$E' = \frac{H_{11} + H_{22}}{2} \pm H_{12} \tag{14.185}$$

That is, if $S_{12} \approx 0$, as supposed above, and if $H_{11} \approx H_{22}$, the two energy states of the system lie at energies $|H_{12}|$ above and below the mean energy $\frac{1}{2}(H_{11} + H_{22})$ calculated from "pure" states. Figure 14.5 illustrates what is occurring as states 1 and 2 interact. The quantity H_{12} is called the *resonance integral* or resonance energy because the mathematically analogous classical problem when $H_{11} = H_{22}$ involves resonant frequencies.

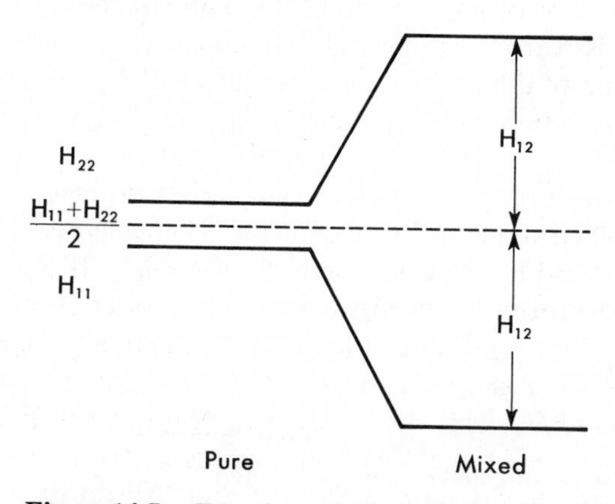

Figure 14.5. Energies of Two States Through Quantum Mechanical Resonance Interaction

Regardless of the assumptions about S_{ij} and H_{ij} in (14.180), when the lowest root E' is known, the linear variation coefficients are found from (14.179). For example, when $v = c_1 v_1 + c_2 v_2$, the c_i's are found from (14.179) in the explicit forms

$$\left.\begin{aligned} c_1(H_{11} - S_{11}E') + c_2(H_{12} - S_{12}E') = 0 \\ c_1(H_{12} - S_{11}E') + c_2(H_{22} - S_{22}E') = 0 \end{aligned}\right\} \tag{14.186}$$

That is, from (14.186)

$$\frac{c_1}{c_2} = -\frac{H_{12} - S_{12}E'}{H_{11} - S_{11}E'} = -\frac{H_{22} - S_{22}E'}{H_{12} - S_{12}E'} \tag{14.187}$$

If $H_{11} = H_{22}$ and if $S_{12} = 0$ then E' as given by (14.185) is $H_{11} \pm H_{12}$ so that (14.187) gives

$$\frac{c_1}{c_2} = -\frac{H_{12}}{H_{11} - E'} = -\frac{H_{11} - E'}{H_{12}} = \pm 1 \tag{14.188}$$

That is, the degenerate states v_1 and v_2 are now split into a reinforcing one with $v = c_1(v_1 + v_2)$ and an interfering one $v = c_1(v_1 - v_2)$. Normalization of v is effected through c_1.

When more than two states intermingle via (14.171), the effects are often spectacular. Several applications of this kind to resonance of electronic structures of molecules are given in the next chapter. Here it is sufficient to note that the Russell-Saunders coupling of spin and orbital angular momentum discussed in Example 14.2 is one application of (14.171) and (14.180) to atomic electronic states. For example, in part (b) of Example 14.2, there are fifteen configurations that yield in (14.180) a determinant with fifteen rows and fifteen columns. Fortunately, because of differing spins or angular momenta, many of the S_{ij}'s and H_{ij}'s vanish so that (14.180) is really a product of determinants of order 1, 2, and 3. In other words, solution of the problem of two equivalent p electrons in the Russell-Saunders approximation gives the energies E' of ${}^1S_0$, ${}^1D_2$, ${}^3P_2$, ${}^3P_1$, and ${}^3P_0$.

Equation (14.180) can sometimes be stated as a numerical problem when S_{ij} and H_{ij} have been evaluated numerically. Expansion as a polynomial in E' allows the roots E' to be found by the usual methods of algebra. If $S_{ij} = 0$, a numerical determinant of the form that results from (14.180) often has roots approximately equal to the values H_{ii}. Substitution of $E' = H_{ii}$ in all diagonal elements $H_{jj} - S_{jj}E'$ except $j = i$ generally yields a new value of E' that is closer to the true root than was H_{ii}. This better root can again be substituted everywhere except at $H_{ii} - S_{ii}E'$; continuation of this process of iteration eventually yields a value of E' that converges upon the true root. All roots can be found by similar processes of iteration.

A more general method of solving (14.180) for E' is to transform from the basis set v_i to a new basis set ϕ_i in such a way that

$$H'_{ij} = \int \phi_i \mathbf{H} \phi_j \, d\tau = 0 \qquad (i \neq j) \tag{14.189}$$

If the ϕ_i are orthogonal, $S'_{ij} = 0$. By thus forcing zeroes in many of the off-diagonal terms $H'_{ij} - S'_{ij}E'$, the determinant can be factored and sometimes even be reduced entirely to factors of the form $H'_{ii} - S'_{ii}E'$. Clearly, after such a transformation, the roots are $E' = H'_{ii}/S'_{ii}$, where the values of H'_{ii} and S'_{ii} are calculated in terms of the functions ϕ_i. For example, if v_1 and v_2 are orthogonal and normalized, then so also are:

$$\left.\begin{aligned} \phi_1 &= v_1 \cos\alpha + v_2 \sin\alpha \\ \phi_2 &= -v_1 \sin\alpha + v_2 \cos\alpha \end{aligned}\right\} \tag{14.190}$$

Orthogonality is easily verified, for since v_1 is orthogonal to v_2,

$$\begin{aligned} \int \phi_1\phi_2\,d\tau &= (\cos^2\alpha - \sin^2\alpha)\int v_1v_2\,d\tau + \sin\alpha\cos\alpha\left(\int v_2v_2\,d\tau - \int v_1v_1\,d\tau\right) \\ &= (\cos^2\alpha - \sin^2\alpha)(0) + (\sin\alpha\cos\alpha)(1-1) \\ &= 0 \end{aligned}$$

Normalization is verified similarly, for with a or $b = 1$ and b or $a = 2$,

$$\begin{aligned} \int \phi_i\phi_i\,d\tau &= \cos^2\alpha\int v_av_a\,d\tau \pm 2\cos\alpha\sin\alpha\int v_av_b\,d\tau + \sin^2\alpha\int v_bv_b\,d\tau \\ &= \cos^2\alpha + \sin^2\alpha = 1 \end{aligned}$$

The parameter α, however, can be adjusted to make $H'_{12} = 0$, for

$$0 = H'_{12} = \int \phi_1 H\phi_2\,d\tau = (\cos^2\alpha - \sin^2\alpha)H_{12} + \sin\alpha\cos\alpha(H_{22} - H_{11}) \tag{14.191}$$

is one equation in one unknown. If $H_{22} = H_{11}$, as in the discussion that led to (14.185) and (14.188), then (14.191) requires $\sin^2\alpha = \cos^2\alpha$, or $\sin\alpha = \pm\cos\alpha$, which gives $\alpha = \pm\pi/4$ and, by (14.190),

$$\left.\begin{aligned} \phi_1 &= \frac{1}{\sqrt{2}}(v_1 + v_2) \\ \phi_2 &= \frac{1}{\sqrt{2}}(v_1 - v_2) \end{aligned}\right\} \tag{14.192}$$

But ϕ_1 and ϕ_2 are the same as v in (14.181) if $c_1 = 1/\sqrt{2}$. If $H_{11} \neq H_{22}$, α is still adjustable to fit (14.191).

Once H'_{12} is reduced to zero, it is possible to transform to still another basis set χ_i if the determinant has more than two rows and columns. Setting $H''_{13} = \int \chi_1\mathbf{H}\chi_3\,d\tau$ equal to zero disturbs $H''_{12} = \int \chi_1\mathbf{H}\chi_2\,d\tau$ from zero, but it is closer to zero than $H_{12} = \int v_1\mathbf{H}v_2\,d\tau$. Eventually it is possible to find a basis set in which H_{ij} is zero for all $i \neq j$. Then, the determinant is diagonal and the values of E' are H_{ii}/S_{ii} as calculated in the final basis set.

With the aid of efficient computers and a variation function of great flexibility, it is possible to calculate values of E' quite close to E_0, the true ground state energy. There is no assurance, however, that a wave function found in this way is of comparable value in calculating the expectation value of another observable. Still, as E' approaches E_0 and $\int v^*u\,d\tau$ approaches unity, the variation function v approaches the true wave function u.

14.12 VIRIAL THEOREM

The virial theorem, which holds in classical as well as quantum mechanics, has many uses. In 1930, Fock found that this theorem was closely connected to varying a scale parameter γ in a variation function. That is, stretching or shrinking all coordinates of a wave function by a factor γ may decrease E', often by a large amount, if the unscaled trial wave function $v(q)$ did not give average values of the kinetic and potential energy in the relation demanded by the virial theorem.

The kinetic energy operator for n particles each of mass m_i when time and position are independent is

$$\mathbf{T} = -\frac{\hbar^2}{2}\sum_{i=1}^{n}\frac{1}{m_i}\left(\frac{\partial^2}{\partial x_i^2}+\frac{\partial^2}{\partial y_i^2}+\frac{\partial^2}{\partial z_i^2}\right) \tag{14.193}$$

Similarly, the potential energy operator for n particles of electric charge $\mathbf{Z}_i e$, the particles being separated by distances r_{ij}, is

$$\mathbf{V} = \frac{e^2}{4\pi\epsilon_0}\sum_{i\neq j}\frac{\mathbf{Z}_i\mathbf{Z}_j}{r_{ij}} \tag{14.194}$$

Moreover, if the coordinates describe the position of a harmonic oscillator, then

$$\mathbf{V} = \sum_{i=1}^{n}\frac{k_i}{2}(x_i^2+y_i^2+z_i^2) \tag{14.195}$$

In view of (14.194) and (14.195), it is not unusual for the potential energy to be of the form

$$\mathbf{V} = \sum_{i=1}^{3n} K_i q_i^m \tag{14.196}$$

where $m = 2$ for a harmonic oscillator problem as in (14.195), $m = -1$ for a coulomb problem as in (14.194), or m may be anything in general. That is, $\mathbf{V}$ is assumed to be, and often is, homogeneous of degree m in the coordinates.

The total Hamiltonian is $\mathbf{T} + \mathbf{V}$ so that the Schrödinger equation of the problem is

$$(\mathbf{T} + \mathbf{V})u = E_0 u \tag{14.197}$$

Here E_0 is the exact energy and u is the exact stationary-state wave function $u = u(q)$, where q stands for the $3n$ position coordinates of n particles. Multiplication of (14.197) by u^* and integration yields $E_0 = \bar{T} + \bar{V}$.

The normalization condition on a variation function $v(q)$ is

$$1 = \int \cdots \int v^*(q)v(q)\,(dq)^{3n} \tag{14.198}$$

Similarly, with the scaled coördinates γq replacing q, (14.198) is

$$\begin{aligned} 1 &= \int \cdots \int v^*(\gamma q)v(\gamma q)\,[d(\gamma q)]^{3n} \\ &= \int \cdots \int \gamma^{3n/2} v^*(\gamma q)\gamma^{3n/2} v(\gamma q)\,(dq)^{3n} \end{aligned} \tag{14.199}$$

That is, when the variation function but not $d\tau$ is scaled, (14.198) and (14.199) require

$$v(q) = \gamma^{3n/2} v(\gamma q) \tag{14.200}$$

The scale factor γ affects $\mathbf{T}$ and $\mathbf{V}$ also, but in different ways. After scaling, the kinetic energy operator is

$$\mathbf{T}_\gamma = -\frac{\hbar^2}{2}\sum \frac{1}{m}\frac{\partial^2}{\partial(\gamma q)^2} = \frac{1}{\gamma^2}\mathbf{T}_1 \tag{14.201}$$

where $\mathbf{T}_1$ is (14.193). Similarly, in view of (14.196),

$$\mathbf{V}_\gamma = \sum K(\gamma q)^m = \gamma^m \mathbf{V}_1 \tag{14.202}$$

Before the variation function is scaled, (14.165) yields

$$E' = \int \cdots \int v^*(q)(\mathbf{T}_1 + \mathbf{V}_1)v(q)\,(dq)^{3n} = \bar{T}_1 + \bar{V}_1 \tag{14.203}$$

After it is scaled, (14.200), (14.201), and (14.202) in (14.203) yield

$$\begin{aligned} E' &= \gamma^{3n} \int \cdots \int v^*(\gamma q)[\gamma^2 \mathbf{T}_\gamma + \gamma^{-m}\mathbf{V}_\gamma]v(\gamma q)\,(dq)^{3n} \\ &= \gamma^2 \int \cdots \int v^*(\gamma q)\mathbf{T}_\gamma v(\gamma q)[d(\gamma q)]^{3n} + \gamma^{-m}\int \cdots \int v^*(\gamma q)\mathbf{V}_\gamma v(\gamma q)\,[d(\gamma q)]^{3n} \\ &= \gamma^2 \bar{T}_1 + \gamma^{-m}\bar{V}_1 \end{aligned} \tag{14.204}$$

where the final result is attained by comparison to (14.203) when γq is replaced by q. If $\bar{T}_1$ and $\bar{V}_1$ are not quite the best, varying γ may lower E'; hence, at the minimum,

$$\begin{aligned} 0 &= \frac{\partial E'}{\partial \gamma} = 2\gamma \bar{T}_1 - m\gamma^{-m-1}\bar{V}_1 \\ 2\gamma^2 \bar{T}_1 &= m\gamma^{-m}\bar{V}_1 \end{aligned} \tag{14.205}$$

Scaling improves $v(q)$ if $\gamma \neq 1$ in (14.205).

If $v(q)$ has been the true wave function $u(q)$, then $\bar{T}_1$ and $\bar{V}_1$ would be, respectively, $\bar{T}$ and $\bar{V}$. Scaling $u(q)$ would similarly lead to (14.205) where $\bar{T}_1 = \bar{T}$, $\bar{V}_1 = \bar{V}$, and $\gamma = 1$. That is, in a real system,

$$2\bar{T} = m\bar{V} \tag{14.206}$$

Equation (14.206) is the most useful result of the virial theorem, which need not be stated here. When all interactions are coulombic, $m = -1$ and

$$2\bar{T} = -\bar{V} \tag{14.207}$$

That is, in a real system of charged particles, the average kinetic energy is half as great as the average potential energy with its sign changed. As a result, increasing the nuclear charge of a two-electron atom like He causes the average potential energy of the electrons to decrease, while their average kinetic energy increases.

On the other hand, when a system consists entirely of harmonic oscillators, $m = 2$ in (14.206) and

$$\bar{T} = \bar{V} \tag{14.208}$$

The (average) energy of a system of harmonic oscillators is divided equally on the average between kinetic and potential energies, for $E = \bar{T} + \bar{V}$. Any change in a system that affects E affects $\bar{T}$ and $\bar{V}$ equally and in the same sense if all potentials are harmonic oscillator potentials. Example 14.3 is a scaling of $v = ce^{-ax^2}$ in accord with (14.208).

Example 14.4 What is the average potential energy of the electron in the $3p$ state of H?

The $3s$, $3p$, and $3d$ states of H are degenerate according to (14.125) with energy

$$E_3 = -\frac{mZ^2e^4}{2(4\pi\epsilon_0)^2\hbar^2}\left(\frac{1}{3^2}\right)$$

By (14.207)

$$E_3 = \bar{T} + \bar{V} = -\frac{1}{2}\bar{V} + \bar{V} = \frac{1}{2}\bar{V}$$

Hence, in the $3p$ state of H,

$$\bar{V} = 2E_3 = -\frac{mZ^2e^4}{9(4\pi\epsilon_0)^2\hbar^2}$$

14.13 PERTURBATION METHOD

Like the variation method, the perturbation method is a scheme for calculating approximate energies and other properties of a system with an improvable wave function. In the variation method, the calculator has complete freedom in his choice of a trial function, and generally the amount of freedom in it is proportional to the agreement of E' with E_0. In the perturbation method, however, the wave function $u^{(0)}$ is known for the system described by the Schrödinger equation

$$\mathbf{H}^{(0)}u^{(0)} = E^{(0)}u^{(0)} \tag{14.209}$$

but u is not known for the real perturbed system described by

$$\mathbf{H}u = Eu \tag{14.210}$$

If the perturbation $\mathbf{H} - \mathbf{H}^{(0)}$ is small enough that the energies $E^{(0)}$ of the unperturbed system are not changed by more than their separations before perturbation, then the perturbation method of finding E and u of (14.210) generally works well. This discussion is limited to only the simplest ideas of the Rayleigh-Schrödinger method, for perturbation theory is well developed.[11]

In order to keep track of the various orders of perturbation, there is introduced into (14.210) a parameter λ(which will eventually be set equal to unity). The perturbation $\mathbf{U}$ is identified by λ, where

$$\lambda\mathbf{U} = \mathbf{H} - \mathbf{H}^{(0)} \tag{14.211}$$

The quantity $\mathbf{U}$ is commonly a small term from the potential energy terms; it may be the additional potential energy of the system because of its presence in an electric or magnetic field, the spin-spin or spin-orbit coupling energies of electrons and/or nuclei, or other energies. For simplicity, the perturbation is assumed to affect a nondegenerate energy state having the wave function $u^{(0)}$ before perturbation and the exact wave function

$$u = \sum_{n=0}^{\infty} \lambda^n u^{(n)} \tag{14.212}$$

after perturbation. The expansion (14.212) is an assumption of the Rayleigh-Schrödinger method, as is the expansion

$$E = \sum_{n=0}^{\infty} \lambda^n E^{(n)} \tag{14.213}$$

Substitution of the expansions (14.212) and (14.213) into (14.210) with account of (14.211) yields

$$(\mathbf{H}^{(0)} + \lambda\mathbf{U})[\sum_{m=0}^{\infty} \lambda^m u^{(m)}] - [\sum_{n=0}^{\infty} \lambda^n E^{(n)}][\sum_{p=0}^{\infty} \lambda^p u^{(p)}] \equiv 0 \tag{14.214}$$

Since (14.214) is true for any λ, the coefficients of $\lambda^0, \lambda, \lambda^2, \ldots$ must be zero. Hence, the terms of order λ^0 yield (14.209), while the terms of order λ yield

[11] J. O. Hirschfelder, W. Byers-Brown, and S. J. Epstein, "Recent Developments in Perturbation Theory," in volume I of *Advances in Quantum Chemistry*, New York: Academic Press, 1964, pp. 255–374.

$$\mathbf{H}^{(0)}u^{(1)} + \mathbf{U}u^{(0)} - E^{(0)}u^{(1)} - E^{(1)}u^{(0)} = 0$$

or

$$[\mathbf{H}^{(0)} - E^{(0)}]u^{(1)} = [E^{(1)} - \mathbf{U}]u^{(0)} \tag{14.215}$$

Similarly, from the λ^2 terms of (14.214) comes $\mathbf{H}^{(0)}u^{(2)} + \mathbf{U}u^{(1)} - E^{(0)}u^{(2)} - E^{(1)}u^{(1)} - E^{(2)}u^{(0)} = 0$, or

$$[\mathbf{H}^{(0)} - E^{(0)}]u^{(2)} = [E^{(1)} - \mathbf{U}]u^{(1)} + E^{(2)}u^{(0)} \tag{14.216}$$

By continuation, it is possible to write equations for any order of λ.

Equations (14.215) and (14.216) can both be simplified by multiplication by $u^{(0)*}$ and integration over $d\tau$. The left side of each is of the form

$$\int u^{(0)*}[\mathbf{H}^{(0)} - E^{(0)}]u^{(i)} d\tau \qquad (i = 1 \text{ or } 2)$$

However, by virtue of (14.40) with $\mathbf{w}_{\text{op}} = [\mathbf{H}^{(0)} - E^{(0)}]$, these become

$$\int [(\mathbf{H}^{(0)} - E^{(0)})u^{(0)}]^* u^{(i)} d\tau = 0$$

since $\mathbf{H}^{(0)}\, u^{(0)} = E^{(0)}u^{(0)}$ in (14.209). Accordingly, (14.215) yields

$$0 = E^{(1)} \int u^{(0)*}u^{(0)}\, d\tau - \int u^{(0)*}\mathbf{U}u^{(0)}\, d\tau$$

or

$$E^{(1)} = \frac{\int u^{(0)*}\mathbf{U}u^{(0)}\, d\tau}{\int u^{(0)*}u^{(0)}\, d\tau} \tag{14.217}$$

That is, the change in energy $E - E^{(0)} = E^{(1)}$ caused by the perturbation $\mathbf{U}$ is equal to $\mathbf{U}$ averaged over the original state of the system. The similarity of (14.217) to (14.172) is also obvious. If $\mathbf{U}$ is of odd parity, $E^{(1)}$ is zero because $u^{(0)*}u^{(0)}$ is always of even parity. Hence, it is often necessary to calculate $E^{(2)}$ if E is to be changed by $\mathbf{U}$.

A value of $E^{(2)}$ is found from (14.216) upon multiplication by $u^{(0)*}$ and integration over $d\tau$. As explained above, the left-hand member is zero; hence,

$$0 = \int u^{(0)*}[E^{(1)} - \mathbf{U}]u^{(1)} d\tau + E^{(2)} \int u^{(0)*}u^{(0)}\, d\tau \tag{14.218}$$

Normalizing u of (14.212) allows (14.218) to be simplified, for by (14.212)

$$1 = \lambda^0 \int u^{(0)*}u^{(0)}\, d\tau + \lambda \int (u^{(0)*}u^{(1)} + u^{(1)*}u^{(0)})\, d\tau + \cdots$$

But if $u^{(0)}$ is normalized, $1 = \int u^{(0)*}u^{(0)}\, d\tau$ and the λ term yields

$$0 = \int u^{(0)*}u^{(1)}\, d\tau + \int u^{(1)*}u^{(0)}\, d\tau$$

That is, when $u^{(0)}$ and $u^{(1)}$ are real, then $u^{(0)}$ and its correction $u^{(1)}$ are orthogonal. Thus, (14.218) becomes simply

$$E^{(2)} = \int u^{(0)}\mathbf{U}u^{(1)}\,d\tau = \int u^{(1)}\mathbf{U}u^{(0)}\,d\tau \qquad (14.219)$$

It can be shown that $E^{(3)}$ can be found from a knowledge of only $u^{(1)}$. Hence the energy can be calculated to the third order by the formula

$$E = E^{(0)} + E^{(1)} + E^{(2)} + E^{(3)}$$

if $u^{(0)}$ and $u^{(1)}$ are known. In general, if $u^{(n)}$ is known for $n = 0, 1, 2, \ldots k$, then the energy can be calculated to the order $2k + 1$.

One way of finding $u^{(1)}$ is to expand it in terms of the known complete set of unperturbed orthogonal normalized wave functions $u_i^{(0)}$. If the perturbation were removed, $u^{(1)}$ would vanish and $u^{(0)}$ would be one of the set $u_i^{(0)}$, say $u_s^{(0)}$. Hence, with s to label the state being perturbed,

$$u_s^{(1)} = \sum_i c_{si}u_i^{(0)} \qquad (14.220)$$

The coefficients c_{si} are found by substituting (14.220) into the simplest equation involving $u^{(1)}$, namely (14.215). After noting that $\mathbf{H}^{(0)}u_i^{(0)} = E_i^{(0)}u_i^{(0)}$, the result is

$$\sum_i c_{si}[E_i^{(0)} - E_s^{(0)}]u_i^{(0)} = [E_s^{(1)} - \mathbf{U}]u_s^{(0)} \qquad (14.221)$$

Multiplication by $u_j^{(0)}$ and integration yields zero on the left if $i \neq j$ because the $u_i^{(0)}$ are orthogonal functions. Hence, if $i \neq j \neq s$, there results

$$c_{sj}[E_j^{(0)} - E_s^{(0)}] = -\int u_j^{(0)}\mathbf{U}u_s^{(0)}\,d\tau = -U_{js}^{(0,0)} \qquad (14.222)$$

whence

$$c_{sj} = -\frac{U_{js}^{(0,\,0)}}{E_j^{(0)} - E_s^{(0)}} \qquad (14.223)$$

When it happens that $s = i$, (14.221) is simply $0 = [E_s^{(1)} - \mathbf{U}]u_s^{(0)}$ and the result of multiplication by $u_i^{(0)} = u_s^{(0)}$ and integration is $0 = E_s^{(1)} - U_{ss}^{(0,\,0)}$, which is (14.217). Hence, by (14.212), (14.220), and (14.223), the perturbation $\mathbf{U}$ causes $u_s^{(0)}$ to become

$$u_s = u_s^{(0)} - \sum_{\substack{i \\ (i\neq s)}} \frac{U_{is}^{(0,\,0)}}{E_i^{(0)} - E_s^{(0)}}\,u_i^{(0)} \qquad (14.224)$$

which is correct to first order.

Equation (14.224) has two interesting features. First of all, and in contrast to the arbitrariness of the variation method, the perturbed wave function u_s is molded by the very nature of the perturbation $\mathbf{U}$. Secondly, the degree to which $u_s^{(0)}$ is affected by $\mathbf{U}$ depends on the natures (i.e. $u_i^{(0)}$) of each of the unperturbed states of the system. Other things being equal, the states with energies $E_i^{(0)}$ near the starting energy $E_s^{(0)}$ cause most of the change in $u_s^{(0)}$ because it is for these states that c_{si} is large, as indicated by (14.223).

The degeneracy of a state may be removed in various ways according to the nature of the perturbation. When all the many summations are carried out for the perturbation of a degenerate level, there results an equation very much like (14.180). It is called the *secular equation* because in similar problems of classical mechanics a perturbation may require a long time (in Latin, *saeculum* means a long period of time) to act before its effect is obvious. While most applications of perturbation theory in quantum chemistry involve initially degenerate levels, it seems sufficient here merely to contrast perturbation theory as an approximate method to the variation method, which has generally been more widely used in chemistry.

Example 14.5. Calculate the difference in zero-point energies of two one-dimensional harmonic oscillators with nearly equal classical frequencies
(a) exactly;
(b) to the first order by perturbation theory.
Then compare the results of (a) and (b).

(a) Let $\mathbf{V}_1 = 2\pi^2 m\, \nu_1^2\, x^2$ be the potential energy of the first harmonic oscillator, while $\mathbf{V}_2 = 2\pi^2 m\, \nu_2^2\, x^2$ is the second's. Then, by (14.64) or (14.82), the zero-point energy of the first is $(1/2)(h\nu_1)$, while that of the second is $(1/2)(h\nu_2)$. The difference in their zero-point energies is exactly $(1/2)h\,(\nu_1 - \nu_2)$.

(b) If the first oscillator is perturbed so as to make it like the second, its new potential energy is $\mathbf{V}_2$. The old Hamiltonian was $\mathbf{H}^{(0)} = \mathbf{T} + \mathbf{V}_1$, but the new one is $\mathbf{H} = \mathbf{T} + \mathbf{V}_2 = \mathbf{H}^{(0)} + \mathbf{V}_2 - \mathbf{V}_1$. That is, the perturbation suffered by the first oscillator is $\mathbf{U}_1 = \mathbf{V}_2 - \mathbf{V}_1 = 2\pi^2 m\,(\nu_2^2 - \nu_1^2)x^2$. Similarly, the second suffers the perturbation $\mathbf{U}_2 = \mathbf{V}_1 - \mathbf{V}_2 = 2\pi^2 m(\nu_1^2 - \nu_2^2)x^2$.

The unperturbed wave function $u_0^{(0)}$ of the ground state of the first oscillator, as given by (14.90), is

$$u_{01}^{(0)} = \left(\frac{\alpha_1}{\sqrt{\pi}}\right)^{1/2} e^{-\xi_1^2/2}$$

where $\xi_1 = \alpha_1 x$ and $\hbar\alpha_1^2 = 2\pi\, m\nu_1$ by (14.67). Hence, by (14.217), the first-order correction to the energy of the first oscillator is

$$\begin{aligned}
E_1^{(1)} &= \int_{-\infty}^{\infty} u_{01}^{(0)} \mathbf{U}_1 u_{01}^{(0)}\, dx \\
&= \frac{\alpha_1}{\sqrt{\pi}} \int_{-\infty}^{\infty} e^{-\xi_1^2/2} [2\pi^2 m(\nu_2^2 - \nu_1^2)x^2] e^{-\xi_1^2/2}\, dx \\
&= \frac{2\pi^2 m(\nu_2^2 - \nu_1^2)}{\alpha_1^2\sqrt{\pi}} \int_{-\infty}^{\infty} \xi_1^2\, e^{-\xi_1^2}\, d\xi_1 \\
&= \frac{2\pi^2 m(\nu_2^2 - \nu_1^2)}{\alpha_1^2\sqrt{\pi}} \int_0^{\infty} y^{(3/2)-1} e^{-y}\, dy \\
&= \frac{2\pi^2 m(\nu_2^2 - \nu_1^2)}{\alpha_1^2\sqrt{\pi}} \Gamma\left(\frac{3}{2}\right) \\
&= \frac{\pi^2 m(\nu_2^2 - \nu_1^2)}{\alpha_1^2} = \frac{\pi\hbar}{2\nu_1}(\nu_2^2 - \nu_1^2) \\
&= \frac{h}{2}\left(\frac{\nu_2 + \nu_1}{2\nu_1}\right)(\nu_2 - \nu_1)
\end{aligned}$$

But since $\nu_1 \approx \nu_2$, $E_1^{(1)} \approx (h/2)(\nu_2 - \nu_1)$ and, by (14.213), the energy of the first oscillator after perturbation is

$$E_1 = E_1^{(0)} + E_1^{(1)} + \cdots \approx \frac{h\nu_1}{2} + \frac{h}{2}(\nu_2 - \nu_1) = \frac{h\nu_2}{2}$$

Similarly, the first-order correction to the energy of the second oscillator is

$$E_2^{(1)} = \frac{h}{2}\left(\frac{\nu_1 + \nu_2}{2\nu_2}\right)(\nu_1 - \nu_2)$$

and its zero-point energy, correct to first-order after perturbation, is

$$E_2 = E_2^{(0)} + E_2^{(1)} \approx \frac{h\nu_1}{2}$$

These values of E_1 and E_2 match the exact values of (a) only because it was assumed along the way that $(\nu_1 + \nu_2)/2\,\nu_2$ or $(\nu_2 + \nu_1)/2\,\nu_1$ was unity. The amount by which these differ from unity is a measure of the accuracy of the perturbation method for this problem.

14.14 FUNDAMENTAL PARTICLES

It is not clear whether it is meaningful to say that everything is composed of certain species that act as fundamental or elementary particles. Tables 14.4 and 14.5 list certain reproducible events that have the nature of particles. Yet some have such short lifetimes (even in terms of the time required to traverse a distance of $\sim 10^{-13}$ cm, which is a typical nuclear radius) that they are plainly not permanent enough. Moreover, there seem to be so many listed in Tables 14.4 and 14.5 that it is not appealing to say all are elementary. Finally, even the well

Table 14.4 Fermions: Particles of Half-Integral Spin.

Particle		Antiparticle		Spin	Magnitude of Lifetime (sec)	Relative Mass
Name	Symbol	Name	Symbol			
Elneutrino	ν_e^0	Antielneutrino	$\bar{\nu}_e^0$	1/2	stable	0
Muneutrino	ν_μ^0	Antimuneutrino	$\bar{\nu}_\mu^0$	1/2	stable	0
Electron	e^-	Positron	e^+	1/2	stable	1
Negative Muon	μ^-	Positive Muon	μ^+	1/2	10^{-6}	207
Proton	p^+	Antiproton	p^-	1/2	stable	1836
Neutron	n^0	Antineutron	$\bar{n}^0$	1/2	10^3	1839
Lambda	Λ^0	Antilambda	$\bar{\Lambda}^0$	1/2	10^{-10}	2183
Positive Sigma	Σ^+	Negative Antisigma	$\bar{\Sigma}^-$	1/2	10^{-10}	2327
Neutral Sigma	Σ^0	Neutral Antisigma	$\bar{\Sigma}^0$	1/2	10^{-14}	2333
Negative Sigma	Σ^-	Positive Antisigma	$\bar{\Sigma}^+$	1/2	10^{-10}	2342
Neutral Xi	Ξ^0	Neutral Antixi	$\bar{\Xi}^0$	1/2	10^{-10}	2570
Negative Xi	Ξ^-	Postive Antixi	$\bar{\Xi}^+$	1/2	10^{-10}	2585

Table 14.5 Bosons: Particles of Zero or Integral Spin.

Particle		Antiparticle		Spin	Magnitude of Lifetime (sec)	Relative Mass
Name	Symbol	Name	Symbol			
Photon	γ^0	(itself)	γ^0	1	stable	0
Neutral Pion	π^0	(itself)	π^0	0	10^{-16}	264
Positive Pion	π^+	Negative Pion	π^-	0	10^{-8}	273
Positive Kaon	K^+	Negative Antikaon	K^-	0	10^{-7}	966
Neutral Kaon	K^0	Neutral Antikaon	$\overline{K^0}$	0	10^{-7} and 10^{-10}	974
Eta	η^0			0	10^{-20}	1074
Rho	$\rho^{\pm}, \rho^0$			1	10^{-21}	1468
Omega	ω^0			1	10^{-20}	1530
Phi	ϕ^0			1	10^{-20}	1995
Omega Minus	Ω^-			0	10^{-10}	3278

known neutron is unstable and the equally "fundamental" proton has been found to have structure, as though it were a meson cloud about a core of some kind. It is therefore relatively unimportant whether the lists in Tables 14.4 and 14.5 are complete or not. They do indicate something of the nature of the problem confronting the physicist. Indeed, it is very much like the problem of the chemist before the periodic table, and perhaps before the Bohr atom as well.

Since this book does not deal at length with nuclear phenomena, these two tables of particles are perhaps sufficient. It is, nevertheless, interesting to remark that every particle is expected to have an antiparticle with the same mass, spin, and lifetime, but opposite charge. Another way of classifying particles is by spin. Particles and antiparticles with zero or integral values of spin are *bosons*; species with half-integral values of spin (e.g. $\pm\frac{3}{2}$, $\pm\frac{1}{2}$) are *fermions.* The wave function of a system must be symmetric with respect to interchanges of identical bosons, but it must be antisymmetric with respect to interchange of any two identical fermions. Examples of antisymmetric wave functions for electrons were illustrated in Section 14.9. In any change, bosons may be generated or destroyed in any number, but the net number of fermions is conserved. Indeed, the law of conservation for fermions is applied separately to two classes of fermion. The fermions $\mu^{\pm}$, $e^{\pm}$, and the four neutrinos are called *leptons*; the more massive $p^{\pm}$, n^0, $\bar{n}^0$, and the 12 hyperons (Λ, Σ, Ξ) are called *baryons.* In any change, the net number of leptons and the net number of baryons are each conserved. For this record, the net number of each is the number of particles diminished by the number of antiparticles. For example, when the energy of one or more photons is converted into mass, leptons and/or baryons are generated in pairs, one of the pair being a particle while the other is an antiparticle. Similarly, the process of annihilation, which is the reverse of pair-production, is the conversion of a particle and its antiparticle into one or more bosons, usually photons. A particular example of annihilation is $e^+ + e^- \longrightarrow n\gamma^0$, where n is an even or odd integer. Before and afterwards, the net number of leptons is zero. Another particular example is the spontaneous decay of a neutron by the process $n^0 \longrightarrow p^+ + e^- + \bar{\nu}^0$; here, the net number of baryons is one and the net number of leptons is zero.

The two examples $e^+ + e^- \longrightarrow n\gamma^0$ and $n^0 \longrightarrow p^+ + e^- + \bar{\nu}^0$ follow other laws of conservation. Energy in all forms, including the energy-equivalent of mass, is conserved. So also are linear and angular momentum. Since spin is a form of angular momentum, and since the spin of γ^0 is unity, the production of an odd number of photons by $e^+ + e^- \longrightarrow n\gamma^0$ requires the spins of e^+ and of e^- to be alike (both $+1/2$ or both $-1/2$). However, if an even number of photons is generated by $e^+ + e^- \longrightarrow n\gamma^0$ the spins of e^+ and e^- are opposed (one is $+1/2$, the other is $-1/2$), as are the spins of γ^0. Similarly, when $n^0 \longrightarrow p^+ + e + \bar{\nu}^0$, the net spin of the products must be the spin ($\pm 1/2$) of n^0; hence, two of the three spins are alike in the products. It is, of course, not unexpected to find the net charge of products and of reactants unchanged by the reaction. Charge is conserved in all changes.

Matter acts on matter by four kinds of process. The most obvious of these is *gravitation*, and there is some evidence for the existence of a stable boson, of spin 2 and called a graviton, that acts as the quantum of the gravitational field. The photon is the quantum of the electromagnetic field; *electromagnetic interaction* includes the macroscopically observable laws of electricity and magnetism. Of course, Coulomb's law and other electromagnetic behavior operate on the microscopic level of atoms and thus are of paramount importance to chemistry. The two other kinds of interaction are typically physics. The *weak interactions* involve neutrinos and include such processes as beta decay of radioactive nuclei and the spontaneous decay of a muon to an electron and two neutrinos. The fourth kind of interaction is the *strong interaction*; it is responsible for nuclear binding and, on occasion, its effects are observable to the senses in fission and fusion reactions. The particle that is typically involved in binding protons and neutrons into nuclei is the *pion*, whose range of action extends over distances of the order of 10^{-12} cm and less. Like the *graviton* for the gravitational field and the *photon* for the electromagnetic field, a *meson* is the quantum for the nuclear field, and a *nucleon* is a source of virtual mesons that act between interacting nucleons. The lifetime of such a meson is of the order of the time uncertainty $\Delta t = \hbar/\Delta E$, where $\Delta E = c^2 M$ is the energy-fluctuation of a nucleon and is the energy-equivalent of a meson's mass M. If Δt is about the time it takes a meson to pass a nucleus of radius R at the speed of light, then $\Delta t = R/c \approx 10^{-23}$ sec. Hence, $M = \hbar/c^2\,\Delta t \approx 10^{-25}$ g, which corresponds to a particle with a mass between that of an electron (ca. 10^{-27} g) and that of a proton (ca. 10^{-24} g).

14.15 NUCLEAR STRUCTURE

The natures of nuclei are of interest to chemists who use radioactive or stable tracers, who establish atomic weights by mass spectral methods (Section 14.16), who need to know the influence of nuclear properties on the energy states of molecules so as to calculate thermodynamic properties properly from molecular events by statistical mechanics (Chapter 17), who correlate as in magnetic resonance spectroscopy the energy states of nuclei with chemical properties of molecules, and so on and on. It is always wise to be somewhat familiar with the aims and problems of a subject like physics, which often provides keys to thorough understanding of chemistry. Still, this modest section must be confined merely to a few remarks, some of which may provoke study elsewhere in more depth.

The first clues about nuclear structure came from radioactivity. In 1896 Becquerel discovered radioactivity in uranium ores and found it to be independent of the chemical state of uranium. Actually recent findings have shown that the rate of decay of certain radioactive nuclei of very light elements does depend slightly on their chemical state, which influences the wave function of the extranuclear (chemical) electrons at the nucleus, which has finite size. Nevertheless, Becquerel's observation called for a nonchemical explanation of radioactivity. By 1900, the characteristic α, β, and γ rays were distinguished in the various sources of radioactivity, and by 1903 the Rutherford-Soddy rules had been formulated.

Alpha decay decreases the atomic weight by four and changes the chemical family of an element, as if it had moved toward lighter elements by two places in the periodic table. Nowadays, this displacement would be described as $\Delta A = -4$ and $\Delta Z = -2$, where A is the mass number and Z is the atomic number. Beta decay was recognized as causing $\Delta A = 0$ and $\Delta Z = +1$, while gamma decay causes no change in A or Z. Rutherford and Royds showed in 1909 that α particles became He after passage through thin glass walls into an evacuated vessel where they were identified spectroscopically. In 1911 Rutherford scattered alpha particles off atoms in metallic foils and interpreted his results by classical mechanics in terms of the familiar nuclear atom. He estimated the radius of a typical nucleus to be of the order of 10^{-11} cm. By 1919 he had caused the first artificial nuclear disintegration

$$^{4}_{2}\mathrm{He} + {}^{14}_{7}\mathrm{N} \longrightarrow {}^{1}_{1}\mathrm{H} + {}^{17}_{8}\mathrm{O}$$

The protons that were generated had too long a range to be confused with the bombarding alpha particles ($^{4}_{2}\mathrm{He}^{2+}$). Mass number and nuclear charge are conserved in such changes; hence, given the reactants and protons, the other product was inferred to be $^{17}_{8}\mathrm{O}$. Sometimes such changes are described in the abbreviated form $^{14}_{7}\mathrm{N}(\alpha, p)^{17}_{8}\mathrm{O}$.

Gamow, Gurney, and Condon in 1928 viewed α-decay as if an α particle in the unstable nucleus tunneled through a barrier in the nuclear potential, for the kinetic energy of some α particles was much less than that expected of coulombic repulsion if the α were generated at rest at the surface of a nucleus of radius ca. 10^{-12} cm. It is not (and was not) certain that α's exist as such within nuclei. With Chadwick's discovery of the neutron in 1932 (the year of the first particle accelerator), Heisenberg and Iwanenko were able to discard the theory that a nucleus of mass number A and atomic number Z consists of A protons and $A - Z$ electrons. They said that nuclei consist of Z protons and $A - Z$ neutrons. The electron-proton theory was unsatisfactory in expecting the electron to contract to nuclear size and in explaining nuclear spin. For example, if electrons really exist in nuclei of odd charge, the nuclear spin should be half-integral because the $A - Z$ proton-electron pairs would yield integral spin (perhaps zero) while the odd proton would have no partner, not even another proton of half-integral spin. Yet molecular spectroscopy showed many nuclei of odd Z with integral spin ($i = 1$ for ${}^{14}_{7}N$, ${}^{2}_{1}H$, and others). Moreover, ${}^{15}_{7}N$ had half-integral spin and yet would be expected to have an even number of protons plus electrons (15 + 7). If, however, nuclei consist of neutrons and protons, then ${}^{15}_{7}N$ has an odd number of nucleons and half-integral spin, while ${}^{14}_{7}N$ and ${}^{2}_{1}H$ have even numbers and integral spin, as observed.

The mass of a nucleus is always less than the sum of the masses of its constituent neutrons and protons. The loss Δm in mass is interpreted as an energy ΔE of combination by the familiar equation

$$\Delta E = c^2 \Delta m \tag{14.225}$$

Figure 14.6 shows the smoothed trend in binding energies, calculated by dividing ΔE by the number of nucleons in the nucleus. There are near $A = 62$, $A = 88$, $A = 120$, $A = 140$, and $A = 208$ very slight rises that indicate minor changes in binding energy. The truly remarkable feature of Figure 14.6 is that

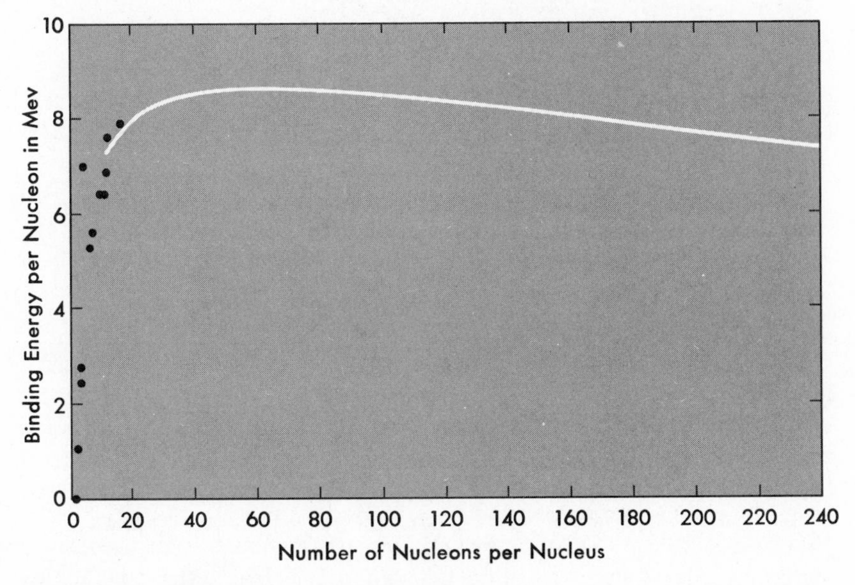

Figure 14.6. Binding Energy Per Nucleon

the binding energies of nuclei with more than about 20 nucleons are all close to 8 Mev, or almost 0.001 atomic mass unit per nucleon. This constancy indicates that addition of a nucleon results in its own stabilization but no net stabilization through its interaction with all other nucleons already present. For if each new nucleon interacted equally with all A others already present, the binding energy curve should rise at a rate proportional to A. Indeed, the slight decline in slope is attributed to protons' coulombic repulsions.

Figure 14.7 lists the numbers of neutrons and protons in stable nuclei. It is clear that heavy stable nuclei have more neutrons than protons. A close study of Figure 14.7 would show that there are never more than two stable nuclei with the same atomic number Z if Z is odd. When binding energies, abundances of nuclei, number of isotopes (same Z, different $N = A - Z$) and isotones (same N, different Z), cross sections for the capture of neutrons, nuclear electric quadrupoles, and half-lives of γ- and neutron-emission are studied, it becomes clear that certain numbers of neutrons or protons confer extraordinary stability on nuclei. These so-called "magic numbers" are 2, 8, 20, 28, 50, 82, and 126; sometimes 6 and 14 are also listed. Nuclei like $^{16}_{8}O$, $^{40}_{20}Ca$, $^{208}_{82}Pb$ are doubly "magic" and have even greater stability and even smaller tendency to capture neutrons than do nuclei like $^{58}_{28}Ni$ and $^{88}_{38}Sr$, which have only one magic number. Nuclei with a magic number of nucleons have low electric

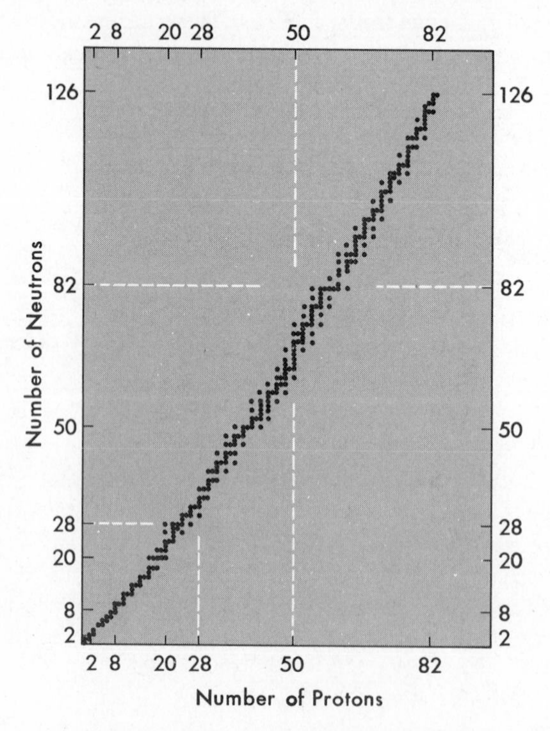

Figure 14.7. Numbers of Neutrons and Protons in Stable Nuclei

quadrupoles; hence, these are nearly spherical. Nuclei needing only one neutron to attain a magic number have unusually great cross sections for neutron capture. On the other hand, nuclei with one nucleon beyond a magic number hold that extra nucleon only loosely or emit a neutron by delayed emission (short-term radioactive decay).

It is now generally believed that the various nuclei have been built from hydrogen in stars. Various processes generate nuclei near Fe with evolution of energy. Then, in a great puff of neutrons in a supernova (stellar explosion), nuclei like Fe capture many neutrons all at once. It is likely that the flux of neutrons ends suddenly and that the nuclei now observed are the result of decay processes that bring the numbers of neutrons and protons ever closer to the dots of Figure 14.7. It is even possible that matter has undergone several cycles of nuclear synthesis and fission.

As physicists learned more and more about nuclei, they proposed models to explain their knowledge in the hope of predicting new facts or at least suggesting new experiments. The two main models, the *liquid-drop model* and the *shell model*, were first proposed in the 1930's. The liquid-drop model imagines the nucleus as a domain through which nucleons are almost free to roam by their wavelike delocalization and zero-point energy. The domain is limited, however, by the powerful short-range nuclear forces which appear to be caused by exchange of pi mesons. The binding energy is analogous to the heat of vaporization of an ordinary liquid, and the decline in binding energy for nuclei with less than 20 nucleons is attributed to a rise in surface energy like that of small liquid droplets as their surface area rises upon division of droplets. Too many nucleons, or vibrations of a drop through addition of neutrons, cause pulsating vibration of a large nucleus and perhaps its fission. This model accounts also for the observation that nuclear matter has almost a constant density. When $10 < Z < 80$, the effective radius of a nucleus containing A nucleons is about $(\frac{5}{4})A^{1/3} \times 10^{-15}$ meters. That is, $R^3 \propto A$.

The shell model, which has come to renewed favor with the introduction of *j-j* coupling (cf Section 14.10) in 1949, is more specific than the liquid-drop model. Like the extranuclear electrons of an atom, the nucleons follow the Pauli exclusion principle and seem to occupy certain energy states which become fully occupied at the magic numbers. Although atomic electrons move in the strong central field of the nucleus and interact with all other electrons through the coulomb field of virtual photons, the interactions of nucleons are not dominated by one central force and occur between pairs of nucleons with little interaction with other nucleons present in the nucleus, except that all obey the exclusion principle with regard to limited occupancy of each available state. The nucleons are presumed to obey the Schrödinger equation in the form

$$-\frac{\hbar^2}{2}\sum_{i=1}^{A}\frac{1}{M_i}\left(\frac{\partial^2 u}{\partial x_i^2}+\frac{\partial^2 u}{\partial y_i^2}+\frac{\partial^2 u}{\partial z_i^2}\right)+\sum_{i>j}V_{ij}u = Eu$$

where a nucleon of mass M_i is at x_i, y_i, z_i, under the action of a potential V_{ij}

when E is the energy of the nucleus. Although V_{ij} is unknown, some information about it can be surmised if the E's of a nucleus are known by observation and if a shrewd guess is made about u. The nucleon-nucleon potential V_{ij} is close to being a two-body interaction, flat-bottomed like a square well of radius $\sim 10^{-15}$ cm. The magic numbers 2, 8, and 20 come from a flat-bottomed square well, and the magic numbers 50 and 82 come if a hump is added at the center of the nucleus. The shell model gives a satisfactory account of the parity of nuclear ground states (minimum E), of the energy distribution of low-lying states, and of nuclear magnetic moments. For example, the angular momenta of nuclei of odd mass number is, in the ground state, correlated with the angular momentum of the odd nucleon.

The requirement for atomic electrons that the orbital angular momentum quantum number l range from zero to one less than the principal quantum number stems from the requirement that the radial function $R(r)$ be properly bounded as $r \longrightarrow \infty$. The radial dependence for the nuclear wave function is such, however, that there is no analogous limit on the integral values of spatial angular momentum of nucleons in a nucleus. That is, l is not limited by the size of the radial quantum number, which is like the quantum number of a particle

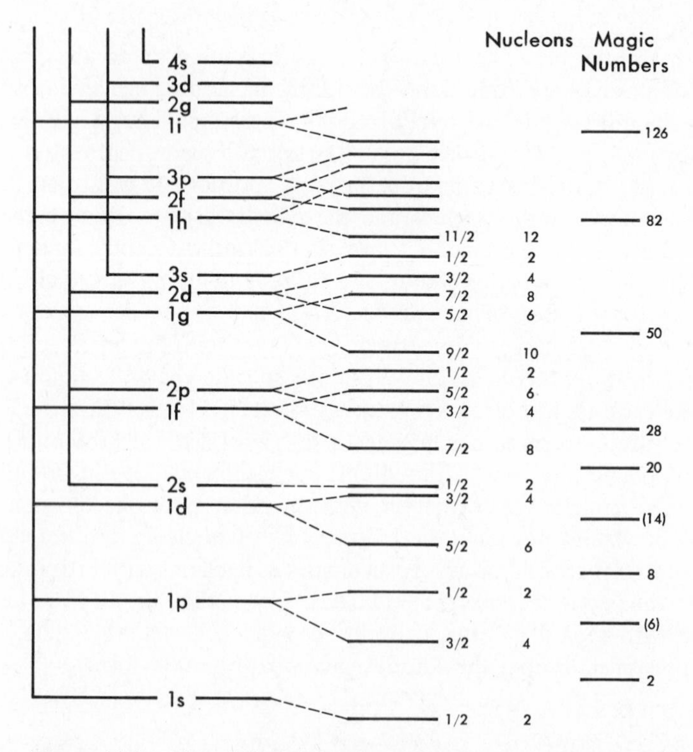

Figure 14.8. How Magic Numbers Come From Nuclear Energy States (*nlj*)

in a one-dimensional box. Thus it is possible to have states 1*s*, 1*p*, 1*d*, 1*f*, 1*g*, . . . 2*s*, 2*p*, 2*d*, 2*f*, 2*g*, . . . and so on, where, as usual, *s* means $l = 0$, *p* means $l = 1$, *d* means $l = 2, \ldots$

Besides these two quantum numbers (radial and angular), nucleons have spin ($+1/2$ or $-1/2$) and a component of total angular momentum along a preferred direction. The coupling of spin and angular momentum according to the scheme of *j*-*j* coupling yields, for each value of l_i for nucleon *i*, two energy states, a more stable one with total angular momentum $j_i = l_i + 1/2$ and a less stable one with $j_i = l_i - 1/2$. The degeneracy of each state is $2j_i = 2l_i \pm 1$, for the possible values of j_i are $j_i, j_i - 1, j_i - 2, \ldots +1/2, -1/2, -3/2, \ldots -j_i$ in an external magnetic field that causes one direction to be preferred. A proper spacing of the states of various j_i allows significant energy gaps at the magic numbers, as shown in Figure 14.8. A simple mnemonic device for the order of states nl_i is offered in Figure 14.9.

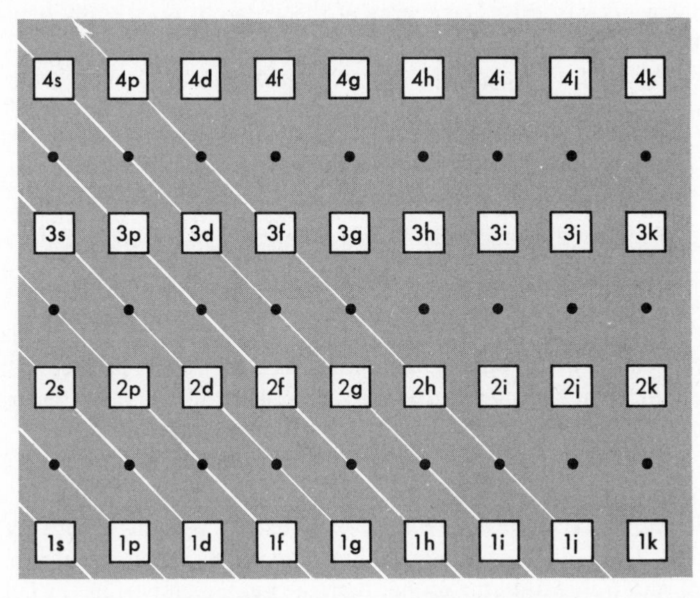

Figure 14.9. Mnemonic Device for Energies of Nucleons in Nuclei

14.16 MASS SPECTROSCOPY

A mass spectroscope is a device for producing and accelerating ionized gas molecules, or fragments thereof, by an electric field, for separating these gaseous ions according to their various masses, and for detecting the numbers of such ions after their separation. If detection is by photography, the device is called a mass spectrograph; if by electrical measurement, a mass spectrometer. Mass spectroscopes can separate isotopes, even in macroscopic amounts (e.g. ^{235}U or stable tracers), perform difficult analyses (e.g. hydrocarbon mixtures), measure isotopic abundances for determining atomic weights or the ages of minerals, and measure atomic (i.e. nuclear) masses within 1 part in 10^8 for calculations of binding energies and atomic weights. Connected to a vacuum apparatus with leaks, a portable mass spectrometer that reacts to He is used to detect the leaks when a jet of He is directed externally at various suspicious parts of the vacuum apparatus. Besides such qualitative and quantitative analysis, it is possible to determine molecular weights and even molecular structure.

The actual separation of gaseous ions of different mass is done at a pressure of less than 10^{-6} mm Hg. In many instruments, molecules leak into this evacuated region from a storage region at a pressure of about 10^{-2} mm Hg. Solid and liquid samples can be heated to attain such a pressure. A beam of electrons directed transverse to the direction of the beam of neutral molecules bombards them and thus generates ions. The energy of the electrons is carefully regulated and often lies near 70 ev. Such energy is sufficient to ionize molecules and cause them to disintegrate into fragments. Organic chemists are familiar with such decays of carbonium ions as well as with the stability of aromatic molecules that have lost just an electron. A direct determination of molecular weight can be made whenever an ion has not decayed. Besides bombardment with electrons, it is possible to generate ions of a sample by ionization at a heated surface. The neutral molecules may approach the surface as a gas or may be deposited as a solid on the surface before it is heated. When the work function ϕ of the surface heated to temperature T is less than the ionization potential I of the element to be studied, the ratio of positive to neutral gas molecules generated at the heated surface is $\exp[e(\phi - I)/kT]$. Such surface ionization may offer greater sensitivity than electron bombardment, the most common method of generating gaseous ions. Many other devices for producing ions are known.

Upon generation, the ions are accelerated by a potential difference up to several kilovolts. In a time-of-flight mass spectrometer, about 3000 volts are applied in pulses. Massive ions reach a modest velocity while light ions reach a higher velocity. The light ions thus run the standard distance, about a meter, to the electron-multiplier detector sooner than the more massive ions. A pulse of ions reaches the detector, which measures the number of ions by measuring their charge, in successive flights, each flight of the pulse having one mass. An oscilloscope synchronized with the pulses, displays the ion currents of the several flights as they arrive during a pulse. The time of flight is proportional to the square root of the ratio of mass to charge. A mass-resolution of 1 in 400 is readily achieved. The main advantages of a time-of-flight mass spectrometer are its high scan rate, which allows analysis of fast chemical reactions, and its small mass, for the instrument needs no large magnetic field.

A mass-resolution of 1 in 10^5 is possible in a mass spectroscope that sorts ions by means of both electric and magnetic fields. In 1913, J. J. Thomson was just able in the first mass spectroscope to resolve $^{20}Ne^+$ from $^{22}Ne^+$. By 1918 and 1919, Dempster and Aston in their spectroscopes were able to resolve 1 in 100. Many arrangements of fields have been tried in the meantime. At the present time, with a double-focusing device, a resolution of 1 in 10^5 is possible and relative atomic masses can be observed to 1 part in 10^8. Figure 14.10 is a schematic diagram of a very simple mass spectrometer with a resolution of about

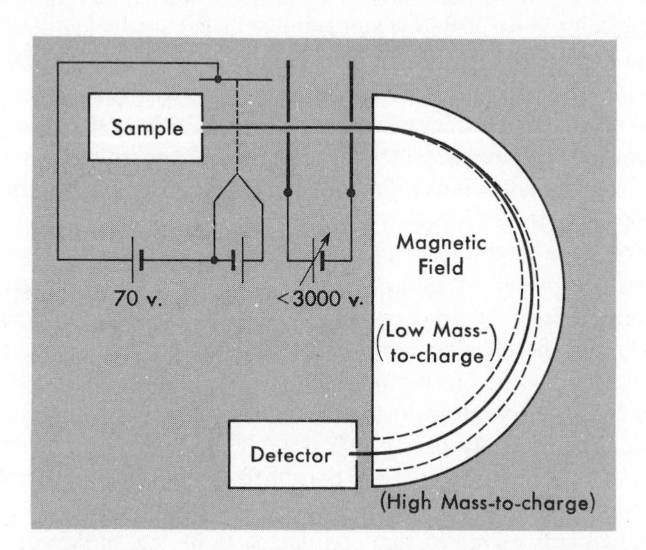

Figure 14.10. Schematic Diagram of Mass Spectrometer Using Magnetic Resolution

1 in 700. The radius of curvature of the ion path is inversely proportional to the intensity of the uniform magnetic field, which has lines of force perpendicular to the plane of the molecule's trajectory. The radius of curvature is also proportional to the square root of the mass-to-charge ratio and to the square root of the electric potential used to accelerate the ions. Although both electric and magnetic fields may be varied, especially to accommodate greatly different ranges of mass, within a range of mass it is common to hold the magnetic field intensity constant and let the electric potential decrease slowly. As this occurs, the masses of the ions recorded at the fixed detector increase. The total electric charge detected is proportional to the number of ions. Instead of total charge, it is common to use peak height as a measure of the number of ions of a particular mass-to-charge (usually unit charge) ratio.

A pure organic sample may yield several ions of different mass because of decay of its carbonium ions. Typical organic chemistry reasoning with the use of bond energies and resonance stabilization energies can usually account for all observed peaks. When a sample contains several kinds of molecule, the peak height H_m at a particular mass may be caused by different ions. If A_{im} is the proportionality constant (called the sensitivity) linking the partial pressure p_i of species i in the sample to its peak height h_{im} under standard conditions of operation, then at the peak of mass m, the total intensity due to C components is

$$\sum_{i=1}^{C} A_{im} p_i = \sum_i h_{im} = H_m \tag{14.226}$$

A typical aliphatic hydrocarbon may have ten times as many peaks as it has carbon atoms because of the various ions and isotopes. As the electric potential rises, more and more kinds of ions result. If at least C equations like (14.226) are available, these simultaneous linear equations can be solved (by a computer, usually) for the unknown, but desired, partial pressures p_i. The sensitivities A_{im} are known by calibration with the use of standard samples. Modern instruments seldom use photography to detect ions because the response of the photographic plate is not the same for all ions.

Molecular weights are determined directly when it is possible to identify the *parent peak*, the one caused by molecules that have lost only one electron under electron bombardment. The parent peak is usually intense for aromatic hydrocarbons and other species whose ions are stabilized by resonance. The parent peak may not be the one of greatest mass-to-charge ratio, for a parent ion may abstract a hydrogen atom from another molecule to produce what is called a $p + 1$ peak. The intensity of a $p + 1$ peak is, however, proportional to the square of the sample pressure p_i, while that of the parent peak is proportional to p_i.

The number and kinds of molecular ions decreases as the energy of the bombarding electrons decreases. The minimum energy required to eject an electron from a molecule and remove it to an infinite distance while electron and

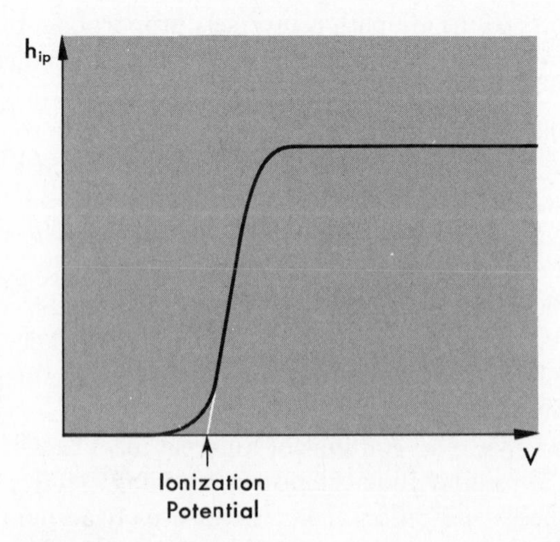

Figure 14.11. Determination of Ionization Potential of a Molecule by Mass Spectroscopy

molecule-ion are at rest is called the *ionization potential* of the molecule. Figure 14.11 shows how the ion current h_{ip} of a parent peak p depends on the potential V accelerating the electron beam. If the electron beam is not regulated to have electrons of just one energy, a few parent ions are produced when V is less than the true ionization potential. The tail at low V is easily eliminated by linear extrapolation as shown in Figure 14.11. Ionization potentials are sometimes useful in identification, in constructing energy cycles to determine or check bond energies, and in understanding valence. Much can also be learned about the elementary steps of gaseous reactions of ions as they collide with other species in mass spectroscopes.

14.17 SUMMARY

This has been a long chapter. The first four sections have introduced different postulatory bases of quantum mechanics in as simple a mathematical framework as possible in order that different viewpoints might paint a picture of the landscape and in their variety offer at least one explanation that makes good sense at first sight. It is amazing how such different mathematics can describe the same world.

The fifth and sixth sections on the harmonic oscillator and one-electron atom are truly most important because they are among the few problems having simple analytic solutions for the energy and wave function. The harmonic oscillator is important in describing the generation and destruction of photons and any vibrating system with quantized energy, such as crystals and molecules. And the one-electron problem, the prototype of all problems having central forces, furnishes the various quantum numbers and angular wave functions that help to keep account of electrons in atoms and, by analogy, in molecules. The most important result of the harmonic oscillator problem is

$$E = \sum_i \left(n_i + \frac{1}{2}\right) h\nu_i \tag{14.95}$$

while the angular wave functions in Figure 14.3 are the most important result of the one-electron atom.

The remainder of the chapter develops several general theorems and mathematical techniques that are quite useful in describing molecules. The power of operators to give certain very general results is shown by its treatment of angular momentum. The Pauli exclusion principle affects every facet of microscopic events and spills over into the macroscopic world in its effect on populations of states and the calculation of thermodynamic properties by quantum statistical mechanics. The virial theorem in the simple form

$$2\bar{T} = m\bar{V} \tag{14.206}$$

offers an understanding of what a quantum mechanical system is really doing. It also, of course, is related to the use of scale parameters in the variation method.

Since problems of real interest are generally far too complex for exact treatment, the theoretician is obliged to become an artist in the manipulation of the Schrödinger equation (or its mathematical equivalent). The variation method, which calls for a minimum in

$$E' = \int v^*(\tau)\mathbf{H}v(\tau)\,d\tau \tag{14.165}$$

with a hope that E' is close to reality, is probably the most used and most useful tactic. When $v(\tau)$ is a superposition of various simpler situations, the variation in their relative contributions to a pseudostate of minimum energy E' leads to the secular equation

$$|H_{ij} - S_{ij}E'| = 0$$

which can be used at once without continual rederivation.

Another major tactic in extracting a reluctant energy from the Schrödinger equation is the perturbation method. In competent hands, it need not be limited to small changes in systems of known behavior. Its conspicuous advantage is that the perturbation itself reshapes and refines the approximate wave function of the unperturbed state. It is even possible to use the variation method on results calculated by perturbation theory and thus benefit doubly. Perturbation theory is particularly good for calculating properties other than the energy, for a zero-order wave function can yield the energy correct to second order, while other properties are correct only to first order. To get the others to second order, one needs the wave function with its first-order correction, which perturbation theory finds easily and in a manner that best fits the nature of the perturbation.

What has been set forth in very general terms in this chapter has use not only for physicists but also for chemists, as the next chapter will amply show. If some of the problems are difficult to understand now, they may make more sense after a study of the next chapter.

PROBLEMS

1. What modification in the rules of baseball would allow the description of a player's reaching second base to be analogous to the trajectory of a wave-particle from home to second base?
   Answer: Make it unnecessary for a batter to go to second via first base.
2. Explain why a classical particle ($S \gg \hbar$) cannot stray from its classical path (S is an extremum), while a wave-particle ($S \approx \hbar$) can meander.
   Answer: Classical particle has short λ and destructively interferes with itself even a short way off its classical path.

3. In spherical polar coordinates show that the angular momentum operator $\mathbf{M}_z$ for rotation about the z axis is $-i\hbar\, \partial/\partial\phi$.

4. Find the wave function and allowed energies of a nonisotropic ($\nu_x \neq \nu_y \neq \nu_z \neq \nu_x$) three-dimensional harmonic oscillator.
Answer: $E = (n_x + 1/2)h\nu_x + (n_y + 1/2)h\nu_y + (n_z + 1/2)h\nu_z$ and $u(x, y, z) = w(\xi_x)\, w(\xi_y)\, w(\xi_z)$.

5. With the aid of the remarks at the end of Section 14.6 and the fact that $R(r)$ for s-electrons is not zero at $\rho = 0$, sketch the radial wave functions $R(r)$ for $1s$, $2s$, $3s$, $4s$, $2p$, $3p$, $4p$, $3d$, $4d$, and $4f$ states of H.

6. Show that the hydrogen angular wave functions for $l = 1$ have maxima along the directions of the Cartesian axes.

7. Show that the three normalized $2p$ angular wave functions of H obey the relation

$$\sum_{m=-1}^{m=+1} \Theta_{1m}^* \Phi_m^* \Theta_{1m} \Phi_m = 3$$

8. Evaluate the energies of a one-electron atom in terms of the fine-structure constant $\alpha = e^2/4\pi\epsilon_0\hbar c$.
Answer: $E_n = -mc^2\alpha^2/2n^2$.

9. By the use of operators, show that $\mathbf{M}_z$ commutes with $\mathbf{M}_x^2 + \mathbf{M}_y^2 + \mathbf{M}_z^2$.

10. The eigenvalue equation for angular momentum about the z axis is $\mathbf{M}_z\, u_z = m u_z$ where m is a number. Transform $\mathbf{M}_z$ to plane polar coordinates r, ϕ (where $x = r \cos \phi$ and $y = r \sin \phi$) and find u_z.
Answer: $u_z =$ (const.) $\exp\,(i\, m\, \phi)$.

11. Show that a system of two weakly interacting alpha particles has a wave function that is approximately symmetric to interchange of alphas. Is this system's wave function really symmetric? Explain.
Answer: No, for it consists of particles of half-integral spin (neutrons and protons).

12. Show that the Russell-Saunders states for three equivalent p electrons are ${}^4S$, ${}^2D$, and ${}^2P$.

13. If the variation trial function ϕ is not normalized, show that the real energy is

$$E_0 \leqslant \frac{\int \phi^* \mathbf{H} \phi \, d\tau}{\int \phi^* \phi \, d\tau}$$

14. By varying the coefficients in the linear variation function $v = c_1\phi_1 + c_2\phi_2 + c_3\phi_3$, find the more stable stationary state of a particle whose behavior is described by a superposition of states with wave functions ϕ_1, ϕ_2, and ϕ_3. Assume $H_{11} = H_{22} = H_{33}$ and that $H_{ij} = H_{ji}$, $S_{ii} = 1$, and $S_{ij} = S_{ji} = 0$ if $j \neq i$.
(a) *Case I* (as if states 1, 2, and 3 were collinear with 1 far from 3): $H_{13} = 0$ while $H_{ij} < 0$ otherwise.
(b) *Case II* (as if states 1, 2, and 3 were in a ring with interaction only by pairs): $H_{ij} < 0$ for all $i \neq j$. In which case does the particle have the lower energy? [Hint: In solving (14.183) for E', it is helpful to divide the determinant by H_{12}^3.]
Answer: Case I: $E_I' = H_{11} + \sqrt{2}\, H_{12}$; Case II: $E_{II}' = H_{11} + 2H_{12} < E_I'$.

15. For a free particle with constant potential energy everywhere, one expects the

average kinetic energy to equal the total energy. Yet the virial theorem with $m = 0$ predicts zero average kinetic energy. Explain.

16. By means of a term diagram (with Russell-Saunders symbols) account for the observed transitions [W. C. Martin, *J. Res. Nat. Bureau Standards* **64A,** 19 (1960)] of He and calculate the energy of the unobserved changes $1s^2 - 1s\,2s$ and $1s^2 - 1s\,3s$.

Terminal States	Energy (cm^{-1})		
$1s^2$—$1s\,2p$	169086.94	171135.00	
$1s^2$—$1s\,3p$	185564.68	186209.47	
$1s^2$—$1s\,4p$	191492.82		
$1s\,2s$—$1s\,2p$	4857.454	9231.4 $\pm$ 0.4 (three states)	
$1s\,2s$—$1s\,3p$	19931.925	25708.594	
$1s\,2s$—$1s\,4p$	25215.271	31361.07	
$1s\,3s$—$1s\,2p$	13729.936	14148.964	14150.000
$1s\,3s$—$1s\,4p$	6627.881		

Answer: 159856.069 and 166277.55; 183236.892 and 184864.94 cm^{-1}.

17. What is the effect of a field ($V = \pm ax$) on the low-energy states of a particle in a one-dimensional box?

18. What is the wave length of a neutrino of energy E if particles of zero mass have energies $E = pc$, where p is momentum and c is the velocity of light.
Answer: $\lambda = hc/E$.

19. What is the atomic weight of a sample of sulfur containing 95.0% ${}^{32}_{16}S$ (31.9822), 4.16% ${}^{34}_{16}S$ (33.9786), 0.77% ${}^{33}_{16}S$ (32.9819), and 0.016% ${}^{36}_{16}S$? The percentages are by atom abundance.
Answer: 32.0724.

20. Calculate the reversible isothermal work required to separate a mixture of C kinds of molecule.

Answer: $w = -T\Delta S = RT \sum_{i=1}^{C} X_i \ln X_i$

21. If the probability of tunneling through a square one-dimensional barrier is the ratio of $|u|^2$ upon exit to $|u|^2$ upon entry, then what is the probability that an electron may tunnel through a barrier 100A thick if its energy-height above the electron's energy is 500 cm^{-1}? If 50.0 cm^{-1}?
Answer: 8.5×10^{-12}; 3.3×10^{-4}.

22. Show that $\mathbf{x}\mathbf{p}_x - \mathbf{p}_x\mathbf{x} = i\hbar$ but that $\mathbf{x}\mathbf{p}_y - \mathbf{p}_y\mathbf{x} = 0$. Relate these results to the uncertainty principle.

23. By actual calculation, show that $0 = \int_{-\infty}^{\infty} w_1(\xi)w_0(\xi)\,d\xi$.

24. Find the direction in which the angular wave functions of hydrogen for $l = 2$ have maxima.
Answer: If $m = 0, \theta = \pi n$; if $m = +1, \phi = \pi n$ and $4\theta = 2n' + 1$; if $m = -1$, $2\phi = \pi(2n + 1)$ and $4\theta = \pi\,(2n' + 1)$; if $m = -2$, $4\phi = \pi(2n + 1)$ and $2\theta = \pi n'$; if $m = +2$, $2\phi = \pi n$ and $2\theta = \pi n'$. (The symbol n is not the principal quantum number here.)

25. When $\mathbf{V} = V(r)$, show that $\mathbf{M}^2 = \mathbf{M}_x^2 + \mathbf{M}_y^2 + \mathbf{M}_z^2$ commutes with $\mathbf{H}$.

26. Construct a wave function for a system of two identical fermions and a boson.

27. Show that the Russell-Saunders states for two nonequivalent p electrons are ^3D, ^3P, ^3S, ^1D, ^1P, ^1S.

28. In electric dipolar radiation, whether the coupling of electrons is $j - j$ or Russell-Saunders, show that the quantum number for electronic orbital angular momentum must change by unity.
Answer: Laporte rule: $g \rightleftharpoons u$.

29. With a variation function of the form $c \exp(-ar^2)$, calculate the lowest energy of the hydrogen atom in terms of the real lowest energy E_1.
Answer: $E' = 8E_1/3\pi$.

30. Find the lowest stationary-state energy of a particle that is delocalized throughout four equivalent states, each of equal energy if occupied alone in the absence of the other states. The four states interact
(a) pairwise with each other, as though each were at the corner of a regular tetrahedron with equal interaction along every edge;
(b) pairwise with nearest neighbors, as though each were in a four-membered ring with no interaction diagonally across the ring;
(c) pairwise with nearest neighbors, as though each were in a linear array with no interaction between terminal states or with states separated by another state.
[Hint: In writing (14.183), assume $S_{ii} = 1$ and $S_{ij} = 0$ if $i \neq j$.]
Answer: (a) $E' = H_{11} + 3H_{12}$; (b) $E' = H_{11} + \sqrt{2}H_{12}$; (c) $E' = H_{11} + 1.618\, H_{12}$.

31. The average potential energy of a system rises x times as fast as its total energy. If the potential energy is a homogeneous function of the coordinates, of what degree is this homogeneous function?
Answer: $2(1 - x)/x$.

32. Show that u_n and $\mathbf{H}u_n$ are infinitesimals of the same order near nodes in u_n.

33. Since angular momentum, including spin, must be conserved in any event, show that an odd number of neutrinos is involved in the decay of:
(a) A pi meson into a mu meson.
(b) A neutron into a proton and an electron.

34. Pi mesons are said to bind nucleuses together by converting neutrons into protons and vice versa. Suggest possible reactions of this kind that conserve charge and momentum.

35. It is probable that all nucleuses of all atomic and mass numbers were about equal in abundance on formation. If true for ^{238}U ($t_{1/2} = 4.5 \times 10^9$ yr) and ^{235}U ($t_{1/2} = 0.71 \times 10^9$ yr), about how long has it been since these two isotopes were formed if now ^{238}U is 138 times as abundant as ^{235}U?
Answer: 6.0×10^9 yr.

---

36. When $\hbar$ is sufficiently small, show in one dimension that the Schrödinger equation reduces to the classical equation of mechanics by following these steps:
(a) If $S(x, \dot{x})$ is the classical action as in (14.17), show that $p_x = \partial S/\partial x$ is the linear momentum.
(b) If $S(x) = S_0(x) + \hbar S_1(x) + \hbar^2 S_2(x) + \ldots$ and if the stationary-state wave function is $u(x) = \exp[iS(x)/\hbar]$, show (by equating coefficients of equal powers of $\hbar$) that $u(x)$ in the Schrödinger equation yields the classical result $E = V(x) + (p_x^2/2m)$.

37. In view of the preceding problem, show that

$$S_1(x) = \frac{i}{4} \ln \left[\frac{2m(E - V)}{\hbar^2}\right]$$

38. Calculate $\bar{V}$ (the average value of the potential energy) of a one-dimensional harmonic oscillator for $n = 0$ and $n = 1$. Then find the average kinetic energy indirectly from this result and the total energy. The average value of the potential energy V is $\bar{V} = \int w^* V w \, dx$.
Answer: $\bar{V}_0 = \bar{T}_0 = h\nu_0/4$; $\bar{V}_1 = \bar{T}_1 = 3h\nu_0/4$.

39. Show that the Schrödinger equation for a rigid body that rotates in a plane about a fixed point is

$$-\frac{\hbar}{i} \frac{\partial \psi}{\partial t} = -\frac{\hbar^2}{2I} \frac{\partial^2 \psi}{\partial \phi^2}$$

where ϕ is the angle of rotation and $\psi = \psi(\phi, t)$. What kind of degeneracy exists here?

40. Find the energies and energy eigenfunctions of a particle free in a box with impenetrable walls and the shape of a right circular cylinder.

41. Show that the Russell-Saunders states for two equivalent d electrons are ^3F, ^3P, ^1G, ^1D, ^1S. Do likewise for eight equivalent d electrons.

42. By actual integration for a harmonic oscillator, show that $\Delta n = \pm 2$ and $\Delta n = \pm 3$ are forbidden for electric dipole radiation when one of the states (initial or final) is the ground state ($n = 0$).

43. Estimate the energy of the ground state of two-electron atoms of nuclear charge Z (e.g. He if $Z = 2$) by use of a variation function $e^{-a(r_1+r_2)}$ where r_i is the position of electron i from the fixed nucleus. It is useful to know that

$$\int_0^\infty \int_0^\infty e^{-2ar_1} \left(\frac{1}{r_{12}}\right) e^{-2ar_2} r_1^2 r_2^2 \, dr_1 \, dr_2 = \frac{5}{128a^5}$$

Answer: For He, $E = 5.696\, E_1$ where E_1 is the energy of H in its ground state ($n = 1$).

44. With a variational function v of the form axe^{-cx^2} find the lowest energy of the harmonic oscillator. In terms of parity of the wave function, explain why this energy is not $h\nu_0/2$.
Answer: $3\pi\hbar\nu_0$.

45. With a variational function of the form ae^{-Ar} in center-of-mass coordinates, find the lowest energy of the hydrogen atom. Or do the same for the harmonic oscillator if $v = ae^{-cx^2}$.
Answer: For H, $E = -\mu e^4/2\hbar^2$; for harmonic oscillator, $E = \pi\hbar\nu_0$.

46. If two states differ by 10.0 cm^{-1} in energy because of an interaction that removes their degeneracy, what would be the relative energies of three such degenerate states when their degeneracy is removed by an equal interaction? As usual, assume $S_{ii} = 1$ and $S_{ij} = 0$ if $i \neq j$. Each of the three states interacts equally with the others.
Answer: Most stable state stabilized by 10.0 cm^{-1} while other states destabilized by 5.0 cm^{-1} each.

47. Show that the third-order perturbation energy is

$$E^{(3)} = \int u^{(1)}[\mathbf{U} - E^{(1)}]\,u^{(1)}d\tau$$

when **U** is the perturbation, $E^{(1)}$ is the first-order perturbation energy, and $u^{(1)}$ is the first-order correction to the wave function.

48. Show how a linear transformation of space variables in the Schrödinger equation for a polyelectronic atom with nuclear charge $\mathbf{Z}e$ can bring all electron replusion terms to a perturbation of order $1/\mathbf{Z}$ while other terms of the polyelectronic wave equation are of order $(1/\mathbf{Z})^0$.
Answer: Let new space coordinates be $\mathbf{Z}r_{ij}$.

49. Show that u_n has a cusp at nuclei, where $|V| \longrightarrow \infty$.

50. What is the minimum kinetic energy of an electron free in a three-dimensional box about 10^{-12} cm on an edge? How does this compare to the energy of a typical β particle?
Answer: 10^{10} ev.

51. In mirror nuclei, the number of protons in one nucleus equals the number of neutrons in the other (that is, $N_1 = Z_2$ and $N_2 = Z_1$). The coulomb energy of Z protons distributed uniformly throughout a sphere of radius R is $3\,Z\,(Z-1)$ $e^2/(4\pi\epsilon_0)\;5R$. If the difference in coluomb energy of mirror nuclei is the sole cause of their difference in mass, estimate R for ${}^{19}_{9}\text{F}$ (19.00445) and ${}^{19}_{10}\text{Ne}$ (19.00794).
Answer: 4.78×10^{-15} m.

52. Natural bromine consists of almost equal numbers of ^{79}Br and ^{81}Br. What peak heights and mass differences are expected (under 1/700 resolution) in mass spectra of molecules containing
(a) one bromine atom per molecule
(b) two bromine atoms per molecule
Answer: (a) equal peak heights with $\Delta m = 2$; (b) three peaks with intensities $1 - 2 - 1$ and separations $\Delta m = 2$.

15 MOLECULAR STRUCTURE

15.1 INTRODUCTION

Every chemist is familiar with the electron-pair theory of chemical bonding as first described by G. N. Lewis in 1916. However, it has remained for mathematical chemists of a subsequent age to use the Schrödinger equation to explain how and why electrons hold nuclei together in molecules. The behavior of the electron is indeed the fundamental question of chemistry. And what is explained in this chapter for isolated molecules holds true for crystals, which are super molecules with periodic potentials because of the regular repetition of nuclei and electrons in space.

The Bohr theory of the one-electron atom could not be extended successfully, even by Sommerfeld, to explain the nature of the two-electron atom He or the one-electron molecule H_2^+. The masterful work of Hylleraas and others in eminently successful explanations of the energies and polarizability of He and the pioneering work of Burrau on H_2^+ and of Heitler and London on H_2, all done before 1930 with the Schrödinger equation, gave early assurance that the Schrödinger equation is worth trying to solve for very complicated molecules. The only problem is that the simple equation $\mathbf{H}\psi = E\psi$ is very, very hard to solve. It is good to know that $\mathbf{H}\psi = E\psi$ is the correct equation. It is easy to write out $\mathbf{H}\psi = E\psi$ explicitly, for the potential energy is merely the summation of the electrical attractions between nuclei and electrons and the repulsions of nucleus for nucleus or electron for electron. What is really troublesome, after a few straightforward simplifications have been made in the Schrödinger equation for molecule or polyelectronic atom, is keeping the electronic motions continuously correlated so that electrons, on the whole, avoid meeting each other.

If the two electrons of He are put into 1*s* orbitals, if their wave function is scaled to meet the demand of the virial theorem (14.207) that $2\bar{T} = -\bar{V}$, and if the electronic wave function is antisymmetric to satisfy the exclusion principle, there still inevitably remains an error of about 2% in the lowest energy of He when the electrons are not somehow kept apart. This is the so-called electronic correlation error. It is not negligible, for in He it is 1.5 electron volts with scaled $1s^2$ electrons and 1.14 ev with the best possible spherically symmetric function having equivalent electrons. However, when one electron is forced to be farther from the nucleus than the other, the discrepancy between theory and reality falls to 0.8 ev. Adding *p*, *d*, *f*, *g* character reduces it to 0.013 ev, for the new angular dependence of the wave function as directed by the variation principle allows not only radial (in-out) correlation but also angular (side-to-side) correlation of electronic position. Much of the remaining error is caused by neglecting relativity and the motion of the nucleus. With care, theory agrees exactly with experiment.

Vindication of the wave equation for He comes only with the aid of high-speed computers that manipulate algebra like an unerring slave and remember whatever is to be remembered. All the troubles that plague an exact solution for polyelectronic atoms remain for molecules, and the existence of more than one center of positive charge by having more than one nucleus adds new kinds of mathematical headaches. Although computers are yielding good results for molecules having about ten electrons, the intermediate machine processes are necessarily hidden within the computer and the final results, though trustworthy, seldom have any vivid chemical interpretation beyond their own meaning. For example, the machine cannot explain simply what additive terms contribute to an energy or a probability density of matter, and an exact molecular wave function is a mess. For these reasons, then, this chapter does not aim at exact answers. Its main purpose is to give clear qualitative explanations of the behavior of molecular electrons.

It is worthwhile, at the start, to note the nature and value of some general approaches to solving the Schrödinger equation for molecules.

First of all, it is common to use a scale factor as a variable parameter of a variation function. The calculated energy can be minimized directly by setting its derivative with respect to the scale parameter equal to zero to find the best value of that parameter. The same result can be achieved, however, by requiring the scale factor to satisfy the virial theorem in the form $2\bar{T} = -\bar{V} = -2E$ when $\bar{T}$ or $\bar{V}$ is calculated like E.

Secondly, one can set aside the ideal of basing every result only on the values of fundamental physical constants like h, e, and c. Instead, it is expeditious to evaluate certain parameters and integrals by reference to observation and attempt to use such semiempirical results in analogous calculations on different molecules. Or, again, it is often helpful to replace the real potential with its natural curves by a simpler model such as a square-well potential with its sharp corners. This eases calculations and yet gives qualitatively correct results.

Thirdly, many theoreticians, even when armed with a good computer, frequently assume that each electron moves in the average smoothed potential of all other electrons and, of course, nuclei. For an atom of several electrons, this *Hartree-Fock approximation* is equivalent to solving several one-electron stationary-state equations, each with a radial potential of the form

$$V(r_1) = \sum_{\alpha>\beta} \frac{\mathbf{Z}_\alpha \mathbf{Z}_\beta e^2}{4\pi\epsilon_0 R_{\alpha\beta}} - \sum_{\alpha} \frac{\mathbf{Z}_\alpha e^2}{4\pi\epsilon_0 r_{\alpha 1}} + \int \frac{u_2^* e^2 u_2 d\tau_2}{4\pi\epsilon_0 r_{12}} \tag{15.1}$$

where $\mathbf{Z}_\alpha e$ and $\mathbf{Z}_\beta e$ are the charges on nuclei separated by $R_{\alpha\beta}$, where $r_{\alpha 1}$ is the distance from nucleus α to electron 1, and where r_{12} is the distance between electron 1 and an average electron density $u_2^* u_2$ attributable to the average behavior of all electrons except 1. The several equations of the form

$$-\frac{\hbar^2}{2m_i} \nabla_i^2 u_i + V(r_i) u_i = E_i u_i \tag{15.2}$$

have wave functions u_i of the form

$$u_i = Q_{nl}(r_i)\Theta_{lm}(\theta)\Phi_m(\phi) \tag{15.3}$$

because $V(r_i)$ is independent of angles. The real forms of $\Theta_{lm}(\theta)\Phi_m(\phi)$ were shown in Figure 14.3. The wave function of all N electrons is a product of the form

$$u = u_1 u_2 = \prod_{i=1}^{N} u_i \tag{15.4}$$

This method was first conceived in 1928 by Hartree and was improved in 1930 by Fock by making u of (15.4) properly antisymmetric by use of a Slater determinantal form like (14.155). In 1930, Slater showed that the variation method with a trial wave function that is a product of one-electron functions leads to essentially the same result as the Hartree-Fock self-consistent field. The radially symmetric field of the other $N - 1$ electrons is called self-consistent because the N one-electron equations of form (15.2) are solved by guessing u_2 in (15.1), finding u_i, until further adjustments in u_2 make no change in u and give u really equal to $u_1 u_2$ for any electron that happens to be labeled 1. While the Hartree-Fock method gives good results, it can never yield perfect results because the self-consistent field of the other electrons, even if it were to depend on angles, is an average and, therefore, makes no allowance for the instantaneous correlations that real electrons really achieve.

Fourthly, the Hellman-Feynman theorem, discovered independently in 1937 and 1939, provides remarkable insight into the forces on nuclei and electrons. This theorem says that the force on a nucleus is correctly computed by classical methods which use the positions of other nuclei and the electron density of the molecule as the locations of charge in the classical form of Coulomb's law. In 1964, Parr reformulated this remarkable result in a more general form for any process that occurs in a system of a fixed number of electrons and nuclei.[1] If R is an internuclear distance *or any other parameter* in the Hamiltonian operator, then, when ψ is the true normalized wave function,

$$\frac{\partial E}{\partial R} = \int \psi^* \frac{\partial \mathbf{H}}{\partial R} \psi \, d\tau \tag{15.5}$$

Since E is a minimum with respect to changes in internuclear distance when ψ is the full description of the molecule, the left side of (15.5) is zero, while the right represents the various forces on the nuclei and electrons since $\mathbf{H}$ depends on internuclear distance only through the potential energy. Of course, (15.5) is more general than the Hellman-Feynman theorem because R may be any parameter in $\mathbf{H}$: a bond angle, a nuclear charge, ...

Finally, as a fifth general remark, it is appropriate to describe the Born-Oppenheimer approximation, first justified theoretically in 1927. The nuclei and electrons of a molecule have coulombic energies of roughly the same magnitude. Their masses differ, however, by more than three powers of ten. Hence, an electron typically goes ten to one hundred times as far as a nucleus in a given time. That is, the motion of electrons occurs in an environment of essentially fixed nuclei. (The Hartree self-consistent field goes a bit farther and assumes that each electron sees not only fixed nuclei but an average of the other electrons.) The Born-Oppenheimer approximation thus breaks the problem of nuclear and electronic motion into two parts. The first part involves the motion of electrons in the field of fixed nuclei, their equation being

$$(\mathbf{T}_e + \mathbf{V})u_e = E_e u_e \tag{15.6}$$

where $\mathbf{T}_e$ is the kinetic energy operator for electrons. Here $\mathbf{V}$ is the potential energy of nuclei and electrons, namely

$$\mathbf{V} = \sum_{\alpha>\beta} \frac{\mathbf{Z}_\alpha \mathbf{Z}_\beta e^2}{4\pi\epsilon_0 R_{\alpha\beta}} - \sum_{\alpha,\,i} \frac{\mathbf{Z}_\alpha e^2}{4\pi\epsilon_0 r_{\alpha i}} + \sum_{i>j} \frac{e^2}{4\pi\epsilon_0 r_{ij}} \tag{15.7}$$

where $R_{\alpha\beta}$ is an internuclear distance, $r_{\alpha i}$ is an electron-nucleus distance, and r_{ij} is an electron-electron distance. For given nuclear geometry, (15.6) yields E_e as a function of the parameters $R_{\alpha\beta}$. Then E_e is used as a potential energy $E_e(R)$ in the nuclear equation

$$[\mathbf{T}_N + E_e(R)]u_N = Eu_N \tag{15.8}$$

---

[1] R. G. Parr, *J. Chem. Phys.* **40,** 3726 (1964); E. F. Hayes and R. G. Parr, *J. Chem. Phys.* **44,** 4650 (1966).

which gives the total energy E of the molecule. This approximation works because u_e does not vary rapidly with respect to changes in nuclear coordinates R. If the molecular wave function is

$$u = u_N(R)u_e(r, R) \tag{15.9}$$

then $\mathbf{T}_N u \approx u_e \mathbf{T}_N u_N$ because derivatives of u_e with respect to R are small compared to $\mathbf{T}_N u_N$. Hence, after multiplication by u_e, (15.8) can be rewritten as

$$(\mathbf{T}_N + E_e)u = Eu \tag{15.10}$$

Similarly because $\mathbf{T}_e u_N$ is zero, and because $\mathbf{V}$ is merely a factor like u_N, multiplication of (15.6) by u_N and a look at (15.9) yields

$$(\mathbf{T}_e + \mathbf{V})u = E_e u \tag{15.11}$$

Addition of (15.10) and (15.11) yields the molecule's wave equation

$$(\mathbf{T}_N + \mathbf{T}_e + \mathbf{V})u = Eu \tag{15.12}$$

where E is the total energy of the molecule.

As in (14.95) and (14.109), additivity of energy and product wave functions go together. And, as in (14.185), separate quantization of energy goes with great differences in magnitudes of wavelength, time of one cycle of motion, and the like. For great disparity in such matters implies small interaction of the motions and separate quantization.

It is time to consider molecules in detail, but always in the light of the variation theorem of Section 14.11.

15.2 HYDROGEN MOLECULE ION

The hydrogen molecule ion H_2^+ is generated from H_2 by loss of an electron. In the Born-Oppenheimer approximation its energy has been calculated exactly (1 in 10^6) and its electronic wave functions are known accurately.[(2)] Consisting of two protons and just one electron, it is the simplest molecule and chemical. It was the first chemical application of the Schrödinger equation (Burrau, 1927). As in (15.7), its potential energy is

$$\mathbf{V} = \frac{e^2}{4\pi\epsilon_0 R_{AB}} - \frac{e^2}{4\pi\epsilon_0 r_A} - \frac{e^2}{4\pi\epsilon_0 r_B} \tag{15.13}$$

where r_A and r_B are the distances of the electron from protons A and B, which are apart by R_{AB}. In the Born-Oppenheimer approximation, which holds well even for the unmassive nuclei, the wave equation of the electron of mass m at x, y, z in a coordinate system fixed to the stationary protons is

(2) D. R. Bates, K. Ledsham, and A. L. Stewart, *Trans. Roy. Soc.* (London) **A246,** 215 (1953).

$$-\frac{\hbar^2}{2m}\left(\frac{\partial^2 u}{\partial x^2}+\frac{\partial^2 u}{\partial y^2}+\frac{\partial^2 u}{\partial z^2}\right)+\frac{e^2}{4\pi\epsilon_0}\left(\frac{1}{R_{AB}}-\frac{1}{r_A}-\frac{1}{r_B}\right)u \equiv \mathbf{H}u = Eu \tag{15.14}$$

As R_{AB} becomes either very small or very great, **V** assumes a simpler form. If the repulsion term for the protons is ignored as R_{AB} approaches zero, r_A approaches r_B and

$$\mathbf{V} \approx -\frac{2e^2}{4\pi\epsilon_0 r}$$

On the other hand, as R_{AB} approaches infinity, if the electron is near one of the protons,

$$\mathbf{V} \approx -\frac{e^2}{4\pi\epsilon_0 r}$$

In either limit the lone electron lies in a hydrogen-like potential and its wave function is also hydrogen-like. Just as the atomic problem is to find an atomic orbital for an atomic electron, the problem here is to find a *molecular orbital*, an orbital having more than one center.

As R_{AB} becomes great, the wave function of the electron becomes u_A when it is primarily under the influence of proton A and becomes u_B while near proton B. Since neither proton is to be preferred over the other, the law of superposition of probability amplitudes suggests a solution of the form

$$v = u_A \pm u_B \tag{15.15}$$

where u_A (or u_B) is a solution of the H atom equation

$$-\frac{\hbar^2}{2m}\left(\frac{\partial^2 u_A}{\partial x^2}+\frac{\partial^2 u_A}{\partial y^2}+\frac{\partial^2 u_A}{\partial z^2}\right)-\frac{e^2 u_A}{4\pi\epsilon_0 r_A} \equiv \mathbf{H}_A u_A = E_A u_A \tag{15.16}$$

The values of E_A and u_A in (15.15) were found in Section 14.6. In view of (15.16) and with v of (15.15) in place of u, (15.14) yields

$$\begin{aligned}\mathbf{H}v &= \left[\mathbf{H}_A + \frac{e^2}{4\pi\epsilon_0}\left(\frac{1}{R_{AB}}-\frac{1}{r_B}\right)\right]u_A \pm \left[\mathbf{H}_B + \frac{e^2}{4\pi\epsilon_0}\left(\frac{1}{R_{AB}}-\frac{1}{r_A}\right)u_B\right. \\ &= E_A u_A \pm E_B u_B + \frac{e^2}{4\pi\epsilon_0}\left(\frac{u_A \pm u_B}{R_{AB}} - \frac{u_A}{r_B} - \frac{u_B}{r_A}\right)\end{aligned} \tag{15.17}$$

As in (14.174), with $S = \int u_A u_B \, d\tau$ and with $1 = \int u_A u_A \, d\tau = \int u_B u_B \, d\tau$, it follows that

$$\begin{aligned}\int vv \, d\tau &= \int (u_A \pm u_B)(u_A \pm u_B)\, d\tau \\ &= \int u_A u_A \, d\tau + \int u_B u_B \, d\tau \pm 2\int u_A u_B \, d\tau \\ &= 2(1 \pm S)\end{aligned} \tag{15.18}$$

At the same time, (15.17) yields similarly

$$\int v\mathbf{H}v\,d\tau = E_A \pm E_A S \pm (E_B \pm E_B S) + \frac{2e^2(1 \pm S)}{4\pi\epsilon_0 R_{AB}}$$
$$-\frac{e^2}{4\pi\epsilon_0}\int \frac{(u_A \pm u_B)u_A}{r_B}\,d\tau \mp \frac{e^2}{4\pi\epsilon_0}\int \frac{(u_A \pm u_B)u_B}{r_A}\,d\tau \qquad (15.19)$$

But the symmetry of the situation requires $E_A = E_B$ and

$$J = -\frac{e^2}{4\pi\epsilon_0}\int \frac{u_A u_A}{r_B}\,d\tau = -\frac{e^2}{4\pi\epsilon_0}\int \frac{u_B u_B}{r_A}\,d\tau \qquad (15.20)$$

and

$$K = -\frac{e^2}{4\pi\epsilon_0}\int \frac{u_A u_B}{r_B}\,d\tau = -\frac{e^2}{4\pi\epsilon_0}\int \frac{u_A u_B}{r_A}\,d\tau \qquad (15.21)$$

Hence, with account of (15.20) and (15.21), (15.19) yields

predicted energy

$$\int v\mathbf{H}v\,d\tau = 2E_A(1 \pm S) + \frac{2e^2(1 \pm S)}{4\pi\epsilon_0 R_{AB}} + 2(J \pm K) \qquad (15.22)$$

According to the variation principle, the actual energy of H_2^+ is less than that predicted by (15.22) and (15.18), namely

nuclear repulsion

$$E' = \frac{\int v\mathbf{H}v\,d\tau}{\int vv\,d\tau} = E_A + \frac{e^2}{4\pi\epsilon_0 R_{AB}} + \frac{J \pm K}{1 \pm S} \qquad (15.23)$$

The term $e^2/4\pi\epsilon_0 R_{AB}$ is clearly nuclear repulsion, and E_A is the energy of an electron about one lone proton. The stability of H_2^+ comes through the so-called *coulomb integral J*, which in (15.20) looks like the energy of an electron density u^2 attracted by the other proton, and through the so-called *exchange* (or *resonance*) *integral K*, which represents the energy of an electron on A and B simultaneously as it is attracted by one proton. Without K, H_2^+ is more stable than H and a proton only by virtue of polarization of H by H^+ and a slight decrease in energy below E_A because of the polarization. With K, however, the observed stability of H_2^+ is largely explained. The dashed lines of Figure 15.1 represent the nuclear energy $e^2/4\pi\epsilon_0 R_{AB}$ and the electronic energy $E_A + (J \pm K)/(1 \pm S)$. The solid lines of Figures 15.1 represent the net energy of (15.23), the state with $v_+ = u_A + u_B$ yielding a stable minimum near $3a_0$, the state with $v_- = u_A - u_B$ yielding no configuration of minimum energy.

Figure 15.2 shows the probability density of the electron in H_2^+ by means of coutours of constant density. In the more stable state with $v_+ = u_A + u_B$, the electron has two strong cusps at the nuclei and a modest density between the nuclei. Were it not for the two cusps, the electron density along the internuclear line would resemble the square of the wave function for the most stable state of a particle in a one-dimensional box. Similarly, as a sum of $1s$-like orbitals of H, the rise of v_+ near the nuclei resembles the wave function of the most stable

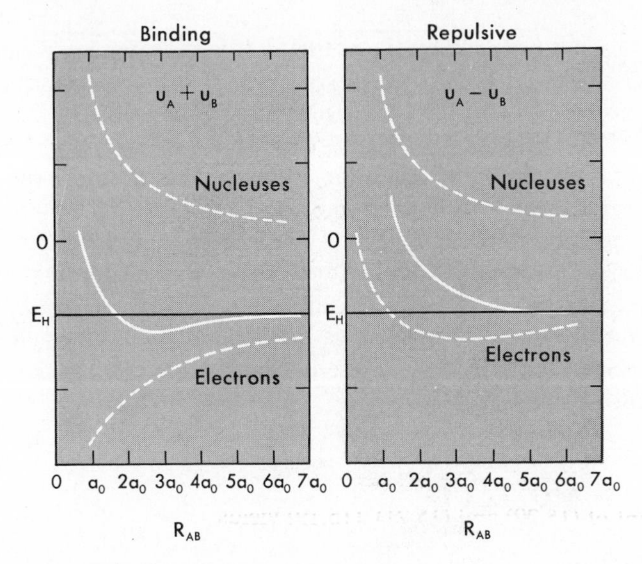

Figure 15.1. Energy Curves of H_2^+†

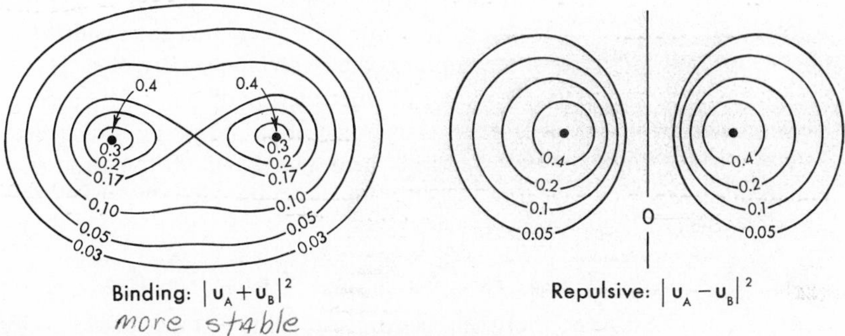

Figure 15.2. Contours of Constant Electron Density in H_2^+‡

state of a particle in a one-dimensional box. Analogous comparisons hold for the first excited states of H_2^+ and the boxed particle, even to the existence of a node in v_- halfway between protons.

Since the curvature of v_+ and v_- is great near the protons and small halfway between them, the kinetic energy of the electron is great near the nuclei and small halfway between them. But since the virial theorem requires $2\bar{T} = -\bar{V}$, the average potential energy of the electrons is very low at the nuclei. That is, H_2^+ is held together not by the low energy of the electron cloud between the protons but rather by the stability of the electron near its *two* protons.

†Adapted from C. A. Coulson, *Valence*, Oxford [1952], p. 80, by permission of the Clarendon Press, Oxford.
‡Adapted from C. A. Coulson, *Valence*, Oxford [1952], p. 80., by permission of the Clarendon Press, Oxford.

Although H_2^+ cannot be made by the bottleful, it is still of great chemical significance. For the electron in H_2^+ occupies an orbital with two centers. By analogy with an atomic orbital in H, the electron in H_2^+ is said to occupy a *molecular orbital* (MO). The orbitals found here for H_2^+ by a *linear combination of atomic orbitals* (LCAO) are the simplest molecular orbitals. Rather sophisticated (but mathematically easy to handle) molecular orbitals with the general nature of Slater atomic orbitals can be expressed in terms of confocal elliptic coordinates. In fact, transformation of (15.14) to these elliptic coordinates allows (15.14) to be separated into three total differential equations, just as the equation for H is readily separated in spherical polar coordinates. Such elliptic orbitals can be expected to be of as much use in simple molecular calculations as are Slater orbitals for atoms.

15.3 HYDROGEN MOLECULE

Like H_2^+, the neutral hydrogen molecule H_2 was an early test of the Schrödinger equation. The first realistic solution, due to Heitler and London in 1927, and another straightforward solution using the aufbau principle on H_2^+ are explained below. Even by 1933, James and Coolidge had calculated the result to within 1 part in 10^4. With the aid of a computer, the electronic energy E_e of H_2 has been calculated[3] for an extended range of internuclear distance for three different electronic states to 1 in 10^8. It has thus taken about 40 years to complete a calculation which involves two electrons near two fixed protons and has as its potential merely

$$\mathbf{V} = \frac{e^2}{4\pi\epsilon_0}\left(-\frac{1}{r_{1A}} - \frac{1}{r_{2B}} - \frac{1}{r_{2A}} - \frac{1}{r_{1B}} + \frac{1}{r_{12}} + \frac{1}{R_{AB}}\right) \tag{15.24}$$

where R_{AB} is the distance between protons, r_{12} is the distance between electrons, and the other r's are electron-proton distances.

As R_{AB} becomes very small, r_{1A} becomes r_{1B} and r_{2A} becomes r_{2B}; without proton-proton repulsion, (15.24) then suits He. Chemical intuition suggests, however, that the limit for large R_{AB} is more meaningful. As R_{AB} approaches infinity, if electron 1 stays on proton A and 2 stays on B,

$$\mathbf{V} \approx \frac{e^2}{4\pi\epsilon_0}\left(-\frac{1}{r_{1A}} - \frac{1}{r_{2B}}\right) \tag{15.25}$$

because r_{12}, r_{1B}, and r_{2A} approach infinity with R_{AB}. In this approximation of two hydrogen atoms, the wave function of H_2 is

$$v = u_A(1)u_B(2) \tag{15.26}$$

where u_A (1) is a hydrogen-like wave function for electron 1 around proton A

[3] W. Kolos and L. Wolniewicz, *J. Chem. Phys.* **43**, 2429 (1965).

while $u_B(2)$ is for electron 2 around proton B. However, (15.26) is altogether unacceptable, for it yields a binding energy, relative to atoms each in the 1*s* state, of only 0.2 ev, whereas the observed binding energy is 4.75 ev. Moreover, (15.26) is not antisymmetric.

The solution for H_2^+, which has identical protons, is the key to improving (15.26). Here, for H_2, the identity of protons *and* electrons requires

$$v = u_A(1)u_B(2) \pm u_A(2)u_B(1) \tag{15.27}$$

There is no way to decide which electron is on which proton, or which belongs to which. With (15.27), the calculation can be carried forward, as for H_2^+, by reference to hydrogen-atom equations $\mathbf{H}_A u_A = E_H u_A$. If $S = \int u_A u_B \, d\tau = \int u_B u_A \, d\tau$ and if $1 = \int u_A u_A \, d\tau = \int u_B u_B \, d\tau$, then

$$\begin{aligned} \iint vv \, d\tau_1 \, d\tau_2 &= 1 \pm 2 \iint u_A(1)u_B(2)u_A(2)u_B(1) d\tau_1 \, d\tau_2 + 1 \\ &= 2 \pm 2 \int u_A(1)u_B(1) d\tau_1 \int u_A(2)u_B(2) d\tau_2 \\ &= 2 \pm 2 S^2 \end{aligned} \tag{15.28}$$

If $\mathbf{H}$ is the correct Born-Oppenheimer Hamiltonian, then reference to (15.24) and $\mathbf{H}_A(1)u_A(1) = E_H u_A(1)$ gives

$$\mathbf{H} = \mathbf{H}_A(1) + \mathbf{H}_B(2) + \frac{e^2}{4\pi\epsilon_0 R} + \frac{e^2}{4\pi\epsilon_0}\left(\frac{1}{r_{12}} - \frac{1}{r_{1B}} - \frac{1}{r_{2A}}\right) \tag{15.29}$$

It is also clear that $\mathbf{H}_B(1)u_B(1)$ involves r_{1B} and leaves r_{1A} for mention in the parentheses of (15.29). Hence, with v given by (15.27) and with $E_A = E_B = E_H$, it follows that

$$\begin{aligned} \mathbf{H}v &= u_B(2)E_A u_A(1) + u_A(1)E_B u_B(2) \pm u_A(2)E_B u_B(1) \pm u_B(1)E_A u_A(2) \\ &\quad + \frac{e^2}{4\pi\epsilon_0}\left(\frac{1}{R} + \frac{1}{r_{12}}\right)[u_A(1)u_B(2) \pm u_A(2)u_B(1)] \\ &\quad + \frac{e^2}{4\pi\epsilon_0}\left(-\frac{1}{r_{1B}} - \frac{1}{r_{2A}}\right)[u_A(1)u_B(2)] \\ &\quad \pm \frac{e^2}{4\pi\epsilon_0}\left(-\frac{1}{r_{1A}} - \frac{1}{r_{2B}}\right)[u_A(2)u_B(1)] \\ &= \left[2E_H + \left(\frac{e^2}{4\pi\epsilon_0}\right)\left(\frac{1}{R} + \frac{1}{r_{12}}\right)\right]v \\ &\quad + \frac{e^2 u_A(1)u_B(2)}{4\pi\epsilon_0}\left(-\frac{1}{r_{1B}} - \frac{1}{r_{2A}}\right) \pm \frac{e^2 u_A(2)u_B(1)}{4\pi\epsilon_0}\left(-\frac{1}{r_{1A}} - \frac{1}{r_{2B}}\right) \end{aligned}$$

Accordingly, with a glance at (15.28), it follows that

$$\iint v\mathbf{H}v \, d\tau_1 \, d\tau_2 = \left[2E_H + \frac{e^2}{4\pi\epsilon_0 R}\right] 2(1 \pm S^2) + I_{12} + I_{AB} \tag{15.30}$$

where

$$I_{12} = \frac{e^2}{4\pi\epsilon_0} \iint v\left(\frac{1}{r_{12}}\right) v \, d\tau_1 d\tau_2 \tag{15.31}$$

$$I_{AB} = \frac{e^2}{4\pi\epsilon_0} \iint v\left[\left(-\frac{1}{r_{1B}} - \frac{1}{r_{2A}}\right) u_A(1) u_B(2) \pm \left(-\frac{1}{r_{1A}} - \frac{1}{r_{2B}}\right) u_A(2) u_B(1)\right] d\tau_1 \, d\tau_2 \tag{15.32}$$

In computing I, integration over the volume element $d\tau_2$ for electron 2 can be done at once if r_{2A} or r_{2B} is not present in the integrand. Similarly, integration over $d\tau_1$ can be done if r_{1A} or r_{1B} is not present. However, r_{12} involves the positions of both electrons so that I_{12} cannot be so simplified. Actually I_{12} is very difficult to calculate; its form is, after a glance at the derivation of (15.28),

$$\begin{aligned} I_{12} = &\left(\frac{e^2}{4\pi\epsilon_0}\right) \iint \frac{u_A(1) u_A(1) u_B(2) u_B(2)}{r_{12}} \, d\tau_1 \, d\tau_2 \\ &\pm 2\left(\frac{e^2}{4\pi\epsilon_0}\right) \iint \frac{u_A(1) u_B(2) u_A(2) u_B(1)}{r_{12}} \, d\tau_1 \, d\tau_2 \\ &+ \left(\frac{e^2}{4\pi\epsilon_0}\right) \iint \frac{u_A(2) u_A(2) u_B(1) u_B(1)}{r_{12}} \, d\tau_1 \, d\tau_2 \end{aligned}$$

Since electron labels are interchangeable, it then follows that

$$I_{12} = 2\left(\frac{e^2}{4\pi\epsilon_0}\right)\left[\iint \frac{u_A^2(1) u_B^2(2)}{r_{12}} \, d\tau_1 \, d\tau_2 \pm \iint \frac{u_A(1) u_B(1) u_A(2) u_B(2)}{r_{12}} \, d\tau_1 \, d\tau_2\right] \tag{15.33}$$

Similarly, it follows from (15.27) and (15.32) that

$$\begin{aligned} I_{AB} = &-\frac{e^2}{4\pi\epsilon_0}\left[\int \frac{u_A(1) u_A(1)}{r_{1B}} \, d\tau_1 \pm S \int \frac{u_B(1) u_A(1)}{r_{1B}} \, d\tau_1 \right. \\ &\left. + \int \frac{u_B(2) u_B(2)}{r_{2A}} \, d\tau_2 \pm S \int \frac{u_A(2) u_B(2)}{r_{2A}} \, d\tau_2\right] \\ &- \frac{e^2}{4\pi\epsilon_0}\left[\pm S \int \frac{u_A(1) u_B(1)}{r_{1A}} \, d\tau_1 + \int \frac{u_B(1) u_B(1)}{r_{1A}} \, d\tau_1 \right. \\ &\left. \pm S \int \frac{u_A(2) u_B(2)}{r_{2B}} \, d\tau_2 + \int \frac{u_A(2) u_A(2)}{r_{2B}} \, d\tau_2 \right. \end{aligned}$$

With account of J and K in (15.20) and (15.21), it then follows that

$$\begin{aligned} I_{AB} &= J \pm SK + J \pm SK \pm SK + J \pm SK + J \\ &= 4(J \pm SK) \end{aligned} \tag{15.34}$$

As before, J is the attraction between a proton and the other proton's electrons, while K is the exchange integral, the electron-wave being on A and B while either proton attracts it. The double integrals of (15.33) have analogous interpretations. The first describes the classically expected repulsion between electron 1 on A and electron 2 on B. The second double integral of (15.33) is of wave mechanical origin, like K; it measures the repulsion of an electron-wave on A and B for another such delocalized electron-wave. With this approach of Heitler and London, it is possible to get a binding energy of $2E_H - 3.20$ ev. This same attack yields an energy of $2E_H - 3.78$ ev when the wave function (15.27) is scaled by a variable nuclear charge. That is, the simple solution yields a dissociation energy of 3.20 ev for the reaction $H_{2(g)} \longrightarrow 2H_{(g)}$. Although far by chemical standards from the true value of 4.75 ev, this is nonetheless a suitable qualitative account of why H_2 exists. This method has become known as the valence-bond (VB) method.

The electronic wave function v of (15.27) for the most stable state of H_2 has the positive sign and is, therefore, symmetric to an interchange of electrons. With the antisymmetric spin factor of (14.153), it becomes antisymmetric in accord with the exclusion principle; hence, in the VB approximation, the most stable state of H_2 has

$$v_{VB} = [u_A(1)u_B(2) + u_A(2)u_B(1)][\alpha(1)\beta(2) - \alpha(2)\beta(1)] \tag{15.35}$$

As in He, the electrons have opposite spin and there can be no more than two of them.

A second method of describing the bond in H_2, the simplest of all covalent bonds, begins with a different arbitrary starting point. In the VB method, the classical starting point was two neutral atoms far apart. In the molecular-orbital (MO) method, a second electron is added to H_2^+. Its nonclassical behavior is acknowledged by giving it the same kind of spatial freedom as the first electron in H_2^+. Hence, the spatial wave function is

$$v_{MO} = [u_A(1) + u_B(1)][u_A(2) + u_B(2)] \tag{15.36}$$

As in (15.35), an antisymmetric spin factor makes (15.36) properly antisymmetric. As a result, each molecular orbital can hold no more than two electrons.

The calculation of the energy proceeds as before, with, however, certain additional terms. Expansion of (15.36) yields

$$v_{MO} = u_A(1)u_B(2) + u_A(2)u_B(1) + u_A(1)u_A(2) + u_B(1)u_B(2) \tag{15.37}$$

The third and fourth terms are interpreted as hydride ions, both electrons being on either proton A or proton B. These extra terms in (15.37) naturally yield certain new integrals which are left to the student for formulation. With $\mathbf{Z} = 1$ for both nuclei, the lowest energy is calculated to be $2E_H - 2.65$ ev with the use of $1s$ functions for u_A and u_B. This is not quite as good as the parallel VB value of $2E_H - 3.20$ ev, but it is still suitable as a qualitative description of a covalent bond. With variable **Z** in 1*s* orbitals, the lowest MO energy of H_2 is $2E_H - 3.49$ ev.

15.4 COMPARISON OF VALENCE-BOND AND MOLECULAR-ORBITAL METHODS

The molecular-orbital and valence-bond methods are approximations. Both describe the covalent bond in H_2 in terms of paired electrons shared by both protons. Although bond energies are calculated in terms of position coordinates and coulomb and exchange integrals, electron spin is a guide to allowed electron population. Pairing of electron spins in the molecular-orbital method is formally akin to pairing of electrons in atomic orbitals, but pairing in the valence-bond method is directly related to the antisymmetric nature of an electronic wave function. The energy of pairing itself is negligible; the main energy of the bond comes from the size of the spatial integral.

These two methods really approach the same observable limit if the wave functions are made more flexible. If the valence-bond variation function of H_2 is

$$v = [u_A(1)u_B(2) + u_A(2)u_B(1)] + a[u_A(1)u_A(2) + u_B(1)u_B(2)] \qquad (15.38)$$

a binding energy $(E - 2E_H)$ of -4.02 ev is achieved[4] for $a = 0.256$ and an effective atomic number of 1.193. The terms following a describe ionic structures A^-B^+ and A^+B^-. If a variable atomic number is included as a parameter in the simple molecular-orbital calculation,[5] $(E - 2E_H) = -3.49$ ev. The reason that this molecular orbital calculation does not yield a lower energy is that its wave function (15.37) requires $a = 1$ in (15.38), thus limiting the flexibility of the variation function and requiring that ionic structures be as important as purely covalent ones. As the variation functions are made more flexible and complex, the calculated energy approaches the observed energy.

In general, the molecular-orbital method places too much emphasis on ionic terms and too little on electron repulsion. It is poor at large internuclear separations because it often predicts wrong dissociation products, whereas the valence-bond method is superior at large distances and predicts correct dissociation products because the zero-order wave function suits large R_{AB}. The valence-bond method, however, underestimates ionic contributions and is generally less tractable mathematically. The molecular-orbital method deals with electrons as individuals, even in excited states, and describes in a simple and natural way the unusual one-electron bond of H_2^+. Since each method makes errors of the order of one or two electron volts in binding energy, neither is clearly to be pre-

[4] Weinbaum, S., *J. Chem. Phys.*, **1**, 593 (1933).
[5] Coulson, C. A., *Trans. Faraday Soc.*, **33**, 1479 (1937).

ferred. Rather, if the use of both methods yields a particular prediction of an observable other than the energy, one is safe in expecting the real situation to lie somewhere between these two extremes.[6]

The pure VB and MO methods of Section 15.3 are arbitrary starting points that begin with some vague classical reasonableness about them. The integrals that result and their interpretation are likewise arbitrary, for a different start would give different integrals.

There are certain regularities, of course. For example, it may be just luck, but it happens that the electron correlation energy (r_{12} terms) is 1.1 ev in He and in H_2. Nevertheless, the arbitrariness of the VB and MO at the start has trapped many into saying that it is the coordinated exchange of electrons that makes H_2 as stable as it is, for K is clearly the dominant term of (15.34). Or a MO interpreter might point out that much stability is conferred not only by K but also by the attraction of a nucleus for "its own" electrons. Ruedenberg[7] has given a very penetrating and detailed account of why bonds are formed. He concludes that

(a) the energy of the atoms rises somewhat as atomic electrons are promoted to a nonstationary valence state;
(b) the energy of these valence-state atoms is changed slightly by electrostatic interaction;
(c) the energy is greatly decreased (system is stabilized) by electrons' wave-like motion in atomic orbitals;
(d) the energy rises somewhat as electrons on different atoms interpenetrate each other's domains; and
(e) the energy may finally be adjusted slightly if the bond is ionic enough to require a transfer of charge.

In other words, careful analysis of why a bond forms and exists eventually calls for mathematics and a minimum of slogans.

15.5 CORRELATION DIAGRAMS OF DIATOMIC MOLECULES

The periodic table of elements in modern form describes the energy states of electrons as they can exist in atoms. Quantum numbers suitable for H and the Pauli exclusion principle are the basis of the table. Although the electrons of large atoms really interact in complicated ways, their correlation still does not

---

[6] For a comparison of the molecular-orbital and valence-bond methods, see: Coulson, C. A., *Valence*. By permission of the Clarendon Press, Oxford. New York: Oxford University Press, 1960.
[7] K. Ruedenberg, *Revs. Modern Phys.* **34**, 368 ff (1962).

alter the number of electronic states or their fundamental symmetry. That is, the same number and kind of quantum numbers are useful for H and polyelectronic atoms.

Correlation diagrams are for diatomic molecules what the periodic table is for atoms. *A correlation diagram* lists the number of electronic states in a diatom and assigns quantum numbers to the states according to the symmetry of the molecular orbitals. And the various molecular electronic states so classified can be correlated with atomic electronic states through a perturbation that molds atomic states into molecular states without changing the number of states, their general symmetry, or their quantum numbers. Gradual changes thus made in quantum theory without discontinuity in the states are called an *adiabatic change*. (Here "adiabatic" has no connection with heat.)

The most stable state of H_2 is directly comparable to the most stable state of He. The wave function of each has no node, does not change sign upon inversion through a center at the center of mass, and does not change sign upon reflection across a plane through the nucleus of He or both nuclei of H_2. Moreover, since the spatial electronic wave function is the same for each electron and unchanged in sign upon interchange of electrons, the exclusion principle requires that the electrons differ in spin and that the spin function be antisymmetric so that the total electronic wave function is antisymmetric. In forcing electrons to exist in pairs in orbitals of various spatial character, the exclusion principle helps in its way to minimize interelectronic repulsions. Thus, a properly antisymmetric electronic wave function provides, as a bonus, an easy way to minimize the so-called correlation energy (r_{12} terms) of electrons. A problem of $N!$ permutations of N electrons is thus approximately reduced to one of $(1/2)N(N-1)$ problems of pairs of electrons, as though electron-pair bonds and all the long-recognized regularities of bond length, bond energy, and so on can be built easily into a rather good molecular wave function.[8]

The internuclear axis of a diatom (or any linear molecule) fixes a preferred direction. By analogy with atomic *s*-states, an orbital having no component of angular momentum along the internuclear axis is called a σ orbital. If an orbital has a minimum nonzero component, it is called a π orbital, by analogy with atomic *p* states. If it has twice as much as the minimum, it is called a δ orbital, and so on. Since a nonzero component can be positive or negative, π, δ, ϕ, . . . orbitals have a degeneracy of order two.

Figure 15.3 shows how two 1*s* orbitals can approach each other to form a molecular orbital with cylindrical symmetry along the molecular axis. Both electron densities of the one-electron densities of H_2^+ in Figure 15.2 show this cylindrical symmetry. The electron density of the more stable orbital $u_A + u_B$ looks like a football at some distance from the nuclei, but near the nuclei at a high electron density the orbital would look like a dumbbell or even two balls, both on the axis. Eventually they coalesce into a 1*s*-like orbital. The electron

[8] See, e.g., Section 15.7.

density of the less stable orbital $u_A - u_B$ looks like two unround balls almost in contact at any electron density, even in the $2p$-like limit upon coalescence at $R_{AB} = 0$. The cylindrical symmetry of the electron density in Figure 15.2 holds also for the wave functions in Figure 15.3. In fact, it is the sign of the wave function and its symmetry that are of interest here, the remarks on Figure 15.2 being only of pedagogical values as a step toward Figure 15.3. Figure 15.3 also shows how two $2s$ orbitals approach when they reinforce and interfere.

Figure 15.4 shows how two atoms, each with a $2p_z$ orbital directed along the internuclear axis z, are able to form a cylindrically symmetric σ bond. The combination is $u_{2pA} - u_{2pB}$. The symbol σ means that the component of electronic orbital angular momentum along the internuclear axis is zero, the non-

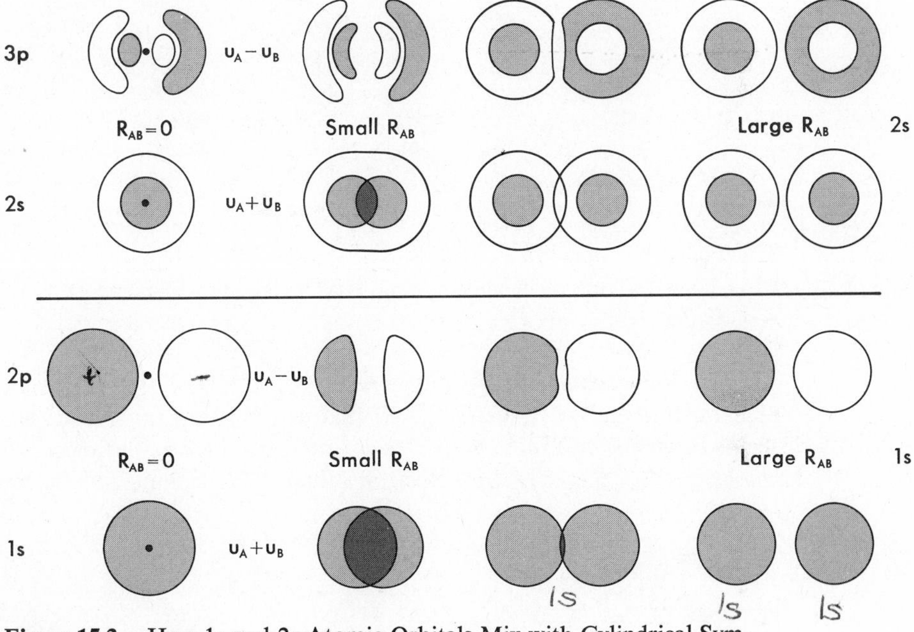

Figure 15.3. How $1s$ and $2s$ Atomic Orbitals Mix with Cylindrical Symmetry (Schematic).

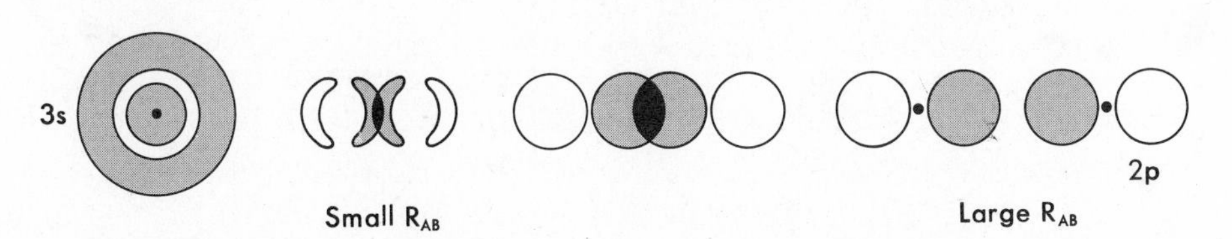

Figure 15.4. How $2p$ Atomic Orbitals Mix to Form a Molecular Orbital with Cylindrical Symmetry (Schematic).

zero atomic components being equal but opposed to give a net of zero (3*s*-like) as combined.

Atomic *p*-states can combine to form a good MO in another way, as shown in Figure 15.5. If one 2*p* orbital with lobes perpendicular to the molecular axis *z* combines by superposition with a similar off-axis 2*p* orbital on the other center, as in Figure 15.5, the result is a MO without cylindrical symmetry and with unit angular momentum along the *z* axis through the nuclei. It is a π MO with wave function $u_{2pA} + u_{2pB}$. Each real $2p_x$ or $2p_y$ atomic orbital has a nodal plane containing the *z* axis. The more stable orbital has both positive lobes on the same side of coincident nodal planes, with gray and white to indicate differing signs. A similar π orbital with lobes perpendicular to the former π and to the *z* axis also exists and will hold two other electrons.

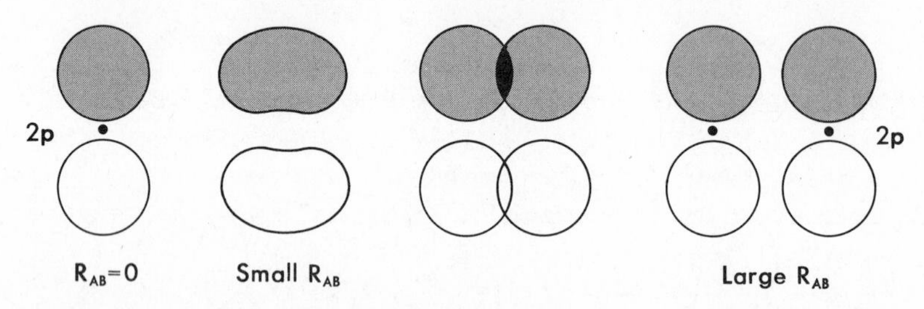

Figure 15.5. How 2*p* Atomic Orbitals Mix to Form a Molecular Orbital Lacking Cylindrical Symmetry and Having Angular Momentum ($v = u_A + u_B$)

Figure 15.6 shows how $2p_x$ and $2p_y$ atomic orbitals on two atoms combine to give a cylindrically symmetrical MO that can hold up to 4 electrons. Four electrons in such a π orbital contribute no net electronic angular momentum to the molecule. If it has only three electrons, then the electronic angular momen-

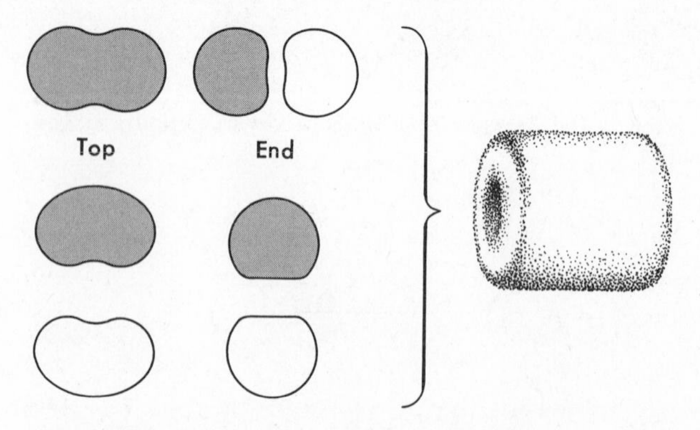

Figure 15.6. Top and End Views of Degenerate π Orbitals That Mix to Give a Cylindrically Symmetric Molecular Orbital

tum contributed to the molecule is $(\pm 1)\hbar$, just as one electron in a π MO yields $(\pm 1)\hbar$. When just two electrons find two πMO's ($u_{2pxA} \pm u_{2pxB}$ and $u_{2pyA} \pm u_{2pyB}$) equally available, the two electrons may enter one with paired spins or they may enter both with spins paired or unpaired.

When a molecule has no net electronic angular momentum (along the molecular axis z, of course, for that is *the* preferred axis), the electron density $|u|^2$ has cylindrical symmetry. The molecule can be rotated on its axis by any angle without a change in $|u|^2$. Reflection across a plane containing both nuclei leaves $|u|^2$ unchanged. In terms of one set of Cartesian axes having z along the molecular axis, reflection in, say, a plane containing the y and z axes means $x \longrightarrow -x$ with y and z unchanged. However, $|u|^2$ is unchanged if $u(x, y, z) = \pm u(-x, y, z)$. That is, u may or may not change sign upon reflection in a plane containing the nuclei if the electrons are as a whole cylindrically symmetric. If $u(x, y, z) = +u(-x, y, z)$, the electronic state is positive (+); if $u(x, y, z) = -u(-x, y, z)$, it is negative (−). This element of symmetry is useful in describing electronic states of diatoms having no net electronic angular momentum.

Another symmetry operation, of immediate concern in correlation diagrams, is inversion (whereby $x \longrightarrow -x$, $y \longrightarrow -y$, $z \longrightarrow -z$) at a center halfway between nuclei of equal charge. Since the electron density $|u|^2$ must be unchanged in sign upon inversion, $u(x, y, z) = \pm u(-x, -y, -z)$. If $u = +u$ upon inversion, the electronic state is labelled g (German: *gerade* = even); if $u = -u$, it is labelled u (German: *ungerade* = uneven). The labels g and u have no meaning for molecules having nuclei of unequal charge.

With these remarks on inversion symmetry and $\sigma, \pi, \delta, \ldots$ MO's, it is possible to classify the various electronic states of a diatomic molecule in terms of the electronic states of atoms for very small or very large internuclear separations. When atoms of the same atomic number are far apart, they interact feebly to produce a g- and a u-state from each of the states they have when isolated. Moreover, this feeble interaction establishes a preferred direction in space along which angular momentum is quantized. These states of feeble interaction of separated atoms are listed with their origins at the right of Figure 15.7. For example, the even and odd s-states of the separated atoms can have no component of orbital angular momentum along the internuclear axis and so produce only σ-states. However, the even or odd p-states of the separated atoms have orbital angular momentum: if ± 1 along the axis, π-states result (Figure 15.5); if 0 along the axis, σ-states result (Figure 15.4).

At the left of Figure 15.7 levels are labeled σ and π because the incipient division of the nucleus into halves acts like an incipient electric field. If $m_l = 0$, a σ-state results; if $m_l = \pm 1$, a π-state results. Here the s-, d-, . . . states are g while the p-, f-, h-, . . . states are u.

States with internuclear distance with intermediate values can be described in terms of these same quantum numbers. The quantum numbers, which indicate the symmetry and nature of the wave function, are conserved (adiabatic) in going from united to separated atoms. That is, σ_g joins σ_g, σ_u joins σ_u, π_g joins π_g, π_u

joins π_u, and so on, the correlation beginning at the bottom with the most stable states. Each σ correlation line describes a molecular orbital capable of holding two electrons with paired spins, while each π or δ line can accommodate four electrons because of the degeneracy of order two.

Bonding molecular orbitals usually have correlation lines that slope downward to the left. The scales of energy and distance in Figure 15.7 are, however,

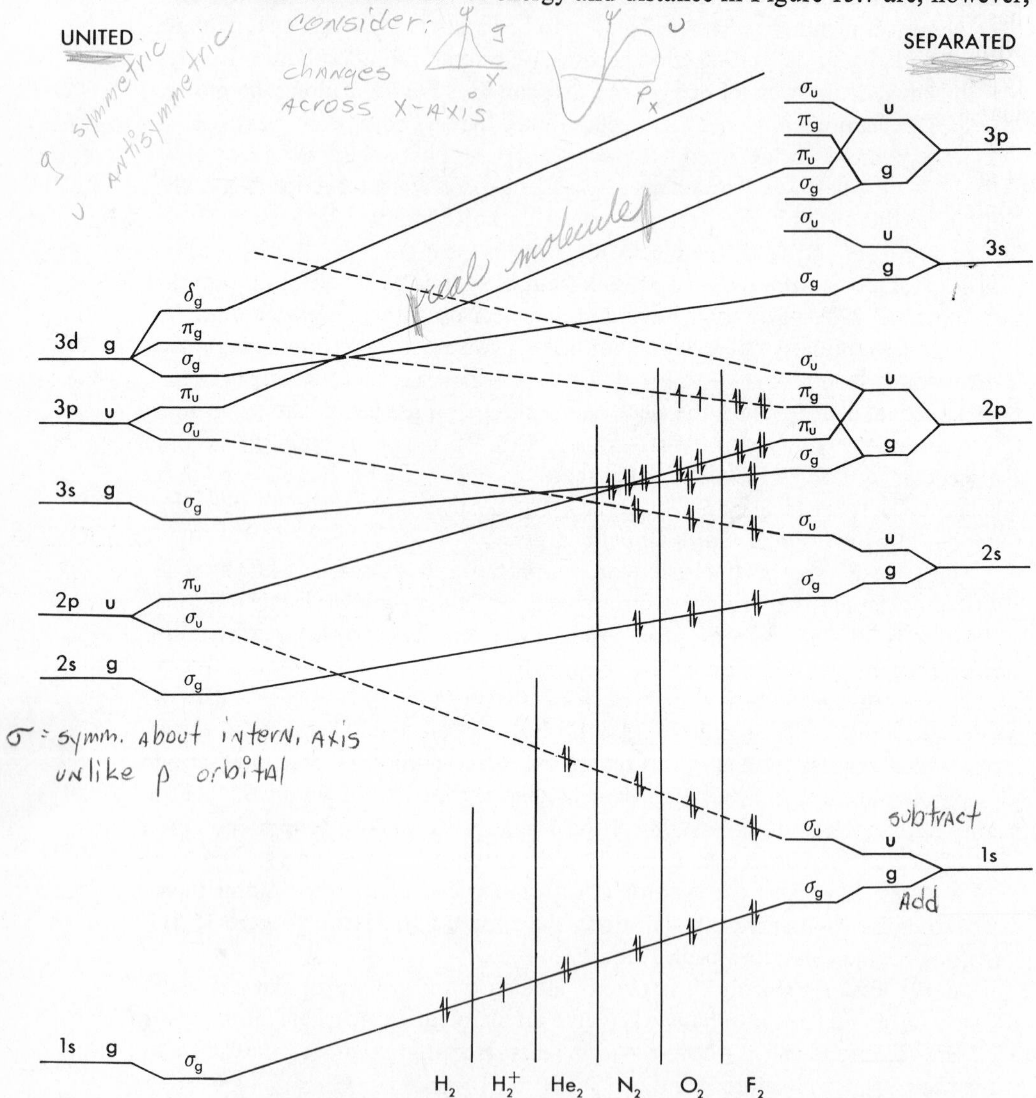

Figure 15.7. Correlation Diagram of Electronic States of Diatom Having Equal Nuclear Charges†

†R. S. Mulliken, *Revs. Modern Phys.* **4**, 1 [1932]

of only qualitative meaning. The most stable states of electrons in H_2^+, H_2, He_2, N_2, O_2, and F_2 are listed in the figure, paired arrows indicating paired spins. The state He_2 is nonbonding because the bonding effect of σ_g^2 is more than undone by the antibonding effect of σ_u^2. These two molecular orbitals hold the inert pairs in the K-shells. In N_2, with neglect of the two K-shells, the bonding electrons are $\sigma_g^2\pi_u^4\sigma_g^2$ while σ_u^2 are antibonding. Because a π-orbital may have

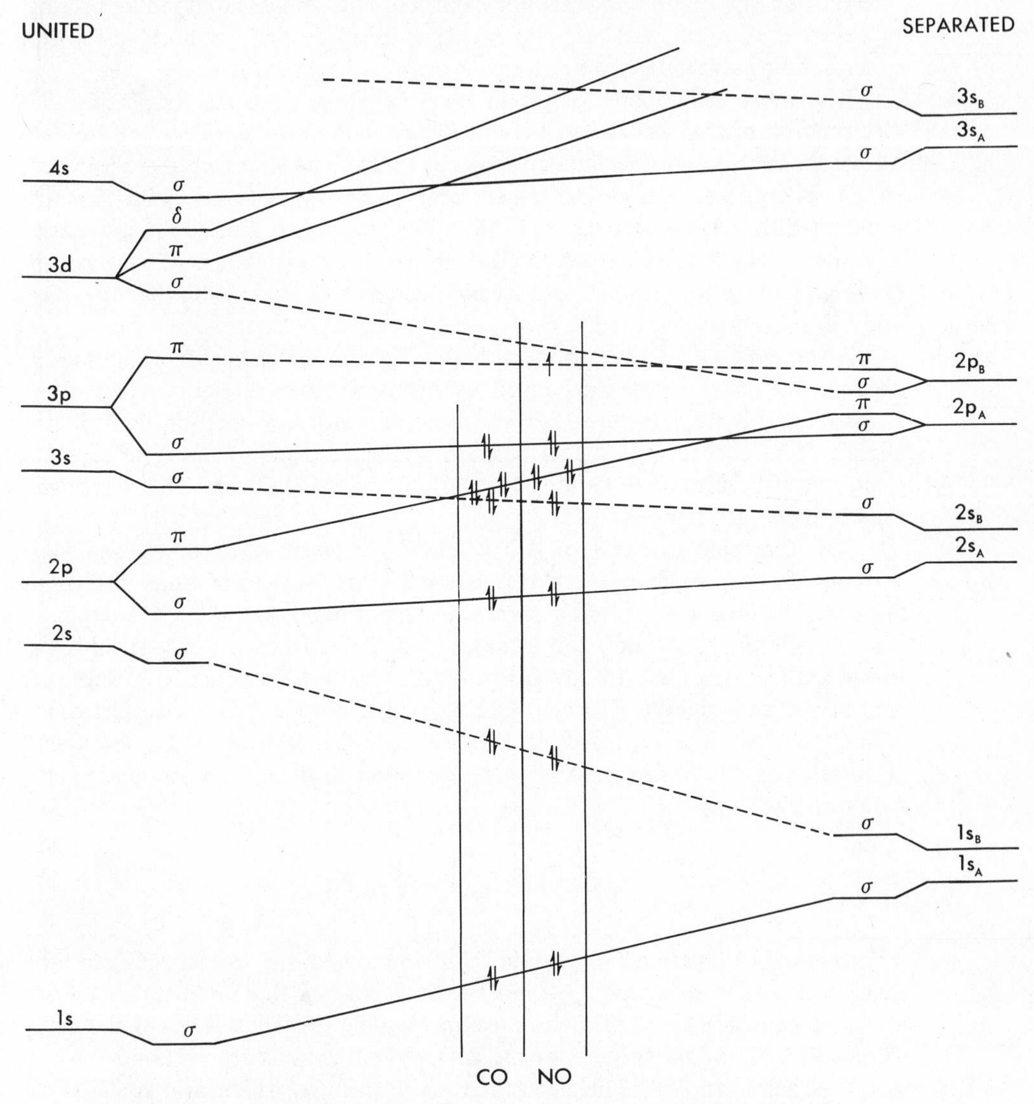

Figure 15.8. Correlation Diagram of Electronic States of Diatom Having Unequal Nuclear Charges†

†R. S. Mulliken, *Revs. Modern Phys.* **4,** 1 [1932]

angular momentum component of $+1$ or -1 along the axis, it can hold up to two pairs of electrons. The bond in N_2 is said to be a triple bond because there is a net of three pairs of bonding electrons, σ_g^2 and σ_u^2 having nearly equal opposed effects. The electron structure in N_2 is cylindrically symmetric, for the π^4 electron distribution depends only on the distance from the axis (Figure 15.6), while the σ^2 combinations are also symmetrical. Similarly, in F_2, the only pair of electrons in a bonding orbital not balanced by a similar nonbonding orbital of electrons is σ_g^2 of $2p$. These two electrons form the single σ-bond of F_2, the other bonding and antibonding electrons having opposed effects.

The most stable state of O_2 involves bonding electrons (neglecting *K*-electrons) in $\sigma_g^2\pi_u^4\sigma_g^2$ as N_2 and F_2, but the antibonding electrons $\sigma_u^2\pi_g^2$ are not all paired because the spins in π_g need not differ. The states π_u^4 and π_g^2 are of similar energy and are almost degenerate. These six electrons, with the net bonding effect of two electrons, are said to form two three-electron bonds, each with about half the strength of an electron-pair bond. The most stable state of O_2 is sometimes written $:\mathrm{O} \overset{\cdots}{\underset{\cdots}{-}} \mathrm{O}:$, which means a superposition of $:\dot{\underset{\cdot\cdot}{\mathrm{O}}}-\ddot{\underset{\cdot}{\mathrm{O}}}:$ and $:\ddot{\underset{\cdot}{\mathrm{O}}}-\dot{\underset{\cdot\cdot}{\mathrm{O}}}:$ as waves.

Although g and u have no meaning for diatoms of unequal nuclear charge because $|u|^2$ need not be unchanged by inversion, the correlation rules σ to σ, π to π, . . . remain. Figure 15.8 lists the states with a correlation that differs slightly from that in Figure 15.7 because of this change in rules. The general electronic structures of NO and CO remain like those of O_2^+ and N_2 except for even-odd character.

The electronic structure of NO is midway between those of N_2 and O_2. Without *K*-electrons, bonding electrons are $\sigma^2\pi^4\sigma^2$ and antibonding electrons are $\sigma^2\pi$. The excess σ^2 orbital provides a single σ-bond, and the $\pi^4\pi$ combination provides a π-bond (π^2) and a three-electron bond ($\pi^2\pi$). Without this unpaired antibonding π-electron, NO forms NO^+, as in the production of sulfuric acid by the lead chamber process. With a true triple bond, NO^+ is isoelectronic with CO and N_2. The stable form of NO with its three-electron bond is described chemically as $:\mathrm{N} \overset{\cdots}{=} \mathrm{O}:$, namely some quantum mechanical combination of structure like

$$:\overset{\uparrow}{\mathrm{N}} = \ddot{\mathrm{O}}: \quad \text{and} \quad :\underset{-}{\ddot{\mathrm{N}}} = \underset{+}{\overset{\uparrow}{\mathrm{O}}}:$$

Figure 15.9 illustrates the various contributions of the several MO's to the electron densities of H_2, N_2, O_2, and F_2. Each contour line indicates a double of the electron density, all the outermost lines having equal density from diagram to diagram. All nodal surfaces of the MO wave functions are, of course, preserved as zeroes in $|u|^2$. The electronic wave functions which are squared to give these electron densities change sign as a nodal surface is crossed. Thus, $1\sigma_u$ is like $u_A - u_B$ where u_A dominates near nucleus A while $-u_B$ dominates near nucleus B. Similarly, in Figure 15.5, the wave function of $1\pi_u$ is positive above

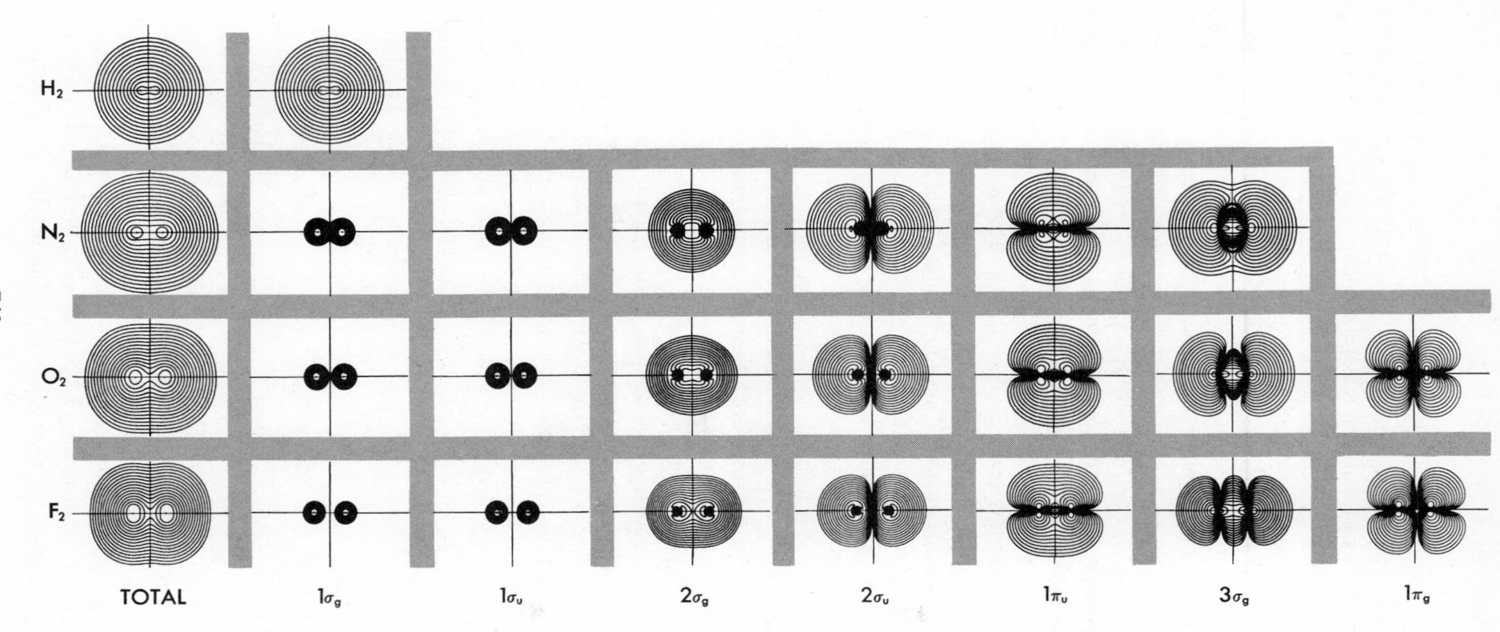

Figure 15.9. Electrons Densities of Various Molecular Orbitals in H_2, N_2, O_2, and F_2 (Ground States)†

†A. C. Wahl, *Science*, **151**, pp. 961–967, February 25, 1966. Copyright 1966 by the American Association for the Advancement of Science.

the nodal plane and negative below it, whereas the wave function of $1\pi_g$ has four lobes (with alternating signs) separated by nodal planes perpendicular to and containing the internuclear axis. This alternation in sign of u is achieved by turning one of the $2p$'s in Figure 15.5 around so that a positive lobe of one is is near a negative lobe of the other. The contour diagrams of Figure 15.9 are close to the best Hartree-Fock (self-consistent field) molecular orbitals.

Electronic states of diatoms are described like electronic states of atoms. Atomic *j-j* coupling has its molecular analogue for diatoms of heavy atoms. The most common of several modes of coupling electronic spin and angular momentum is, however, the analogue of Russell-Saunders coupling (Section 14.10). Completely filled molecular orbitals make no net contribution to electronic angular momentum, but electrons in incompletely filled MO's do. If their net angular momentum (component) along the nuclear axis is zero, the electronic state of the diatom is $\Sigma\,(\Lambda = 0)$, by analogy with atomic S states $(L = 0)$. Similarly, unit angular momentum along the axis $(\Lambda = \pm 1)$ gives Π electronic state (like P for atoms). One source of a Π state is one unpaired π electron. Two π electrons yield a Δ state $(\Lambda = \pm 2)$ as well as a Σ state $(\Lambda = 0)$. The electron spin multiplicity is determined exactly as for an atom. If all electrons are paired, it is a singlet state; hence, N_2, CO, and H_2 are ${}^1\Sigma$ in their most stable states. If one electron is unpaired, its spin may be α or β and it is thus a doublet; hence, O_2^+ and NO are ${}^2\Pi$. Two electrons in different MO's yield a singlet state if paired or a triplet state if spins are alike (the ground state of O_2 is ${}^3\Sigma$).

Besides multiplicity and axial component of electronic angular momentum, certain auxiliary facts may be noted. For example, there are two states of NO having total angular momenta (axial + spin) of $1 + (1/2) = 3/2$ and $1 - (1/2) = 1/2$; these states have the symbols ${}^2\Pi_{3/2}$ and ${}^2\Pi_{1/2}$. In Σ states, the + and − symmetry of the wave function for reflection across any plane containing both nuclei is indicated as a superscript; for example, H_2 N_2, and CO are ${}^1\Sigma^+$, while the ground state of O_2 is ${}^3\Sigma^-$. Finally, for diatoms having nuclei of equal charge, inversion symmetry is indicated by a subscript. Thus, H_2, N_2 and F_2 are ${}^1\Sigma_g^+$ in their ground states, while the ground state of O_2 is ${}^3\Sigma_g^-$. Just as the Laporte rule requires "even" to go to "odd" and vice versa, allowed electronic transitions in diatoms follow various rules. Among these, which guide experimenters to a proper classification of electronic states, are:

$$\Sigma^+ \rightleftharpoons \Sigma^+ \qquad\qquad \Sigma^- \rightleftharpoons \Sigma^-$$

$$g \rightleftharpoons u \qquad\qquad \Delta\Lambda = 0 \text{ or } \pm 1$$

Hence, great intensity is expected of these transitions, which are allowed:

$$\Sigma_g^+ \rightleftharpoons \Pi_u \qquad\qquad \Pi_g \rightleftharpoons \Pi_u$$

Multiplicity is usually conserved so that ${}^3\Pi_g \rightleftharpoons {}^3\Pi_u$ is more likely than ${}^3\Pi_g \rightleftharpoons {}^1\Pi_u$. On the other hand, O_2 molecules in the excited ${}^1\Delta_g$ state decay only slowly to ${}^3\Sigma_g^-$ because the transition is forbidden for three reasons: the multiplicity changes, $\Delta\Lambda = \pm 2$, and g $\rightleftharpoons$ g. Absorption and emission of photons is a good way to find the energies of various electronic states of diatoms, but the energies of all states, even those that cannot be detected optically, can be found by careful measurement of the energies of bombarding electrons that cause changes in electronic states.[9]

It is common knowledge that the very light elements (H to Ne) behave most individualistically. It is generally true that as the number of particles in a system increases, the characteristic quantum mechanical behavior tends to be damped toward classical behavior. Thus, as atoms and molecules get bigger and bigger, their orbitals become less concentrated in angle and extent so that their peculiar orbital geometry is smeared away. Moreover, large atoms tend to hold each other off by repulsions of electrons in inner shells so that the close approach so necessary for strong π orbitals is difficult. Hence, the tendency for the very light elements to form strong double bonds declines as atoms grow in size, rises a bit as many d orbitals become available for delocalization of electrons, and then gradually wanes until even single bonds between very heavy atoms are weak.

The chemical behavior of diatoms is primarily a function of their electronic state and not of the nuclei. That is, $^3\Sigma$ states act alike, $^1\Pi$ states act alike, $^1\Sigma$ states act alike, and so on. The diatoms made of light atoms are very intense in their electronic natures, while diatoms of heavy atoms are more tractable. Their various electronic states differ less in energy than do similar states of light diatoms. In fact, even the distinction between bonding and antibonding electrons and orbitals tends to be erased by the plethora of electrons and orbitals in heavy diatoms.

Correlation diagrams are obviously at least as important as the periodic table. In fact, the periodic table is a special case of the correlation diagrams.

15.6 DISSOCIATION ENERGY

Solution of the electronic wave equation $(\mathbf{T}_e + \mathbf{V})u_e = E_e u_e$ (for fixed nuclei with the Born-Oppenheimer approximation) yields the electronic energy E_e as a function of the parameter R_{AB}, the distance between nuclei. The calculations are excessively difficult even for H_2 and become almost impossible for present-day computers when there are more than about ten electrons. It is possible, however, to combine certain spectroscopic observations and derive an empirical electronic potential energy curve $E(R)$. Figure 15.10 illustrates the general nature of such a curve.

Many empirical curves have been offered,[10] but the best containing just three parameters is the Rydberg function

$$E(R) = -D_e(1 + q)e^{-q} \tag{15.39}$$

[9] A. Kuppermann & L. M. Raff, *J. Chem. Phys.* **37,** 2497 (1962).
[10] Y. P. Varshni, *Rev. Mod. Phys.* **29,** 664 (1957).

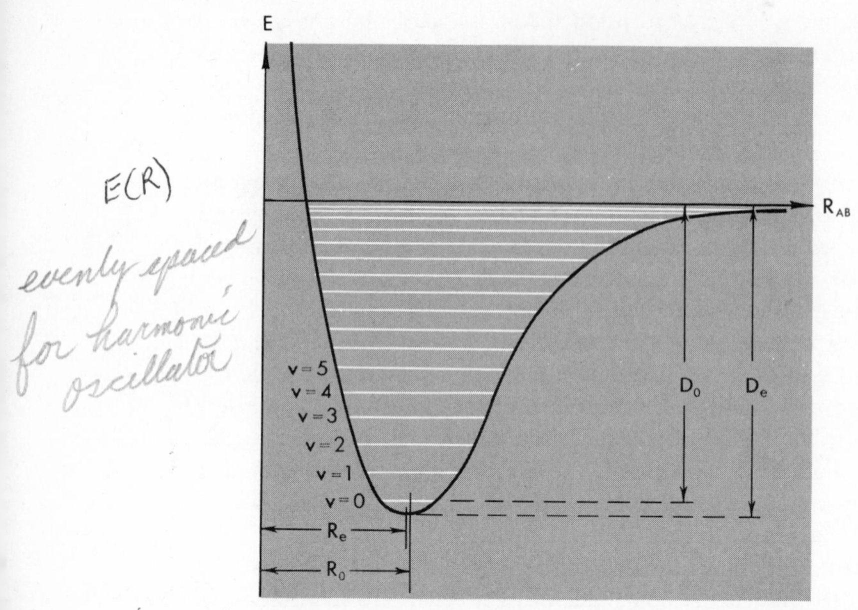

Figure 15.10. Typical Electronic Potential Energy $E_e(R_{AB})$ and Vibrational Energies of a Diatom AB

where the dimensionless (scaled) parameter of distance is

$$q = b(R - R_e) \tag{15.40}$$

and where R_e is the internuclear separation at equilibrium. When $R = R_e$, q is zero and $E(R_e) = -D_e$. The energy D_e is the difference between the energy of the minimum at R_e and the limit at $q = \infty$ where $E = 0$. That is, D_e is the energy required to dissociate a hypothetical isolated diatom lacking zero-point energy and bring the atoms to rest at an infinite distance from each other. The curve $E_e(R)$ is a classical construct and exists by virtue of the Born-Oppenheimer separation of variables. The scale parameter is related to the classical vibrational force constant k_e at the minimum of $E(R)$. For a harmonic oscillator of frequency ν_e and reduced mass m_e, classical mechanics requires at $R = R_e$

$$k_e = 4\pi^2 m_e \nu_e^2 = \left(\frac{d^2E}{dR^2}\right)_{R_e} \tag{15.41}$$

But by (15.39) and (15.40)

$$\begin{aligned}\frac{d^2E}{dR^2} &= -D_e\frac{d}{dR}\left[-(1+q)e^{-q}\frac{dq}{dR} + e^{-q}\frac{dq}{dR}\right]\\ &= +bD_e\frac{d}{dR}(qe^{-q}) = b^2D_e(e^{-q} - qe^{-q})\end{aligned}$$

Since q is zero near $R = R_e$, it follows from (15.41) that

$$k_e = 4\pi^2 m_e \nu_e^2 = b^2 D_e \tag{15.42}$$

Each electronic state of a diatom has its own curve $E(R)$ with its own D_e, R_e, and ν_e. Many electronic states have no minimum; the repulsive state of H_2^+ with $v = u_A - u_B$ is an example, dispersion excepted. Some electronic potential energy curves have two minima, the second one being weak and at large R where van der Waals or other long-range forces operate.

Zero-point vibration prevents any real diatom from having an energy $E_e = -D_e$, just as a harmonic oscillator cannot attain the energy of the minimum in its $V = (1/2)kx^2$. Figure 15.10 shows typical energy states of a diatom, part of the energy being vibrational energy. The energy of the most stable real state of a diatom relative to separated atoms at rest is $-D_0$, as indicated in Figure 15.10. The slight anharmonicity in $E(R)$ near R_e causes the average internuclear distance R_0 of the real most stable state to exceed R_e.

Almost all diatoms vibrate very much like harmonic oscillators. Slight anharmonicity in general exists because the "spring" of the electrons is weakened as the nuclei separate. Thus the equal increments in vibrational energy required by (14.95) of an ideal harmonic oscillator decrease gradually as the vibrational quantum number $n_i = v$ rises. Empirically this change is described by the series

$$\frac{E(v)}{hc} \equiv G(v) = \omega_e(v + \tfrac{1}{2}) - x_e\omega_e(v + \tfrac{1}{2})^2 + y_e\omega_e(v + \tfrac{1}{2})^3 + \cdots \tag{15.43}$$

where $y_e\omega_e \ll x_e\omega_e \ll \omega_e$ and where $E(v)$ is the vibrational energy to be added to $E_e(R)$ to give the actual energy of a rotationless diatom. The values of ω_e, $x_e\omega_e$, and sometimes $y_e\omega_e$ (which is very small) are found by proper assignment of vibrational quantum numbers v to infrared spectra, where only v changes as a photon is absorbed or emitted, or to visible and ultraviolet spectra, where the vibrational energy changes are a small part of the energy changes due to a change of electronic state.

There is no selection rule for changes in v. The Frank-Condon principle, which summarizes trends in intensities of vibrational-electronic transitions, merely says that when v exceeds about 3 or 4, the most likely change (greatest intensity) is one in which nuclei do not move. Vibration is semiclassical at large v, with nuclear motion being slow at the classical turning points where $E_e(R)$ equals the total energy. Since nuclei thus spend much time almost resting at the maximum and minimum distances of their vibration, the most intense transitions occur virtually at constant R from $E''(R)$ to $E'(R)$. When v is small, however, it is important in estimating intensities to calculate $\bar{R} = \int u''(R)Ru'(R)\,dR$, where $u''(R)$ is the vibrational wave function of one electronic state with energy $E''(R)$ and $u'(R)$ is for the other electronic state. This is especially important for states with $v = 0$, for the most probable place to find the oscillator, as in the harmonic oscillator, is halfway between the classical turning points.

The difference in energy from v to $v + 1$ for a particular electronic state gradually decreases as v rises and as the classical turning points given by $E(R)$ spread apart. When $y_e\omega_e$ is negligible or unknown, as is usual, the difference in energy of adjacent vibrational levels is

$$\begin{aligned}\Delta G(v + \tfrac{1}{2}) &= G(v + 1) - G(v) \\ &= [\omega_e(v + \tfrac{3}{2}) - x_e\omega_e(v + \tfrac{3}{2})^2] - [\omega_e(v + \tfrac{1}{2}) - x_e\omega_e(v + \tfrac{1}{2}] \\ &= \omega_e - x_e\omega_e(2v + 2) \qquad (15.44)\end{aligned}$$

When $\Delta G(v + \frac{1}{2})$ is at last zero, the diatom may be viewed as dissociating by vibration. If (15.44) holds, this occurs when

$$v_0 + \frac{1}{2} = \frac{\omega_e}{2x_e\omega_e} - \frac{1}{2} \qquad (15.45)$$

Really ΔG seldom declines linearly with v as in (15.44). However, with $(v_0 + \frac{1}{2})$ in $G(v)$ of (15.43), the vibrational energy relative to the minimum electronic

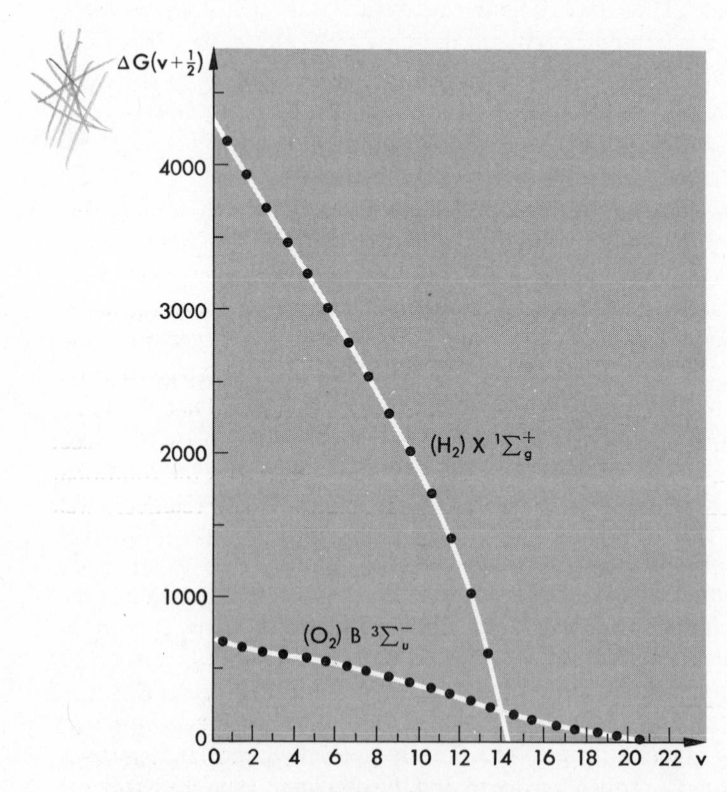

Figure 15.11. Birge-Sponer Plot of Differences in Vibrational Energy $\Delta G(v + \frac{1}{2})$ to Dissociation at $\Delta G = 0$.

energy at $E_e(R_e) = -D_e$ is

$$G(v_0) = \omega_e\left(\frac{\omega_e}{2x_e\omega_e} - \frac{1}{2}\right) - x_e\omega_e\left(\frac{\omega_e}{2x_e\omega_e} - \frac{1}{2}\right)^2$$

$$= \frac{\omega_e^2}{4x_e\omega_e} - \frac{x_e\omega_e}{4} \tag{15.46}$$

Since the vibrational energy of the most stable state ($v = 0$) is

$$G(0) = \frac{\omega_e}{2} - \frac{x_e\omega_e}{4} \tag{15.47}$$

if follows from (15.46) and (15.47) and a glance at Figure 15.10 that

$$D_0 = G(v_0) - G(0) = \frac{\omega_e^2}{4x_e\omega_e} - \frac{\omega_e}{2} \tag{15.48}$$

When the gradual convergence of $\Delta G(v + \frac{1}{2})$ toward zero at v_0 is nonlinear, D_0 is found by summing the ΔG's from $v = 0$ to v_0 or as great a v as data allow. Figure 15.11 shows how $\Delta G(v + \frac{1}{2})$ is customarily plotted against increasing v to yield the sum of ΔG's as the area below the curve. This is the celebrated method of Birge and Sponer for finding dissociation energies. If the extrapolation at high v is short, very reliable and accurate values of D_0 are found by summing numerical ΔG's to the end of their observation and adding a graphical correction for what remains. Since (15.44) seldom holds at all v, the use of (15.48) without data at large v gives only approximate values of D_0. Usually the D_0's found by (15.48) are too great by up to 30%.

Table 15.1 lists several values of D_0, ω_e, and $x_e\,\omega_e$ for various molecules in various electronic states. Values of D_0 have been found not only from convergence of $\Delta G(v + \frac{1}{2})$ to zero but also from thermochemical cycles, from electron impact with perhaps mass spectroscopy, and from predissociation limits. Sometimes the closely spaced rotational energy levels (see Section 15.8) become diffuse above a certain energy because such molecules have a short lifetime Δt. According to the uncertainty principle, their energies become ill defined to the extent $\Delta E \approx \hbar/\Delta t$. If Δt is long compared to a cycle of vibration ($\sim 10^{-13}$ sec) and yet short compared to a cycle of rotation ($\sim 10^{-10}$ sec), then the rotational energy states become diffuse while the vibrational states remain relatively well defined in energy. The disturbance is a radiationless transition from one electronic state to another state at a crossing of their potential energy curves. Upon crossing to a repulsive curve, molecules dissociate to atoms within one vibration of the new state. Usually during such a change of $E(R)$, there is no change in multiplicity (spin) or g-u symmetry, Λ may change by 0 or ± 1, and if $\Lambda = 0$ then the + or − reflection symmetry is unchanged. The rotational quantum number may be unchanged also. The great advantage of establishing a predissociation limit, especially a sharp one, is that it forces D_0 to assume one of a few definite values according to the state of electronic excitation (if any) of the product atoms. Establishing predissociation is not always straightforward, however.

Table 15.1 Spectroscopic Constants of Diatomic Molecules.

Molecule	Electronic State†	ω_e (cm^{-1})	$x_e\,\omega_e$ (cm^{-1})	D_0 (ev)	D_0 (kcal/mole)	Ref. (Below)
$^1H^1H$	$X\,^1\Sigma_g^+$	4395.2	117.90	4.476	103.22	(1)
$^1H^1H$	$C\,^1\Pi_u$	2242.72	67.03			(1)
$^1H^2H$	$X\,^1\Sigma_g^+$	3817.09	94.958	4.511	104.03	(1)
$^2H^2H$	$X\,^1\Sigma_g^+$	3118.5	64.10	4.554	105.02	(1)
$^{12}C^1H$	$X\,^2\Pi$	2868.5	64.4	3.47	80.0	(2), (3)
$^{16}O^1H$	$X\,^2\Pi$	3735.21	82.81	4.45	103	(1), (2)
$^{12}C^{14}N$	$X\,^2\Sigma^+$	2068.705	13.144	8.1	187	(1), (2)
$^{12}C^{16}O$	$X\,^1\Sigma^+$	2170.21	13.461	11.11	256.2	(1), (2)
$^{12}C^{16}O$	$A\,^1\Pi$	1515.61	17.2505			(1)
$^{14}N^{14}N$	$X\,^1\Sigma_g^+$	2359.61	14.456	9.762	225.1	(1), (2)
$^{16}O^{16}O$	$X\,^3\Sigma_g^-$	1580.361	12.0730	5.1148	117.95	(1), (5)
$^{16}O^{16}O$	$a\,^1\Delta_g$	1509.	13.			(1)
$^{16}O^{16}O$	$b\,^1\Sigma_g^+$	1432.687	13.9501			(1)
$^{127}I^{16}O$	$X\,^2\Pi_{3/2}$	681.5	4.3	1.9	44.	(2), (4)
$^{127}I^{35}Cl$	$X\,^1\Sigma^+$	384.18	1.465	2.153	49.65	(1), (2)
$^{79}Br^{81}Br$	$X\,^1\Sigma_g^+$	323.2	1.07	1.971	45.4	(1)

† The ground (most stable) electronic state is indicated by X.
(1) Herzberg, G., *Molecular Spectra and Molecular Structure* I. Spectra of Diatomic Molecules. Princeton, N. J.: D. Van Nostrand Company, Inc., 1950, Table 39, pp. 501–581.
(2) Gaydon, A. G., *Dissociation Energies and Spectra of Diatomic Molecules.* London: Chapman & Hall, Ltd., 1947, 1953.
(3) N. H. Kiess and H. P. Broida, *Astrophys. J.* **123**, 166 (1956).
(4) Reproduced by permission of the National Research Council of Canada from the *Canadian Journal of Physics* **38**, 444 (1960).
(5) Reproduced by permission of the National Research Council of Canada from the *Canadian Journal of Physics* **32,** 110 (1954).

Example 15.1. The $B\,^3\Sigma_u^-$ state of $O_{2(g)}$ dissociates to $O_{(g)}$ (^3P at 0 cm^{-1}) and $O_{(g)}$ (^1D at 15,870 cm^{-1}) and the lowest vibrational state of the B state is 49,360 cm^{-1} above the lowest vibrational state of the ground electronic state. Calculate the dissociation energy D_0 of the ground state to unexcited (^3P) atoms. Use Figure 15.11.

The sum of the ΔG's or the area under the O_2 curve of Figure 15.11 is about 7760 cm^{-1}. The energy of O (^3P) + O (^1D) above the $v = 0$ state of the ground electronic state is $7760 + 49{,}360 = 57{,}120$ cm^{-1}. Since the products have excitation energy of 15,870 cm^{-1}, the energy of 2O(^3P) above $v = 0$ of the ground electronic state is about $57{,}120 - 15{,}870 = 41{,}250$ cm^{-1}. With 1 ev equal to 8066 cm^{-1}, $D_0 = 5.11$ ev. A more accurate value is given in Table 15.1.

15.7 BOND ENERGY[11]

Chemists have for many years known and used the fact that many molecular properties are additive and that chemical bonds tend to be independent of their

[11] Much of the first part of this section is based on J. L. Allen and H. Shull, *J. Chem. Phys.* **35,** 1644 (1961).

environment. As more and more complex quantum mechanical calculations of molecular energies are undertaken, it is becoming clear that electron correlation must be allowed for. Nearly all correlation that is required can, however, be effected by a careful and adequate description of each pair of electrons in its own MO. For the natural isolation and near-independence of electron-pairs even extends to each of the two or three electron-pairs of double and triple bonds.

A worthwhile step beyond the one-electron approximation of many MO calculations and beyond the self-consistent field of one-electron Hartree-Fock calculation considers an electronic wave function of a molecule to be a product of *geminals*. Whereas an orbital is a one-electron function (as for H), a geminal describes a pair of electrons, but the electrons may have like spin if a triplet multiplicity is needed, and only one electron may be present if the molecule is a free radical. Ordinarily, though, a geminal holds the two spin-paired electrons of a single covalent bond. The success of using geminals will, of course, equal the emipirical success of the chemist's traditional view of bonding in molecules. Like bonds, geminals are usually localized in a certain region of the molecule and thus relieve interelectronic repulsion, but it is possible for certain geminals to extend over much of a molecule, as π electrons do in aromatic systems. To the extent that a bond or geometrical environment for two electrons is the same in different molecules, the same geminal is useful in both molecules.

When the electronic wave function of a molecule is a product of geminals (and within the Born-Oppenheimer approximation), the kinetic energy of the molecule is the sum over geminals of the electronic kinetic energy of each pair of electrons. That is,

$$\bar{T} = \sum_I T_I \tag{15.49}$$

where T_I is the kinetic energy of the electrons in geminal I. Furthermore, when the nuclei are at their equilibrium positions, the virial theorem (14.207) requires $2\bar{T} = -\bar{V}$. The total molecular energy, with all internuclear and electronic energies included, is

$$E = \bar{T} + \bar{V} = -\bar{T} = -\sum_I T_I \tag{15.50}$$

where (15.49) has been used. Equation (15.50) says that molecular energy is a sum of terms T_I attributable individually to geminals. Moreover, the terms T_I are identified with the energy of a geminal (electron-pair) in the molecule. This energy is the energy of the electrons relative to a zero of energy for separated nuclei and electrons. And this energy is exactly equal to the kinetic energy of the electrons in the geminal (with its sign changed).

There are many reasons why the kinetic energy of electrons in a geminal might depend on the environment of the geninal. However, Allen and Shull conclude that there are several reasons why it does not depend on the rest of the molecule. What is truly significant about this attitude toward molecular electrons is the possibility of calculating parts of molecular wave functions for use in many other related molecules. This scheme also allows analysis of parts of multiple bonds, attributing independent energies to nonvalence electrons, and studying the effect of minor differences in large molecules.

Values of bond energies are stated for 0°K when spectroscopic or extensive thermodynamic data are available. Without these, 25°C is the usual basis. The difference in bond energies is small but real at these temperatures. Dissociation energies, even of O_2 which has long been one of the well established values, are sometimes changed. Since the final state of the process for which a bond energy is calculated is one or more ground-state atoms at rest, a change in dissociation energy involves a change in the reference of energy. Before about 1955, there was great debate and confusion about $D_0(N_2)$ and the energy of $C_{(g)}$ relative to graphite.

Still another misunderstanding involves the meaning of a bond energy. There are two general kinds: an average bond energy and a bond-dissociation energy. An average bond energy, when multiplied by the number of bonds broken, is equal to the total energy required to break in one step all bonds of a certain kind in a gaseous molecule and remove the atoms (and molecular fragments, if any remain) to an infinite distance from each other. For example, by Tables 9.6 and 15.1, at 0°K

$$\begin{array}{ll} H_2O_{(g)} \longrightarrow H_{2(g)} + \tfrac{1}{2}O_{2(g)} & \Delta H_0^\circ = +57.10 \text{ kcal} \\ H_{2(g)} \longrightarrow H_{(g)} + H_{(g)} & \Delta H_0^\circ = +103.22 \text{ kcal} \\ \tfrac{1}{2}O_{2(g)} \longrightarrow O_{(g)} & \Delta H_0^\circ = +58.98 \text{ kcal} \\ \hline H_2O_{(g)} \longrightarrow H_{(g)} + H_{(g)} + O_{(g)} & \Delta H_0^\circ = 219.30 \text{ kcal} \end{array}$$

The average bond energy of the O–H bonds in H_2O is, therefore, $(\tfrac{1}{2})(219.30) = 109.65$ kcal. If the OH bond is unchanged in H_2O_2, alcohols, and so on, this average bond energy is useful for estimating the stability of a whole molecule or molecular fragment relative to atoms in their most stable electronic states.

The difference between an average bond energy and a bond-dissociation energy involves the difference between breaking all the bonds and breaking a particular one. For example, from Table 15.1 and the result above for $H_2O_{(g)}$,

$$\begin{array}{ll} O_{(g)} + H_{(g)} \longrightarrow OH_{(g)} & \Delta H_0^\circ = -D_0(\text{OH}) = -103 \text{ kcal} \\ H_2O_{(g)} \longrightarrow H_{(g)} + H_{(g)} + O_{(g)} & \Delta H_0^\circ = +219 \text{ kcal} \\ \hline H_2O_{(g)} \longrightarrow H_{(g)} + OH_{(g)} & \Delta H_0^\circ = +116 \text{ kcal} \end{array}$$

That is, the bond-dissociation energy of the first O–H bond of water is 116 kcal, while the second is only 103 kcal. It is clear that in estimating ΔH° for single chemical events, perhaps to limit ΔH_a for a forward or reverse step of a mechanism, only a bond-dissociation energy is useful. An average bond energy is of no direct use except when all bonds of a certain kind are broken, for the average bond energy makes no allowance for electronic rearrangements in the fragments of dissociation.

Bond-dissociation energies are generally found from kinetics, for highly reactive species are usually involved. Spectroscopic measurements also yield bond-dissociation energies. Mass spectrometers are very useful for identifying the unstable species and the minimum energy for their generation. Optical spectroscopy is frequently handicapped because it is difficult to identify with certainty what molecular species is absorbing or emitting photons of a certain energy. Thermodynamics, of course, contributes to bond energies of both kinds through calorimetry and Hess's law.

There is one more dissociation energy that has theoretical value but requires very judicious use. It is concerned with the energy required to break one or all bonds of a certain kind and produce one or more atoms in their valence state. An atom in a valence state has the same electronic status as it does in the molecule. In its valence state, an atom is in a nonstationary quantum state. Hence, its energy exceeds that of the ground atomic state, which is the usual reference of bond-energy calculations. The difference between the energy to break all bonds with atoms being formed in their valence states and the sum of the average bond energies for the bonds broken is the summation of the valence state energies of the atoms. The valence-state energy of H is almost zero because only the $1s$ state of H is stable enough to contribute significantly to its bonding. The $1s - 2s$ energy difference is 235 kcal mole^{-1}, a great handicap to the use of any orbital besides $1s$ (or to a valence of two for H). If O in OH is indeed in its valence state, then the valence state energy of O in H_2O is $2(116) - 219 = 13$ kcal mole^{-1}. Valence state energy, like bond energy, has been defined in many ways.

15.8 ROTATIONAL ENERGY

Bond energies are additive and bonds in a molecule are independent whenever the interaction between their electrons is small or negligible. Analogous statements hold for many other kinds of possible interaction, as among electronic energy E_e and vibrational energy E_v and rotational energy E_J. It is generally possible to use a linear variation function to calculate the extent of nonadditive interactions; hence, (14.184) would yield a more realistic energy E' than either of the unperturbed energies H_{11} or H_{22}. The interaction is greatest when H_{12} is greatest, often when v_1 is like v_2 and $H_{11} \approx H_{22}$. The interaction is least when $H_{12} = 0$, for then (14.184) yields the energies H_{11} and H_{22}. Qualitatively, H_{12} can be expected to be negligible whenever the times for one cycle of motion are different in the two mixed states.

It is generally true that E_e, E_v, and E_J involve greatly different frequencies or time-cycles so that the total energy of a molecule is merely their sum (with perhaps other lesser energies of no immediate interest here). That is,

$$E = E_e + E_v + E_J + \dots \tag{15.51}$$

where E_e and E_v are calculated as in previous sections of this chapter. Typically, $E_J \ll E_v \ll E_e$, while the times of a typical cycle h/E increase from $\sim 10^{-15}$ sec for E_e through $\sim 10^{-13}$ sec for E_v to $\sim 10^{-10}$ sec for E_J.

For a rigid rotor, conceived as a nonvibrating dumbbell, the rotational energy is

$$E_J = \frac{\hbar^2 J(J+1)}{2\mu R^2} \tag{15.52}$$

where the rotational quantum number J is 0, 1, 2, 3, . . . , and where μ is the reduced mass of the rotor, which is thought of as a mass m_1 and mass m_2 held apart at a distance R. That is,

$$\frac{1}{\mu} = \frac{1}{m_1} + \frac{1}{m_2} \tag{15.53}$$

where m_1 and m_2 are the atomic masses of the atoms, their nuclei being a distance R apart. Equation (15.52) comes from (14.112) with $V(r) = 0$ because the rotor is free, with $dR/dr = 0$ because it is rigid, and with $l = J$. Equation (15.52) can also be related to the results of Section 14.8 on angular momentum. A rotor with moment of inertia

$$I = \mu R^2 \tag{15.54}$$

has a kinetic energy $(1/2)I\omega^2$ at an angular velocity ω (not ω_e!) and angular momentum $I\omega$. But by (14.147), the square of the total angular momentum, with J replacing l, is $I^2\omega^2 = J(J+1)\hbar^2$. Hence, the kinetic (total) energy of the rotor in center-of-mass coordinates is

$$E = \frac{(I\omega)^2}{2I} = \frac{\hbar^2 J(J+1)}{2I} \tag{15.55}$$

where $I = \mu R^2$ as in (15.54). [Nuclei sometimes show rotational energies in accord with (15.55) because of their nucleon structure.]

In the infrared and visible spectra, energy differences are customarily measured in cm^{-1} so that the usual notation for (15.52) or (15.55) is

$$F(J) = \frac{E_J}{hc} = BJ(J+1) \tag{15.56}$$

where the rotational constant is

$$B = \frac{h}{8\pi^2 cI} \tag{15.57}$$

Rotation of a nonrigid diatom requires (15.56) to become

$$F(J) = BJ(J+1) - DJ^2(J+1)^2 \tag{15.58}$$

where D accounts for centrifugal stretching. Approximately,

$$D \approx \frac{4B^3}{\omega_e^2} \ll B \tag{15.59}$$

Affected also by vibrational stretching, B and D depend on the vibrational quantum number; in standard spectroscopic notation, B becomes

$$B_v = B_e - \alpha_e(v + \tfrac{1}{2}) \tag{15.60}$$

and D becomes

$$D_v = D_e - \beta_e(v + \tfrac{1}{2}) \tag{15.61}$$

The values B_e and D_e apply at the minimum in $E_e(R)$.

The equations above apply to Σ electronic states of a diatom; all rotational energy is about either of two axes perpendicular to the internuclear axis. When electronic angular momentum exists around this axis, $\Lambda \neq 0$ and (15.56) becomes for $\Pi, \Delta, \ldots$ states

$$F(J) = BJ(J+1) - (A - B)\Lambda^2 \tag{15.62}$$

where Λ, which is analogous to m, is the component of electronic angular momentum along the molecular axis. The value of J cannot decrease below Λ; hence $J = \Lambda, \Lambda + 1, \Lambda + 2, \ldots$. However, $A \gg B$ because A is proportional to a reciprocal of the moment of inertia of the electrons.

The formulas above apply also to linear molecules of more than two atoms. Examples are HCN, CO_2, COS, and C_2H_2. When a polyatomic molecule is not linear and yet has enough symmetry to have two equal moments of inertia, it is called a symmetric top. For such molecules (15.62) becomes

$$F(J) = BJ(J+1) - (A - B)K^2 \tag{15.63}$$

where, analogous to B, A is related to the moment of inertia I_A about the axis of high symmetry (threefold or greater) by

$$A = \frac{h}{8\pi^2 c I_A} = \frac{h}{8\pi^2 c \mu_A R_A^2} \tag{15.64}$$

Now A is comparable in size to B. In (15.63), K is the component of angular momentum about the symmetry axis and takes the values $0, \pm 1, \pm 2, \ldots$ along the axis. Since J measures the total angular momentum, $J \geqslant K$.

Infrared radiation has an energy of the order of 1000 cm^{-1} and thus involves both vibrational and rotational energy. For a harmonic oscillator, the Laporte rule requires $\Delta v = \pm 1$, but this rule is not perfect because vibrations are slightly anharmonic. For a diatom in a Σ electronic state ($\Lambda = 0$), $\Delta J = \pm 1$ because the even and odd character of the rotational levels alternate as J rises by one. For a diatom not in a Σ state, however, the Laporte rule yields as the selection rule $\Delta J = 0, \pm 1$. Similarly, for a symmetric top, photons are absorbed or emitted when $\Delta K = 0$ and $\Delta J = 0, \pm 1$. It is customary to label spectra originat-

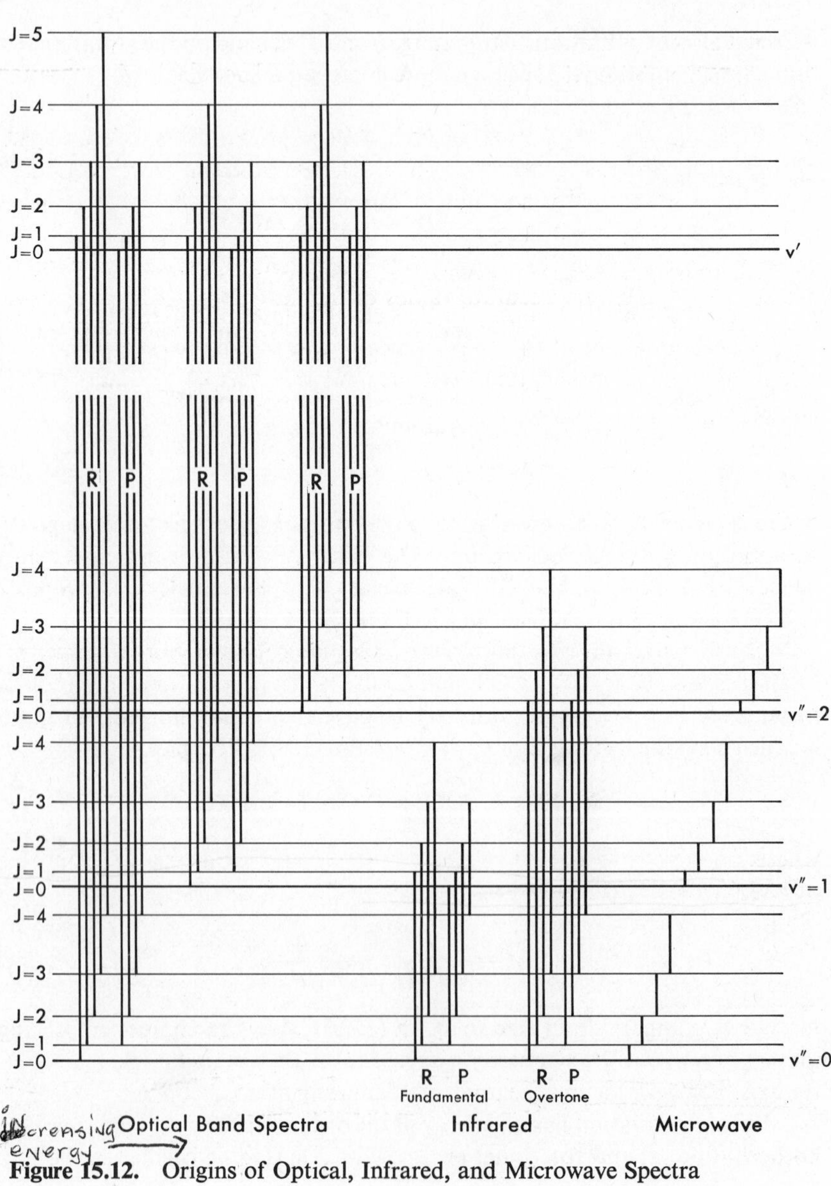

Figure 15.12. Origins of Optical, Infrared, and Microwave Spectra

ing from $\Delta J = -1$ a P branch when the initial and final vibrational states are constant; from $\Delta J = 0$, a Q branch; and from $\Delta J = +1$, an R branch.

Figure 15.12 illustrates for a few rotational and vibrational states how photon energies are related to molecular energy states. The Frank-Condon principle weakly guides the changes in v'' for the ground electronic state and v' for a vibrational state of the excited electronic state. Generally, electronic transitions involve energies of a few electron volts so that the spectra fall in the visible and ultraviolet. Infrared spectra have energies of the order of ω_e (Table 15.1), or about 1000 cm^{-1}. This is a wavelength of 10^{-3} cm $= 10^5$ A. Microwave spectra are pure rotational spectra with $\Delta J = \pm 1$ and no change in vibrational or electronic state (Section 15.10).

The object of interpreting optical and infrared spectra is to learn something of the structure and vibrational properties of a molecule. Any molecule yields spectra in the optical range, but in the infrared and microwave regions the molecule must have an electric dipole moment. Table 15.2 lists values of the rotational constant B for several linear molecules. These are of great value because they yield very accurate values of the moment of inertia I_B about axes perpendicular to the molecular axis, and from I_B come internuclear distances. Since the electronic potential energy is but little affected, if at all, by isotopic substitution, one molecular parameter can be found for each different B. Thus B's yield the structure of even polyatomic species.

Table 15.2 Rotational Constants for Linear Molecules from Optical and Infrared Spectra.

Molecule		B_e (15.60) (cm^{-1})	B_0 (15.60) (cm^{-1})	Reference (Below)
$^{79}Br\,^{81}Br$	$X\,^1\Sigma_g^+$	0.08091		(1)
$^{12}C^1H$	$X\,^2\Pi$	14.457		(1)
$^{35}Cl^{35}Cl$	$X\,^1\Sigma_g^+$	0.2438		(1)
$^{12}C\,^{16}O$	$X\,^1\Sigma^+$	1.93139		(1)
$^1H^1H$	$X\,^1\Sigma_g^+$	60.809		(1)
$^1H^2H$	$X\,^1\Sigma_g^+$	45.655		(1)
$^2H^2H$	$X\,^1\Sigma_g^+$	30.429		(1)
$^1H^{35}Cl$	$X\,^1\Sigma^+$	10.5909		(1)
$^{14}N^{14}N$	$X\,^1\Sigma_g^+$	2.010		(1)
$^{16}O^{16}O$	$X\,^3\Sigma_g^-$	1.44567		(1)
$^{16}O^1H$	$X\,^2\Pi$	18.871		(1)
$^{16}O^{12}C^{16}O$	(CO_2)	0.3906	0.3895	(2)
$^1H^{12}C^{12}C^1H$	(C_2H_2)	1.1838	1.17692	(2)
$^1H^{12}C^{12}C^2H$	(C_2HD)	0.9967	0.99141	(2)

(1) G. Herzberg, *Molecular Spectra and Molecular Structure* I. Spectra of Diatomic Molecules. Princeton, N. J.: D. Van Nostrand Co. Inc., © 1950 Table 39, pp. 501–581.
(2) G. Herzberg, *Molecular Spectra and Molecular Structure* II. Infrared and Raman Spectra of Polyatomic Molecules. © 1945 Princeton, N. J.: D. Van Nostrand Co. Inc., p. 396.

Example 15.2. From the data of Table 15.2, calculate the internuclear distances in H_2, HD, and D_2.

By (15.54) and (15.57),

$$R_e = \sqrt{\frac{I_e}{\mu}} = \sqrt{\frac{\hbar}{4\pi c B_e \mu}}$$

Since $m_H = 1.00782$ and $m_D = 2.01410$, in atomic units (15.53) yields

$$\mu(H_2) = \frac{m_H m_H}{m_H + m_H} = \frac{m_H}{2} = 0.50391$$

$$\mu(HD) = \frac{m_H m_D}{m_H + m_D} = 0.67171$$

$$\mu(D_2) = \frac{m_D}{2} = 1.00705$$

In cgs units,

$$R_e(H_2) = \left(\frac{6.6256 \times 10^{-27} \times 6.0225 \times 10^{23}}{8 \times \pi^2 \times 2.9979 \times 10^{10} \times 60.809 \times 0.50391}\right)^{1/2}$$

$$= 0.74172 \times 10^{-8} \text{ cm}$$

Similarly, $R_e(HD) = 0.74142 \times 10^{-8}$ cm and $R_e(D_2) = 0.74170 \times 10^{-8}$ cm. Not all five significant figures have real meaning in the usual sense, for R_e as calculated is really a reciprocal root mean square distance, B_e being an average value of the reciprocal of the moment of inertia. Moreover, the uncertainty principle and the distinction between R_e and R_0 must be considered. A meaningful distance would seem to be 0.742 A for H_2 and D_2 and 0.741 A for HD. The essential equality of the internuclear distances is one indication that isotopic substitution does not alter the electronic potential energy function.

15.9 INFRARED AND RAMAN SPECTRA

The same influences and conditions that keep bond energies constant also tend to keep vibrational frequencies constant from molecule to molecule when the local environment within each is the same. For example, the fundamental stretching vibration of H against its molecule has an energy of $\sim$ 3000 cm^{-1}, while single, double, and triple bonds have stretching vibrations with (fundamental) energies of about 900 cm^{-1}, 1600 cm^{-1}, and 2000 cm^{-1} respectively. In general, stretching energies are more characteristic and constant than are bending energies. However, because stretchings and bendings combine to form combination frequencies ($\nu_1 + \nu_2$) or overtones ($\nu_1, 2\nu_1, 3\nu_1, \ldots$), the infrared spectrum is often simplest to interpret below about 1000 cm^{-1}. Figure 15.13 indicates the energies of various vibrations with energies in the far infrared, below ca. 800 cm^{-1}.

With standard spectra of reference species at hand it is clearly possible to identify unknowns and even to make reasonable conjectures about their structures. Sometimes certain functional groups are very clearly indicated. When observations of nuclear magnetic resonance (Section 15.12) and mass spectroscopy (Section 14.16) are combined with infrared data, identity of a substance and its structure are usually established with assurance. The details of such correlations and identification and the practical matters of operating infrared spectrometers, which have reached a high level of sophistication, are left for laboratory work.

A rather interesting spectroscopic method, less widely used than the three just mentioned, depends on light scattered incoherently, that is, with a change of wavelength characteristic of the scatterer. Predicted in 1923 by Smekal and first observed in India in 1928 by Raman, this radiation depends on a change in molecular polarizability during a vibration. Raman spectra are excited by intense electromagnetic radiation; mercury arcs are used and lasers may be used in the future. If ν_i is a Raman active frequency of a substance, and if ν_0 is the frequency of the intense source, then Raman lines have the frequencies $\nu_0 \pm \nu_i$. These are observed in a direction perpendicular to the rays from the intense source and have varying degrees of polarization. Rayleigh scattering, which is coherent and of unchanged frequency ν_0, also is observed.

RAMAN

The lines at $\nu_0 + \nu_i$ are called *Stokes lines.* They originate from transitions of unexcited molecules of the irradiated substance from a low-energy state (often the ground vibrational state) to a virtually intermediate state (unobserved) to a final state of energy $h\nu_i$ above the initial energy. The lines at $\nu_0 - \nu_i$, called *anti-Stokes lines*, are much less intense than Stokes lines because they originate in excited states of energy $h\nu_i$ above the final state, these excited states being less populated by virtue of the usual Boltzmann distribution of energy states in the irradiated sample.

There are two great values of Raman spectra. It is possible to observe fundamental vibrational frequencies that are not active in the infrared. Secondly, the infrared and Raman frequencies together may determine the general symmetry of a molecule. For example, if a molecule has a center of symmetry (e.g. CCl_4, SF_6), then fundamental vibrations are active *either* as Raman or infrared, but not in both.

FAR INFRARED VIBRATIONAL FREQUENCY CORRELATION CHART

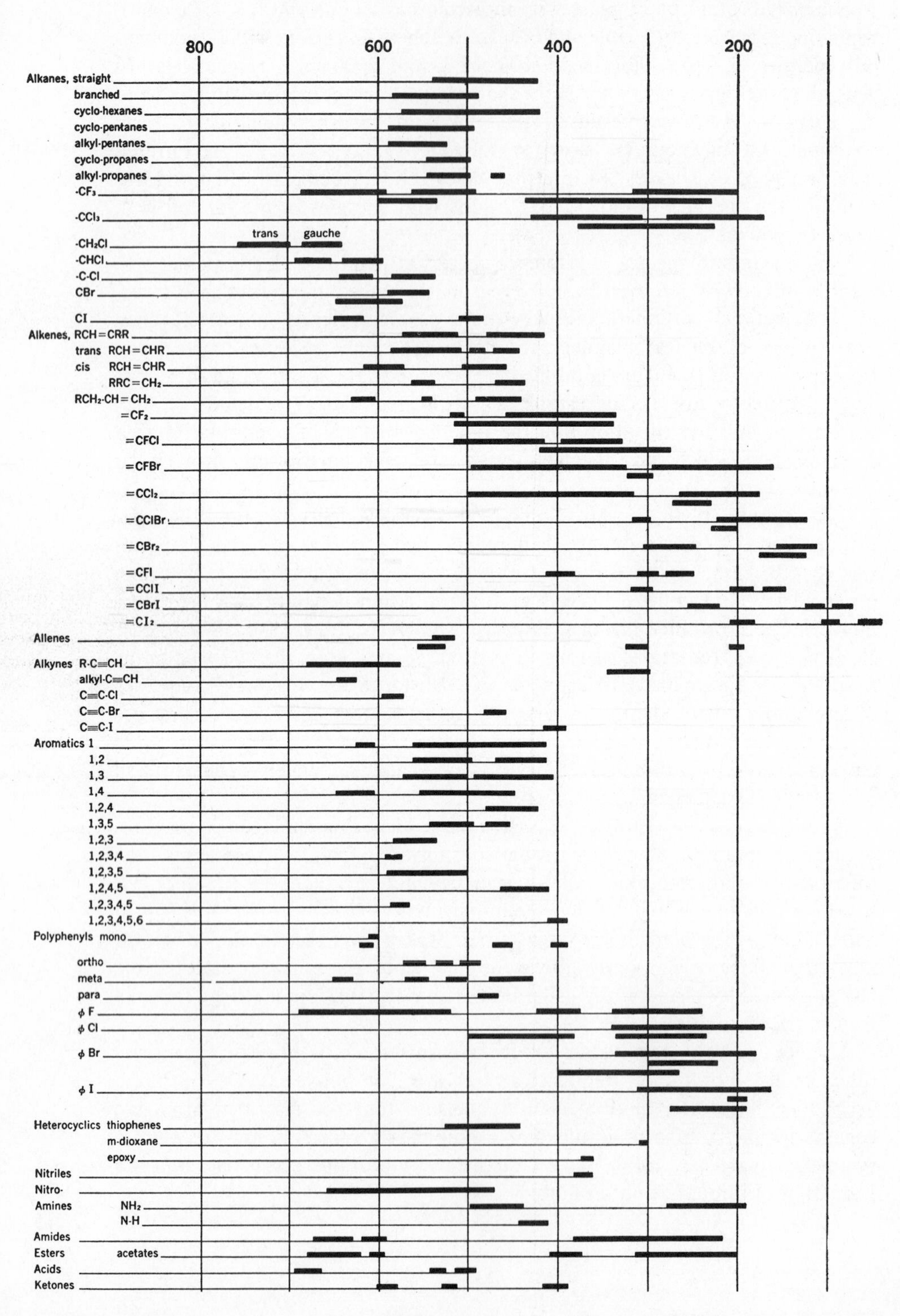

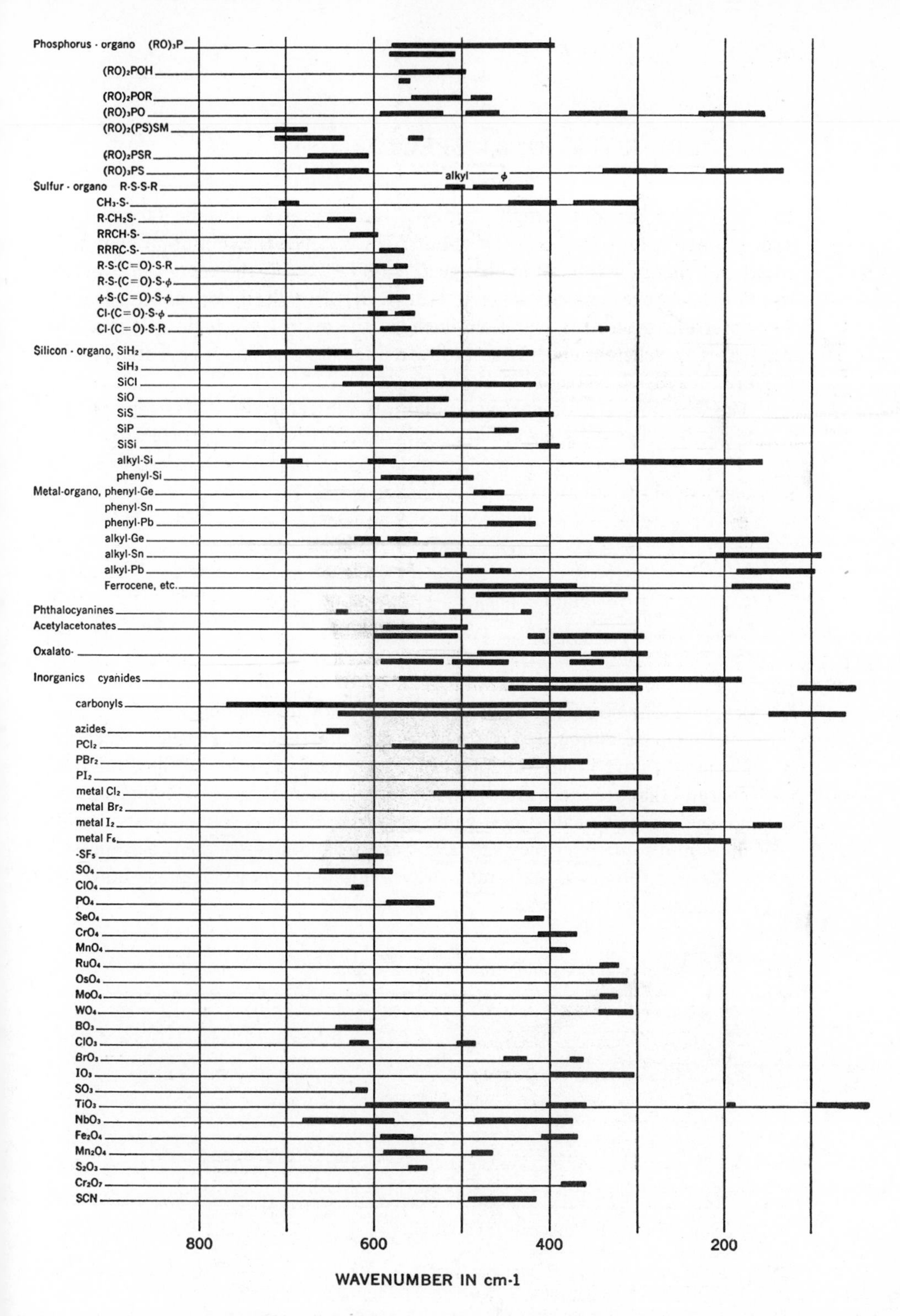

Figure 15.13. Far Infrared Vibrational Frequency Correlation Chart†

†J. E. Stewart, Beckman Instruments, Inc., Fullerton, Calif. 92634

15.10 PURE ROTATIONAL SPECTRA

Except for diatoms containing H, values of the rotational constant B for diatoms and symmetric tops are less than about 2 cm^{-1}. Since the minimum change in rotational energy involves the change $J'' = 0$ to $J' = 1$, the energy of a purely rotational change exceeds $F(1) - F(0) = B[1(2) - 0(1)]$, or about 4 cm^{-1}. The spectral region near $\lambda = 1$ cm is called the microwave region. It is at the very-short-wavelength end of the radio frequencies and merges eventually with the far infrared, which begins at about 10 cm^{-1}.

The selection rule for electric dipolar radiation is $\Delta J = \pm 1$. Ordinarily it is by absorption that such spectra are seen; hence, it is the R branch with $\Delta J = J' - J'' = +1$ that is important. From (15.63) with $\Delta K = 0$, as required, the frequency of absorbed radiation is, with $J' = J'' + 1$,

$$\begin{aligned} \nu = \frac{E}{h} &= c\Delta F = cB[J'(J'+1) - J''(J''+1)] \\ &= cB[(J''+1)(J''+2) - J''(J''+1)] \\ &= 2Bc(J''+1) \end{aligned} \tag{15.65}$$

where J'' is the rotational quantum number of the initial state. Figure 15.12 shows transitions described by (15.65); were it not for the dependence of $F(J)$ on centrifugal stretching, (15.65) with B constant would describe absorption frequencies that are linear functions of J'', namely a series of spectral lines with energies that are exact multiples of the fundamental at $\nu_0 = 2Bc$. To avoid dependence on the so-called best value of c, microwave spectroscopists usually report cB, and sometimes they call it B. Table 15.3 illustrates the precision with which cB can be observed in the microwave region. The molecule must, however, have a nonzero electric dipole.

Table 15.3 Rotational Constants from Microwave Spectra.

	Substance	$10^{-10} \times cB(\text{sec}^{-1})$	J''
(a)	$^{1}H^{12}C^{14}N$	4.431597	0
	$^{1}H^{13}C^{14}N$	4.316983	0
	$^{2}H^{12}C^{14}N$	3.6207395	0
	$^{2}H^{13}C^{14}N$	3.5587565	0
(b)	$^{14}N^{14}N^{16}O$	1.26267	0
	$^{15}N^{14}N^{16}O$	1.21996	0
(c)	$^{121}Sb^{35}Cl_3$	2.4554	6
	$^{123}Sb^{35}Cl_3$	2.4510	6

(a) J. W. Simmons, W. E. Anderson, and W. Gordy, *Phys. Rev.* **77,** 77 (1950) and *ibid.,* **86,** 1055 (1952).
(b) Calculated from B_e in A. E. Douglas and C. K. Møller, *J. Chem. Phys.* **22,** 275 (1954).
(c) P. Kisliuk and C. H. Townes, NBS Circular 518, p. 75

Microwave spectra are really much more complicated than is suggested by (15.65). The exceedingly great precision in observing frequencies allows observation of very small molecular energies. The effect of centrifugal stretching and vibration on B and D can, of course, be observed. The permanent dipole moment can be observed from the change of ν in an electric field (Stark effect), and nuclear magnetic moments and electron spin, in a magnetic field. Nuclear electric quadrupoles, electronic-nuclear magnetic interactions, barrier heights for internal molecular rotations (e.g. CH_3—), and the interaction of nuclear magnetic dipoles with each other can also be observed. Here, however, it is sufficient to examine B because each B yields a moment of inertia from which one molecular parameter can be determined. Isotopic substitution yields several B's and one parameter for each B. The extreme accuracy of B cannot be transferred to the molecular parameters, however, for: (1) physical constants like h may not be known to the same accuracy as B; (2) the observed quantity B contains a distance that has been squared as part of its denominator (I) so that solving for an R involves a complicated kind of average; (3) the uncertainty principle as expressed in zero-point vibration limits the meaning of internuclear distances to about ± 0.001A.

Example 15.3. With data from Table 15.3, find the structure of N_2O, which is linear.

For $^{14}N\ ^{14}N\ ^{16}O$, (15.57) yields a moment of inertia of

$$I_1 = \frac{h}{8\pi^2 cB} = \frac{6.626 \times 10^{-27}}{8\pi^2 \times 1.26267 \times 10^{10}} = 6.645 \times 10^{-39}\ \text{g cm}^2$$

Since one atomic mass unit is 1.660×10^{-24}g, and since $1\ \text{A} = 10^{-8}$ cm, it follows that for $^{14}N^{14}N^{16}O$

$$I_1 = \frac{6.645 \times 10^{-39}\ \text{g cm}^3}{1.660 \times 10^{-24}\ \text{g/amu}} \times \left(\frac{10^8\text{A}}{1\ \text{cm}}\right)^2 = 40.02\ \text{amu} - \text{A}^2$$

Similarly, for $^{15}N^{14}N^{16}O$, $I_2 = 41.43$ amu $-$ A^2.

Let r_1 be the position of the terminal N, r_2 be the position of the central N, and r_3 be the position of the O, all from an arbitrary origin. The molecular parameters to be found are the N-N distance, which is $R_{NN} = r_2 - r_1$ in $^{14}N\ ^{14}N\ ^{16}O$ and $R'_{NN} = r'_2 - r'_1$ in $^{15}N\ ^{14}N\ ^{16}O$, and the N-O distance, which is either $R_{NO} = r_3 - r_2$ or $R'_{NO} = r'_3 - r'_2$. It is assumed that isotopic substitution does not affect the bonding or mean nuclear positions so that $R_{NN} = R'_{NN}$ and $R_{NO} = R'_{NO}$.

$$r_3 - r_2 = r'_3 - r'_2 \tag{a}$$

$$r_2 - r_1 = r'_2 - r'_1 \tag{b}$$

It is convenient to choose the centers-of-mass as the origins of r_1 and r'_i. Hence, since the center-of-mass is specified by $\Sigma m_i r_i = 0$, it follows that

$$14.00\ r_1 + 14.00\ r_2 + 16.00\ r_3 = 0 \tag{c}$$

$$15.00\ r'_1 + 14.00\ r'_2 + 16.00\ r'_3 = 0 \tag{d}$$

And, finally, since the moment of inertia about a center-of-mass at $r = 0$ is defined as $I = \Sigma m_i r_i^2$, the microwave data yield

$$I_1 = 40.02 = 14.00\, r_1^2 + 14.00\, r_2^2 + 16.00\, r_3^2 \tag{e}$$

$$I_2 = 41.43 = 15.00\, r_1'^2 + 14.00\, r_2'^2 + 16.00\, r_3'^2 \tag{f}$$

Solution of the six simultaneous equations (a) to (f) for their six variables yields

$$R_{NN} = r_2 - r_1 = r_2' - r_1' = 1.126 \text{ A}$$

$$R_{NO} = r_3 - r_2 = r_3' - r_2' = 1.186 \text{ A}$$

15.11 ELECTRON DIFFRACTION

The wavelength of an electron depends on its kinetic energy $T = p^2/2\,m$ through the de Broglie relation (13.41), namely

$$\lambda = \frac{h}{p} = \frac{h}{\sqrt{2mT}} \tag{15.66}$$

Since electrons are very strongly absorbed by matter, their wave nature is directly observed only in vacuum systems where their energy is all kinetic. Of course, (15.66) needs correction when the velocity of the electron approaches that of light, for then relativistic effects are not negligible, as supposed in (15.66).

A brief passage through matter may cause an electron to be scattered coherently, without change of λ, or incoherently, with a change of λ. Incoherent scattering is rather intense, but is of interest here only because it must be corrected for. Careful control of the accelerating potential, which is the same as control of the electron energy, yields a beam of electrons of one wavelength. These may then be directed through matter to yield a diffraction pattern, due to systematic reinforcement and interference, if the matter has any order reminiscent of the regularity of a diffraction grating. The order of atoms in crystals of Ni first showed this wave property of electrons in 1927 in the pioneer work of Davisson and Germer. Since electron diffraction by solids is similar to X-ray diffraction, it will be described in the next chapter on solids. What is truly amazing is that the various interatomic distances of a molecule, even a tumbling gaseous molecule, are sufficiently regular in space to diffract monochromatic electrons in a definite interference or diffraction pattern that can be related to the molecular structure. Figure 15.14 illustrates the kind of apparatus used in electron diffraction. A potential V, often of the order of 40 kilovolts to give $\lambda \approx$ 0.06 A, accelerates electrons from a hot tungsten filament F. The beam of electrons may be focused electrostatically by a bias voltage B or by magnetic fields not shown in Figure 15.14. Pinholes P and P collimate the beam so that when it is scattered in a small region by a small jet of the sample S, the scattered electrons will appear to come from one region of space. The sample must be condensed

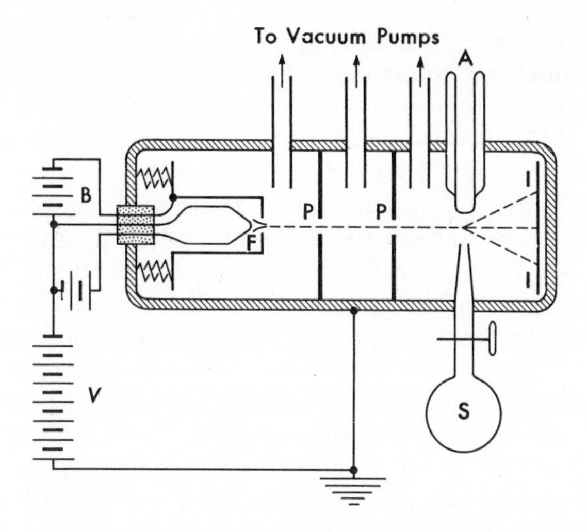

Figure 15.14. Sketch of Electron Diffraction Apparatus

immediately on a liquid air cold finger A to keep the vacuum. A flat photograph $I - I$ records the scattered electron intensity.

The successful interpretation of electron diffraction from molecules by Brockway and Pauling and co-workers in the 1930's involves learning how to make a visual correction for the intense incoherent scattering that necessarily accompanies the structurally interesting coherent scattering. It is possible to design rotating sectors, partly cut away absorbing discs rotating in front of the photograph, to reduce the rapid rate of decline in scattered intensity as the scattering angle increases. Such devices have been skillfully made by O. Bastiansen and his Norwegian co-workers, by I. and J. Karle, by Brockway, and by others, and their use brings objectivity to the interpretation of the photographs. Nevertheless, the human eye has an amazing ability to outperform densitometers on photographs taken without a rotating sector. With practice, one learns to see against a rapidly declining smooth background a structure-sensitive diffraction intensity I that can be correlated with internuclear distances R_{ij} by the formula

$$I(s) = \sum_{i>j} \frac{(Z-f)_i(Z-f)_j}{R_{ij}} e^{-a_{ij}s^2} \sin(R_{ij}s) \tag{15.67}$$

The scattering variable

$$s = \frac{4\pi \sin \theta/2}{\lambda} \tag{15.68}$$

depends on the electron wavelength λ and the angle θ by which the electron beam is deviated from its original direction. (Rutherford used this variable s in his classical interpretation of alpha-ray scattering by nuclei in 1910!) The electrons are scattered by the nuclei, which lie apart by various distances R_{ij}. The effect of the atomic number Z is tempered, however, by an atomic form factor f that declines from Z to zero as s increases. Actually, f measures the extent to which electrons shield their nucleus. It measures the relative cooperation of electrons at various distances from the nucleus as they interfere with each other in scattering X-rays, when a photon is scattered by an atom's electron cloud. (The visual interpretation correlated with I of (15.67) generally makes $(Z-f)_i(Z-f)_j$ appear to be merely the product Z_iZ_j of the atomic numbers of atoms i and j.) The quantity a_{ij} is related to the amplitudes of vibration of the molecule and to the characteristic sizes of the pinholes and sample jet.

The desired internuclear distances R_{ij} are extracted from $I(s)$ by Fourier analysis. The result is a probability density function $R\,D(R)$

$$R\,D(R) = \int_0^{s'} I(s)e^{-as^2} \sin Rs\,ds \tag{15.69}$$

where data are observed from $s = 0$ to $s = s'$. The constant a is adjusted to bring the amplitude of $I(s)$ close to zero at s' so as to avoid spurious peaks in $R\,D(R)$ because of the sudden cutoff in the integration, which is performed as a sum by a computer. The maxima in $R\,D(R)$ correspond to the most probable distances in the molecules of the sample. These peaks in $R\,D(R)$ are Gaussian, centered at R_{ij}, and the area of each peak is approximately proportional to Z_iZ_j/R_{ij}. Thus heavy atoms and distances R_{ij} that occur several times by virtue of molecular symmetry yield the most important peaks in the radial distribution curve $R\,D(R)$.

In the hands of V. Schomaker and his co-workers, the visual method of interpreting electron diffraction by molecules has yielded many structures of molecules containing up to about 20 atoms. As in any art, the interpretation is subjective and the results are subject to some uncertainty, even with regard to overall molecular shape in difficult cases. To remove such uncertainty, the use of densitometers on photographs taken with rotating sectors has been painstakingly developed. The Norwegian school regularly attains accuracies of ± 0.002A and has been able to identify each of the several chlorinated isomers of cyclohexane, where it is only the long nonbonded Cl — Cl interactions that differ. The usual error with the visual method is ± 0.02A.

Many molecular parameters can be determined at once by electron diffraction. The molecule need not have a dipole moment, and it need not be a symmetric rotor [which is required by (15.65)]. Figure 15.15 illustrates how one of five independent parameters of trifluoromethyl acetylene was fixed after four independent conditions on them had been found by microwave methods. The final parameter was taken to be the FCF angle. The curve Visual I was inserted as $I(s)$ into (15.69) to yield the radial distribution curve, which ordinarily would suggest trial models. There are clearly spurious peaks at the incredible internuclear distances $R = 0.2$A and $R = 0.4$A. The solid vertical lines indicate

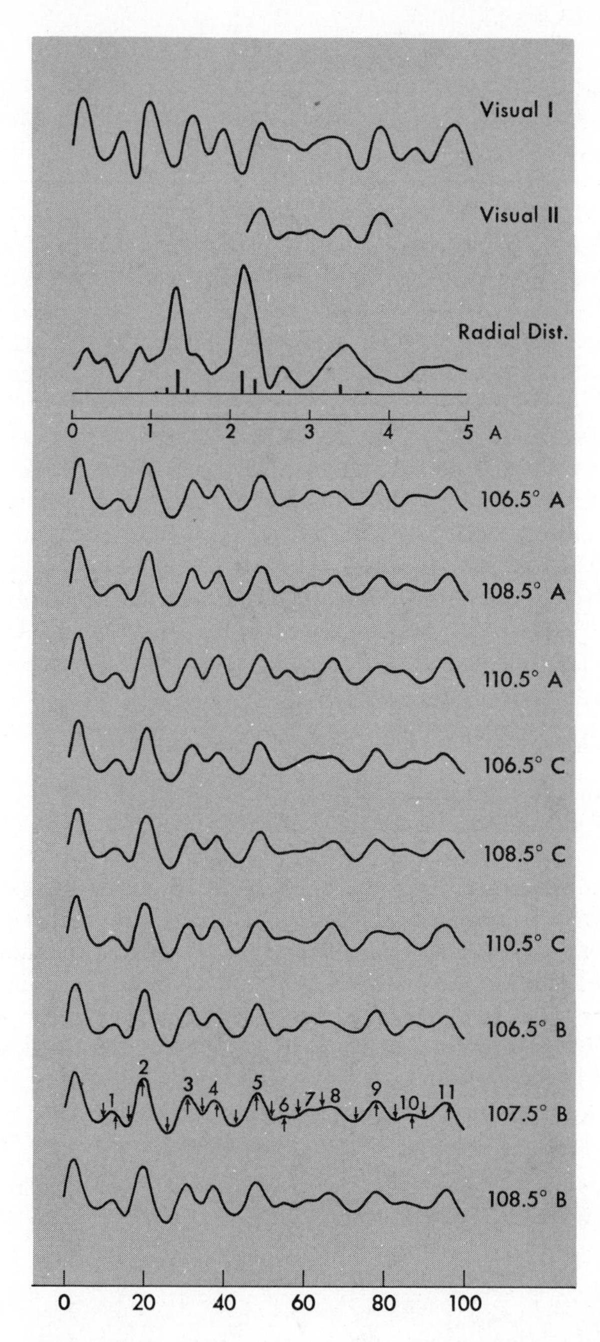

Figure 15.15. Determination of a Structural Parameter of Trifluoromethylacetylene†

†J. N. Shoolery, R. G. Shulman, W. F. Sheehan, Jr., V. Schomaker, and D. M. Yost, *J. Chem. Phys.* **19,** 1364 [1951]

the values of R finally derived. Shown in Figure 15.15 are nine curves $I(s)$ calculated by (15.67) for various FCF angles. The letters A, B, and C indicate different choices of the constants a_{ij}. The final choice of FCF angle is 107.5°, because of various visual estimates of relative depths of minima, especially near maxima 10. Visual II is a second observer's impression of the photographs; its similarity to and difference from Visual I and the theoretical curves indicate typical problems in the visual method, where much depends on how the eye subtracts off the rapidly changing background.

The quantum mechanical theory that leads to results like (15.67) for $I(s)$ assumes that the perturbation offered by the molecule's atoms to the monochromatic electrons is small. When Z is great, this condition is not always satisfied. In general, structures found by electron diffraction are valid if based on R_{ij}'s between atoms of roughly the same atomic number. This condition is amply satisfied for almost all organic determinations. The great advantage of electron diffraction methods, especially with the use of sectored photographs, is that the molecule need not be a symmetric rotor and need not have a dipole moment—both required for use of (15.65). Despite its limitations, electron diffraction offers a valuable alternative method of determining molecular structure. It is also of great value in studying the surfaces of crystals, for X-rays penetrate too deeply and thus see the substrate solid and not the surface.

15.12 MAGNETIC RESONANCE SPECTROSCOPY

The two common kinds of magnetic resonance spectroscopy involve electrons (EPR) and nuclei (NMR). In each, a strong external magnetic field removes the degeneracy of a system and thus makes possible the absorption and emission of photons between states that would have had essentially the same energy in the absence of the external field. If the external magnetic field H_z is uniform over the system, the energy of the system, relative to its energy E_0 when the field is nil, is

$$E - E_0 = -g\mu \mathrm{H}_z m_z \tag{15.70}$$

The factor g is the Landé splitting factor when (15.70) applies to magnetic moments due to electrons in the system. It has the value

$$g_e = 1 + \frac{j(j+1) + s(s+1) - l(l+1)}{2j(j+1)} \tag{15.71}$$

Free radicals generated from stable molecules by loss of an electron usually have $l = 0$, but for ions of transition elements or for electrons in solids, l may differ from zero. If $l = 0$, then $j = l + s = s = \frac{1}{2}$ and $g_e = 2$; these values hold for a free electron or for most free radicals that come from stable molecules having electron-pair bonds upon loss of one electron. (Actually, a quantum electrodynamic correction requires $g_e = 2.0023$.) When (15.70) applies to nuclear magnetic moments in H_z, g takes values characteristic of the nucleus in question, the most important being ^1_1H with $g = 5.5854$. For many nuclei, g is near unity.

The second factor μ of (15.70) is the fundamental magnetic moment of the species aligned by H_z. For an electron, it is called the Bohr magneton and has the value

$$\mu_e = \frac{e\hbar}{2mc} = -0.92732 \times 10^{-20} \text{ erg oersted}^{-1} \tag{15.72}$$

The intensity of the magnetic field imposed from the surroundings is measured in oersteds. For electron spin (paramagnetic) resonance (ESR or EPR), H_z is commonly about 3000 oersteds, while for nuclear magnetic resonance H_z is often over 10,000 oersteds, with about 50,000 oersteds possible by the use of superconducting metals in the coils of the electromagnet. The value of μ for nuclei is the nuclear magneton,

$$\mu_N = \frac{e\hbar}{2Mc} = 5.0505 \times 10^{-24} \text{ erg oersted}^{-1} \tag{15.73}$$

The quantum number m_z in (15.70) is the integer or half-integer that describes the component of angular momentum in the direction z of the uniform magnetic field of intensity H_z. When (15.70) refers to electron(s), m_z takes the $2j + 1$ values $j = l + s, j - 1, j - 2, \ldots, -j$, where j may be either integral or half-integral and thus pass through zero with the values $\ldots + 2, +1, 0, -1, \ldots$ or with the values $\ldots +3/2, +1/2, -1/2, -3/2, \ldots$. Similarly, when (15.70) refers to nuclei of spin i, there are $2i + 1$ values of m_z: $i, i - 1, \ldots +1, 0, -1, \ldots -i$ when i is integral; $i, i - 1, \ldots +1/2, -1/2, \ldots -i$ when i is half-integral. If the nuclear mass number is odd, i is half-integral ($i = 1/2$ for ^1_1H, $^{13}_6C$, $^{15}_7N$, $^{19}_9F$, $^{29}_{14}Si$, $^{31}_{15}P$; $i = 3/2$ for $^{11}_5B$). If the mass number is even, then i is 0 when Z is even ($i = 0$ for $^{12}_6C$, $^{16}_8O, \ldots$) but i is integral when Z is odd ($i =$ 1 for ^2_1H, ^7_3Li, $^{14}_7N$; $i = 2$ for $^{36}_{17}Cl$; $i = 3$ for $^{10}_5B \ldots$).

The signs and magnitudes of μ_e and μ_N are interesting. The negative sign of μ_e indicates that the more stable state of an electron has $m_z = \beta = -1/2$. The increase in energy as the spin of an electron changes from $-1/2$ to $+1/2$ is, by (15.70),

$$E_\alpha - E_\beta = -g_e\mu_eH_z[1/2 - (-1/2)] = -g_e\mu_eH_z = g_e\,|\mu_e|\,H_z \tag{15.74}$$

where g_e is given by (15.71) and μ_e by (15.72). The resonant frequency at which this increase in energy occurs is found by equating $E_\alpha - E_\beta$ to the photon energy $h\,\nu_0$; hence, from (15.74), the resonant frequency is

$$\nu_0 = \frac{g_e\,|\mu_e|\,H_z}{h} \tag{15.75}$$

If $g_e = 2$ and $H_z = 3.00 \times 10^3$ oersteds, then

$$\nu_0 = \frac{2 \times 0.927 \times 10^{-20} \times 3.00 \times 10^3}{6.626 \times 10^{-27}} = 0.839 \times 10^{10} \text{ sec}^{-1}$$

This frequency is very close to the X-band in the microwave region and thus is experimentally convenient because generation equipment is already available.

The positive sign of $\mu_{N'}$, on the other hand, means that the more stable state of a proton has $m_z = i = +1/2$. (Some nuclei have $g_N < 1$.) The selection rule for absorption or emission of radiation is, for electrons or nuclei, $\Delta m_z = \pm 1$. Hence, for a nucleon, (15.70) yields

$$\Delta E = g_N \mu_N H_z = h\nu_0 \tag{15.76}$$

where ν_0 is the resonant frequency. When the nucleon is a proton, g_N is 5.5854 so that (15.73) and (15.76) yield, when $H_z = 10.00 \times 10^3$ oersteds, a resonant frequency of about

$$\begin{aligned}\nu_0 &= \frac{5.5854 \times 5.0505 \times 10^{-24} \times 10.0 \times 10^3}{6.6256 \times 10^{-27}} \\ &= 42.6 \times 10^6 \text{ sec}^{-1}\end{aligned}$$

This ν_0 for protons is at an accessible radio frequency. For ${}^2_1H$, ν_0 is 6.54×10^6 sec^{-1}; for ${}^{19}_9F$, ν_0 is $40.0 \times 10^6 \text{ sec}^{-1}$. Not only are the ν_0's for nuclei less than those for electrons by a factor of $\sim 10^4$, but the energy differences of the states ($h\nu_0$) also differ by 10^4. In fact, with account of the usual Boltzmann distribution, the energy difference of the nuclear states is so low that the difference in populations of proton levels $i = +1/2$ and $i = -1/2$ at $H_z \approx 10^4$ oersteds is negligible at temperatures above 1°K. For example, if $T = 300$°K,

$$\begin{aligned}\frac{N_+}{N_-} &= \exp\left(\frac{h\nu_0}{kT}\right) \\ &= \exp\left(\frac{6.6 \times 10^{-27} \times 43 \times 10^6}{1.38 \times 10^{-16} \times 300}\right) \\ &= \exp(6.8 \times 10^{-6}) \\ &\approx 1.0000068\end{aligned}$$

In other words, the differences in the magnitudes of μ_e and μ_N are such that energy differences of nuclei are much less than those of electrons in the same magnetic field. And at any temperature above 1°K, the populations of nuclear states are nearly equal at the uniform magnetic fields presently attainable.

A typical nuclear magnetic spectrometer is a device for observing and controlling ν_0 and H_z in (15.76). It consists of: (1) a large electromagnet capable of generating a uniform magnetic field of 10^4 oersteds or more throughout a sample volume of the order of one cm^3; (2) a coil for transmitting electromagnetic radiation through a sample it surrounds; and (3) a detection coil, having a known but small coupling to the transmitter coil, but having a great sensitivity to small changes in the intensity of radiation of frequency near ν_0 as the sample absorbs and emits such resonant radiation. It happens to be easier to vary H_z than ν_0. Hence, the resonant condition (15.76) is achieved by slow adjustment of H_z. The reason that NMR is chemically interesting is that, even for a particular nucleus, the resonant value of H_z at fixed ν_0 depends on the molecular structure. The same is true of the resonant H_z in EPR.

There are two main reasons why the NMR resonant H_z depends on structure. Both stem from the fact that the magnetic field experienced by a particular kind of nucleus differs from the external field H_z. Any magnetic field acts on matter in such a way as to induce a contrary magnetic field; this is called *diamagnetism.* It can be pictured as an operation of Lenz's law for all the sample's electrons. That is, the atomic electrons about a nucleus tend, by their diamagnetism, to shield the nucleus from H_z and thus reduce the effective field intensity at the nucleus. A bare proton would require the least H_z to reach resonance, while well-shielded protons, such as those in $Si(CH_3)_4$ (which has highly polarizable electrons), could achieve resonance only when a somewhat increased H_z was imposed externally. In general, H_z increases as the electron density at ${}^1_1H$ increases; hence, protons on electronegative atoms are ionic, less shielded, and require less H_z at resonance. Similarly, H_z is more sensitive to shielding in ${}^{19}_9F$ and ${}^{13}_6C$ than in ${}^1_1H$ because F and C have more *s*-type electrons with nonzero electron density at the nucleus than ${}^1_1H$ does. This diamagnetic shielding is called the *chemical shift.* Because diamagnetism is proportional to the external field, the chemical shift is proportional to H_z. If the shift is $H_0 = \sigma_0 H_z$ in a standard like $Si(CH_3)_4$, and if it is $H_x = \sigma_k H_z$ in an unknown substance, then a comparison of unknown and standard at fixed ν_0 yields a chemical shift of

$$\delta_{x0} H_z = \sigma_x H_z - \sigma_0 H_z \tag{15.77}$$

It is customary to report only δ in ppm so that if H_x and H_0 are the fields at resonance with the unknown and with the standard, then

$$\delta = \frac{H_x - H_0}{H_0} \times 10^6 \tag{15.78}$$

The size of δ is a rough indication of the chemical environment of the nucleus under study. For protons, δ ranges from 0 to about -15 as its ionicity rises. For ${}^{19}_9F$ and ${}^{13}_6C$, δ covers a range of about 250.

The chemical shift $H_x - H_0$ increases as the intensity of the external field increases. The second important structural effect on the resonant condition (15.76) is independent of H_z. Dependence or independence of H_z thus distinguishes these two effects. This field-independent effect occurs because of magnetic moments on nearby nuclei, which act to modify the local magnetic field experienced by other nuclei. The energy effects here are of the order of $h\Delta\nu_0$ with $\Delta\nu_0 \approx 5\ \text{sec}^{-1}$. The classic example of this multiplet splitting is ethanol, which contains three kinds of protons. The three protons of the CH_3 are equivalent; each of them experiences H_z and the spins of the two protons on the adjacent carbon. These two protons have a net spin of $+1/2 + 1/2 = +1$, $+1/2 - 1/2 = 0$, $-1/2 + 1/2 = 0$, or $-1/2 - 1/2 = -1$. That is, the three H's of CH_3 see a field H_z modified by $+1, 0, 0$, or -1 because of two H's on —CH_2— immediately adjacent. As a result, the three H's on CH_3 attain resonance at three values of H_z, the intensity of peaks within the triplet being 1 — 2 — 1 (because two configurations yield O, while only one yields either $+1$ or -1). Likewise, the identical protons on —CH_2— experience H_z and the net effect of the three on CH_3, which form a quartet with $+3/2, +1/2, -1/2, -3/2$ and relative intensities 1–3–3–1. The proton on O is a singlet, too far from the others to be affected directly. Thus, the NMR spectrum of ethanol is a 1–2–1 triplet chemically shifted to high field, a 1–3–3–1 quartet chemically shifted less (inductive effect of electronegative O), and a singlet at low field. The integrated area of the triplet is 3 times the singlet and that of the quartet is 2 times the singlet, to correspond to the number of protons contributing to each.

The NMR spectrum of PH_3 in Figure 15.16 is a ${}^{31}_{15}P$ resonance as affected by the three magnetic moments of the three protons. There is no chemical shift within the PH_3 because only one ${}^{31}P$ exists. Of course, this P would resonate at a different H_z from a P in H_3PO_4. The relative heights of peaks within a multi-

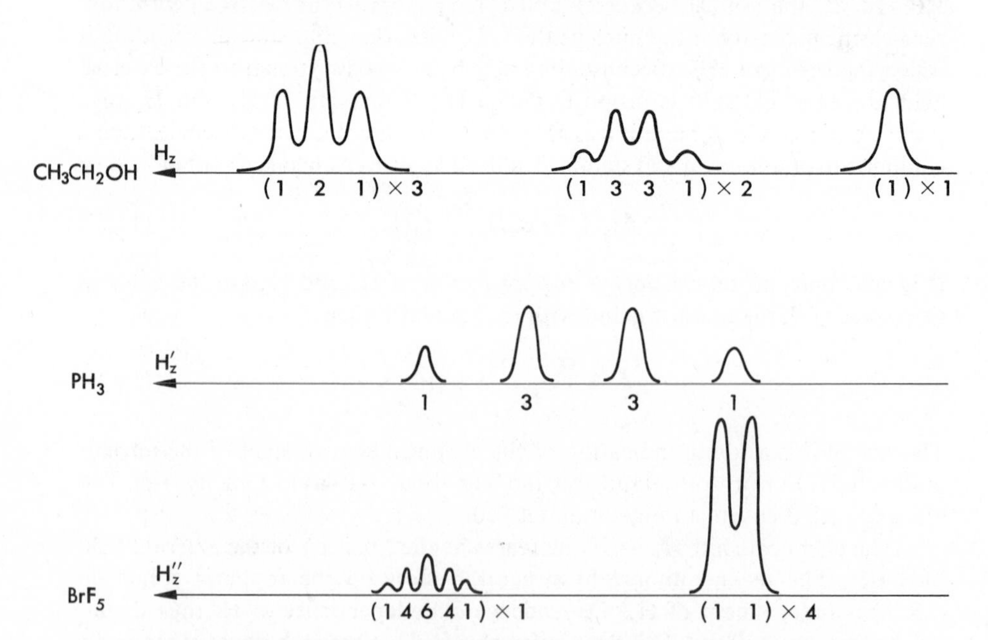

Figure 15.16. Schematic NMR Spectra of CH_3CH_2OH, PH_3, and BrF_5
H. S. Gutowsky and C. J. Hoffman, *J. Chem. Phys.*, **19**, 1259 (1951).

plet are equal to the number of ways of taking two spins, some one way and some the other way, in all possible ways. This combinatorial problem is summarized by Pascal's triangle:

Heights	Multiplet	Neighbors
1 1	Doublet	One Nucleus
1 2 1	Triplet	Two Nuclei
1 3 3 1	Quartet	Three Nuclei
1 4 6 4 1	Quintet	Four Nuclei

In view of the list above, the structure of BrF_5, as judged from the areas of its ^{19}F resonances, involves four fluorines of one kind and one fluorine with a somewhat greater electron density than the other four. The 1–4–6–4–1 multiplet confirms the existence of 4 F's that are equivalent. The whole spectrum thus confirms a tetragonal pyramidal arrangement of F's about the Br.

If it were not for a reasonably short lifetime of the excited state, the absorption of EPR or NMR radiation would soon depopulate the lower state and attenuation of the transmitted ν_0 could not be observed. That is, the signal would fade. However, the excited states often have a half-life for decay of the order of 1 to 20 seconds. This is sufficient to prevent fading and yet not short enough to smear the spectrum by virtue of the uncertainty principle. Indeed, NMR line-broadening can yield rate constants when the species observed by NMR have small lifetimes because they are undergoing chemical change. This time span nicely extends well into a time-region that was exceedingly difficult to study because of severe limitations on speeds of mixing reagents and difficult decisions on when to start the clock.

15.13 OPTICAL ROTATION

Some crystals and molecules can rotate the plane of plane-polarized light that passes through them. A molecule (or a crystal considered as a very great molecule) is optically active in this way if translation and rotation in space cannot lead to superposition of it on its mirror image. Mirror images are related as left hand is to right, the mirror plane being midway between facing hands. The two forms that cannot be superposed are called *dextro-* and *levo-rotary*, and are identical in every way except in the arrangement in space of equivalent chemical groupings.

Any molecule or crystal that exhibits a rotation-inversion axis as part of its own symmetry cannot be optically active. A onefold rotation-inversion involves a rotation by 360° followed by movement of all atoms from $+x, +y, +z$ to $-x, -y, -z$, It is nothing else than a center of inversion. If a symmetry operation transforms the molecule into a configuration that is indistinguishable from the original one, the molecule is said to possess the *element of symmetry*. Many molecules including H_2, N_2, C_2H_4, and SF_6 possess a center of inversion. The staggered form of C_2H_6, shown with C_2H_2 and C_2H_4 in Figure 15.17, contains a center of inversion midway between the carbon atoms. Ethene is planar and ethyne is linear.

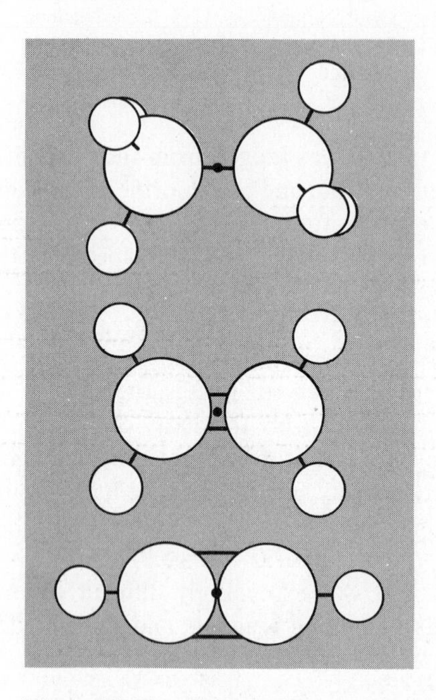

Figure 15.17. Centers of Inversion in Ethane, Ethene, Ethyne

A twofold rotation-inversion axis involves a rotation by 360°/2 followed by inversion. A rotation by 180° around the *z*-axis transforms *x*, *y*, *z* into $-x$, $-y$, *z*; subsequent inversion yields *x*, *y*, $-z$. Accordingly, a twofold rotation-inversion is equivalent to reflection across a mirror plane in the *x*-*y*-plane, for the net change is *x*, *y*, *z* to *x*, *y*, $-z$. Similarly, an *n*-fold rotation inversion involves rotation by 360°/*n* followed by inversion. Since most situations of interest involve rotation-inversion axes that contain mirror planes or centers of inversion as subgroups, the usual guide to optical activity is this: Optical activity is possible in a molecule that has neither a mirror plane nor a center of inversion. There are, however, exceptions to this last statement.[12]

The simplest type of optically active molecule would be SbFClBr or NHDT, an isotopically substituted NH_3. Here SbX_3 and NH_3 are pyramidal in form. The two forms of optically active ammonia are shown in Figure 15.18. They are

[12] Wells, A. F., *Structural Inorganic Chemistry*. New York: Oxford University Press, 1950, pp. 207–10. Also Bunn, C. W., *Chemical Crystallography*. New York: Oxford University Press, 1945, p. 88. By permission of the Clarendon Press, Oxford.

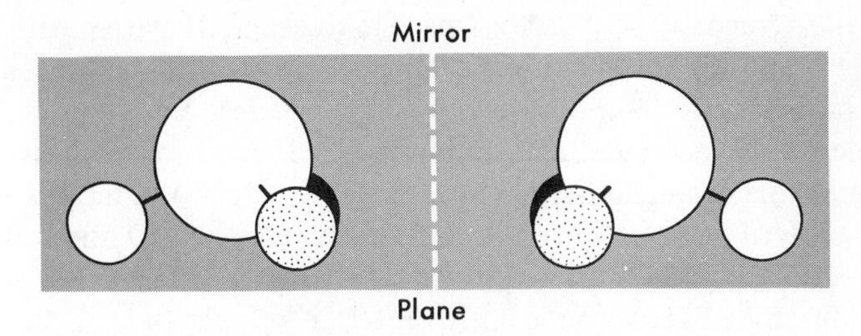

Figure 15.18. Optically Active Ammonia

related to each other by reflection in a mirror plane and no rotation or movement in space can turn them so that the two forms can be superposed. Ordinary ammonia (NH_3) or NH_2D is not optically active because each has a vertical mirror plane. Reflection in such a plane interchanges protons, which are indistinguishable from one another. Planar BFClBr, however, is not optically active because, by a rotation about an axis in the plane of the molecule, two forms that appear to be mirror images can in fact be superposed. Indeed, because the molecule is planar, its plane is a mirror plane, the twofold rotation inversion axis being perpendicular to the plane of the molecule.

Optical activity frequently results from an asymmetric carbon atom, a carbon holding four unlike groups. Thus, there exist two forms of CHFClBr. Every optically active site presents two possibilities, a left- and a right-hand form. As a result, a sugar containing four asymmetric carbon atoms will have 2^4 isomers.

The angle α_R through which the plane of polarization is rotated by an optically active substance or its solution is proportional to the concentration of the optically active substance and to the length of the optical path. If the length of the optical path is l decimeters and if g grams of the substance are in V milliliters of fluid (solution or pure liquid or gas), then

$$\alpha_R = [\alpha_R]_T^\lambda \frac{lg}{V} \tag{15.79}$$

Table 15.4 Specific Rotations in Aqueous Solution.†

Substance	Temperature	Specific Rotation[a]	(Na D)
Dextrose (d-glucose)	20°C	$+52.5 + 0.025d$	$(1 < d < 18)$
Levulose (d-fructose)	25°C	$-88.5 - 0.145d$	$(2.6 < d < 18.6)$
Sucrose	20°C	$+66.412 + 0.01267d - 0.000376d^2$	$(0 < d < 50)$
Nicotine	20°C	-77	$(1 < d < 16)$

[a] d = grams per 100 g solution.
† *Handbook of Chemistry and Physics*. 48th ed., R.C. Weast, ed. Cleveland, O.: The Chemical Rubber Publishing Co., 1967, p. E-184.

The proportionality constant $[\alpha_R]_T^\lambda$ is the specific rotation. It varies with the wavelength of light and the temperature, is almost independent of concentration, and is a characteristic of the optically active species. Equation (15.79) provides a simple, rapid, accurate, and nondestructive means of analysis that is used routinely in the sugar industry. Table 15.4 lists specific rotations of a few substances dissolved in water when the convenient yellow Na D line is used. When the plane of polarization is rotated to the right on proceeding in the direction of the light, the angle of rotation is positive; to the left, negative.

Example 15.4. Calculate the angle of rotation caused by a solution containing 10.0 g sucrose in 90.0 g water at 20°C when the sodium *D* line is used and when the optical path is 20.00 cm in length.

The density of such a solution is 1.038 g ml^{-1}; hence,

$$\frac{g}{V} = \frac{10.0}{\left(\frac{100}{1.038}\right)} = 0.1038 \text{ g ml}^{-1}$$

From Table 15.4 for $d = 10$,

$$[\alpha_R]_T^\lambda = 66.412 + 0.127 - 0.038 = 66.501$$

Finally, by (15.79),

$$\alpha_R = 66.501 \times 2.000 \times 0.1038 = 13.81°$$

The reason for the rotation of plane polarized light is a difference in the index of refraction of a substance for left- and right-circularly polarized light. There is also a difference in the absorption of left- and right-circularly polarized light in optically active substances. Several quantum mechanical theories of optical activity were developed in the 1930's by Kirkwood, Eyring, and others.

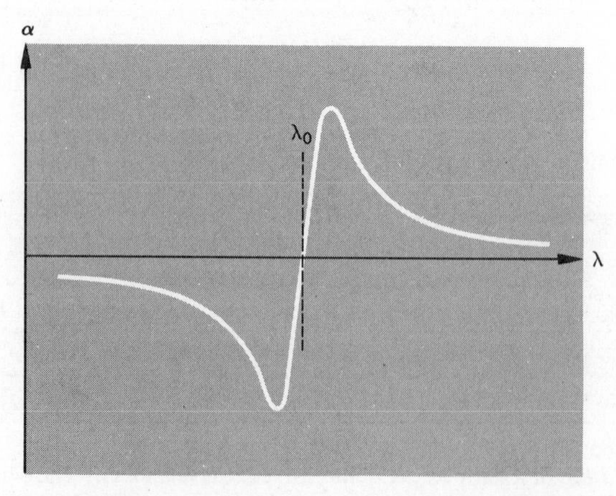

Figure 15.19. Simple Optical Rotatory Dispersion Curve

These theories agree in their predictions concerning the real configuration of butanol–2 and its rotation of light. Fortunately, the theories' predictions agree not only with the long established arbitrary convention of Fischer introduced in 1890 but also with experimental verification by Bijovet in about 1950.

Figure 15.19 illustrates in an ideal way how α changes with λ. At λ_0 there is an electronic absorption by a group of atoms that find themselves in an asymmetric environment in the molecule or ion exhibiting optical activity. Observation at the yellow Na D line is usually well removed from λ_0, which is typically in the ultraviolet for colorless organic substances. One substance may exhibit several λ_0's and complicated dispersion curves. With the advent of automatic commercial apparatus for observing optical rotatory dispersion curves into the ultraviolet, these curves have been established for many standard substances and are used for routine analysis of natural organic products like steroids and proteins.

15.14 HYBRIDIZATION

Of interest to chemists are diatomic molecules at high temperatures or in flames where molecules like OH and CN are among the main species. A few simple gases like N_2 and Cl_2 are also diatomic. In general, however, interest lies with polyatomic molecules. Because rigorous calculation is impractical and because the chemist finds empirically that the electron-pair bond localized between two particular atoms is often a good first approximation, the previous discussion of H_2^+, H_2, and diatomic molecules can be extended almost without modification to polyatomic molecules. It is merely necessary to view any molecule as an array of atoms joined by bonds that are almost independent of each other.

As for H_2^+ and H_2, wherever the atomic wave functions overlap greatly there is high electron density and a strong chemical bond. The greater the overlap, the stronger the bond. Since atomic *s*-orbitals are spherically symmetric, being independent of θ and ϕ, they show no preferred direction of bonding. Atomic *p*-orbitals are highly directional in nature, as Figure 14.3 shows, and this preference for specific directions is shown by molecules like PH_3 and H_2S. The HSH angle in H_2S is 92° because S has two 3*p*-orbitals available for bonding. Any two of the three *p*-states of Figure 14.3 would make 90° the preferred angle. Similarly, P offers three mutually perpendicular atomic orbitals, the observed HPH angles being only a few degrees greater than 90°.

In view of the peculiarities of wave mechanics, it is probably not surprising that an atom which has *s*- and *p*- and even *d*-electrons of similar energy in its valence shell will rearrange its electrons without regard to their atomic quantum states in order to minimize the molecular energy. Nor is it surprising that the result is often a hybrid of bonding orbitals less related to *s*-, *p*,- and *d*-orbitals than a mongrel dog is to its progenitors. Some of the many possible hybridizations are listed in Table 15.5. The hybrid orbitals form equivalent σ-bonds with maxima in directions that point to bonded atoms. The principal quantum number n and indeed the radial part of the wave function are assumed to be of secondary importance in determining the strength and symmetry of these hybrid combinations.

A simple exhibition of the meaning and use of these hybrid combinations involves the configurations expected in $Ni(CO)_4$ and $Ni(CN)_4^{--}$. A coordination number of four at once suggests tetrahedral arrangement as in carbon with sp^3 hybrid orbitals. The valence shell of neutral Ni is $3d^{10}$. This leaves a $4s$- and three $4p$-orbitals free to accept electron pairs from 4 CO; the arrangement is tetrahedral, with four equivalent sp^3-bonds. Dipositive Ni, however, has one stable $3d$-orbital vacant, and dsp^2-bonds form when 4 CN^- ions form coordinate covalent bonds with Ni^{++}. Pauling predicted $Ni(CN)_4^{--}$ and similar species to be planar on the basis of this kind of argument.[13]

Table 15.5 Configurations of Hybrid Orbitals†

Coordination Number	Atomic Orbitals	General Configuration	Strong π— Orbitals
2	sp	linear	p^2d^2
2	dp	linear	p^2d^2
3	sp^2	trigonal plane	pd^2
3	dp^2	trigonal plane	pd^2
3	d^2s	trigonal plane	pd^2
3	d^3	trigonal plane	pd^2
4	sp^3	tetrahedral	d^2
4	d^3s	tetrahedral	d^2
4	dsp^2	tetragonal plane	d^3p
4	d^2p^2	tetragonal plane	d^3p
6	d^2sp^3	octahedral	d^3
6	d^4sp	trigonal prism	—
6	d^5p	trigonal prism	—
6	d^3p^3	trigonal prism	—

† Kimball, G. E., *J. Chem. Phys.*, **8**, 188 (1940).

The pure MO's described by the correlation diagrams of Figure 15.7 and 15.8 are in real molecules various mixtures of the usual arbitrary reference states, atomic $s, p, d, \ldots$ atomic states. A very little bit of hybridization causes truly profound stabilization in energy relative to these arbitrary states. The reason is that admixture of a little of another quite different type of orbital can use the most flattering parts of the newly introduced orbital while discarding parts of the old that are either plentiful or disadvantageous to proper correlation of the electrons' positions or to the most adventitious positioning of electrons near nuclei. The extent of hybridization depends largely on general similarity in sym-

[13] Pauling, L., *Nature of the Chemical Bond.* Ithaca, N. Y.: Cornell University Press, 1960, pp. 153 et seq.

metry and on use of states of low energy. Since $2s$ and $2p_z$ from each atom of a diatom can contribute to a bonding σ_g orbital and antibonding σ_u orbital correlated to $2s$ and to a bonding σ_g orbital and antibonding σ_u orbital correlated to $2p$, it is generally advantageous to adjust the relative amounts of $2s$ and $2p_z$ character in the σ_g's and σ_u's to attain the most flattering admixture. In N_2, about one-fourth of an electron moves from $2s$ to $2p_z$; at the same time, the unoccupied $2p\ \sigma_u$ MO accepts the less useful parts of the atomic $2s$ to the extent that they are rejected in forming the best occupied MO's of σ character. Of course, if diatomic MO's are arbitrary hybrids of pure atomic states, so also are the MO's of polyatomic molecules. In general, hybridization that strengthens one bond of a central atom tends at the same time to weaken other bonds of that atom. While σ-bonds, hybrid or pure, determine the general configuration of a molecule, the actual internuclear distances are determined by the number of bonding electrons between atoms. The most typical multiple bonds occur in ethene and ethyne, whose structures are shown in Figure 15.17. The planar configuration of ethene is dominated by sp^2 hybridization on each carbon, with the carbon-carbon distance of 1.33 A such as to allow maximum overlap of the atomic p-orbitals perpendicular to the plane of the molecule. These p-orbitals form a π-bond or double bond. Again, the linear configuration of ethyne is dominated by sp hybridization on each carbon, while the carbon-carbon distance of 1.20 A is such as to allow maximum overlap of two pairs of atomic p-orbitals perpendicular to the axis of this linear molecule. These π-electrons form the second and third parts of ethyne's triple bond and are similar to the π bonding electrons in N_2. Withdrawing two protons from nitrogen nucleuses would in fact transform $:N{\equiv}N:$ into $H{-}C{\equiv}C{-}H$ just as a united N atom can become separated CH atoms. The next section describes how such multiple bonds are related to single bonds.

A third method of describing the orbitals used by a central atom from the transition elements ($3d$, $4d$, or $5d$ electrons being added) is called the *ligand field theory*. Its main idea is to follow the removal in the degeneracy of the five d orbitals in the perturbing field of ionic ligands situated in various symmetrical positions about the central species having the d orbitals. If six octahedrally situated ions remove the d-degeneracy of order five, the result is a set of three equivalent degenerate d orbitals (d_{xy}, d_{xz}, and d_{yz} of Figure 14.3) at low energy and a set of two equivalent degenerate d orbitals ($d_{x^2-y^2}$ and d_{z^2}) of high energy. The state of the electrons on the hexaligated central ion depends on whether its electrons tend to prefer the triplet of d orbitals because they are very stable or whether its electrons prefer to use all d orbitals and thus spread themselves out in space to avoid electron-electron repulsions, as they would according to Hund's rules in an isolated atom where all d orbitals have the same energy. A tetrahedral arrangement of ligands stabilizes a pair of degenerate d orbitals ($d_{x^2-y^2}$, d_{z^2}) while at the same time destabilizing a set of three equivalent d orbitals (d_{xy}, d_{xz}, d_{yz}). It is possible to visualize these splittings of the d orbitals into two sets by imagining repulsions from the ligands in their given arrangements. However, a purely electrostatic repulsion is far too naive, and any refinement leads via hybridization, MO's, and VB methods toward the real bonding situation. The ligand field theory is capable of remarkably simple correlations of magnetic moments and electronic transitions of transition-metal ions and their complexes, but its description of bonding is unsophisticated.

15.15 BOND LENGTHS

Covalent radii are easily found merely by halving the observed single-bond distance between like atoms. The carbon-carbon distance of 1.542 A in diamond yields at once a covalent single-bond radius of 0.771 A for carbon. This same distance of 1.54 A is also observed in saturated hydrocarbons. Similarly, all atoms have a characteristic single-bond radius that does not depend strongly upon environment. That is, in ordinary circumstances the single-bond distance between like atoms is a definite distance. Half of this distance is the element's single-bond radius r_i. Pauling's commonly used covalent atomic radii are listed in Table 15.6. The value for Cl, for example, is half the distance observed in Cl_2.

In general, these radii are additive, for the C-S bond length is observed to be about 1.82 A and the C-H bond length is observed to be about 1.09 A. When the atoms joined by a single bond of length R_{AB} differ considerably in electronegativity, additivity fails. Schomaker and Stevenson[14] have suggested an empirical rule relating interatomic distance R_{AB} to atomic electronegativities x_A and x_B thus:

$$R_{AB} = r_A + r_B - 0.09\,|x_A - x_B| \tag{15.80}$$

For example, gaseous and crystalline compounds have single Si-C bonds invariably close to 1.89 A in length, but additivity without correction for electronegativity difference predicts 1.94 A. Electronegativities of a few elements are given in parentheses in Table 15.6. Electronegativities of metals decrease smoothly from 1.8 near Fe and 1.7 near W to 0.8 ± 0.2 for the alkali metals. The observed As-F distance in pyramidal AsF_3 is 1.72 A, in agreement with the prediction of (15.80) that

$$\begin{aligned} R_{AsF} &= r_{As} + r_F - 0.09\,|x_F - x_{As}| \\ &= 1.21 + 0.72 - 0.09(4.0 - 2.0) = 1.75\text{ A} \end{aligned}$$

The length of a bond is a measure not only of the sizes of the atoms but also of the strength of the bond. The lengths of single, double, and triple C-C bonds are typically 1.54 A, 1.33 A, and 1.20 A. In terms of bond order n, somewhat greater than half the number of bonding electrons between atoms because

(14) Schomaker, V., and D. P. Stevenson, *J. Am. Chem. Soc.*, **63**, 37 (1941).

Table 15.6 Covalent Atomic Radii (A) and Some Electronegativities†

H 0.30																	H(2.1) 0.30
Li 1.225	Be 0.889	B 0.80											C(2.5) 0.771	N(3.0) 0.74	O(3.5) 0.74		F(4.0) 0.72
Na 1.572	Mg 1.364	Al 1.248											Si(1.8) 1.173	P(2.1) 1.10	S(2.5) 1.04		Cl(3.0) 0.994
K 2.025	Ca 1.736	Sc 1.439	Ti 1.324	V 1.224	Cr 1.172	Mn 1.168	Fe 1.165	Co 1.157	Ni 1.149	Cu 1.173	Zn 1.249	Ga 1.245	Ge(1.8) 1.223	As(2.0) 1.21	Se(2.4) 1.17		Br(2.8) 1.142
Rb 2.16	Sr 1.914	Y 1.616	Zr 1.454	Nb 1.342	Mo 1.291	Tc	Ru 1.241	Rh 1.247	Pd 1.278	Ag 1.339	Cd 1.413	In 1.497	Sn 1.412	Sb 1.41	Te 1.37		I(2.5) 1.334
Cs 2.35	Ba 1.981	La 1.690	Hf 1.442	Ta 1.343	W 1.299	Re 1.278	Os 1.255	Ir 1.260	Pt 1.290	Au 1.336	Hg 1.440	Tl 1.549	Pb 1.538	Bi 1.52	Po 1.53		At

† Pauling, L., *J. Am. Chem. Soc.*, **69**, 542 (1947); and *Nature of Chemical Bond*. Ithaca, N. Y.: Cornell University Press, 1960.

of resonance stabilization, Pauling[15] finds that the interatomic distance $R(n)$ is related to the single-bond distance $R(1)$ by

$$R(n) = R(1) - 0.706 \log_{10} n, \qquad (n > 1) \tag{15.81}$$

The values for C-C bonds fix the single empirical constant 0.706. Equation (15.81) is postulated for any bond between any atoms provided the bond order n is greater than unity. The bond between apparently singly bonded carbon atoms immediately adjacent to a triple bond is generally about 1.46 A in length. Because of various resonant forms, this bond has some π character; how much can be estimated from (15.81) thus:

$$1.46 = 1.54 - 0.706 \log_{10} n$$

$$\log_{10} n = \frac{0.08}{0.706} = \log 1.3$$

Although other bond-shortening influences may be at work, up to 30% double-bond character can be ascribed to this bond.

In graphite, where four bonds hold each carbon to its three neighbors in its layer, the bond number (half the number of bonding electrons) is $\frac{4}{3}$. Without distinction between bond number and bond order, $R(\frac{4}{3})$ is predicted to be $1.54 - 0.706 \log \frac{4}{3} = 1.45$ A. The observed value is less by 0.03 A because resonance greatly strengthens the bond. Similarly, the value predicted for benzene with $n = \frac{3}{2}$ is 1.42 A, longer than observed by 0.03 A.

When there are more stable bonding orbitals than bonding electrons, as in metals, $n < 1$ and (15.81) is modified to read

$$R(n) = R(1) - 0.600 \log_{10} n \qquad (n < 1) \tag{15.82}$$

The new constant 0.600 automatically adjusts for the uninhibited resonance in electron-deficient substances. For them, n is the ratio of the number of valence electrons of a neutral atom to its coordination number. Equation (15.82) is the basis of a valence-bond theory of metals[16] and a unifying interpretation of the unusual structures of boron hydrides.[17] Other interpretations of bond distances emphasize the kinds of hybridization, intramolecular repulsions, and each such basis of correlation can usually be made to account entirely for the observed bond distances.

Bond lengths have been related directly to the strength of a bond by Huggins' equation

$$R = r_A^* + r_B^* - \tfrac{1}{2} \log_{10} D_{AB} \tag{15.83}$$

where D_{AB} is the dissociation energy (to atoms) of the bond between A and B

---

(15) Pauling, L., *J. Am. Chem. Soc.*, **69,** 542 (1947).
(16) See, for example: Pauling, L., *J. Am. Chem. Soc.*, **69,** 542 (1947); and *Proc. Roy. Soc. (London,) Series A*, **196,** 343 (1949).
(17) Hedberg, K., *J. Am. Chem. Soc.*, **74,** 3486 (1952).

and r_i^* is a constant energy distance characteristic of atom i. The energy D_{AB} is expressed in kilocalories per mole of bonds. Table 15.7 lists values of r_i^*, most of which are about 0.40 A greater than radii of Table 15.6

Table 15.7 Constant Energy Radii (A)†

			H 0.84
C 1.22	N 1.12	O 1.12	F 1.11
Si 1.57	P 1.53	S 1.46	Cl 1.44
Ge 1.61	As 1.63	Se 1.58	Br 1.56
Sn 1.80	Sb 1.83	Te 1.79	I 1.73

† Huggins, M. L., *J. Am. Chem. Soc.*, **75**, 4126 (1953).

Example 15.5 Discuss the bonding in Cl_2O and ClO_2 in view of the tabulated data [F. D. Rossini *et al.*, Circular of the National Bureau of Standards 500 (1952); J. D. Dunitz and K. Hedberg, *J. Am. Chem. Soc.*, **72,** 3108 (1950)]. The dissociation energies of Cl_2 and O_2 are 57.1 and 117.2 kcal mole^{-1}.

Property	Cl_2O	ClO_2
Heat of Formation ($\Delta H°_f$)	18.2 kcal mole^{-1}	24.7 kcal mole^{-1}
Dipole moment	Small	Small
Cl-O distance	1.70A	1.49A
Angle between bonds	111°	116°

The Schomaker-Stevenson rule (15.80) predicts a single-bond Cl-O distance of $0.74 + 0.994 - 0.09 \times (3.5 - 3.0) = 1.69$ A in argeement with the observed value in Cl_2O. If two p-orbitals on O form angular p^2 σ-bonds, the deviation from the expected 90° is to be attributed to repulsion between Cl atoms. The mean dissociation energy D of a Cl-O bond in Cl_2O is 48.8 kcal, for

$$\begin{array}{lll} Cl_{2(g)} \longrightarrow 2\,Cl_{(g)} & & \Delta H = +57.1 \text{ kcal} \\ \frac{1}{2}O_{2(g)} \longrightarrow O_{(g)} & & \Delta H = +58.6 \text{ kcal} \\ Cl_2O_{(g)} \longrightarrow Cl_{2(g)} + \frac{1}{2}O_{2(g)} & & \Delta H = -18.2 \text{ kcal} \\ \hline Cl_2O_{(g)} \longrightarrow 2Cl_{(g)} + O_{(g)} & & \Delta H = +97.5 \text{ kcal} \end{array}$$

Rule (15.83) yields $R = 1.44 + 1.12 - \frac{1}{2}\log 48.8 = 1.71$ A.

For ClO_2, the mean dissociation energy per Cl-O bond is similarly found to be 60.6 kcal; hence, by (15.83), $R = 1.67$ A, far in excess of the observed 1.49 A. Rule (15.81) suggests the that Cl-O bonds are double bonds, for

$$1.49 = 1.69 - 0.706 \log n$$

$$\log n = \frac{0.20}{0.71} = \log 1.92$$

After some discussion and comparison with SO_2, Dunitz and Hedberg favor the electronic structure

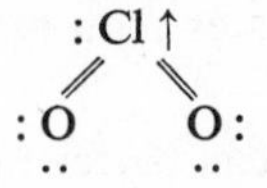

$$\begin{array}{c} :\mathrm{Cl}\uparrow \\ \diagup\!\!\!\diagup \quad \diagdown\!\!\!\diagdown \\ :\underset{\cdot\cdot}{\mathrm{O}} \qquad \underset{\cdot\cdot}{\mathrm{O}}: \end{array}$$

The chlorine atom uses six orbitals, some of which are 4*s* or 3*d* atomic orbitals. These and the stable 3*p*-orbitals can form angular σ-bonds with strong π-bonds for the double bonds.

15.16 RESONANCE ENERGY

In classical mechanics, resonance occurs when the frequency of an externally impressed vibration equals a natural frequency of vibration of the undamped system upon which it is impressed. In quantum mechanics, resonance is said to occur when two or more arbitrarily chosen approximate wave functions combine as amplitudes to produce wave functions that represent more exactly the true state of the system.

Resonance of one electron between equivalent protons explains the stability of H_2^+ in the way characteristic of wave mechanics. The mutual exchange of electrons between equivalent hydrogen atoms similarly explains the stability of H_2. Resonance is in fact the characteristic feature of wave mechanics.

In a more restricted sense, resonance is said to occur in molecules with several similar electrons or valence structures of comparable stability. The real valence or electron structures of such chemical species are found experimentally not to be explained simply in terms of these several simple structures. A nonad-

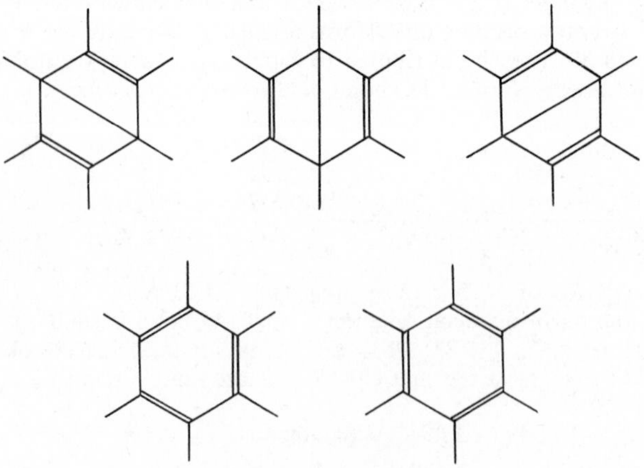

Figure 15.20. Some Resonating Structures of Benzene

ditive influence is at work. For example, benzene has five rather stable simple structures shown in Figure 15.20. Experimental chemists find only one kind of benzene with all carbon-carbon bonds and carbon-hydrogen bonds alike in reactivity. Structural chemists observe only one carbon-carbon bond distance and spectroscopists insist that the molecule is planar with sixfold symmetry. In terms of quantum mechanics, the true state of benzene is described by a superposition of wave functions for each of the rather arbitrary zero approximations of Figure 15.20. The result is a better approximation to the true wave function and true nature of real benzene.

Example 15.6. If the standard molar heats of formation of gaseous benzene, cyclohexene, and cyclohexane are 19.8 kcal, −0.8 kcal, and −29.4 kcal, calculate the resonance energy of benzene.

For the hydrogenation of cyclohexene

$$3\ C_6H_{10(g)} + 3\ H_{2(g)} \longrightarrow 3\ C_6H_{12(g)}, \qquad \Delta H^{\ominus} = -85.8 \text{ kcal}$$

For the hydrogenation of what seem to be three double bonds in benzene,

$$C_6H_{6(g)} + 3\ H_{2(g)} \longrightarrow C_6H_{12(g)}, \qquad \Delta H^{\ominus} = -49.2 \text{ kcal}$$

The difference of 36.6 kcal represents the extraordinary stability of benzene, its resonance energy.

It is possible to make certain very simple calculations for the electrons of molecules like ethene, butadiene-1, 3, benzene, and aromatics in general. The scheme was first introduced by Hückel and assumes that each electron of the π bonds is regulated by an effective Hamiltonian $\mathbf{H}^{(\pi)}$ that has somehow built into it the average potential experienced by the electrons as it exists on the framework of σ bonds that give the molecule its shape. The Hückel approach is thus akin to the Hartree-Fock approach in considering one electron in an average situation. The one-electron wave function v_a for electron a satisfies the equation

$$\mathbf{H}^{(\pi)} v_a = E_a v_a \tag{15.84}$$

The total energy of the n π electrons relative to their σ-bonded framework is

$$E = \sum_{a=1}^{n} E_a \tag{15.85}$$

The Hückel approach succeeds largely because it calculates only a small energy E relative to a very large (unmentioned) negative energy for the framework.

The wave functions v_a are assumed to be superpositions of N atomic orbital wave functions u_{ai} so that

$$v_a = \sum_{i=1}^{N} c_i u_{ai} \tag{15.86}$$

That is, v_a is an LCAO MO like $u_A \pm u_B$ for H_2^+. In (15.86), however, u_{ai} is typically a $2p_z$ orbital on atom i with lobes perpendicular to the plane of the σ-bonded molecular framework. In C_2H_4, C_4H_6, and C_6H_6, these frameworks lie in the xy plane and have these shapes:

```
H       H          H       H
 \     /            \     /
  C—C                C—C        H
 /     \            /     \    /
H       H          H       C—C
                          /     \
                         H       H

              H
              |
        H     C     H
         \  /   \  /
          C       C
          |       |
          C       C
         /  \   /  \
        H     C     H
              |
              H
```

The energies E_a for the n electrons satisfy the secular equation (14.180) in the form

$$|H_{ij}^{(\pi)} - S_{ij}E_a| = 0 \tag{15.87}$$

where, as in (14.174) and (14.175),

$$S_{ij} = \int u_{ai}^* u_{aj} d\tau \tag{15.88}$$

$$H_{ij}^{(\pi)} = \int u_{ai}^* \mathbf{H}^{(\pi)} u_{aj} d\tau \tag{15.89}$$

The next step usually taken is to let S_{ij} and H_{ij} be zero when atoms i and j are not adjacent each other in the σ-framework. The chemical reason for this is that a double bond exists only between adjacent atoms. The mathematical reason for this is that u_{ai}^* is small where u_{aj} is large when i and j are far apart. It is frequently convenient to set $S_{ij} = 0$ if $i \neq j$ even though S_{ij} may really be about 0.2. If the atoms i are equivalent, then $H_{ii}^{(\pi)} = \alpha$ is constant, and $H_{ij}^{(\pi)} = \beta$ is also constant for neighbors. The greatest use of the Hückel method has been to assume α and β to be constant from molecule to molecule and thus to compare their energies. The examples show how α and β can be evaluated empirically and how molecular energies and resonance energies can be compared. More refined and complicated adaptations of the Hückel approach are widely used today.

Example 15.7. By the Hückel method, calculate the energy of benzene and evaluate β from the result of Example 15.6.

There are 6 π electrons on 6 equivalent carbon atoms. If S_{ij} is zero when $i \neq j$ and if $S_{ii} = 1$, then (15.87) for electron a reads

$$\begin{vmatrix} \alpha - E_a & \beta & 0 & 0 & 0 & \beta \\ \beta & \alpha - E_a & \beta & 0 & 0 & 0 \\ 0 & \beta & \alpha - E_a & \beta & 0 & 0 \\ 0 & 0 & \beta & \alpha - E_a & \beta & 0 \\ 0 & 0 & 0 & \beta & \alpha - E_a & \beta \\ \beta & 0 & 0 & 0 & \beta & \alpha - E_a \end{vmatrix} = 0$$

The zeroes occur because, for example, atoms 1 and 3 are so far apart that u_{a1}^* is small where u_{a3} is large, and vice versa. That is, atoms 1 and 3 have no direct chemical π bonding. Division of this secular equation by β^6 and the substitution $\varepsilon = (\alpha - E_a)/\beta$ gives

$$\begin{vmatrix} \varepsilon & 1 & 0 & 0 & 0 & 1 \\ 1 & \varepsilon & 1 & 0 & 0 & 0 \\ 0 & 1 & \varepsilon & 1 & 0 & 0 \\ 0 & 0 & 1 & \varepsilon & 1 & 0 \\ 0 & 0 & 0 & 1 & \varepsilon & 1 \\ 1 & 0 & 0 & 0 & 1 & \varepsilon \end{vmatrix} = 0$$

Expansion of the determinant yields

$$(\varepsilon + 1)^2(\varepsilon - 1)^2(\varepsilon + 2)(\varepsilon - 2) = 0$$

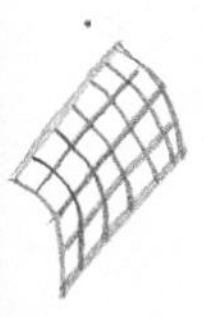

That is, since $\beta < 0$, the six roots in order of increasing ε and energy are

$$\varepsilon_1 = \frac{\alpha - E_a}{\beta} = -2 \qquad \text{(nondegenerate)}$$

$$\varepsilon_2 = \varepsilon_3 = \frac{\alpha - E_a}{\beta} = -1 \qquad \text{(degenerate; of order two)}$$

$$\varepsilon_4 = \varepsilon_5 = \frac{\alpha - E_a}{\beta} = +1 \qquad \text{(degenerate; of order two)}$$

$$\varepsilon_6 = \frac{\alpha - E_a}{\beta} = +2 \qquad \text{(nondegenerate)}$$

By the aufbau principle, with a pair of spin-opposed electrons in each orbital, one has six electrons distributed thus:

Two electrons in ε_1: $E_a = \alpha + 2\beta$ (lowest energy)
Two electrons in ε_2: $E_a = \alpha + \beta$
Two electrons in ε_3: $E_a = \alpha + \beta$

The total energy is, by (15.85),

$$E = 2(\alpha + 2\beta) + 4(\alpha + \beta) = 6\alpha + 8\beta$$

The secular equation for 1, 3, 5-cyclohexatriene (not benzene!) is, with $\varepsilon = (\alpha - E_a)/\beta$,

$$\begin{vmatrix} \varepsilon & 1 & 0 & 0 & 0 & 0 \\ 1 & \varepsilon & 0 & 0 & 0 & 0 \\ 0 & 0 & \varepsilon & 1 & 0 & 0 \\ 0 & 0 & 1 & \varepsilon & 0 & 0 \\ 0 & 0 & 0 & 0 & \varepsilon & 1 \\ 0 & 0 & 0 & 0 & 1 & \varepsilon \end{vmatrix} = 0$$

for atoms 1 and 2 have overlapping $2p_z$ atomic orbitals that do not interact with carbons 3 or 6, while the same can be said of 3—4 and 5—6. But this secular equation yields

$$(\varepsilon^2 - 1)^3 = 0$$

$$\varepsilon = -1 \qquad \text{(degenerate; of order three)}$$

$$\varepsilon = +1 \qquad \text{(degenerate; of order three)}$$

If six electrons are assigned to $\varepsilon = -1$, their total energy is $E_0 = 6(\alpha + \beta) = 6\alpha + 6\beta$. With the value 36.6 kcal from Example 15.6, it follows that the resonance energy is

$$36.6 = E_0 - E = (6\alpha + 6\beta) - (6\alpha + 8\beta) = -2\beta$$

$$\beta = -18.3 \text{ kcal}$$

Example 15.8. Estimate the resonance energy of butadiene-1, 3. (The observed value is 6 kcal mole^{-1}.)

The resonating structures involving 4 π electrons in 4 atomic orbitals ($i = 1, 2, 3, 4$) are

$\underset{1}{C}=\underset{2}{C}\diagdown\underset{3}{C}=\underset{4}{C}$ and $\underset{1}{C}-\underset{2}{C}\diagdown\!\!\diagdown\underset{3}{C}-\underset{4}{C}$

Hence, the secular equation (15.87) is

$$\begin{vmatrix} \varepsilon & 1 & 0 & 0 \\ 1 & \varepsilon & 1 & 0 \\ 0 & 1 & \varepsilon & 1 \\ 0 & 0 & 1 & \varepsilon \end{vmatrix} = 0$$

where $\beta_{14} = 0$ because C (1) and C (4) are far apart. Expansion yields $\varepsilon^4 - 3\varepsilon^2 + 1 = 0$; whence

$$\varepsilon^2 = \frac{+3 \pm \sqrt{9-4}}{2} = \frac{+3 \pm \sqrt{5}}{2} = \frac{+3 \pm 2.236}{2}$$

$$= +2.618 \text{ or } +0.382$$

$$\varepsilon = \pm 1.618 \text{ or } \pm 0.618 \qquad \text{(each nondegenerate)}$$

With two electrons in $\varepsilon = -1.618$ and two in $\varepsilon = -0.618$, one finds the energy to be

$$E = 2(\alpha + 1.618\,\beta) + 2(\alpha + 0.618\,\beta)$$
$$= 4\alpha + 4.472\,\beta$$

However, since $E_0 = 4(\alpha + \beta)$, as for the nonresonating form of benzene, the resonance energy is expected to be

$$E_0 - E = -0.472\beta$$

If $\beta = -18.3$ kcal, $E_0 - E = 8.63$ kcal. Of course, it is unlikely that β will be the same in benzene and butadiene, and even within butadiene the differences in C-C distances make it unlikely that $\beta_{12} = \beta_{34}$ is the same as β_{23}.

Example 15.9. Solve the secular equation that describes the resonance in NO_3^- or $CO_3^=$.

The three structures with 2 π electrons in four AO's are

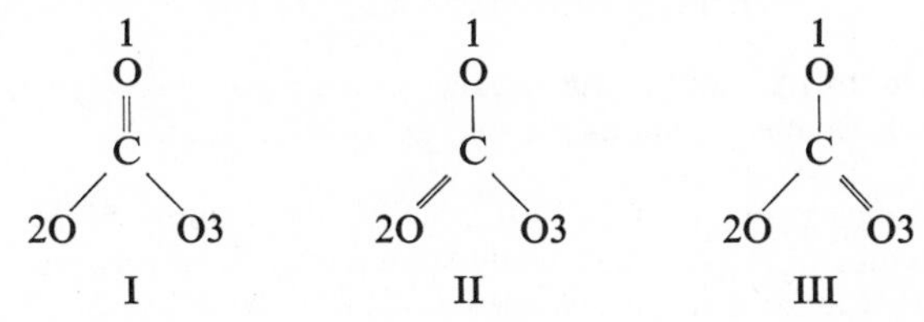

In I, $\beta_{1c} \neq 0$ while $\beta_{2c} = \beta_{3c} = 0$; in II, $\beta_{2c} \neq 0$; in III $\beta_{3c} \neq 0$. Hence, (15.87) is

$$\begin{vmatrix} H_{cc} - E_a & \beta & \beta & \beta \\ \beta & H_{oo} - E_a & 0 & 0 \\ \beta & 0 & H_{oo} - E_a & 0 \\ \beta & 0 & 0 & H_{oo} - E_a \end{vmatrix} = 0$$

That is, after division by β^4,

$$\begin{vmatrix} \varepsilon' & 1 & 1 & 1 \\ 1 & \varepsilon & 0 & 0 \\ 1 & 0 & \varepsilon & 0 \\ 1 & 0 & 0 & \varepsilon \end{vmatrix} = 0$$

where

$$\varepsilon' = \frac{H_{cc} - E_a}{\beta} \quad \text{and} \quad \varepsilon = \frac{H_{oo} - E_a}{\beta}$$

Expansion yields

$$0 = \varepsilon'\varepsilon^3 - 3\varepsilon^2 = \varepsilon^2(\varepsilon'\varepsilon - 3)$$
$$\varepsilon = 0 \qquad \text{(degenerate; of order two)}$$
$$\varepsilon'\varepsilon = 3 \qquad \text{(two energies that differ)}$$
$$(H_{cc} - E_a)(H_{oo} - E_a) = 3\beta^2 = H_{cc}H_{oo} - (H_{oo} + H_{cc})E_a + E_a^2$$
$$E_a = \frac{1}{2}\left[H_{oo} + H_{cc} \pm \sqrt{(H_{oo} - H_{cc})^2 + 12\beta^2}\right]$$

If only one of the three structures has $\beta \neq 0$, then (15.87) is

$$\begin{vmatrix} \varepsilon' & 1 & 0 & 0 \\ 1 & \varepsilon & 0 & 0 \\ 0 & 0 & \varepsilon & 0 \\ 0 & 0 & 0 & \varepsilon \end{vmatrix} = 0 = \varepsilon^2(\varepsilon'\varepsilon - 1)$$

Whence $\varepsilon = 0$ (degenerate, of order two) or

$$(H_{cc} - E_a^{(0)})(H_{oo} - E_a^{(0)}) = \beta^2$$

$$E_a^{(0)} = \frac{1}{2}\left[H_{oo} + H_{cc} \pm \sqrt{(H_{oo} - H_{cc})^2 + 4\beta^2}\right]$$

The resonance energy of the two π electrons is, therefore,

$$2(E_a^{(0)} - E_a) = -\sqrt{(H_{oo} - H_{cc})^2 + 4\beta^2} + \sqrt{(H_{oo} - H_{cc})^2 + 12\beta^2}$$

If $\beta^2 \ll (H_{oo} - H_{cc})^2$, the resonance energy is $2(E_a^{(0)} - E_a) \approx 4\beta^2 [|H_{oo} - H_{cc}|]^{-1}$

Example 15.10. Solve the secular equation that describes the resonance in CO_2, which has a resonance energy relative to O=C=O of about 40 kcal mole^{-1}.

The electrons in CO_2 are cylindrically symmetric for the same general reason that C_2H_2 is cylindrically symmetric. However, the resonance is to be calculated relative to a structure having a π bond fashioned of $2p_x$ on O and C and a π bond fashioned of $2p_y$ on C and the "other O." The molecular axis is z on all atoms. However, an equivalent situation exists when $2p_y$ is used on O and C while $2p_x$ is used on C and the "other O." The C is assumed to use $2s$ and $2p_z$ in a linear sp hybrid to form its two σ bonds to O and "other O." That is, there are six AO's for 4 π electrons. The Hückel secular equation (15.87) is

$$0 = \begin{vmatrix} H_{oo}^{(xx)} - E_a & 0 & \beta & 0 & 0 & 0 \\ 0 & H_{oo}^{(yy)} - E_a & 0 & \beta & 0 & 0 \\ \beta & 0 & H_{cc}^{(xx)} - E_a & 0 & \beta & 0 \\ 0 & \beta & 0 & H_{cc}^{(yy)} - E_a & 0 & \beta \\ 0 & 0 & \beta & 0 & H_{oo}^{(xx)} - E_a & 0 \\ 0 & 0 & 0 & \beta & 0 & H_{oo}^{(yy)} - E_a \end{vmatrix}$$

where $H_{ii}^{(xx)}$ refers to $2p_x$ on i, while $H_{ii}^{(yy)}$ refers to $2p_y$ on i, and so on. By symmetry, all β's are equal to zero if the interaction is between adjacent $2p_x$ and $2p_y$. They are also zero between nonadjacent O's. When $\beta \neq 0$, it is constant because of the symmetry about C. As usual S_{ij} has been taken to be zero if $i \neq j$. Division by β^6 and regrouping of rows and columns yields

$$0 = \begin{vmatrix} \varepsilon_o & 1 & 0 & 0 & 0 & 0 \\ 1 & \varepsilon_c & 1 & 0 & 0 & 0 \\ 0 & 1 & \varepsilon_o & 0 & 0 & 0 \\ 0 & 0 & 0 & \varepsilon_o & 1 & 0 \\ 0 & 0 & 0 & 1 & \varepsilon_c & 1 \\ 0 & 0 & 0 & 0 & 1 & \varepsilon_o \end{vmatrix}$$

where

$$\varepsilon_o = \frac{H_{oo} - E_a}{\beta} \qquad \varepsilon_c = \frac{H_{cc} - E_a}{\beta}$$

Solution yields the degenerate (of order two) values $\varepsilon_o = 0$ and $\varepsilon_o\varepsilon_c = 2$, whence

$$H_{oo} - E_a = 0\,; \qquad E_a = H_{oo}$$

$$(H_{oo} - E_a)(H_{cc} - E_a) = 2\beta^2; \quad E_a = \tfrac{1}{2}\left[(H_{oo} + H_{cc}) \pm \sqrt{(H_{oo} - H_{cc})^2 + 8\beta^2}\right]$$

The energy of resonating CO_2 with 4 π electrons is, therefore,

$$E = 2\left[(H_{oo} + H_{cc}) - \sqrt{(H_{oo} - H_{cc})^2 + 8\beta^2}\right]$$

If there were no resonance, the Hückel equation for 4 electrons in 4 AO's would be

$$O = \begin{vmatrix} H_{oo}^{(xx)} - E_a' & \beta & 0 & 0 \\ \beta & H_{cc}^{(xx)} - E_a' & 0 & 0 \\ 0 & 0 & H_{cc}^{(yy)} - E_a' & \beta \\ 0 & 0 & \beta & H_{oo}^{(yy)} - E_a' \end{vmatrix}$$

whence, with degeneracy of order two,

$$(H_{oo} - E_a')(H_{cc} - E_a') = \beta^2$$

$$E_a' = \tfrac{1}{2}\left[(H_{oo} + H_{cc}) \pm \sqrt{(H_{oo} - H_{cc})^2 + 4\beta^2}\right]$$

By the aufbau principle, the energy of nonresonating CO_2 with 4 π electrons is

$$E_0 = 2\left[(H_{oo} + H_{cc}) - \sqrt{(H_{oo} - H_{cc})^2 + 4\beta^2}\right]$$

As before, if $\beta^2 \ll (\mathrm{H}_{oo} - \mathrm{H}_{cc})^2$, the resonance energy of CO_2 is

$$E_0 - E \approx 2\beta^2[\| H_{cc} - H_{oo} \|]^{-1}$$

15.17 HYDROGEN BONDS

A *hydrogen bond* is an essentially electrostatic attraction of a covalently bonded hydrogen toward a region of high electron density. This region of negative charge may be an ion or an unshared pair of electrons. Hydrogen bonds are linear, or almost so, and link only rather electronegative atoms, usually just N, O, and F. Small in size, the hydrogen can be coordinated with only two atoms. Because it has only one orbital stable enough to form a bond, the hydrogen cannot involve two covalent bonds. It remains covalently bonded to one atom at a single-bond distance, and commonly lies at a distance from the second atom which is about 0.8 A greater than that atom's single-bond radius. Thus, the proton is not symmetrically located between its two electronegative atoms. A notable exception is FHF^-, where the proton is exactly midway between fluoride ions which are about 2.26 A apart (see Example 9.15).

Hydrogen bonds are of paramount importance in biological systems. The configuration of proteins is controlled largely by hydrogen bonds. The packing of oxide and hydroxide ions in ionic crystals involves hydrogen bonds. Ice has a very low density because the formation of hydrogen bonds does not allow efficient packing of water molecules. Each oxygen in ice is surrounded tetrahedrally by only four other oxygens. A proton lies along each tetrahedral line, two covalently bonded and two from other water molecules held in line by hydrogen bonds.

The effects of hydrogen bonds on physical properties are manifest. Increased dielectric constants, viscosities, melting and boiling points, heats of vaporization and sublimation are common when hydrogen bonds link molecules. Intramolecular hydrogen bonds are, however, possible, as in salicaldehyde, where the phenolic hydrogen is hydrogen-bonded to the oxygen of the aldehyde group. Intramolecular hydrogen bonds generally cause increased solubility and volatility. Salicaldehyde can be steam-distilled, but *p*-hydroxybenzaldehyde cannot because the crystal has intermolecular hydrogen bonds. Similarly, CH_4 is much more volatile than NH_3, H_2O, and HF.

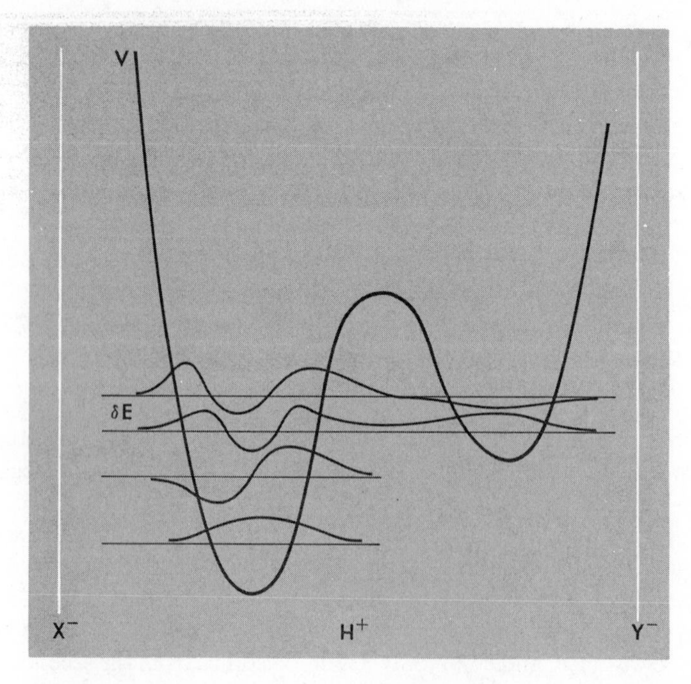

Figure 15.21. Proton Wave Functions in Hydrogen-Bond Potential

Most hydrogen bonds have energies of about four to eight kilocalories per mole of bonds, a few have energies of 10 kcal, and that of FHF^- is extraordinarily great, for[18]

$$F^-_{(g)} + HF_{(g)} \longrightarrow FHF^-_{(g)} \quad \Delta H^{\circ} = -58 \text{ kcal} \qquad (25°C)$$

The distance between electronegative atoms generally ranges from 2.7 A to 2.8 A, but the distance in FHF^- is only 2.26 A. Indeed, the distances in FHF^- are short enough and the bonds are ionic enough that, in addition to electrostatic attraction, resonance of the form ($F^- \cdots$ H-F; F-H $\cdots F^-$) contributes significantly to the stability of the anion. In unsymmetrical hydrogen bonds the proton is too far from one atom to form a strong covalent bond with it, and yet it is too massive to tunnel between two positions 0.8 A apart at a rate approaching the "rate of movement" of electrons in resonating systems.

Although the proton is indeed massive and is ordinarily closer to one of the two atoms most of the time, there is a finite probability that it may be found near the other atom. An inverse measure of the time it would require to move from one minimum to the other is the square of its wave function in the classically forbidden region of the maximum (Figure 15.21). Or the time Δt might be calculated from the uncertainty principle $\Delta E \cdot \Delta t \geqslant \hbar$ where ΔE is the difference in energy of the symmetric and antisymmetric energy states.

15.18 SUMMARY

Quantum and wave mechanics are a way of thinking that is best developed by a study of many situations from various viewpoints. This freedom to approach a solution in several ways is very clearly exemplified by the valence-bond, molecular-orbital, and ligand-field methods of describing chemical bonds. Each method has its strengths and weaknesses, of course, but together their strengths are powerful theory indeed. It is a matter of taste, in a way, for a chemist to decide when the calculation he has made is, for him, good enough to meet his elastic criteria and tiring enough to induce him to stop challenging the Schrödinger equation or its mathematical equivalent. Although the Hückel π electron theory is poor for calculating the energies of excited electronic states, it is sometimes just sufficient in accuracy and mathematical tractability for on-the-spot guidance. For, as chemists learn to trust the Schrödinger equation and their ability to extract some of its content for their use, it is likely that calculations of the kind offered in this chapter will become second nature even to the experimentalist.

It is clear that much of this chapter has avoided a fundamental mathematical approach in the hope of clarity and brevity. The specialist, armed

[18] T.C. Waddington, *Trans. Faraday Soc.* **54,** 25 (1958)

with much time and a good computer, however, can be expected to do more. He may be able to predict equilibrium situations for very reactive species at high temperature or in planetary atmospheres. His goal is surely an adequate theory of chemical kinetics in living systems as well as in dilute gases. There is clearly plenty of work for everyone.

PROBLEMS

1. Since the Born-Oppenheimer approximation is expected to fail when the linear momenta of nuclei and electrons are comparable, what order of magnitude of nuclear kinetic energy is required for a failure of this approximation in a system consisting of
   (a) two helium atoms in collision if the first ionization energy of He is about 25 ev?
   (b) wildly vibrating H_2 if the first ionization energy of H is 13.6 ev?
   Answer: (a) 0.005 ev; (b) 0.01 ev.
2. Use the secular equation with the variation function $v = c_1 u_\alpha + c_2 u_\beta$ to find the energy of H_2^+ and the values of c_1 and c_2.
3. What advantage would scaling both electronic and protonic charges in H_2 have?
   Answer: The relative importance of the r_{12} terms would change.
4. Write out explicitly the potential for Li H and Li_2.
5. Show that there are three real states of H_2 with coordinate electron wave function $u_A(1)\, u_B(2) - u_A(2)\, u_B(1)$.
6. Write an electronic wave function for H_2 in an excited state.
   Answer: e.g. $[u_A(1)\, u_B(2) - u_A(2)\, u_B(1)]\, \alpha(1)\, \alpha(2)$.
7. By a drawing, explain how a σ bond might be formed between a $1s$ orbital and one of these:
   (a) $2s$
   (b) $2p$
   (c) $3d$
8. Reproduce from memory correlation diagrams for homonuclear and heteronuclear diatomic molecules.
9. Plot accurate electronic potential energy curves for three states of H_2. The $2p - 1s$ energy difference can be calculated from the Bohr equation (13.34). [For data see W. Kolos and L. Wolniewicz, *J. Chem. Phys.* **43,** 2429 (1965)]. Then fit a Rydberg function to each.
10. With the aid of Figure 15.11, verify that $D_0\,(H_2) = 4.48$ ev.
11. Plot $E_e(R)$ for $X\,^1\Sigma_g^+$ of H_2 with data from Table 15.1.
12. Calculate the force constants k_e for the three isotopic species of H_2 ($X\,^1\Sigma_g^+$) in Table 15.1. Assume $m\,(^1_1H) = 1.00782$ and $m\,(^2_1H) = 2.01410$.
    Answer: $k_e = 5.735 \times 10^5$ dynes cm^{-1} for $^1H^1H$; 5.766×10^5 for $^1H^2H$; 5.770×10^5 for $^2H^2H$.
13. What is the average bond energy of the C–H bond in CH_4? Use Tables 9.6 and 15.1.
    Answer: 98.2 kcal mole^{-1}.

14. Calculate the internuclear distances in Cl_2 and Br_2 from data in Table 15.2.
Answer: 1.988 A and 2.284 A.

15. Calculate the zero-point energy of a real diatomic molecule.

16. Absorption cells of infrared spectrometers sometimes use KBr as windows. These transmit light from $\lambda = 2000$ A to $\lambda = 270{,}000$ A. To what energies do these limits correspond?
Answer: 50,000 cm^{-1} (6.2 ev) to 370 cm^{-1} (0.046 ev).

17. If $\Delta K = 0$ and $\Delta J = +1$, find a formula for microwave absorption valid when centrifugal stretching is observed ($D \neq 0$) for a fixed vibrational state of a symmetric top.
Answer: $\nu = 2\,cB\,(J'' + 1) - 4\,cD\,(J'' + 1)^3$.

18. From data in Table 15.3, find R_{CO} of CO.
Answer: 1.131A.

19. If Boltzmann statistics obtain, at what temperature in a magnetic field of 10.0 $\times\ 10^3$ oersteds is the population of electrons with spin $-1/2$ and $l = 0$ twice that of electrons with spin $+1/2$ and $l = 0$?
Answer: 1.94°K.

20. It is said that an inversion at an optically active carbon atom having four dissimilar groups has a half-life for tunneling to its enantiomer of the order of 10^9 years. This time uncertainty corresponds to what energy difference of the symmetric and antisymmetric linear combinations of the two enantiomer wave functions? What wavelength of electromagnetic radiation would link the two states?
Answer: 3.34×10^{-44} erg; 5.94×10^{25} m.

21. Explain why a square arrangement of ligands about a transition element splits its five 3 d orbitals into a pair (d_{xz}, d_{yz}), and three singlets (d_z^2 more stable than d_{xy} or $d_{x^2-y^2}$).

22. In terms of the valence-bond and molecular-orbital theories, describe and compare:
(a) N_2 and C_2H_2.
(b) Ne, HF, H_2O, NH_3, and CH_4.

23. Describe the hybridized bonding orbitals on the central atom in:
(a) Octahedral SF_6.
(b) Linear HgX_2.
(c) Linear Hg_2X_2.

24. Write the resonating structures of CO_3^{2-} and NO_3^-. Compare to BF_3.

25. Describe the electronic structures of SO_2 and SO_3 if R(SO) is observed to be 1.43 A in each.

26. What is the expected effect upon the angle between sigma p^2-bonds as their s-character increases?
Answer: Angle increases.

27. Discuss electronic structures of ClO_2 in terms of three-electron bonds.

28. Write out and solve the Hückel secular equation for the five benzene structures of Figure 15.21. Note that β-across-the-ring differs from β-adjacent-atoms.

29. Write and solve the secular equation for the interaction of the three structures of $CO_3^=$ in Example 15.8 in terms of three-structure wave functions rather than in terms of one-electron wave functions.

Answer:

$$0 = \begin{vmatrix} H_{11} - E & H_{12} & H_{12} \\ H_{12} & H_{11} - E & H_{12} \\ H_{12} & H_{12} & H_{11} - E \end{vmatrix}; \quad \frac{H_{11} - E}{H_{12}} = 2, 1, -1$$

30. Solve the Hückel secular equation for a nitro-group attached to an aromatic ring.

31. Why is the problem of the electrons in propadiene different from that in CO_2?
Answer: The H's force sp^2 hybridization at the terminal C's and thus leave only one $2p$ orbital on each for π electrons.

32. Explain how the two equivalent proton-positions between oxygen atoms 2.8 A apart may have a symmetrical vibrational potential before the proton appears, while afterwards the proton is closer to one than the other.
Answer: H^+ is in a nonstationary state or H^+ changes the potential by changing one O more than the other.

---

33. How good is the Born-Oppenheimer approximation for two protons held together by a negative μ meson at $R \approx 2 \times 10^{-15}$m?
Answer: Little good.

34. Write out the secular equation for H_2^+ when the linear variation function uses $1s$ and $2p$ orbitals on each proton. Assume $1s_A$ is orthogonal to $1s_B$ and $2p_B$.

Answer:
$$\begin{vmatrix} H_{11} - E & H_{12} & H_{23} & H_{23} \\ H_{12} & H_{22} - E & H_{23} & H_{23} \\ H_{23} & H_{23} & H_{33} - E & H_{34} \\ H_{23} & H_{23} & H_{34} & H_{44} - E \end{vmatrix} = 0$$

where
$$H_{11} = H_{22} = \int u_A(1s)\mathbf{H}u_A(1s)\, d\tau$$
$$H_{33} = H_{44} = \int u_A(2p)\mathbf{H}u_A(2p)d\tau$$
$$H_{12} = \int u_A(1s)\mathbf{H}u_B(1s)d\tau$$
$$H_{34} = \int u_A(2p)\mathbf{H}u_B(2p)d\tau$$
$$H_{23} = \int u_A(1s)\mathbf{H}u_B(2p)d\tau$$

35. Carry out the VB energy calculation for H_2 when $u_A(1)$ is a different kind of orbital from $u_B(2)$ (for example, $u_A(1)$ is $2p_A$ while $u_B(2)$ is $1s_B$) and compare the result to the VB energy calculation for HeH^+.

36. By reference to (15.34), explain why the amount of overlap, as measured by $S = \int u_A\, u_B\, d\tau$, might be used by chemists as a measure of bonding intensity.
Answer: $K \ll J$; hence, the K term dominates I_{AB}, which exceeds I_{12} in effect on bonding.

37. By reference to Figure 15.9, sketch the positions of nodal planes and the signs of electronic wave functions of π_u, π_g, δ_g, and δ_u MO's.

38. In terms of atomic one-electron wave functions, explain why atomic *s*-, *d*-, ... states are g while atomic *p*-, *f*-, *h*- states are u.

39. By means of a correlation diagram with added electrons, describe the binding in BeO, Ne_2, and OH.
Answer: BeO: $(KK)\sigma^2\pi^4\sigma^2$; Ne_2 $(KK)\sigma_g^2\sigma_u^2\sigma_g^2\pi_u^4\pi_g^4\sigma_u^2$; OH: $(K\sigma^2)\,\sigma^2\sigma^2\pi^3$.

40. There are two low-lying electronic states of C_2: $X\,^1\Sigma_g^+$ and an excited $^3\Pi_u$ state. Explain why their energies are almost alike in terms of molecular orbitals.

41. By a linear Birge-Sponer extrapolation, find D_0 for N_2 and ICl and compare to the values of Table 15.1.
Answer: D_0 extrap (N_2) = 11.79 ev; D_0 extrap (ICl) = 3.10 ev.

42. With data from Tables 15.1 and 9.6, find ΔH° at 0°K for $CO_{2(g)} \longrightarrow CO_{(g)} + O_{(g)}$ and compare the result to the average bond energy of the C–O bonds in CO_2.
Answer: $\Delta H_0^\circ = 125.36$ kcal; average bond energy = 190.9 kcal mole^{-1}. CO is unusually stable.

43. From B_e and B_0 in Table 15.2, find the structure of CO_2 if it is linear and without a dipole moment.
Answer: 1.162 A = R_{CO}.

44. If the heats of formation of $H_{(g)}$, $C_{(g)}$, $CH_{3(g)}$, $CH_{4(g)}$, and $C_2H_{6(g)}$ are 52.1, 171.7, 32.0, −17.9, and −20.2 kcal mole^{-1}, calculate:
(a) The strength of C—H and C—C bonds.
(b) The heat of formation of $C_5H_{12(g)}$.
(Data from F. D. Rossini et al., Circular of the National Bureau of Standards 500 (1952).)
Answer: 99.5 (or 102.0) kcal for CH; 79.2 (or 84.2) kcal for CC; (b) −27.1 kcal.

45. If the fundamental stretching energy of a C—H bond is 3000 cm^{-1}, what is the force constant of this bond?
Answer: 5.34×10^5 dynes cm^{-1}.

46. From data in Table 15.3, find the structure of HCN.
Answer: Linear; $R_{HC} = 1.064$ A; $R_{CN} = 1.156$ A.

47. A second scale of chemical shifts in NMR defines the position of proton resonance in Si $(CH_3)_4$ to be 10.000. Show that $\tau + \delta = 10$ if τ is the index on the second scale for a chemical shift of δ.

48. Allyl magnesium bromide has an NMR proton spectrum consisting of a quintet of unit intensity (total) and a doublet of total area four [J. E. Nordlander and J. D. Roberts, *J. Am. Chem. Soc.* **81,** 1769 (1959).] Suggest a structure for the allyl radical as it exists in this Grignard solution.
Answer: A resonance hybrid of $H_2C = CH - CH_2^- \rightleftharpoons {}^-H_2C - CH = CH_2$.

49. Predict the angle of rotation of plane-polarized Na D light due to passage through 2.00 decimeters of aqueous solution at 20°C if 100.0 g of solution of density 1.03 g ml^{-1} contains:
(a) Ten g *d*-glucose.
(b) Eight g *d*-glucose and 2.0 g *l*-glucose.
Answer: (a) 10.9°; (b) 6.51°.

50. Describe the hybridized bonding orbitals on the central atom in:
(a) Planar BX_3, each X equivalent to the others.
(b) Tetrahedral SiF_4.
(c) Octahedral SiF_6^{--}.

51. Predict structures (configurations and interatomic distances) of PBr_3, C_2N_2, S_2Cl_2, and $VOCl_3$.

52. Discuss the bonding and probable bond lengths in these molecules if each be tetrahedral:
(a) CF_4.

(b) POF_3.
(c) OsO_4.

53. If the distance between fluorine nucleuses in HF_2^- is 2.26 A and if the proton is midway between fluorines, discuss the bonding.

54. If the $^1\Delta_g$ state of O_2 has an equilibrium internuclear distance of 1.22 A, what can be said of the bonding?
Answer: Ordinary double bond.

55. Which has the more stable singly changed carbonium ion $C_5H_5^+$: cyclopentadiene or pentadiene?

56. Solve the Hückel secular equation for hexatriene -1, 3, 5.

---

57. Consider the approach of a proton to He^+ or of an alpha particle to H. Write suitable wave functions for the most stable state and evaluate roughly the linear variation coefficients.
Answer: $u = u_{He} \pm c\, u_H$ where $c \ll 1$.

58. Carry out the MO treatment of H_2 as suggested in Section 15.3.

Answer: $$E = 2E_H + \left(\frac{e^2}{4\pi\epsilon_0}\right)\left[\frac{1}{R_{AB}} - \frac{2K' + 2K}{1 + S} + \frac{J_1 + J_2 + 2J_3 + 4J_4}{2(1 + S^2)}\right]$$

where $$K' = \int \frac{u_A(1)u_A(1)}{r_{1A}}\, d\tau_1$$

$$J_1 = \iint \frac{u_A(1)u_A(1)u_A(2)u_A(2)}{r_{12}}\, d\tau_1 d\tau_2$$

$$J_2 = \iint \frac{u_A(1)u_A(1)u_B(2)u_B(2)}{r_{12}}\, d\tau_1 d\tau_2$$

$$J_3 = \iint \frac{u_A(1)u_B(1)u_A(2)u_B(2)}{r_{12}}\, d\tau_1 d\tau_2$$

$$J_4 = \iint \frac{u_A(1)u_A(2)u_A(1)u_B(2)}{r_{12}}\, d\tau_1 d\tau_2$$

59. Redraw the correlation diagram for HeH, LiH, and BeH with careful account of the differences in separated atom energies. Show why HeH and BeH are probably repulsive, except perhaps for long-range weak van der Waals attraction.

60. By means of a correlation diagram with added electrons, describe the free radicals CN, C_2, CH. Estimate internuclear distances from the net number of bonding electrons.
Answer: CN 1.19 A (obs. 1.17); C_2 1.33 A (obs. 1.31 A); CH 1.03 A (obs. 1.12 A)

61. Atomic $3p$ orbitals have one radial node while $2p$ have none. However, $3p$ and $2p$ atomic wave functions each change sign upon inversion through a center. By a sketch, describe the nodal surfaces of the π_u bonding orbital derived from two $3p$ atomic orbitals.
Answer: Like two superimposed π_u bonding orbitals derived from two $2p$ atomic orbitals, but one of the two so superimposed is turned upside-down and expanded so as to generate a nodal surface that is an ellipsoid of revolution.

62. On one graph plot Rydberg functions of $X\,^1\Sigma_g^+$ (which dissociates to ^3P C and ^3P O) and of $A\,^1\Pi$ (which dissociates to ^1D C at 10,190 cm^{-1} and ^1D O at 15,870 cm^{-1}). For the X state, $R_e = 1.128$ A while for the A state $R_e = 1.235$ A. As-

sume D_e for the A state is given by a Birge-Sponer linear extrapolation (15.47) to get b for the A state. Then find the energy of the minimum of the A state above that of the X state. The observed value is 38,910 cm^{-1}.

63. At 1500°C, $K_p = 2.12 \times 10^{-5}$ for $SO_{2(g)} \rightleftharpoons SO_{(g)} + (1/2)O_{2(g)}$, while at 1250°C, $K_p = 4.22 \times 10^{-8}$ for $S_{2(g)} + 2\,SO_{2(g)} \rightleftharpoons 4\,SO_{(g)}$ [E. W. Dewing and F. D. Richardson, *Trans. Faraday Soc.* **54,** 679 (1958).]
(a) With the aid of free energy functions in the library (e.g. Landolt—Bornstein), find two independent values of $\Delta H_0^\ominus$ at 0°K for the reaction $S_{2(g)} + O_{2(g)} \longrightarrow 2\,SO_{(g)}$.
(b) If $D_0(O_2) = 5.12$ ev and $D_0(SO) = 5.02$ ev, determine which of the possible spectroscopic values (3.3 ev, 3.6 ev, and 4.4 ev) is correct for $D_0\,(S_2)$.
(c) Find the average bond energy of the SO bonds in SO_2.
(d) Find D_0 for the reaction $SO_2 \longrightarrow SO + O$.
Answer: (a) $\Delta H_0^\ominus = -30.6$ kcal; (b) $D_0(S_2) = 3.58$ ev.

64. From Table 15.2, find the structure of acetylene.
Answer: $R_e(CC) = 1.203$ A, $R_e(CH) = 1.060$ A.

65. Explain how Λ, the component of electronic angular momentum along the axis of a diatom, can be observed if the rotational energy states are spectroscopically resolved.
Answer: Λ is the minimum value of J.

66. From data in Table 15.3, find the structure of $SbCl_3$ if it is pyramidal with a threefold axis.
Answer: $R_{SbCl} = 2.32$ A; Cl—Sb—Cl = 100°.

67. Suggest a molecular structure for P_4S_3 from these data. The compound P_4S_3 has an electric dipole moment and its infrared and Raman spectra suggest that it has a threefold rotation axis. It is well known that P_4O_6 and P_4O_{10} retain the tetrahedral arrangement of P's as in P_4; little change in the P geometry is expected in P_4S_3. The NMR spectrum of P_4S_3 consists of a doublet of intensity 3 and a quartet of intensity 1 at lower field, the relative peaks within the quartet being of intensity 1–3–3–1 [C. F. Callis, J. R. Van Wazer, J. N. Shoolery, and W. A. Anderson, *J. Am. Chem. Soc.* **79,** 2719 (1957)].
Answer: Trigonal pyramid: P_3 S_3 P.

68. Explain the presence or absence of optical activity in:
(a) The several pentanols.
(b) Glycine ($HOOCCH_2NH_2$).
(c) Lactic acid ($HOOCCHOHCH_3$).
(d) The several dichlorocyclopropanes.
(e) $K_3Co\,(C_2O_4)_3$.

69. Describe the bonding in tetrahedral VCl_4 and octahedral $Mo(CO)_6$.

70. The internuclear distances of the most stable states of Li_2, B_2, C_2, N_2, O_2, and F_2 are approximately 2.7 A, 1.6 A, 1.3 A, 1.1 A, 1.2 A, and 1.4 A. Their most stable electronic states are all ${}^1\Sigma_g^+$ except for those of B_2 and O_2, which are ${}^3\Sigma_g^-$. However, a ${}^3\Pi_u$ state of C_2 has almost exactly the same energy as its ${}^1\Sigma_g^+$ ground state. Use these facts to order the relative energies of the MO's at various distances in a correlation diagram.

71. At 25°C, the heat of sublimation of $As_{(s)}$ to monatomic atoms is 50.74 kcal $mole^{-1}$, the dissociation energy of F_2 is 38.4 kcal $mole^{-1}$, and the heat of formation of $AsF_{3(g)}$ is -218.3 kcal $mole^{-1}$ [F. D. Rossini et al, Circular of the

National Bureau of Standards 500 (1952)]. By means of Table 15.7 and (15.83), predict the length of the As–F bond in AsF_3.
Answer: 1.72 A.

72. Certain Rydberg-like states of NO have $^2\Sigma$ electronic states and internuclear distances of 1.07 A. Describe these states.
Answer: Triple bond between N and O with extraneous e^- at large distances about NO^+.

73. Predict an internuclear distance for the most stable state of CN^+.
Answer: Like C_2, 1.33A.

74. Which is more stable: linear H_3^+ or cyclo H_3^+?
Answer: Cyclo.

75. Find the linear variation coefficients c_i for the Hückel wave function of butadiene -1, 3 and compare them to the first four vibrational functions of the harmonic oscillator.

16
CRYSTALS

16.1 INTRODUCTION

A crystal is a solid with much internal order. The regular repetition of species usually occurs in three dimensions, although some condensed phases have crystalline order among molecules or ions in just two dimensions or one. Moreover, the order of a crystal extends not only to the immediate environment of each constituent atom, ion, or molecule but also through large distances embracing millions of repetitions of the fundamental structural pattern. This chapter begins with general remarks on crystalline order and its detection. It continues with descriptions of ideal structural types that occur frequently and to which many less common types of structure can be compared. It ends with thermodynamic, structural, and quantum mechanical views on ideal and real crystals. For almost all of the first part of the chapter, what is required for adequate understanding is just elementary chemistry and geometrical intuition.

The beauty and simplicity of form of crystalline solids has interested and charmed men of all ages. In the age of alchemy, mineralogists and metallurgists surely pondered the regular exteriors of their materials. Kepler, astronomer and mathematician, penned a semiserious essay on hexagonal snow in 1611. By 1669, Steno had recognized that quartz exhibits constant angles between perpendiculars to its naturally occurring faces. It was only in 1784, however, that Häuy was able to account for this regularity of angles and for the remarkable ability of $CaCO_3$ to be broken and cleaved into smaller and smaller and smaller crystals having the same external shape and symmetry. Häuy concluded that it was the order within the crystal that caused the remarkably smooth faces with their characteristic angles, and that the eye did not see the fine microstructure of the seemingly smooth faces. His law of rational indexes (Section 16.3) accounts for the angles in a precise mathematical way and thus represents the start of the science of crystallography.

Crystallography has grown with chemistry, for it was in 1774 that Priestley first prepared O_2 (Scheele had done so in 1772), it was in 1777 that Lavoisier explained combustion correctly, and it was about 1803 that Dalton proposed the atomic theory and the structural elements that could be repeated to yield Häuy's order within crystals. The enumeration and description of the fourteen space lattices by Bravais in 1848 was, of course, a truly significant event. By 1891, the mathematicians Fedorov and Schoenflies had derived the 230 space groups. These summarize all possible self-consistent combinations of symmetry elements in arrays having regular repetition of their parts throughout three-dimensional space. These mathematical concepts and Häuy's hypotheses were finally confirmed by experiments in 1912 and 1913. At the suggestion of von Laue, his assistants, Friedrich and Knipping, used various solids as diffraction gratings for X-radiation in 1912. Fortunately, some of their solids were crystalline and caused obvious diffraction. And in 1913, W. H. Bragg and his son, Sir Lawrence Bragg, determined the atomic arrangement of diamond and the positions of Na^+ and Cl^- in salt. It is true that the kinetic theory offered a clear explanation of the structure of gases long before 1912. In 1865, Kekulé had proposed the hexagonal ring for benzene. In 1874, van't Hoff and Le Bel had explained their reasons for the tetrahedral carbon atom. By 1890, Fischer and many other organic chemists before him had developed methods of providing structural formulas. In 1893, Werner had explained isomerism in complex ions. Yet, despite these brilliant early contributions to the shapes of molecules and ions, structural chemistry seems properly to be dated from 1912 and 1913 when both shape and scale were established by the start of crystallography.

Structural chemistry has matured with quantum and wave mechanics. The structures of atoms and molecules have supplied the questions and applications of the new mechanics, and crystals of Ni educed the wave nature of electrons for Davisson and Germer in 1927 to vindicate de Broglie's hypothesis that particles act like waves. At first, only simple ionic substances were studied by X-ray diffraction, generally with the aid of Fourier analysis of the observed spectra to get electron densities. However, by the 1930's many structural chemists and crystallographers, among whom were Robertson, Lonsdale, and Pauling, were undertaking with their associates difficult and tedious studies of organic crystals. The remarkable successes of the many investigators of the 1940's and 1950's has culminated in apparatus that shines X-radiation on a crystal (grown and selected by hand as yet) and automatically prepares an electron-density map of its structure in three dimensions. In a way, the challenge is gone from determining ideal structures; it now resides in investigating irregularities.

16.2 CRYSTALLINE PROPERTIES

Gases are easy to understand because of their randomness and disorder. Crystals are simple because of their internal order and regularity. Disorder in a gas leads to isotropy, while order in a crystal leads to anisotropy.

The clearest manifestation of order and anisotropy in crystalline substances is the perfection and regularity of the faces of individual crystals. The particular form of a crystal depends upon the conditions of growth. Precipitation from a slightly supersaturated solution or a very slowly cooling melt allows all naturally occurring faces to grow. If the growing crystal is completely bathed in a homogeneous environment, its growth generally proceeds in such a way as to develop highly symmetrical crystals like those of Figure 16.1. However, if precipitation alters the concentration near a face or if all faces of a growing crystal are not bathed in the solution or melt, perhaps because the crystal rests on the bottom of its container, or passes through its liquor in one direction, then imperfect crystals are expected. Sometimes rapid growth in a melt or greatly supersaturated solution may allow quickly growing faces to develop so fast that they disappear. For example, if the octahedral faces of Figure 16.1(f) were to grow more rapidly than the cubic faces, (f) would become (d), and finally (a). Thus, the observed faces are usually the most slowly growing ones, but minerals often grow so slowly and from solutions that are so very slightly supersaturated that many faces are developed. Traces of impurities such as dyes often greatly modify the relative rates of growth of various faces and thus lead to unusual crystalline forms.[1]

Under special circumstances, it is possible to grow perfect whiskers of crystalline Si by solution of Si in a liquid droplet that is slightly supersaturated with Si. Diamonds are grown at high pressure and temperature by solution of graphite in a molten metal and precipitation of diamond therefrom. In these cases and many more, the liquid acts like a zone in fractional crystallization (Section 7.9). However, almost always a dislocation or imperfection of some kind (Section 16.12) is required to aid the growth of the macroscopically perfect face, just as snow forms drifts near obstructions. The slight supersaturation that drives the irreversible process of crystallization is often evaporation of solvent or a changing temperature. Crystals may also be grown by chemical reactions of gases at a solid, by condensation of a gas, or by cooling of a melt. Crystals grown by electrolysis generally have preferred orientation and particular faces developed. When a crystal grows because of a phase change caused by a change in pressure or temperature, the new crystals are often aligned preferentially with respect to the gradient of P or T. Impurities present in the liquor

[1] Buckley, H. E., *Crystal Growth*. New York: John Wiley & Sons, Inc., 1951.

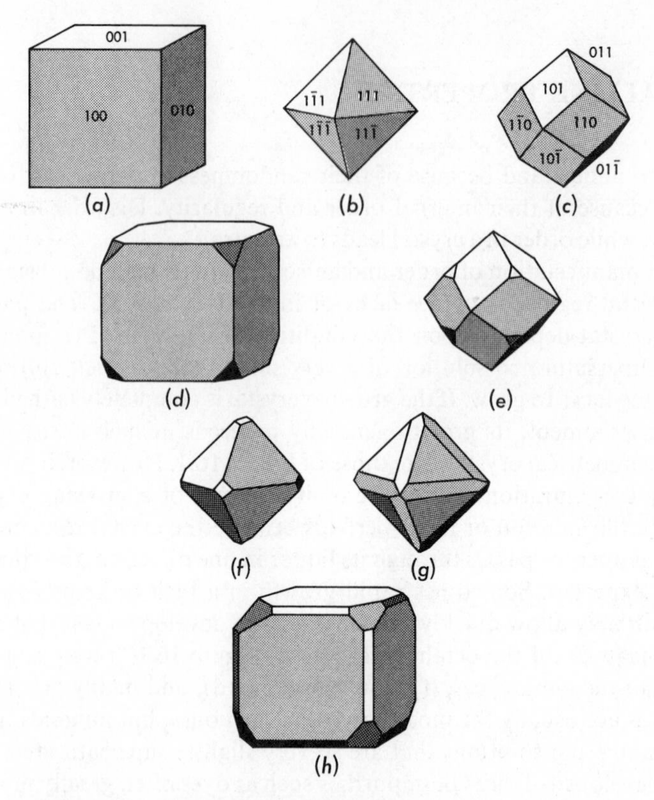

Figure 16.1. Some Crystalline Habits
(a) Cube [NaCl, PbS, Cu_2O]
(b) Octahedron [Au, NaCl, Cu_2O, $MgAl_2O_4$, Fe_3O_4]
(c) (Irregular) Dodecahedron [Cu_2O, Fe_3O_4]
(d) Cube and Octahedron [KCl, PbS]
(e) Dodecahedron and Octahedron [Fe_3O_4]
(f) Octahedron and Cube [PbS, Cu_2O, C]
(g) Octahedron and Dodecahedron [$MgAl_2O_4$]
(h) Cube-Octahedron-Dodecahedron [Cu_2O]

may tend to accumulate in a particular face. If such an impurity changes the rate of crystallization, it clearly can affect the resulting crystalline habit.

Despite the defects that inevitably occur in real crystals because of impurities, dislocations, and so on, the various macroscopic properties of crystals are generally characteristics of the gross symmetry and bonding within the crystal. It is as if the defects that occur in a particular kind of crystal always act on its ideal properties in the same way. Table 16.1 lists some typical properties for the four main kinds of crystal. Mineralogists have long used properties like color, index of refraction, streak, specific gravity, lustre, fusibility, solubility, and hardness to identify crystals. For example, Moh's scale of hardness establishes an order of increasing resistance to a surface's being scratched. Each successive

Table 16.1 General Crystalline Properties of Four Kinds of Crystal.

Kind of Crystal	Molecular	Ionic	Covalent	Metallic
Chemical Species	Molecules	Ions	Atoms	Atoms
Kind of Bonding	Van der Waals or hydrogen-bonding	Ionic	Electron pairs	Electron waves in lattice
Melting Point	Low	High	High	High or low
Mechanical Properties	Soft	Hard and brittle	Hard and tough	Often ductile and malleable
Electrical Conductivity	Low	Variable (by impurities)	Variable (by impurities)	High
Density	Low	Intermediate	High or low	High or low
Geometrical Determinant	Efficient packing	Efficient packing of large ions	Hybridized orbitals	Efficient packing

standard of the scale scratches others before it. The standards, with their hardness numbers and typical formulas, are: 1. Talc ($3MgO \cdot 4SiO_2 \cdot H_2O$); 2. Gypsum ($CaSO_4 \cdot 2H_2O$); 3. Calcite ($CaCO_3$); 4. Fluorite ($CaF_2$); 5. Opalite [$Ca_5F(PO_4)_3$]; 6. Orthoclase ($KAlSi_3O_8$); 7. Quartz ($SiO_2$); 8. Topaz [$Al_2F(OH)SiO_4$]; 9. Corundum ($Al_2O_3$); 10^+. Diamond (C). The hardest in this series have covalent bonds or ionic bonds between very efficiently packed ions that are difficult to polarize. As the close-packing of ions becomes disordered, the hardness decreases. The softest, on the other hand, are hydrates. Identification in a modern laboratory frequently depends on a precise measurement of a few properties: specific gravity, index of refraction at a certain wavelength, crystalline habit and angles between verticals to faces, and X-ray diffraction pattern. It is sometimes possible to analyze a mixture with only the X-ray diffraction pattern of finely ground crystals.

16.3 LAW OF RATIONAL INDEXES

Although the perfection of crystals of a substance is variable, the angles between the normals to the various faces are characteristic and distinctive features of a substance. Identification of a crystalline species depends in part upon measurements of the interfacial angles. With large crystals a contact goniometer may be used to measure these angles, but for tiny crystals a reflection goniometer is used. A beam of light is reflected from a face as from a mirror in order to measure the angles between faces. From the interfacial angles it is possible to derive a set of crystallographic axes that describe the crystal. The law of rational indexes (Häuy, 1784) says: *For any crystalline species there is a set of axes in terms of which all naturally occurring faces have reciprocal intercepts proportional to small integers (hkl).*

The three axes appropriate to the description of the crystalline species of Figure 16.1 are mutually perpendicular to one another and are of equal length. Each face, if extended sufficiently, would cut each axis. Each face of the cube cuts one axis at a distance a from the origin and cuts the other two axes at infinity. The reciprocal intercepts are a^{-1}, 0, and 0 in terms of this set of axes. If the proportionality constant is a, then the small integers are (100). If the positive sense of the first axis is outward from the figure and if the positive senses of the second and third axes are to the right and upward, then the front face of the cube is (100). Similarly, the right-hand face is (010) and the top face is (001). Because they intercept the negative axes, the back, left-hand, and bottom faces are $(\bar{1}00)$, $(0\bar{1}0)$, and $(00\bar{1})$, respectively, where the symbol $\bar{1}$ means *minus unity*. The indexes appropriate to the visible faces of the other simple crystals of Figure 16.1 are inscribed on the various faces. The (111) face of the octahedron is so labeled because it intercepts each of the axes at $+a$. The (110) face of the dodecahedron intercepts the first two axes at $+a$ and the third axis at infinity. The actual magnitude of the proportionality constant a is not established by the interfacial angles. Rather, all that can be said is that the (111) face cuts all three axes at the same distance from the origin.

The set of axes described above is not the only choice that leads to small integers. If axes rotated by $\pi/4$ about the vertical had been chosen, (111) of (*b*) would have been (101), (100) and (010) of (*a*) would have been $(1\bar{1}0)$ and (110), and so on. The set chosen originally is, however, the simplest set of many possible choices. It is seldom necessary to choose integers greater than 5 regardless of the complexity of the crystalline development. The integers (*hkl*) are called the *Miller indexes of a face*. They define the orientation of a face or plane relative to the three noncoplanar axes fixed in the crystal. These axes may be of any length and may be inclined at any angle. When several sets that yield small integers are at hand, that set which most fully describes the symmetry of the crystals is chosen. Several examples of Miller indexes of planes are described in Figure 16.2, the order of the axes being ***a***, ***b***, ***c***.

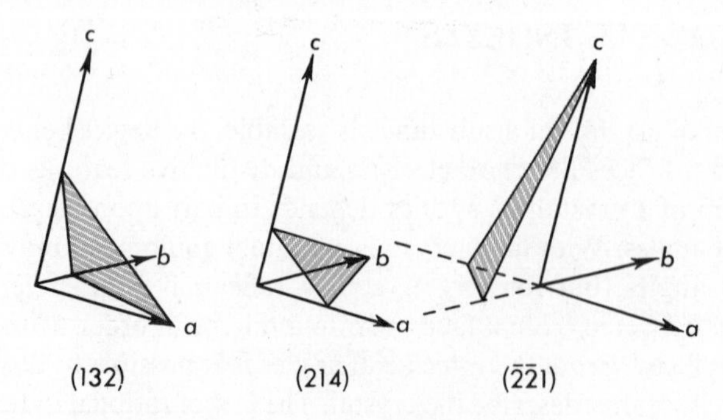

Figure 16.2. Examples of Miller Indexes

16.4 LATTICES

A lattice is a mathematical construct for describing the order of a structure. A lattice is defined as an infinite set of points repeated regularly throughout space. In one dimension, a set of points that are repeated at a distance ***a*** along a line is a one-dimensional lattice. A line of identical equally spaced telephone poles provides a simple example of a structure based on such a lattice. The characteristics of such a lattice are that each lattice point is identical with any other lattice point and that the distance between any two lattice points is an integral multiple of the distance ***a***. The various lattice sites are occupied by congruent figures that may or may not be points. Movement by an integral multiple of the primitive translation ***a*** leads inevitably to a corresponding position on a congruent figure at the final position. The figure that is repeated endlessly throughout space is the *motif* of the lattice. The motif of a line of equally distant identical telephone poles is one such pole. But if the poles were painted alternately red and green, the motif would be a pair of poles and the primitive translation would be twice as great as it was when the poles were not distinguished by color.

In two dimensions, a lattice is an infinite set of points recurring regularly in a plane. A field of identical cornstalks provides a homely example of a structure based upon such a lattice. Two translations that are not parallel fix the positions of all lattice sites. The directions taken by the two translations must, however, be specified just as their lengths are specified. Since a vector is a mathematical quantity having magnitude and direction, such a two-dimensional lattice is appropriately described by two vectors. Some of the many possible choices of two such vectors of a particular lattice are indicated in Figure 16.3. In fact, the choices of Figure 16.3 are a few of the many ways in which a *primitive pair* of vectors may be chosen for the lattice, a primitive pair being a pair that includes only one lattice site in its parallelogram, namely, that at the origin. A primitive

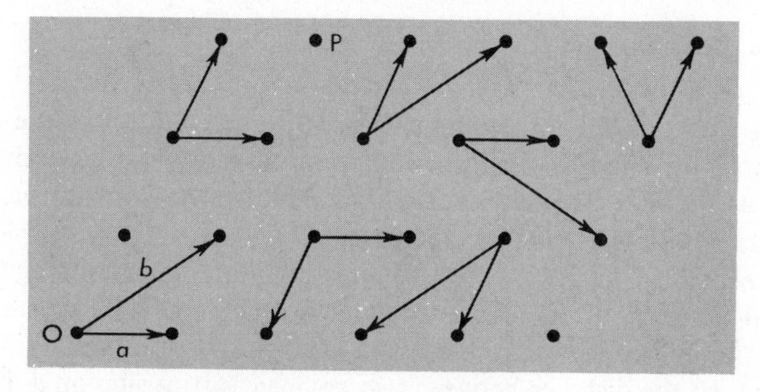

Figure 16.3. Some Primitive Vector-Pairs

pair is found systematically by choosing $\boldsymbol{a}$ between two successive sites along a line of sites and then choosing $\boldsymbol{b}$ as the vector from the tail of $\boldsymbol{a}$ to any point in one of the closest lines of sites parallel to $\boldsymbol{a}$. The region included by the parallelogram that could be generated from primitive pairs of vectors is called the *primitive unit cell of the lattice.* The primitive unit cell of a one-dimensional lattice is just the vector that links successive identical points on the line in one dimension.

As with the one-dimensional lattice, the two-dimensional lattice is a mathematical device for finding equivalent positions in a structure composed of regularly repeated congruent figures. If $\boldsymbol{a}$ and $\boldsymbol{b}$ are the two primitive vectors of the lattice, then a movement by

$$\boldsymbol{r} = u\boldsymbol{a} + v\boldsymbol{b} \tag{16.1}$$

such that u and v are integers, would lead to an equivalent position on a congruent figure. For example, to achieve point P from point O in Figure 16.3 $u = -2$ and $v = 3$. A beetle that was moved by $\boldsymbol{r}$ while napping could not distinguish his new ear of corn or its stalk from the one he occupied before he was spirited through his field.

The familiar lines of cornstalks in a field are lines that have certain Miller indexes (hk) once a pair of vectors has been chosen for the planar lattice. Figure 16.4 illustrates the assignment of indexes. Lines labeled (10) do not intersect

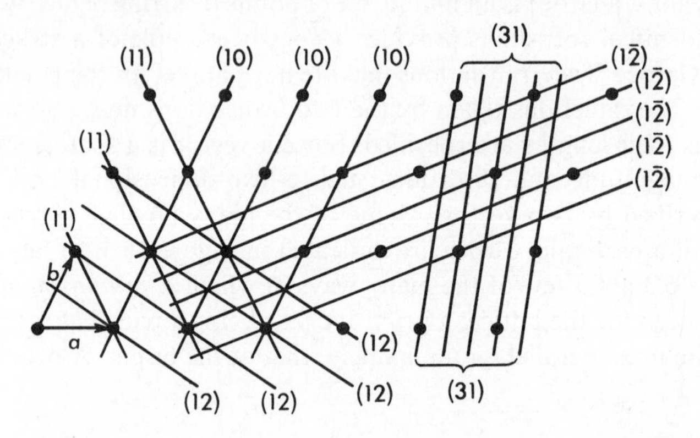

Figure 16.4. Indexes of Some Rows in a Planar Lattice

b; (11) intersects $\boldsymbol{a}$ and $\boldsymbol{b}$ with equal frequency; and so on. A study of the rows of this figure shows that lattice sites generally become more and more distant along the rows as the indexes increase and that the distance between parallel rows generally decreases as the indexes increase.

A three-dimensional lattice has lattice sites that are repeated regularly throughout three dimensions. Three noncoplanar primitive vectors $\boldsymbol{a}$, $\boldsymbol{b}$, and $\boldsymbol{c}$ that describe such a lattice can be found by an extension of the method in two dimensions. First, let the distance between two adjacent lattice sites on a line of sites be the primitive vector $\boldsymbol{a}$. Extension of this line yields lattice sites along the line at ua, where u is an integer. Second, choose a plane containing this line and any lattice site not on the line, and in this plane find the primitive vector **b** as in a two-dimensional lattice. Third, find an equivalent parallel plane that is as near to the plane of $\boldsymbol{a}$ and $\boldsymbol{b}$ as is any other such plane. A vector $\boldsymbol{c}$ from any lattice site of one plane to a lattice site in such an immediately adjacent parallel plane is the third noncoplanar vector $\boldsymbol{c}$ of the triple of primitive vectors $\boldsymbol{a}$, $\boldsymbol{b}$, and $\boldsymbol{c}$. This triple, of course, may not be the simplest possible choice of primitive vectors.

Any movement **r** between equivalent points in this three-dimensional lattice is then

$$\boldsymbol{r} = u\boldsymbol{a} + v\boldsymbol{b} + w\boldsymbol{c} \tag{16.2}$$

where u, v, and w are integers that each range from $-\infty$ to $+\infty$. Indeed, the lattice can be generated from a point by letting u, v, and w assume all integral values. As a mathematical construct designed to label equivalent positions in a structure, the lattice is infinite in extent while the structure is bounded by the finiteness of the number of its elements,

Plane faces such as those developed by crystals are indexed by integers (hkl). These are the same integers called *Miller indexes*. The requirement of the law of rational indexes that these integers be small means that planes that develop naturally in crystals have a high surface density of lattice sites, just as in a two-dimensional lattice rows having small indexes generally have more sites per unit length than rows with large indexes. Figure 16.5 illustrates the indexing of a few planes in a three-dimensional lattice.

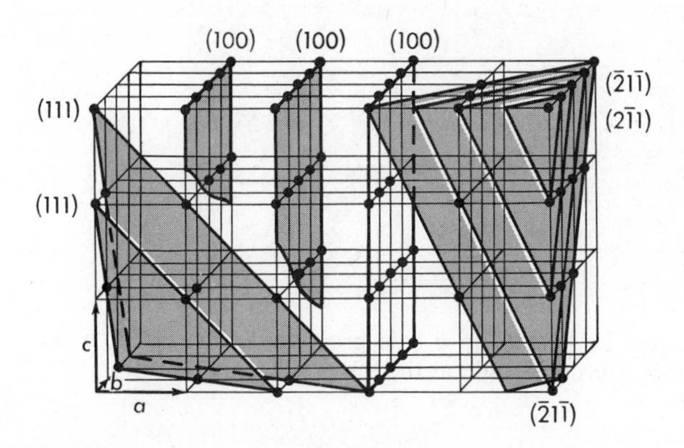

Figure 16.5. Some Indexed Planes

16.5 SPACE LATTICES

There are 14 different ways of arranging lattice points in three-dimensional space. These 14 ways were first described by Bravais in 1848 and are called the *Bravais lattices*. The axes chosen for these lattices display the full symmetry of the structures that they describe. Figure 16.6 exhibits for each of these 14 Bravais lattices its unit cell, the smallest part of the lattice that is repeated throughout space in order to generate the whole lattice.

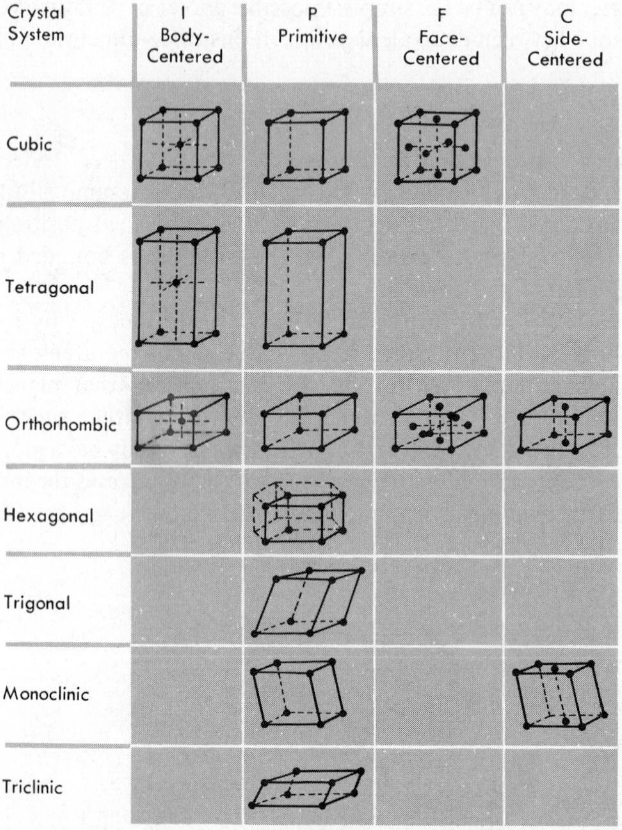

Crystal System	I Body-Centered	P Primitive	F Face-Centered	C Side-Centered
Cubic				
Tetragonal				
Orthorhombic				
Hexagonal				
Trigonal				
Monoclinic				
Triclinic				

Figure 16.6. Bravais Lattices (The *a* axis proceeds to the right; *b* to, the rear; *c*, upwards from the origin at the lower left front.)

The lattices are classified according to the seven crystal systems (cubic, tetragonal, orthorhombic, hexagonal, trigonal, monoclinic, and triclinic) and according to the number and kind of lattice sites in the unit cell. Primitive unit cells are labeled *P* and contain only one lattice site at the origin. The position of this site is described as 000, the three zeroes indicating that the site is not displaced from the origin along ***a***, ***b***, or ***c***. More than the minimum number of lattice sites is shown in Figure 16.6 in order to show the symmetry of the unit cells. In each *P* cell, the seven additional lattice points not at 000 in the cells shown are in fact at 000 in the seven cells that are immediately above, to the right of, and behind the cell shown.

Nonprimitive unit cells are labeled *I*, *F*, and *C*, and are chosen as nonprimitive in order to match the full symmetry of the lattice. Body-centered unit cells, labeled *I* from the German *innenzentriertes Gitter*, contain two lattice sites per unit cell, one at the origin 000 and one at the position $\frac{1}{2}\frac{1}{2}\frac{1}{2}$ displaced from the origin by $\frac{1}{2}\boldsymbol{a} + \frac{1}{2}\boldsymbol{b} + \frac{1}{2}\boldsymbol{c}$. Face-centered lattices are labeled *F* and contain, besides the site at 000, three more sites in the centers of the faces at displacements from the origin $\frac{1}{2}\boldsymbol{a} + \frac{1}{2}\boldsymbol{b}$, $\frac{1}{2}\boldsymbol{a} + \frac{1}{2}\boldsymbol{c}$, and $\frac{1}{2}\boldsymbol{b} + \frac{1}{2}\boldsymbol{c}$. In terms of fractional displacements along the vectors that describe the unit cells, these four sites per unit cell of a face-centered lattice are at 000, $\frac{1}{2}\frac{1}{2}0$, $\frac{1}{2}0\frac{1}{2}$, and $0\frac{1}{2}\frac{1}{2}$. Side-centered lattices in which the (001) face, the one intersecting only $\boldsymbol{c}$, is the only face centered are labeled *C*. Such *C* cells contain two sites per unit cell, one at 000 and another at $\frac{1}{2}\frac{1}{2}0$. [If the (100) face were centered, the lattice would be labeled *A*; if (010), *B*.]

The *I*, *F*, and *C* lattices that appear to be missing from Figure 16.6 may not really be lattices, or may, in fact, be equivalent to one of the 14 lattices already

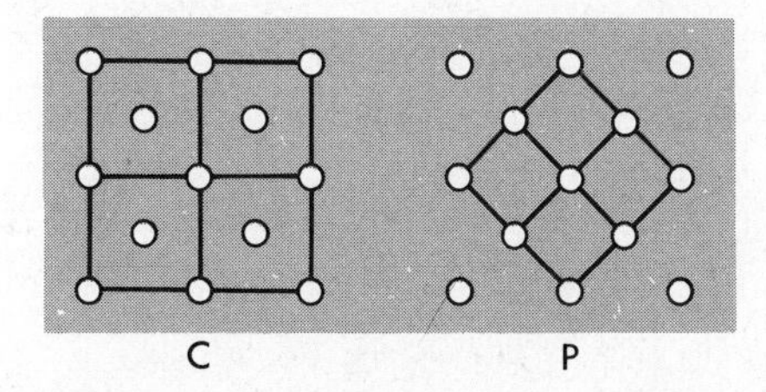

Figure 16.7. The (001) Face of Four Unit Cells of Tetragonal C and P Lattices and Their Equivalence

set forth. A cubic *C* lattice is not a cubic lattice because centering the *C* face would make the $\boldsymbol{c}$-axis different from the $\boldsymbol{a}$- and $\boldsymbol{b}$-axes and would thus lead to tetragonal symmetry. On the other hands, a tetragonal *C* lattice can be described more simply in terms of a primitive lattice based on axes rotated by $\pi/4$ relative to those used to describe the *C* unit cell, as Figure 16.7 explains. It is easy to show that tetragonal *F* is tetragonal *I*.

Table 16.2 lists the parameters that must be specified in order to define the size and shape of a unit cell in any of the seven crystal systems. The length of the edge of the cubic unit cell is the only variable that must be specified in the cubic system. Less symmetrical systems require the specification of more variables than just the scale of size. For example, three different cell lengths must be specified in the orthorhombic system. The triclinic system has so little symmetry that all six parameters, three lengths and three interaxial angles, must be specified in order to fix the size and shape of the unit cell.

Table 16.2 also lists the symmetry characteristic of a crystal system and the parameters that are fixed by this symmetry. The symmetry operations that are listed are rotations. If rotation by $2\pi/n$ about an axis leads to an arrangement identical to that which existed before rotation, the element of symmetry that exists is called an n-fold axis. Only one-, two-, three-, four-, and sixfold axes

Table 16.2 Symmetry and Parameters of Crystal Systems.

Crystal System	Characteristic Symmetry	Parameters† Fixed By Symmetry	Parameters† to Be Specified
Cubic	Four threefold axes perpendicular to (111), $(\bar{1}11)$, $(\bar{1}\bar{1}1)$, $(1\bar{1}1)$	$a = b = c$ $\alpha = \beta = \gamma = \frac{\pi}{2}$	a
Tetragonal	One fourfold axis perpendicular to (001)	$a = b$ $\alpha = \beta = \gamma = \frac{\pi}{2}$	a; c
Orthorhombic	Three mutually perpendicular twofold axes	$\alpha = \beta = \gamma = \frac{\pi}{2}$	$c < a < b$
Hexagonal	One sixfold axis perpendicular to (001)	$a = b$ $\alpha = \beta = \frac{\pi}{2}$ $\gamma = \frac{2\pi}{3}$	a; c
Trigonal	One threefold axis perpendicular to (111)	$a = b = c$ $\alpha = \beta = \gamma$	a α
Monoclinic	One twofold axis perpendicular to (010)	$\alpha = \gamma = \frac{\pi}{2}$	$c < a$; b $\beta > \frac{\pi}{2}$
Triclinic	Onefold axes	None	$c < a < b$ α, β, γ

† The values of a, b. and c are the magnitudes of the vectoros $\boldsymbol{a}$, $\boldsymbol{b}$, and $\boldsymbol{c}$. The angle α is the angle between $\boldsymbol{b}$ and $\boldsymbol{c}$; β between $\boldsymbol{a}$ and $\boldsymbol{c}$; γ, between $\boldsymbol{a}$ and $\boldsymbol{b}$.

are allowed in lattices; five-, eight- and higher-fold axes are forbidden by the repetition that is the essence of a lattice. The four threefold axes characteristic of the cubic system transform the a-, b-, and c-axes into each other. For example, rotation by $2\pi/3 = 120°$ around the axis perpendicular to (111) transforms $\boldsymbol{a}$ into $\boldsymbol{b}$, $\boldsymbol{b}$ into $\boldsymbol{c}$, and $\boldsymbol{c}$ into $\boldsymbol{a}$. The triangular faces of the octahedron in Figure 16.1 clearly show the effect and character of these four axes of rotation. The fourfold axis of the tetragonal system transforms $\boldsymbol{a}$ into $\boldsymbol{b}$ and $\boldsymbol{b}$ into $-\boldsymbol{a}$; if applied three more times, both axes would return to their initial position. However, each rotation by $2\pi/4$ would lead to a configuration that could not be distinguished from others of the series.

Certain kinds of symmetry operations leave at least one point in space unmoved. Reflection of left hand into right hand across a plane halfway between them leaves all points in the plane of reflection unmoved; rotation about an axis leaves points on the axis unmoved; rotation followed by reflection in a plane perpendicular to the axis of rotation leaves one point unmoved. On the other hand, other kinds of symmetry operations transform similar figures into each other by translations in space coupled with rotations and reflections. A screw rotation is a rotation followed (or preceded) by a translation parallel to the axis of rotation; a gliding reflection is a reflection followed (or preceded) by a translation parallel to the plane of reflection. There are in all just 230 space groups that combine all possible space operations of three-dimensional lattices. The mathematicians Fedorov and Schoenflies derived these 230 space groups in 1890. There are 32 crystallographic point groups that combine all the elements of symmetry allowed at a lattice point into a group of operations that leave at least one point in space invariant. For molecules free of a lattice, many more point groups are possible and observed. For the student who cares to pursue this fascinating study further, a list of carefully selected references is given in the footnotes.[2]

16.6 POWDER DIFFRACTION EQUATION

Although the electron microscope has revealed to "direct" observation the regular stacking of huge virus molecules into a lattice, no one has actually seen how ions, atoms, and small molecules are arranged in lattices. Information about the positions and sizes of atoms, ions, and molecules has come through the interpretation of the interference patterns caused when X-rays with wavelengths of the same order of magnitude as atomic sizes are diffracted from the lattice as from a diffraction grating. The success of the Braggs with C, NaCl, and soon thereafter with KCl, ZnS, CaF_2, and other substances was due in part to their recognition of the X-ray patterns as the results of diffraction and to their simple mathematical formulation of the spectra.

The interaction of X-radiation with a crystal is conceived as a reflection of radiation from one of the many sets of planes that exist in a three-dimensional

[2] (a) Herzberg, G., *Molecular Spectra and Molecular Structure, Volume II, Infrared and Raman Spectra*. Princeton, N. J.: D. Van Nostrand Co., Inc., 1945, Introduction. (b) Margenau, H. and G. M. Murphy, *The Mathematics of Physics and Chemistry*. Princeton, N. J.: D. Van Nostrand Co., Inc., chapter on group theory in late editions. (c) *Tables of Interatomic Distances and Configuration in Molecules and Ions*, edited by L. E. Sutton et al. Special Publication Nos. 11 (1958) and 18 (1965), London: The Chemical Society, Burlington House, W.1. (d) Henry, N. F. M., and K. Lonsdale, eds., *International Tables for X-ray Crystallography, Volume I, Symmetry Groups*. Birmingham, England: The Kynoch Press, 1952.

lattice. Suppose that a set of such planes separated by the distance d is viewed edge-on as in Figure 16.8. Reflection of a beam of X-radiation is said to occur when the angle θ between the incident beam and the planes equals the angle θ between the planes and the reflected beam. The reflected beam can have an intensity greater than zero only when the difference in path length along two

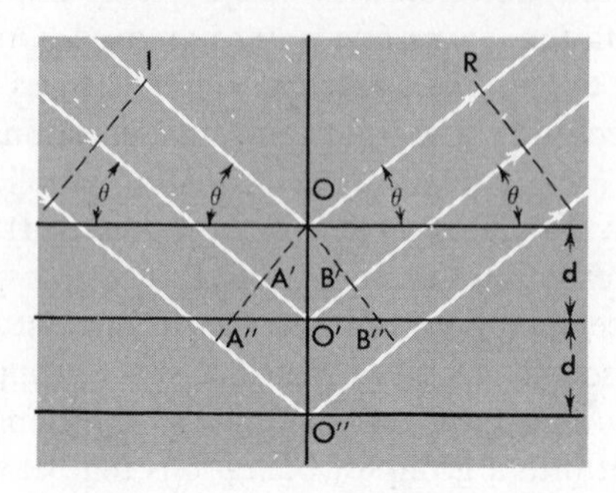

Figure 16.8. Bragg Reflection of X-Radiation

reflected rays from the wavefront at I to that at R is an integral number n of wavelengths λ. Otherwise, the interference that occurs because of the very many sites in the reflecting planes is complete and the intensity is zero in the reflected wave. If OA' and OB' are perpendicular to the ray that is reflected at O, this difference in path length is $A'O' + O'B'$. Since the sides of the angles $A'OO'$ and $B'OO'$ are perpendicular to the sides of the angles θ, both angles are equal to θ; whence it follows at once from the definition of the sine that in the right triangles $O'OA'$ and $O'OB'$, $O'A' = O'B' = d \sin \theta$. Since the difference in path length ($A'O' + O'B'$) must equal $n\lambda$ for reinforcement of the reflected radiation, it follows that

$$n\lambda = 2d \sin \theta \qquad (16.3)$$

For the plane through O'', the path difference is $2n\lambda$ and is equal to $2(2d \sin \theta)$, again yielding (16.3), the famous Bragg equation. It can also be derived very elegantly by vector methods.[3]

Provided the wavelength λ is small enough relative to the spacing d between lattice planes, several values of n, the *order of the reflection*, are possible for $0 \leqslant \theta \leqslant \pi/2$, the allowed range of θ. Figure 16.9 shows three orders of reflection from planes separated by d. The order n can be suppressed altogether from the Bragg equation by a transformation that is equivalent to imagining the existence of fictitious planes parallel to the real Bragg planes. Division of the Bragg equation (16.3) by n yields

[3] James, R. W., *The Crystalline State, Volume II, The Optical Principles of the Diffraction of X-rays*. London: George Bell & Sons, Ltd., 1950, pp. 2-3.

$$\lambda = 2\left(\frac{d}{n}\right)\sin\theta \tag{16.4}$$

This has the same form as the Bragg equation in first order; but between the real planes, which are populated with lattice sites and separated by the distance d, there are $(n - 1)$ new imaginary planes that divide the distance d into n equal parts of length (d/n).

The form of (16.4) is convenient because the value of (d/n) can be claculated very simply from the indexes (hkl) when these indexes are any three integers. True Miller indexes are always taken to be relatively prime. But if the indexes are not relatively prime and thus contain a common factor, it happens that this common factor is n, the order of the reflection. It can be shown geometrically for a lattice in which $\alpha = \beta = \gamma = \pi/2$ that the interplanar spacing d_{hkl} depends upon the triple of integers (hkl) in the simple manner

$$\frac{1}{d_{hkl}^2} = \frac{h^2}{a^2} + \frac{k^2}{b^2} + \frac{l^2}{c^2} \tag{16.5}$$

When h, k, and l are referred to axes of a primitive unit cell, d_{hkl} is the distance d between real planes of lattice sites only if h, k, and l are true Miller indexes, relatively prime. If h, k, and l contain a common factor n, (16.5) yields $d_{hkl} = d/n$, where d is the distance between planes really populated by lattice sites. Equation (16.4) then reads simply

$$\lambda = 2d_{hkl}\sin\theta \tag{16.6}$$

Equation (16.6) is generally more convenient than (16.3). In Figure 16.10 real planes are shown as solid lines and imaginary planes are shown as dashed lines.

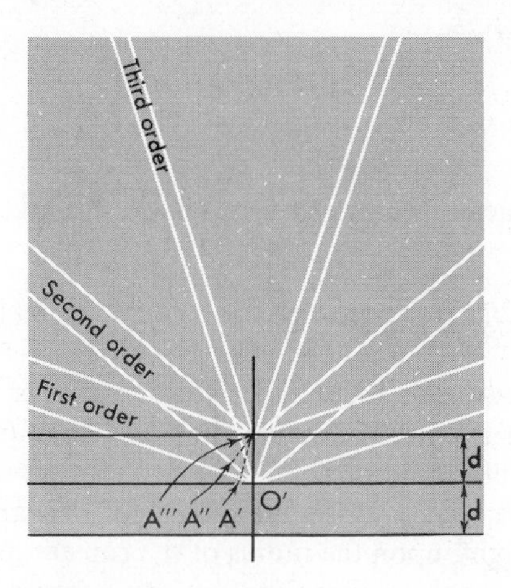

Figure 16.9. Bragg Reflection in Three Orders ($\lambda = 2[A'O']$; $2\lambda = 2[A''O']$; $3\lambda = 2[A'''O']$)

In second order, $2\lambda = 2(A'O') = 4(A''O'')$. In pseudo-first-order reflection from both kinds of plane, $\lambda = 2(A''O'') = 2(d/2) \sin \theta$.

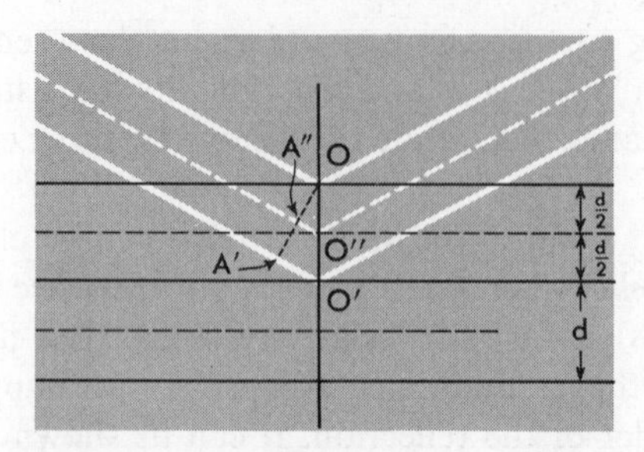

Figure 16.10. Bragg Reflection from Fictitious Planes. Real planes are solid lines; fictitious planes are dashed lines. In the second order, $2\lambda = 2(A'O') = 4(A''O'')$; hence, $\lambda = 2(A''O'')$.

If h, k, and l are referred to axes of nonprimitive unit cells and contain a common factor n [e.g., $n = 2$ for (200)], planes that might be expected to be imaginary on the basis of this discussion may really be populated by lattice sites. For example, all (200) planes in either body-centered or face-centered cubic lattices are in fact equally populated by lattice sites. Section 16.7 discusses the effect this has on the intensities of reflections.

The interplanar spacings in lattices in which α, β, or γ differs from $\pi/2$ depend upon the indexes (hkl) and lattice parameters in somewhat more complicated ways.[4] Since all lattices except monoclinic and triclinic can be referred to mutually perpendicular axes, albeit less than the best axes in the hexagonal and trigonal cases, Equation (16.5) will suffice.

16.7 EXTINCT REFLECTIONS

The intensity of X-radiation in a diffracted beam relative to that of the incident beam is

$$I = KF^2p\left(\frac{1 + \cos^2 2\theta}{\sin^2 \theta \cos \theta}\right)e^{-\delta^2 s^2/2} \tag{16.7}$$

The proportionality constant K depends upon the number of unit cells per unit volume, upon the mass and charge of the electron, upon the wavelength of X-radiation, upon the length of the arc produced on the photograph or upon the length of the slits that define the X-ray beam, upon the volume of the sample that can reflect, upon the velocity of light, upon the radius of the camera, upon

[4] See, for example, Buerger, M. J., *X-ray Crystallography*. New York: John Wiley & Sons, Inc., 1942, p. 103.

the degree to which the sample absorbs the X-rays, and upon the characteristics of the recording process. The factor $(1 + \cos^2 2\theta)/\sin^2 \theta \cos \theta$ takes account of the polarization of the X-rays and of the fact that the angle of the cone that describes the diffracted beam permits more radiation to fall on the recording device when θ is near 0 or $\pi/2$ than it does when θ is near $\pi/4$. The factor exp $(-\delta^2 s^2/2)$ is called the *temperature factor* because it accounts for the decrease in intensity due to lattice vibrations: δ^2 is the mean square displacement of the elements of the structure and $s = (4\pi \sin \theta)/\lambda$. The factor p in (16.7) is the multiplicity of the reflection (hkl); it is the number of equivalent planes that have the same value of d_{hkl}. For example, in a cubic crystal, $p = 24$ for (230) because the 2 and 3 may be positive or negative if the sample consists of randomly oriented crystals and because the order of indexes is unimportant in determining d_{hkl} by (16.5) when $a = b = c$. With four independent choices for sign $(2 \times 2 \times 1)$, three independent choices for the first index (2, 3, or 0), two remaining choices for the second index, and no free choice for the third, $p = (2 \times 2 \times 1) \times 3 \times 2 \times 1 = 24$.

The factor of (16.7) that is of real interest is F, the structure factor. Only F depends upon the arrangement of the elements of the structure. For an ordinary crystal's reflection indexed (hkl), it is

$$F(hkl) = \sum_i f_i e^{-2\pi i(hx_i + ky_i + lz_i)} \tag{16.8}$$

The summation upon i proceeds over all atoms in the unit cell; their positions are x_i, y_i, z_i. The atomic scattering factor f_i depends upon the scattering variable $s = (4\pi \sin \theta)/\lambda$ because each atom is not a point and thus yields diffracted radiation that is more and more out of phase as θ increases. At small θ or s, however, f_i is equal to the number of electrons per atom or ion, for it is the electrons that scatter or reflect the X-rays. The value of f_i decreases continuously and in a theoretically predictable manner as s increases. Equation (16.8) obtains also for electron and neutron diffraction, but the values of f_i differ from those for X-rays. Whereas X-rays are scattered by electrons, neutrons are scattered by nuclei or regions having a magnetic moment. The values of f_i for neutrons scattered by nuclei depend only slightly on atomic number. In fact, there is generally less than a factor of two between such f_i's; hence, it is possible to find H among heavy atoms by neutron diffraction but not by X-ray diffraction. However, the great f_i for a heavy atom in X-ray diffraction is often a help in finding the algebraic sign of $F(hkl)$, for only F^2 is ordinarily observed.

In (16.8), h, k, and l are the indexes of the reflection and x_i, y_i, and z_i are the fractional displacements of atom i along $\boldsymbol{a}$, $\boldsymbol{b}$, and $\boldsymbol{c}$. If lattice sites are occupied by single atoms, x_i, y_i, and z_i are zero in P lattices, assume the values 000 and $\frac{1}{2}\frac{1}{2}\frac{1}{2}$ in I lattices, assume the value 000 and $\frac{1}{2}\frac{1}{2}0$ in C lattices, and assume the values 000, $\frac{1}{2}\frac{1}{2}0$, $\frac{1}{2}0\frac{1}{2}$, and $0\frac{1}{2}\frac{1}{2}$ in F lattices. In P lattices, $F = \sum_i f_i$ for all possible integral triples (h, k, l); that is, all reflections are allowed in a primitive lattice. However, in nonprimitive lattices, certain combinations of (hkl) yield

$F = 0$ and lead to what are called *extinct reflections:* reflections of zero intensity because of the nature of the lattice. The three simplest extinction laws are derived below.

In a C lattice that contains one atom with a scattering factor f at each lattice site (000 and $\frac{1}{2}\frac{1}{2}0$), (16.8) provides the following condition upon h and k when F is zero and the reflection is extinct.

$$F = fe^{-2\pi i(0+0+0)} + fe^{-2\pi i[h/2)+(k/2)+0]}$$

$$0 = f[1 + e^{-\pi i(h+k)}]$$

$$e^{-\pi i(h+k)} = -1 = \cos(h+k)\pi - i\sin(h+k)\pi$$

$$h + k = 2m + 1 \quad (m = 0, \pm 1, \pm 2, \cdots)$$

That is, when $(h + k)$ is odd, F is zero and the reflection is extinct. Allowed (nonzero) reflections are possible only when $(h + k)$ is even. This rule applies in general, for each atom of a complex at each lattice site could have been chosen as the reference atom at 000 and $\frac{1}{2}\frac{1}{2}0$.

In an analogous way, for I lattices, which have lattice sites at 000 and $\frac{1}{2}\frac{1}{2}\frac{1}{2}$, the extinction condition is $0 = f[1 + e^{-\pi i(h+k+l)}]$. This yields the conditions $0 = \sin(h + k + l)\pi$ and $0 = f[1 + \cos(h + k + l)\pi]$. With $(h + k + l)$ as an integer, $\sin(h + k + l)\pi$ is zero. Since $f \neq 0$, $(h + k + l)$ must be odd. Hence, (111) is extinct while (110) and (211) are allowed.

For F lattices, which have lattice sites at 000, $\frac{1}{2}\frac{1}{2}0$, $\frac{1}{2}0\frac{1}{2}$, and $0\frac{1}{2}\frac{1}{2}$, the extinction condition is $0 = f[1 + e^{-\pi i(h+k)} + e^{-\pi i(h+l)} + e^{-\pi i(k+l)}]$. When $f \neq 0$, and since $\sin(n)\pi$ is zero when n is any integer, this condition becomes $0 = 1 + \cos(h + k)\pi + \cos(h + l)\pi + \cos(k + l)\pi$. If $(h + k)$ is odd, then $\cos(h + k)\pi$ is -1 and the condition is $0 = \cos(h + l)\pi + \cos(k + l)\pi$; whence, either $(h + l)$ or $(k + l)$ must be odd while the other is even. But if, as supposed, $(h + k)$ is odd, then either h or k is odd (not both odd). To get either $(h + l)$ or $(k + l)$ odd (but not both odd), l must be even. Thus only one of the indexes h, k, l must be odd while the others must be even, if $(h + k)$ is odd. On the other hand, if $(h + k)$ is even, then $\cos(h + k)\pi$ is $+1$ and the extinction condition is $0 = 2 + \cos(h + l)\pi + \cos(k + l)\pi$. If h and k are each even, then $(h + k)$ is even, as assumed, and l must be odd to satisfy the condition for extinction. If h and k are each odd, then $(h + k)$ is even, as assumed, and l must be even to satisfy the condition. Thus, the indexes h, k, l cannot be all even or all odd if $F(hkl)$ is zero. Accordingly, in an F lattice, (111) is allowed while (110) and (211) are extinct.

Inadequate intensity or accidental structural features may make $F(hkl)$ so small that the reflection is unobserved. Hence, in reasoning from extinctions to symmetry, one must be certain that a strong attempt has been made to find small F's. It is thus often satisfactory to state extinction rules in terms of what reflections are allowed. A reflection from an F lattice need not be extinct if

h, k, and l are all even or all odd. For if they are all even or all odd, the integers $(h + k)$, $(h + l)$, and $(k + l)$ are each even, contrary to what is required by the extinction condition.

Table 16.3 Indexes of Cubic Crystals

Indexes (hkl)	$(h^2 + k^2 + l^2)$†	Lattice Type That Allows Reflection
100	1	*P*
110	2	*P I*
111	3	*P F*
200	4	*P F I*
210	5	*P*
211	6	*P I*
220	8	*P F I*
300, 221	9	*P*
310	10	*P I*
311	11	*P F*
222	12	*P F I*
320	13	*P*
321	14	*P I*
400	16	*P F I*
410, 322	17	*P*
411, 330	18	*P I*
331	19	*P F*
420	20	*P F I*
421	21	*P*
332	22	*P I*
422	24	*P F I*
500, 430	25	*P*

† When h, k, l, m, and n are integers, the following is impossible: $h^2 + k^2 + l^2 = (7 + 8m)4^n$.

The process of finding lattice parameters and indexes (hkl) for the diffraction lines of a powder photograph or for the diffraction spots due to reflections from single crystals is called *indexing*. Standard methods are available for indexing patterns of the simpler lattice types.[5] Indexing with respect to the correct unit cell generally makes evident systematic extinctions such as those derived above for C, F, and I lattices. Distinguishing F and I cubic lattices is quite simple, as shown by Table 16.3, which lists all possible integer triples the sum of whose squares is less than 26.

Diffraction patterns of tetragonal and orthorhombic structures obey the same extinction rules as cubic structures. However, because the axes are not all equal, many more reflections are possible. For example, in an orthorhombic lattice, a (220) reflection will occur at an angle that differs from that of a (202) reflection because the values of d_{220} and d_{202} differ. The planes (202), $(20\bar{2})$,

[5] See, for example, Bunn, C. W., *Chemical Crystallography*. New York: Oxford University Press, 1946. By permission of the Clarendon Press, Oxford.

($\bar{2}02$), and ($\bar{2}0\bar{2}$) will, of course, reflect at the same angle and yield a multiplicity p of 4 for (202).

Figure 16.11 lists the intensities and angles at which samples of powdered, randomly oriented crystals of those substances reflect X-radiation of wavelength $\lambda = 1.541$ A.

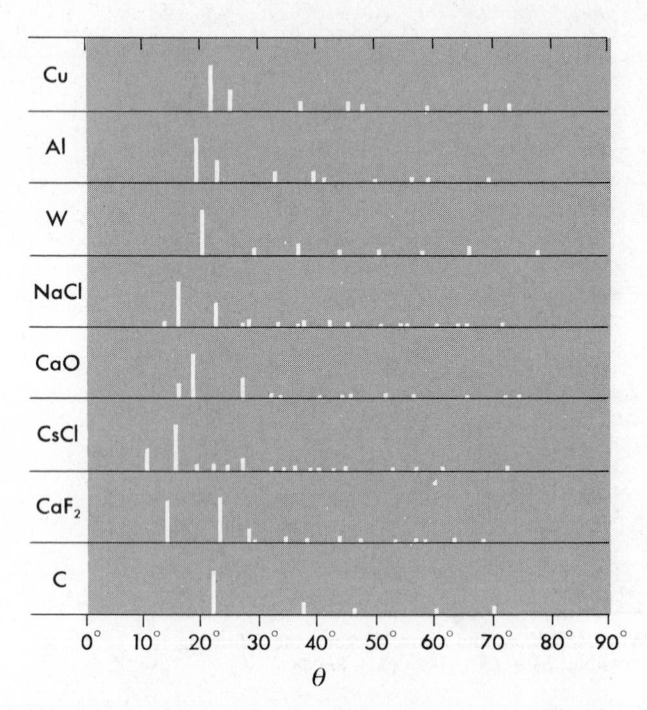

Figure 16.11. X-ray Spectra of Powdered Cu, Al, W, NaCl, CaO, CsCl, CaF_2, and Diamond ($\lambda = 1.541$ A)†

Example 16.1. At 20°C, elemental silver reflects X-radiation of wavelength 1.5418 A at $\theta = 19.076°, 22.171°, 32.256°, 38.743°, 40.816°, 49.004°$, and so on. These are the only reflections observed at angles less than 50°. Determine the kind and size of the cubic unit cell of silver metal from these data.

The Bragg equation (16.6) yields six values of d_{hkl} from the wavelength $\lambda = 1.5418$ A and the six Bragg angles. For example, if $\lambda = 19.076°$,

$$d_{hkl} = \frac{1.5418}{2 \times \sin 19.076°} = \frac{1.5418}{2 \times 0.32682} = 2.3588\text{A}$$

The six spacings calculated in this way are listed in the accompanying table.

†Calculated from *Standard X-ray Diffraction Powder Patterns*, National Bureau of Standards Circular 539 Washington, D. C. 1953: Vol. I by H. E. Swanson and E. Tatge; Vol. II by H. E. Swanson and R. K. Fuyat

θ	d_{hkl} (A)	If Body-Centered (hkl)	a (A)	If Face-Centered (hkl)	a (A)
19.076°	2.3588	110	3.3358	111	4.0855
22.171°	2.0428	200	4.0856	200	4.0856
32.256°	1.4444	211	3.5382	220	4.0855
38.743°	1.2318	220	3.4840	311	4.0855
40.816°	1.1794	310	3.7296	222	4.0855
49.004°	1.0214	222	3.5382	400	4.0856

Since it is given that silver crystallizes in the cubic system, it must be possible to calculate these six spacings from six triples of integers (the indexes) and just one parameter, the length of the edge of the cubic unit cell. Since P cubic lattices having only one atom per unit cell have not been observed, the possibility that more than one atom is associated with each lattice site is ignored and only I and F cubic lattices need be investigated. The first six allowed sets of indexes listed in Table 2.2 are assigned to these spacings and values of a, the length of the cell edge, as calculated from (16.5) are also listed. For example, for the (220) reflection if the lattice is F,

$$\frac{1}{d_{220}^2} = \frac{2^2}{a^2} + \frac{2^2}{a^2} + \frac{0}{a^2} = \frac{1}{1.4444^2} = \frac{8}{a^2}$$

$$a = 1.4444\sqrt{8} = 4.0855\text{A}$$

It is clear from the values of a that the unit cell is face-centered and that $a = 4.086$ A. A body-centered cubic unit cell cannot explain the observed reflections in terms of its sole parameter a.

16.8 CALCULATION OF DENSITY

The *density* of a substance is the ratio of its mass to its volume. A knowledge of the lattice type and unit-cell dimensions and a knowledge of the mass associated with each lattice site permit a calculation of density because the large visible crystal is merely an ordered repetition of unit cells. Imperfect crystals with voids or vacant lattice sites would of course exhibit densities lower than expected, while crystals with extra matter would have densities higher than expected.

The mass per lattice site is the molecular or formula weight M of matter associated with a site divided by Avogadro's number N. The amount of matter per unit cell is the mass per lattice site (M/N) times the number Z of lattice sites per unit cell. In P lattices, $Z = 1$; in C- and I-type lattices, $Z = 2$; and in F-type lattices, $Z = 4$. If v is the volume of the unit cell, the calculated density is, then,

$$\rho = \frac{ZM}{Nv} \tag{16.9}$$

The volume of a cubic unit cell is a^3; of a tetragonal unit cell, a^2c; of an orthorhombic unit cell, abc; and so on.

Example 16.2. Calculate the density of silver at 20°C if it crystallizes in a face-centered cubic lattice with one atom per lattice site and a unit cell that is 4.086 A in length.

There are four lattice sites per unit cell: 000, $\frac{1}{2}\frac{1}{2}0$, $\frac{1}{2}0\frac{1}{2}$, $0\frac{1}{2}\frac{1}{2}$. At each site there is one silver atom. Since the atomic weight of silver is 107.88, the density is

$$\rho = \frac{ZM}{Nv} = \frac{4 \times 107.87}{0.60225 \times 10^{24} \times 4.086^3 \times 10^{-24}} = 10.503 \text{ g cm}^{-3}$$

Equation (16.9) permits the calculation of any one of its five variables from a knowledge of the other four. Long before absolute wavelengths of X-rays were established by diffraction from ruled gratings, the Braggs used (16.9) to fix the wavelength of their X-rays. Barlow and Pope had proposed several hypothetical structures for NaCl. When the Braggs found by their experiments that one of these proposed structures was true, it was a simple matter to calculate v from (16.9) by assuming that Z was four, as required for the proposed structure. Since M, N, and ρ were known, the value of a was at once fixed through v. Then, through the Bragg equation, λ was fixed and thus the scale of all dimensions determined by X-ray diffraction was fixed.

Now that the wavelengths of X-radiation are known independently of (16.9), this equation is commonly used to determine Z or M. It has also been used to fix the value of Avogadro's number, but crystalline imperfections limit its use for the determination of N.

Example 16.3. Tobacco seed globulin has a density of 1.287 g cm^{-3} and crystallizes in a face-centered cubic unit cell with $a = 123$ A (Donnay, J. D. H., and W. Nowacki, *Crystal Data*. Geological Society of America 1954). Calculate the molecular weight of tobacco seed globulin.

By (16.9),

$$M = \frac{\rho N v}{Z} = \frac{1.287 \times 0.6022 \times 10^{24} \times 123^3 \times 10^{-24}}{4} = 3.60 \times 10^5$$

16.9 DIFFRACTION APPARATUS

As a qualitative and quantitiave analytical method, X-ray diffraction provides several advantages over chemical methods. Without destroying the sample, analysis by X-ray powder diffraction examines small samples so as to reveal the size, shape, and perfection of crystals, their identity, and the relative amounts of several crystalline substances in mixtures. It reveals these things swiftly and often with great accuracy.

An X-ray diffraction pattern can be recorded in several ways. Early investigators like the Braggs used single crystals and large spectrometers containing iomization chambers that held gases like SO_2. Reflected X-radiation that entered the ionization chamber through slits would ionize the gas according to its intensity and wavelength, and the degree of ionization was measured electrically. From the very beginning until now, X-radiation has been recorded photographically, for the degree of blackening of a negative is directly proportional to the intensity of X-radiation of any given wavelength. Modern X-ray apparatus available commercially since about 1955 records X-ray spectra photographically (ten-second development without a darkroom is possible) or by means of Geiger counters, proportional counters, scintillation crystals and photomultiplier tubes, or other means.

The angles at which the diffracted X-rays emerge from the crystals are measured in various kinds of spectrometers. Each type of spectrometer produces a diffraction pattern of reflections that is useful for answering a particular question about the nature and structure of the sample. The two spectrometers whose operation is most easily understood are the Bragg spectrometer of Figure 16.12 and the powder camera of Figure 16.13. In the Bragg spectrometer, X-radiation that is almost monochromatic originates in an X-ray tube at X and is collimated by slits S into a beam of almost parallel rays that meet the reflecting planes of the crystal at an angle θ. The crystal C is mounted on a table that rotates through an angle θ while the ionization chamber or counter R, which receives the radiation through the slits S', rotates through an angle 2θ. The table and counter may be geared to rotate together or may be rotated independently. Reflections are recorded only when (16.6) is satisfied. Some modern diffractometers have powder at C and a modern counter at R.

In a powder camera, almost monochromatic X-radiation from X is collimated by slits S and falls on a sample C that contains many small crystals oriented at random. The sample is generally rotated in order to assure that the orientation of the crystals appears random relative to the X-ray beam. As the

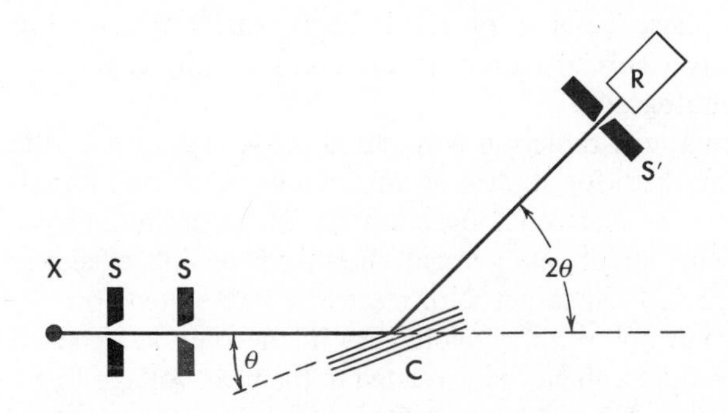

Figure 16.12. Top Schematic View of Bragg Spectrometer

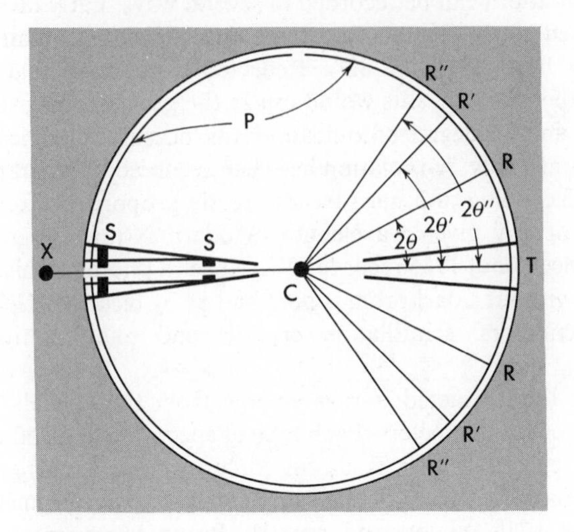

Figure 16.13. Top Schematic View of Powder Camera

sample C rotates, various of its crystals assume just the right angle θ for reflection and several diffracted beams are recorded at $R, R', R'', \cdots$ on a strip of photographic film P that is pressed tightly inside the cylindrical camera. The X-radiation that is not diffracted is caught in a beam trap T to prevent its fogging the film. The film is mounted unsymmetrically to facilitate corrections for film expansion and contraction when the positions of the reflections R, R', R'', are measured from the developed negative.

If a properly oriented single crystal is examined in an X-ray spectrometer of more complex design than those of Figure 16.12 and 16.13, the reflections that are recorded electrically or photographically have certain values of h, k, or l fixed by the crystal's orientation. From the record the other values of the indexes can be deduced so that $|F|^2$ is then known as a function of (hkl). By Fourier inversion (summation over the Miller indexes), the positions x_i, y_i, z_i can be found when the phase factor $e^{i\delta}$ on F is known, usually by astute guesswork. This kind of study yields structural details that generally cannot be deduced from a powder photograph.

Almost monochromatic X-radiation is required for X-ray powder diffraction and, it may be remarked, for studies of amorphous solids and liquids by techniques analogous to the electron diffraction study of gaseous molecules. X-rays are produced with about one percent energy-conversion efficiency by bombardment of a water-cooled target with electrons accelerated from a hot W filament by more than about 20 kilovolts. As in the photoelectric effect, here reversed, the maximum frequency ν_0 is related to the peak voltage V_0 by the energy equation $eV_0 = h\nu_0$. If V_0 is 35 kilovolts, λ_0 is 0.355 A. The bombarding electrons eject electrons from the inner atomic orbitals of atoms in the target, and X-rays are emitted as these are filled by atomic electrons from states of higher energy. All wavelengths greater than the minimum λ_0 are generated as radiation characteristic of the target's atomic energy states or as continuous (so-called white) radiation of all wavelengths. White radiation is generated by inelastic collision of electrons with the target. Figure 16.14 illustrates the intensity I of radiation from a copper target as a function of wavelength λ. The characteristic K_α doublet at $\lambda = 1.544$ A and 1.540 A is ten times as intense as the K_β lines at 1.39 A. The K_α radiation comes from the transition $2p \longrightarrow 1s$, while the K_β is due mostly to $3p \longrightarrow 1s$.

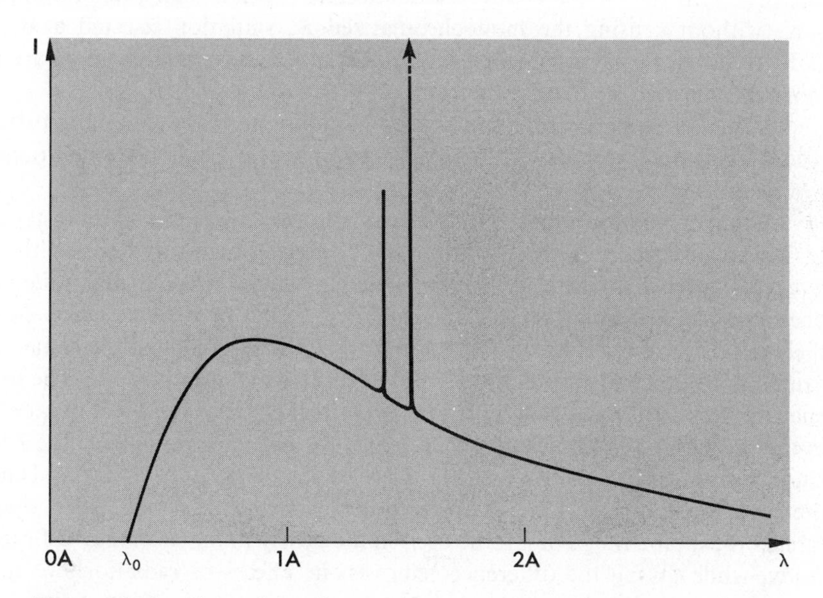

Figure 16.14. X-ray Intensity I as a Function of Wavelength λ (Cu target).

The most common way to monochromatize X-radiation is to interpose a thin piece of metal between the X-ray tube and the camera or spectrometer. The metal is chosen to absorb the K_β and short wavelength white radiation very strongly while allowing K_α and long wavelengths to pass with little absorption. Air strongly absorbs radiation with λ greater than about 2A, and what remains is almost all K_α because of its great intensity relative to the white radiation at any particular λ. In general, mass absorption coefficients (μ/ρ) vary as $Z^4\lambda^3$, where Z is the atomic number of atoms in the absorber. As λ decreases the coefficient increases almost discontinuously whenever the photon energy becomes sufficient to eject electrons from atomic orbitals of lower (more stable) energy. For example, Ni is used to filter Cu radiation because its K absorption edge $(1s \longrightarrow \infty)$ lies at 1.49A, between the K_α and K_β lines of Cu.

A second way to monochromatize X-radiation is to use Bragg reflection from a single crystal. The beam from such a preliminary reflection has wavelengths that satisfy $n\lambda = 2d \sin \theta$ because the angle θ is specified, as is d by the orientation of the single crystal. This reflected beam then acts as the incoming beam for the experiment that requires X-rays of one λ. Some monochromator crystals that deliver reasonable intensities, are stable, and are mechanically suitable are topaz ($d = 1.36$ A); quartz ($d = 1.38$ A or $d = 3.34$ A), LiF ($d = 2.02$A), CaF_2 ($d = 3.15$ A), NaCl ($d = 2.82$ A), and, for very long λ, lead stearate ($d = 50.4$ A). The second order ($n = 2$) from CaF_2 is very weak because $F(222)$ is much less than $F(111)$. Hence, the white radiation, which increases in intensity with the characteristic K radiation as V_0 rises, can extend almost to $\frac{1}{3}\ K_\alpha$ without causing the monochromatized K_α radiation selected at θ_{111} of CaF_2 to have much $\lambda/2$ present. Neutron beams from thermal reactors are also monochromatized by Bragg reflection.

A third way to measure neutron or X-radiation of only one λ is to use a recording device like a proportional counter set to select only one small range of wavelengths.

A fourth way to monochromatize radiation with less loss of intensity than by Bragg reflection is to use two filters in two experiments and record the difference in intensity. One filter absorbs strongly when λ is less than λ_0'; the other does so when λ is less than λ_0''. The thickness of the filters is adjusted so that their effect for any λ outside the range from λ_0' to λ_0'' is almost the same. This can be done generally since, away from edges, (μ/ρ) varies as $Z^4\lambda^3$. The difference in intensities recorded in the two experiments yields the effect of radiation in the range λ_0' to λ_0'', which can be narrow (± 0.1A) and can include the strong characteristic radiation (e.g., K_α doublet) of the X-ray tube's target. That is, the near discontinuities in mass absorption coefficients at λ_0' and λ_0'' for the two filters bracket the range of λ to be used in the nearly monochromatic diffraction study, while taking the difference removes the effects of radiation not in the range from λ_0' to λ_0''.

16.10 X-RAY ANALYSIS

Diffraction experiments with X-rays are a powerful way to find structure; organic chemists may even depend on a crystal structure to aid their work, especially in natural products having unusual rings. Powder photography is a swift means of nondestructive analysis with very small samples. The values of d_{hkl} and the intensities of the reflections of an unknown mixture, regardless of the complexity of its pattern, can be compared to pure standards for qualitative identification. And the amounts of components present can be estimated by comparison to synthetic mixtures or by accurate measurement of intensities. Powder cameras are easily run at high T and, with care at 25°C, lattice constants can be observed to six significant figures. Since lattice constants may be linear functions of content (Vegard's law) when the crystal is a solid solution, such accuracy is of direct value for quantitative analysis.

Diffraction is not the only way that X-rays are used in analysis, however. Elemental analysis by X-ray absorption makes use of the discontinuities in mass absorption coefficients (μ/ρ) at certain wavelengths like λ_0. If λ_1 just exceeds λ_0, $(\mu/\rho)_1$ is small at λ_1 and the transmitted intensity at λ_1 is $I^{(1)} = I_0^{(1)} \exp [-(\mu/\rho)_1 \rho x]$, where x is the sample thickness, where ρ is the density of the element sought, and where ρx is the mass per unit area of the element in the X-ray beam. The intensity $I_0^{(1)}$ is the intensity that would have been transmitted in the absence of the element sought. Again, if λ_2 is just less than λ_0, then $(\mu/\rho)_2$ is great for the element with absorption edge at λ_0 and at λ_2 the transmitted intensity is $I^{(2)} = I_0^{(2)} \exp [-(\mu/\rho)_2 \rho x]$. Since λ_1 is close to λ_2, $I_0^{(1)}$ is about equal to $I_0^{(2)}$. In general, however, the amount of element per unit area is

$$\rho x = \left[\left(\frac{\mu}{\rho}\right)_2 - \left(\frac{\mu}{\rho}\right)_1\right]^{-1} \left[\ln \frac{I_0^{(2)}}{I^{(2)}} - \ln \frac{I_0^{(1)}}{I^{(1)}}\right] \tag{16.10}$$

The mass absorption coefficients $(\mu/\rho)_2$ and $(\mu/\rho)_1$ are known by calibration with a standard, and the four intensities are observed with a particular sample, the element sought being absent when I_0's are measured (really or by calculation). The intensities $I^{(i)}$ and $I_0^{(i)}$ at λ_i are distinguished from intensities at other wavelengths by the use of a Bragg spectrometer set at a suitable angle θ_i such that $n\lambda_i = 2d \sin \theta_i$ is satisfied, d being the monochromator crystal's spacing.

A second kind of elemental analysis that uses X-rays without diffraction is called *X-ray fluorescence*. A sample intensely irradiated with X-rays of all λ absorbs the radiation and then re-emits X-radiation characteristic of its elements. If it were convenient to place the sample in a vacuum and if the sample were capable of withstanding high temperatures, it could of course itself be made the target of the electron beam in order that its characteristic radiation might be excited. Fluorescent radiation excited by the high-intensity radiation source is just more convenient. The wavelengths emitted are nearly independent of the state of chemical binding because the transitions involve electrons in inner, nonvalence atomic orbitals. (See, however, the Mössbauer effect in Section 16.24.) The wavelengths emitted identify the element; the intensities at each interesting λ are measured in a Bragg spectrometer, which resolves the characteristic λ's by the Bragg equation. The amount of a high atomic number element in a matrix of atoms of low atomic number (e.g., Pt supported on silica gel or Pb in gasoline) is nearly a linear function of the intensity of its fluorescent radiation. However, when the matrix has elements of high atomic number, absorption may be great and the amount present may have to be found by comparison to empirical calibrations. Except perhaps for radiation damage, both X-ray absorption and X-ray fluorescence involve no change in the sample. This can be a major advantage if chemical separation is time-consuming.

16.11 CRYSTALLITE SIZE

There are many methods of measuring the sizes of crystals and essentially perfect crystalline domains, and there are almost as many ways of defining crystallite size. A tedious but straightforward method is to count particles in a weighed sample by optical or electron microscopy. Other ways include empirical correlation with rates of solution, rates of chemical reaction, adsorption of gases or solutes, and so on. Here it is appropriate to mention the broadening of X-ray spectra caused by subdivision of a solid. The X-ray apparatus causes a so-called instrumental broadening b through such things as slit size, divergence of the X-ray beam, and absorption by the sample. According to the widely accepted method of Warren, the observed angular broadening B of a powder spectrum is related to the pure diffraction broadening β and the instrumental broadening b by

$$B^2 = \beta^2 + b^2 \tag{16.11}$$

The quantities B and b in (16.11) are observed half-widths (in radians) of diffraction peaks at half-maximum intensity. Equation (16.11) assumes that the intensity of a peak as a function of angle is a Gaussian distribution; this assumption is close to correct in many cases. It is also a rare sample that does not offer a distribution in sizes of crystallites. Values of B for the small crystallites of interest and of b for deliberately added large crystals of another standard substance are frequently observed at nearly the same angles 2θ on the same photograph or in the same sequence of intensity measurements with a counter.

When β (in radians) is thus found by (16.11) for a particular reflection (hkl), it yields the linear dimension t measured perpendicular to the Bragg planes d_{hkl} through the equation

$$t = \frac{K\lambda}{\beta \cos \theta} \tag{16.12}$$

The angle θ is the Bragg angle at which d_{hkl} reflects X-rays of wavelength λ. The constant K in (16.12) is close to unity and may depend on (hkl), the crystal system, the exact way B and b are observed if (16.11) is not used, and other parameters. What is important about (16.12) is that it provides comparative values and that β varies as $\sec \theta$ when the broadening is attributable to small sizes of crystallites. The absolute value of t may be in error by 25%, but still (16.12) is of great value for very precise determination of relative sizes in related experiments and for establishing directions in which crystallite dimensions are observed when t depends on (hkl).

A powder spectrum may also be broadened beyond pure instrumental broadening by other influences, one of which is a variation in d_{hkl}. These uncertainties in d_{hkl} may be caused by changes in chemical composition (solid solutions, crystalline defects, etc.) or by mechanical strain. The effects these have on angle of diffraction are easily assessed, for at constant λ, the Bragg equation (16.6) yields $0 = \delta\lambda = \delta(2d_{hkl} \sin \theta) = 2d_{hkl} \cos \theta \, \delta\theta + 2 \, \delta d_{hkl} \sin \theta$. Whence, the broadening in radians is

$$\delta\theta = -\frac{\delta d_{hkl}}{d_{hkl}} \tan \theta \tag{16.13}$$

That is, broadening caused by variation in lattice constants is proportional to $\tan \theta$ while (16.12) requires that broadening proportional to $\sec \theta$ be attributed instead to fine division of the crystals. In order to distinguish these two additive sources of broadening, it is necessary to observe several spectra at several angles θ. If the indexes (hkl) are several orders of the same planes [e.g., (200), (400), (600), (800), . . .], the dependence of crystallite size on direction in the crystal is eliminated; hence, β and K in (16.12) are constant.

Really perfect crystals have a natural diffraction width of a few seconds of arc. Most real crystals are mosaics, that is, juxtaposed and intergrown tiny perfect crystals loosely attached with alignments to within less than a degree of arc. Hence, equations (16.11) and (16.12) are useful only when b is small compared to B, the crystallite size t being less than about 200 A. The value of t is a weighted average of whatever distribution of size may exist in the sample for a particular direction (hkl). In the same way, when $\delta\theta$ in (16.13) depends on (hkl), that dependence tells how strain, dislocations, stacking errors, and so on depend on direction within the crystals. Macroscopic measurements of strain generally do not give such detailed directional data.

Some examples of interest with regard to size are: proof that certain methods of crystallization of $CaCO_3$ yield needles of aragonite; rate of growth of crystallites of graphite on cracking catalysts; state of division of Pt crystallites supported on Al_2O_3 for hydrogenation; uniformity of hydration of clays, which expand and contract with gain and loss of water; extent of cold-working of metals.

16.12 DISLOCATIONS

A truly perfect crystal is never achieved, for every real crystal is disorganized relative to its ideal pattern, the lattice. Every real crystal vibrates since 0°K is unattainable, is subject to irradiation by light or cosmic rays, contains impurities despite the advances in zone refining, and has a surface because matter in a particular crystal does not match the mathematical infinity of its lattice. Nevertheless, even with these defects, some real crystals are so nearly perfect that they diffract X-rays with intensities proportional to $F(hkl)$ rather than $|F|^2$.

The dependence upon F^2 observed for most crystals led Darwin to postulate in 1913 that most real crystals consist of a mosaic of perfect domains about 10^3A on a side. These domains are not quite perfectly aligned and so reflect X-rays over a small range of angles, generally several hundred seconds. Reflection from planes of a perfect crystal is not additive in the same way as from a mosaic crystal which is very imperfect on the microscopic level. In a perfect crystal, a reflected ray emerges at an angle such that it can be re-reflected from the inner side of the planes that first caused its reflection. Multiple reflections and reduced intensity are the result, but what intensity there is is concentrated into a few seconds of arc. Grinding or thermal or mechanical shock readily transforms these unusual crystals into the very common kind of single crystal with spectral intensities proportional to $|F|^2$.

A *dislocation* is a kind of structural imperfection that extends for many unit cell lengths through a crystal. Typically the distances are hundreds of angstroms, and a particular set of related irregularities can be traced along their unifying feature, the dislocation line, sometimes from one surface of a crystal deviously to another surface. A dislocation may be much less a disturbance than the imperfections that yield the mosaic structure. Dislocations exist with or without chemical impurities, which can be reduced by zone refining to less than one part in a million.

A more definite description of disclocations classifies them as *screw* and *edge*. Suppose that a path is followed from atom to atom or from ion to ion in a real crystal. If this path returns upon itself, it is called a *Burgers circuit*. If the same path in the lattice that typifies the structure does not return upon itself so that the beginning and end do not lie on the same atom, as they did in the real crystal, then the Burgers circuit encloses one or more dislocations. The vector that completes the closed circuit in the lattice is the *Burgers vector*. It measures the magnitude of the dislocation.

If the Burgers vector is parallel to the line that locates the dislocation, it is called a *screw dislocation*. The shortest screw dislocation is analogous to the vertical movement of a helical (sometimes ineptly called spiral) staircase that rises by one step per revolution. The end of such a dislocation is shown in Figure 16.15. The dislocation line is perpendicular to the upper face. Far from this line, the structure looks almost ideal: all planes are approximately parallel and correctly spaced.

On the other hand, if the Burgers vector is perpendicular to the dislocation line, it is an *edge dislocation*. The simplest edge dislocation is an incomplete plane of atoms or ions interleaved between two normal planes as in Figure 16.16. It is analogous to a book mark between the pages of a book. On one side of the dislocation line, the planes separate to make room for the extra layer; on the other side, there is a compression due to the absent layer.

In general, a dislocation is part screw and part edge. Darwin himself thought only warping might be sufficient to account for the F^2-intensity dependence. In a well-annealed crystal, dislocations are about 10^4A apart but cold-

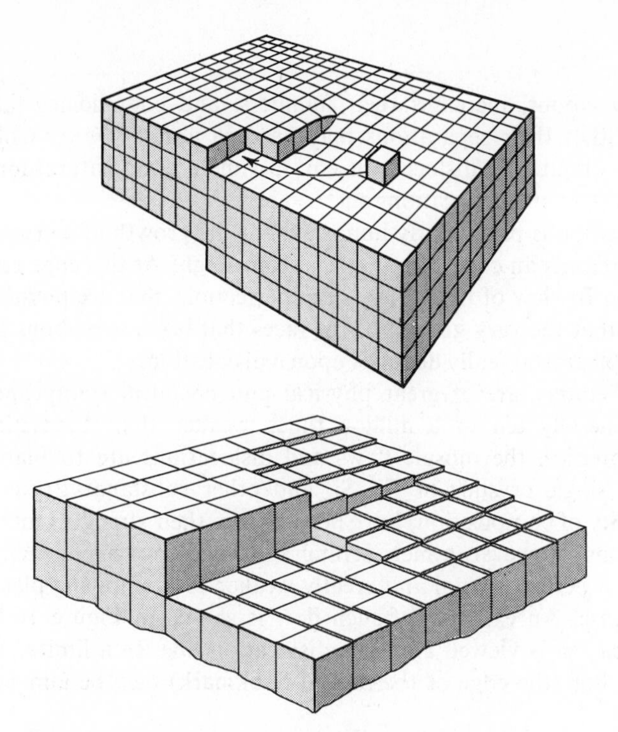

Figure 16.15. End of a Screw Dislocation†

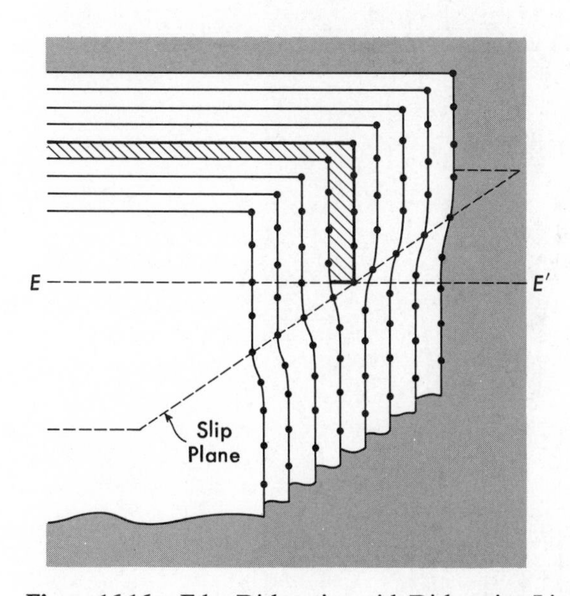

Figure 16.16. Edge Dislocation with Dislocation Line *EE′* in a Slip Plane

†Reproduced from W. T. Read, Jr., *Dislocations in Crystals*, New York: McGraw-Hill Book Co., Inc. 1953, Figures 10.3 and 10.4

working moves them about, increases their numbers, and complicates their interrelationships so that their separations may become about 10^2 A. Cold-working may lead to about 10^{12} dislocations cm^{-2}, while a good natural ionic crystal may have less than 10^8 dislocations cm^{-2}.

The screw dislocation is particularly important for the growth of a crystalline face. It always presents an edge one or a few atoms high. At this edge continued growth is easy. In view of the variety of imperfections that are possible, it is indeed startling that the very growth of the faces that tell much about the symmetry and order of crystal really depends upon a dislocation.

Dislocations, of course, are of great physical and chemical significance. Real crystals are generally ten to a million times weaker than theoretical calculations would predict; the mosaic flaws and dislocations are to blame. When really perfect single crystals of Fe, Si, and other substances (usually elements for uniformity of composition) have been grown, their strengths match theoretical expectations. However, a mere scratch on the surface may generate a dislocation in such a perfect crystal and greatly weaken it by allowing plastic flow to occur with ease. An example of such flow is shown in Figure 16.17, where an edge dislocation is viewed along its dislocation line. In a limited region, the dislocation line (the edge of the ragged bookmark) may be almost a

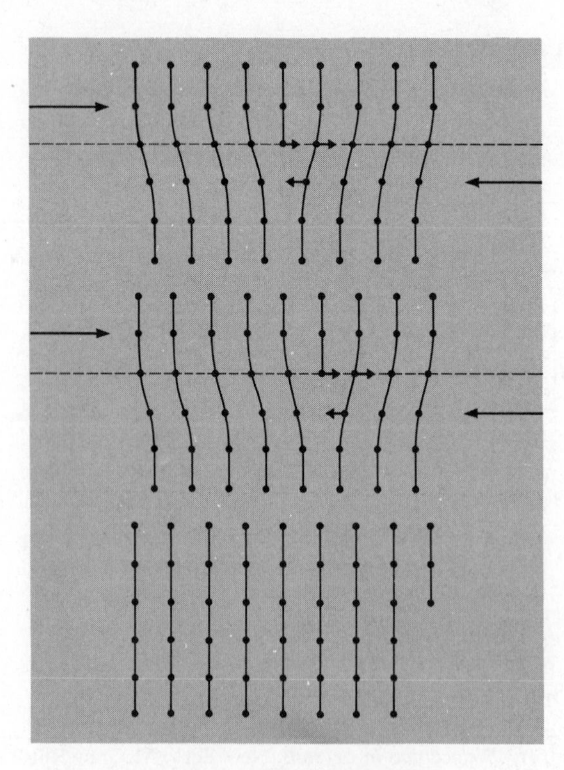

Figure 16.17. Slip at an Edge Dislocation

straight line. Any plane containing a segment of the dislocation line is a *slip plane*. The edge dislocation moves easily through a crystal because, as Figure 16.17 shows, motion in the slip plane involves only slight displacement of the structural elements. That is, the slip planes provide a low-energy intermediate state by which a crystal can be reorganized. Naturally they also provide weak spots in a crystal. The slip plane in a screw dislocation also contains the dislocation line, and slip adjusts the displacement per turn about the dislocation line. While slip is perpendicular to the dislocation line of an edge dislocation, slip is parallel to the dislocation line of a screw dislocation. Cold-working involves complicated slip at many dislocations that eventually become greatly entangled so that eventually slip is possible only for short distances without interruption by another dislocation.

Dislocations are sources of easy recrystallization during annealing and avenues of diffusion for chemical reaction. They are large-scale defects, sometimes identifiable with the mosaic structure, and the points at which chemicals attack the phalanx that is a crystal.

16.13 BODY-CENTERED CUBIC STRUCTURES

Twenty-three metallic elements crystallize in the body-centered cubic structure, some only at temperatures well removed from room temperature. In this type of structure, one atom occupies a lattice site and has eight equivalent nearest neighbors. Besides these eight, each atom has six other neighbors that are only slightly farther away along the directions of the cubic axes.

Distances between atoms in structures having all angles between axes equal to right angles are readily calculated by the Pythagorean theorem. Consider the body-centered cubic structure of Figure 16.18. In the plane of the front face,

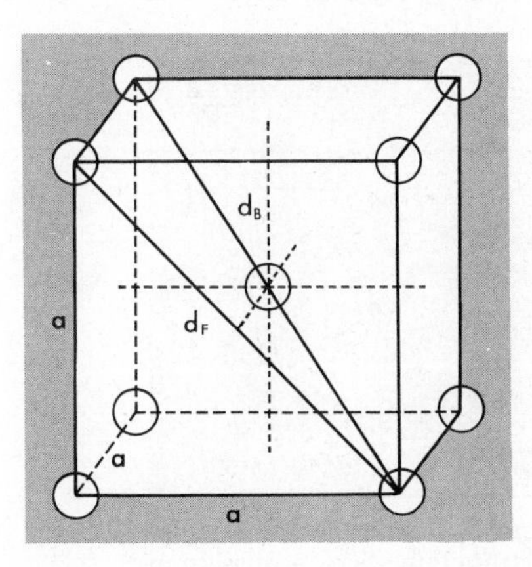

Figure 16.18. Body-Centered Cubic Unit Cell

the theorem of Pythagoras says that the length a of the edge of the unit cell is related to the length d_F of the face diagonal by the relation $d_F^2 = a^2 + a^2$. That is, $d_F = \sqrt{2}a$. The third axis, perpendicular to the front plane, is perpendicular to all lines in that plane; therefore, it is perpendicular to the face diagonal d_F. The lines labeled d_F and d_B in Figure 16.18 then form two of the three sides of a right triangle in which, according to Pythagoras, $d_B^2 = a^2 + d_F^2$. On elimination of d_F^2 through $d_F^2 = a^2 + a^2$, the length d_B of the body diagonal of the cube is related to a thus: $d_B^2 = a^2 + a^2 + a^2 = 3a^2$, or $d_B = \sqrt{3}a$. Although the shortest distance between atoms along lines parallel to the cubic axes is a, the shortest distance between atoms is $d_B/2$, or $\sqrt{3}a/2$.

If the atoms of a body-centered structure are conceived as spheres, knowledge of the size of the unit cell not only fixes the radius of the atom as $\sqrt{3}a/4$ but also fixes the fraction of the total volume that actually is occupied by the spheres. Each unit cell has a total volume of a^3 and contains two spheres, each of volume $4\pi r^3/3$. Since $r = \sqrt{3}a/4$, it follows at once that the ratio of occupied to total volume is

$$\frac{2\left(\frac{4}{3}\pi r^3\right)}{a^3} = \frac{\frac{8}{3}\pi\left(\frac{\sqrt{3}}{4}a\right)^3}{a^3} = \frac{\pi\sqrt{3}}{8} = 0.680$$

Only about 68% of the volume is actually occupied by identical spheres packed according to a body-centered cubic lattice.

Unit cell dimensions of some elements that crystallize with the body-centered cubic structure are listed in Table 16.4. Note the accuracy that has been attained for tungsten. Indeed, accurate measurement of unit cell dimensions at various temperatures is a method of evaluating the coefficient of expansion. This method is particularly valuable for polycrystalline substances because in non-

Table 16.4 Dimensions of Body-Centered Cubic Unit Cells†

Element	Temperature (°C)	Dimension (a) A
Cr	25	2.8839
α-Fe	25	2.8665
β-Fe	800	2.91
δ-Fe	1425	2.94
K	−268	5.225
K	−195	5.247
Na	20	4.2906
Ta	25	3.3058
V	25	3.0240
W	25	3.16469

† R. W. G. Wyckoff, *Crystal Structures* (Second Edition) Vol. 1. New York: Interscience Publishers, a division of John Wiley and Sons, Inc. © 1963, p. 16.

cubic systems the coefficient of expansion differs in different crystallographic directions.

There are many structures based upon a body-centered cubic lattice that have more than one atom at each lattice site: alloys, oxides, nitrides, sulfides, and so on. Among the organic compounds which have a whole molecule at each lattice site in a body-centered cubic lattice are hexamethylene tetramine and tetramethylorthothiocarbonate III.

Example 16.4. With the aid of Table 16.4, calculate the density of β-Fe at 800°C and the apparent radius of Fe in β-Fe at 800°C.

According to (16.9) with $M = 55.85$ for Fe, with $Z = 2$ for its I lattice with sites at 000 and $\frac{1}{2}\frac{1}{2}\frac{1}{2}$, and with $v = a^3$, the density of β-Fe at 800°C is

$$\rho = \frac{2 \times 55.85}{0.602 \times 10^{24}(2.91 \times 10^{-8})^3} = 7.53 \text{ g cm}^{-3}$$

Since the radius of touching spheres in the I lattice is $a\sqrt{3}/4$, the radius of Fe in β-Fe at 800°C is

$$r = \frac{2.91 \times 10^{-8}\sqrt{3}}{4} = 1.26 \times 10^{-8} \text{ cm} = 1.26 \text{ A}$$

16.14 THE CESIUM CHLORIDE STRUCTURE

The structure of CsCl, shown in Figure 16.19, would appear at first sight to be body-centered cubic. However, CsCl is really primitive cubic because the species at $\frac{1}{2}\frac{1}{2}\frac{1}{2}$ differs from that at 000. Elements clearly do not take this structure. About 35 alloys of two elements and about 15 ionic substances like CsCl have this structure. Each species is surrounded by 8 nearest neighbors of the other kind arranged at the corners of a cube. The eight gray Cl^- about Cs^+ are obvious

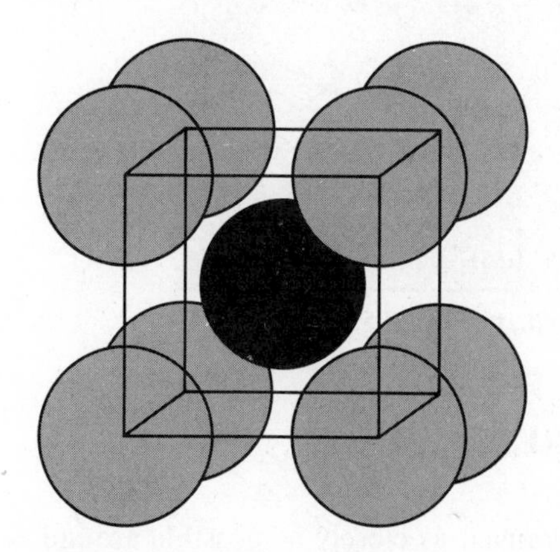

Figure 16.19. Unit Cell of CsCl

in Figure 16.19, and the eight black Cs^+ about one of the Cl^- lie at $\frac{1}{2}\frac{1}{2}\frac{1}{2}$ in the eight unit cells that meet at Cl^-.

This structural type presents a theoretical limit of interest with regard to ionic sizes and packing. If the anions with radii r_- are regarded as touching as spheres, then the edge of the unit cell is $a = 2r_-$. The body diagonal has the length $a\sqrt{3}$, as shown above. If the cations of radii r_+ are of such size as just to touch the 8 touching anions without disturbing them, then along the body-diagonal $2(r_+ + r_-) = a\sqrt{3}$. Elimination of a from this and $a = 2r_-$ yields $r_+ + r_- = \sqrt{3}\,r_-$, whence

$$\frac{r_+}{r_-} = \sqrt{3} - 1 = 0.7321 \tag{16.14}$$

This ratio marks the theoretical limit of stability of ionic structures of the CsCl type. If r_+ is smaller, the cation may rattle around in its void among anions, the differently charged ions will not generally be as close as their electrical attraction might otherwise place them, and the anions will be touching and repelling each other. On the other hand, if r_+ exceeds the limit (16.14), then the anion-anion repulsions are eased and the cation-anion contacts are as close as possible with no rattling about. Thus, the CsCl-type structure is expected to be stable if r_+/r_- exceeds $\sqrt{3} - 1$, provided ions can be assigned meaningful radii. Fortunately, they can. Table 16.5 lists cell dimensions of a few substances with the CsCl type structure.

Table 16.5 Dimensions of Cubic Unit Cells of Substances Like CsCl†

Substance	Dimension (a) (A)	Temp.
CsCl	4.123	25°C
CsBr	4.286	
CsI	4.5667	20°C
TlCl	3.8340	
TlBr	3.97	
TlI	4.198	
NH_4Cl	3.8756	26°C
CuZn	2.945	
AgCd	3.33	
AgZn	3.156	
AlNi	2.881	

† R. W. G. Wyckoff, *loc. cit.*, pp. 104–105.

16.15 CLOSE-PACKED SPHERES

If identical coins or golf balls are arranged as closely as possible around each other in a plane, each unit of the planar array that results has six nearest neighbors. The sixfold rotation axis characteristic of the hexagonal system is at once evident in Figure 16.20. This type of array can be extended indefinitely in all directions with each unit's assuming a role identical to any other unit.

A planar array of close-packed spheres becomes a three-dimensional close-packed array by the addition of layers above (and below) the first layer. Among each triplet of spheres in a layer there is a hollow into which a fourth sphere can nestle, as a cannon ball does among three that support it in display. Once this first sphere of the new layer is set in place, all others in its layer naturally fall into place in similar hollows in the layer below. This newly created second layer is also close-packed; it is shown shaded in Figure 16.21.

A third layer can be added to the second just as the second was added to the first. A twofold choice of hollow now exists; either the initial layer can be repeated as the third layer as in Figure 16.21(a), or a third layer [black in Figure 16.21(b)] can be generated over the hollows in the first layer that were

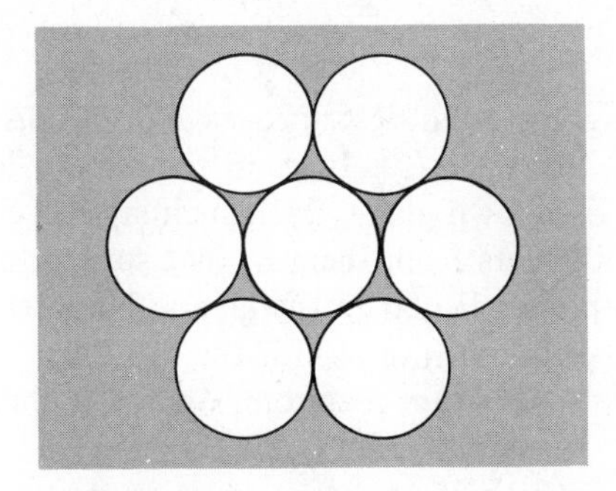

Figure 16.20. Close-Packing in a Plane

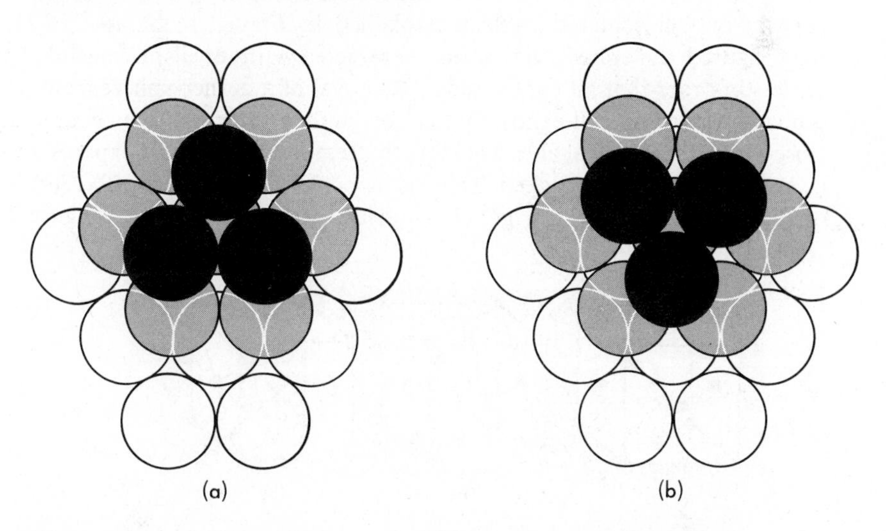

Figure 16.21. Close-Packed Layers of Identical Close-Packed Spheres

never populated when the second layer was added. Both types of array are close-packed because each is built of close-packed layers that fit into each other as four cannon balls do when stacked for display. Yet the two arrays differ in the third layer as a trigonal prism differs from a trigonal antiprism in Figure 16.22.

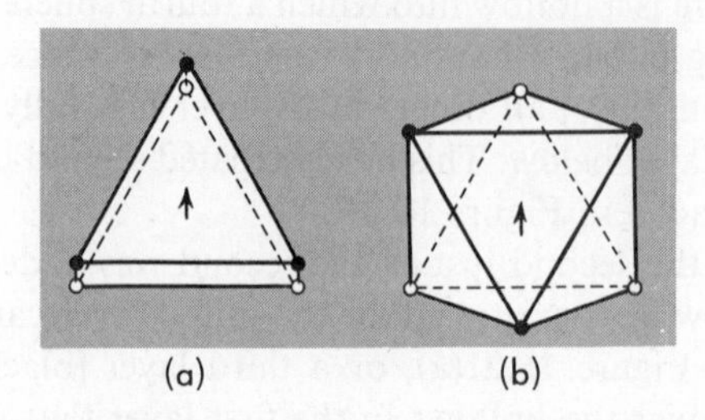

Figure 16.22. Trigonal Prism and Antiprism Viewed Almost Along Threefold Axes

These two types of close packing are often described as ABABABA ··· for type (a) and ABCABCABCA··· for type (b). In each sequence a letter indicates a layer that is close-packed in its own plane. Each such layer is close-packed relative to adjacent layers but differs from them in that superposition requires more than just a translation perpendicular to the layers. The first two layers, which differ, are AB. The two choices (a) or (b) for the third layer lead to A, which is directly above the first layer atom for atom, or to C, which is directly above neither A nor B.

The sequence ABABABA··· in which every other layer is repeated is *hexagonal close packing*. That the sequence ABCABCABCA··· is *cubic close packing* or face-centered cubic is explained in Figure 16.23 and 16.24. (In these figures, the spheres have been contracted without displacement of their centers in order that all can be seen.) Removal of a corner sphere from a face-centered cubic unit cell exposes its hollow among three (at face centers) and a close-packed layer parallel to a (111) face. Removal of those six exposes another layer that is also close-packed. This last exposed layer in Figure 16.23(c) is one of the eight faces of the trigonal antiprism of Figure 16.22(b). Figure 16.24

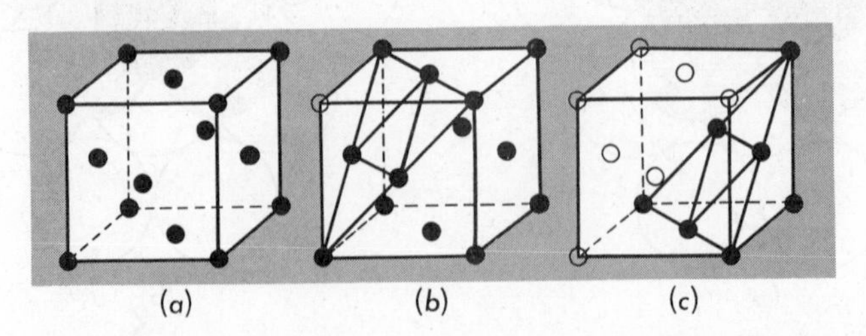

Figure 16.23. Close-Packed Layers in Face-Centered Cubic Structure

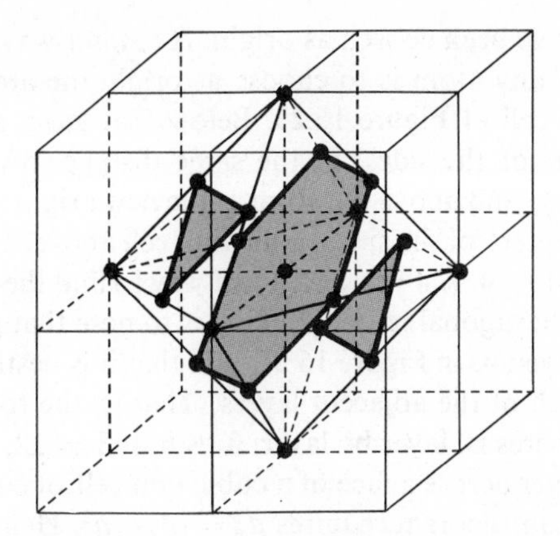

Figure 16.24. Close-Packed Layers in Face-Centered Cubic Unit Cells

illustrates the orientation and size of this trigonal antiprism (which is really an octahedron) as it exists in eight face-centered cubic unit cells. Each edge of the octahedron has halfway along it a sphere from the center of a unit-cell face. Spheres occupy all its corners and its center. A plane through the center and parallel to any of the octahedral faces has six spheres close-packed around the central sphere, as in Figure 16.20.

Each atom in a face-centered cubic structure has 12 equivalent nearest neighbors. The 12 atoms closest to the atom at the origin in Figure 16.25 are at the centers of the 12 faces that meet at the origin. The same environment obtains

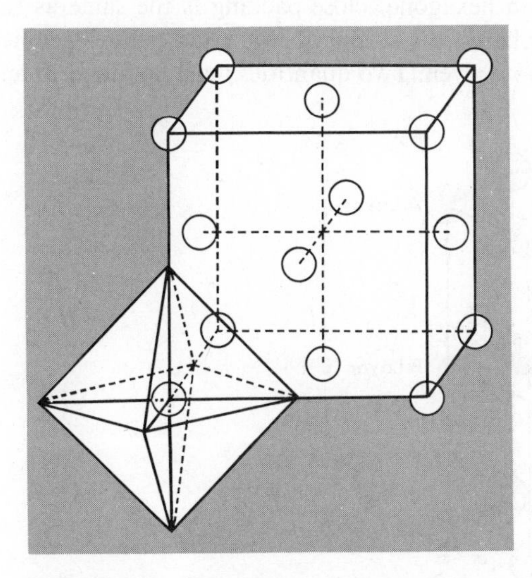

Figure 16.25. Face-Centered Cubic Unit Cell with the Twelve Planar Faces that Meet at a Point

at all lattice points, for each could have been chosen as origin. A second way to describe the 12 nearest neighbors of any atom is to choose as origin the atom that centers the top face of the unit cell of Figure 16.25. Below that atom are four equidistant atoms at the centers of the sides; at the same distance away are four more atoms at the top corners; and above the atom at the new origin are four more equidistant atoms at the centers of the sides of the unit cell above. The total number of equidistant atoms is $4 + 4 + 4 = 12$. A third way to find the 12 nearest neighbors in cubic (and also hexagonal) close-packing is to note that six are close-packed about it in its own layer, as in Figure 16.21, and that it is nestled like a cannonball among three in each of the adjacent layers. That is, the total number of equidistant (touching) spheres is, layer by layer, $3 + 6 + 3 = 12$.

The distance from corner to corner across a face of a cubic unit cell of edge a is $d_F = a\sqrt{2}$, since the Pythagorean theorem requires $d_F^2 = a^2 + a^2$. Hence, the distance between the centers of nearest neighbors is $\sqrt{2}a/2$. If the atoms are thought of as rigid spheres in contact, their radii are $\sqrt{2}a/4$. Since there are four lattice sites per unit cell, the ratio of the volume of these four spheres to the volume of the unit cell is

$$\frac{4\left(\frac{4}{3}\pi r^3\right)}{a^3} = \frac{\frac{16\pi}{3}\left(\frac{\sqrt{2}a}{4}\right)^3}{a^3} = \frac{\sqrt{2}\pi}{6} = 0.741$$

About 74% of the volume is actually occupied by identical speres close-packed according to a face-centered cubic lattice.

Although it should be intuitively obvious that the fraction of the volume actually occupied by spheres in hexagonal close-packing is the same as for a face-centered cubic array of spheres, the straightforward but tedious geometrical exercise of proving this is now given. Two quantities must be found in terms

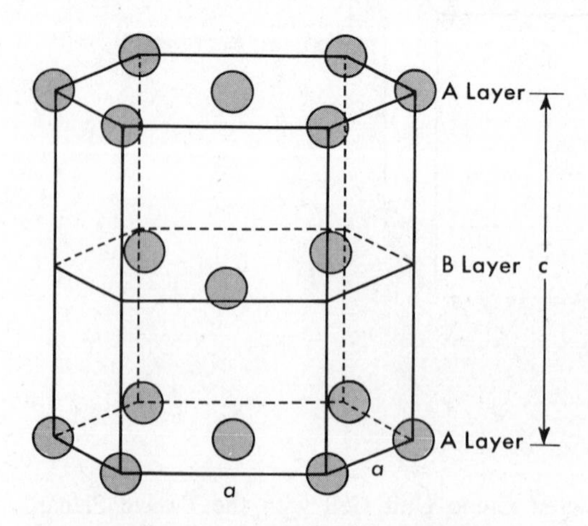

Figure 16.26. Hexagonal Close-Packing

of the radius of the identical spheres: the area of the hexagonal base of the prism of Figure 16.26 and its altitude c. The altitude is just twice the distance from the center of a sphere to the plane of the three that are in contact with it. This distance ($c/2$) is readily found by reference to a face-centered cubic lattice with unit cell length a. In such a lattice, the distance between close-packed layers is one-third of the body diagonal, or $\sqrt{3}\,a/3$, and the radius of the close-packed spheres is one-fourth of the face diagonal, or $\sqrt{2}\,a/4$. That is, in the hexagonal lattice of Figure 16.26 as well, the distance between layers is $c/2 = \sqrt{3}\,a/3$, and $r = a\sqrt{2}/4$ is the sphere radius. Elimination of a yields

$$c = \frac{2\sqrt{3}}{3}a = \frac{2\sqrt{3}}{3} \times \frac{4r}{\sqrt{2}} = \frac{8}{\sqrt{6}}r$$

The hexagonal base consists of six equilateral triangles each with side $2r$. Since the altitude of each of these triangles is $\sqrt{3}\,r$, the area of each triangle is $\frac{1}{2}(\sqrt{3}\,r)(2r)$, and the area of the hexagonal base is $6\sqrt{3}\,r^2$. The volume of the prism of Figure 16.26 is, then, $24\sqrt{2}\,r^3$.

The hexagonal prism contains several spheres. The three in the B layer are wholly within the prism. One of the two at the centers of the bases is to be ascribed to the prism. And of the 12 at the corners, two are to be ascribed to the prism shown because only one-sixth of each is within the prism. There are, then, effectively six spheres per prism. The fraction of the volume of the prism actually occupied by the sphere is thus

$$\frac{6\left(\frac{4}{3}\pi r^3\right)}{24\sqrt{2}\,r^3} = \frac{\sqrt{2}\,\pi}{6} = 0.741$$

This is the same value found for a face-centered cubic structure of identical spheres. Both are close-packed.

16.16 STRUCTURES BASED ON CLOSE-PACKING

Close-packing of spheres is important because it offers a simple and widely applicable standard of reference for many, many structures. Most of the structures so described are not perfectly close-packed, but comparison to such an ideal aids the memory, passes over details that may be of interest to a few expert crystallographers, and emphasizes structural similarities even between crystals of different systems. Close-packing unites a subject teeming with details and exceptions.

Thirty or so elements crystallize with the face-centered cubic unit cell of Figures 16.23 or 16.25. Among these are Ne, Ar, Kr, and Xe, but not He, which is hexagonal close-packed. The relative stabilities of cubic and hexagonal close-packing involve delicate differences in interactions among next-to-nearest neighbors. For example,[6] although Ar is cubic close-packed when pure, it happens that crystals of Ar containing only 1% N_2 in solid solution, with N_2 molecules replacing Ar molecules, are hexagonal close-packed if liquid Ar containing N_2 is present. The change to hexagonal may be induced by the slight increase in volume attendant on introduction of N_2 molecules, which act as though they are slightly larger than Ar molecules. It is worth noting also that N_2 brings with it a preferred direction and that hexagonal crystals are nonisotropic while cubic ones are isotropic. Other diatoms also do what N_2 does to crystals of Ar.

Table 16.6 Dimensions of Face-Centered Cubic Unit Cells†

Element	Temperature (°C)	Dimension (a) A
Ag		4.0862
Al	25	4.04958
Ca		5.576
Cu	18	3.61496
γ-Fe	22	3.5910
Ni	25	3.52387
Pt	25	3.9231

† R. W. G. Wyckoff, *loc. cit.*, p. 10

Table 16.6 lists the unit cell sizes of a few of the elements that crystallize with one atom at each lattice site of F cubic lattice, which is of course close-packed.

Substances that crystallize in a structure based on the face-centered cubic lattice and have more than one atom per lattice site are quite common: halides of group I elements; sulfides, selenides, and tellurides of group II elements; phosphides and arsenides of group III elements; perchlorates; methane; alloys; ferricyanides and related species; diamond; many ionic oxides; and many other

Table 16.7 Dimensions of Hexagonal Unit Cells of Elements†

Element	Temperature (°C)	a (A)	c (A)
β-Ca	450.	3.98	6.52
Cd	26.	2.97887	5.61765
Cr		2.722	4.427
Mg	25.	3.20927	5.21033
Ti	25.	2.950	4.686
Zn	25.	2.6648	4.9467

† R. W. G. Wyckoff, *loc. cit.*, p. 11.

(6) C. S. Barrett and L. Meyer, *J. Chem. Phys.* **42**, 107 (1965).

types of substances. Of these, the structures of NaCl, CaF_2 and ZnS are described in detail below.

Table 16.7 lists the dimensions of the unit cells of some elements that crystallize in a lattice that is at least approximately hexagonal close-packing. Ideally, for a nonprimitive cell like the hexagonal prism of Figure 16.26, the ratio of the altitude c to the edge of the hexagonal cell a is

$$\frac{c}{a} = \frac{8r/\sqrt{6}}{2r} = \frac{2\sqrt{6}}{3} = 1.63299\cdots \tag{16.15}$$

Most of the elements listed in Table 16.7 deviate from this ideal axial ratio because bonds to neighbors in adjacent layers differ in strength and length from those to neighbors in the same layer. It is interesting to note, however, that the ratio c/a remains fixed at the ideal value (16.15) when a little N_2 changes Ar to hexagonal close-packing and that the lattice parameters c and a are linear functions of the mole fraction of N_2 at 22°K.[7]

Identical spheres can be close-packed in only two ways, cubic and hexagonal, if each sphere of such an array is to exist in an environment identical to those of all other spheres. There are, however, many different close-packed arrays in which the environments of spheres may differ. The arrangement ABACABAC··· is close-packed; but the spheres in the A layers are in a cubic environment because immediately adjacent layers differ, while spheres in the B or C layers are in a hexagonal environment, immediately adjacent layers being both A. Many other close-packed arrays are possible. Indeed, the sequence of layers of types A, B, and C in elemental cobalt may be random.

Whether or not a particular complex structure is considered to be based upon close-packing depends upon the degree of perfection expected in the close-packing and also upon the view taken of the structure. Many complex halides, oxides, hydroxides, and sulfides are very simply described in terms of approximately close-packed anions with smaller cations in the voids. These cations generally disturb the packing because they do not quite fit into the interstices. It frequently happens that such disturbance is small and that the close-packed array is obvious in its general nature. Sometimes the relation to close-packing is unexpected: SnI_4, WCl_6, and UCl_6 can be thought of as close-packed halogen atoms with metal atoms arranged in just the right way so that individual molecules are preserved. The volatility, compressibility, and low melting points of these substances indicate that the crystals consist of molecules rather than ions. Sometimes the relation to close-packing is somewhat artificial: NaCl, ZnS, CaF_2, and TiO_2 can be considered to be based upon close packing of Cl^-, S^{--}, Ca^{++}, or O^{--}.

The inert gases are not the only molecular crystals that consists of close-packed molecules. Crystalline HCl, HBr, HI, H_2S, H_2Se, NH_3, CH_4, SiH_4, and H_2 are approximately close-packed. In these structures, the molecules are

(7) C. S. Barrett and L. Meyer, *ibid.*

generally freely rotating. These substances also exhibit at very low temperatures crystalline species in which rotation is restricted or absent.

Like the metallic elements, many alloys are best described in terms of close-packed atoms. Many carbides, nitrides, and hydrides are described very simply as solutions of N, C, and H atoms in the voids of cubic close-packed metallic atoms. But most important of all are the oxide systems. More than 90% of the volume of the lithosphere consists of oxide ions.[8] Most of these oxides are silicates and are described very simply as close-packed oxide ions containing ions of Si, Al, Fe, Mg, Ca, Na, K, Ti, H, and so forth. In order to understand these three important classes—alloys, interstititial solutions, and oxides—it is necessary to investigate the kinds, sizes, and numbers of voids in close-packed arrays; for it is in these voids that the small atoms or ions are considered to reside.

There are three kinds of void. The smallest is among three touching spheres and is in their plane. Figure 16.27 illustrates this trigonal void. The largest sphere of radius r_+ that can be inserted among three identical touching spheres of radius r_- is found thus. The centers of the three large spheres are at the corners of an equilateral triangle of side $2r_-$. The distance from the center of this triangle to a corner, $r_+ + r_-$, is the hypotenuse of a small right triangle with a side r_-. The third side of this small right triangle is $(r_+ + r_-)/2$ because it is opposite an angle of $\pi/6$. By the Pythagorean theorem, in this small triangle it follows that

$$(r_+ + r_-)^2 = \left(\frac{r_+ + r_-}{2}\right)^2 + r_-^2$$

Whence $3(r_+ + r_-)^2 = 4r_-^2$; $r_+ + r_- = 2r_-/\sqrt{3}$

$$\frac{r_+}{r_-} = \frac{2\sqrt{3} - 3}{3} = 0.1547 \qquad (16.16)$$

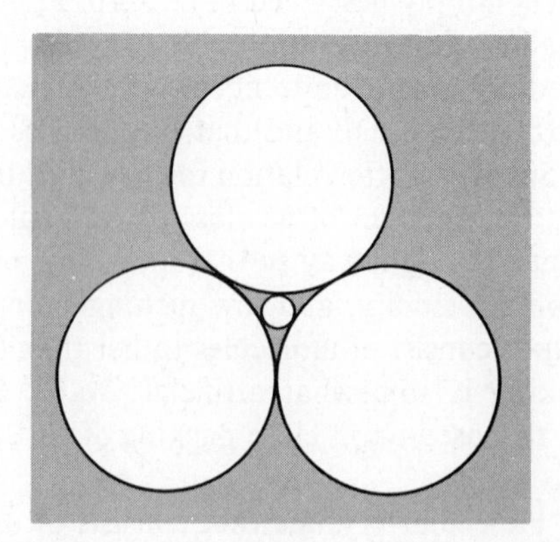

Figure 16.27. Trigonal Void Among Close-Packed Spheres

[8] Wells, A. F., *Structural Inorganic Chemistry*. New York: Oxford University Press, 1950, pp. 570, 375–85. By permission of the Clarendon Press, Oxford.

Only B^{+3} ion appears to occupy this type of void among oxide ions, and even then its coordination may be influenced by bonding that is covalent rather than ionic.

A somewhat larger void exists at the center of a tetrahedron whose corners are the centers of four identical touching spheres. This tetrahedral void exists among four cannon balls stacked for display. Between two close-packed layers there are two sets of such tetrahedral voids: one set is below the spheres of the upper layer in the hollows of triples of spheres in the lower layer; the second set is above the spheres of the lower layer under the hollows of triples of spheres in the upper layer. Since each of these two sets has one tetrahedral void per sphere per layer, there are twice as many voids of this kind as there are close-packed spheres.

The size of a tetrahedral void among close-packed anions of radius r_- is readily found from Figure 16.28, where the anions in gray are slightly shrunken for clarity. The length of the face diagonal of the reference cube of edge a is $4r_- = a\sqrt{2}$. In the one-eighth cube that has the black tetrahedrally coordinated cation of radius r_+ at its body center, the length of the body diagonal is $2(r_+ + r_-) = a\sqrt{3}/2$. Eliminating a from this and $4r_- = a\sqrt{2}$ yields $r_+ + r_- = r_-\sqrt{3/2}$; whence,

$$\frac{r_+}{r_-} = \sqrt{\frac{3}{2}} - 1 = 0.2247 \qquad (16.17)$$

At this limit the cation of radius r_+ just touches the four tetrahedrally situated and mutually touching spherical anions without disturbing them.

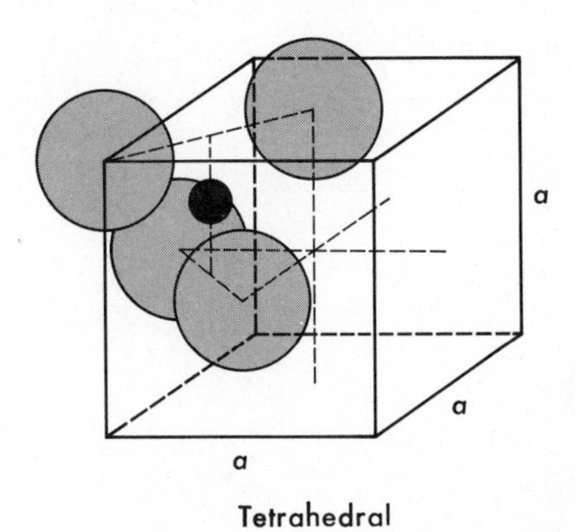

Figure 16.28. A Tetrahedral Void Among Close-Packed Spheres

Since the oxide ion has a radius of about 1.40 A, it would appear that ions of radius of about 0.32 A are the largest that such a void could accommodate. Actually, however, larger ions fill such voids because expansion attendant upon entry of ions with radii greater than 0.32 A relieves the coulombic repulsions between oxide ions. Ions of Li, Be, B, and Si, and sometimes of Al and Ge, can be accommodated in tetrahedral voids among close-packed oxide ions.

The largest void in close-packed identical spheres is octahedral, so called because the polyhedron that has its corners at the centers of the spheres that define the void is an octahedron. The center of this void is halfway between adjacent layers and is equally distant from three adjacent spheres in each layer. In Figures 16.29 and 16.30, which depict two close-packed layers, the octahedral voids are indicated by the black spheres. From their arrangement over the third type of position (C if the layers shown in Figure 16.30 are A and B), it is clear that the number of octahedral positions equals the number of close-packed spheres. The radius r_+ of the largest sphere that can be inserted into these octahedral voids without disturbing the close-packed spheres of radius r_- is readily calculated by reference to Figure 16.29. In this figure, the spheres are in cubic

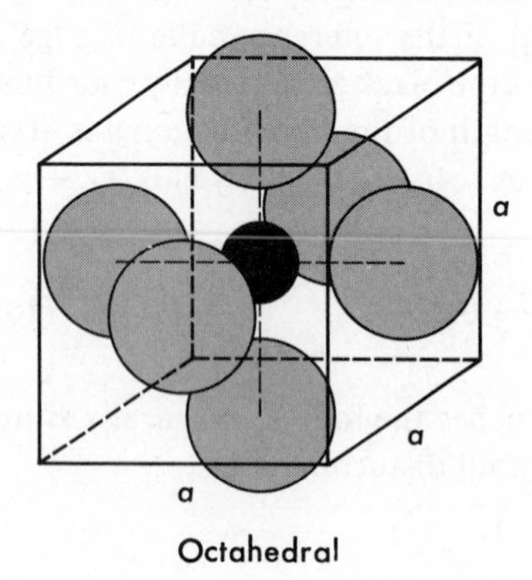

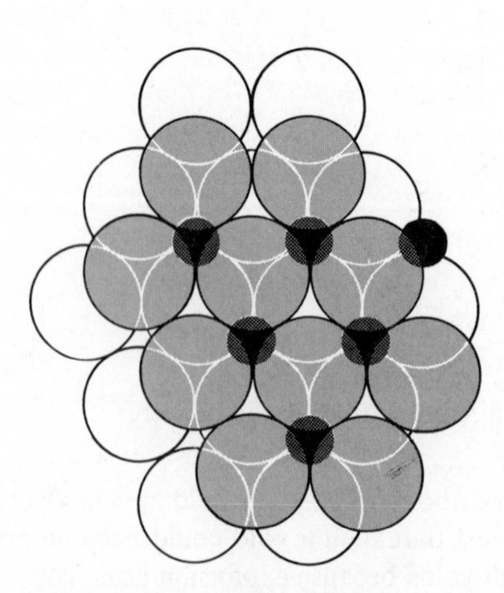

Figure 16.30. Octahedral Voids Among Close-Packed Spheres

close-packing. The centers of octahedral voids occur at the center of the cube and at the centers of the cell edges. Since r_- equals $\sqrt{2}/4$ times the cell edge, and since the cell edge equals $2(r_+ + r_-)$, it follows that

$$\frac{r_+}{r_-} = \sqrt{2} - 1 = 0.4142 \tag{16.18}$$

At this limit the cation of radius r_+ just touches the six octahedrally situated and close-packed spherical anions without disturbing them.

The largest cation that can fit among close-packed oxide ions each of radius 1.40 A is therefore 0.58 A. Cations with radii less than 0.58 A occupy tetrahedral positions because in so doing they cause the oxide ion array to expand, electrical repulsions among oxide ions thus being relieved. Cations with radii greater than 0.58 A occupy octahedral positions among oxide ions. [It has been shown in Section 16.14 that when (r_+/r_-) exceeds $\sqrt{3} - 1$, eight or more anions can pack around one cation. Hence, octahedral voids in close-packed oxide ions are occupied by cations with radii from 0.58A to 1.02 A.] Some ions that prefer octahedral voids among oxide ions are Al^{+3}, Fe^{+2}, Fe^{+3}, Mg^{+3}, Ca^{+2}, Na^{+}, Ti^{+4}, and, in fact, most ions of the transition elements.

Silicates can be thought of as close-packed arrays of oxide, hydroxide, and fluoride ions. The hydroxide and fluoride ions are almost the same size as the oxide ion. Silicon, with an ionic radius of about 0.40 A, always assumes a tetrahedral position. Although aluminum prefers an octahedral position, it may sometimes assume a tetrahedral position. Monovalent and divalent ions like Na^{+}, K^{+}, Mg^{+2}, Ca^{+2}, Fe^{+2}, and so on are present in numbers sufficient to render the whole assembly of ions electrically neutral. The enormous number of ways of packing anions and cations is matched by the great variety of known silicate minerals and synthetic silicates.

Besides the silicates, the three most important types of oxide have the structures characteristic of spinel, ilmenite, and perovskite. Important features of these types of mineral are listed in Table 16.8. From the formulas it is obvious that only part of the voids is filled. The examples listed have been chosen from among the 85 or more known spinels, the 14 substances known to be like ilmenite, and the 175 substances known to have structures like that of perovskite. Most of these perovskite-like structures are slightly distorted cubic structures. For example, $BaTiO_3$ is like perovskite, but is trigonal below −80°C, orthorhombic from −80°C to 0°C, tetragonal from 0°C to 120°C, and cubic above 120°C. These changes in symmetry are associated with its ferroelectric properties. Or again, $KMgF_3$ is monoclinic with cell edges of 8.02 A and β equal to about 91°.[9] The structure of $CaTiO_3$ itself is not quite the ideal cubic structure of perovskite in Figure 16.31. An interesting and lucid explanation of the natures of these three kinds of oxide is given by Wells.[10]

---

[9] Ludekens, W. L. W. and A. J. E. Welch, *Acta Crystallographica*, **5**, 841, 1952.
[10] Wells, *loc. cit.*

Table 16.8 Characteristics of Important Types of Oxide.

Characteristic	Name of Type		
	Spinel	Ilmenite	Perovskite
Formula	$MgAl_2O_4$	$FeTiO_3$	$CaTiO_3$
General Formula	AB_2O_4	ABO_3	ABO_3
Type of Close-Packing	Cubic	Slightly Distorted Hexagonal	Cubic
Close-Packed Species	O^{--}(or S^{--})	O^{--}	A; O^{--}(or F^-)
Species in Tetrahedral Voids	A	none	none
Species in Octahedral Voids	B	A, B	B
Examples	$FeAl_2O_4$ $MoAg_2O_4$ $ZnAl_2O_4$ WNa_2O_4 $FeCr_2O_4$ Fe_3O_4 $TiCo_2O_4$ $MnIn_2S_4$ VMg_2O_4 Ni_3S_4	$CoTiO_3$ $MgTiO_3$ Cr_2O_3 α-Al_2O_3 α-Fe_2O_3	$BaCeO_3$ $BaThO_3$ $LaFeO_3$ $NaWO_3$ $RbCaF_3$

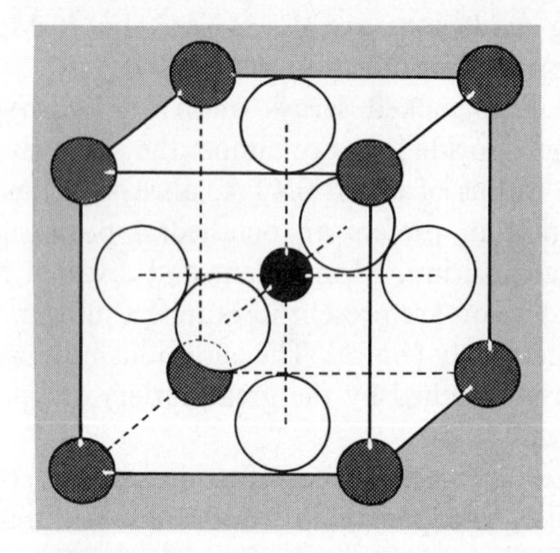

Figure 16.31. Ideal Perovskite Structure ABO_3 (A at 000; B at $\frac{1}{2}\frac{1}{2}\frac{1}{2}$; oxide at face centers)

16.17 COMMON STRUCTURAL TYPES

One of the simplest and most common structural types is that of NaCl. Hydrides halides, cyanides, and hydrosulfides of the alkali metals; oxides, sulfides, selenides, and tellurides of divalent metals, especially the alkaline earths; and many nitrides and carbides have this structure. (Halides of rubidium can be transformed from the NaCl- to CsCl-structure under pressures of several thousands of atmospheres.) Figure 16.32 shows the unit cell of this structural type. Except for the iodides, it is perhaps best not to classify the NaCl structure as close-packed anions with an equal number of cations in octahedral voids. The

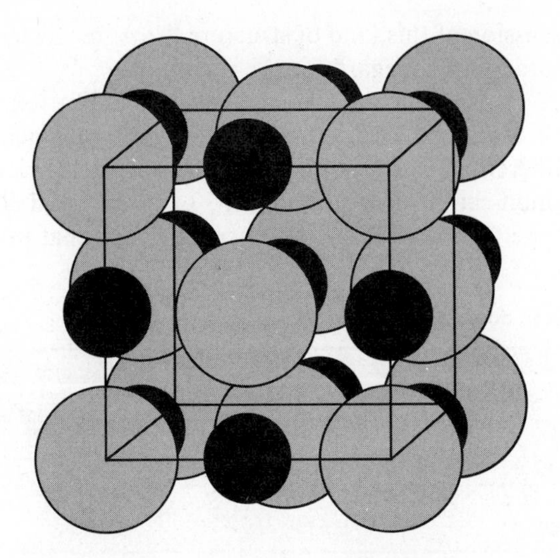

Figure 16.32. Cubic Unit Cell of NaCl

reasons are that the anions generally do not touch, and that such a view does little to simplify study of this highly symmetrical structure.

Table 16.9 lists unit cell dimensions of a few of the 100 or more substances known to have this simple structure. The simplicity of this arrangement has

Table 16.9 Dimensions of Cubic Unit Cells of Substances Like NaCl†

Substance	Temperature (°C)	Dimension (a) (A)
AgBr		5.7745
NaCl	18°C	5.63978
NaCl	26°C	5.64056
KF		5.347
KCl	25°C	6.29294
KBr	25°C	6.6000
KI	25°C	7.06555
CsCl	450°C	7.02
LiH		4.085
MgO	21°C	4.2112
CaO		4.8105
CdO	27°C	4.6953
MnO	26°C	4.4448
VN		4.128
LaN		5.295
UN		4.880
TiC		4.3186
VC		4.182
KCN	25°C	6.527

† R. W. G. Wyckoff, *loc. cit.*, pp. 86–91.

inspired much theoretical discussion of this kind of structure.[11] A few remarks on ionic radii are perhaps in order in this regard.

A glance at Figure 16.32 reveals that the distance between unlike ions is one-half the length of the cell edge. If the anions were either all in contact or all not in contact, regular differences in interionic distance would be obvious. The comparisons made of anion-cation distances in LiF, LiI, RbF, and RbI in Table 16.10 belie such a hope. The reason for the discrepancies is that in all

Table 16.10 Interionic Distances in Some Alkali Halides†

Anion / Cation	Fluoride	Iodide	Difference
Lithium	2.01 A	3.02 A	1.01 A
Rubidium	2.82 A	3.66 A	0.84 A
Difference	0.81 A	0.64 A	Anion / Cation

† Pauling L., *The Nature of the Chemical Bond.* Ithaca, N. Y.: Cornell University Press, 1960, p. 520.

halides of lithium except LiF, the halide ions are in direct contact. The lithium ion thus lies loose in its octahedral void among close-packed anions. But if the iodide ions in LiI are close-packed, their radii are then equal to $\sqrt{2}/4$ times the length of the face-centered cubic unit cell. In 1920, Landé proposed this simple method of calculating the radius of an iodide ion and thus of apportioning to anion and cation their proper shares of the interionic distance. The radius calculated for iodide in this way is 2.13 A. A more commonly accepted value calculated in another way is 2.16 A.

With a value of the radius of iodide ion, simple subtraction from 3.66 A for the $Rb^+ - I^-$ distance yields a rubidium ion radius of 1.50 A. Next, from the $Rb^+ - F^-$ distance of 2.82 A and the value of 1.50 A for Rb^+, the fluoride ion's radius is expected to be 1.32 A. When such calculations are done systematically for all the alkali halides having the NaCl arrangement, it is clear that radii are not quite additive. Various adjustments with theoretical bases can be made, however, that yield agreement to within about 0.001 A.[11]

An example of the difficulties involved is shown in LiF, for which the observed interionic distance is somewhat large. This expansion is attributed to double repulsion, for the radius ratio is so close to the critical $\sqrt{2} - 1$ of (16.18) that both anions and cations are almost in contact. Each repels its own kind vigorously.

The radius ratio limits of (16.14) to (16.18) are theoretically exact, but the NaCl-type structure refuses to be bound by its limits at 0.4142 and 0.7321. Of

[11] See, for example, Pauling, L., *The Nature of the Chemical Bond.* Ithaca, N. Y.: Cornell University Press, 1960, Chapter 13.

the alkali halides with the NaCl structure, only about half fit the limits. The lower actual limit seems to be 0.28 for LiI, and the upper real limit seems to be 0.81, which is r_+/r_- for RbCl and is r_-/r_+ for CsF. However, KF has r_+/r_- equal to 0.98 and RbF has a value of 1.09. Why the NaCl-type structure has such a large range of observed radius ratios is not known. The NaCl and CsCl structures are, however, the only reasonable and simple possibilities for symmetrical crystalline packing of ions, and, as the pressure-induced transformations of RbX suggest, their energies are not greatly different. The NaCl-type structure is capable also of entertaining up to about 25% ion vacancies of either kind in defect structures of various transition-metal oxides. Perhaps the common imperfections can find suitable abodes in NaCl more readily than in other standard types so that NaCl usurps their domains of stability.

The salient feature of the NaCl structure is that each ion is surrounded octahedrally by six of the opposite kind. The coordination number is said to be six.

It is easy to describe the $CdCl_2$ type structure relative to NaCl, if NaCl is viewed as cubic close-packed Cl^- with Na^+ in all octahedral voids. The formula $CdCl_2$ clearly requires that half of the available octahedral voids be vacant if the Cl^- are close-packed. Actually, $CdCl_2$ is like NaCl with alternate (111) layers of octahedral voids free of cations. Viewed perpendicular to (111) planes, which parallel the close-packed layers of Figure 16.30, $CdCl_2$ is seen as a layer structure with Cd^{2+} in octahedral voids within a pair of close-packed Cl^- layers and with van der Waals contacts between Cl^- ions from adjacent Cl-Cd-Cl sandwiches. Some of the 20 or so substances that are known to follow more or less closely the $CdCl_2$ arrangement are $ZnCl_2$, $ZnBr_2$, ZnI_2, $CdCl_2$, $CdBr_2$, $MgCl_2$, and many dihalides of Fe, Co, and Ni. Ideally, the radius ratio limits are 0.4142 and 0.7321 as for NaCl.

Besides NaCl, another very important structural type involving anions close-packed at cubic positions is the cubic form of ZnS, called sphalerite or zinc blende. The Zn^{2+} occupy half of the tetrahedral voids among cubic close-packed S^{2-}. If the sulfides are at 000, $\frac{1}{2}\frac{1}{2}0$, $\frac{1}{2}0\frac{1}{2}$, and $0\frac{1}{2}\frac{1}{2}$ as in a cubic F lattice, then Zn^{2+} are at $\frac{1}{4}\frac{1}{4}\frac{1}{4}$, $\frac{3}{4}\frac{3}{4}\frac{1}{4}$, $\frac{3}{4}\frac{1}{4}\frac{3}{4}$, and $\frac{1}{4}\frac{3}{4}\frac{3}{4}$. That is, the Zn^{2+} positions are displaced from S^{2-} positions by $\frac{1}{4}\frac{1}{4}\frac{1}{4}$ and thus find themselves in cubic close-packed positions. In other words, each kind of ion is electrically close-packed relative to its own kind and is immediately surrounded by four equidistant ions of the opposite kind. Figure 16.33 shows the unit cell of ZnS (with axial order for the Zn^{2+} positions listed above being to the right, rear, up).

The sphalerite structure is found for almost 40 compounds, among which are: SiC; AgI; halides of Cu^+; sulfides, selenides, and tellurides of divalent metals like Zn, Cd, and Hg; and certain nitrides, phosphides, arsenides, and stibnides of trivalent metals like Al and Ga. Diamond (as well as Si, Ge, and gray Sn) has the sphalerite structure if all 8 sites of Zn and S are occupied by one kind of atom. The series CuBr, ZnSe, GaAs, Ge from one row of the periodic table indicates that there is a nearly continuous range of bonding character from possibly ionic ZnS to surely covalent C. Hence, the bonding in these

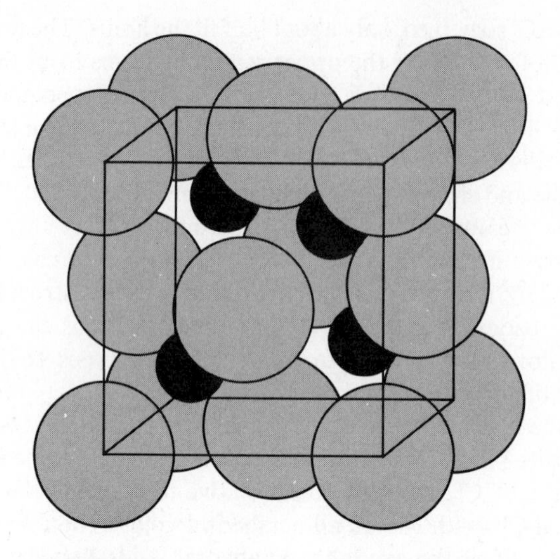

Figure 16.33. Cubic Unit Cell of ZnS (Sphalerite)

structures may be covalent, even for ZnS. If it is ionic, the ideal radius ratio limits are 0.2247 and 0.4142; if covalent, then sp^3 tetrahedral hybridization dominates the arrangement.

Sets of covalent or ionic radii for all the substances of this kind are very simply derived from the observed interatomic distances. Predicted and observed distances agree within about 0.02 A. Values of this kind as derived by Pauling and Huggins are listed in Table 16.11. The interatomic distances r predicted from this table are related to the edge a of the cubic unit cell by the Pythagorean theorem thus:

Table 16.11 Tetrahedral Covalent Radii (A)†

	Be 1.06	B 0.88	C 0.77	N 0.70	O 0.66	F 0.64
	Mg 1.40	Al 1.26	Si 1.17	P 1.10	S 1.04	Cl 0.99
Cu 1.35	Zn 1.31	Ga 1.26	Ge 1.22	As 1.18	Se 1.14	Br 1.11
Ag 1.52	Cd 1.48	In 1.44	Sn 1.40	Sb 1.36	Te 1.32	I 1.28
	Hg 1.48					

† Pauling, L., *The Nature of the Chemical Bond*. Ithaca, N. Y.: Cornell University Press, 1960, p. 246.

$$r^2 = \left(\frac{a}{4}\right)^2 + \left(\frac{a}{4}\right)^2 + \left(\frac{a}{4}\right)^2 = \frac{3a^2}{16}; \qquad r = \frac{\sqrt{3}}{4}a$$

The structures of $ZnBr_2$ and HgI_2 are probably ionic with halide ions nearly cubically close-packed and cations organized in one-fourth of the tetrahedral sites. That is, $ZnBr_2$ and HgI_2 are like sphalerite without half of its cation sites populated. There are also structures with one kind of ion cubically close-packed as in sphalerite, but with all tetrahedral voids occupied by oppositely charged ions. These are discussed below as the fluorite (CaF_2) type structure.

Wurtzite is ZnS with sulfides hexagonally close-packed and zinc ions in half of the tetrahedral voids in an organized way. About 25 compounds are known to have this structure; among them are ZnO, ZnS, ZnSe, ZnTe, CdS, AgI, SiC, GaN. The oxygen atoms of ice occupy both the Zn and S positions of wurtzite. Each oxygen has two covalently bonded H's pointed directly toward neighboring O's to form hydrogen bonds and has two H's from other water molecules pointed towards itself in hydrogen bonds. Thus, along each O–O line there is a proton closer to one O than the other. Many orientations of the H_2O's are possible and ordinarily realized. The packing and symmetry of ice is dominated by the hydrogen bonds. The O–H single-bond distance is about 1.00 A while the O···O distance in ice is 2.76 A; hence, the length of the hydrogen bond is 1.76 A. A few dihalides MX_2 are also like wurtzite with half of its cation positions empty; that is, these dihalides have X^- hexagonally close-packed and one-fourth of the tetrahedral voids occupied by cations M^{2+}.

Besides NaCl and ZnS, a third very important structural type is that of NiAs. Ideally, the As atoms are hexagonally close-packed in the sequence ABABABA··· and the Ni atoms occupy all octahedral voids halfway between these layers, the sequence of close-packed atoms being ACBCACBCACBCA··· if the Ni are considered to be, instead, part of the close-packed array and are labeled C. The Ni layers are all C type and thus lie directly over each other atom by atom of Ni. The As atoms are surrounded by six Ni at the corners of a trigonal prism and the Ni atoms are each surrounded by six As at the corners of a trigonal antiprism, an octahedron being a trigonal antiprism with all edges equal in length.

Over 50 substances have the NiAs arrangement in a general sort of way. This structural type is somewhat variable in its axial ratio c/a and readily accommodates many atomic vacancies. That is, the formula AB is an ideal seldom achieved by real crystals of this type. Substances with this structure are typically 3*d*-transition metals combined with S, Se, Te, As, Sb, or Sn.

The structure of CdI_2 may be viewed as NiAs with half of its Ni positions vacant. That is, CdI_2 may be compared to hexagonally close-packed I^- with Cd^{2+} in half of the octahedral voids. The Cd^{2+} ions are arranged in layers perpendicular to the sixfold axis. The sequence of occupied positions, without distinction between differing ions, is ACBACBACBACBA··· as in Figure 16.34 with C positions occupied by Cd^{2+}.

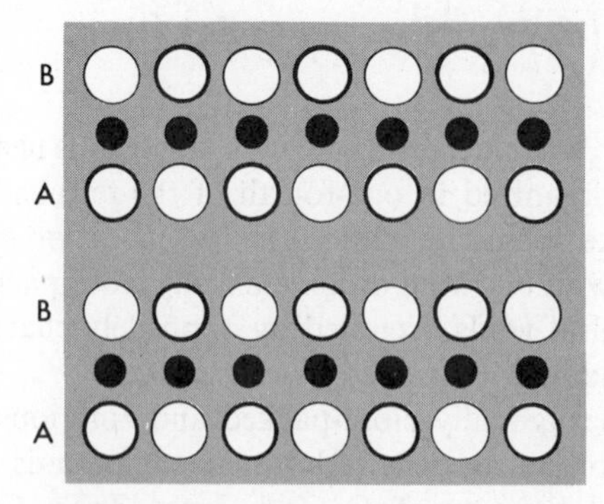

Figure 16.34. Layers in CdI_2 Viewed Perpendicular to the Sixfold Axis

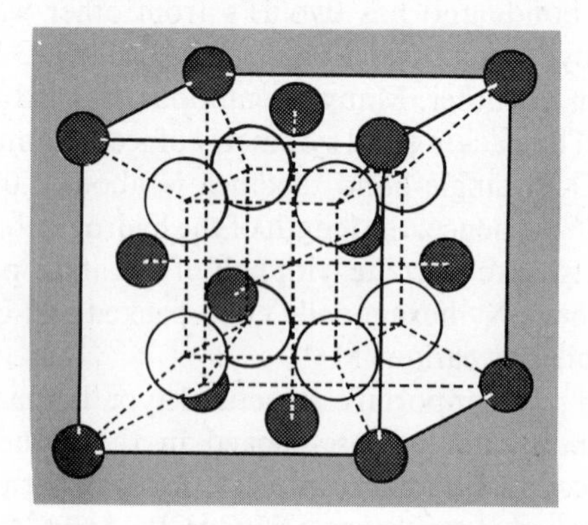

Figure 16.35. Cubic Unit Cell of CaF_2

Besides NaCl, ZnS, and NiAs, a fourth very important type of structure is that of CaF_2. Figure 16.35 shows that each F^- is surrounded by 4 Ca^{2+} at tetrahedral angles. It also shows that the Ca^{2+} are at face-centered cubic positions, as though the highly charged cations were close-packed to minimize their mutual electrical repulsions in a milieu of anions, just as billiard balls become close-packed to minimize their mutual volume repulsions in space. Actually the F^- are larger in volume than the Ca^{2+}, as shown in Figure 16.35, where the fluorides are white. A consideration of that figure also shows that each Ca^{2+} is surrounded by 8 equidistant F^- ions. Thus the structure of CaF_2 is like CsCl with half of the Cs^+ positions vacant checkerboard-fashion in three dimensions. As for CsCl, the critical lower limit to the radius ratio is expected to be 0.7321, a limit that is well respected.

The substances that are known to crystallize with this structure are: about ten fluorides of metals having rather large divalent ions; about 15 oxides of metals having rather large quadrivalent ions; about ten oxyfluorides of trivalent metals; a few chlorides, nitrides, and complex fluorides; about 15 alloys; oxides, sulfides, selenides, and tellurides of the alkali metals in which the roles of cation and anion are interchanged from their roles in CaF_2 (the so-called antifluorite structure was referred to at the end of the sphalerite discussion); and a few other types of substance. Unit cell dimensions of a few of these substances are listed in Table 16.12.

Table 16.12 Dimensions of Cubic Unit Cells of Substances Like CaF_2†

Substance	Dimension (a) (A)	Temperature (°C)
CaF_2	5.46295	28°C
SrF_2	5.7996	26°C
BaF_2	6.2001	25°C
β-PbF_2	5.92732	18°C
ThO_2	5.5997	
UO_2	5.4682	26°C
$SiMg_2$	6.39	
$SnMg_2$	6.765	
K_2O	6.436	

† R. W. G. Wyckoff, *loc. cit.*, p. 241.

When the radius ratio of cation to anion falls below $\sqrt{3} - 1$, octahedral coordination is favored. About 14 oxides of tetravalent metals and about seven fluorides of divalent metals are known to crystallize with the structure characteristic of TiO_2. In this structure, anions are almost close-packed and half the octahedral voids are occupied by cations. The following are some of the substances that crystallize in the tetragonal structure of this kind: MgF_2, NiF_2, ZnF_2, MnO_2 (if it exists), PbO_2, SnO_2, and TiO_2.

In general, as the value of n in the formula MX_n increases beyond 2, the arrangement of ions or atoms tends to deviate more and more from close-packing of X, or M and X. Frequently the environment of M among the X is unsymmetrical and unrelated to expectations of σ-bond hydridization in free molecules.

In general ionic crystals may be viewed as close-packed arrays of their large ions, usually the anions. To the extent that the radius ratio limits influence the kind of void and kind of structure realized by a cation, it seems fitting to provide in Table 16.13 a set of anionic radii and radius ratio limits to aid in deciding what kind of structure is likely for a cation of given size.

The structures of $CdCl_2$ and CdI_2 have been shown to be layer structures. These substances are easily cleaved along the planes where van der Waals forces hold the bread of the X-Cd-X ionic sandwiches. In both $CdCl_2$ and in CdI_2, the Cd^{2+} ions are surrounded octahedrally by anions.

The compounds WS_2 and MoS_2 differ from the CdX_2 structures in the environment about W or Mo. The sulfur atoms are arranged as in a trigonal

Table 16.13 Radii of Anions† and the Cation Sizes at Various Limits

		Coordination Number	4	6	8
		Structural Types	ZnS	NaCl, CdX_2	CsCl, CaF_2
Anion	r_-				
F^-	1.36 A	0.31 A	0.56 A	1.00 A	—
O^{2-}	1.40	0.31	0.58	1.02	—
Cl^-	1.81	0.41	0.75	1.32	—
S^{2-}	1.84	0.41	0.76	1.35	—
Br^-	1.95	0.44	0.81	1.43	—
Se^{2-}	1.98	0.44	0.82	1.45	—
H^-	2.08	0.47	0.86	1.52	—
I^-	2.16	0.48	0.89	1.58	—

† L. Pauling, *The Nature of the Chemical Bond*, Ithaca, N. Y.: Cornell University Press 1960, p. 514.

prism about the metal atom instead of being arranged octahedrally. The contacts between sulfur atoms in different sandwiches remain close-packed, as do the arrangements of sulfur atoms in their own layers.

Easy cleavage between S-S layer-contacts is probably why MoS_2 is useful as a lubricant and why, also, a little I_2 lubricates Ti and stainless steel, for FeI_2 and TiI_2 have the CdI_2 structure.

Certain kinds of silicate minerals, the swelling clays and mica-like silicates, form layer structures in analogous ways. Aluminum and silicon ions bind two or more close-packed layers of oxide ions into a complex that extends indefinitely in two dimensions. Monovalent and divalent ions may bind these layer-like complexes. Cleavage occurs between such complexes and absorption of water, glycerol, or other small molecules between such layers causes swelling in a direction perpendicular to the layers.

A final example of a layer structure is graphite. Each layer is a polynuclear aromatic condensed ring system that extends indefinitely in all directions in its own plane. Each ring is a hexagon of carbon atoms, each of which has three nearest neighbors at a distance of 1.42 A. The distance between carbon atoms in benzene is 1.39 A, and in polynuclear aromatic hydrocarbons like naphthalene, anthracene, and phenanthrene, carbon-carbon distances range from about 1.38 A to 1.42 A.

Adjacent layers are stacked so that half their atoms are directly above or below atoms of the adjacent layers. The other half of the atoms are directly over or under the centers of hexagons of adjacent layers. The distance between layers is 3.35 A, the great length indicating only weak interlayer forces. Graphite is very easily cleaved by separation of these layers, and most expansion due to a rise in temperature occurs in a direction perpendicular to the layers. The lubricating properties of graphite are attributed to absorption of molecules between the layers.

In ordinary graphite, every other layer is an exact repetition; the packing of layers is ABABAB··· as in Figure 16.26, where c/a is much too small for graphite. A second, rare type of graphite exhibits layer packing of the type ABCABC· · ·. Pyrolyzed organic substances, such as the "coke" deposited on silica-alumina cracking catalysts, may consist of this kind of layer. A layer of this kind is essentially a huge polynuclear aromatic hydrocarbon having hydrogen atoms on its periphery and extending about 30 A in its plane. The coke consists of several layers stacked parallel, but with random orientation relative to adjacent layers.

16.18 LATTICE ENERGY

The energy of an ionic crystal is mainly the coulomb energy of attraction and repulsion tempered by the repulsion energy associated with the finite sizes of ions. Because the square of the electronic wave function of an ion approaches zero only asymptotically, the size of an ion is a matter of defining where $|u|^2$ becomes negligible. Because ions have an indefinite but finite size, calculating the energy of an ionic crystal would be difficult were it not for the spherical symmetry of many ions and the simplicity of ionic structures.

The lattice energy U_0 of an ionic crystal is the energy required per gram formula weight to separate the ions and bring them to rest at infinity. For example, for $NaCl_{(s)} \longrightarrow Na^+_{(g)} + Cl^-_{(g)}$, $\Delta E = U_0$. In keeping with the usual development,[12] if R is the shortest interionic distance, the potential energy V of the crystal is

$$V = -\frac{Ae^2z^2}{4\pi\epsilon_0 R} + \frac{Be^2}{4\pi\epsilon_0 R^n} \tag{16.19}$$

The constant A in the term that contains all coulombic interactions is the *Madelung constant*, a characteristic number that depends upon the nature of the

Table 16.14 Madelung Constants†

Structural Type	Madelung Constant A	Internuclear Distance R_0
CsCl	1.76268	3.570623 A
NaCl	1.74756	2.813840 A
$CdCl_2$	4.489	2.6633 A
ZnS (cubic)	1.63805	2.340867 A
ZnS (hex)	1.64073	2.339051 A
CdI_2	2.988222	4.383 A
CaF_2	5.03879	2.360352 A

† Q. C. Johnson and D. H. Templeton, *J. Chem. Phys.* **34**, 2004 (1961).

[12] Sherman, J., *Chemical Reviews*, **11**, 93 (1932). Copyright © 1932, The Williams and Wilkins Co., Baltimore.

lattice. The term containing B is a repulsive term, and n is of the order of ten. The value of z is the absolute value of the charge of the negative ions of the lattice. Table 16.14 lists values of the Madelung constants for some simple lattices.

At the observed equilibrium distance R_0, the potential energy is a minimum; hence,

$$\frac{dV}{dR} = 0 = \frac{Ae^2z^2}{4\pi\epsilon_0 R_0^2} - \frac{nBe^2}{4\pi\epsilon_0 R_0^{n+1}}$$

$$B = \left(\frac{z^2 R_0^{n-1}}{n}\right)A \qquad (16.20)$$

Since n can be found experimentally from the compressibility of a crystal, B can be evaluated if R_0 is also known from diffraction experiments. At equilibrium, substitution of (16.20) into (16.19) yields

$$V_0 = -\frac{Ae^2z^2}{4\pi\epsilon_0 R_0}\left[1 - \frac{1}{n}\right] \qquad (16.21)$$

For one gram formula weight, the lattice energy is

$$U_0 = -N_0 V_0 = \frac{N_0 Ae^2z^2}{4\pi\epsilon_0 R_0}\left[1 - \frac{1}{n}\right] \qquad (16.22)$$

The famous Born-Haber cycle, devised in 1919, relates the lattice energy to other quantities which can be calculated or observed. This isothermal cycle for a crystal $MX_{(s)}$ like NaCl is this:

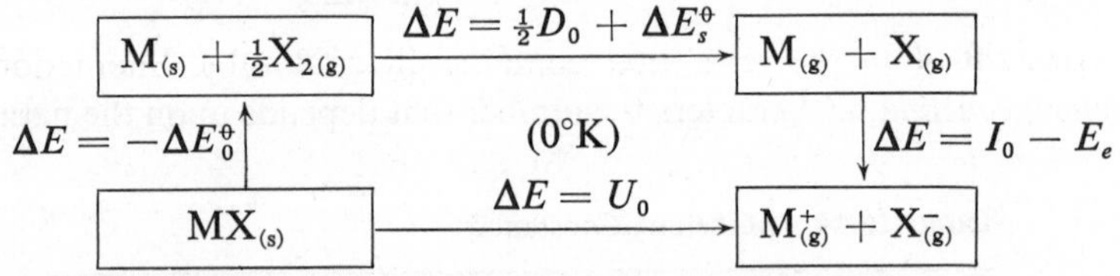

$$\begin{array}{ccc} \boxed{M_{(s)} + \tfrac{1}{2}X_{2(g)}} & \xrightarrow{\Delta E = \frac{1}{2}D_0 + \Delta E_s^\circ} & \boxed{M_{(g)} + X_{(g)}} \\ \uparrow \Delta E = -\Delta E_0^\circ & (0^\circ K) & \downarrow \Delta E = I_0 - E_e \\ \boxed{MX_{(s)}} & \xrightarrow{\Delta E = U_0} & \boxed{M^+_{(g)} + X^-_{(g)}} \end{array}$$

Here ΔE_0° is the change in energy at absolute zero for the formation of $MX_{(s)}$ from the elements in standard states, D_0 is the dissociation energy of $X_{2(g)}$, ΔE_s° is the standard sublimation energy of $M_{(s)}$ at absolute zero, I_0 is the ionization energy of $M_{(g)}$, and E_e is the electron affinity of $X_{(g)}$. Because ΔE is independent of the path,

$$U_0 = -\Delta E_0^\circ + \tfrac{1}{2}D_0 + \Delta E_s^\circ + I_0 - E_e \qquad (16.23)$$

Any one of the six energies in (16.23) can be calculated from the others; it also serves as a check if all are known. The cycle is also often written at 25°C because data are readily available at 25°C for ΔH_f° of the species in the cycle.

Written for ZnS in terms of enthalpy changes at one atm at 25°C, the Born-Haber cycle is

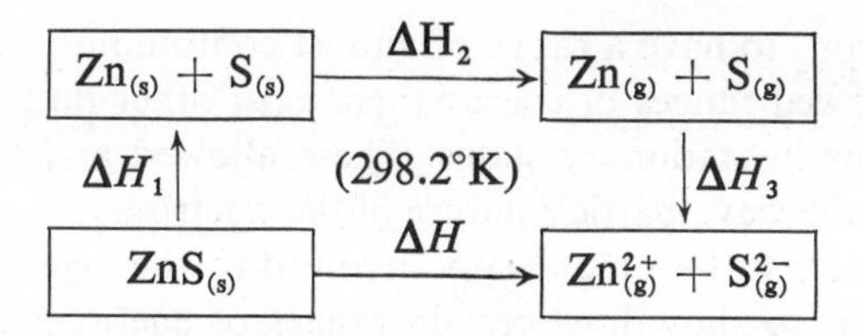

Here $-\Delta H_1$ is the standard enthalpy of formation of $ZnS_{(s)}$, while ΔH_2 is the sum of the sublimation enthalpies of Zn and S. The value of ΔH_3 is equal to the first and second ionization energies of Zn plus the electron affinities of S and S^-, the PV terms for the electrons adding to zero in the net ΔH_3. Actually it is sometimes convenient to calculate $\Delta H_2 + \Delta H_3$ as a unit from enthalpies of formation of the gaseous ions. With a $\Delta(PV)$ correction, U_0 for $ZnS_{(s)}$ becomes equal to ΔH. The cycle, of course, requires ΔH to equal $\Delta H_1 + \Delta H_2 + \Delta H_3$.

Lattice energies of alkali halide crystals are about 200 kcal/mole, while those of ZnS-type crystals are about 800 kcal/mole. The factor of four between these U_0's is roughly the ratio of the products of the charges of the contacting ions, as though the structure were unimportant. The type of structure is important, as the values of the Madelung constants in Table 16.14 attest.

The present discussion has neglected polarization of ions. The fat electron clouds of anions like S^{2-} and Br^- are easily distorted by the approach of a concentrated charge of a lean cation like Zn^{2+} or Li^+. Polarization, which essentially is a tendency toward covalent character in the bonding, contributes about 15 kcal/mole to the stabilization of AgI, and more to ZnS. Covalent bonding is, of course, the limit of extreme polarization.

The Born-Haber cycle was used at first to calculate electron affinities E_e. Now that these can be calculated with some assurance of accuracy by quantum mechanics, the cycle is used as a check and to calculate U_0 in the hope of explaining heats of solution and sublimation, crystalline surface tension, energies of vacant ion sites, and various mechanical and thermal properties of ionic cyrstals.

Example 16.5. Calculate the lattice energy of $NaCl_{(s)}$ if $n = 9$.
From Table 16.9, for NaCl, $a_0 = 5.64$ A at room temperature. Since R_0 is the distance of closest approach of ions, $R_0 = 2.82$ A. By (16.22) with $z = 1$,

$$U_0 = \frac{0.602 \times 10^{24} \times 1.748 \times (1.602 \times 10^{-19})^2}{4\pi\epsilon_0 \times 2.82 \times 10^{-10}}\left[1 - \frac{1}{9}\right]$$

$$= 7.63 \times 10^5 \text{ joules mole}^{-1} = 182.2 \text{ kcal mole}^{-1}$$

16.19 BAND THEORY AND ZONES

A crystal can be viewed either as an assembly of atoms into a macromolecule or as a periodic potential for electrons. Both views when fully developed require the crystal's electrons to have a range of almost continuously variable energies. Between these allowed ranges of energy there exist other ranges of energy forbidden to electrons in stationary states. These allowed and forbidden energy bands result from the wave-particle nature of the electron.

It is unnecessary to become deeply involved in the algebraic complexities of three dimensions to show how certain ranges of energy are not allowed to electrons that roam over a potential with the periodic properties of a lattice. One dimension x is sufficient. In the absence of any potential ($V = 0$), the wave function of an electron is $u = Ae^{ik_x x}$ where A is a constant and where the propagation number k_x is $p_x/\hbar = 2\pi/\lambda_x$, as explained in Section 13.8. Bloch in 1928 showed that when V is periodic and not zero the wave function of the electron is of the form

$$u(x) = f(x)e^{\pm ik_x x} \tag{16.24}$$

In three dimensions, x is replaced by $\mathbf{r}$. When (16.24) is inserted into the one-dimensional Schrödinger equation (13.97), it is necessary that $f(x)$ be a solution of

$$\frac{d^2 f}{dx^2} + 2ik_x \frac{df}{dx} = \frac{2m}{\hbar^2}\left[V + \frac{\hbar^2 k_x^2}{2m} - E\right] f \tag{16.25}$$

When V is zero, the left side of (16.25) is zero because $f(x)$ is constant, u being of the form $Ae^{ik_x x}$. If f is constant but not zero, (16.25) then yields

$$E^{(0)} = \frac{\hbar^2 k_x^2}{2m} \tag{16.26}$$

which is (13.69) in one dimension since $\hbar k_x = h/\lambda_x = p_x$. Comparison of (16.26) to (13.90) yields

$$\frac{\pi n_x}{a} = k_x = \frac{2\pi}{\lambda_x}$$

Whence

$$n_x \lambda_x = 2a \tag{16.27}$$

Equation (16.27) is the Bragg equation in one dimension.

However, when V is not zero, $f(x)$ is not constant, and the left side of (16.25) is not zero. For present convenience and simplicity, V is assumed to act only in the immediate neighborhood of lattice sites, which in one dimension lie along x with a distance a between nearest sites. The short range of x over which V is not zero means that it is possible to assume that

$$a\frac{d^2 f}{dx^2} \gg \frac{df}{dx} \tag{16.28}$$

Hence, in view of (16.26), it follows from (16.25) that

$$\frac{d^2f}{dx^2} = \frac{2m}{\hbar^2}[V - (E - E^{(0)})]f \tag{16.29}$$

As in Section (13.10), if $V > E - E^{(0)}$, f is of the real form

$$f(x) \sim e^{\pm Bx} \tag{16.30}$$

with

$$B^2 = \frac{2m}{\hbar^2}[V - (E - E^{(0)})] \tag{16.31}$$

The condition (16.28) with (16.30) yields $|aB| \gg 1$. But if $f(x)$ in (16.30) is to be almost constant near a site where $V \neq 0$, then Bx must be small as x ranges over the site. That is, if δ is the distance over which V acts, then $B\delta \ll 1$ and, since $|aB| \gg 1$, it follows that $\delta \ll a$, as already supposed. Solution of (16.31) for the energy E that might be realized gives

$$E = E^{(0)} + V - \frac{\hbar^2 B^2}{2m} \tag{16.32}$$

On the other hand, if $V < E - E^{(0)}$, Section 13.9 requires a solution of the form

$$f(x) \sim e^{\pm iCx} \tag{16.33}$$

with

$$C^2 = \frac{2m}{\hbar^2}[(E - E^{(0)}) - V] \tag{16.34}$$

Solution of (16.34) for the energy E that might be realized by the electron gives

$$E = E^{(0)} + V + \frac{\hbar^2 C^2}{2m} \tag{16.35}$$

Since B^2 and C^2 are each greater than zero, (16.32) and (16.35) indicate that there is a range of energies from

$$E^{(0)} + V - \frac{\hbar^2 B^2}{2m} \quad \text{to} \quad E^{(0)} + V + \frac{\hbar^2 C^2}{2m} \tag{16.36}$$

that cannot be realized when $V \neq 0$. This gap of forbidden energy states is near or contains the state of energy $E^{(0)}$ since B^2 and C^2 vary linearly with V. And when E is approximately equal to $E^{(0)}$, the one-dimensional Bragg equation $n_x\lambda_x = 2a$ is approximately satisfied. That is, when V acts, the electron energies that go with $n_x\lambda_x = 2a$ are forbidden since they lie in the range (16.36).

These key results are presented graphically in Figure 16.36. The dashed parabola is (16.26), which obtains when $V = 0$. As soon as the periodic potential V exists, E rises discontinuously as k_x passes through the values $\pi n_x/a$. The solid s-shaped lines indicate the actual values of E when $V \neq 0$ for a typical case.

When these ideas are extended to three dimensions, analogous forbidden and allowed ranges of energy are generated from a previously unrestricted range of E. Forbidden ranges occur when the Bragg equation $n\lambda = 2d \sin \theta$ is satisfied. Thus the (hkl) planes at which the Bragg equation holds can be presented in k space (with coordinates k_x, k_y, and k_z) as the forbidden ranges were presented in k_x space in Figure 16.36. The first zones of allowed energy are terminated at (100) in primitive cubic (P), at (110) in body-centered cubic (I), and at a combination of (111) and (200) in face-centered cubic (F), as shown in Figure 16.37. For the disturbance is roughly proportional to $|F(hkl)|^2$. It is, of course, not limited to cubic systems, for any crystal qualifies as a source of a

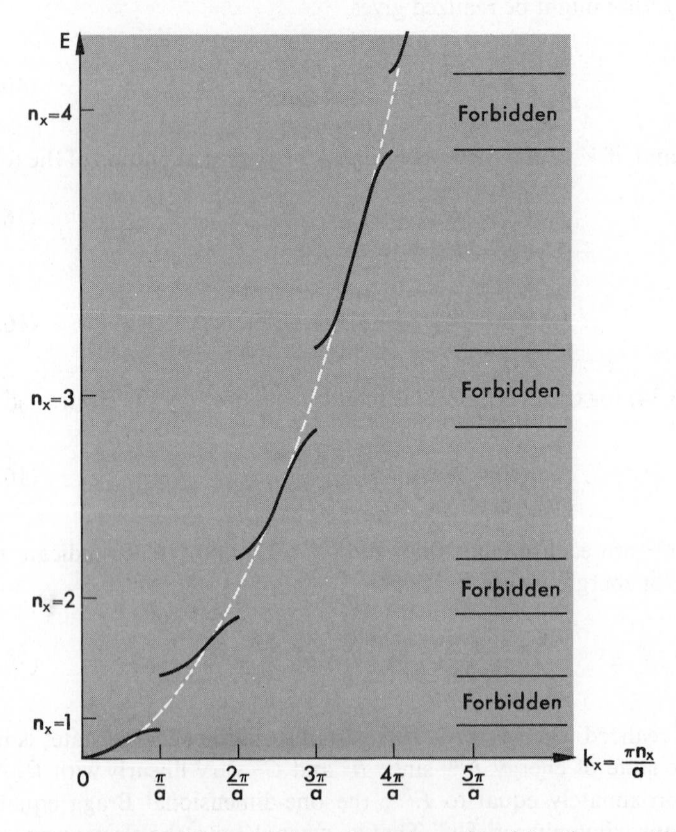

Figure 16.36. Energy E in a One-Dimensional Lattice as a Function of Progagation Number k_x and Lattice Constant a

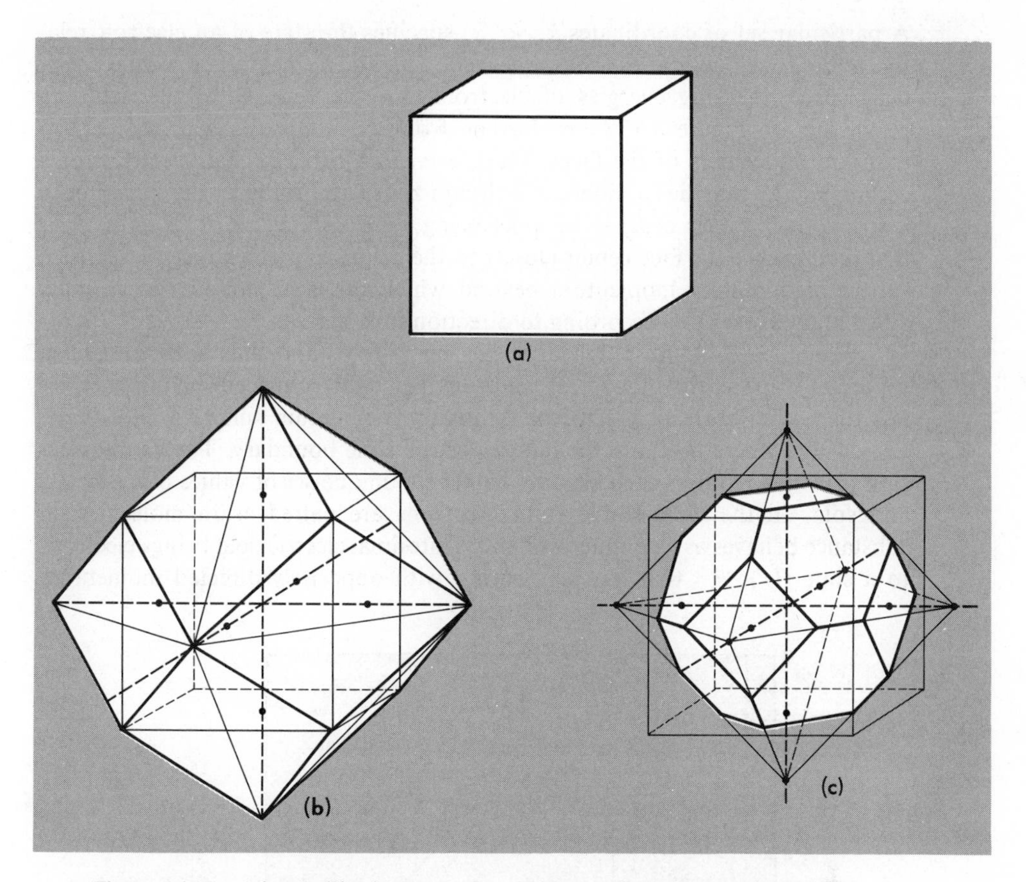

Figure 16.37. First Brillouin Zones for Cubic Lattices (a) Simple Cubic (100) (b) Body-Centered Cubic (110) (c) Face-Centered Cubic (111) and (200)

periodic potential. The second zones of cubic crystals end at (110) for P, at (200) for I, and at a different combination of (111) and (200) for F. The third zone of F would end at a polyhedron (dodecahedron) based on (220). These zones, called *Brillouin zones* after one of their first investigators, are fixed by the nature of the lattice and lie between the polyhedra in k space. That is, the lattice presents a mild periodic potential V that causes certain electron waves to be so thoroughly reflected from Bragg planes for which $F(hkl) \neq 0$ that such electrons do not exist in the crystal because they cannot be propagated over several unit cells.

The energy of a nearly free electron is, as in (13.69),

$$E \approx \frac{\hbar^2}{2m}(k_x^2 + k_y^2 + k_z^2) \qquad (16.37)$$

A particular set of coordinates k_x, k_y, k_z specifies the state of an electron relative to the zone boundaries. The values of k_x, k_y, and k_z that fall on a zone boundary specify varying energies of electrons, for the vertexes of the Brillouin polyhedra of Figure 16.37 are farther from $k_x = k_y = k_z = 0$ and $E = 0$ than are the centers of the faces. Thus, even in a cubic crystal, electrons of a certain energy may lie in different Brillouin zones according to the direction in k space, their values of $k_x^2 + k_y^2 + k_z^2$ being equal. The value of $k_x^2 + k_y^2 + k_z^2$ that just reaches the face center closest to the origin in a cubic system defines a sphere of minimum momentum beyond which the zone boundaries strongly affect allowed energies according to direction in k space.

When the Brillouin polyhedron has many faces and thus approximates a sphere in k space, the number of electrons per cubic unit cell having energies less than what corresponds to the minimum momentum sphere is $(\pi/3)(h^2 + k^2 + l^2)^{3/2}$, where (hkl) are the indexes of the zone boundary. The Pauli exclusion principle requires each electron to have a unique set of values of k_x, k_y, k_z, and spin. In the most stable state, electrons are paired as in molecules. A substance behaves as a conductor if an infinitesimal electric field brings electrons to a state $f(x)e^{+ik_xx}$ that has no electron with oppositely directed momentum

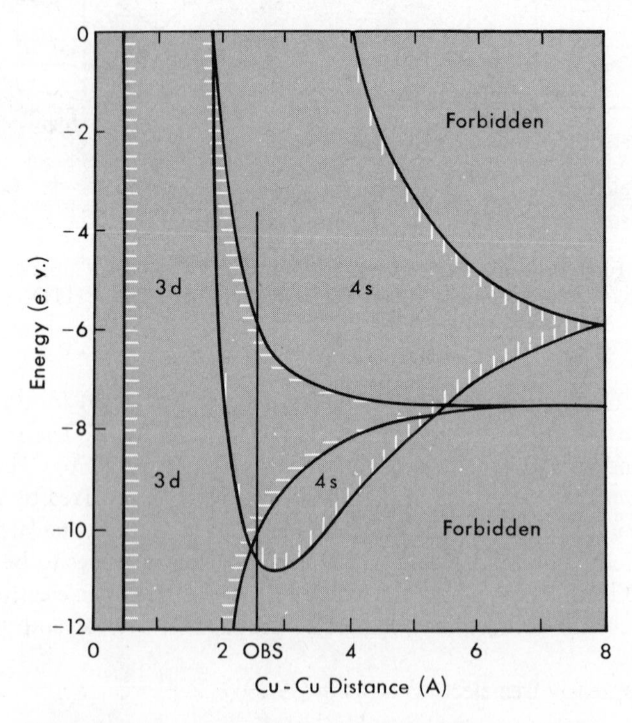

Figure 16.38. Bands of Energy in Crystalline Copper†

†Adapted from H. M. Krutter, *Phys. Rev.* **48**, 664 [1935]

and wave function $f(x)e^{-ik_zx}$. Zones are said to overlap in energy if different choices of k_x, k_y, k_z of the same energy place electrons in different zones because the zone boundary is not a sphere but is a set of planes. When exactly the right number of electrons fill a zone that does not overlap another in energy, the crystal is a nonconductor in its lowest state (unless it is a superconductor). A magnetic or electric field of sufficient strength, a photon, or thermal energies (vibrations of structure) may excite electrons across a gap of forbidden energies and produce mobile electrons.

Brillouin zones suppose a weak lattice potential perturbing the states of electrons free in a box the size of the crystal. A second quantum mechanical approximation to describe electrons in a crystal assumes that the electrons are very strongly held by each nucleus, which is somehow associated with a lattice site. This second approach is like the LCAO molecular approach.

Viewed as a macromolecule, a crystal is the result of many interactions of many identical atoms. Since the interaction of just two atoms leads to states of slightly different energy, it is not surprising that the interaction of many atoms

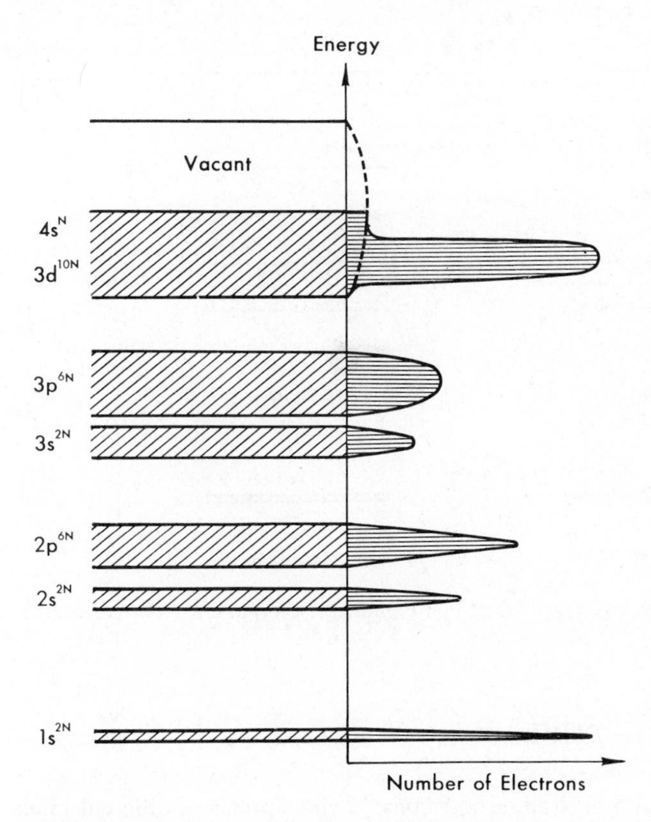

Figure 16.39. Distribution of Electrons of Various Energies in Copper (Schematic)

with discrete energies should lead to many states of similar energy with perhaps certain ranges of impossible energies. Figure 16.38 illustrates this smearing of the topmost atomic energy levels of Cu as the distance between copper atoms decreases. All the energy bands of Cu containing electrons are shown schematically in Figure 16.39 with the general density of electrons in each band. With N atoms, the s-bands can accommodate up to $2N$ electrons, the p-bands up to $6N$ electrons, the d-band up to $10N$ electrons, and so on. Figure 16.40 contrasts the electron populations of conducting Na and nonconducting Ne.

The band theory explains electrical conductivity and magnetic properties of crystals well. These physical properties are of considerable chemical importance. For example, the rate of hydrogenation of double bonds is said to depend on the nature of the d-band in catalytic metals. Heats of adsorption of molecules on metallic surfaces can be related to their electronic structure. Of course, bulk chemical properties of crystals, including their reaction kinetics and states of chemical equilibrium, depend on electronic structure as described by band theory.

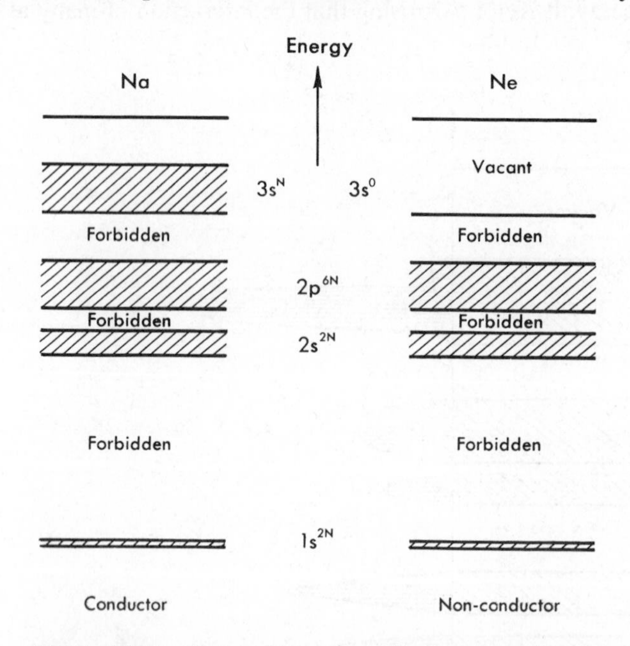

Figure 16.40. Energy Bands in a Conductor (Na) and a Non-Conductor (Ne)

16.20 SUPERLATTICES

A *solid solution* is a crystalline substance having species of different kinds randomly distributed at predictable locations. Its composition and lattice constants are continuously variable over certain ranges. If the different kinds of species could not be distinguished [for example, if isotopes are not distinguished, or if Cu and Zn are not distinguished because their scattering factors $f(\theta)$ are nearly equal], a solid solution would appear to be an ordinary pure crystalline substance. Thus, a solid solution of Cu and Zn would have the same diffraction pattern as Fe, except for lattice constant. What is regularly repeated in space in a solid solution is sometimes this and sometimes that with no order except where this or that is found.

A *superlattice* is a crystalline array of various species that are organized so that what is regularly repeated in space is as definitely predictable as is its position. A superlattice is an organized solid solution with a definite formula and definite order on the atomic or molecular level. At absolute zero, a solid solution has zero-point entropy that is lost on attaining equilibrium either by formation of a superlattice, which is a crystalline compound, or by separation into pure crystals, each of one kind of species.

Alloys of the types AB and A_3B are often prone to a disordering phenomenon in which metal atoms can be arranged regularly but without distinction between atoms of kind A and those of kind B. There are about 40 alloys of the type AB (e.g., CuZn, AgCd, AuMg, MgTl, ZnCe) in which the disordered structure appears to be body-centered cubic. On annealing, however, the distinction between the two kinds of atom leads to an ordered structure like that shown in Figure 16.41. There, kind A is at 000 and kind B is at $\frac{1}{2}\frac{1}{2}\frac{1}{2}$, and the lattice is no longer body-centered because these two lattice sites are no longer equivalent. Actually, the lattice is the CsCl type. In alloys of the type A_3B (e.g., Cu_3Au, Ni_3Fe), the disordered state has both types of atoms arranged in a face-centered cubic structure. In the ordered state, atoms of kind A take the positions at the centers of faces and atoms of kind B take the positions at the cube corners, as in Figure 16.42. Ordered AB and A_3B are very simple examples of superlattices. The unit cells of some superlattices contain hundreds of atoms.

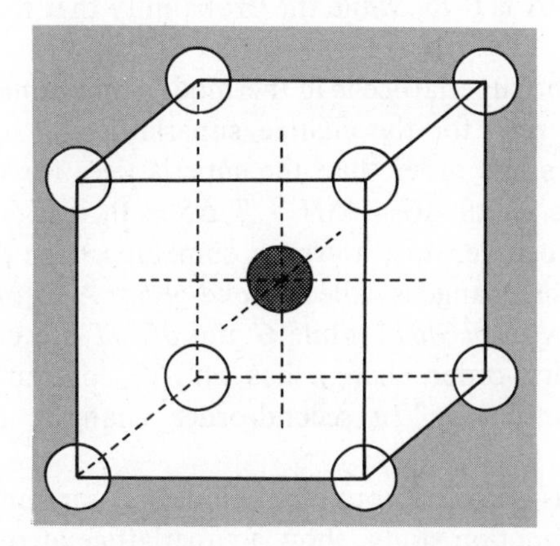

Figure 16.41. Cubic Unit Cell of Ordered Alloy AB

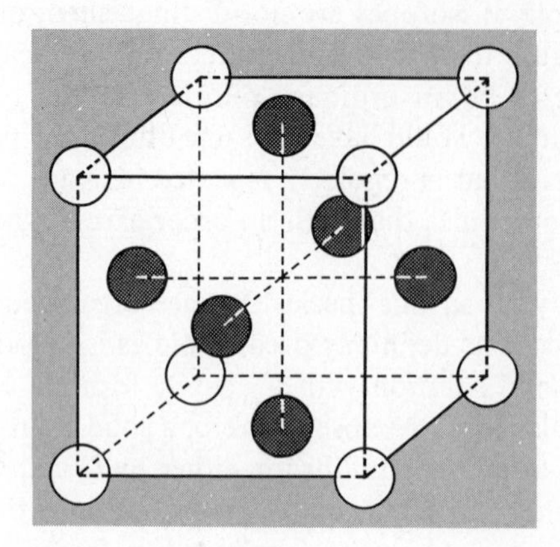

Figure 16.42. Cubic Unit Cell of Ordered Alloy A_3B

In the solid-solution or disordered state of AB, the X-ray powder pattern of $CuZn_x$ is like that of Na or K, with reflections appearing only if $(h + k + l)$ is even. As annealing below a certain critical temperature gradually brings order by allowing diffusion of atoms to organized sites, new diffraction spectra, weak and broad at first, appear for any $(h + k + l)$ because the ordered state (Figure 16.41) is primitive. The new spectra become stronger and sharper as the superlattice develops. The superlattice generally has a lower electrical resistance than the solid solution phase because its greater order facilitates wavelike propagation of electrons. It is also generally stronger and harder than the disordered phase. The superlattice A_3B behaves like AB. As a solid solution above the critical temperature or at any temperature if not annealed after swift crystallization from the melt, it has three-fourths of its sites occupied by A and one-fourth occupied by B, there being no organization of A and B. That is, the probability that a particular site has A is 0.75, while the probability that it has B is 0.25.

At the critical temperature T_c, the superlattice is in thermodynamic equilibrium with the solid solution; ΔG is zero for the change superlattice $\longrightarrow$ solid solution. Since the solid solution has less order than the superlattice, for this change ΔS is expected to be positive. With $\Delta G = \Delta H - T_c\Delta S = 0$, it is clear that ΔH is positive if ΔS is indeed positive. It is, however, sometimes true that ΔS is zero for such a change. If so, the change is called *second-order*. A second-order change involves a discontinuity in $\partial^2G/\partial T^2$ while G and $\partial G/\partial T$ are each continuous, whereas an ordinary first-order change has only G continuous $(\Delta G = 0)$ with $\partial G/\partial T = -S$ discontinuous. In second-order changes, ΔH and ΔV are zero like ΔS.

Alloys of the types AB and A_3B as well as various other kinds of compounds, when examined by neutrons in a diffraction study, show a superlattice attributable to organization of magnetic moments. For example, MnO, MnS, and MnSe each have the NaCl-type structure when examined by X-rays. When examined by neutrons, they are observed to have a trigonal unit cell with ions placed as in NaCl. The edge of the trigonal unit cell is twice that observed by X-rays and the angle between axes is close to $\pi/2$. The cell edge is doubled because the neutrons find that alternate (111) layers of Mn^{2+} have their ions' magnetic moments pointed in opposite directions. That is, all Mn^{2+} of a (111) layer have their magnetic moments equal and opposed to the Mn^{2+} of adjacent (111) layers. Any substance like MnO, MnS, or MnSe that has internal magnetic order but no net macroscopic magnetic moment because of cancellation through symmetry is said to be *antiferromagnetic*. Some alloys AB are antiferromagnetic, and most solid free radicals are expected to be so, too, as though neighboring radicals were tending to form incipient long-range covalent bonds.

In general, there are two ways of describing *ferromagnetism*. In Fe, Co, Ni, and the like, whole bands of electrons achieve a cooperative and spontaneous magnetization. In many ionic crystals containing ions of transition metals or of rare earths, the magnetic moments of the ions are aligned to form extended domains of the crystal in a strong, spontaneous magnetization. Among alloys of type AB, some that are ferromagnetic are FeCo, FeV, FeRh, and MnZn, while among the A_3B type one finds Pt_3Co to be ferromagnetic. With the NiAs-type structure, MnAs is ferromagnetic and MnTe is antiferromagnetic.

If certain species have their magnetic moments opposed to moments of other species while their moments are unequal, the substance is termed *ferrimagnetic*. For example, Pt_3Cr is like A_3B and is ferrimagnetic because all Pt moments are opposed to all Cr moments without causing exact cancellation. Another ferrimagnetic substance is Fe_3O_4, which may be described as approximately close-packed oxide ions with Fe^{2+} and Fe^{3+} filling octahedral voids. The cations' magnetic moments are unequal and do not cancel each other over the whole crystal.

By analogy with these magnetic situations, some crystals are capable of entertaining minor motions or adjustments in positions of whole groups of ions to give crystals with spontaneous electric polarization that reinforces itself throughout crystalline domains. The resulting crystals are termed *ferroelectric*. Among the ferroelectrics are $BaTiO_3$ (Section 16.16) and similar substances, KH_2PO_4, and sodium potassium tartrate.

16.21 SEMICONDUCTORS

Semiconductors have conductivities intermediate between metals and insulators. Their conductivity is of two kinds: *intrinsic*, because of thermal excitation of electrons from the valence band across a narrow forbidden energy gap into the empty states of the conduction band; and *impurity*, because of a few energy states within the forbidden region between valence and conduction bands.

Ordinarily intrinsic conductivity is important only at temperatures where the energy gap is of the order of *RT*. As the energy gap approaches zero, valence and conduction bands merge, and conduction becomes metallic when filled and vacant bands join.

Impurity conductivity is due to foreign atoms and lattice imperfections. Ultrapure Si and Ge are insulators at very low temperatures and conduct an electric current at higher temperatures because valence electrons from a filled band are excited thermally to a low-energy vacant band. Such Si and Ge, prepared by zone refining, can be transformed into impurity semiconductors by the deliberate and controlled addition of very small amounts of elements with similar sizes and chemical natures. If P or As is added to Si or Ge, the foreign atom is built right into the lattice in place of Si or Ge. The extra electron associated with each foreign atom remains nearby because of the extraordinary charge on the nucleus of the foreign atom. This extra electron cannot be accommodated in the usual valence band of crystalline Si or Ge. It seeks a state of low energy that may be in the range of energies forbidden to electrons in pure Si or Ge. This is an *n*-type (negative charge carrier) semiconductor.

If B, Al, or Ga were added as impurity to Si or Ge, the foreign atom would again substitute for Si or Ge. Lacking four valence electrons, each foreign atom has associated with it a "hole," namely, an electron energy state in the valence band that would have been filled if Si or Ge had been at the lattice site instead of the electron-deficient foreign atom. Because electrons are mobile, this hole can migrate about like an electron. However, if it leaves the foreign atom, that foreign atom has a negative charge associated with it because its octet of electrons is complete like Si or Ge. This is a *p*-type (positive charge carrier) semiconductor for positive holes carry the current.

The energies of electrons in an *n*-type semiconductor are shown schematically in Figure 16.43. These donor impurity levels lie near the top of the forbid-

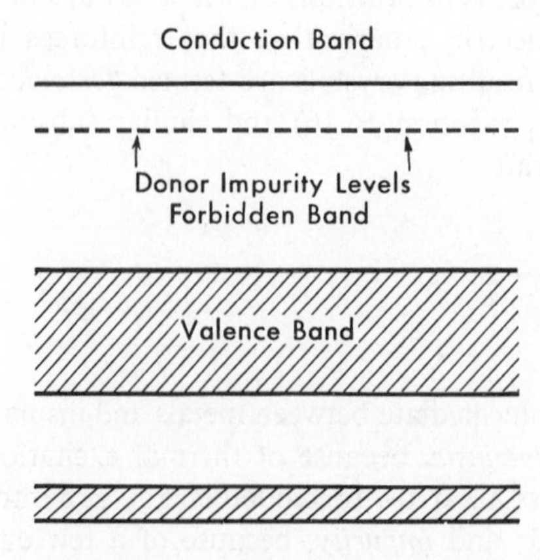

Figure 16.43. Electron Energy States in *n*-Type Semiconductor

den band and are indicated by short lines to suggest that they are localized near the impurity center. These levels are no longer forbidden because the structure is no longer perfect. Electron transfer among states in the forbidden band occurs by tunneling, but a conduction band may develop if much impurity is present.

Well over 100 substances have been characterized as semiconductors.(13) Their most common structural type is cubic ZnS, although the wurtzite, NaCl, and CdI_2 types are not uncommon. Most of the widely used semiconductors contain a metal combined with O, S, Se, Te, P, As, or Sb. Some organic crystals show semiconductivity, and among the pure elements, the following act like semiconductors: B, C, Si, Ge, Sn, P, As, Sb, S, Se, Te, and I_2.

Some of the characteristics of electrons in impurity levels can be estimated by likening the state of such an electron near its positively charged foreign atom to a hydrogen-like electron near its proton. The lattice is supposed to act as a homogeneous dielectric. The various equations for hydrogen are readily modified to this situation provided the e^2 is replaced by e^2/κ (or $\mathbf{Z}$ by $\mathbf{Z}/\kappa$), where κ is the dielectric constant of the lattice.

Example 16.6. Estimate the least energy required to transfer an electron from its most stable impurity level in n-type Si to the conduction band. The dielectric constant of Si is 13.

By (14.125) modified for a nonvacuum, $E = -(\mu \mathbf{Z}^2 e^4 / 2\hbar^2 n^2 (4\pi\epsilon)^2)$. In the state of lowest energy, $n = 1$; hence, the least energy I to ionize an electron bound to an impurity center with $\mathbf{Z} = 1$ is

$$I = \left| \frac{\mu e^4}{2\hbar^2 (4\pi\epsilon)^2} \right| = \frac{\left(\dfrac{10^{-3}}{1836 \times 0.602 \times 10^{24}} \right) \times (1.602 \times 10^{-19})^4}{(4\pi\epsilon_0)^2 2 \times \left(\dfrac{6.626 \times 10^{-34}}{2\pi} \right)^2 13^2}$$

$$= 1.28 \times 10^{-20} \text{ joule electron}^{-1}$$

$$= 1.84 \text{ kcal mole}^{-1} = 0.080 \text{ ev}$$

16.22 CHEMICAL POTENTIAL OF LATTICE ELECTRONS

Lattice vibrations have energies of the order of RT. At room temperature, this is 600 cal mole^{-1} or about 0.025 ev. Only those electrons within about this energy of a vacant state are likely to be excited thermally into that vacant state. Since forbidden band gaps are of the order of 1 volt or more, very few electrons are available for conduction in insulators. Moreover, even in metals, where the highest energy electrons have vacant states only infinitesimally greater in energy, most of the electrons are in stable states well removed in energy from vacant

(13) G. M. Reimherr, *A General Survey of the Semiconductor Field*, Washington, D. C.: U. S. Government Printing Office, NBS Technical Note 153 (August) 1962.

bands and states. Only the electrons within 0.05 volt or so of the top are thermally active at room temperature.

The effective average energy of the electrons in thermal equilibrium with the surroundings is the *Fermi energy*. It is the energy at which half of the available states are on the average actually populated with electrons at thermal equilibrium. For metals, it is approximately the energy of the electrons that can be thermally promoted to a conduction state. At absolute zero in a metal, it is the energy of the most energetic electron. In insulators, the Fermi energy level lies about in the middle of the forbidden region above the topmost valence band. Thermal excitation of an insulator produces a few conduction electrons and an equal number of mobile holes in the valence band. The average energy of these current-carrying holes and electrons clearly lies in the energy gap that separates them. In k space, the Fermi energy is described by what is called the *Fermi surface*, the locus of those points that have an energy such that at thermal equilibrium half of the states are occupied by electrons.

The Fermi energy is the thermodynamically significant energy of lattice electrons. The thermodynamic name for this energy is the chemical potential of the electrons. That is to say, the chemical potential of electrons and the Fermi energy of those electrons are the same. Since phases in contact at equilibrium must have equal electronic chemical potentials, it follows at once that the Fermi energies of electrons in phases at equilibrium are equal. Achieving equilibrium often calls for considerable modification of band structure in the contact layer and incipient transfer of electrons through the phase boundaries.

The energy required to take an electron with the Fermi energy to an infinite distance from a metal is called the *work function* ϕ of the metal. One way of evaluating ϕ is to measure the least energy of a photon that can cause emission of a photoelectron. Part, and sometimes much, of the EMF of an electrochemical cell is attributable to a difference in work functions of the electrodes. Table 13.1 lists work functions for several elements.

16.23 VACANCIES AND INTERSTITIAL IONS

Many kinds of defects have already been described: dislocations, impurities, solution disorder, vibrations, stray particles from outer space, the crystal's own surface, and so on. No mention has yet been made of two well known defects in crystals that can be viewed as ionic. These defects are:

1. *Frenkel defect*. This defect is a misplaced ion, generally a cation held in the wrong place in a region that would otherwise be a perfect array of ions. For every interstitial ion of this kind there is also a vacant ion site, perhaps on the surface of the crystal, so that the crystal may remain electrically neutral.

2. *Schottky defect.* This defect is a vacant ion site. Anions and cations are both missing from what might have been a perfect structure. The ions from the vacated sites are considered to be moved to the surface of the crystal.

Because cations are generally smaller than anions, a Frenkel defect is usually a cation jammed into an otherwise vacant void. In NaCl-type structures, a misplaced cation would usually be in a tetrahedral void. Frenkel defects occur in AgCl and AgBr with Ag^+ in a tetrahedral void among close-packed Cl^- or Br^-. Since one form of AgI is like ZnS, it seems that Ag^+ finds tetrahedral coordination acceptable. The radius ratio rule here is of little value, for AgCl and AgBr are largely covalent. Frenkel defects are very rare indeed in NaCl, and the radius of Ag^+ is larger than Na^+'s by 0.3 A. If the radius ratio rule has any significance, it would suggest the possibility of Frenkel defects when r_+/r_- is close to the low limit of 0.4142.

Schottky defects are much more common than Frenkel defects in almost all kinds of crystal. While the latter are favored by ions of greatly different size and ions of high polarizability, Schottky defects are favored by the opposite conditions: slightly polarizable ions of about the same size. A given crystal, accordingly, seldom exhibits both kinds of defect even under greatly different thermodynamic conditions. The ion defects in the alkali halides are Schottky defects, and the typical nonstoichiometry of the NiAs-type structure also involves absences at either the Ni or As sites, or both.

Many substances are capable of compositions that vary greatly from the ideal with its ideal numbers of ions or atoms.[14] Some substances that absorb excess metal are NaCl, KCl, KBr, and perhaps ThO_2, CeO_2, and PbS. Some substances that take on excess nonmetal with cation vacancies are Cu_2O, FeO, NiO, CoO, NaCl, KBr, KI, CuI, FeS, CrS, and perhaps PbS and SnS. These two kinds of substance exhibit Schottky defects in which the extra electrons or holes reside. It is possible, however, for the added ions to be Frenkel defects. Two substances that absorb excess metal interstitially are ZnO and CdO, while ThO_2 absorbs excess oxygen interstitially.

If the observed density of a nonstoichiometric crystal exceeds the density calculated from observed unit cell constants and an assumed stoichiometric formula, the excess atoms or ions are undoubtedly interstitial. However, it is not always true that an increase in density after incorporation of a nonstoichiometric excess of one element means that Frenkel defects have been generated. The reason is that the crystal whose density is observed may have had Schottky defects which were later filled. Another possibility is that the newly added excess may so alter ionic radii and packing that there occurs a significant change in the size of the unit cell. If chemical analysis can detect nonstoichoimetry, then it is

[14] F. S. Stone, "Lattice Defects in Ionic Crystals," in W. E. Garner, ed., *Chemistry of the Solid State*, London: Butterworths Scientific Publications, 1955, pp. 20–56.

likely that X-ray powder diffraction can detect changes in cell size. These with an observation of density then establish the nature of the defect with certainty, if the ideal structure is known.

Wustite, which departs greatly from the ideal formula FeO, has the NaCl type of structure. All X-ray reflections for the preparations listed in Table 16.15 could be accounted for in terms of the NaCl structure. As the ratio of iron atoms to oxygen atoms decreases, both the density and edge length of the unit cell decrease. Some possible explanations for these chemical analyses are Fe^{2+} vacancies, substitution of O for Fe, or interstitial O^{2-}.

Table 16.15 Densities and Unit Cell Lengths of Wustite†

Fe (wt.-%) (obs.)	Fe (atom-%)	Density (g cm^{-3}) (obs.)	Unit Cell Edge[a] a(A) (obs.)
76.08	47.68	5.613	4.2907
76.20	47.85	5.624	4.2938
76.42	48.15	5.643	4.3000
76.48	48.23	5.658	4.3012
76.72	48.56	5.726	4.3091

† E. R. Jette and F. Foote, *J. Chem. Phys.* **1**, 29 (1933).
[a] Adjusted to a(NaCl) = 5.6400 A.

If the structure of wustite were lattice-perfect, there would be four Fe^{2+} and four O^{2-} in each unit cell of volume a^3. The mass of iron actually present in the unit cell of the 76.08 percent sample, as calculated from the observed density of 5.613 g cm^{-3} and from the observed cell length of 4.2907 A, is $0.7608 \times 5.613 \times (4.2907 \times 10^{-8})^3 = 3.373 \times 10^{-22}$ g. Since the atomic weight of Fe is 55.847, the number of iron atoms or ions per unit cell is observed to be

$$\frac{3.373 \times 10^{-22}}{55.847/(0.6023 \times 10^{24})} = 3.638$$

Results of similar calculations for the Fe and O atoms of all the samples are listed in Table 16.16.

Table 16.16 Observed Numbers of Atoms per Unit Cell of Wustite

Weight Percentage Fe	Atoms per Unit Cell Fe	O
76.08	3.638	3.992
76.20	3.659	3.989
76.42	3.698	3.982
76.48	3.713	3.986
76.72	3.796	4.015

It is evident from Table 16.16 that in wustite Fe^{2+} ions are occasionally absent while O^{2-} are all present. The deviations of the number of O^{2-} per unit cell from 4.000 are of the magnitude expected from errors in the measurements of density of the order of 0.5 percent. A very thorough thermodynamic study of the defects in wustite ("FeO"), hematite (Fe_2O_3), and magnetite has been made.[15]

16.24 ACTION OF LIGHT ON SOLIDS

Although electrons with energies of 0.5 ev less than the Fermi energy are little affected by ordinary temperature changes, any electron in any state can be affected by light of sufficiently short wavelength. Red light ($\lambda = 7000$ A) has an energy of about 1.8 ev, while blue light ($\lambda = 4000$ A) has an energy of 3.1 ev. Absorption of a photon of blue light can thus increase the energy of an electron by about 3 ev. If the final state of the electron is in the conduction band, the crystal becomes photoconductive.

There are many ways in which an excited electron can be stabilized. It may radiate its energy at once or bit by bit as it interacts with lattice imperfections. If it happens to achieve a long-lived excited state, it is said to be *trapped.* The natures of traps vary greatly. The electron may remain in a trap with only a small probability of radiating or it may be obliged to await thermal excitation into a less stable state before radiating and achieving a state of low energy. Some excited states are not well localized in traps; an electron-hole pair may proceed through the structure much like a diffuse hydrogen atom until it collides with an imperfection and is destroyed or changed. The defects in photographically important silver halides are interstitial silver ions (Frenkel defects). Photoelectrons commonly are trapped by silver ions near grain boundaries or other lattice imperfections and form tiny crystals of metallic silver. These form a latent image, which is strengthened by chemical development.

It is possible to introduce measurable excesses, up to about 10^{19} atoms per cm^3, of alkali metal into alkali halide crystals by heating the crystals in metallic vapor and quenching the crystals to stabilize the impurities. Density measurements indicate that the metal enters or generates ion vacancies (Schottky defects) rather than form interstitial ions or atoms (Frenkel defects). Heating doped crystals of NaCl at 400°C causes their yellow color to fade and change to blue with the formation of colloidal particles containing of the order of 100 atoms of Na. The same color occurs with any of the alkali metals in NaCl, and the reddish-purple color associated with excess alkali metal in KCl does not depend on which alkali metal has been added in excess. This suggests that the defect is associated with the lattice. Magnetic measurements yield a Landé g factor of

[15] O. N. Salmon, *J. Phys. Chem.* **65,** 550 (1961).

close to 2.00, the value for an electron. Irradiation with light makes crystals with excess metal photoconductive. Called F centers, these defects have been studied widely since Pohl and his coworkers began their characterization in the 1930's.

Light is strongly absorbed by F centers. As the alkali metal ion or halide ion of the host crystal increases in size, the most strongly absorbed photon energy decreases. For example, in the series NaF-NaCl-NaBr, the energies are 3.6 ev-2.7 ev-2.3 ev. Similarly, in the series LiCl-NaCl-KCl, the energies are 3.2 ev-2.7 ev-2.2 ev. The various energy states of an F center are described semi-quantitatively by the hydrogen-like formula

$$E = -\frac{hcR}{(4\pi\epsilon)^2 n^2}$$

where n is a kind of principal quantum number and where ϵ is the dielectric constant of the crystal with its impurities. The energies quoted above correspond roughly to a $1s$-$2p$ transition. Thus, an F center is viewed as an electron held near an anion vacancy, which really is a positive region spread over the six metal ions around the halide ion vacancy. The orbital of the electron is a hybrid containing p and other character in addition to its predominant s character. The electron moves from site to site by tunnelling, and at room temperature spends of the order of 10^7 seconds at each site before moving on. If an F center absorbs enough energy, generally from a photon, it may move at once to a conducting band or even to another F center where it can pair with the electron already present to form what is called an F' center, namely a pair of paired electrons in a halide ion vacancy. An F' center absorbs about one ev of energy and in doing so becomes two F centers.

Irradiation of pure colorless alkali halide crystals with ultraviolet light or X-rays or bombardment with electrons or neutrons generates F centers and what are called V centers. Since V centers can be made by heating crystals in gaseous halogens, they seem to be holes associated with a halogen atom. A V center annihilates an F center if both are present and properly excited thermally or by photons. There are also several other kinds of impurity center in alkali halide crystals. Indeed, all these kinds of center are expected in almost any kind of crystal. It just happens that the alklai halides are theoretically appealing in the simplicity of their structure.

Example 16.7. Estimate the difference in energy of one F' center and two F centers in NaCl ($\kappa = 2.5$) if the first and second ionization potentials of He are 24.6 and 54.4 ev.

As in Example 16.6, the ionization energy in free space is κ^2 times as great as in the crystal. However, He and He^+ are analogous to F' and F only if $\mathbf{Z} = 2$ for the helium nucleus is reduced to $\mathbf{Z} = 1$ for the anion vacancy. Since the energy is proportional to $\mathbf{Z}^2$, it follows that the energy necessary to transfer an F-center electron into the conduction band of the crystal is $(54.4/2^2\kappa^2) = (54.4/4 \times 2.5^2) = 2.18$ ev. Similarly, the energy necessary to remove the first electron from an F' center and place it in the conduction band is $(24.6/2^2\kappa^2) = (24.6/4 \times 2.5^2) = 0.98$ ev. The difference in energy of one F' center containing electrons of energy -0.98 ev and -2.18 ev and two F centers with energy -4.36 ev is therefore expected to be 1.20 ev.

Molecules trapped in inert solid matrices may have unusual states and configurations that can be characterized by the radiation absorbed or emitted by them. For example, besides NO_2 and the common planar N_2O_4, there exist in solid O_2 and Ar a nonplanar form of N_2O_4 and more than one form of $ONONO_2$.[16] Structures were assigned these species on the basis of their infrared vibrational spectra. Another interesting set of observations finds a rarity among diatoms, a quartet state, namely the $^4\Pi_{5/2}$ state of NO, when NO is trapped in solid Ne, Ar, or Kr and irradiated by X-rays. The lifetime of the excited quartet state as it decays to the ground state is 156, 93, and 35 msec in Ne, Ar, and Kr. Other NO bands were only slightly affected by the crystal lattice, but a general red shift in all frequencies of the $B^2\Pi \longrightarrow X^2\Pi$ bands was noted.[17]

The absorption and emission of photons by electrons in a crystal is a major source of chemical information about crystals. The Mössbauer effect, which involves gamma radiation from nuclei in crystals, also yields chemical information along with data of great importance to physicists. Through observation of small differences in frequency of monochromatic gamma radiation, it is possible to learn something of the s-electron density at nuclei in crystals and of the symmetry and intensity of electric and magnetic fields at nuclei in crystals. The fields there tell something of the atom's p-, d-, and f-electron structure. The Mössbauer effect involves observing the exact wavelength of radiation absorbed by nuclei or the exact wavelength of fluorescent radiation emitted by nuclei that have absorbed radiation from another emitter of the same kind. What is truly significant about this effect is the remarkable uniformity of energy of the gamma photons.

When any atom or system of mass m emits or absorbs a photon of energy $h\nu$, its momentum changes and it recoils with an energy $(h\nu)^2/2mc^2$. This recoil energy changes the observed energy of the photon (its frequency). Relative motion of radiation source and observer may also lead to changes in the observed energy of photons. This is the *Doppler effect*, common to all wave motion and noticeable as the sudden lowering in pitch of a train whistle or whine of a car motor as the vehicle passes. The spread in observed photon energies because of the Doppler effect on species emitting or absorbing photons of energy $h\nu$ is $2h\nu\ (v/c)$, where v is the relative velocity and c is the velocity of light. Both the recoil and Doppler spreads increase as $h\nu$ increases.

The uncertainty principle also requires that there be a natural spread in the energy of a photon that results from a transition between states of finite half-life $t_{1/2}$. If Γ_0 is the minimum observable natural line width, the uncer-

---

[16] R. V. St. Louis and B. Crawford, Jr., *J. Chem. Phys.* **42,** 857 (1965).
[17] R. P. Frosch and G. W. Robinson, *J. Chem. Phys.* **41,** 367 (1964).

tainty principle requires

$$\Gamma_0 t_{1/2} = \hbar \ln 2 = 0.731 \times 10^{-34} \text{ joule sec} \tag{16.38}$$

The ground state has an infinite lifetime, and the typical lifetime of an excited state of a nucleus or electron in an atom as it decays to the ground state is 10^{-8} sec. Hence, Γ_0 is of the order of 10^{-26} joule. Typically, then, a photon has an uncertainty of about 10^{-26} joule in its energy. Recoil and Doppler broadening may increase this minimum line width.

Example 16.8. At what wavelength is the recoil energy of a species of atomic mass 50 equal to 0.731×10^{-26} joule, the typical natural line width Γ_0?

Since the recoil energy is $(h\nu)^2/2mc^2$, it follows that

$$(h\nu)^2 = (0.731 \times 10^{-26})\left(\frac{2 \times 50 \times 10^{-3}}{0.602 \times 10^{24}}\right)(3.00 \times 10^8)^2$$

$$= 10.92 \times 10^{-35}$$

$$h\nu = \frac{hc}{\lambda} = 1.045 \times 10^{-17} \text{ joule}$$

$$\lambda = \frac{6.626 \times 10^{-34} \times 3.00 \times 10^8}{1.045 \times 10^{-17}} = 190.3 \times 10^{-10} m$$

That is, recoil of a species of mass 50 broadens radiation of wavelength 190 A as much as a half-life of 10^{-8} sec.

The fundamental discovery of Mössbauer in 1957 was the fact that the recoil energy of an absorber or emitter in a crystal can be transferred directly to the whole crystal. In other words, the mass m in $(h\nu)^2/2mc^2$ may be a macroscopic quantity like the mass of a crystal rather than the mass of an atom or molecule as in Example 16.8. This change, of course, reduces the recoil energy by a factor of the order of 10^{20} or more and thus leaves only the Doppler effect to interfere with the best possible observation of λ or photon energy.

Vibrations of atoms have a typical frequency of the order of 10^{13} sec^{-1}. Within a time of the order of 10^{-13} sec the atom has moved (twice) through its range of about 0.1 A. This time is so short compared to an excited state half-life that the Doppler energy spread $2h\nu(v/c)$ is generally negligible. It becomes significant when $h\nu$ is great and line widths approach Γ_0, the minimum value. In his experiments of discovery in 1957, Mössbauer actually used the Doppler effect to compensate for the small recoil energy. By moving the emitter he exactly matched the frequency of the radiation to that absorbed by the like system. For the intensity of absorption depends strongly on the extent to which line widths of emitter and absorber overlap in energy. When they nearly coincide, relative motion allows the small adjustment needed to attain exact resonance for best possible absorption or to measure line widths as absorption efficiency varies. The velocity of a free molecule is related to its kinetic energy $\frac{3}{2}kT$, and temperature also influences the amplitude of vibration of an atom in a crystal.

To minimize the Doppler effect, crystal temperatures less than 100°K are sometimes used.

The optimum circumstances for the Mössbauer experiment occur when the line width is $h\nu \times 10^{-12\pm2}$. Since Γ_0 is of the order of 10^{-26} joule, $h\nu$ is about 10^{-14} joule; hence, λ is about 0.2 A. Some isotopes with γ-radiation in this range are ^{57}Fe, ^{61}Ni, ^{67}Zn, ^{73}Ge, ^{85}Rb, ^{99}Ru, ^{101}Ru, ^{107}Ag, ^{109}Ag, ^{117}Sn, ^{119}Sn, ^{123}Sb, ^{123}Te, ^{125}Te, ^{129}I, ^{133}Cs, many of the lanthanides and actinides, several isotopes of W, Os, and other heavy elements, most of which have many nuclear excited states of low energy. Unfortunately, the light elements have few excited states, and these are usually at high energy and thus too short a λ.

One of the items of chemical interest available when such exact photon energies can be observed (e.g., 1 in 10^{13}) is the electron density $|u(0)|^2$ at a nucleus. The value of $|u(0)|^2$ is sensitive to changes in crystalline environment and in atomic electronic structure such as that caused by a difference in valence. For example, $^{57}Fe^{2+}$ and $^{57}Fe^{3+}$ have different resonant frequencies, as do atoms bonded in different covalent environments. The reason is that the extranuclear electrons act on the nucleus by virtue of its finite size. If δR is a difference in nuclear radii, then the change in resonant frequency is

$$\delta\nu_0 = k\,\delta R[|u_1(0)|^2 - |u_2(0)|^2] \tag{16.39}$$

where k is a proportionality constant and $|u_i(0)|^2$ is the electron density at nucleus i. The Mössbauer experiment permits k, δR, nuclear radii R, and the $|u_i(0)|^2$'s to be observed by judicious use of (16.39). The differences in s-electron density thus found are of value in estimating ionic character and kinds of hybridization.

Lasers involve another kind of interaction of photons with species distributed and held in crystals. If a frequency ν_0 generates an excited electronic state in an ion or other species in a crystal, then ν_0 is also able to stimulate that excited state to emit another photon of energy $h\nu_0$. Thus, one photon of energy $h\nu_0$ meets an excited ion and from it generates a second photon of the same energy $h\nu_0$, both photons being exactly in phase with each other. Ordinary light sources are neither in phase nor exactly monochromatic. For such a photon-stimulation process to amplify itself like a chain letter, the number of species in the excited state must exceed the number in the lower state reached as the second photon is generated. The excited state ordinarily has a lifetime of about 10^{-6} sec and is itself produced as a metastable state by decay of more highly excited states produced by strong radiation with frequencies greater than ν_0. If this temperature-inverted population does not exist, absorption of the first photon is more likely than stimulated emission and the laser goes out at once as absorption dominates the action. Great amplification is achieved by continual reflections of the original and stimulated photons within the crystal. Various kinds of arrangements of mirrors make the multiple internal reflections possible as the stimulated photons multiply. A beam can be withdrawn through a partially reflecting mirror. Laser beams are remarkable for their high intensity, the non-divergence of their beams after many reflections between parallel mirrors during growth of the photon horde, and coherence (being in phase). Lasers may be of theoretical and practical use in photochemistry and kinetics of reactions influenced by light.

16.25 TRANSFERENCE IN SOLIDS

Transference in solids is analogous to transference in solutions and the ideas and methods of Sections 11.4 and 11.5 are still useful. In solids, however, it may not be possible to analyze directly for the charge carriers if they are impurities, ion defects, or loose species migrating along dislocations. Moreover, in aqueous solutions the contribution of electrons as conductors is usually negligible. The very action of electrochemical cells depends on this lack of electronic conduction from electrode to electrode within the cell. In solids, electronic transport often competes with and even overwhelms ionic motion. The summation rule (11.10) must be modified to

$$t_e + t_+ + t_- = 1 \tag{16.40}$$

where the new quantity t_e is the transference number of the electron. It is conceivable that a term for holes might also be included.

Many kinds of experiment have been used to observe transference numbers in solids. In the hard, brittle ionic crystals of the alkali halides and in the soft silver halides, t_+ is about 0.9 and t_e is negligible. The values of t_+ decrease as T rises and as anions contribute more to the flow of charge. In crystals of the kind MX_2 (e.g., BaF_2, UO_2, oxides of the rare earths, . . .), the anions carry the major part of the current and t_- exceeds t_+. Despite their greater size, the anions in these solids are more mobile, perhaps because they create a lesser electric disturbance than the more highly charged cations do. Finally, in some crystals, notably those with many vacancies and in the oxide and halides of Cu^+, electrons carry most of the charge, t_e often approaching unity.

The mechanism of charge transfer involves motion of and through ion vacancies in some crystals and, in other crystals, motion of impurities. These are essentially point defects, but the greater spatial extent of dislocations is often important as well. It is possible to use (16.21) and other expressions for lattice energy to estimate changes in chemical potential as a function of R_0, the distance between ions, when compressive and tensile forces are at work in surfaces and dislocations to influence the rate of transfer of matter.

Transference numbers can be found by passing electricity through a series of tightly held pellets, the analogue of the ionic solution, and weighing them and the electrodes again after an accurately monitored amount of charge has passed.

Care must be taken that whiskers of an electrode are not weighed with a pellet after penetrating it during electrolysis or that the boundaries of pellets are not somehow mechanically altered. An indirect and now classic method, due to Wagner in 1933, may be less difficult than such a Hittorf approach. Figure 16.44 shows how a metal M, a nonmetal X, and two pellets of their compound MX are placed and allowed to react at constant T to produce more MX by the reaction $M + X \longrightarrow MX$. The problem, besides measuring the rate of reaction, is to decide whether the reaction occurs at the interface at x_M or at x_X or perhaps at both interfaces. If the reaction proceeds by diffusion of M or by electron transfer and migration of M^{+z}, then Pellet B gains mass at x_X to the same extent that M and X lose mass. (If the temperature is very high, it may be necessary to correct all masses for sublimation.) If, however, X or X^{-z} migrates through both pellets toward M, then Pellet A is observed to gain mass at x_M. If both pellets gain mass at the expense of M and X, an unusual event, then both migrating species have nonzero transference numbers in MX. An ionic crystal seldom if ever accommodates nonionic species so that the migrating species are M^{+z} and/or X^{-z} if MX is ionic. In general it is the cation that moves, and it does so as the rate-limiting step of the chemical reaction because electronic conduction in MX is very swift.

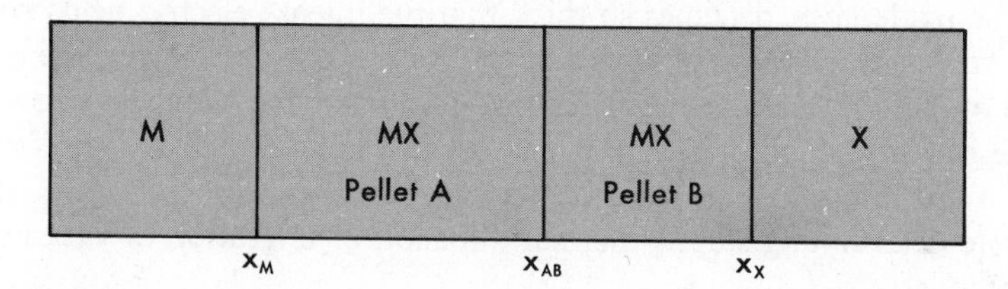

Figure 16.44. Two-Pellet Method of Determining Transference Numbers during a Chemical Reaction

16.26 REACTIONS OF SOLIDS

Traditional theories of metallic oxidation[18] suppose the formation of an effectively uniform and continuous coating of oxide upon metal. Exceptions, at least in the beginning of oxidation, are those metals whose oxides occupy less volume per mole of metal than does one mole of pure metal. The oxide coating of many metals behaves however, as though it were continuous, like a film of paint. For example, clean aluminum reacts rapidly at room temperature with traces of O_2 to form a stable layer of oxide apparently uniform with a thickness

[18] The first part of this section is based on T. B. Grimley, "Oxidation of Metals," in *Chemistry of the Solid State*, ed. by W. E. Garner, London: Butterworths Scientific Publications 1955, pp. 336–366.

of about 20 A. This layer protects the metal from further reaction. Further oxidation requires temperatures above a certain critical temperature which for Al is about 300° C. For Cu the critical temperature is a little above room temperature and the limiting thickness of Cu_2O is about 20 A.

As the temperature rises above the critical value, the oxide layer grows. If the oxide can accommodate excess metal, as ZnO and Al_2O_3 do, gaseous oxygen adsorbed on the surface of the oxide becomes part of the oxide ion array by taking electrons already freed by the excess metal. The interstitial metallic ions then migrate under the influence of the intense electric field generated by the anions at the oxide-oxygen surface. As the oxidation proceeds, metal atoms enter the oxide phase at the metal-oxide surface and at once become interstitial ions and electrons.

If instead of having excess metal, the oxide layer is deficient in metal, as Cu_2O and NiO are, the adsorbed O_2 generates vacancies in the metallic ion lattice. These vacancies move toward the metal in a slow process that really involves gradual movement of many different metallic ions outward from the metal. Eventually, a vacancy occurs at the metal-metal oxide surface. Then metal atoms enter the oxide and their electrons are rapidly drawn across the oxide layer to convert the adsorbed O_2 into ions. Again, an intense electric field is generated across the thin oxide layer by the reaction itself.

When the oxide layer becomes so thick that the intense electric fields near the surfaces are largely without influence on the bulk of the oxide layer, the rate of oxidation often follows the parabolic law of Tammann and Wagner. This law describes the rate of oxidation of many metals when the oxide layer is uniform and already a few hundred angstroms in thickness. In these circumstances, the slowest or rate-determining step is thermal diffusion or migration of vacancies or interstitial ions.

The law of Tammann and Wagner says that the rate of growth in thickness of the layer is inversely proportional to the thickness of the layer when temperature and other variables like partial pressure of O_2 are constant. If z is the thickness of the oxide layer, assumed to be continuous like a coat of paint, then

$$\frac{dz}{dt} = \frac{k_{TW}}{z} \tag{16.41}$$

where k_{TW} is the Tammann-Wagner rate constant at T for a particular kind of metal. If the thickness is z_1 at t_1 and is z_2 at t_2, integration of (16.41) yields

$$\int_{z_1}^{z_2} z\,dz = k_{TW} \int_{t_1}^{t_2} dt$$

$$z_2^2 - z_1^2 = 2k_{TW}(t_2 - t_1) \tag{16.42}$$

The integrated form (16.42) is often referred to as the *parabolic rate law*. It is interesting to note in passing that the mean square displacement of a species subject to random flights is proportional to the time interval of observation, as though the layer were acting as a medium for random motion of ions. The existence of concentration gradients and electric fields surely modifies this kind of ideal motion, however.

Some of the metals whose rates of oxidation are described by this law are Be, Al, Ti, V, Cr, Ni, Cu, Zn, Zr, and Ta. Table 16.17 lists parabolic rate constants k_{TW} for Be and V at 0.100 atm O_2 at various temperatures. For the same thickness of oxide layer, these constants provide a direct comparison of rates of oxidation.

Table 16.17 Parabolic Rate Constants (k_{TW}).

Oxidation Reaction	$p(O_2)$ (atm)	Temp. (°C)	k_{TW} ($cm^2\ sec^{-1}$)
$2Be_{(s)} + O_{2(g)} \longrightarrow 2BeO_{(s)}$	0.100	400	0.050×10^{-14}
	0.100	500	0.104
	0.100	600	0.147
	0.100	700	0.70
	0.100	800	1.20
	0.100	900	27.8
$4V_{(s)} + 3O_{2(g)} \longrightarrow 2V_2O_{3(s)}$	0.100	400	0.20×10^{-13}
	0.100	450	1.75
	0.100	500	7.05
	0.100	550	24.2
	0.100	600	51.2

SOURCES: (Be) E. A. Gulbransen and K. F. Andrew, *J. Electrochem. Soc.* **97**, 383 (1950); (V) Gulbransen and Andrew, *ibid.*, p. 396.

Example 16.9. What time is required at 500°C in 0.100 atm O_2 for a layer of V_2O_3 300 A thick to become 1000 A thick?

From Table 16.17, k_{TW} is 7.05×10^{-13} $cm^2\ sec^{-1}$. Hence, with $z_1 = 300 \times 10^{-8}$ cm and $z_2 = 1000 \times 10^{-8}$ cm in (16.42), the time is

$$t_2 - t_1 = \frac{(1.00 \times 10^6 - 0.09 \times 10^6) \times 10^{-16}}{2 \times 7.05 \times 10^{-13}} = 64.5 \text{ sec}$$

When the oxide film does not adhere closely to the metal, the rate of growth in the thickness of the oxide layer is independent of z at fixed temperature and oxygen pressure; hence, the rate being constant, $z_2 - z_1 = k_0(t_2 - t_1)$. Except for Be, the metals with one or two s electrons beyond an inert-gas electronic configuration follow this linear law of oxidation. The most common metals of this kind are Na, Mg, and Ca.

The traditional theories of metallic oxidation have been subject since about 1950 to critical review. New observations have been possible by electron microscopy and electron and X-ray diffraction. These show single crystals of oxide growing in O_2 on the surface of certain metals the way grass grows on a field.

Growth occurs at special places, probably dislocations, whose properties depend on previous treatment of the metallic surface. The shapes and sizes of these crystals in the noncontinuous oxide layers depend also on the temperature and content of the gaseous atmosphere. There appear to be no generalizations for such growth like the parabolic law, which applies only to layers that are continuous and several hundred angstroms thick.

The Tammann-Wagner rate law (16.42) is macroscopically useful for many kinds of solid state reaction, not only oxidations. For example,[19] when weighed pellets of MgO and Cr_2O_3 are held in contact at constant T (in a flow of air to prevent sublimation of Cr_2O_3 to MgO), the square of the gain in weight of the MgO pellet is a linear function of reaction time at 1000°C to 1250°C. The increase in mass of the MgO pellet corresponds to the loss in mass of the Cr_2O_3 pellet (after due correction for sublimation loss by the Cr_2O_3). X-ray examination finds the spinel $MgCr_2O_4$ in the MgO pellet. Table 16.18 lists values of k_{TW} for the reaction $MgO_{(s)} + Cr_2O_{3(s)} \longrightarrow MgCr_2O_{4(s)}$. Other reactions, from many that might have been listed, are the formation of the hydrobromide of 1, 1-diphenylurea from $HBr_{(g)}$ and the urea[20] and the formation of HfN from Hf and N_2.[21]

Table 16.18 Parabolic Rate Constants for the Formation of $MgCr_2O_4$ from MgO and Cr_2O_3.†

Temperature °C	k_{TW} g^2 cm^{-4} hr^{-1})
1000	0.226×10^{-7}
1100	1.81×10^{-7}
1200	3.54×10^{-7}
1250	10.4×10^{-7}

† G. Parravano, *J. Am. Chem. Soc.* **74**, 6123 (1952).

Many kinds of reaction between solids have been investigated. Besides being influenced by the reactants' general chemical properties, it is clear that the reactivity of solids depends on such things as the presence of fluxes, impurities, defects, dislocations, and the state of division and mixing. Of paramount importance, of course, is temperature. Tammann was the first to express the view that, all other things being equal, the temperature at which a solid becomes noticeably reactive is a constant fraction of its absolute melting point. In other words, a kind of critical temperature of reaction exists for each solid. Surface diffusion of atoms and ions appears to occur at about 0.3 T_f, where T_f is the absolute melting point of the solid. Similarly, volume diffusion seems to begin about 0.5 T_f. This temperature of 0.5 T_f is called the Tammann temperature and repre-

(19) G. Parravano, *J. Am. Chem. Soc.* **74**, 6123 (1952).
(20) F. E. Massoth and W. E. Hensel, Jr., *J. Phys. Chem.* **65**, 636 (1961).
(21) R. K. Edwards and G. T. Malloy, *J. Phys. Chem.* **62**, 45 (1958).

sents roughly the minimum temperature at which the solid shows noticeable chemical reactivity. At such a temperature, the average distance that an atom or ion moves through the solid without a stop is of the order of 10 A. It is also well known that solids having more than one kind of structure are exceptionally reactive near temperatures at which transformations of structure normally occur.

16.27 NONCRYSTALLINE STRUCTURES

Solids are generally distinguished from liquids by their rigidity. Both solids and liquids have their own volume, but a solid does not conform to the shape of its container. Glass apparently should be classed as a solid at room temperature. However, glass does not exhibit a crystalline habit of well-developed faces, cannot be cleaved like most crystals, and displays a rather indistinct X-ray diffraction pattern that lacks the well-defined rings so typical of metals, salts, and minerals. Moreover, as a glass forms on cooling, there is no discontinuity in density, index of refraction, or viscosity. Rather, the viscosity rises continuously to about 10^{25} poise at room temperature; this viscosity is so great that the substance is apparently a solid. Because the X-ray diffraction pattern of glass is obviously like the diffraction patterns of substances that are clearly liquids, glass must indeed be a liquid.

The characteristic feature of crystalline structures is their lattice-like order. When this kind of regularity extends for only 5 or even 10 A, structures lose their crystallinity. While long-range order may be gone, generally the short-range order involving nearest and next-to-nearest neighbors remains, with little modification, what it might have been if crystallization had occurred.

The radial distribution function $4\pi r^2 \rho(r)\, dr$ for vitreous SiO_2 is presented in Figure 16.45. This curve is the sum of the probability densities of electrons at various distances from either an oxygen atom or a silicon atom. The upward sweep is caused by the r^2-dependence. Peaks, which represent most likely distances, occur at 1.62 A, 2.65 A, and so on. The distance 1.62 A is characteristic of the Si-O bond, and 2.65 A is to 1.62 A as the distance between corners of a tetrahedron is to the distance from a corner to its center. This and all other features are interpreted in terms of a structure in which each silicon atom is surrounded tetrahedrally by four oxygen atoms, each of which is bonded to two silicon atoms. That is, the structure may be imagined to consist of SiO_4 tetrahedra linked at their corners by oxygen atoms common to two tetrahedra. The various distances in cristobalite, to which vitreous silica devitrifies, are shown with their relative importance at the top of Figure 16.45. The correspondence is excellent. The difference in the structures of vitreous silica and cristobalite is in the long-range order of the latter. Silica gel is similar to vitreous silica in its short-range order, but the diffraction pattern of silica gel indicates

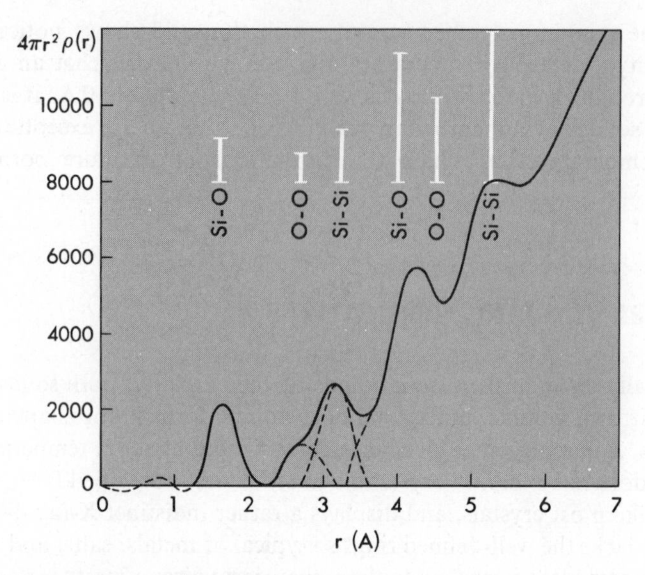

Figure 16.45. Probability Distribution of Interatomic Distances in Vitreous Silica†

that there are large discontinuities and voids in its structure. Vitreous silica, however, is a continuous structure in which the SiO_4 tetrahedra form one vast and continuously linked network.

Water resembles ice (Section 16.17) in the arrangement of hydrogens and oxygens. There are, however, somewhat less than four oxygen atoms arranged tetrahedrally around any one oxygen. That is, water is a broken-down ice structure in which hydrogen bonds are continually broken and remade. Water is, however, denser than ice because, as the temperature rises, the molecules tend to approach a close-packed arrangement. X-ray diffraction has shown that atoms in liquid Hg and liquid Na exist in an environment that is approximately close-packed. While short-range order calls for about 12 nearest neighbors, random movements so loosen the close packing that long-range order is absent.

16.28 SUMMARY

The study of crystalline imperfections and their interactions with each other and their host crystal promises to require more effort and time than the study of ideal structures. For everyone makes his own kinds of defects in great variety and often without control. What is important is to realize their profound in-

†B. E. Warren, H. Krutter, and O. Morningstar, *J. Amer. Ceramic Soc.* **19,** 202 [1936]

fluence on all crystalline properties. Imperfections offer the means of adjusting almost continuously the behavior of crystals to fit man's particular need.

It would be tedious to recite many facts to illustrate the breadth of knowledge at hand concerning crystals. The excess oxygen in this catalyst closely parallels the activity it has in a certain conversion. The electron structure of that alloy is like that in this alloy. Or the mechanism of corrosion, which wastes billions of dollars annually, might be reviewed. And the great variety of silicate structures might be described. The obvious impossibility of giving details on all or even most structures of interest has required this brief chapter to be directed instead toward general principles. Like close-packing and the radius ratio rule, generalities have many exceptions, especially in this subject. Yet such guides are needed to organize some of the details of this vast subject.

The key equations, for those students who are fortunate enough to be examined by working problems, would appear to be the Bragg equation (16.6), equation (16.5) relating d_{hkl} to cell edges, the density equation (16.9), the radius ratio limits, the lattice energy equation (16.22), and the parabolic rate law (16.41). As always, clear understanding makes problems easier. Toward the attainment of adequate understanding of general structural principles, there would appear to be no substitute for wide and even random reading, and eventually research.

PROBLEMS

1. Well-formed large crystals of a pure substance were formed by rapid growth and by very slow growth. Which set is expected to have fewer faces, and why?
   Answer: Rapid growth makes certain faces disappear by growth to a point.
2. Precipitate NaCl from its saturated solution:
   (a) By slow evaporation.
   (b) By adding concentrated HCl swiftly.
   (c) Containing about 10% dissolved urea by slow evaporation.
   Note differences in the crystals of NaCl.
3. Account for the following:
   (a) Petrification of wood, etc.
   (b) Growth of stalagmites and stalactites.
   (c) Conchoidal fracture of glass.
   (d) Easy deformability of annealed copper as contrasted to cold-worked copper.
4. Distinguish between lattice and structure, with a large automobile parking lot as example.
5. Show that face-centered tetragonal is really body-centered tetragonal.
6. Draw a face-centered cubic unit cell, and outline in it a primitive unit cell. Repeat for a body-centered cubic lattice.
7. Justify Equation (16.5) for a few particular triples (hkl) and also in general by means of analytic geometry.

8. A sample of iridium had its first ($h00$) reflection at $\theta = 23.7°$, its first ($hh0$) reflection at 34.7°, and its first (hhh) reflection at 20.4° with radiation of wavelength 1.542 A. Calculate the lattice type, dimension of the cubic unit cell, and the density of iridium if there is one atom per lattice site.
Answer: F.C.C. $a = 3.84$ A; $\rho = 22.6$ g cm^{-3}.

9. Metallic vanadium, with a density of 6.02 g cm^{-3}, diffracts X-radiation of wavelength 0.710 A so that the first ($h00$) reflection is at $\theta = 13.5°$, the first ($hh0$) reflection is at $\theta = 9.50°$, and the first (hhh) reflection is at $\theta = 23.9°$. From these data and the atomic weight, and if there is one atom per lattice site, find:
(a) The kind and size of the cubic unit cell.
(b) The distance of closest approach of V atoms.
(c) Avogadro's number.
(d) The angles at which the next reflections of the types above will occur.
Answer: (a) B.C.C.; (b) 2.63 A; (c) 0.602×10^{24}; (d) $\theta_{400} = 27.8°$, $\theta_{220} = 19.3°$, $\theta_{444} = 54.0°$.

10. A substance with cubic crystals exhibits X-ray powder reflections at $\theta = 28.5°$, 42.6°, 55.9°, and 73.0° (but at no other angles less than 73°) when $\lambda = 1.937$ A.
(a) What is the shape and size of the cubic unit cell?
(b) What mass is associated with each lattice site if the density of the crystals is 7.86 g/cm^3?
(c) What is the shortest distance between lattice sites?
Answer: (a) I, with $a = 2.865$ A; (b) 55.7; (c) 2.48 A.

11. The first five powder spectra of Ce occur at $\theta = 15.05°$, 17.45°, 25.08°, 29.81°, and 31.32° with $\lambda = 1.542$ A Find the type and size of the cubic unit cell of Ce.
Answer: F, with $a = 5.14$ A.

12. Calculate the density of europium metal, which crystallizes with one atom at each lattice site in a body-centered cubic lattice with $a = 4.58$ A.
Answer: 5.26 g/cm^3.

13. By a drawing whose plane is perpendicular to the dislocation line of a screw dislocation, explain how addition of matter at the step of the dislocation tends to form a spiral, but explain also why the step is not exactly a spiral.

14. Explain how two edge or two screw dislocations might annihilate each other and leave behind a perfect crystal.
Answer: Equal but opposed Burgers vectors.

15. Determine the location and size of the largest sphere that can exist among identical touching spheres in a body-centered cubic structure without disturbing that structure.
Answer: 0.225 at $\frac{1}{2}\frac{1}{8}\frac{1}{8}$.

16. Determine the densities of KCl and KBr with data from Table 16.9.
Answer: 1.9866 and 2.7489 g/cm^3.

17. Calculate the coefficient of linear expansion of NaCl with data from Table 16.9.
Answer: 17.3×10^{-6} deg^{-1}.

18. Calculate the densities of TlCl and AlNi with data from Table 16.5.
Answers: 7.0650 and 5.9474 g/cm^3.

19. Carborundum (SiC) has the ZnS-type structures and others of equal density. If the Si-C internuclear distance is 1.89 A, what is the density of SiC?
Answer: 3.20 g/cm^3.

20. With $a = 4.21$ A, MgO has the NaCl-type structure. Calculate the distance

between nearest oxide ions and the angles at which the first five allowed X-ray powder spectra appear if $\lambda = 1.542$ A.
Answer: 2.98 A; $\theta = 18.5°, 21.5°, 31.2°, 37.4°, 39.4°$.

21. Predict the kinds of structure expected of EuF_2, EuO, EuS, and $EuBr_2$ if the ionic radius of Eu^{2+} is 1.12A
Answer: EuF_2 like CaF_2; EuO like CsCl; EuS like NaCl; $EuBr_2$ like CdI_2.

22. Calculate the densities of sphalerite and wurtzite with data from Table 16.11.
Answer: 4.04 g/cm^3.

23. Are the sulfide ions of WS_2 and MoS_2 all close-packed? Explain.
Answer: No; trigonal prism of S^{2-} about metal ion is not close-packed array of S^{2-}.

24. What is the expected range of cubic unit cell length for sulfides with the NaCl-type structure?
Answer: 5.2 A to 6.4 A.

25. If $n = 9$, what is the lattice energy of ZnS(s)?
Answer: 823 kcal/mole.

26. Draw the second Brillouin zones of P and of I cubic.
Answer: P has (110) dodecahedron; I has (200) cube mixed with (211).

27. Draw the energy bands of diamond and K.

28. Draw the actual population of electrons in conduction and valence bands for a pure insulator acting as an intrinsic conductor at an elevated temperature.

29. If there are 1.00×10^{18} F centers per cm^3 in KCl, and if the F centers are close-packed, what is the shortest distance between F centers? About how many unit cells are associated with one F center?
Answer: 112 A; 4020 unit cells.

30. At what wavelength does the recoil energy of an atom of mass 50 equal its photon energy?
Answer: $\lambda = 1.33 \times 10^{-17}$ m.

31. What is the activation energy of the reaction of Table 16.18?
Answer: 50 kcal/mole.

32. How long will it take a layer of BeO 400 A thick to become 1000 A thick at 400°C in O_2 at 0.100 atm?
Answer: 8.40×10^4 sec.

---

33. Explain why crystals from the cubic system are harder to identify than are those from the tetragonal system when index of refraction and interfacial angles are the only properties observed.
Answer: Cubic crystals have only one index of refraction and only a limited number of faces to develop because of their high symmetry.

34. What circumstances favor the formation of dendritic (treelike) crystals such as snowflakes?
Answer: Rapid growth from high supersaturation.

35. Find the interfacial angles of an octahedron and of a regular dodecahedron. (A scalar product of vectors eases the calculation.)
Answer: (Octahedron) 70.53°, 109.48°, and 180°; (dodecahedron) 63.43°, 116.57° and 180°.

36. By two calculations, show that the volume of the primitive trigonal unit cell

having the same lattice as face-centered cubic is one fourth the volume of the cubic cell.

37. Give examples of lattice-like arrangements from everyday experience of one-, two-, and three-dimensional structures.

38. Give the results of rotation of a cubic crystal by $2\pi/3$ around the perpendicular to: (a) $(1\,\bar{1}\,\bar{1})$. (b) $(\bar{1}\,1\,1)$.

39. Show that a primitive hexagonal lattice can be described as an end-centered orthorhombic lattice, and find a restriction upon the orthorhombic axial lengths.
Answer: $a = a$; $b = a\sqrt{3}$; $c = c$.

40. By a drawing, show several choices of a monoclinic unit cell for the same set of lattice points.

41. Why must the X-radiation used in powder photography be almost monochromatic?
Answer: With several λ, each d_{hkl} gives several spectra and pattern is cluttered.

42. Metallic molybdenum has a density of 10.22 g cm^{-3}. From a powder photograph of Mo taken with X-radiation of wavelength 0.711 A, the first ($h00$) reflection occurred at $\theta = 13.1°$, the first ($hh0$) reflection occured at $\theta = 9.2°$, and the first (hhh) reflection occurred at $\theta = 23.1°$. From these data, if there is one atom per lattice site, calculate:
(a) The type and size of cubic unit cell.
(b) The distance of closest approach of Mo atoms.
(c) Avogadro's number.
(d) The angle θ at which the (211) reflection should occur.
Answer: (a) I, $a = 3.14$ A; (b) 2.72 A; (c) 0.607×10^{24}; (d) 16.1°.

43. When niobium metal diffracts X-radiation of wavelength 1.542 A, the first ($h00$) reflection lies at $2\theta = 55.64°$, the first ($hh0$) reflection lies at $2\theta = 38.54°$, and the first (hhh) reflection lies at $2\theta = 108.10°$. The metal is cubic, has a density of 8.57 g cm^{-3}, and has a specific heat of 0.065 cal g^{-1} deg^{-1}. In one of its oxides, the equivalent weight of the metal is 18.54. From only these data, calculate Avogadro's number if there is one atom per lattice site.
Answer: 0.601×10^{24}.

44. At 89°K, krypton exists in a cubic lattice with density of 3.00 g cm^{-3}. The first three X-ray reflections occur at $\theta = 13.54°$, 15.68°, and 22.46° when the wavelength is 1.542 A. From gas density measurements the atomic weight of krypton is known to be 83.8. Calculate the type and size of the cubic unit cell and the diameter of a krypton atom.
Answer: F; $a = 5.707$ A; 4.03 A.

45. Calculate for a face-centered lattice containing one atom with atomic scattering factor f at each lattice site the structure factors $F(hkl)$ as follows:
(a) $F(000)$. (b) $F(100)$. (c) $F(110)$. (d) $F(111)$. (e) $F(200)$. (f) $F(210)$. (g) $F(211)$. (h) $F(220)$.
Answer: (a) (d) (e) (h) $F = 4f$; otherwise, $F = 0$.

46. Repeat Problem 45 for a body-centered lattice.
Answer: (b) (d) (f) $F = 0$; otherwise, $F = 2f$.

47. What is the multiplicity of:
(a) ($h00$) in the cubic system.
(b) ($hk0$) in the orthorhombic system.
Answer: (a) 6; (b) 4.

48. If thorium has a density of 11.7 g/cm^3 and face-centered cubic crystals with one atom per lattice site and a shortest internuclear distance of 3.60 A,
(a) what are the five smallest Bragg angles at which powder spectra occur with $\lambda = 1.542$ A?
(b) what is the atomic weight of Th?
Answers: (a) 15.21°, 17.94°, 25.37°, 30.16°, 31.68°; (b) 232.5.

49. On a powder photograph taken with $\lambda = 1.541$ A radiation, the (111) reflection of Pt ($a = 3.92$ A) had a half-width at half-height of 1.00 degree, while a highly crystalline reference had reflections with half-widths at half-height of 0.200 degree at about the same Bragg angle. What is the crystallite size of Pt if all its broadening is caused by instrumental and crystallite size effects?
Answer: If K is 1.00, $t = 96.0$ A.

50. Show by a mathematical derivation that with a given uncertainty in Bragg angle, d_{hkl} and lattice constants can be determined more precisely at large Bragg angle than at small Bragg angle.

51. What is the ratio of atomic radii of a metal that has the same density in I and in F cubic structures?
Answer: 1.0287.

52. Calculate the squares of the structure factors of NaCl for the (100), (200), (300), (111), (222), and (333) reflections if $f(Na^+) = 10$ and if $f(Cl^-) = 18$.
Answer: $F^2(100) = F^2(300) = 0$; $F^2(200) = F^2(222) = 112^2$; $F^2(111) = F^2(333) = 32^2$.

53. Make a perspective drawing of the NiAs structure with a tracing of Figure 2.21 as a start.

54. With F^- at 000, give the relative coordinates of Ca^{2+} in CaF_2.
Answer: $(\frac{1}{4}\,\frac{1}{4}\,\frac{1}{4})$ $(\frac{3}{4}\,\frac{3}{4}\,\frac{1}{4})$ $(\frac{1}{4}\,\frac{3}{4}\,\frac{3}{4})$ $(\frac{3}{4}\,\frac{1}{4}\,\frac{3}{4})$.

55. How far apart are the closest tetrahedral voids among hexagonally close-packed spheres of radius r_-?
Answer: $r_-\sqrt{2/3}$.

56. Calculate the electron affinity of S^{2-} if at 0°K the standard heat of formation of cubic ZnS is −48.5 kcal/mole, the standard heats of formation of gaseous Zn and S (each atomic) are 30 and 52 kcal/mole, and the energy to remove two electrons from gaseous Zn to yield gaseous Zn^{2+} is 633 kcal/mole. Assume $n = 9$.
Answer: −59 kcal/mole.

57. Draw the second Brillouin zones of face-centered cubic by using up the rest of the (111) octahedron and (200) cube not used in the first zone.

58. Diagram the band energies of Mg and Al.

59. Certain oxides (e.g., γ-Al_2O_3 and γ-Fe_2O_3) have 32 oxide ions close-packed as in spinels in each cubic unit cell. Explain how and why these substances are disordered and how their cations might be arranged.

60. Show that the Fermi surface of electrons free in a box is a sphere.
Answer: See (16.37).

61. With the zero of energy at the top of the valence band, draw acceptor levels (hole energy levels) in the range of forbidden energies in a p-type semiconductor like Si.

62. The work function of Se in Table 16.12 is 4.87 ev and yet Se is a photoconductor in the presence of visible light. Explain.

Answer: Conduction band at less than 1.8 ev.

63. What wavelength of light is perhaps absorbed by an F center in NaCl as light ionizes it?
Answer: 5700 A.

64. What is the formula of PbS that has 10^{19} excess atoms of S per cm^3? What is its density if the defects are Schottky defects and if $a = 5.924$ A for the cubic unit cell? Let Pb = 207.19 and S = 32.064.
Answer: $PbS_{1.00052}$; 7.640 g cm^{-3}.

65. What is the energy of the Doppler spread of a gaseous atom of mass 50 at 300°K?
Answer: $2.35 \times 10^{-6}\ h\nu$.

66. An oxide layer 1000 A thick is growing at a rate of 1.00 A/sec. What is k_{TW}?
Answer: 1.00×10^{-13} cm^2 sec^{-1}.

67. The rate of transformation of metastable cubic AgI into hexagonal AgI was followed by X-ray powder photography by measuring the intensities of cubic and hexagonal reflections [G. Burley, *J. Phys. Chem.* **68,** 1111 (1964)]. Show that the transformation is first-order and find the activation energy from these data:
(a) At 120°C, mole percent hexagonal at various times (hrs):
30(0); 32(2); 34(4); 37(8); 41(15); 45(24).
(b) At 137°C, mole percent hexagonal at various times (hrs):
30(0); 34(2); 40(5); 45(8); 49(12); 56(20).
(c) At 146°C, mole percent hexagonal at various times (hrs):
30(0); 45(2.25); 53(4.50); 55(5); 57(5.75); 59(6.25).
Answer: $\Delta H_a = 10.3$ kcal/mole.

---

68. Some solids, called plastic crystals, have an unusually low entropy of fusion because of lattice disorder. If its enthalpy of fusion is normal, what is expected of the melting point of a plastic crystal?
Answer: High melting point because $\Delta G = \Delta H - T\Delta S = 0$.

69. In the cubic system, what is the angle between these pairs of faces? (110) and (111); (100) and (210).
Answer: 35.3°; 26.6°.

70. Draw a portion of a planar rectangular lattice and inscribe lines with indexes (2, 1), (4, 2), (3, 0), (2, 1) after defining axes.

71. Metallic aluminum, with one atom per lattice site and a density of 2.70 g cm^{-3} at 25°C, exhibits its first four X-ray reflections at $\theta = 19.25°$, 22.38°, 32.58°, and 39.15°. If the wavelength of radiation is 1.542 A, determine:
(a) The type and size of cubic unit cell.
(b) The atomic weight of Al.
(c) The distance between closest Al atoms.
(d) The angle θ at which (400) reflection occurs.
Answer: (a) F, $a = 4.05$ A; (b) 27.0; (c) 2.86 A; (d) 49.6°.

72. Show that the (222) reflection of CaF_2 is weak and explain why this is an advantage when CaF_2 is used as a monochromator.

73. The (200) reflection of metallic lithium at −183°C is at $\theta = 26.272°$ when the wavelength of X-rays is 1.5418 A. At 20°C the same reflection is at 26.062°. Calculate the coefficient of linear expansion of Li. Must the wavelength of X-rays be known?
Answer: 3.7×10^{-5} deg^{-1}.

74. Index the spectra of Figure 16.11 and determine the sizes of the cubic unit cells.
Answer: See tables except for a(Al) = 4.05 A and a(C) = 3.57 A.

75. Powder of a cubic crystal gives X-ray reflections at $\theta = 20.52°$, 23.88°, 34.90°, 42.15°, 44.50°, 54.05°, 62.00°, 64.95°, and greater angles. What are the indexes of these spectra?
Answer: (111) (200) (220) (311) (222) (400) (331) and (420).

76. A certain virus has a density of about 1.30 g/cm³ with cubic I or F crystals. The only two powder reflections observed with $\lambda = 1.542$ A lie at $\theta = 0.158°$ and 0.274°. If these spectra are among those possible with the three or four smallest values of $h^2 + k^2 + l^2$ allowed by I or F cubic lattices, what is the length of the edge of the cubic unit cell and what is the molecular weight of the virus if there is only one molecule of it per lattice site?
Answer: $a = 395$ A; $M = 24.1 \times 10^6$.

77. Solid solutions of Cu and Ni have lattice constants that vary linearly with mole fraction. Predict the density of a solid solution of 3 Cu atoms for every one Ni.
Answer: 8.929 g/cm³.

78. The mass absorption coefficients of Al are 5.28, 48.6, and 93.5 cm²/g at $\lambda = 0.710$ A, 1.540 A, and 1.933 A respectively. What values are expected at $\lambda = 4.00$ A and at 8.00 A if the K absorption edge is at 7.95 A?
Answer: At 4 A, 824. cm²/g; at 8 A, a value cannot be predicted because the K edge discontinuity is not given.

79. Explain how reflection broadening caused by crystallite size and by strain might be resolved into separate contributions if these sources of broadening are additive.
Answer: Plot $\beta \cos \theta$ vs $\sin \theta$.

80. Find the relative radius of a sphere situated among 8 identical spheres arranged in a square Archimedean antiprism. The 8 large spheres are in contact with each other and the central one just fits in among them.
Answer: $r_+/r_- = 0.646$.

81. For cubic and hexagonal arrangements of identical close-packed spheres, calculate the number of equivalent next-to-nearest neighbors and their distance as a multiple of a sphere radius r.
Answer: Six at $2\sqrt{2}\, r$.

82. What is to NiAs as CaF_2 is to CsCl?
Answer: CdI_2.

83. Rutile (a form of TiO_2) is tetragonal with $a = 4.59373$ A and $c = 2.95812$ A at 25°C. Titanium atoms lie at (000) and ($\frac{1}{2}\frac{1}{2}\frac{1}{2}$), and oxygen atoms lie at: (0.3053, 0.3053, 0); (0.8053, 0.1947, 0.5000); (0.6947, 0.6947, 0); and (0.1947, 0.8053, 0.5000). [R. W. G. Wyckoff, *Crystal Structures*, (Second Edition) Vol. 1, New York: Interscience Publishers, a division of John Wiley and Sons © 1963, p. 251]
(a) Draw a sketch of the unit cell with its atoms.
(b) Calculate the density of rutile.
(c) Determine the coordination number of Ti.
(d) Find the average Ti—O distance.
Answer: (b) 4.248 g/cm³; (c) 6; (d) four at 1.947 A and two at 1.983 A give 1.96 A.

84. A metal forms a sulfide MS describable as close-packed sulfide ions with cations in tetrahedral voids. It also forms an oxide MO describable as close-packed oxide

ions with cations in octahedral voids. Theoretically, what limits can be placed on the effective ionic radius of M^{2+}?
Answer: 0.58 A to 0.76 A.

85. When one mole of sphalerite is transformed into wurtzite, 3 kcal of heat are absorbed at 25°C at one atm. If $n = 9$, if polarization effects are alike in these two forms of ZnS, and if their heat capacities are alike at all T, what can be said of R_0, the shortest internuclear distance, in these crystals?
Answer: R_0 in wurtzite exceeds R_0 in sphalerite by 0.089 A, contrary to Table 16.14.

86. If Frenkel defects in a certain crystal are about 1000 times rarer than Schottky defects, and if each type could have been generated, what is the order or magnitude of the energy difference of these two types of defect?
Answer: $7RT$.

87. Explain the electrical conductivities of diamond, ZnS, NaCl, Fe, and CdS containing traces of $CuCl_x$ in place of Cd.

88. Calculate the Bohr radius of an electron in its most stable state near a positively charged ($\mathbf{Z} = 1$) impurity center in n-type semiconducting silicon. How many Si atoms are within a sphere with twice this distance as radius?
Answer: 550 atoms.

89. Indicate by a schematic diagram the contact layer and its distorted bands when:
(a) Two different metals touch.
(b) An insulator contacts a metal.
(c) An n-type semiconductor contacts a metal.

90. Calculate the energy states of a hole-electron combination in a homogeneous dielectric with $\kappa = 2.5$.
Answer: $E = -1.09/n^2$ (ev).

91. Explain why a laser that operates between one excited state and another excited state might be more easily maintained in a continuously emitting state.
Answer: If the lower state is not the ground state, use of an exciting frequency greater than the laser frequency can easily populate the higher excited state more than the lower excited state. For each excited state is subject to Boltzmann statistics relative to the ground state if radiation is absent.

92. If an oxide consists of close-packed oxide ions ($r_- = 1.40$ A), about how many NaCl-type unit cells are being added per second to a layer 1000 A thick if k_{TW} is 1.00×10^{-12} cm²/sec?
Answer: 2.5.

93. At about what T does vanadium with an exposed area of 1.00 cm² gain mass at a rate of 2.00 μg/min if the V_2O_3 layer is 6000 A thick and has a density of 4.80 g/cm³ and if the partial pressure of oxygen is 0.100 atm?
Answer: 510°C.

94. At about 700°C, with $CaF_{2(s)}$ as a barrier capable of conducting F^- interstitially, and with catalysts (oxides of Cr and Pb) present to speed electrode reactions, the cell

$$(Pt)O_{2(g)}\,|\,CaO_{(s)}\,|\,CaF_{2(s)}\,|\,CaSiO_{3(s)}\,|\,SiO_{2(s)}\,|\,O_{2(g)}(Pt)$$

has an EMF of 0.461 volt [R. Benz and C. Wagner, *J. Phys. Chem.* **65**, 1308 (1961)]. If the $CaSiO_3$ and SiO_2 are replaced by $Ca_3Si_2O_{7(s)}$ and $CaSiO_{3(s)}$, the EMF is 0.418 volt at about 700°C, while it is 0.060 volt if they are replaced by $Ca_2SiO_{4(s)}$ and $Ca_3Si_2O_{7(s)}$. Explain by half-reactions how this cell works and find ΔG for the reaction $4\,CaO_{(s)} + 2SiO_{2(s)} \longrightarrow 2Ca_2SiO_{4(s)}$ at 700°C.

Answer: $CaO_{(s)} + 2F^- \longrightarrow \frac{1}{2}O_{2(s)} + CaF_{2(s)} + 2e^-$ and $2e^- + CaF_{2(s)} + \frac{1}{2}O_{2(g)} + SiO_{2(s)} \longrightarrow CaSiO_{3(s)} + 2F^-$; or $CaO_{(s)} \longrightarrow \frac{1}{2}O_{2(g)} + Ca^{2+} + 2e^-$ and $2e^- + Ca^{2+} + \frac{1}{2}O_{2(g)} + SiO_{2(s)} \longrightarrow CaSiO_{3(s)}$; and so on; $\Delta G = -270{,}000$ j.

95. The reduction $CuO_{(s)} + H_{2(g)} \longrightarrow Cu_{(s)} + H_2O_{(g)}$ proceeds in three steps: induction, autocatalytic stage, and decreasing-rate stage. The last two stages are described by the equation [W. D. Bond, *J. Phys. Chem.* **66,** 1573 (1962)]

$$\frac{dx}{dt} = \frac{k_1}{2x_i}(1 - 2x_i + x)(1 - x)$$

where t is time, k_1 is a temperature-dependent rate constant, x is the fraction of CuO decomposed, and x_i is 0.35 (the mole fraction at maximum rate). With $k_1 = 0.0500\ \text{min}^{-1}$ at 450°K, how long will it take for a mixture of CuO and Cu containing ten mole percent Cu to be reduced to a mixture containing seventy mole percent Cu?
Answer: 21.7 min.

17
STATISTICAL MECHANICS

17.1 INTRODUCTION

The ancient Greek philosophers invented atoms to explain change. The atom stands for whatever is common to initial and final states, and the atom's motion and rearrangements stand for whatever distinguishes initial state from final state. This intuitive correlation is not quantitative in the sense expected by modern physical science.

The brief exposition of the kinetic theory in the first chapter and the four chapters just completed constitute a description of the 'atoms' of modern science. It has been possible on a few occasions to proceed quantitatively from the microscopic level of single events to the macroscopic, generally the thermodynamic, level of ordinary chemistry. For example, the kinetic theory has already yielded the perfect gas equation of state, root-mean-square velocities of free molecules, and understanding of diffusion and viscosity, and a phenomenological account of nonideal behavior of fluids. Sections 4.12 to 4.15 have introduced the Boltzmann distribution, the statistical temperature variable $\beta = 1/kT$, equipartition of energy, and how entropy is related to order and disorder in a qualitative sense.

The present brief chapter cannot be theoretically exhaustive. It aims rather to be practical and to offer physical insight into the behavior of systems of many particles. It reaches toward the ultimate goal of the theoretical chemist: to relate chemical behavior on the macroscopic or molar level to mechanical behavior on the microscopic or single-event level. Much modern research is devoted to this attempt for time-dependent processes. For equilibrium states and reversible processes, however, the broad outlines are well established and previous matter of this book provides several interesting examples that can be discussed properly here.

From the very beginning of this text observed facts have been related at least qualitatively to the structure of matter. The kinetic theory yielded a mechanical explanation of pressure and explained heat as disorganized mechanical motion. Faced with a detailed calculation of the trajectories and collisions of 10^{24} particles, one was forced to admit that the details were of secondary importance. Observables had to be averages and a full and complete knowledge was not only impossible but unnecessary. Still, averages must be used with caution for they involve uncertainties. In fact, as soon as one admits that he must use statistics he also admits his ignorance about a particular system and attempts to compensate for his lack of knowledge by recourse to what little he does know of similar systems. It is often easier to do this instead of getting precise data and complete facts for one system. While the actual information may then be less than the maximum that might somehow be attained, it is sufficient to satisfy present needs. Moreover, the uncertainties of quantum and wave mechanics are such that a cautious student might rightly question whether a wave-particle view of matter could give anything familiar, especially on the macroscopic level of observation. It happens, however, that it is easier to perform the required calculations correctly by use of discrete energies than it is to do the analogous classical calculations in violation of the uncertainty principle.

Statistical mechanics bridges the gap between single event and thermodynamics. It provides a method of calculating the few thermodynamic quantities of a macroscopic system from the immense number of individual events that together constitute the state of a system. Many similar but different microscopic states exhibit essentially the same macroscopic variables, so almost any reasonable set of microscopic events will yield thermodynamic sense. Almost any method of averaging also yields essentially the same result; the most probable state has macroscopic properties that differ only negligibly from any kind of average. As a result, the average behavior of an ensemble of similar microscopic systems in a suitable range of states is said to be the average behavior of a particular mechanical system actually studied. While its exact microscopic state may be incompletely specified, its thermodynamic state is indeed well specified.

A remark about notation: Wide use has established E_n as the symbol for the energy of a single microscopic system in the wave equation $\mathbf{H}u_n = E_n u_n$. Henceforth, however, the symbol ε_n replaces E_n for the energy of a single microscopic event or molecule, as in Chapter 4. That is, E and E_n now refer to macroscopic energies involving many molecules, while ε and ε_n refer to the energy of just one atom or molecule or other single event.

17.2 ENTROPY POSTULATE

Boltzmann made a remarkable and most fundamental discovery when he found that the function $\int\int f(p, q) \ln f(p, q)\, dp\, dq$ provides a macroscopically suitable measure of the deviation from equilibrium or degree of removal from equilibrium of a system with probability distribution $f(p, q)$. The symbols p and q stand for all the momenta and positions of the particles of the system. This function tends to decrease to a minimum as time passes and as equilibrium is approached. Entropy, on the contrary, tends spontaneously to increase as equilibrium is approached from some arbitrary initial state described by $f(p, q)$. Gibbs and many others after him thus postulate that

$$S = -k \int\int f \ln f\, dp\, dq \tag{17.1}$$

The change of sign means that S increases spontaneously on approach to equilibrium and the constant k fixes the dimensions of S, the entropy. Equation (17.1) is classical in that conjugate momenta p and positions q are assumed to have exactly specifiable values.

Stationary states, which as time-independent are expected to be the basis of equilibrium predictions, are characterized by their accurately specified energies ε_n in quantum mechanics. Time and energy are conjugate variables. The classical formulation of the entropy postulate is thus modified to read

$$S = -k \sum_n P_n \ln P_n \tag{17.2}$$

where P_n is the probability of a stationary state with energy ε_n. The summation proceeds over all allowed states just as the integrations in the classical expression (17.1) proceeded over all allowed values of p and q. As defined, S is identified with the macroscopically observable entropy of thermodynamics. Similarly, the thermodynamic energy E is identified with the mean energy

$$E = \sum_n P_n \varepsilon_n \tag{17.3}$$

The probabilities P_n of the energies ε_n can be calculated by the methods of quantum mechanics by taking appropriate averages of $|\psi|^2$. They are normalized so that for each molecule

$$1 = \sum_n P_n \tag{17.4}$$

At equilibrium, E is a minimum subject to the constraints of constant S and (17.4). Or again, at equilibrium, S is a maximum subject to the constraints of constant E and (17.4). By the method of undetermined multipliers A and $(\beta k)^{-1}$, either condition for an extremum (or stationary value) requires that

$$\delta E - A - \left(\frac{1}{\beta k}\right)\delta S = 0 \tag{17.5}$$

Since the several energies ε_n are specified, they remain fixed while the P_n's change; hence,

$$\delta E = \sum_n \varepsilon_n \, \delta P_n = 0 \tag{17.6}$$

From (17.4), a change in probabilities accompanying a virtual change in the system yields

$$\delta(1) = \sum_n \delta P_n = 0 \tag{17.7}$$

Similarly, from (17.2),

$$\delta S = -k \sum_n \left[\delta P_n \ln P_n + P_n \left(\frac{\delta P_n}{P_n} \right) \right] = 0$$

But because of (17.7), this is equivalent to

$$\delta S = -k \sum_n \delta P_n \ln P_n = 0 \tag{17.8}$$

Substitution of (17.6), (17.7), and (17.8) into (17.5) then yields

$$\sum_n \left[\varepsilon_n - A + \left(\frac{1}{\beta} \right) \ln P_n \right] \delta P_n = 0 \tag{17.9}$$

For arbitrary δP_n, it is necessary that

$$\ln P_n = \beta(A - \varepsilon_n) \tag{17.10}$$

$$P_n = e^{\beta(A-\varepsilon_n)} \tag{17.11}$$

The probability distribution of (17.10) and (17.11) is the most likely one and P_n, the probability that the system it represents is in state n with energy ε_n, is a maximum. The ensemble from which the mechanical system was chosen is called *canonical.* It represents a thermodynamic system at equilibrium with a constant temperature heat reservoir. The undetermined multipliers A and β have thermodynamic meaning and can be evaluated by (17.3) and (17.4).

17.3 IDENTIFICATION OF THERMODYNAMIC FUNCTIONS

Because ordinary macroscopic systems contain very great numbers of individuals, the probability distribution is quite sharply peaked at its single maximum. As a result, the most probable value of a quantity and its mean value cannot be distinguished experimentally. Such a distinction might be noticed for small systems such as a colloidal particle undergoing Brownian motion. However, for systems of ordinary or molar size, the average, most probable, and observed values are alike. Equation (17.3) states this for energy, and in general for some property G_n, the macroscopic value G is postulated to be

$$G = \sum_n G_n P_n \tag{17.12}$$

In particular, with $\ln P_n$ given by (17.10), (17.2) yields for the entropy

$$S = -k \sum_n P_n[\beta(A - \varepsilon_n)] = -k\beta[A \sum_n P_n - \sum_n P_n \varepsilon_n]$$

By virtue of (17.3) and (17.4), this becomes

$$S = -k\beta(A - E) \tag{17.13}$$

The various energies ε_n will in general depend upon *external parameters* x_i that can be specified at will by the experimenter. Such parameters might be electric, magnetic, or gravitational fields or the position of barriers such as vessel walls. If X stands for these external parameters and in particular for the volume, then the statisticomechanical equivalent of (5.10) is

$$T = \left(\frac{\partial E}{\partial S}\right)_X \tag{17.14}$$

Equation (17.14) is the most sophisticated and final definition of absolute temperature T. In particular, with values of δE and δS as given in (17.6) and (17.8)

$$T = \frac{\sum_n (\delta P_n)\varepsilon_n}{-k \sum_n (\delta P_n) \ln P_n} = \frac{\sum_n (\delta P_n)\varepsilon_n}{-k\beta \sum_n \delta P_n (A - \varepsilon_n)}$$

Since $\sum_n \delta P_n A = A \sum_n \delta P_n = 0$ because of (17.7), it follows at once that β fixes a reciprocal temperature scale, for

$$\beta = \frac{1}{kT} \tag{17.15}$$

Equation (17.13) then reads $S = (E - A)/T$. Since this yields $A = E - TS$, the undetermined multiplier A is the Helmholtz free energy. The various external parameters x_i are part of the surroundings and are under the control of an observer in the surroundings. Adjusting the x_i may cause ε_n and P_n both to change, for the values of x_i specify the nature of the quantum mechanical problem that gives the ε_n and $P_n = |\Psi_n|^2$. A change in a particular x_i, which may specify the (average) position of a vessel wall, is viewed as work if the P_n's are not changed. Hence, the work done on the system to change x_i by dx_i is

$$dw_i = \frac{\partial \varepsilon_n}{\partial x_i} dx_i \tag{17.16}$$

The coefficient of dx_i is the generalized force along the parameter x_i when the number of species of energy ε_n, as measured by P_n, is unchanged. The total work done on the system is the average of the sum of the dw_i's; hence,

$$dw = \sum_n P_n \sum_i \frac{\partial \varepsilon_n}{\partial x_i} dx_i = \sum_n P_n \, d\varepsilon_n \tag{17.17}$$

where the purely mathematical substitution of $d\varepsilon_n$ for its equivalent has been made.

The differential of E when both ε_n and P_n vary is found from (17.3) to be

$$dE = \sum_n \varepsilon_n \, dP_n + \sum_n P_n \, d\varepsilon_n \tag{17.18}$$

But since the last term of (17.18) is dw by virtue of (17.17), the first law in the form $dE = dq + dw$ requires that the heat absorbed by the system be

$$dq = \sum_n \varepsilon_n \, dP_n \tag{17.19}$$

That is, heat is absorbed when there is a change in the number of species in the various states of fixed energy ε_n. Work, as (17.17) suggests, involves a change in the energy levels, while heat, as (17.19) suggests, involves a change in the occupation of given energy states. From (17.8), (17.10) and (17.15), a change in entropy is

$$\begin{aligned} \delta S &= -k \sum_n \delta P_n [\beta(A - \varepsilon_n)] \\ &= \frac{1}{T} \sum_n \varepsilon_n \, \delta P_n \end{aligned}$$

as required by the second law if (17.19) holds in the form $\delta q = \sum \varepsilon_n \delta P_n$.

17.4 PARTITION FUNCTION

Actual calculation of values of E, S, A, and other thermodynamic variables generally involves the partition function Q, sometimes called the *sum-of-states*. By definition, the canonical partition function Q is

$$Q = \sum_n e^{-(\varepsilon_n/kT)} \tag{17.20}$$

Because of (17.4) and (17.11),

$$1 = \sum_n P_n = \sum_n e^{\beta(A-\varepsilon_n)}$$

But $\beta = 1/kT$ and A is independent of n so that

$$1 = e^{A/kT} \sum e^{-(\varepsilon_n/kT)}$$

$$e^{-(A/kT)} = Q$$

$$A = -kT \ln Q \tag{17.21}$$

It happens that the logarithm of Q is more convenient in calculations than is Q itself, as the following calculations show. For statistical mechanics, pressure P is defined by

$$-P = \left(\frac{\partial A}{\partial V}\right)_T \tag{5.17}$$

The partition function Q depends upon external parameters like V because the energies ε_n calculated by the wave equation depend upon boundary conditions like positions of vessel walls. By virtue of (17.21), pressure is

$$P = kT\left(\frac{\partial \ln Q}{\partial V}\right)_T \tag{17.22}$$

The logarithm of Q is involved also in E and C_V, for by (17.3) and (17.11),

$$E = \sum_n E_n e^{\beta A - \beta\varepsilon_n} = e^{\beta A} \sum_n E_n e^{-\beta\varepsilon_n}$$

Because of (17.20) and (17.21),

$$E = \frac{1}{Q}\left(-\frac{\partial Q}{\partial \beta}\right)_X = -\left(\frac{\partial \ln Q}{\partial \beta}\right)_X \tag{17.23}$$

In terms of T, (17.23) reads

$$E = -\left(\frac{\partial \ln Q}{\partial T}\right)_X \left(\frac{\partial T}{\partial \beta}\right)_X = kT^2\left(\frac{\partial \ln Q}{\partial T}\right)_X \tag{17.24}$$

Similarly, from the definition of C_V,

$$C_V = \left(\frac{\partial E}{\partial T}\right)_X = k\frac{\partial}{\partial T}\left[T^2\left(\frac{\partial \ln Q}{\partial T}\right)_X\right]_X \tag{17.25}$$

With values of V specified by the experimenter in advance, with values of E and S as postulated, and with values of T, P, and C_V as calculated from $\ln Q$, all thermodynamic functions can be calculated by the usual methods of thermodynamics.

Example 17.1. Express the Gibbs free energy G in terms of $\ln Q$ and its derivatives.

By definition, $G = E + PV - TS = A + PV$; hence, by (17.21) and (17.22),

$$G = kT\left[V\left(\frac{\partial \ln Q}{\partial V}\right)_T - \ln Q\right]$$

The straightforward but usually tedious way to evaluate the partition function Q is to sum (17.20) directly over all possible states with known energies ε_n at some temperature T of interest. States with ε_n large compared to kT contribute little or almost nothing to Q so that states with energies in excess of a certain value can be neglected in calculating Q within a specified accuracy. Most, and frequently all, energies of molecules can be found experimentally with great precision by spectroscopic methods since $\Delta\varepsilon = h\nu$.

Whether observed or calculated energies are used to evaluate the partition function, it is necessary to take account of the fact that identical particles or molecules cannot be distinguished from each other. Classically each individual of a system could in principle be numbered and followed along its observed or predicted trajectory in phase space forever. However, in order to assure that the entropy of a homogeneous system is an extensive property, Gibbs was forced to conclude that only the numbers and not the individual identities of like particles in the several states were of importance. Quantum mechanics by its nature insists on the same idea; identical particles are in principle indistinguishable. Thus, the $N!$ permutations of N identical particles comprising a system cannot even in classical statistical mechanics be considered to lead to new situations. Accordingly, permutations and interchanges of identical units do not generate really different circumstances and the partition function must be divided by $N!$ to take account of this indistinguishability of identical units.

Although in the last analysis any interaction whatsoever removes degeneracies and affects energies, it is often convenient and quite accurate to neglect interactions among almost independent units such as molecules of a perfect gas. Each molecule if isolated would have the same spectrum of energies ε_k. By analogy with (17.20) there is for each molecule a partition function

$$Q_1 = \sum_k e^{-\beta\varepsilon_k} \tag{17.26}$$

The system energies E_n become merely a summation of N terms each of which is one of the molecular energies ε_k. There is a system energy E_n for each way of distributing the various molecular energies ε_k among the N molecules considered as distinguishable. The number of times a particular value of $E_n = E_m$ occurs in Q is the number of ways of distributing the same set of molecular energies among the N distinguishable molecules, namely the coefficients C_m in

$$\left(\sum_k e^{-\beta\varepsilon_k}\right)^N = \sum_m C_m e^{-\beta E_m}$$

Here each value of E_m differs from every other. With $(N!)^{-1}$ to correct for indistinguishability,

$$Q = \frac{1}{N!}\sum_n e^{-\beta\varepsilon_n} = \frac{1}{N!}\sum_m C_m e^{-\beta E_m} = \frac{1}{N!}\left(\sum_k e^{-\beta\varepsilon_k}\right)^N$$

Substitution of Q_1 into the expression for Q yields for an ideal gas

$$Q = \frac{1}{N!} Q_1^N \tag{17.27}$$

In deriving (17.27) no limitation was placed upon the number of identical molecules with like spectra of energies ε_k. If the number of energy states available to the molecules greatly exceeds their actual number, (17.27) is adequate because it is unlikely that more than one molecule should achieve the same state as another molecule. Quantum mechanics, however, places limitations upon the number of molecules that can exist in exactly like states.

If each of the N molecules contains an odd number of elementary particles with half-integral spin, the wave function of the system must be antisymmetric with respect to interchange of any two molecules. Since interchange of an even number of elementary particles of half-integral spin does not change the sign of the wave function, the wave function of the system must be antisymmetric only if each molecule contains an odd number of such elementary particles. If their number is even in each molecule and if elementary particles with integral spin (light quanta, π-mesons, and the like) are present, the wave function of the system must be symmetric with respect to interchanges of molecules. Wave functions that are only partly symmetric or antisymmetric are not allowed.

Systems with symmetric wave functions may have any number of molecules in each quantum state, but systems with antisymmetric wave functions may have only one or none per state. Systems that can have only one or none per state are subject to the Pauli exclusion principle and are regulated by Fermi-Dirac statistics (Section 17.12). Systems that can have more than one unit in the same state follow Bose-Einstein statistics (Section 17.13). In the limit of high temperature or low density of units per available state both these kinds of statistics reduce to Boltzmann statistics for which (17.27) is true.

What follows in this chapter are explicit evaluations of ln Q. Sometimes this is possible because, at least for low energies, an approximately or asymptotically correct formula is known for ε_k as a function of quantum numbers over which the summation can be done. In favorable cases, when the number of states in an energy range of the order of kT is great, the summation becomes an integral that can be evaluated. It is appropriate here to rewrite (17.26) for the case when ε_k has a degeneracy of order g_k. With all terms containing ε_k grouped together, the partition function of a molecule is

$$Q_1 = \sum_k g_k e^{-\beta\varepsilon_k} \tag{17.28}$$

If the degeneracy is removed, only (17.26) is correct. The factors $e^{-\beta\varepsilon_k}$ may not differ sufficiently, however, when the splitting of the degeneracy is small compared to kT, to warrant use of (17.26) when (17.28) is available with fewer terms. Simplifications of this kind and hypothesizing models for which such simplifications are possible are the main concern of what follows.

17.5 PERFECT MONATOMIC GAS

With the methods of calculation now developed it is possible to calculate Q explicitly for several situations. One of the simplest of these is the ideal monatomic gas consisting of N identical point masses free in a volume V. The energies ε_k are given by (13.84), where k stands for the integer triple (n_x, n_y, n_z).

$$\varepsilon_k = \frac{\pi^2\hbar^2}{2m}\left(\frac{n_x^2}{a^2} + \frac{n_y^2}{b^2} + \frac{n_z^2}{c^2}\right) \tag{13.84}$$

If the box with sides a, b, and c is very large, the energies ε_k are closely spaced and, if the gas is dilute, (17.27) holds. The atoms have $g_k = 1$ in Q_1 of (17.28) if they have no internal energy states. It is easy, however, to allow each atom to have g_0 degenerate states so that (17.28) yields

$$\begin{aligned} Q_1 &= g_0 \sum_k e^{-\beta\varepsilon_k} \\ &= g_0 \sum_{n_x=1}^{\infty}\sum_{n_y=1}^{\infty}\sum_{n_z=1}^{\infty} \exp\left[-\frac{\beta\pi^2\hbar^2}{2m}\left(\frac{n_x^2}{a^2} + \frac{n_y^2}{b^2} + \frac{n_z^2}{c^2}\right)\right] \end{aligned} \tag{17.29}$$

Just as (17.20) becomes (17.27), the sum (17.29) becomes a product of sums, each taken over just one quantum number. In the approximation suitable for a rarefied gas in a big box,

$$\sum_{n=1}^{\infty} \exp\left[-\frac{\beta\pi^2\hbar^2}{2m}\left(\frac{n^2}{a^2}\right)\right] = \int_0^{\infty} \exp\left[-\frac{\beta\pi^2\hbar^2 n^2}{2ma^2}\right] dn$$

By the usual methods of transformation, this becomes

$$\frac{1}{2}\left(\frac{2ma^2}{\beta\pi^2\hbar^2}\right)^{1/2} \int_0^{\infty} x^{-1/2} e^{-x}\, dx = \left(\frac{ma^2}{2\beta\pi^2\hbar^2}\right)^{1/2} \Gamma\left(\frac{1}{2}\right) = \left(\frac{ma^2}{2\beta\pi\hbar^2}\right)^{1/2}$$

If $V = abc$, it therefore follows from (17.29) and (17.27) that

$$Q_1 = \left(\frac{2\pi mkT}{h^2}\right)^{3/2} g_0 V \tag{17.30}$$

and

$$Q = \left(\frac{2\pi mkT}{h^2}\right)^{3N/2} g_0^N \frac{V^N}{N!} \tag{17.31}$$

In order to obtain a simple expression for $\ln Q$, use is made of the Stirling approximation for factorials of large numbers:

$$\ln N! \approx N \ln N - N + \tfrac{1}{2} \ln 2\pi N \tag{17.32}$$

Since N is at least of the order of 10^{18}, the last term of (17.32) is negligible. With (17.32), (17.31) yields

$$\begin{aligned} \ln Q &= N \ln \left(\frac{2\pi mkT}{h^2}\right)^{3/2} + N \ln V - \ln N! + N \ln g_0 \\ &= N \ln \left[\left(\frac{2\pi mkT}{h^2}\right)^{3/2} g_0 \frac{Ve}{N}\right] \end{aligned} \tag{17.33}$$

The calculation of the thermodynamic functions given $\ln Q$ is straightforward. By (17.22), with $R = Nk$,

$$P = kT\left(\frac{\partial \ln Q}{\partial V}\right)_T = \frac{RT}{V}$$

Similarly, by (17.24),

$$E = RT^2 \frac{d \ln T^{3/2}}{dT} = \frac{3}{2} RT$$

Although these expressions are familiar, the absolute value of the entropy S is not. With the aid of (17.21),

$$S = \frac{E - A}{T} = \frac{3}{2} R + k \ln Q$$

With $PV = RT$ and $M = Nm$, it follows from (17.33) that

$$S = -R \ln P + \frac{5}{2} R \ln T + R \ln \left[\left(\frac{2\pi M}{Nh^2}\right)^{3/2} g_0 (ke)^{5/2}\right] \tag{17.34}$$

where P is in dynes/cm^2. If P is expressed in atmospheres and S in calories per mole per degree,

$$S = -R \ln P + \tfrac{5}{2} R \ln T + \tfrac{3}{2} R \ln M + R \ln g_0 - 2.3150 \tag{17.35}$$

These equations are suitable only for dilute gases in which almost all molecules are in the same state with degeneracy of order g_0 at the temperature T.

Example 17.2. What is the absolute entropy of He at 298.16°K? The accepted value is 30.126 cal mole^{-1} deg^{-1} [F. D. Rossini *et al.*, Circular of the National Bureau of Standards 500 (1952)].

Since $M = 4.003$, $g_0 = 1$, and $P = 1.000$ atm, (17.35) yields

$$\begin{aligned} S^\ominus &= \tfrac{5}{2} R \ln 298.16 + \tfrac{3}{2} R \ln 4.003 - 2.315 = 28.306 + 4.135 - 2.315 \\ &= 30.126 \text{ cal mole}^{-1} \text{ deg}^{-1}. \end{aligned}$$

17.6 PERFECT DIATOMIC GAS

When a molecule consists of mechanical parts or has accessible to it at the temperature of interest more than one intramolecular energy state, the partition function Q_1 depends upon more than just the translational energies of the preceding section. This discussion of intramolecular energies considers four kinds: electronic, vibrational, rotational, and nuclear spin energies. Since these energies merely add to the translational energy of the molecule,

$$Q_1 = \left(\frac{2\pi mkT}{h^2}\right)^{3/2} g_0 V Q_i \tag{17.36}$$

Here Q_i is an internal partition function, namely,

$$Q_i = \sum_i e^{-(\varepsilon_i/kT)} \tag{17.37}$$

where ε_i represents the several intramolecular energies.

The energy differences among various nuclear spin states are very small and are comparable to kT at less than 0.01°K even in strong magnetic fields. Accordingly, the several states that arise because of the several possible values of the components of an isotope's spin along the direction of a magnetic field are of almost equal energy. If the spin of the isotope is i, then the number of states of almost equal energy is $2i + 1$. Since each of these states has one term in Q_i, it follows that

$$Q_i = (2i + 1)Q_{im} \tag{17.38}$$

where Q_{im} is the internal partition function of the monatomic molecule without nuclear spin. An alternate way of accounting for this degeneracy of order $(2i + 1)$ is to set g_0 equal to $(2i + 1)$ in (17.36). Then Q_i is equal to Q_{im}. Henceforth, g_0 of (17.36) will be reserved for whatever unrecognized degeneracy there might be that is neglected through ignorance. That is, g_0 is effectively unity, held in reserve until needed.

In a diatomic molecule in which both atoms have nonzero nuclear spin, each contributes almost independently to Q_i. If the nucleuses differ,

$$Q_i = (2i_A + 1)(2i_B + 1)Q_{id} \tag{17.39}$$

where i_A and i_B are the spins on nucleuses A and B and where Q_{id} is the internal partition function of the heteronuclear diatomic molecule without nuclear spin. If the nucleuses are alike, the requirement for a symmetric or antisymmetric molecular wave function requires (17.39) to be modified. The modified form, generally required only for molecules such as H_2 and D_2 at temperatures less than room temperature, is

$$Q_i = i(2i + 1)Q_{id}^{(p)} + (i + 1)(2i + 1)Q_{id}^{(o)} \tag{17.40}$$

The superscripts refer to para and ortho modifications. The para form of a homonuclear diatom ($^{14}_{7}N^{14}_{7}N$, but not $^{14}_{7}N^{15}_{7}N$) has a total wave function with a factor that is antisymmetric (changes algebraic sign) upon interchange of identical nuclei. The total wave function of the ortho form has a factor that is symmetric upon interchange of the identical nuclei. The only really significant difference between $Q_{id}^{(p)}$ and $Q_{id}^{(o)}$ is in their rotational energies (15.55). The coefficients $i(2i + 1)$ and $(i + 1)(2i + 1)$ in (17.40) give the relative populations of the para and ortho forms because of the several degenerate states attributed to various alignments of nuclear spins. In the absence of catalysts (like free radicals) or magnetic fields, the interaction of nuclear spins with other molecular energies is so weak that collisions and vaporizations and similar events have only a small probability of changing ortho molecules into para ones, and vice versa. Moreover, if the nuclear spin is zero ($i = 0$), then only ortho states exist. That is, the ratio of the number of antisymmetric nuclear spin factors in the total wave function to the number of symmetric ones is $i/i + 1$.

The total wave function of a homonuclear diatom is, to a good approximation, a product of factors, each describing a certain kind of additive intramolecular energy. It is a product of a center-of-mass part (symmetric to interchanging nuclei that are alike), a vibrational part (which depends only on internuclear distance R and is thus of no concern for interchanging nuclei), an electronic part [which is symmetric to an interchange of electrons (or, what is equivalent, of nuclei) if it is +g or −u (see Section 15.5 for this notation), but is antisymmetric to an interchange of electrons (or nuclei) if −g or +u], a rotational part (which is symmetric to an interchange of identical nuclei if the rotational quantum number J is even, but antisymmetric if J is odd), and a nuclear spin part (which is symmetric to an interchange of identical nuclei if ortho, but antisymmetric if para, as described above). The Pauli exclusion principle requires the total wave function to be antisymmetric upon interchange of nuclei that act like fermions (that is, have an odd number of nucleons). The total wave function is symmetric to an interchange of identical nuclei consisting of an even number of nucleons, for an even number of sign changes means no net change in sign. Moreover, an interchange of identical nuclei cannot change the density of matter; hence, the total wave function must be either symmetric or antisymmetric in such interchange. It cannot be partly symmetric and/or partly antisymmetric.

The ground state of H_2 is $^1\Sigma_g^+$; hence, the electronic factor is symmetric. Since each nucleus is a proton in $^1H^1H$, its total wave function must be antisymmetric upon interchange of protons. If the rotational factor is symmetric (J even), then the nuclear spin factor must be antisymmetric (para); and vice versa. That is, para states with nuclear degeneracy $i(2i + 1)$ have only even J, while ortho states have only odd J. This combination keeps the total wave function antisymmetric to the interchange of protons in the $X^1\Sigma_g^+$ state of $^1H^1H$.

On the other hand, the ground states of D_2 and N_2 are also $^1\Sigma_g^+$ but their ortho states have only even J while their para states have only odd J. The reason is that their nuclei have integral spin and even numbers of nucleons, and thus behave like bosons. With +g electronic states, the rotational and nuclear spin factors must be both symmetric (ortho, even J) or both antisymmetric (para, odd J). The ratio of intensities in the rotational spectra or the presence or absence of states of even or odd J has in the past told the values of nuclear spin. The isotopes ^{17}O and ^{18}O were first discovered in O_2 because of the appearance of rotational states of $^{17}O^{16}O$ and $^{18}O^{16}O$ not allowed to $^{16}O^{16}O$. Again, in $^{14}N^{14}N$ all even J(ortho) have twice the population of odd J (para) so that $i + 1/i = 2$, with $i = 1$ as a result. In $^1H^1H$, the ratio of ortho to para is $(\frac{1}{2} + 1)/(\frac{1}{2})$, or 3 to 1, at very high T where many rotational states are populated. Cooling hydrogen in the absence of catalysts preserves this ratio of 3 ortho to 1 para with the result that at low T the state $J = 1$ (ortho) is for a while more heavily populated than is the lowest state $J = 0$ (para). For most molecules containing identical nucleuses, several rotational energy levels are well populated at room temperature. If so, (17.40) reduces to $\frac{1}{2}Q_i$ of (17.39) because only half of the rotational states are accessible to each modification.

The net effect of nuclear spin states is thus to add ln $(2i + 1)$, ln $(2i_A + 1)(2i_B + 1)$, or approximately $2 \ln(2i + 1) - \ln 2$ to ln Q_1. These terms affect only the entropy. Since only a nuclear reaction can change nuclear spin, this entropy term (except $-\ln 2$) is suppressed or ignored by convention.

Another contribution to entropy that is generally suppressed is the entropy of mixing of isotopes. As long as the change of interest produces no separation of isotopes, the whole system can be classified as one giant molecule that suffers no change in its entropy due to isotope redistribution. Most changes do change electronic, vibrational, and rotational states so that their influence on the several thermodynamic functions must now be calculated.

As is generally the case, direct summation over all molecular states except nuclear spin states will yield Q_i. Because electronic energies are commonly great relative to kT and also few in number, Q_i for electronic states of any molecule—monatomic, diatomic, or polyatomic—is best evaluated by direct summation. In addition to its characteristic vibrational and rotational energy, each state of a certain electronic state has a common electronic energy ε_e. Each term of Q_i for each electronic state thus has a common factor $e^{-(\varepsilon_e/kT)}$ so that

$$Q_i = \sum_e Q_e Q_{rv}^{(e)} \tag{17.41}$$

Equation (17.41) really says that electronic energy and rotational-vibrational energy are additive. The summation upon e in (17.41) is over electronic states with

$$Q_e = g_e e^{-(\varepsilon_e - \varepsilon_0)/kT} \tag{17.42}$$

where $\varepsilon_e - \varepsilon_0$ is the energy difference of the lowest vibrational-rotational state of state e and that of the ground state with energy ε_0. Ordinarily ε_0 is the origin of energy so that $\varepsilon_0 = 0$. The factor g_e is the degeneracy of state e, that is, the number of electronic states of almost equal energy for every vibrational-rotational state. For most stable chemicals, g_e is unity in the ground state. Oxygen and NO are notable exceptions. The ground state of O_2 is ${}^3\Sigma_g^-$, the three states of the triplet being separated by only about 1 cm^{-1}. This is a negligible energy difference even below 100°K so that at ordinary T, $g_e = 3$. The situation for NO is explained in Example 17.4.

It happens that rotational and vibrational energies are at least approximately additive so that for a particular electronic state e

$$Q_{rv}^{(e)} = Q_r^{(e)} Q_v^{(e)} \tag{17.43}$$

Except for H_2, HD, CH_4, and other molecules with small moments of inertia, above room temperature Q_r can be evaluated by integration. Moreover, the summation over vibrational states represented by Q_v can be evaluated in closed form if the vibration is harmonic. Thus, Q_{rv} can be expressed explicitly in terms of molecular parameters.

From the development above it is clear that

$$Q_v = \sum_v e^{-[\varepsilon(v)/kT]} \tag{17.44}$$

where, as in (14.95), $\varepsilon(v) = (v + \frac{1}{2})2\pi\hbar\nu_0$. Substitution and factoring yield

$$Q_v = e^{-(\pi\hbar\nu_0/kT)} \sum_{v=0}^{\infty} e^{-(2\pi\hbar\nu_0 v/kT)} \tag{17.45}$$

The summation is the sum of a geometric progression with a term-to-term ratio of $\exp(-2\pi\hbar\nu_0/kT)$; hence, as in Section 13.2, Equation (13.5),

$$Q_v = e^{-(\pi\hbar\nu_0/kT)}[1 - e^{-(2\pi\hbar\nu_0/kT)}]^{-1} \tag{17.46}$$

Values of ν_0 for several molecules can be calculated from values of ω_e in the ground state in Table 15.1 by the relation $\nu_0 = c\omega_e$.

The evaluation of Q_r by integration is justified when $B_e hc \ll kT$. Since there are $(2J + 1)$ states of energy $\varepsilon(J) = hcB_e[J(J + 1)]$ it follows that

$$Q_r = \sum_{J=0}^{\infty} (2J + 1)e^{-\{hcB_e[J(J+1)]/kT\}} \tag{17.47}$$

If $hcB_e = wkT$ and if $w \ll 1$,

$$Q_r = \int_0^{\infty} (2J + 1)e^{-w(J^2+J)}\,dJ = \frac{1}{w}\int_0^{\infty} e^{-x}\,dx = \frac{1}{w}\Gamma(1) = \frac{1}{w}$$

By (15.57),

$$Q_r = \frac{4\pi c I_e kT}{h\hbar c} = \frac{2I_e kT}{\hbar^2} \tag{17.48}$$

Combination of all these results yields for the internal partition function Q_i of a heteronuclear diatomic molecule in its nondegenerate ground electronic state, subject of course to the various restrictions noted above,

$$Q_i = (2i_A + 1)(2i_B + 1)\left(\frac{2I_e kT}{\hbar^2}\right)\left[\frac{e^{-(\pi\hbar\nu_0/kT)}}{1 - e^{-(2\pi\hbar\nu_0/kT)}}\right] \tag{17.49}$$

If $A = B$ certain rotational levels are unpopulated and Q_i contains an extra factor of $\frac{1}{2}$. For a system of N identical diatomic gas molecules, then,

$$\ln Q = N \ln\left[\left(\frac{2\pi mkT}{h^2}\right)^{3/2} \frac{Ve}{N} Q_i\right] \tag{17.50}$$

where Q_i is given by (17.49) or its equivalent. These formulas are full of traps; hence, several examples follow to illustrate their use.

Example 17.3. Calculate the heat content function of N_2 at 2000°K and compare with the value of Table 9.4.

Since $H = E + PV$, it seems necessary to calculate PV as well as E by statistical mechanics. But Q_i is independent of V so that $PV = RT$ for N_2 as well as a monatomic perfect gas. Hence, at 0°K, PV vanishes and E is zero by convention. The heat function is thus

$$\frac{H_T^\ominus - H_0^\ominus}{T} = \frac{[E(T) + RT] - [E(0) + 0]}{T} = \frac{E(T)}{T} + R$$

Only E needs calculation at 2000°K. By (17.24), (17.49), and (17.50), with the effects of nuclear spin in this homonuclear molecule accounted for by an extra factor of $\frac{1}{2}$,

$$\begin{aligned}
\frac{E(T)}{T} &= kT\left(\frac{\partial \ln Q}{\partial T}\right)_V \\
&= RT\frac{\partial}{\partial T}\ln\left[\left(\frac{2\pi mkT}{h^2}\right)^{3/2}\left(\frac{Ve}{N}\right)\frac{1}{2}\left(\frac{2I_e kT}{\hbar^2}\right)\left(\frac{e^{-(\pi\hbar\nu_0/kT)}}{1 - e^{-(2\pi\hbar\nu_0/kT)}}\right)\right] \\
&= RT\frac{\partial}{\partial T}\left\{\ln T^{5/2} - \frac{\pi\hbar\nu_0}{kT} - \ln\left[1 - e^{-(2\pi\hbar\nu_0/kT)}\right]\right\} \\
&= RT\left[\frac{\frac{5}{2}T^{3/2}}{T^{5/2}} + \frac{\pi\hbar\nu_0}{kT^2} + \frac{e^{-(2\pi\hbar\nu_0/kT)}(2\pi\hbar\nu_0/kT^2)}{1 - e^{-(2\pi\hbar\nu_0/kT)}}\right] \\
&= \frac{5}{2}R + \frac{Nh\nu_0}{T}\left[\frac{1}{2} + \frac{e^{-(2\pi\hbar\nu_0/kT)}}{1 - e^{-(2\pi\hbar\nu_0/kT)}}\right] \\
&= \frac{5}{2}R + \frac{Nh\nu_0}{T}\left[\frac{1}{2} + \frac{1}{e^{(2\pi\hbar\nu_0/kT)} - 1}\right]
\end{aligned}$$

According to Table 15.1, $\omega_e = 2359.61\ \mathrm{cm}^{-1}$; hence,

$$\frac{h\nu_0}{kT} = \frac{hc\omega_e}{kT} = \frac{6.626 \times 10^{-27} \times 2.998 \times 10^{10} \times 2.360 \times 10^3}{1.380 \times 10^{-16} \times 2.000 \times 10^3} = 1.698$$

and $e^{1.698} = 5.464$.

Since the real state at 0°K is given zero energy, the term $Nh\nu_0/2T$ must be suppressed for it is due to zero-point energy $Nh\nu_0/2$, which has as its reference the minimum of potential energy rather than the lowest vibrational state. Accordingly, at 2000°K,

$$\frac{H_T^{\ominus} - H_0^{\ominus}}{T} = R + \frac{5}{2}R + \frac{Nh\nu_0}{2000} \times \left(\frac{1}{5.464 - 1}\right)$$

$$= \frac{7}{2}R + \frac{6.023 \times 10^{23} \times 6.626 \times 10^{-27} \times 2.360 \times 10^3 \times 2.998 \times 10^{10}}{2.000 \times 10^3 \times 4.464 \times 4.184 \times 10^7}$$

$$= 6.955 + 0.756 = 7.711\ \mathrm{cal\ mole^{-1}\ deg^{-1}}$$

The value in Table 9.4 is 7.750 cal mole^{-1} deg^{-1}, higher through anharmonicity.

Example 17.4. Find Q_i for NO if nuclear spin is ignored.

From the discussion of NO in Section 15.5 it is necessary to conclude that the ground electronic state involves electronic spin and a nonzero component of electronic angular momentum along the internuclear axis. Because the electronic angular momentum states differ little in energy, these π-states with components $+1$ and -1 cause every energy level to be doubled; hence, $g_e = 2$. The two electronic spin states are separated by an energy $\varepsilon_e = 120\ \mathrm{cm}^{-1}$, which is comparable to kT at 200°K; it is thus improper to correct by a factor of two or to ignore the more energetic state. Since the vibrational and rotational energies of both electronic spin states are almost alike, (17.41), (17.42), and (17.49) yield

$$Q_i = 2\left[1 + e^{-(\varepsilon_e/kT)}\right]\left(\frac{2I_e kT}{\hbar^2}\right)\left[\frac{e^{-(\pi\hbar\nu_0/kT)}}{1 - e^{-(2\pi\hbar\nu_0/kT)}}\right]$$

Example 17.5. Calculate the equilibrium constant K_p for the gaseous reaction $^{14}N^{14}N + {}^{16}O^{16}O \longrightarrow 2\,{}^{14}N^{16}O$ at 2000°K from these data if there are no other states of lower electronic energy.

Molecule	State	D_e (ev)	ε_e (cm^{-1})	ω_e (cm^{-1})	R_e (A)
N_2	$X\,^1\Sigma_g^+$	9.76	0	2360	1.098
N_2	$a\,^1\Pi_g$		69300	1690	1.214
O_2	$X\,^3\Sigma_g^-$	5.08	0	1580	1.208
O_2	$a\,^1\Delta_g$		7920	1510	1.216
O_2	$b\,^1\Sigma_g^+$		13200	1430	1.227
NO	$X\,^2\Pi_{1/2}$	6.49	0	1900	1.151
NO	$X\,^2\Pi_{3/2}$		120	1900	1.151
NO	$A\,^2\Sigma^+$		44000	2370	1.064

Since Δn_g is zero, $\Delta A^{\ominus} = \Delta G^{\ominus} = -RT \ln K_p$ by Section 9.2. Equation (17.21), which is $A = -kT \ln Q$, gives the Helmholtz free energy $A(T)$ of a substance at T relative to $A(0)$ at $T = 0$ when the zero of energy for Q is the ground state of that substance, as in the tabulated values of ε_e. However, at

$T = 0$, $\Delta E_0^{\ominus} = \Delta A_0^{\ominus}$ is not zero for the chemical reaction; it is really $\Delta A_0^{\ominus} = 2\,A_{\rm NO}^{\ominus}(0) - A_{\rm NN}^{\ominus}(0) - A_{\rm OO}^{\ominus}(0)$. The dissociation energies D_e tabulated above are referred to gaseous atoms at rest in their ground electronic states. Hence, for the reaction at $T = 0$,

$$\Delta A_0^{\ominus} = 2(-6.49) - (-9.76) - (-5.08) = 1.86 \text{ ev} = 42.9 \text{ kcal/mole}$$

With (17.21) in the form $A(T) - A(0) = -kT \ln Q$, there results for the gaseous reaction

$$\begin{aligned}\Delta A^{\ominus} &= 2A_{\rm NO}^{\ominus}(T) - A_{\rm NN}^{\ominus}(T) - A_{\rm OO}^{\ominus}(T)\\ &= \Delta A_0^{\ominus} - kT \ln [Q_{\rm NO}^{\ominus}\, Q_{\rm NO}^{\ominus} / Q_{\rm NN}^{\ominus} Q_{\rm OO}^{\ominus}]\end{aligned}$$

Since $\Delta A^{\ominus} = -RT \ln K_p$ and since $R = Nk$, it follows that at 2000°K

$$\begin{aligned}\ln K_p &= -\frac{\Delta A_0^{\ominus}}{RT} + \frac{1}{N} \ln \left(\frac{Q_{\rm NO}^{\ominus}\, Q_{\rm NO}^{\ominus}}{Q_{\rm NN}^{\ominus} Q_{\rm OO}^{\ominus}}\right)\\ &= -\frac{42.9 \times 10^3}{1.987 \times 2000} + \frac{1}{N} \ln [\Pi Q^{\ominus}]\\ &= -10.79 + \frac{1}{N} \ln [\Pi Q^{\ominus}]\end{aligned}$$

where the meaning of $\Pi Q^{\ominus}$ is clear. Each $Q^{\ominus}$ in $\Pi Q^{\ominus}$ has as its zero of energy the ground state of its own gaseous diatom at one atm pressure.

According to (17.49) and (17.50), the variables needed to calculate the Q's are the moments of inertia I_e, the vibrational frequencies ν_0, the masses m of the diatoms, and (to get $Q^{\ominus}$ rather than Q) the volumes V occupied by a mole of diatoms at one atm at 2000°K. (Nuclear spin is ignored conventionally, but it is necessary to include a factor of 1/2 in $Q_i^{\ominus}$ of N_2 and O_2.) A closer study of these equations and the definition above for $\Pi Q^{\ominus}$ indicates much cancellation of various factors. Indeed, by (17.50) there results simply

$$\ln [\Pi Q^{\ominus}] = N \ln \left(\frac{m_{\rm NO}^{3/2}\, Q_{i\rm NO}\, m_{\rm NO}^{3/2}\, Q_{i\rm NO}}{m_{\rm NN}^{3/2}\, Q_{i\rm NN}\, m_{\rm OO}^{3/2}\, Q_{i\rm OO}}\right)$$

This result will be used below after various factors in Q_i are evaluated.

Excited electronic states do not contribute significantly to Q_i when ε_e is very great. How great depends on T. In the $b\ {}^1\Sigma_g^+$ state of O_2

$$\begin{aligned}\exp\left(-\frac{\varepsilon_e}{kT}\right) &= \exp\left(-\frac{6.626 \times 10^{-27} \times 2.998 \times 10^{10} \times 13200}{1.380 \times 10^{-16} \times 2000}\right)\\ &= \exp(-9.50) = 10^{-4.12} = 7.6 \times 10^{-5}\end{aligned}$$

Within 1 part in 10^4 this state of O_2 and all states of O_2 of higher energy can be neglected. So also can the $a\ {}^1\Pi_g$ state of N_2 and $A\ {}^2\Sigma^+$ state of NO be neglected within the same accuracy. The $a\ {}^1\Delta_g$ state of O_2 is not negligible, for

$$\exp\left(-\frac{\varepsilon_e}{kT}\right) = \exp(-5.70) = 10^{-2.48} = 3.34 \times 10^{-3}$$

It is clear also that the ${}^2\Pi_{3/2}$ state of NO cannot be neglected since for it

$$\exp\left(-\frac{\varepsilon_e}{kT}\right) = \exp(-0.0864) = 0.9228$$

According to Example 17.4, therefore, for NO

$$Q_{i\text{NO}} = 2(1.9228)\left(\frac{2I_{e\text{NO}}kT}{\hbar^2}\right)Q_{v\text{NO}}$$

where $Q_{v\text{NO}}$ as given by (17.46) is the same for both $^2\Pi$ states. Nitrogen has $g_e = 1$ because $X\,^1\Sigma_g^+$ is nondegenerate, has $Q_e = 1$ because $X\,^1\Sigma_g^+$ is the only electronic state of interest, and has a factor of 1/2 in $Q_{i\text{NN}}$ for ortho-para correction; hence,

$$Q_{i\text{NN}} = \frac{1}{2}\left(\frac{2I_{e\text{NN}}kT}{\hbar^2}\right)Q_{v\text{NN}}$$

where $Q_{v\text{NN}}$ is given by (17.46). At 2000°K (or even only 100°K) the $X\,^3\Sigma_g^-$ state of O_2 can be treated as triply degenerate with $g_e = 3$. The $a\,^1\Delta_g$ state of O_2 is doubly degenerate with $g_e = 2$ because the component of electronic angular momentum along the molecular axis may be either $+2$ or -2 in states of almost equal energy; this is called *lambda doubling*. With a factor of 1/2 for ortho-para correction

$$Q_{i\text{OO}} = \frac{1}{2}\left[3\left(\frac{2I''_{e\text{OO}}kT}{\hbar^2}\right)Q''_{v\text{OO}} + 2 \times 3.34 \times 10^{-3}\left(\frac{2I'_{e\text{OO}}}{\hbar^2}\right)Q'_{v\text{OO}}\right]$$

where a double prime refers to the $^3\Sigma_g^-$ state and a single prime refers to the $^1\Delta_g$ state.

The rotational factors $(2I_ekT/\hbar^2)$ can be calculated from R_e for each species, since (15.54) requires $I_e = \mu R_e^2$ where μ is the diatom's reduced mass. The common factor at 2000°K has the cgs value

$$\frac{2kT}{\hbar^2} = \frac{2 \times 1.380 \times 10^{-16} \times 2000}{(1.0545 \times 10^{-27})^2} = 49.6 \times 10^{40}$$

The table below summarizes the results for the rotational factors of interest.

Molecule	State	R_e (cm)	μ (g)	I_e (g cm^2)	$\frac{2I_e kT}{\hbar^2}$
$^{14}N^{14}N$	$X\,^1\Sigma_g^+$	1.098×10^{-8}	11.61×10^{-24}	14.01×10^{-40}	695.5
$^{16}O^{16}O$	$X\,^3\Sigma_g^-$	1.208	13.28	19.39	962.5
$^{16}O^{16}O$	$a\,^1\Delta_g$	1.216	13.28	19.64	975.5
$^{14}N^{16}O$	$X\,^2\Pi$	1.151	12.39	16.41	815.0

The vibrational contributions of these states can be found from ω_e, for at 2000°K

$$\frac{\pi\hbar\nu_0}{kT} = \frac{h\nu_0}{2kT} = \frac{hc\omega_e}{2kT} = 3.596 \times 10^{-4}\,\omega_e$$

The following table lists the values of Q_v calculated from ω_e by (17.46).

Molecule	State	$\omega_e(\text{cm}^{-1})$	$\frac{\pi\hbar\nu_0}{kT} = u$	e^{-u}	e^{-2u}	Q_v
N_2	$X\,^1\Sigma_g^+$	2360	0.848	0.428	0.183	0.467
O_2	$X\,^3\Sigma_g^-$	1580	0.568	0.567	0.321	0.835
O_2	$a\,^1\Delta_g$	1510	0.543	0.581	0.338	0.877
NO	$X\,^2\Pi$	1900	0.683	0.505	0.255	0.678

Inserting these results for Q_v and $(2I_ekT/\hbar^2)$ into the expressions for Q_i derived above yields

$$Q_{i\text{NO}} = 2(1.9228)(815.0)(0.678) = 2125$$
$$Q_{i\text{NN}} = \tfrac{1}{2}(695.5)(0.467) = 162.4$$
$$Q_{i\text{OO}} = \tfrac{1}{2}[(3 \times 962.5 \times 0.835) + (2 \times 3.34 \times 10^{-3} \times 975.5 \times 0.877)] = 1208$$

All of these results for Q_i then yield

$$\begin{aligned}\ln[\Pi Q^\ominus] &= N \ln\left[\left(\frac{m_{\text{NO}}m_{\text{NO}}}{m_{\text{NN}}m_{\text{OO}}}\right)^{3/2}\left(\frac{Q_{i\text{NO}}Q_{i\text{NO}}}{Q_{i\text{NN}}Q_{i\text{OO}}}\right)\right] \\ &= N\ln\left[\left(\frac{30.0 \times 30.0}{28.0 \times 32.0}\right)^{3/2}\left(\frac{2125 \times 2125}{162.4 \times 1208}\right)\right] \\ &= N \ln 23.2 = 3.14N\end{aligned}$$

Therefore, from far above,

$$\ln K_p = -10.79 + \frac{1}{N}\ln[\Pi Q^\ominus] = -10.79 + 3.14 = -7.65$$

$$K_p = 4.8 \times 10^{-4}$$

This result for K_p differs from the value 3.94×10^{-4} of Example 9.16. The neglect of changes in ω_e and R_e as the vibrational quantum number rises causes an error of 0.15 in $\ln K_p$, small partly because errors in $Q_{i\text{NO}}$ are partly offset by like errors in $Q_{i\text{NN}}$ and $Q_{i\text{OO}}$. The free energy functions calculated thus are in error by about 20%, but their combination in $\Delta G^\ominus$ is in error by only 5%.

17.7 PERFECT POLYATOMIC GAS

Because polyatomic molecules have many more electronic and vibrational energy states than diatomic molecules, their spectra are quite complex compared to diatomic spectra. As a result, the interpretation of their spectra in terms of simple and uniquely identified energy states is difficult. Although the expressions for the several forms of molecular energy are similar in kind to those for diatomic molecules, they are more lengthy. Each added term in the molecular energy adds a factor to the partition function.

If electronic energies are ignored and if other molecular energies can be separated into additive contributions from nuclear spin, rotation, and vibration, there is in the partition function of a molecule (1) a factor $(2i + 1)$ for each nucleus with nonzero spin; (2) a factor $(2I_e kT/\hbar^2)^{1/2}$ for each nonzero moment of inertia; (3) a factor $\{e^{-(\pi\hbar\nu_0/kT)}/[1 - e^{-(2\pi\hbar\nu_0/kT)}]\}^{g_v}$ for each vibrational frequency, where g_v is the degree of vibrational degeneracy; (4) a correction factor $\sqrt{\pi}/\sigma$, where σ is the finite order of the pure rotational subgroup of the point group of the nonlinear molecule. Because molecular symmetry and internal rotations generally require detailed application often tailored to fit a particular kind of molecule, these remarks on polyatomic molecules and their partition functions must suffice here.

At modest temperatures the partition function of many molecules depends only mildly upon vibrations. Often it is sufficient to use only approximate frequencies of vibration guessed by analogy with similar molecules or by use of an empirical force-constant formula. With moments of inertia from data on molecular structure it is then possible to calculate free energies and equilibrium constants for gaseous reactions, as in Example 17.5 above.

17.8 DIPOLES IN A STATIC FIELD

The preceding sections have shown how the partition function can be evaluated and used to describe the thermodynamic behavior of gaseous systems. Both term-by-term summation and summation by integration have been used, the latter when many energy states are populated and their differences in energy are small compared to kT. This is essentially a classical limit wherein energy is almost continuously variable. The action of an electric field on the orientation of electrically unsymmetrical molecules of a gas is another example of this essentially classical limit.

A very intense electric field may ionize the gas, and by accelerating ions and electrons produce by bombardment many more ions until a gaseous discharge occurs. If the field is not intense enough to transform or destroy molecules, however, it tends merely to orient electrically unsymmetrical molecules so that a part of a molecule that is preponderantly negative in charge tends toward the positive pole of the external electric field while the positively charged part of a molecule tends toward the negative pole. Because the molecule is neutral it does not migrate, and because it is continually bombarded by other molecules its alignment in the field is far from perfect.

In a symmetrical molecule like Ne or N_2 the external electric field may actually induce a movement of charges within the molecule so as to effect a separation of charge proportional to the strength of the field. Unsymmetrical molecules like HCl and CH_3Cl, however, present to the field a permanent separation of centers of positive and negative charge. The product of the distance of separation l and the amount of charge ze (z is the effective number of electronic charges e of magnitude 4.80223×10^{-10} esu) is the dipole moment. It is a vector directed from the center of negative charge to the center of positive charge. Its magnitude is μ_0, where

$$\mu_0 = zel \tag{17.51}$$

It happens that dipole moments are by custom stated with cgs units. In this treatment, μ_0 will be assumed to be independent of the electrostatic field.

Because the molecule as a whole is uncharged, there is no force acting on it as a whole and its energy is independent of the position of its center of mass in the field. The molecule's orientation in the field is, however, influenced by the field. Let the angle from the direction of the field **E** to the dipole moment be θ, with $\theta = 0$ when alignment is ideal and the energy of the dipole in the field is a minimum. Then the potential energy of the dipole for any orientation is $V(\theta)$, where

$$V(\theta) = -\mu_0 \mathbf{E} \cos\theta \tag{17.52}$$

Here $V(\theta)$ is essentially non-quantized energy in excess of the kinetic energy enjoyed by each molecule.

Just as the Boltzmann distribution specifies the distribution of molecules according to their kinetic energies, it similarly specifies their numbers according to their potential energies $V(\theta)$ relative to their energies in the absence of the field. Since the component of the dipole moment in the direction of the field is $\mu_0 \cos\theta$, the average value of the dipole moment is the sum of the components $\mu_0 \cos\theta$ for all molecules divided by the total number of molecules. This is the same as the sum of the expected values of the function $\mu_0 \cos\theta$ for all possible angles. The average value of μ_0 is then

$$\bar{\mu}_0 = \frac{\int_0^{2\pi}\int_0^{\pi} \mu_0 \cos\theta e^{-(-\mu_0\mathbf{E}\cos\theta)/kT} \sin\theta \, d\theta \, d\phi}{\int_0^{2\pi}\int_0^{\pi} e^{-(-\mu_0\mathbf{E}\cos\theta)/kT} \sin\theta \, d\theta \, d\phi}$$

$$= \frac{\int_0^{\pi} \mu_0 \cos\theta e^{\mu_0\mathbf{E}\cos\theta/kT} \sin\theta \, d\theta}{\int_0^{\pi} e^{\mu_0\mathbf{E}\cos\theta/kT} \sin\theta \, d\theta}$$

The appearance of these integrals is simplified by transformation to the convenient variable $x = (\mu_0\mathbf{E}/kT)\cos\theta$. Since μ_0, **E**, k, and T are independent of θ, by the rules of calculus $dx = (\mu_0\mathbf{E}/kT)(-\sin\theta \, d\theta)$. When $\theta = 0$, $x = (\mu_0\mathbf{E}/kT)$ and when $\theta = \pi$, $x = -(\mu_0\mathbf{E}/kT)$. Hence,

$$\bar{\mu}_0 = \frac{\mu_0\left(\frac{kT}{\mu_0\mathbf{E}}\right)^2 \int_{(\mu_0\mathbf{E}/kT)}^{-(\mu_0\mathbf{E}/kT)} xe^x \, dx}{\left(\frac{kT}{\mu_0\mathbf{E}}\right) \int_{(\mu_0\mathbf{E}/kT)}^{-(\mu_0\mathbf{E}/kT)} e^x \, dx} \tag{17.53}$$

But

$$\int xe^x\,dx = \int x\,d(e^x) = xe^x - \int e^x\,dx = xe^x - e^x + C$$

Accordingly (17.53) becomes

$$\bar{\mu}_0 = \mu_0\left(\frac{kT}{\mu_0\mathbf{E}}\right)\frac{\Big[xe^x - e^x\Big]_{x=\left(\frac{\mu_0\mathbf{E}}{kT}\right)}^{x=-\left(\frac{\mu_0\mathbf{E}}{kT}\right)}}{\Big[e^x\Big]_{x=\left(\frac{\mu_0\mathbf{E}}{kT}\right)}^{x=-\left(\frac{\mu_0\mathbf{E}}{kT}\right)}}$$

$$= \mu_0\left(\frac{kT}{\mu_0\mathbf{E}}\right)\frac{\left[-\left(\frac{\mu_0\mathbf{E}}{kT}\right)e^{-\mu_0\mathbf{E}/kT} - e^{-\mu_0\mathbf{E}/kT}\right] - \left[\left(\frac{\mu_0\mathbf{E}}{kT}\right)e^{\mu_0\mathbf{E}/kT} - e^{\mu_0\mathbf{E}/kT}\right]}{[e^{-\mu_0\mathbf{E}/kT} - e^{\mu_0\mathbf{E}/kT}]}$$

$$= \mu_0\left(\frac{e^{\mu_0\mathbf{E}/kT} + e^{-\mu_0\mathbf{E}/kT}}{e^{\mu_0\mathbf{E}/kT} - e^{-\mu_0\mathbf{E}/kT}} - \frac{kT}{\mu_0\mathbf{E}}\right)$$

$$= \mu_0\left[\coth\left(\frac{\mu_0\mathbf{E}}{kT}\right) - \frac{1}{\left(\frac{\mu_0\mathbf{E}}{kT}\right)}\right] \tag{17.54}$$

$$= \mu_0 L(y) \qquad \left(y = \frac{\mu_0\mathbf{E}}{kT}\right) \tag{17.55}$$

Of importance in the theory of paramagnetism as well as for the orientation of electric dipoles is the function $L(y)$ called the *Langevin function*, where

$$L(y) = \coth y - \frac{1}{y} \tag{17.56}$$

Since molecular dimensions are of the order of 10^{-8} cm and since ze is of the order of 5×10^{-10} esu, electric dipole moments are of the order of 5×10^{-18} cm $\times$ esu. The usual field $\mathbf{E}$ is less than 3000 volts cm^{-1}, or 10 electrostatic volts cm^{-1}. At room temperature, kT is about 4×10^{-14} ergs molecule^{-1}. Thus it happens that

$$y = \frac{\mu_0\mathbf{E}}{kT} \approx \frac{5 \times 10^{-18} \times 10}{4 \times 10^{-14}} \approx 10^{-3}$$

Since $L(y)$ is required only for values of y much less than unity, it is convenient to expand $L(y)$ as a rapidly convergent power series in y. The result is

$$L(y) = \frac{y}{3}\left(1 - \frac{y^2}{15} + \cdots\right) \tag{17.57}$$

Since only the first term is of importance, by (17.55) and (17.57),

$$\bar{\mu}_0 = \frac{\mu_0^2 \mathbf{E}}{3kT} \tag{17.58}$$

The Langevin function's variable for magnetic dipoles μ in a magnetic field **H** is $\mu\mathbf{H}/kT$, by analogy with electric dipoles in an electric field. The magnetic dipole of one electron is of the order of 10^{-20} erg/oersted. A magnetic field of the order of 10^4 oersteds is commonly available to study paramagnetic substances like crystals containing ions with unpaired electrons. Since kT is of the order of 5×10^{-14} erg at room temperature,

$$y = \frac{\mu\mathbf{H}}{kT} = \frac{10^{-20} \times 10^4}{5 \times 10^{-14}} \approx 2 \times 10^{-3}$$

Again only the first term of the series expansion of $L(y)$ is needed and the magnetic polarization of a paramagnetic substance at room temperature is

$$\bar{\mu} = \frac{\mu^2 \mathbf{H}}{3kT} \tag{17.59}$$

At low T, in very intense magnetic fields, and for ferromagnetic substances, $L(y)$ cannot validly be approximated by (17.57).

17.9 MOLAR POLARIZATION

In addition to the average electric dipole moment $\bar{\mu}_0$, there is in gases composed of symmetrical or unsymmetrical molecules an electric moment induced by the electric field. This induced moment μ_i exists only when the field exists and is proportional to the field intensity **E**.

$$\mu_i = \alpha \mathbf{E} \tag{17.60}$$

The proportionality constant α is the polarizability of the molecule. The induced moment is attributed to an electronic polarization in which the field displaces electrons relative to nucleuses and to an atomic polarization in which the field deforms the molecule by moving atoms relative to others in the same molecule. Although the value of α depends upon the direction within the molecule, a mean value averaged over all angles is adequate for fluids. Since these induced and orientational moments are almost independent, the total average moment $\bar{\mu}$ per molecule is then, by (17.58) and (17.60)

$$\bar{\mu} = \left(\alpha + \frac{\mu_0^2}{3kT}\right)\mathbf{E} \tag{17.61}$$

For a gas of N molecules in a volume V, the polarization $\mathbf{P}$ per unit volume is

$$\mathbf{P} = \frac{N}{V}\left(\alpha + \frac{\mu_0^2}{3kT}\right)\mathbf{E} \tag{17.62}$$

Since the dielectric constant κ is related to the electric field strength $\mathbf{E}$ and the polarization $\mathbf{P}$ by the relation

$$\frac{\kappa - 1}{4\pi} = \frac{\mathbf{P}}{\mathbf{E}} \tag{17.63}$$

it follows from (17.62) that

$$\kappa - 1 = 4\pi\left(\frac{N}{V}\right)\left(\alpha + \frac{\mu_0^2}{3kT}\right) \tag{17.64}$$

Equation (17.64) is the Debye equation for the dielectric constant of gases as a function of temperature. It applies to gases that are so dilute that intermolecular forces that would tend to cause molecules to influence the orientation of their neighbors are negligible. When the neighboring molecules do exert an effect upon the orientation of a molecule, the molecule finds itself in a kind of average local field $\mathbf{E}_{\text{local}}$, where

$$\mathbf{E}_{\text{local}} = \mathbf{E} + \tfrac{4}{3}\pi\mathbf{P} \tag{17.65}$$

Here $\mathbf{E}_{\text{local}}$ is the field in the center of a spherical cavity in a polarized dielectric. Since it is this local field that is effective in inducing an electrical moment μ_i and in orienting the permanent moment μ_0, it follows from (17.61) and (17.62) that

$$\mathbf{P} = \left(\frac{N}{V}\right)\left(\alpha + \frac{\mu_0^2}{3kT}\right)\left(\mathbf{E} + \frac{4}{3}\pi\mathbf{P}\right) \tag{17.66}$$

whence

$$1 = \left(\frac{N}{V}\right)\left(\alpha + \frac{\mu_0^2}{3kT}\right)\left(\frac{\mathbf{E}}{\mathbf{P}} + \frac{4}{3}\pi\right)$$

By (17.63),

$$1 = \left(\frac{N}{V}\right)\left(\alpha + \frac{\mu_0^2}{3kT}\right)\left(\frac{4\pi}{\kappa - 1} + \frac{4\pi}{3}\right) = \left(\frac{N}{V}\right)\left(\alpha + \frac{\mu_0^2}{3kT}\right)\left(\frac{4\pi}{3}\right)\left(\frac{3}{\kappa - 1} + 1\right)$$

whence

$$\frac{\kappa - 1}{\kappa + 2} = \frac{4}{3}\pi\left(\frac{N}{V}\right)\left(\alpha + \frac{\mu_0^2}{3kT}\right) \tag{17.67}$$

Equation (17.67) is a second form of the Debye equation (17.64), and it reduces to (17.64) for dilute gases because their dielectric constants are essentially unity.

The molar polarization $\mathscr{P}_M$ of a substance is defined by (17.68), where V_M is the molar volume of the substance.

$$\mathscr{P}_M = V_M\left(\frac{\kappa - 1}{\kappa + 2}\right) \tag{17.68}$$

When the local field approximation is valid, as it is in gases (and in dilute liquid solutions of polar substances in nonpolar solvents), $\mathscr{P}_M$ is almost independent of density. Pure nonpolar liquids yield the same value of $\mathscr{P}_M$ that they exhibit as gases. Here $\mathscr{P}_M$ is not expected to be the same for gaseous and condensed phases of polar substances, for the local field approximation fails because of preferred positions in the liquid and solid. From (17.67) for those substances for which the local field approximation is valid, $\mathscr{P}_M$ depends upon the temperature as in (17.69), where N is Avogadro's number.

$$\mathscr{P}_M = \frac{4}{3}\pi N\left(\alpha + \frac{\mu_0^2}{3kT}\right) \tag{17.69}$$

Measurement of the dielectric constant κ at two or more temperatures allows a calculation of α and μ_0. If $\mathscr{P}_M$ is independent of temperature, as it is for nonpolar substances, μ_0 is zero. The dipole moment is important in valence theory. Moreover, with α and μ_0 known, (17.67) or (17.69) permits a calculation of κ at any density and temperature for which the local field is a valid approximation.

The dielectric constant is usually measured by measuring the capacitance of a condenser in an alternating electric field. The ratio of its capacitance filled with fluid to the capacitance evacuated is κ. The varying electric field must be of a low enough frequency that the molecules can rotate with the field. Radio frequencies of the order of 10^8 cycles per second are satisfactory. At higher frequencies the orientational term containing μ_0 gradually decreases in importance because molecules are unable to rotate fast enough to keep pace with a field that alternates faster than about 10^{10} times per second. For frequencies from 10^{10} to 10^{12} cycles per second, atomic and electronic polarizations contribute to $\mathscr{P}_M$; but beyond 10^{12} cycles into the visible and ultraviolet regions of the electromagnetic spectrum, atomic movements that result in atomic polarizations are too slow to keep pace with the field. Fortunately, the atomic polarization of a substance is a small fraction (often about 5%) of the induced polarization. It is therefore possible to estimate the induced polarization from measurements with visible light. Figure 17.1 exhibits the dependence of $\mathscr{P}_M$ on temperature at radio frequencies for several simple molecules. In addition to the obvious increases in $\mathscr{P}_M$ due to a dipole moment, Figure 17.1 illustrates how $\mathscr{P}_M$ increases as the number of electrons in a molecule increases. The molar polarizations of the rare gases increase from Ar at 4.12 through Kr at 6.26 to Xe at 10.09. For Ne and He, $\mathscr{P}_M$ is 1.00 and 0.54 cc, respectively. However, due mainly to the great attraction of the highly positive osmium nucleus for its inner elec-

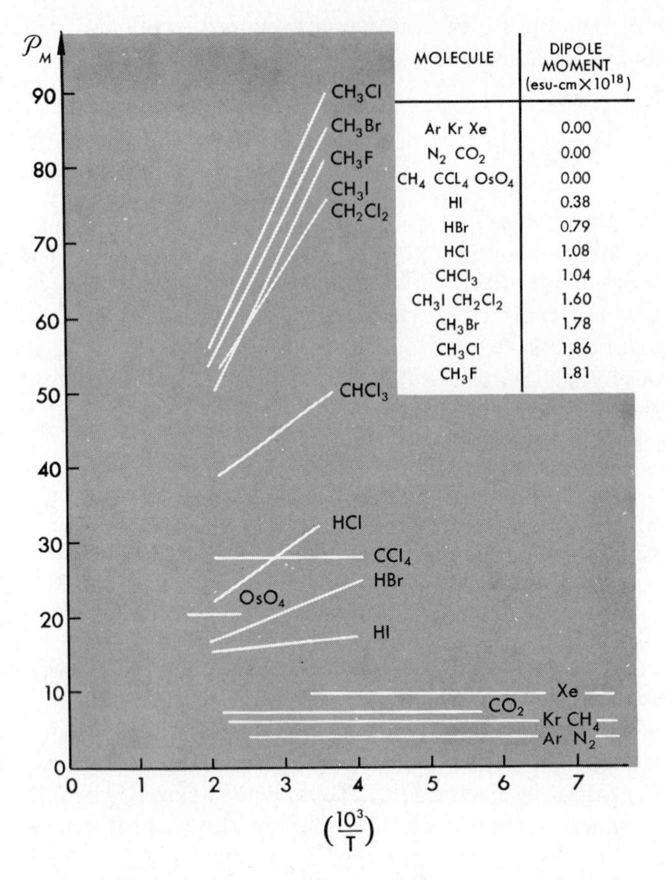

Figure 17.1. Molar Polarization ($\mathcal{P}_M$) as a Function of Reciprocal Temperature (T)†

trons, the molar polarization of OsO_4 with its 108 electrons is less than that of CCl_4 which has only 80 electrons.

Example 17.6. The molar polarizations $\mathcal{P}_M$ of gaseous H_2O at 1 atm at several temperatures are listed below [Hurdis, E. C. and C. P. Smyth, *J. Am. Chem. Soc.*, **64,** 2829 (1942)]. From these data: (a) calculate the dipole moment μ_0 of gaseous H_2O; (b) calculate the moment associated with an OH bond if the angle subtended by the bonds in H_2O is 105°; and (c) estimate the ionic character of the OH bond in H_2O if the OH bonds in H_2O are each 0.957 A in length.

$\mathcal{P}_M$(cc)	57.4	53.5	50.1	46.8	43.1
T(°K)	384.3	420.1	444.7	484.1	522.0

† Data from Landolt-Bornstein, *Zahlenwerte und Funktionen* . . . , *I* Band, *3.* Teil, Springer-Verlag, Berlin (1951), pp. 386 ff. and pp. 514–7.

(a) In Figure 17.2, $\mathscr{P}_M$ is plotted as a function of the reciprocal of absolute temperature. The slope of the best straight line is 2.08×10^4 cc $\times$ deg. This value is equal to the coefficient of T^{-1} in (17.68) so that $2.08 \times 10^4 = (4/3)\pi N (\mu_0^2/3k)$; whence,

$$\mu_0 = \sqrt{\frac{9k \times 2.08 \times 10^4}{4\pi N}} = \sqrt{\frac{9 \times 1.380 \times 10^{-16} \times 2.08 \times 10^4}{4 \times \pi \times 0.6022 \times 10^{24}}}$$

$$= 1.85 \times 10^{-18} \text{ esu} \times \text{cm}$$

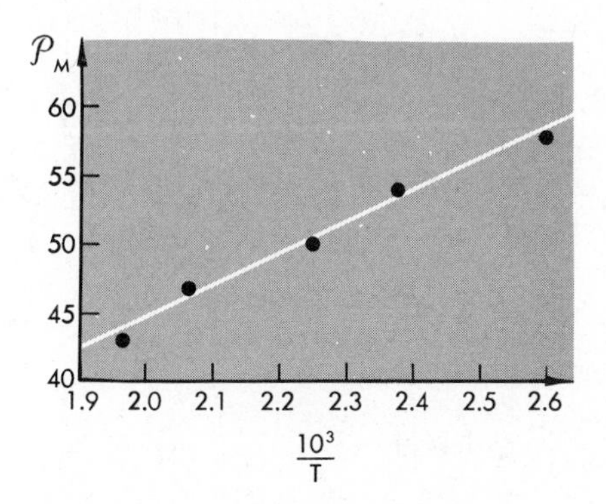

Figure 17.2. Molar Polarization ($\mathscr{P}_M$) of Gaseous Water as a Function of Reciprocal Temperature (T)

(b) The molecule of H_2O is planar. The component of the bond moment μ_{OH} along the axis of the molecule is

$$\mu_{OH} \cos\left(\frac{105°}{2}\right) = \mu_{OH} \cos(52.50°)$$

Since two bonds contribute to the molecular moment of 1.85×10^{-18} esu $\times$ cm,

$$1.85 \times 10^{-18} \text{ esu} \times \text{cm} = 2\mu_{OH} \cos(52.50°)$$

$$\mu_{OH} = 1.52 \times 10^{-18} \text{ esu} \times \text{cm}$$

The bond moment is thus 1.52×10^{-18} esu $\times$ cm.

(c) By (17.51), the fractional charge z separated by 0.957×10^{-8} cm is

$$z = \frac{\mu}{el} = \frac{1.52 \times 10^{-18}}{4.80 \times 10^{-10} \times 0.957 \times 10^{-8}} = 0.33$$

Each OH bond is thus expected to have one-third ionic character. (Since the unshared pairs of electrons on the oxygen atom may contribute to the moment of the molecule and since the OH bonds may interact, this result must not be taken too seriously.)

Example 17.7. Landolt-Bornstein, *Zahlenwerte und Funktionen* (Berlin: Verlag Julius Springer, 1951, Band I., 3. Teil, pp. 386 *et seq.* and pp. 514–517) list many atomic and electronic molar polarizations and many dipole moments. For NH_3, the dipole moment is reported to be about 1.44×10^{-18} esu $\times$ cm and the atomic and electronic molar polarizations total about 6.0 cc. Calculate the low-frequency dielectric constant of NH_3 at $\frac{1}{2}$ atm at 0°C if NH_3 is a perfect gas.

By (17.69),

$$\mathscr{P}_M = \frac{4}{3}\pi N\alpha + \frac{4}{3}\pi N\left(\frac{\mu_0^2}{3kT}\right)$$

$$= 6.0 + \frac{4}{3}\pi \times 6.022 \times 10^{23}\left(\frac{1.44^2 \times 10^{-36}}{3 \times 1.38 \times 10^{-16} \times 273}\right)$$

$$= 6.0 + 46.2 = 52.2 \text{ cc}$$

Since the molar volume under these conditions is 44.8 l, namely, twice the standard molar volume, by (17.68)

$$\frac{\kappa - 1}{\kappa + 2} = \frac{\mathscr{P}_M}{V_M} = \frac{52.2}{44.8 \times 10^3} = 1.165 \times 10^{-3}$$

$$\kappa - 1 = 0.001165\kappa + 0.00233$$

$$\kappa = \frac{1.00233}{0.99883} = 1.00350$$

17.10 MAGNETIC PROPERTIES

The orbital angular momentum and the spin of an electron give it a magnetic moment. In Russell-Saunders coupling (Section 14.10), an atom or ion has angular momentum $\hbar[L(L+1)]^{1/2}$ due to orbital motion of electrons and angular momentum $\hbar[S(S+1)]^{1/2}$ due to spin of its electrons. Analogous expressions apply to electrons in a molecule or even throughout a large crystalline domain, like those found in ferromagnetic substances. The *total magnetic moment* of an atom or ion is

$$\mu = g\,\mu_e[J(J+1)]^{1/2} \tag{17.70}$$

where g is the Landé g factor of (15.71) and where μ_e is the Bohr magneton of (15.72).

Just as an external electric field induces an electric moment $\mu_i = \alpha\mathbf{E}_{\text{local}}$ in matter having a susceptibility α, so also an external magnetic field $\mathbf{H}$ induces a very small magnetic field in all matter. This tiny field is proportional to $\mathbf{H}$ and is opposed to it. A much more important effect, however, is observed in substances having ions or groups of atoms with a permanent moment μ. Their alignment by $\mathbf{H}_{\text{local}}$ is analogous to the alignment of electric dipoles by $\mathbf{E}_{\text{local}}$ and their average moment, if each is free, is given by (17.59). The paramagnetic susceptibility of a substance containing ions, free radicals, or other species with permanent magnetic moments μ is

$$\chi = \frac{\mathbf{M}}{\mathbf{H}} \tag{17.71}$$

where the *magnetization* $\mathbf{M} = \bar{\mu}(N/V)$ is a quantity analogous to electric polarization $\mathbf{P}$. In view of (17.59) and (17.71), one has

$$\chi = \left(\frac{N}{V}\right)\frac{\mu^2}{3kT} = \frac{C}{T} \tag{17.72}$$

Equation (17.72) is the *Curie law of paramagnetism; C* is the Curie constant. Equation (17.72) is analogous to (17.67) and represents the compromise between thermal disorder and alignment by the magnetic field. A graph of χ^{-1} vs T is a straight line through the origin if (17.72) holds.

Many substances follow (17.72), but many do not. In this latter group are ferromagnetic and antiferromagnetic substances. The law describing χ as a function of T for them is explicable by assuming, with Weiss, that there is a local magnetic field $\mathbf{H}_{\text{local}}$ that is the sum of the external field $\mathbf{H}$ and a field attributed to and proportional to the magnetization $\mathbf{M}$ of the neighborhood about μ; hence,

$$\mathbf{H}_{\text{local}} = \mathbf{H} \pm a\mathbf{M} \tag{17.73}$$

The plus sign indicates the fact that the magnetization reinforces $\mathbf{H}$, as it does weakly in crystals of almost independent free radicals or ions and as it does strongly in ferromagnetic substances; the minus sign in (17.73) indicates weak opposition to $\mathbf{H}$ by the environment in antiferromagnetic materials or in crystalline free radicals where the radicals tend to pair their electrons. It follows from (17.71) and (17.73) that

$$\frac{1}{\chi} = \frac{\mathbf{H}}{\mathbf{M}} = \frac{\mathbf{H}_{\text{local}}}{\mathbf{M}} \mp a \tag{17.74}$$

Since $\mathbf{M}$ has a temperature-dependence specified by (17.72), it follows from (17.74) that

$$\frac{1}{\chi} = \frac{T}{C} \mp \frac{aC}{C} = \frac{T \mp T_c}{C} \tag{17.75}$$

where $aC = T_c$, the *Curie temperature*, will fit the behavior of $1/\chi$ for those substances for which (17.72) does not hold. Paramagnetic crystals of a free radical may have a small T_c of the order of 10°K, while ferromagnetic substances have T_c of the order of 1000°K. Both use the minus sign in (17.75) and the plus sign in (17.73). Antiferromagnetic substances use the plus sign in (17.75) and have T_c of the order of 100°K.

17.11 CRYSTALS AND THE THIRD LAW

In a crystal containing N atoms, the energy due to harmonic vibration with $3N$ degrees of freedom is

$$E = \sum_{i=1}^{3N} (n_i + \tfrac{1}{2}) h\nu_{0i} \tag{17.76}$$

Rotational energy is assumed absent because the crystal itself is fixed and because each atom has no moment of inertia. Real crystals of course may contain at lattice sites molecules that may rotate in part or as units either freely or with some hindrance. Electronic energy is also zero, for the crystal is assumed to be in its ground electronic state, the electronic state at absolute zero. This ground state may, however, be degenerate in any of several ways. A simple kind of degeneracy is due to nuclear spin, but even this is presumed to be lost at absolute zero because only one spin state is supposedly most stable.

With g_0 as the degeneracy of the ground state *of the crystal*, the partition function of the whole crystal is

$$\begin{aligned} Q &= g_0 \sum_{n_i=0}^{\infty} \exp\left[-\frac{1}{kT}\sum_{i=1}^{3N}\left(n_i + \frac{1}{2}\right) h\nu_{0i}\right] \\ &= g_0 \prod_{i=1}^{3N} \sum_{n_i=0}^{\infty} e^{-[(n_i+1/2)h\nu_{0i}/kT]} \\ &= g_0 \prod_{i=1}^{3N} \left[\frac{e^{-(\pi\hbar\nu_{0i}/kT)}}{1 - e^{-(2\pi\hbar\nu_{0i}/kT)}}\right] \end{aligned} \tag{17.77}$$

That is, as in (17.46), there is a factor of the form

$$\frac{e^{-(\pi\hbar\nu_{0i}/kT)}}{1 - e^{-(2\pi\hbar\nu_{0i}/kT)}}$$

for each of the $3N$ frequencies or degrees of translational freedom and a factor g_0 for the g_0 levels of almost equal energy at each vibrational state. There is no factor $N!$ in (17.77). Although the N atoms are indistinguishable, they are fixed to distinguishable lattice sites. If tunneling should allow atoms to change sites, (17.77) would have to be divided by $N!$ but g_0 would rise by a factor $N!$ to give (17.77) as it is. If tunneling does not occur, it is sufficient to count energy states as merely g_0-degenerate in one potential minimum and thus to forget the other minima that might be reached by tunneling. Finally, of course, (17.77) yields

$$\ln Q = \ln g_0 - \sum_{i=1}^{3N} \frac{\pi\hbar\nu_{0i}}{kT} - \sum_{i=1}^{3N} \ln\left[1 - e^{-(2\pi\hbar\nu_{0i}/kT)}\right] \tag{17.78}$$

The second term of the right side of (17.78) yields the zero-point energy of the crystal. Since the conventional zero of energy is at this level of energy, the second term of (17.78) is to be omitted. The last term of (17.78) yields the characteristic T^4-dependence of energy and the T^3-dependence of C_V when the proper frequencies ν_{0i} are inserted. This summation is generally done by assuming, with Debye and others, that ν_{0i} ranges over a set of values from zero to a maximum ν_M. Calculation with such a set of continuously varying frequencies does indeed terminate in the proper temperature dependence of E and C_V. It is sufficient here, however, to make the assumption of Einstein of 1907 that all ν_{0i} are alike. This is physically the equivalent of allowing all atoms to vibrate independently in a cubic lattice. With ν_{0i} equal to one common value ν, and after suppression of zero-point energy, (17.78) becomes

$$\ln Q = \ln g_0 - 3N \ln(1 - e^{-h\nu/kT}) \tag{17.79}$$

It is necessary to have the derivative

$$\left(\frac{\partial \ln Q}{\partial T}\right)_X = \frac{3Nh\nu}{kT^2}(e^{h\nu/kT} - 1)^{-1} \tag{17.80}$$

By (17.24) and (17.80), the energy of the crystal is

$$E = 3Nh\nu(e^{h\nu/kT} - 1)^{-1} \tag{17.81}$$

Hence, since V is among the external parameters X, the heat capacity is

$$C_V = \left(\frac{\partial E}{\partial T}\right)_X = 3Nk\left(\frac{h\nu}{kT}\right)^2 (e^{h\nu/kT} - 1)^{-2} e^{h\nu/kT} \tag{17.82}$$

Since l'Hospital's rule yields

$$\lim_{x\to 0} \frac{x^2 e^x}{(e^x - 1)^2} = \lim_{x\to 0} \frac{2x + x^2}{2(e^x - 1)} = \lim_{x\to 0} \frac{2 + 2x}{2e^x} = 1$$

it follows from (17.82), wherein $x = h\nu/kT$, that at high T, C_V approaches $3Nk = 3R$, the classical limit given by equipartition of energy. However, as T approaches absolute zero, the limit of interest is

$$\lim_{x\to \infty} \frac{x^2 e^x}{(e^x - 1)^2} = \lim_{x\to \infty} \frac{2 + 2x}{2e^x} = \lim_{x\to \infty} \frac{2}{2e^x} = 0$$

That is, C_V approaches zero as T approaches zero, in accord with experiment. Although (17.82) is, therefore, qualitatively correct, it does not fit observed data well at low T. The Debye approximation with a range of frequencies ν_{0i} does fit satisfactorily.

By (17.21) and (17.24), the entropy is, in general,

$$S = \frac{E - A}{T} = k\left[\ln Q + T\left(\frac{\partial \ln Q}{\partial T}\right)_X\right] \tag{17.83}$$

Term-by-term differentiation of (17.78) yields, as in (17.80), the perfectly general result

$$\left(\frac{\partial \ln Q}{\partial T}\right)_X = \sum_{i=1}^{3N} \frac{h\nu_{0i}}{2kT^2} + \sum_{i=1}^{3N} \frac{h\nu_{0i}}{kT^2} (e^{h\nu_{0i}/kT} - 1)^{-1} \tag{17.84}$$

Substitution of (17.84) and (17.78) into (17.83) yields

$$\frac{S}{k} = \ln g_0 - \sum_{i=1}^{3N} \ln (1 - e^{-h\nu_{0i}/kT}) + \sum_{i=1}^{3N} \frac{h\nu_{0i}}{kT} (e^{h\nu_{0i}/kT} - 1)^{-1} \tag{17.85}$$

Whence

$$\begin{aligned} \lim_{T\to 0} \left(\frac{S}{k}\right) &= \ln g_0 + \sum_{i=1}^{3N} \lim_{x\to\infty} \frac{x}{e^x - 1} \\ &= \ln g_0 \end{aligned} \tag{17.86}$$

If $g_0 = 1$, the entropy is zero at absolute zero. If there is nuclear spin i at each of N lattice sites, $g_0 = (2i + 1)^N$ and the entropy $S_0^\ominus$ very near absolute zero due to nuclear spin degeneracy is

$$S_0^\ominus = Nk \ln (2i + 1) \tag{17.87}$$

This term is usually suppressed. Terms for isotope mixing are also usually suppressed.

Residual entropy is conventionally acknowledged to exist at absolute zero if g_0 varies as some quantity to a power of the order of N. For solid CO with complete randomness quenched in, $g_0 = 2^N$ for N molecules and

$$S_0^\ominus = Nk \ln 2 \tag{17.88}$$

For ice with randomly located protons, two to an oxygen, $g_0 = (\frac{3}{2})^N$ for NH_2O and[1]

$$S_0^\ominus = Nk \ln \tfrac{3}{2} \tag{17.89}$$

But if $g_0 = C^M$ where M is small compared to N, then

$$S_0^\ominus = \left(\frac{M}{N}\right) Nk \ln C \approx 0 \tag{17.90}$$

That is, residual entropy will be absent at absolute zero in terms of the third law of thermodynamics if the number M of random-sites per gram-mole is very small compared to Avogadro's number.

---

[1] Pauling, L., *Nature of the Chemical Bond*. Ithaca, N. Y.: Cornell University Press, 1960, p. 467.

17.12 DEGENERATE ELECTRON GAS[2]

One of the common circumstances in which Boltzmann statistics utterly fail is for electrons in a metal. The reason is that even at temperatures near the melting points of metals the number of electrons is comparable to the number of states with energy kT. Fermi-Dirac statistics must be used.

Let s be the number of states of about the same energy available to n electrons. Since each state may be either unoccupied or occupied by only one electron because of the exclusion principle, the number of ways of assigning the n electrons to the s states is $s(s-1)(s-2)\cdots(s-n+1)$, for the first electron has s possible states available, the second has $(s-1)$, the third has $(s-2)$, and so on until there remain $(s-n)$ vacant states. But

$$s(s-1)(s-2)\cdots(s-n+1)=\frac{s!}{(s-n)!}$$

Moreover, the n electrons are indistinguishable so that their $n!$ possible orders of being chosen reduces the number of distinguishable arrangements to $s!/n!(s-n)!$. If several groups of states of different ranges of energy exist, the total number of distinguishable eigenstates is the product for all groups of states, namely,

$$P=\prod_i\frac{s_i!}{n_i!(s_i-n_i)!} \tag{17.91}$$

This product is proportional to the probability that the particular arrangement is achieved from all possible arrangements. By maximizing this probability for a constant total number N of electrons and for a constant energy E, the most likely distribution or arrangement is found. And because of the great numbers of electrons and states, the distribution is sharply peaked so that mean and most probable values do not differ significantly. Thus, P of (17.91) is to be maximized provided the following are constant.

$$E=\sum_i n_i\varepsilon_i \tag{17.92}$$

$$N=\sum_i n_i \tag{17.93}$$

According to Stirling's approximation (17.32),

[2] The Fermi-Dirac and Bose-Einstein distributions are derived as in: Tolman, R. C., *The Principles of Statistical Mechanics*. New York: Oxford University Press, 1938, pp. 369–74. By permission of the Clarendon Press, Oxford.

$$\begin{aligned}\ln P &= \sum_i \ln (s_i!) - \sum_i \ln (n_i!) - \sum_i \ln (s_i - n_i)! \\ &= \sum_i [s_i \ln s_i - s_i - n_i \ln n_i + n_i \\ &\qquad - (s_i - n_i) \ln (s_i - n_i) + (s_i - n_i)] \\ &= \sum_i [s_i \ln s_i - n_i \ln n_i - (s_i - n_i) \ln (s_i - n_i)]\end{aligned}$$

Since P is a maximum when $\ln P$ is a maximum, by the method of undetermined multipliers β and F one has $\delta(\ln P) - \beta\, \delta E + \beta F\, \delta N = 0$. On adjusting the various numbers n_i of electrons in the available states,

$$\sum_i (-\ln n_i + \ln (s_i - n_i) - \beta\varepsilon_i + \beta F)\delta n_i = 0$$

The most probable distribution is, therefore,

$$\ln\left(\frac{s_i - n_i}{n_i}\right) = \beta(\varepsilon_i - F) \tag{17.94}$$

The conditions (17.92) and (17.93) fix β and F thus. Equation (17.94) yields the Fermi-Dirac distribution

$$n_i = \frac{s_i}{e^{\beta(\varepsilon_i - F)} + 1} \tag{17.95}$$

When s_i greatly exceeds n_i, as in an ideal gas subject to Boltzmann statistics, $n_i \approx s_i e^{-\beta(\varepsilon_i - F)}$ because unity is small compared to $e^{\beta(\varepsilon_i - F)}$. By (17.93),

$$N = \sum_i s_i e^{-\beta(\varepsilon_i - F)}$$

$$e^{-\beta F} = \frac{1}{N}\sum_i s_i e^{-\beta\varepsilon_i}$$

Then, by (17.92),

$$E = \sum_i s_i \varepsilon_i e^{-\beta(\varepsilon_i - F)} = \frac{N \sum_i s_i \varepsilon_i e^{-\beta\varepsilon_i}}{\sum_i s_i e^{-\beta\varepsilon_i}} = N\bar{\varepsilon}_i$$

As expected, this is like (4.74), the Boltzmann distribution, if $\beta = 1/kT$ and if s_i is the number of states of energy ε_i.

At absolute zero β is infinite. In order that n_i be greater than zero it is necessary that F exceed ε_i. States with energy ε_i less than F have $n_i = s_i$ at absolute zero; that is, the electron gas is completely degenerate with all possible states occupied. States with ε_i greater than F have $n_i = 0$ at absolute zero. The Fermi energy F thus represents the maximum energy of electrons at absolute zero. Figure 17.3 shows how n_i/s_i changes as T rises from absolute zero. As indicated in Sections 16.19 and 16.22, the number of electrons with energy F may be quite great.

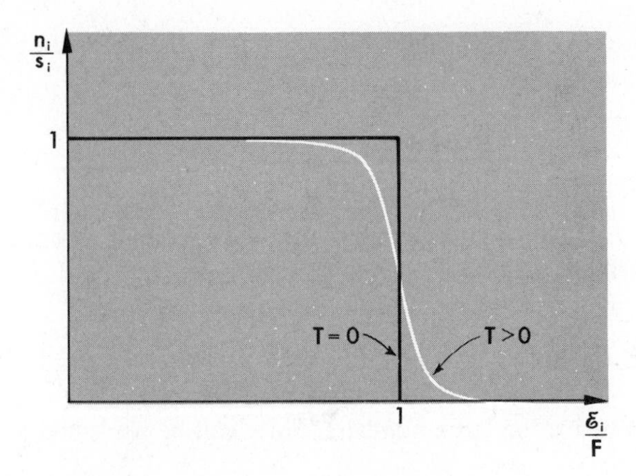

Figure 17.3. Fermi-Dirac Distribution

Above absolute zero F depends upon T. When kT is small compared to $\varepsilon_i - F$, it follows from (17.95) that $n_i/s_i = e^{-[(\varepsilon_i - F)/kT]}$. That is, the probability n_i/s_i that a state with energy well removed from the Fermi level is occupied follows Boltzmann statistics with the zero of energy referred to the Fermi level. At any temperature, states with energy equal to F are half-occupied, for by (17.95) with $\varepsilon_i = F$,

$$n_i = \frac{s_i}{1 + e^0} = \frac{s_i}{2}$$

17.13 RADIATION[3]

The wave function of a system of photons is symmetric for interchanges of identical photons. The statistics are Bose-Einstein and the number of photons possible in any state is unlimited.

The total number of distinguishable eigenstates is best calculated by considering the n photons and the s states available to them in any small range of energies as a line of n photons and $(s - 1)$ markers that divide the n photons into s states of similar energy. These $(n + s - 1)$ objects can be arranged without restriction in $(n + s - 1)!$ ways. But since the $n!$ permutations of the photons and the $(s - 1)!$ permutations of the markers do not lead to distinguishable arrangements, the number of distinguishable arrangements is

$$\frac{(n + s - 1)!}{n!(s - 1)!}$$

[3] See footnote to Section 17.12.

If several groups of states of different ranges of energy exist, the total number of distinguishable eigenstates is

$$P = \prod_i \frac{(n_i + s_i - 1)!}{n_i!(s_i - 1)!} \tag{17.96}$$

On maximizing $\ln P$ at constant N and E as in the preceding section, there results as the most probable distribution

$$\ln\left(\frac{s_i + n_i - 1}{n_i}\right) = \beta(\varepsilon_i - F) \tag{17.97}$$

Since n_i and s_i are assumed to be large numbers, unity can be neglected in the term $s_i + n_i - 1$ and

$$n_i = \frac{s_i}{e^{\varepsilon_i - F/kT} - 1} \tag{17.98}$$

where $1/kT$ replaces β. This is the Bose-Einstein distribution law. Since bosons need not be conserved in number, F may be set equal to zero because the condition that N be constant does not hold.

For photons, $F = 0$ and $\varepsilon_i = h\nu_i$. The total average energy of a system of n_i oscillators with frequency ν_i is

$$E = \sum_i n_i \varepsilon_i = \sum_i \frac{s_i h\nu_i}{e^{h\nu_i/kT} - 1} \tag{17.99}$$

The number of distinguishable photon states in a volume V with frequencies from ν_i to $\nu_i + d\nu_i$ is $8\pi V\nu_i^2 d\nu_i/c^3$. The famous Planck radiation formula for the energy density $E(\nu)$ is, then,

$$E(\nu) = \frac{8\pi V h\nu^3}{c^3(e^{h\nu/kT} - 1)} \tag{17.100}$$

It is here that quantum mechanics began in 1900, as explained in Section 13.2.

17.14 SUMMARY

The key to equilibrium statistical mechanics is $\ln Q$. An adequate model of a system allows a calculation of its energies ε by quantum or classical mechanics, and the partition function is merely $Q = \Sigma e^{-\beta\varepsilon}$. Its calculation is easy, at least for the modern high-speed computer that solved for the ε's. The best way to find Q is to have a list of exactly observed energies and their degeneracies, if any, ready for the computer. Lacking them, one must be satisfied with approximate formulas like those derived in this chapter. Then, with Q as a function of T and any external parameters like V, thermodynamic results are immediately available from the equations

$$A = -kT \ln Q \tag{17.21}$$

$$P = kT\left(\frac{\partial \ln Q}{\partial V}\right)_T \tag{17.22}$$

$$E = kT^2\left(\frac{\partial \ln Q}{\partial T}\right)_X \tag{17.24}$$

$$C_V = k\frac{\partial}{\partial T}\left[T^2\left(\frac{\partial \ln Q}{\partial T}\right)_X\right]_X \tag{17.25}$$

$$S = k\left[\ln Q + T\left(\frac{\partial \ln Q}{\partial T}\right)_X\right] \tag{17.83}$$

and their like. The trouble, of course, is generally with the model, or at least one that facilitates calculations.

An enormous amount of work has been done on liquid models. There are two broad classifications of statistical mechanical models of liquids: those that begin by loosening up a lattice, and those that begin by gathering up a gas. That is, a molecule of a liquid is given a cell in which to roam or a lowered frequency of vibration compared to a crystal. Or it may be given short-range order and long-range disorder by some mathematical trick or by a statistical distribution. One model forces some molecules into a lattice environment while others are as free as molecules of a gas. However it is done, the calculational complexities are fortunately such that they are beyond this humble introduction.

There are sometimes surprises at hand. For example, an elegant calculation of the equation of state of a fluid consisting of ideal gas molecules of mass m and containing either all fermions or all bosons has yielded

$$\frac{PV}{NkT} = 1 \pm \frac{h^3}{2^4(\pi mkT)^{3/2}}\left(\frac{N}{V}\right)$$

where $+$ is for the fermions and $-$ is for the bosons. The final term is only 0.003 at 2°K and is masked by dispersion forces, but there it is. The fermions have a residual quantum repulsion and a higher than expected pressure P while the bosons do the opposite.

Liquid solutions, of course, present the problems of liquids and the problems of semichemical interaction. Here, too, there are surprises. For example, as a mole of gas dissolves in a nonpolar solvent, $\Delta S^\ominus$ is about -10 cal mole^{-1} deg^{-1}. If the same gas dissolves in water, again without interaction chemically with the solvent, $\Delta S^\ominus$ is about -30 cal mole^{-1} deg^{-1}. The difference is caused by the solute's inducing an ordered structure in the water nearby, perhaps because the water molecules cannot carry on their usual antics with the stranger. A useful model would, of course, be expected to foresee this peculiarity and accommodate it without straining its premises.

With much variety calling for study, it is clear that statistical mechanics can be expected to remain a bigger challenge and puzzle than the problems that follow.

PROBLEMS

(Because of the advanced nature of the matter of this chapter and the limited number of readily tractable problems, only one set of problems is given.)

1. Assume that every state of a system has the same probability $f = 1/W$, where W is the number of states. Show that the entropy of the system is $S = k \ln W$ and correlate the result with the third law of thermodynamics.

2. Find enthalpy as a function of $\ln Q$.

   Answer: $H = kT\left[\left(\frac{\partial \ln Q}{\partial \ln T}\right)_V + \left(\frac{\partial \ln Q}{\partial \ln V}\right)_T\right]$

3. Show that for any state of aggregation

$$C_P = C_V + T\left(\frac{\partial P}{\partial T}\right)_V \left(\frac{\partial V}{\partial T}\right)_P$$

   Then find C_P as a function of $\ln Q$.

$$\textit{Answer: } \frac{C_P}{kT} = 2\left(\frac{\partial \ln Q}{\partial T}\right)_V + T\left(\frac{\partial^2 \ln Q}{\partial T^2}\right)_V + \left(\frac{\partial \ln Q}{\partial V}\right)_T \left(\frac{\partial V}{\partial T}\right)_P + T\left(\frac{\partial^2 \ln Q}{\partial V \partial T}\right)\left(\frac{\partial V}{\partial T}\right)_P$$

4. If $E = \frac{3}{2}NkT$ and if $P = -(\partial E/\partial V)$, show that $PV = NkT$. *Hint*: Use (13.84).

5. Test the Stirling approximation (17.32) for 5!, 10!, and 100! (N.B.: $\log_{10} 100! = 157.97$.)

6. If the potential energy inside the container of a classical ideal gas is zero and is infinite outside, calculate Q for a classical ideal monatomic gas of N molecules from the Gibbs phase integral

$$Q = \frac{1}{N!h^{3N}} \iint e^{-\beta \mathscr{H}(p,q)}\, dp\, dq$$

   Answer: $Q = \left[\frac{2\pi mkT}{h^2}\right]^{3N/2} \frac{V^N}{N!}$

7. Show that $C_V = -T(\partial^2 A/\partial T^2)_X$ and with this expression find C_V of a perfect monatomic gas.
   Answer: $C_V = 3Nk/2$.

8. Discuss the analogy between mixing isotopes and allowing one of several nuclear spin states to achieve equilibrium in $(2i + 1)$ states.

9. Find $\ln Q$, E, and S° per mole $F_{(g)}$ at 298.15°K from these data [C. E. Moore,

Atomic Energy Levels, Vol. I, Circular of the National Bureau of Standards 467, Washington, D. C. (1949)]:

State of F	Energy (cm^{-1})	Degeneracy
$^2P_{3/2}$	0.0	4
$^2P_{1/2}$	404.0	2
other	$>10^5$	—

Answer: $\ln Q = 1.0512 \times 10^{25}$; $E = 965$ cal mole^{-1}; $S^\ominus = 37.918$ cal deg^{-1} mole^{-1}.

10. From data of the preceding problem, calculate the free energy functions of $F_{(g)}$ at 298.15°K, 1000°K, 2000°K, and 4000°K.
Answer: −32.69, −39.06, −42.64, and −46.17 cal mole^{-1} deg^{-1}.

11. What are the standard absolute entropies at 25°C of gaseous Ar and gaseous Hg, both of which are monatomic? Assume no electronic excitation. (The values of F. D. Rossini et al., Circular of the National Bureau of Standards 500, 1952, are 36.983 and 41.80 cal mole^{-1} deg^{-1}.)

12. Show that the pressure of a perfect gas is an entropy effect and not an energy effect.

13. Explain how at thermal equilibrium the number of molecules with energy E_2 might exceed the number with energy E_1 even though E_2 exceeds E_1.
Answer: Make degeneracy of state E_2 high.

14. With data from problem 9, calculate K_p for the gaseous reaction $^{19}F_2 \longrightarrow 2\ ^{19}F$ at 1000°K if only the ground state ($X\ ^1\Sigma_g^+$) is important. For it, $\omega_e = 920$ cm^{-1}, $R_e = 1.44$ A, and $D_e = 35.6$ kcal/mole.
Answer: 1.0×10^{-2}.

15. Calculate the partition function of $^{12}_{6}C_{(g)}$ and from it find the free energy function of this monatomic gas at 2000°K. The following are energies of known electronic states of C in cm^{-1}:
$^3P_0$ at 0; $^3P_1$ at 16; $^3P_2$ at 44; $^1D_2$ at 10190; $^1S_0$ at 21650.
Answer: −42.18 cal mole^{-1} deg^{-1}.

16. The ground electronic state $X\ ^1\Sigma_g^+$ of HF has $D_e = 133$ kcal/mole, $R_e = 0.92$ A, and $\omega_e = 4140$ cm^{-1}. With data from problem 9, find K_p for the gaseous reaction $HF \longrightarrow H + F$ at 2000°K.
Answer: 1.4×10^{-9}.

17. With the aid of Example 17.5, calculate the free energy functions of gaseous N_2, O_2, and NO at 2000°K.
Answer: −63.5, −67.9, and −68.8 cal mole^{-1} deg^{-1} respectively.

18. Show that Q_v of a diatomic molecule at very high temperatures is $kT/h\nu_0$.

19. Derive a formula analogous to (17.35) for the entropy of a perfect diatomic gas.

20. Calculate the absolute entropy of $Br_{2(g)}$ at 298.15°K.
Answer: 58.64 cal mole^{-1} deg^{-1}.

21. Compare $B_e hc$ and kT for Br_2, Cl_2, CO, HCl, and H_2. For which of these molecules is (17.48) adequate at 300°K? At 1000°K?
Answer: At 300°, Br_2, Cl_2, and CO; at 1000°, all but H_2.

22. Show that K_p of a gas reaction is greater the larger the
(a) moments of inertia of products;
(b) vibrational frequencies of reactants;
(c) number of low-lying molecular energy states of products.

23. Find for gaseous O_2 in its ground state the temperature above which ortho-para corrections can be corrected by a symmetry number.
Answer: At $T > 10°K$.

24. Evaluate the constant C in the formula

$$-\frac{G_T - E_0}{RT} = -\ln P + C \ln T + \cdots$$

for:
(a) Linear molecules.
(b) Nonlinear molecules.
Both translation and rotation contribute to C.
Answer: (a) 7/2; (b) 4.

25. Consider a nonlinear molecule of n atoms within which there occurs one free rotation described by one angle relative to axes fixed to part of the molecule.
(a) How many degrees of angular freedom exist?
(b) How many coordinates are needed in the internal potential energy?
(c) Estimate C_V for $CH_3 - C \equiv C - CH_3$ at 300°K if all vibrational frequencies contribute $\frac{11}{2}R$.
Answer: (a) $3 + 1$; (b) $3n$–7; (c) $C_V = 9R$.

26. Calculate the dipole moment of nitromethane (CH_3NO_2) from the data below [C. P. Smyth and K. B. McAlpine, *J. Am. Chem. Soc.*, **56**, 1697 (1934)].

T(°K)	339.0	380.7	400.8	435.1	448.8	493.2	494.1
$\mathscr{P}_M$(ml)	231.5	208.5	198.6	185.0	179.6	164.9	164.6

Answer: 3.44×10^{-18} esu cm.

27. Calculate the dipole moments of CH_3Br and CH_3I from the data below [C. P. Smyth and K. B. McAlpine, *J. Chem. Phys.*, **2**, 499 (1934)]. Predict the dipole moments of CBr_3I and CI_3Br if all bond angles are tetrahedral.

CH_3Br		CH_3I	
T(°K)	$\mathscr{P}_M$(ml)	T(°K)	$\mathscr{P}_M$(ml)
306.2	79.60	304.7	71.82
309.1	78.85	313.4	70.15
330.8	74.40	345.9	65.3
368.0	68.40	398.6	59.4
405.9	63.85	446.7	55.5
		494.4	51.8

Answer: $\mu(CH_3Br) = 1.81$; $\mu(CH_3I) = 1.61$; predicted $\mu = 0.20$.

28. The molar polarization $\mathscr{P}_M$ of cis-dichloroethlyene at 301.5°K is 93.13 cc and at 427.0°K is 71.42 cc [A. A. Maryott, M. E. Hobbs, and P. M. Gross, *J. Am. Chem. Soc.*, **63**, 661 (1941)].
(a) Calculate the dipole moment of cis-dichloroethylene.

(b) Predict the dipole moment of planar trans-dichloroethylene.
(c) Calculate the visible index of refraction of liquid cis- or trans-dichloroethylene if the density of each is about 1.28 g ml^{-1} and if the atomic polarization $\mathscr{P}_A$ is about 10% of the induced polarization $\mathscr{P}_D$.
Answer: (a) 1.91×10^{-18} esu-cm; (b) zero; (c) 1.381.

29. Show that $\bar{\mu} = \alpha E_{\text{local}} + \mu_0$ when $\mu_0 E \approx kT$.

30. Plot C_V as a function of T from 0°K to 500°K for a crystal having only one $3N$-fold degenerate vibrational frequency ν.

31. If $\Delta E = 2$ cal mole^{-1} for $CO_{(s)\,(\text{ordered})} \longrightarrow CO_{(s)\,(\text{disordered})}$, then what is the temperature at which ΔG is zero for this process?
Answer: 1.44°K.

32. Explain why electrons in a crystalline conductor contribute very little to C_V at room temperature. What is expected of N free electrons classically?
Answer: $\frac{3}{2}R$.

33. If the Fermi level of a metal has an energy of 100 kcal mole^{-1}, plot n_i/s_i as a function of ε_i at 0°K, 100°K, 300°K, and 500°K.

34. Discuss possible interpretations of the phrase "temperature of radiation."

35. Explain why (17.100) is like (13.11).

36. Show that the Gibbs free energy of N photons at equilibrium with their container is zero by use of (17.99) and (17.100).

18
REACTION RATE THEORY

18.1 INTRODUCTION

The summary of Chapter 10 on *Chemical Kinetics* ended with the hope that it had "somehow indicated the scope and complexity" of the problem of calculating the rate of a chemical reaction from first principles and microscopic events. Even if one attempts this feat in dilute gases so as to avoid the problem of solvent and solutes as much as possible as well as the statistical mechanical problem of the liquid state, the chapters on quantum mechanics would suggest that the first part of this rate problem is hard. The energy states of the reactant(s) alone can be found from first principles (the wave equation) only with great difficulty. Even with this part solved, there then remains the problem of the structure of the activated complex and the statistical mechanical problem of finding a suitable average of observables. It is clear, then, that this brief chapter can merely suggest the general nature of the mathematical and conceptual difficulties by a few well chosen and well considered examples of minimum complexity. It is impossible to be encyclopedic and it is foolish to give the impression that all problems in this area have been solved.

18.2 PHOTOCHEMISTRY

Although a plasma arc might be employed to study thermal reactions at 10,000°K, there would be little chemistry because most diatoms and almost all polyatoms are dissociated to atoms and ionized atoms below 7000°K. There are, however, many other ways to initiate chemical reactions under conditions that are in part those that exist at very high temperatures. Ionization in an electric field or by electron bombardment generates unusual species, shock waves reach high temperatures swiftly, and an intense flash of light can selectively excite many molecules to reactive status. Extreme pressures of the order of 10^4 atm may even initiate unexpected reactions, such as an explosion of sucrose. Of these methods and others, the use of photons of a particular energy is clearly a highly selective way to introduce energy into a system. Indeed, one method of observing very fast reactions with speeds up to those of diffusion-controlled reactions is to inject a sudden bit of energy into a system at equilibrium and follow its return to equilibrium. It is thus possible to study mechanisms, lifetimes of excited states, and spectra of rare and reactive species that would otherwise be so rare as to be almost beyond observation.

The two laws of photochemistry are simple. Only absorbed radiation can act, and one photon activates one molecule in the primary step. What happens after the initial primary step can be and usually is rather complicated.

The laws of Beer and Lambert relate the intensity of radiation transmitted through a substance to the length of the optical path and the concentration of absorber. The combined law of Beer and Lambert says that the rate of decrease in transmitted intensity I with respect to optical path length x is proportional to the intensity and to the concentration C of the absorber. Mathematically,

$$-\frac{dI}{dx} = \kappa IC \tag{18.1}$$

If I_0 is the initial intensity when the thickness of absorber x is zero, then integration of (18.1) yields

$$-\int_{I_0}^{I} \frac{dI'}{I'} = \kappa C \int_0^l dx$$

$$\ln\left(\frac{I_0}{I}\right) = \kappa Cl \tag{18.2}$$

The proportionality constant κ depends upon the wavelength of radiation as well as upon the nature of the absorber and the units of C and x. Since absorption spectroscopists prefer decadic logarithms for calculations, (18.2) is usually written

$$A = \log\left(\frac{I_0}{I}\right) = aCl \tag{18.3}$$

where $2.303a = \kappa$. Here A is called the absorbance and a is the absorptivity if C is given in moles per unit volume.

If one absorbtion cell of length l contains several species i (such as solvent and solutes), at wavelength λ_1 (18.3) reads

$$A^{(1)} = l \sum_i a_i^{(1)} C_i \tag{18.4}$$

That is, each of the i species that absorb is assumed to act independently upon the intensity transmitted by the others. Because the various molar absorptivities depend upon wavelength in a way that varies according to the nature of the absorber and its various excited energy states, at λ_j for the same mixture in the same cell

$$A^{(j)} = l \sum_i a_i^{(j)} C_i \tag{18.5}$$

If the matrix of absorptivities $a_i^{(j)}$ is known at the several wavelengths λ_j for the several species i, (18.5) represents simultaneous linear equations that can be solved for the several C_i. The number of equations must exceed or equal the number of concentrations to be found.

If the values of I_0 and I are measured absolutely in terms of ergs per square centimeter per second, then $I_0 - I$ is the energy absorbed per square centimeter per second. If the radiation is monochromatic with frequency ν, the energy per photon is $\varepsilon = h\nu$. The total number of photons absorbed per second per square centimeter is, therefore, $(I_0 - I)/h\nu$. Even when the intensity is not uniform over an irradiated area $\mathscr{A}$, the second law requires that $[(I_0 - I)/h\nu]\mathscr{A}$ be the number of molecules that absorb per second. The number of moles of absorber that disappear in a volume $V = \mathscr{A}l$ per second is therefore

$$-\frac{dC}{dt} = \left(\frac{I_0 - I}{Nh\nu}\right)\frac{1}{l} = \frac{I_0(1 - e^{-\kappa Cl})}{Nh\nu l} \tag{18.6}$$

When λ, κ, and l are fixed and absorption is modest so that $\kappa Cl \ll 1$, (18.6) becomes the simplest law of photochemical kinetics

$$-\frac{dC}{dt} = \frac{I_0 \kappa C}{Nh\nu} \tag{18.7}$$

That is, for the reaction $A + h\nu \longrightarrow A^*$ the rate of disappearance of A and the rate of formation of A* are proportional to I_0, C_A and κ if absorption is weak. Equation (18.7) is ordinarily suitable even for small range of frequencies if the absorption coefficient does not vary greatly with ν.

Example 18.1. The concentrations of two solutes were estimated in the same solution by absorption spectroscopy at 2 wavelengths. At λ_1, the molar absorptivities were 300 and 30 l mole^{-1} cm^{-1}; at λ_2, 10 and 200 l mole^{-1} cm^{-1}. When measured in a cell 2.00 cm in length, the percentage transmitted (after correction for solvent and cell-window absorption) was 1.77% at λ_1 and 20.3% at λ_2. What were the concentrations of the two solutes?

At λ_1, by (18.3) and (18.4),

$$\log\left(\frac{100}{1.77}\right) = 2.00\,(300C_A + 30C_B)$$

At λ_2, similarly,

$$\log\left(\frac{100}{20.3}\right) = 2.00\,(10C_A + 200C_B)$$

Simultaneous solution of these equations yields

$$C_A = 2.76 \times 10^{-3} \text{ mole l}^{-1}$$

$$C_B = 1.59 \times 10^{-3} \text{ mole l}^{-1}$$

As already noted in Section 10.12, a chain reaction is a reaction that proceeds by the repetition of a certain sequence of reactions. One or more of the reactants in the repeated series of reactions is itself a product of those reactions. This product, which is also a reactant, is generally a radical or excited atom, ion, or molecule. When it is destroyed the chain of reactions is broken and the reaction ceases until another reactive species is generated. This highly reactive intermediate may be generated thermally, by absorption of radiation, or in other ways. Often it is generated in an induction period during which no obvious reaction occurs.

The classic examples of chain reactions are the reactions of hydrogen with bromine or chlorine. Reaction begins with the production of halogen atoms. In the thermal reaction (Section 10.12), there exists the equilibrium $X_2 \rightleftharpoons 2X$. In the photochemical mechanism, halogen atoms X are generated by photolysis of X_2 and are eventually destroyed by a three-body collision.

$$X_2 + h\nu \xrightarrow{k_I} X + X \tag{18.8}$$

$$X + X + M \xrightarrow{k_3} X_2 + M^* \tag{18.9}$$

The chain reaction involves just two steps, namely,

$$\left.\begin{aligned} X + H_2 &\xrightarrow{k_X} HX + H \\ H + X_2 &\xrightarrow{k_H} HX + X \end{aligned}\right\} \tag{18.10}$$

These two steps can occur repeatedly until reactants disappear or until the atomic chain carriers are destroyed by (18.9) or (18.11).

$$\left.\begin{aligned} H + H + M &\longrightarrow H_2 + M^* \\ H + X + M &\longrightarrow HX + M^* \end{aligned}\right\} \tag{18.11}$$

The production of HX is slowed by the addition or formation of HX because (18.10) is reversed.

$$X + HX \longrightarrow X_2 + H \tag{18.12}$$

$$H + HX \xrightarrow{k_2} H_2 + X \tag{18.13}$$

These reverse reactions do not, however, decrease the number of chain-propagating atoms. Reaction (18.11) is relatively unimportant because the concentration of H is small. The photolysis of X_2 yields enough X, however, to make (18.9) of some importance. Reaction (18.12) is highly endothermic and thus is slow because of a great ΔH_a.

The mathematical formulation in a steady state proceeds in the usual way. Without (18.11) and (18.12),

$$\frac{dC_{HX}}{dt} = k_X C_{H_2} C_X + k_H C_{X_2} C_H - k_2 C_{HX} C_H \tag{18.14}$$

$$0 = \frac{dC_H}{dt} = k_X C_{H_2} C_X - k_H C_{X_2} C_H - k_2 C_{HX} C_H \tag{18.15}$$

$$0 = \frac{dC_X}{dt} = -k_X C_{H_2} C_X + k_H C_{X_2} C_H + k_2 C_{HX} C_H - k_3 C_M C_X^2 + 2k_I I C_{X_2} \tag{18.16}$$

The last term in (18.16) follows from (18.7). In view of (18.15), (18.16) becomes simply

$$C_X = \left(2\frac{k_I I C_{X_2}}{k_3 C_M}\right)^{1/2} \tag{18.17}$$

and (18.14) reduces to

$$\frac{dC_{HX}}{dt} = 2k_H C_{X_2} C_H \tag{18.18}$$

Solution of (18.15) for C_H and use of (18.17) to eliminate C_X yields finally

$$\frac{dC_{HX}}{dt} = 2k_H C_{X_2}\left(\frac{k_X C_{H_2}}{k_H C_{X_2} + k_2 C_{HX}}\right)\left(2\frac{k_I I C_{X_2}}{k_3 C_M}\right)^{1/2} \tag{18.19}$$

In the reaction of Cl_2 with H_2, the chain (18.10) may occur up to one million times before it is broken by recombination of atoms at the wall or in a three-body collision. Both chain reactions are swift because they have small activation energies. With Br_2, however, the reaction $Br + H_2 \longrightarrow HBr + H$ is endothermic, as explained in Section 10.12. Since ΔH_a is at least as great as ΔH, the rate of this reaction is slow and recombination can compete, thus limiting the chain length.

The quantum yield of a photochemical reaction is a measure of the efficiency with which radiation is used in a reaction. It is the ratio of the number of molecules of product produced to the number of quanta absorbed. For the production of HCl it may be as high as 10^6; in photosynthesis it is 0.25; in cis-trans isomerizations, it may be as low as 0.05. In the primary step, it is unity by the second law of photochemistry.

Photochemical studies are frequently helpful in understanding mechanisms. The quantum yield may be a key fact. One of the most startling developments is the observation by Sullivan[1] that the gas reaction $H_2 + I_2 \longrightarrow 2HI$ is not the ideal bimolecular one it has long been believed to be. The rate constants for the photochemically induced reaction $2I + H_2 \longrightarrow 2HI$ at room T lie on the same Arrhenius line as those of the thermally induced reaction $2I + H_2 \longrightarrow 2HI$ at about 700°K. Since a few I are thermally produced from I_2 at all T, the rate law for $H_2 + I_2 \longrightarrow 2HI$ cannot be distinguished from the law for $H_2 + 2I \longrightarrow 2HI$. For if $I_2 = 2I$ yields $K = C_I^2/C_{I_2}$, then $(\frac{1}{2})\, dC_{HI}/dt = k_2 C_{I_2} C_{H_2} = (k_2/K) C_I^2 C_{H_2}$. The distinction concerns the distance between I atoms as they attack H_2. (Sullivan finds the decomposition of HI to be ideally bimolecular, as in Section 10.13.)

18.3 COLLISION THEORY

The most obvious classical approach to a calculation of the rate of a thermal bimolecular reaction is to calculate the rate at which unlike molecules collide with enough energy to initiate reaction. This was done in Example 10.18 with the amazing result that the collision cross section σ of the molecules involved was much less than their real size, even less than their internuclear distance. On the other hand, for certain very fast diffusion-controlled reactions such as the neutralization of an acid with ions of charge $Z_A e$ by a base with ions of charge $Z_B e$ in an aqueous solution of dielectric constant κ, the apparent sum σ_{AB} of ion sizes as calculated from

$$k = \frac{4\pi Z_A Z_B e^2 N_0^2 \mathscr{D}}{\kappa RT} \left(e^{Z_A Z_B e^2 N_0/\kappa RT \sigma_{AB}} - 1\right)^{-1} \tag{18.20}$$

is unexpectedly large by a factor of about five. [Equation (18.20) reduces to (10.123) as Z_A and Z_B approach zero.]

A simple way to correct for this kind of discrepancy in apparent size is to add an empirical constant α to the rate law. If Z_{12} of (1.61) is the frequency of collision of unlike gas molecules in a certain constant volume, then the rate of reaction is

$$v = k_2 C_1 C_2 = \alpha Z_{12} e^{-E/RT} \tag{18.21}$$

where $C_i = N_i/V$ is the concentration of i, k_2 is the usual rate constant, and E is the energy of activation. With α, which might show systematic trends in value

[1] J. H. Sullivan, *J. Chem. Phys.* **46**, 73 (1967).

for related reactions, the very reasonable molecular diameters derived from second virial coefficients, self-diffusion studies, Joule-Thomson coefficients, or viscosity measurements (Section 1.10) can be kept.

A potential from which satisfactory values of molecular diameters σ are often derived is the well known Lennard-Jones potential

$$V(R) = 4\varepsilon\left[\left(\frac{\sigma}{R}\right)^{12} - \left(\frac{\sigma}{R}\right)^{6}\right] \tag{18.22}$$

When the intermolecular distance R is equal to σ or ∞, V is zero; at $R = \sigma\sqrt[6]{2}$, V is a minimum with the value $V = -\varepsilon$. This potential combines a long-range attractive R^{-6} term, required of typical dispersion forces, and a short-range repulsive R^{-12} term of the kind already seen in crystals (Section 16.18). Table 18.1 lists typical values of molecular diameters suitable when this potential is used in a partition function to calculate viscosity or nonideal gas behavior. The values are reasonable in view of present knowledge of molecular structure, and they exhibit reasonable trends according to the periodic table. Of those listed, only Hg and CH_3Cl seem really out of place.

It is, however, somewhat presumptuous to use these cross sections, adjusted to fit nonreactive molecular encounters, for chemical encounters wherein electronic energies are severely adjusted. Still another difficulty is establishing the size of an ion even though qualitatively the long-range coulombic potential would suggest that ions, as observed, have cross sections for reaction much larger than neutral free radicals or neutral molecules with all electrons paired.

Table 18.1. Molecular Diameters.

σ (± 0.1 A)	Molecules							
2.6	He							
2.8	Ne			Hg				
3.0		H_2						
3.2								
3.4	Ar	HCl					CH_3Cl	
3.6	Kr	HBr	O_2	NO	F_2			
3.8			N_2	CO		CO_2	CH_4	
4.0	Xe	HI						
4.2					Cl_2	SO_2	C_2H_2	C_2H_4
4.4					Br_2	CS_2	C_2N_2	C_2H_6
4.6								
4.8								
5.0					I_2		C_3H_8	

There are two interpretations of the steric factor α; both are really the same. One conceives α as a probability that the reactants are properly oriented at impact. This would require α to be less than unity for a particular gas reaction, as is usually the case, since there is no long-range order in a gas before collision. Since α in the acid-base neutralization does exceed unity, the explanation is that the proton in an aqueous solution by its tunneling has an unusually large effective range for neutralizing a base. The other form of interpretation of α considers the probability of a reactive impact in terms of entropy as in Section 10.9. For when a reaction like AB + CD = AC + BD reaches equilibrium, (10.62) requires the equilibrium constant to be $K = k_2/k_{-2}$, where k_{-2} refers to the reverse reaction with activation energy E'. In view of (18.21), cancellation of C_1, C_2, and Z_{12} yields

$$-RT \ln K = \Delta E - T(R \ln (\alpha_2/\alpha_{-2})) \tag{18.23}$$

where α_{-2} is the empirical constant for the reverse reaction and $\Delta E = E - E'$ is the energy change for the forward reaction. Since at constant V, $\Delta A^{\ominus}$ equals $-RT \ln K$, the term $R \ln (\alpha_2/\alpha_{-2})$ in (18.23) is an entropy change. Without α, therefore, (18.21) and (18.23) could be true only at $T = 0$.

The frustrating problem with α of course is that it cannot be calculated by methods that in any way approach the simplicity with which it was introduced. The real value of this kind of approach is that it offers an order-of-magnitude for k and, hopefully, a kind of maximum rate for bimolecular gas reactions.

18.4 MOLECULAR BEAMS[(2)]

A molecular beam is a jet of gaseous molecules streaming through a vacuum in a well defined direction. Precisely aligned slits limit the beam's divergence, and a series of synchronized beam-choppers periodically interrupt the beam and so by their concerted action limit the molecules' velocities to a small range. When two such molecular beams intersect, some of the collisions are chemical events in which the initial states of each reactant are as well defined as the beams. Angular distribution of the products then may reveal what really happens in a single event. It is conceivable that the distribution of velocities in strong product beams might also be measured in addition to the intensity in certain directions. Such mechanical details about speed and direction are blurred beyond recovery, of course, when gaseous reactants are, as usual, mixed in the same container so that reactant molecules approach each other from all directions and with a wide spectrum of speeds. Just as spatial separation of reactants in an electrochemical cell yields electric work as an organized flow of electrons and new insight into chemical behavior, so also the use of molecular beams reveals the fine details of the mechanical events in a chemical change.

Typical molecular beams carry up to 10^{14} molecules per second into the reaction volume where the beams meet. There the concentration is of the order

(2) This section is drawn largely from *Molecular Beams*, ed. by John Ross, **10**, Vol. X of *Advances in Chemical Physics*, especially Chapter 9, "Reactive Scattering in Molecular Beams" by D. R. Herschbach, New York: Interscience Publishers, a division of John Wiley and Sons, 1966.

of 10^{10} molecules per cm^3, while in the neighboring regions away from the beams there are perhaps less than 10^9 molecules per cm^3. Their concentration is often kept low by condensation on the cold metal walls of the evacuated vessel, which is immersed in liquid nitrogen. In strategic places throughout the vacuum are placed shields, deflectors, and electric and magnetic fields for focusing and guiding molecules and ions. Detectors that operate by surface ionization record the impacts of 2000 or more of scattered product molecules per second at various angles around the reaction zone. Preparation of the detector surfaces in various ways allows a detector to ignore or record particular kinds of molecules. This permits counting the various species separately or by difference. A rate of 2000 counts per second is, by macroscopic measure, small indeed. When scattering to a particular angle is weak, every effort is made to intensify the reactant beam. Years ago, the beams were made by mere effusion from a heated chamber, but nowadays it is common to produce the beams by squirting a gaseous stream out through a nozzle from a chamber heated strongly enough to establish a pressure of the order of 10 mm Hg.

The observations are a record of intensities of products at various angles for certain orientations of the reactant beams. It is always necessary to subtract a background caused by molecules scattered in nonreactive collisions. The predominant direction and speed of the reactants allows a calculation of the motion of the center-of-mass of the system of reactant molecules. This motion must be subtracted from the apparent motion of the products, as observed by counters fixed to the laboratory coordinates, in order to get the truly interesting velocities of products relative to each other.

Almost all reactions investigated thus far have involved an alkali atom M in one beam and a halogen-containing molecule in the other beam. The type reaction is thus

$$M + XY \longrightarrow MX + Y$$

where X is a halogen. The symbol Y represents things like a halogen atom, a hydrogen atom, an alkyl radical, or another molecular fragment. When the cross section for reaction is small, of the order of 10 A^2, the product MX is usually observed to move backwards from the direction of the M atoms in their beam. Iodoalkanes behave thus. This kind of reaction begins to occur at relatively short range, occurs abruptly, and much of the chemical energy from the breaking and making of chemical bonds appears as translational energy of the products relative to each other. However, the molecules of a beam are not really alike in velocity so that it is not possible to solve uniquely for the distribution of chemical energy among rotation, internal vibration, and relative translation of products. What is usually done is to compare the observed angular distribution of products to what is predicted by a model whose mechanical consequences are calculated by a large computer. Many sets of initial conditions are used in many separate calculations in order to simulate the distribution of speeds and directions of molecules in the beams. That is, as for many X-ray diffraction studies, the consequences of an assumed model are compared to observation so as to eliminate impossibilities and detect reasonable models and behavior.

On the other hand, when reactants attract each other at long range so that the cross section for reaction is of the order of 100 A^2, very little of the chemical energy becomes translational or even rotational energy of the products. Instead, the chemical energy tends to stay in MX as vibrational energy. This happens, for example, when XY is a halogen, Br-CBr_3, Cl-$SnCl_3$, Cl-PCl_2, Br-PBr_2, Cl-SCl, and F-SF_5. In these reactions the alkali halide molecule MX continues in the general direction of the M beam and vibrates wildly. In the 1930's, Polanyi termed this kind of reaction "harpooning." As M approaches XY, it 'shoots' its electron into XY. That is, the highly delocalized *s* electron of M finds XY an attractive spot to lodge. This sudden accumulation of an electron on XY leads to a more stable species XY^- with little or no time for nuclear motion. As a result, XY^- vibrates excitedly, for the new equilibrium internuclear distance in XY^- is generally longer than in XY since the newly added electron is commonly antibonding. Figure 18.1 explains this transition and why XY^- often falls apart into X^- and Y within one-half cycle of vibration.

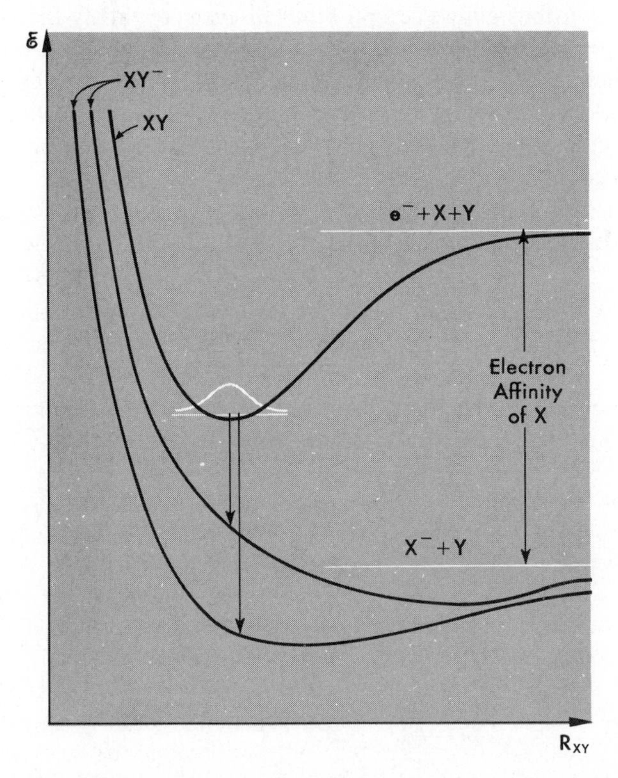

Figure 18.1. How an Extra Electron May Cause XY to Dissociate Within Half a Cycle of Vibration or to Form a Weakly Bonded XY^-

After throwing its electron harpoon, M^+ continues to approach XY^-, or what remains of it. Acting at long range through the coulomb potential, it hauls X^- aboard like a whale. This model explains several kinds of observations. For example, the reactive cross section is large because of the wide range of M's *s* electron. Again, the vigorous vibrations of MX stem from the coalescing of the widely separated ions.

Whether achieved by harpooning or by abrupt short-range action, the chemical collision of M and XY is very brief, often less than 5×10^{-13} seconds. This is less than the time of one rotation of an activated complex. Even in the slower harpooning event, Y may be effectively gone from the scene before M^+ pulls X^- aboard. Hence, when an alkali atom reacts with a halide, the event does not really involve an activated complex or molecular transition state. It is, rather, a direct collision which is nonconservative because of the bond energies hidden in the reactants and products.

Under ideal circumstances, thorough analysis of angles and intensities of products might yield every detail of energy and configuration. At the present time, however, the beams are somewhat heterogeneous and the resolution of the detectors is limited. Uncertainty in how much energy ends up in vibration, translation, and rotation thus allows several kinds of event to satisfy the same record of angular dependence of products. It is the task of the computer to establish limits of the possibilities beyond which the model disagrees with observation. The ideal would, of course, be an observed energy for every possible set of positions and velocities and orientations of reactants and products.

18.5 POTENTIAL ENERGY SURFACES

The electronic energy ε of a diatom is calculated in the Born-Oppenheimer approximation for a particular internuclear distance R. This energy reaches a minimum value $-D_e$ when R equals R_e. It is possible to calculate $\varepsilon(R)$ by the electronic wave equation $\mathbf{H}u = \varepsilon u$ at any arbitrarily fixed R. It is also possible to calculate $\varepsilon(R)$ from the observed vibrational energies $G(v)$. The Rydberg function

$$\varepsilon(R) = -D_e(1 + q)e^{-q} \tag{18.24}$$

[where $q = b(R - R_e)$] is a simple approximation to the true $\varepsilon(R)$. The Morse function

$$\varepsilon(R) = D_e(1 - e^{-q'})^2 \tag{18.25}$$

where

$$q' = b'(R - R_e) \tag{18.26}$$

is a more widely used function, but it errs more than the Rydberg function at about 2.5 R_e, where it predicts too low a value of ε.

These functions describe the potential energy for nuclear vibration, as explained in (15.8). It is as if the electron cloud were an external force acting on the nuclei through $\varepsilon(R)$. Both the Morse function[3] and the Rydberg function[4] have been generalized to describe repulsive states of diatoms and attractive and repulsive states (bonding and antibonding, that is) of triatomic and even polyatomic molecules. This discussion is limited to triatoms because this is sufficient for the type-reaction AB + C ⟶ A + BC.

The energy $\varepsilon_{\text{bond}}$ of H_2^+ was found in the simplest approach to be

$$\varepsilon' = \varepsilon_A + \frac{e^2}{4\pi\epsilon_0 R_{AB}} + \frac{J + K}{1 + S} \tag{15.23}$$

That is, relative to nuclei A and B, one having the electron, at energy ε_A and without nuclear repulsion, the bonding energy of an electron is of the form

$$\varepsilon_{\text{bond}} = \frac{J_{AB} + K_{AB}}{1 + S} \tag{18.27}$$

The VB method for H_2, a method that is recognized to be superior to the MO method at large R, has as its main bonding term the similar result (15.34), which at a similar reference of energy is

$$\varepsilon_{\text{bond}} = 2\frac{J_{AB} + SK_{AB}}{1 + S^2} \tag{18.28}$$

The antibonding states have expressions like (18.27) and (18.28) with minus signs replacing the plus signs. Using the well known Eyring semi-empirical method in somewhat modified form, Sato[3] has evaluated J_{AB} and K_{AB} from attractive and repulsive Morse functions for diatom AB by assuming various constant values of S in expressions like (18.27) and (18.28). About $S^2 = 0.2$ was best.

His purpose in thus finding empirical values of J and K is to use the widely known London formula (18.29) for the energy of three atoms A, B, and C in the neighborhood of the region where both A and C are bonded to B.

$$\varepsilon' = \frac{1}{1 + S^2}\left\{J_{AB} + J_{BC} + J_{CA} - \frac{1}{\sqrt{2}}\left[(K_{AB} - K_{BC})^2 + (K_{BC} - K_{CA})^2 + (K_{CA} - K_{AB})^2\right]^{1/2}\right\} \tag{18.29}$$

The values of J_{ij} and K_{ij} vary, of course, with R_{ij} for each kind of diatom. When ε' is plotted vertically as a function of R_{AB} and R_{BC} for three H's with $R_{AC} = R_{AB} + R_{BC}$, the contours of Figure 18.2 were found. Figure 18.3 was calculated by the use of Morse functions for H_2 and HCl with $R_{HCl} = R_{HH} + R_{HCl}$, one

[3] S. Sato, *J. Chem. Phys.* **23**, 592, 2465 (1955).
[4] W. F. Sheehan, *J. Phys. Chem.* **69**, 923 (1965).

H being between and collinear with Cl and the terminal H in the reaction $H_2 + Cl \rightarrow H + HCl$. Figure 18.4 is the London Potential Energy Surface for three H atoms as calculated semi-empirically from the exact $\varepsilon(R)$ for the electronic states ${}^1\Sigma_g^+$ and ${}^3\Sigma_u^+$ that correlate with ground-state atoms.

The value of S, which is chosen to fit some datum well, is a function of R. This arbitrary choice of a parameter and, indeed, the evaluation of J and K for use in (18.29), can be avoided by attempting to join potential energy curves that approximate either AB + C or A + BC. The result is generally a discontinuity in the space derivative of ε in the neighborhood of the region where $R_{AB} \approx R_{BC}$. This is the region of utmost interest in a collision of diatom and atom, but an interesting result comes from doing so anyway with triatomic Rydberg functions. When A is identical with C, and when the energy of $A \ldots B \ldots A^{\ddagger}$ exceeds the minimum energy $-D_e(AB)$ of diatom and distant atom, the energy of $A \ldots B \ldots A^{\ddagger}$ cannot exceed $-0.736\ D_e$. That is, at the point where B is equally distant from each A and joined with them, the energy

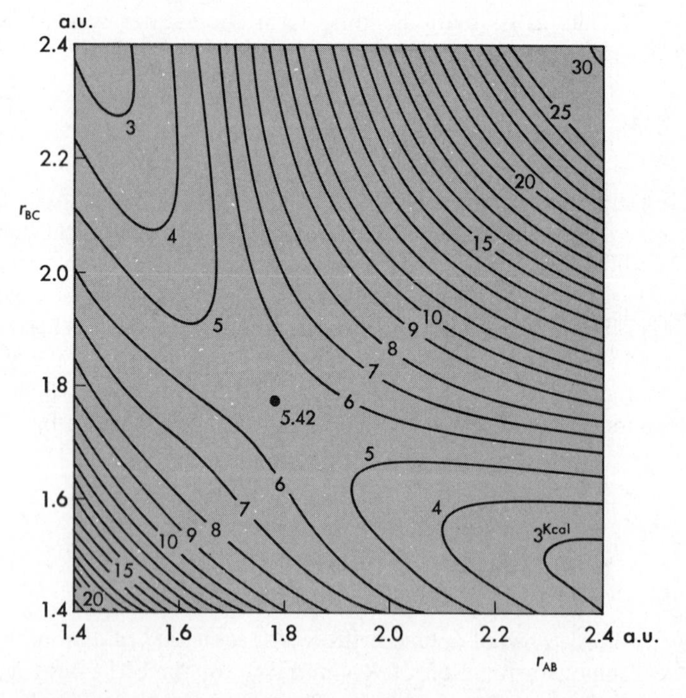

Figure 18.2. Potential Energy Surface of Three Collinear Hydrogen Atoms: Contours of Constant Energy Relative to Zero Energy at Equilibrium Internuclear Distance R_e for H_2†

†S. Sato, *J. Chem. Phys.* **23**, 592 (1955), Fig. 1

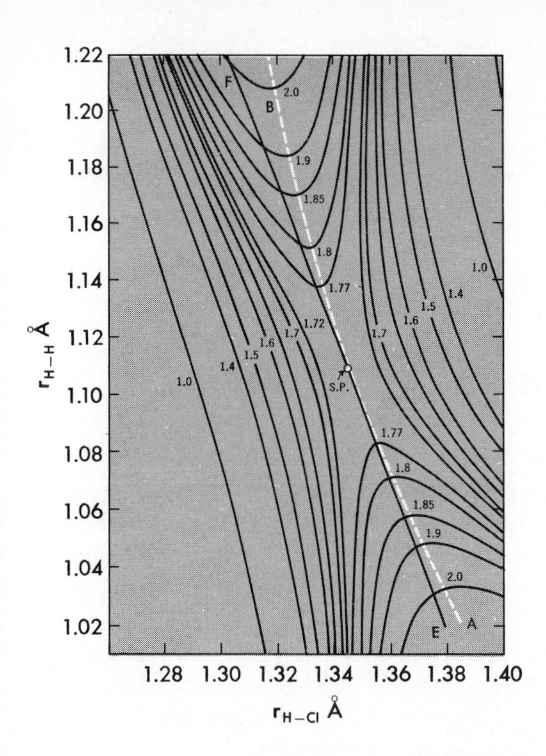

Figure 18.3. Potential Energy Surface of Collinear H, H, and Cl (Cl on end)†

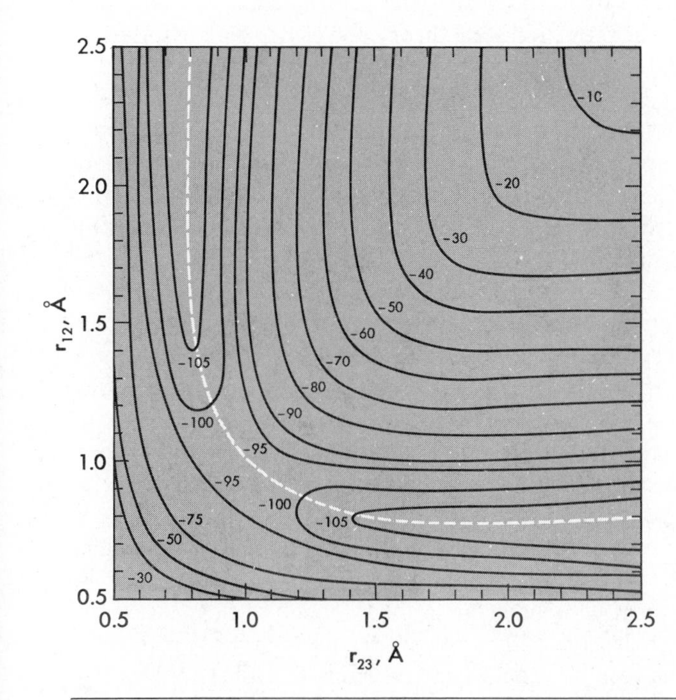

Figure 18.4. London Potential Energy Surface for Three Hydrogen Atoms‡

†A. Persky and F. S. Klein, *J. Chem. Phys.* **44,** 3623 [1966] Fig. 2
‡J. K. Cashion and D. R. Herschbach, *J. Chem. Phys.* **40,** 2358 [1964] Fig. 2

does not exceed 0.264 D_e relative to a zero of energy at the start or end of reaction $A + BA \longrightarrow AB + A$. On the basis of wide experience, it has long been recognized that the height of this mountain pass seldom exceeds 0.30 of the bond energies of the bonds involved in the reaction.

18.6 TRANSITION-STATE THEORY

The preceding section explained how the energy of three collinear atoms A,B, and C might be calculated semi-empirically from observed $\varepsilon(R)$ with guidance from quantum mechanics. When R_{AB} and R_{BC} both increase or decrease together in the region where they are about equal, the energy ε' rises from a minimum atop the saddle at the mountain pass. That is, in a symmetrical (breathing) vibration, the activated complex $ABC^{\ddagger}$ behaves like a stable species. However, when $\delta R_{AB} = -\delta R_{BC}$ in the saddle, the vibration is unsymmetrical and ε' decreases toward the energy and configuration of a diatom and distant atom. Marcelin, using classical mechanics in 1915, was the first to suggest a view of this general kind for rate processes. Early in the 1930's, after a few of the initial valence problems had been satisfactorily answered in a qualitative way, wave mechanics was applied to the transition state theory by Wigner, Polanyi, Eyring, and others.

Before discussing the details of calculating rate constants by statistical and quantum mechanics, it is appropriate to note the breadth of this idea of a transition state. It is an attempt to describe the fine details of a process in terms of an intermediate state of higher-than-normal energy and known structure. This extraordinary energy is the barrier to instantaneous or one-hundred-percent conversion of the initial state into the final state. It is thus possible to use the theory to describe many kinds of process: the transfer of an electron from an electrode to an ion; a rotation of part of a molecule against the rest of it; desorption of a molecule from a surface; evaporation or sublimation; diffusion through a dense fluid; motion of ions through a crystal; and so on to any process that occurs at a finite rate.

To emphasize this breadth of utility, a few remarks on viscosity are in order. Gases exhibit viscosity because each molecule has a mass that resists acceleration and a collisional cross section that allows collisions. The viscosity of a gas increases with the square root of the temperature because the rate of movement perpendicular to the direction of flow increases with $\sqrt{T}$.

In a liquid, displacement perpendicular to the direction of flow is severely limited because of the high density. Although the reason for viscosity, namely, a change of momentum between adjacent layers, remains the same for gas and liquid, the intermolecular forces so dominate flow in liquids that η depends upon T in a different and more marked way. In liquids in general,

$$\ln \eta = \frac{A}{RT} + B \tag{18.30}$$

where B is an empirical constant and A represents an energy of viscous flow due to breaking of bonds or unfavorable intermolecular contacts during flow. In water, A is about 4 kcal per mole.

Table 18.2 Viscosities of liquids (20°C)†

Substance	η (dyne-sec cm^{-2})
Benzene	0.00647
Ethanol	0.011943
Glycerol	10.690
Heptane	0.004163
Mercury	0.01547
Water	0.01002

† Lange's *Handbook of Chemistry*, New York: McGraw-Hill Book Co., Inc., 1967, pp. 1669–74.

18.7 ACTIVATED COMPLEX

The activated complex is the unobservable molecular species that acts as the critical intermediate between reactants and products. It has the energy of the lowest energy-pass connecting reactants and products in a space of several dimensions some combination of which is suitable for describing the spatial progress of the reaction. For a reaction of type $A + B + \cdots \rightarrow AB^{\ddagger} \rightarrow$ products the activated complex $AB^{\ddagger}$ has the energy and configuration of the saddle-point of a figure like those above. If the reaction coordinate were flattened out, the result would be something like Figure 18.5.

With the energy and configuration of the activated complex known by an appropriate calculation, and with vibrational and rotational frequencies known from the shape and curvature of the energy-parameter surface, the *theory of absolute reaction rates* then uses the methods of statistical mechanics to evaluate the rate constant k_n. It is assumed, with ample justification through agreement of calculated and observed rates, that the activated complex is in equilibrium with reactants. The equilibrium

$$A + B + \cdots \rightleftharpoons AB^{\ddagger} \tag{18.31}$$

between reactants A, B, $\cdots$ and activated complex $AB^{\ddagger}$ has an equilibrium constant

$$K_c^{\ddagger} = \frac{C_{AB^{\ddagger}}}{C_A C_B \cdots} = e^{-(\Delta A^{\ddagger}/kT)} \tag{18.32}$$

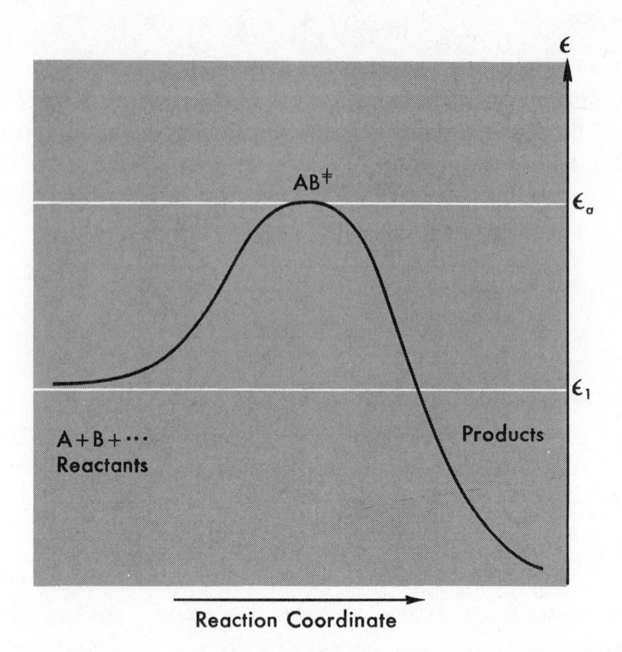

Figure 18.5. Schematic Diagram of Reaction Coordinate

If the activated complex decomposes to products with a probability κ (called the *transmission coefficient*), the rate of the reaction is equal to κ times the frequency $\nu^{\ddagger}$ of vibration along the reaction coordinate times the concentration of activated complex. If $N_{\ddagger}$ molecules of $AB^{\ddagger}$ exist in a volume V, the rate (molecules per unit volume per unit time) is

$$-\frac{d}{dt}\left(\frac{N_{\ddagger}}{V}\right) = \kappa\nu^{\ddagger}\left(\frac{N_{\ddagger}}{V}\right) \tag{18.33}$$

With one molecule per unit volume as the standard state, (18.32) then yields for the rate:

$$\begin{aligned} -\frac{d}{dt}\left(\frac{N_{\mathrm{A}}}{V}\right) &= -\frac{d}{dt}\left(\frac{N_{\mathrm{B}}}{V}\right) = -\frac{d}{dt}\left(\frac{N_{\ddagger}}{V}\right) \\ &= \kappa\nu^{\ddagger}\left(\frac{N_{\mathrm{A}}}{V}\right)\left(\frac{N_{\mathrm{B}}}{V}\right)\cdots e^{-(\Delta A^{\ddagger}/kT)} \end{aligned} \tag{18.34}$$

By analogy with (10.7), which holds at constant V,

$$v = -\frac{dC_{\mathrm{A}}}{dt} = kC_{\mathrm{A}}^{a}C_{\mathrm{B}}^{b} \tag{10.7}$$

it is clear that the rate constant is

$$k_n = \kappa \nu^{\ddagger} e^{-(\Delta A^{\ddagger}/kT)} = \kappa \nu^{\ddagger} K_c^{\ddagger} \tag{18.35}$$

Chapter 17 discusses the calculation of $\Delta A^{\ddagger}$ and other thermodynamic properties from molecular properties. Here it is convenient to make the calculation for one molecule in unit volume; the translational partition function (17.30) for $V = 1$ is merely

$$Q_{tr} = \left(\frac{2\pi mkT}{h^2}\right)^{3/2} \tag{18.36}$$

Then, for one molecule per unit volume, as in (17.36) and (17.21),

$$Q_1 = Q_{tr} Q_i \quad \text{and} \quad A = -kT \ln Q_1 \tag{18.37}$$

Equations (18.36) and (18.37) as applied to (18.31) yield

$$\begin{aligned} \Delta A^{\ddagger} &= A_{\ddagger} - (A_{\mathrm{A}} + A_{\mathrm{B}} + \cdots) \\ &= -kT \ln \left(\frac{Q_{tr}^{\ddagger} Q_i^{\ddagger}}{Q_{tr}^{(\mathrm{A})} Q_i^{(\mathrm{A})} Q_{tr}^{(\mathrm{B})} Q_i^{(\mathrm{B})} \cdots}\right) \end{aligned}$$

Finally, by (18.35)

$$k_n = \kappa \nu^{\ddagger} \left(\frac{Q_{tr}^{\ddagger} Q_i^{\ddagger}}{Q_{tr}^{(\mathrm{A})} Q_i^{(\mathrm{A})} Q_{tr}^{(\mathrm{B})} Q_i^{(\mathrm{B})} \cdots}\right) \tag{18.38}$$

The methods of evaluating Q_i have been discussed in Sections 17.6 and 17.7. Here only two features need to be clarified: how the activation energy originates and how the very low frequency $\nu^{\ddagger}$ of vibration along the reaction coordinate is to be handled.

The activation energy originates from the electronic parts of the Q_i's as in Example 17.5. Each electronic state of a species has an energy ε_e from which vibrational and rotational levels of that electronic state are calculated. As in (17.41) and (17.42),

$$Q_i = \sum_e g_e e^{-(\varepsilon_e - \varepsilon_0)/kT} Q_{rv}^{(e)}$$

The energy of the ground (or most stable) state of most molecules is usually so much less than the energies of all excited states that the sum is dominated by the one term for that one most stable state and $Q_i = g_e e^{-(\varepsilon_e - \varepsilon_0)/kT} Q_{rv}^{(e)}$. With one species it is best to let $\varepsilon_0 = \varepsilon_e$ and Q_i is simply $g_e Q_{rv}^{(e)}$, where g_e is the electronic degeneracy of the ground state.

As in Figure 18.4, it is common to assume that the transition from reactants to products via activated complex can be effected adiabatically in the quantum mechanical sense (that is, with $g_e^{\ddagger} = g_e^{\mathrm{A}} g_e^{\mathrm{B}} \cdots$). In the end, therefore, the g_e's cancel in (18.38) and there remains only the factor

$$\exp -\frac{1}{kT}\left\{(\varepsilon_{\ddagger} - \varepsilon_0) - [(\varepsilon_{\mathrm{A}} - \varepsilon_0) + (\varepsilon_{\mathrm{B}} - \varepsilon_0) + \cdots]\right\}$$

These energies are the lowest vibrational-rotational energies of the most stable electronic states of the several reactants and activated complex and ε_0 is the one arbitrary reference energy common to all. It is customary to choose the lowest vibrational state of each electronic state as the zero of energy in computing $Q_{rv}^{(e)}$ for each species. The activation energy per molecule at absolute zero is

$$\Delta\varepsilon^{\ddagger} = (\varepsilon_{\ddagger} - \varepsilon_0) - [(\varepsilon_{\mathrm{A}} - \varepsilon_0) + (\varepsilon_{\mathrm{B}} - \varepsilon_0) + \cdots]$$

In Figure 18.5, ε_0 would be chosen as ε_1 and $\varepsilon_{\ddagger}$ as ε_a. The zero-point energy of $AB^{\ddagger}$ is not shown in the figure because it involves bendings and stretching along coordinates not depicted there.

The second feature of (18.38) concerns the decomposition vibration $\nu^{\ddagger}$ of the activated complex. If the reference of energy in calculating Q_v of a molecule such as the activated complex is its lowest energy level, its vibrational partition function, as in (17.46), is

$$Q_v = \prod_i [1 - e^{-(2\pi\hbar\nu_i/kT)}]^{-1}$$

For most frequencies, $2\pi\hbar\nu_i \gg kT$ so that Q_v is close to unity. The one low frequency $\nu^{\ddagger}$ of the activated complex corresponding to vibration along the reaction coordinate contributes thus:

$$\lim_{\nu^{\ddagger}\to 0} (1 - e^{-(2\pi\hbar\nu^{\ddagger}/hT)})^{-1} = \lim_{\nu^{\ddagger}\to 0}\left[1 - \left(1 - \frac{2\pi\hbar\nu^{\ddagger}}{kT} + \cdots\right)\right]^{-1} = \frac{kT}{2\pi\hbar\nu^{\ddagger}} \tag{18.39}$$

A nonlinear activated complex of N atoms is treated, therefore, like an ordinary molecule with $3N - 7$ internal degrees of freedom. Six of the total of $3N$ degrees of freedom are rotation and translation and the seventh, not included among the $3N - 7$, is the weak vibration with frequency $\nu^{\ddagger}$.

The internal partition function $Q_i^{\ddagger}$ of the activated complex is the product of (18.39) and an internal partition function $Q_i^{(\ddagger)}$ of the complex devoid of the vibration $\nu^{\ddagger}$. That is, $Q_i^{\ddagger} = (kT/h\nu^{\ddagger})Q_i^{(\ddagger)}$. It follows, therefore, from (18.38) and subsequent equations that

$$k_n = \kappa\left(\frac{kT}{h}\right)\left(\frac{Q_{tr}^{(\ddagger)}Q_i^{(\ddagger)}}{\prod_{j=1}^{n} Q_{tr}^{(j)}Q_i^{(j)}}\right)e^{-(\Delta\varepsilon^{\ddagger}/kT)} \tag{18.40}$$

The $(n + 1)Q_{tr}$'s are given by (18.36) and the Q_i's are calculated for the most stable electronic state whose lowest vibrational-rotational state is the reference of energy for each. The universal frequency factor (kT/h) is 6.21×10^{12} sec^{-1} at 25°C.

The observed activation energy ΔH_a differs slightly from $N\Delta\varepsilon^{\ddagger}$ of (18.40) for several reasons. While $N\,\Delta\varepsilon^{\ddagger}$ applies at $T = 0$, ΔH_a may obtain at any T. In general for ideal gases in (18.31), $\Delta H = \Delta E + (1 - n)RT$ and the choice of standard state is immaterial to ΔE or ΔH. It happens, however, that observed values of ΔH_a and ΔE_a in the Arrhenius equation exceed calculated values like $N\,\Delta\varepsilon^{\ddagger}$ by RT because of the factor kT/h in (18.40). That is, $\Delta H_a = \Delta H^{\ddagger} + RT = N\,\Delta\varepsilon^{\ddagger} + (1 - n)RT + RT = N\,\Delta\varepsilon^{\ddagger} + (2 - n)RT$. With this result and $R = Nk$, (18.40) finally yields for the rate constant

$$k_n = \kappa e^{2-n}\left(\frac{kT}{h}\right)\left(\frac{Q_{tr}^{(\ddagger)}Q_i^{(\ddagger)}}{\prod_{j=1}^{n} Q_{tr}^{(j)}Q_i^{(j)}}\right)e^{-(\Delta H_a/RT)} \tag{18.41}$$

Example 18.2. If all molecules are rigid, if all rotational partition functions $(2I_e kT/h^2)^{1/2}$ are $10^{1.5}$, and if all Q_{tr} are 10^{26}, show that bimolecular reactions between nonlinear reactants are much slower than between atoms even when the activation energies of both reactions are equal.

For bimolecular reactions $n = 2$. If all vibrations are suppressed, the molecules being rigid, all Q_v are unity. For the diatomic activated complex, there are two nonzero moments of inertia and $Q_i = Q_r = (10^{1.5})^2 = 10^3$. For a rigid nonlinear molecule or activated complex, there are three nonzero moments of inertia and $Q_i = (10^{1.5})^3$. The bimolecular reaction between atoms has a rate constant k_{2a} as given by (18.41) with $\kappa = 1$

$$k_{2a} = \left(\frac{kT}{h}\right)\left(\frac{10^{26}\cdot 10^{3}}{10^{26}\cdot 10^{26}}\right)e^{-(\Delta Ha/RT)}$$

Similarly, for the reaction between nonlinear molecules,

$$k_{2m} = \left(\frac{kT}{h}\right)\left(\frac{10^{26}\cdot 10^{4.5}}{10^{26}\cdot 10^{4.5}\cdot 10^{26}\cdot 10^{4.5}}\right)e^{-(\Delta Ha/RT)}$$

It follows at once that $k_{2a} = k_{2m} \times 10^{7.5}$. The rate between atoms exceeds that between nonlinear molecules by 3×10^7. What must be explained by steric factors and collision efficiencies in the collision theory is here explained simply in terms of rotational degrees of freedom.

There remain two troublesome points about (18.41). The value of the transmission coefficient κ is an adjustable parameter. If decomposition of the activated complex is equally likely toward reactants or products, perhaps because writing $K^{\ddagger}$ implies a steady nonzero concentration of activated complex, then κ should be 1/2. In the absence of other information, this value can be used as a convention. It does not allow, however, for what might be termed chemical inertia akin to mechanical momentum across the saddle.

The second troublesome feature of (18.41) is the actual or supposed structure of the activated complex when it has more than three atoms. One may wonder also whether it is reasonable for all three-atom complexes to be linear. The crucial matter is whether an observed pre-exponential factor s from the Arrhenius equation can be calculated by (18.41). A very fair and thorough test[5] has been made for 12 bimolecular reactions listed in Table 18.3. The structures of the activated complexes as shown in Figure 18.6 were assumed to be planar and were guessed so as to be simply related to the products and reactants. Fortunately, what is needed in $Q_i^{(\ddagger)}$ is merely the product $(I_1^\ddagger I_2^\ddagger I_3^\ddagger)^{1/2}$ of the mo-

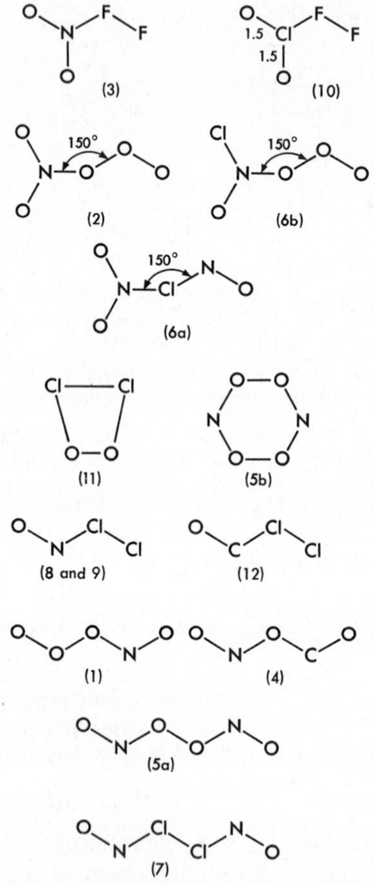

Figure 18.6. Structures of Activated Complexes of Reactions of Table 18.3†

[5] D. R. Herschbach, H. S. Johnston, K. S. Pitzer, and R. E. Powell, *J. Chem. Phys.* **25,** 736 (1956).

†D. R. Herschbach, H. S. Johnston, K. S. Pitzer, and R. E. Powell, *J. Chem. Phys.* **25,** 736 (1956) Fig. 1

ments of inertia and not their individual values in a sensitive combination. This product of I's is not greatly changed when the complex is made nonplanar and when various changes in internuclear distance are made.

Table 18.3 A Comparison of Theoretical and Observed Pre-Exponential Factors of Bimolecular Reactions

Elementary Reaction	ΔH_a (kcal/mole)	s(obs)	$\frac{s}{\kappa}$ (calc)† (10^{12} cc/mole-sec)
1. $NO + O_3 \longrightarrow NO_2 + O_2$	2.5	0.80	0.44
2. $NO_2 + O_3 \longrightarrow NO_3 + O_2$	7.0	5.9	0.14
3. $NO_2 + F_2 \longrightarrow NO_2F + F$	10.4	1.6	0.12
4. $NO_2 + CO \longrightarrow NO + CO_2$	31.6	12.	6.0
5. $NO_2 + NO_2 \longrightarrow 2NO + O_2$	26.6	1.8	(a) 4.5 (b) 0.0017
6. $NO + NO_2Cl \longrightarrow NOCl + NO_2$	6.9	0.83	(a) 0.84 (b) 1.6
7. $NOCl + NOCl \longrightarrow 2NO + Cl_2$	24.5	9.4	0.44
8. $NOCl + Cl \longrightarrow NO + Cl_2$	1.1	11.4	4.4
9. $NO + Cl_2 \longrightarrow NOCl + Cl$	20.3	4.0	1.2
10. $F_2 + ClO_2 \longrightarrow FClO_2 + F$	8.5	0.035	0.082
11. $ClO + ClO \longrightarrow Cl_2 + O_2$	ca. 0	0.058	0.010
12. $COCl + Cl \longrightarrow CO + Cl_2$	0.83	400	1.8

† D.R. Herschbach, H.S. Johnston, K.S. Pitzer, and R.E. Powell, *J. Chem. Phys.* **25,** 736 (1956).

It was, of course, impossible for these investigators to calculate the transmission coefficient; hence, it is left as a parameter of unknown value. It is, nevertheless, close to unity in all cases except 12, which may have an unusual activated complex. Its observed s is certainly unusual. When s is calculated by classical collision theory with the usual molecular diameters, a value of α in (18.21) of the order of 10^{-2} is needed except for reaction 12 where α is about 6. The agreement of calculated and observed s's is an amazing confirmation of the Eyring theory of the activated complex.

The advantages of the Eyring theory are obvious. Through $K^{\ddagger}$, which may have any number of factors in its denominator, it deals automatically with reactions of any molecularity. The theory has as few adjustable parameters as are consistent with the usual ignorance of the activated state. It provides an easy way to calculate rates of closely related reactants if a small change in structure of one of them makes corresponding changes in the free energy of reactant and activated complex.[6] And, as the next section shows, the theory accounts well for the effects of isotopic substitution, and it does so without extraordinary effort.

[6] In this regard, see, e.g., D. R. Herschbach, H. S. Johnston, and D. Rapp, *J. Chem. Phys.* **31,** 1652 (1957).

18.8 ISOTOPE EFFECT

Isotopic substitution in reactants aids in the study of mechanism and provides a suitable test of the Eyring theory of the activated complex because the theory's predictions are definite and easy to identify. As already indicated in Table 18.3, the theory is able to calculate the collision or frequency factor s within a power of ten. When reactants are as similar as molecules containing one different nucleus, the theory can be expected to yield an accurate value of a *ratio* of rate constants because of cancellation of various factors that might otherwise contribute to an inaccurate value of the rate constant itself.

If species A contains the lighter nucleus while species B contains the heavier nucleus, then the most direct comparison is a study of the elementary processes

$$\left.\begin{array}{ll} A + X + \ldots \rightarrow P + \ldots & (k_A) \\ B + X + \ldots \rightarrow P + \ldots & (k_B) \end{array}\right\} \quad (18.42)$$

The rate laws for (18.42) are

$$\left.\begin{array}{l} v_A = -\dfrac{dC_A}{dt} = k_A C_A C_X \ldots \\ v_B = -\dfrac{dC_B}{dt} = k_B C_B C_X \ldots \end{array}\right\} \quad (18.43)$$

From dividing the equations of (18.43) comes the result

$$\frac{dC_A}{dC_B} = \frac{k_A C_A}{k_B C_B} \quad (18.44)$$

which is useful when A and B are in the same system with X. If at $t = 0$ the concentration of A is C_A^0 while that of B is C_B^0, then definite integration of (18.44) yields

$$\frac{k_A}{k_B} = \frac{\ln (C_A^0/C_A)}{\ln (C_B^0/C_B)} \quad (18.45)$$

It is necessary, especially with isotopes of hydrogen, to beware of possible exchange reactions among the reactants, activated state, and/or products as (18.42) occurs before reporting values of C_A and C_B for use in (18.45).

Normally, since lighter atoms usually move more rapidly at a certain T, k_A is greater than k_B. However, it is possible for k_A to be less than k_B in what is called the *inverse isotope effect*. Possible reasons for this are given below. Generally, inverse isotope effects are half as great as normal effects, which find k_A/k_B of the order of 10^2 when ^2H replaces ^1H. Isotopic substitution by first-row elements generally gives a ratio of k_A to k_B of the order of 1.2, of the order of 1.05 for second-row elements, and less and less as the mass of the nucleus increases. (In the limit of zero mass change upon isotopic substitution, the theory does not give a ratio of unity.) The values of k_A and k_B may differ even though the substituted atom is not directly involved in the bond or bonds that are broken.

A straightforward (more elegant ones are possible) application of (18.40) or (18.41) to k_A and k_B yields the theory's prediction for comparison to observed k_A/k_B. The transmission coefficients should be almost equal and thus cancel in the ratio. Any electronic degeneracies will cancel also. The potential energy surfaces should be almost alike; the only contribution here comes from a difference in zero-point energy, which may be very great for H. If ε_{ei} is the energy given by the potential energy surface while ε_{0i} is the energy of the actual ground state of i, then (18.40) for the reaction $A + X \longrightarrow AX^\ddagger$ gives

$$\begin{aligned}\Delta\varepsilon_A^\ddagger &= \varepsilon_{0\ddagger}^{(A)} - \varepsilon_{0A}^{(A)} - \varepsilon_{0X}\\ &= [\varepsilon_{0\ddagger}^{(A)} - \varepsilon_{e\ddagger}^{(A)}] + \varepsilon_{e\ddagger}^{(A)} - [\varepsilon_{0A}^{(A)} - \varepsilon_{eA}^{(A)}] - \varepsilon_{eA}^{(A)} - \varepsilon_{0X}\end{aligned}$$

wherein superscripts identify which isotope is in use. Similarly, there is an equivalent expression for $\Delta\varepsilon_B^\ddagger$ with B with replacing A in the reaction and in the expression's sub- and superscripts. But if the potential energy surface is the same because the electronic states are alike for A and B, then $\varepsilon_{e\ddagger}^{(A)} = \varepsilon_{e\ddagger}^{(B)}$ and $\varepsilon_{eA}^{(A)} = \varepsilon_{eB}^{(B)}$. Hence, (18.40) indicates that the ratio k_A/k_B has the factor

$$\exp\left[\frac{\Delta\varepsilon_B^\ddagger - \Delta\varepsilon_A^\ddagger}{kT}\right] = \exp\left[\frac{\begin{array}{c}[\varepsilon_{0\ddagger}^{(B)} - \varepsilon_{e\ddagger}^{(B)}] - [\varepsilon_{0\ddagger}^{(A)} - \varepsilon_{e\ddagger}^{(A)}]\\ + [\varepsilon_{0A}^{(A)} - \varepsilon_{eA}^{(A)}] - [\varepsilon_{0B}^{(B)} - \varepsilon_{eB}^{(B)}]\end{array}}{kT}\right]$$

For $^1H^1H$, $\varepsilon_0 - \varepsilon_e$ is 2200 cm^{-1}; for $^1H^2H$ it is 1900 cm^{-1}; for $^2H^2H$ it is 1550 cm^1 in the $X\,^1\Sigma_g^+$ state. Such differences are less for other isotopes.

Another factor in k_A/k_B is the ratio of symmetry numbers σ (Section 17.7). For $^1H^1H$ and $^2H^2H$, $\sigma = 2$, but for $^1H^2H$ it is unity. Or again, for CH_4 containing only ^1H, σ is 12; but if one of the H's is replaced by ^2H, σ is only 3 because three of the four threefold axes no longer exist. The value of σ for the activated complex is also of concern, for linear $XXY^\ddagger$ has $\sigma = 1$ while $XYX^\ddagger$ has $\sigma = 2$. The factor σ_i occurs in the denominator of Q_i; hence, the ratio of k_A to k_B has the factor $(\sigma_A\sigma_B^\ddagger/\sigma_B\sigma_A^\ddagger)$.

The translational partition function of a nonlinear species is $(2\pi mkT/h^2)^{3/2}$. Thus, in k_A/k_B there is, if all species are nonlinear, a factor

$$\left(\frac{m_A^\ddagger}{m_B^\ddagger}\right)^{3/2}\left(\frac{m_B}{m_A}\right)^{3/2}$$

Similarly, the moments of inertia I_{1i}, I_{2i}, and I_{3i} about axes 1, 2, and 3 for species i contribute a factor

$$\left[\frac{(I_{1A}^{\ddagger}I_{2A}^{\ddagger}I_{3A}^{\ddagger})}{(I_{1A}I_{2A}I_{3A})} \times \frac{(I_{1B}I_{2B}I_{3B})}{(I_{1B}^{\ddagger}I_{2B}^{\ddagger}I_{3B}^{\ddagger})}\right]^{1/2}$$

Finally, the vibrational effects of the isotopic substitution affect the ratio of Q_v's in a complicated way. The pseudo-frequency $\nu^{\ddagger}$ along the reaction coordinate is not considered in $Q_v^{(\ddagger)}$ and is especially important in this regard because it controls the rate of passage over the energy saddle. If kT is much greater than $h\nu^{\ddagger}$, the net effect of vibration is to yield the factor $\nu_A^{\ddagger}/\nu_B^{\ddagger}$ in k_A/k_B, where $\nu_A^{\ddagger}$ refers to the pseudo-frequency of $AX^{\ddagger}$. If this frequency is proportional inversely to the square root of the reduced mass of the vibrator along this reaction coordinate, then the factor in k_A/k_B is $(\mu_B/\mu_A)^{1/2}$.

When more than one electronic state (potential energy surface) is to be considered, the partition functions are more complicated than envisioned above and individual consideration is required. A factor for tunneling of H through the energy saddle also can be calculated and has been observed experimentally. It is dependent on T because the population of the various states depends on T. An excellent review of isotope effects has been written.[7]

18.9 WAVE PACKET THEORY

The activated complex is not as definite or as well resolved an entity as the preceding discussion would imply. If $\Delta t^{\ddagger}$ is a measure of its lifetime, then the uncertainty principle requires that its energy states be fuzzy by $\Delta\varepsilon^{\ddagger} \approx \hbar/\Delta t^{\ddagger}$. If $\Delta t^{\ddagger}$ is about 10^{-12} sec, then $\Delta\varepsilon^{\ddagger}$ is about 10^{-22} joule, which is about 10^2 joule/mole or 0.02 kcal/mole on the macroscopic scale. Indeed, it is easy to show that the energy states of the activated complex overlap in energy as though its energies formed a band.

In addition to poorly quantized energies, the potential energy surface varies only slowly with respect to distance, especially along the reaction coordinate near the saddle-point. If the total energy ε is almost equal to the potential energy V, then arguments like those of Section 13.11 call for a rather slow space-variation or oscillation in the wave function of the activated complex in the region near the saddle point. That is, the effective wavelength $\lambda = h/p$ of the activated complex's motion is large because $\varepsilon \approx V$ and $p^2/2\mu$ is small. Not only is the energy of the activated complex poorly quantized, but its position, including its crucial internal configurations, is poorly specified. It is clear that a truly adequate account of the details of an elementary chemical event must be formulated in terms of the wave equation rather than classical mechanics. Identifying the potential energy surface too carefully has a tinge of classical thinking in it. It

(7) J. Bigeleisen and M. Wolfsberg, "Theoretical and Experimental Aspects of Isotope Effects in Chemical Kinetics" in Vol. I of *Advances in Chemical Physics*, ed. by I. Prigogine, New York: Interscience Publishers, Inc. 1958.

is better to think of the complex as an unobserved species at the unobserved intermediate states in Figure 14.1.

The initial and final states of a chemical change, in contrast to the activated state, are well defined, long-lived, and almost classically related to each other. The energy of each reactant is reasonably well defined if its lifetime exceeds 10^{-11} sec. A typical vibration takes 10^{-13} sec, and the lifetime of a typical spectroscopic state is 10^{-8} sec. The energy of the initial state of the reaction $AB + C \longrightarrow ABC^{\ddagger} \longrightarrow A + BC$ is the energy ε_C of C plus the energy ε_{AB} of AB plus their relative kinetic energy. Since additive energies yield factors in the wave function, the wave function at the start of reaction ($t = -\infty$) is of the form

$$\psi_1(p_1, q_1, t = -\infty) = \psi_{trC}\psi_{AB}\psi_C \tag{18.46}$$

In (18.46), p_1 and q_1 include the variables specifying the initial momentum and position of AB and C, ψ_{trC} is a wave function for their relative translation, and ψ_{AB} and ψ_C are the wave functions for 'isolated' AB and C, each in essentially a stationary state. Similarly, after reaction,

$$\psi_2(p, q, t) = \psi_{trA}\psi_A\psi_{BC} \tag{18.47}$$

The probability that a reaction has occurred by time t is the probability that the essentially classical configuration $A + BC$ is observed. That is, the probability that A has a momentum p relative to BC at time t is

$$P(p, t) = \int \psi_2^*\psi_2\, dq \tag{18.48}$$

The total probability that reaction has occurred is the summation of $P(p, t)$ over all momenta p consistent with T, other external parameters, and the general preparation of the system. If the reaction is irreversible, this sum approaches unity at $t \longrightarrow \infty$, while $\psi_1^*\psi_1$ approaches zero.

The wave function $\psi_\ddagger$ of the activated complex is a hybrid of ψ_1 of (18.46) and ψ_2 of (18.47). It must be possible for ψ_1 to become $\psi_\ddagger$ near $t = 0$ and for $\psi_\ddagger$ to become ψ_2 thereafter. The rate at which $\psi_\ddagger$ changes with respect to time is (13.53) in the form

$$\frac{\partial \psi_\ddagger}{\partial t} = \left(-\frac{i}{\hbar}\right)\mathbf{H}\psi_\ddagger \tag{18.49}$$

where $\mathbf{H}$ is the Hamiltonian of the system. The short lifetime of the activated state from about $t = -\Delta t^\ddagger$ to about $t = +\Delta t^\ddagger$ makes it necessary to use the time-dependent form of the wave equation.

The best possible characterization of an activated complex with momentum p_0 along the reaction coordinate at position q_0 at $t = 0$ is the wave packet

$$\psi_\ddagger(q) = a \exp\left[-\frac{(q - q_0)^2}{4\Delta q_0^2}\right] \exp\left[\frac{ip_0 q}{\hbar}\right] \tag{18.50}$$

This wave function applies to what is called a *minimum packet* for which $\Delta p \Delta q = \hbar/2$. After the constant a is a Gaussian (error-function) distribution in position with standard deviation $\Delta q_0 \sqrt{2}$. The third factor of (18.50) is the wave of momentum p_0. As time passes, the center of the packet of reduced mass μ moves as p_0 directs it with a speed p_0/μ. At time t, Δq_0^2 in (18.50) must be replaced by

$$\Delta q^2 = \Delta q_0^2 + \frac{\hbar^2 t^2}{4\mu^2 \Delta q_0^2} = \Delta q_0^2 + \frac{\Delta p_0^2 t^2}{\mu^2}$$

That is, the wave packet gradually spreads out in space. The spread is a minimum if $\Delta q_0^2 = \hbar t/\mu$. Presumably, after a while, this wave packet will resolve itself by internal interference into $\psi_1 \pm \gamma \psi_2$ where γ is a constant related to the size of the transmission coefficient. If the products must be either A + BC or AB + C, then $\psi_1^* \psi_2$ is zero, for ψ_1 and ψ_2 are not both large at the same values of p and q when t is not near zero.

The conclusion is inescapable: an elementary chemical event cannot be followed classically in its ultimate detail.

18.10 SUMMARY

It is appropriate now to pause and survey the scenery, for it has been a long trail from the billiard balls of the kinetic theory in Chapter 1 to the present provocative semi-picture of a chemical event. With true elegance, thermodynamics has offered precise and commonplace descriptions of ideal and real gases, heats of reaction between well defined states, macroscopic spontaneity, solutions, surfaces, phase and membrane equilibria, and chemical equilibrium. The terms have familiar explanations in the world of direct experience. The mechanisms of reactions are less obvious, but the collisions of reactants are readily imagined. The motion of ions in an electric field and of electrons in and out of electrochemical cells is also easy to grasp.

The sudden change in attitude at Chapter 13 is not all bad. Many thermodynamic questions are understandable in terms of quanta, but the mathematical treatment in terms of wave-particles is at first a mental strain. However, as energy states become familiar, the energetics of molecules in the new mechanics becomes very simple. The uncertainty principle cuts the amount of information in half. For chemistry, it all seems to reduce to $\Delta\varepsilon = h\nu$, just as an understanding of crystals in general seems to reduce to close-packing of atoms, ions, or at least electric charges, or some minor modification thereof. Finally, the marvelous partition function merely counts the energy states, digests them, and produces the macroscopic variables that really comfort man when properly used.

If these chapters have offered a few facts, an understanding of chemistry, a facility with applied mathematics, and a lot of questions that demand answers, then the time spent in studying them has been well spent.

PROBLEMS

(Because of the difficulty of problems from some sections of this chapter, only one set of problems is offered.)

1. The quantum yield of HI from H_2 and I_2 is two. Explain this upper limit of two.

2. In 1918, Warburg found that 2HI are decomposed to H_2 and I_2 by one photon of suitable energy. Write a mechanism that accounts for this fact.
Answer: $HI + \gamma \longrightarrow H + I$; $H + HI \longrightarrow H_2 + I$; $M + I + I \longrightarrow I_2 + M^*$.

3. A one-molar solution 0.200 mm thick transmits one-tenth of a beam of light. With neglect of absorption by solvent and cell windows, what percentage of the initial intensity will be transmitted by a 2-molar solution in a cell 0.150 mm thick?
Answer: 3.16%.

4. Suggest a mechanism of the photochemical reaction $2\ COCl_2 + O_2 \longrightarrow 2\ CO_2 + 2\ Cl_2$ that is in accord with a quantum yield such that 16.0 mm Hg of $COCl_2$ at 1 atm at room T react when 4×10^{18} quanta are absorbed [C. W. Montgomery and G. K. Rollefson, *J. Am. Chem. Soc.* **55**, 4025 (1933)].

5. By reference to the π electrons of 1,2-disubstituted ethene, explain how light of short enough λ or the presence of halogen X_2 catalyzes the conversion of a cis isomer to a trans isomer.
Answer: X makes single bond between C's by forming a C-X bond and free radical; light makes $\pi^2 \longrightarrow \pi\pi^*$ leaving a single bond C-C.

6. When the quantum yield of a photolytic dissociation (e. g., $MX_n \longrightarrow X + MX_{n-1}$) to unexcited products is found to depend strongly on the temperature of reactants when the maximum frequency of light is used, what can be said of the dissociation energy of that M-X bond?
Answer: The initial state is thermally excited molecules, and the dissociation energy exceeds the energy of the so-called maximum frequency (which really depends on T).

7. If the half-life of M^* is 1.0×10^{-8} sec, what κ is required at 1 atm at 27°C to maintain a pressure of M^* of 1.0×10^{-7} mm Hg with $I_0 = 5.00$ ergs mm^{-2} sec^{-1}? Express κ as a function of ν.
Answer: $\kappa/\nu = 7.3 \times 10^{-8}$ cm^2 sec mole^{-1}.

8. At high pressures of Cl_2, the chain-terminating step in the production of HCl may be

$$Cl_3 + Cl_3 \xrightarrow{k_3} 3\ Cl_2$$

where Cl_3 is generated from and is in near-equilibrium with Cl_2 and Cl.

$$Cl + Cl_2 \underset{k''}{\overset{k'}{\rightleftharpoons}} Cl_3$$

If this is so, derive the rate law that describes the photoproduction of HCl from H_2 and Cl_2 at high Cl_2 pressures.

Answer: $\dfrac{dC_{HCl}}{dt} = \dfrac{2k_H k_X C_{H_2}}{k'(k_H C_{Cl_2} + k_2 C_{HCl})}\left[\left(\dfrac{k''^2 k_I I C_{Cl_2}}{2k_3}\right)^{1/2} + \dfrac{k_I I C_{Cl_2}}{2}\right]$

9. At 40°C with radiation of wavelength 4358 A, the photochemical reaction

$$Cl_{2(g)} + C_2Cl_{4(g)} \longrightarrow C_2Cl_{6(s)}$$

proceeds at a rate that depends upon the intensity of light and the concentration of Cl_2. When p_{Cl_2} was 46.7 mm Hg and $p_{C_2Cl_4}$ was 5.8 mm Hg, the total pressure decreased by 3.40×10^{-3} mm Hg sec^{-1} in a rigid glass vessel of volume 1110 cc when 5.66×10^{-10} einsteins sec^{-1} were absorbed. The energy of 1 einstein is $Nh\nu$. Later, when p_{Cl_2} was 43.2 mm Hg and $p_{C_2Cl_4}$ was 2.3 mm Hg, the total pressure decreased by 1.48×10^{-3} mm Hg sec^{-1} when 1.47×10^{-10} einsteins sec^{-1} were absorbed. If the rate law is

$$-\frac{dC_{Cl_2}}{dt} = kI_a^n C_{Cl_2}$$

where I_a is the intensity of *absorbed* radiation, find k and n. Determine also the quantum yield for each set of conditions if only half of the Cl_2 that disappears absorbs radiation in the primary event. [Data from R. G. Dickinson and J. L. Carrico, *J. Am. Chem. Soc.*, **56,** 1473 (1934).]
Answer: $k = 11.0$; 171 and 287.

10. If the primary event in the photochlorination of C_2Cl_4 is $Cl_2 + h\nu \longrightarrow 2\,Cl$, invent a mechanism that leads to the rate law stated in Problem 9. N. B.: $I_a = I_0 \kappa C/Nh\nu$.
Answer: $Cl_2 + \gamma \longrightarrow 2Cl$; $Cl + C_2Cl_4 \longrightarrow C_2Cl_5$; $C_2Cl_5 + Cl_2 \longrightarrow C_2Cl_6 + Cl$; $2C_2Cl_5 \longrightarrow C_2Cl_6 + C_2Cl_4$ (or $Cl_2 + 2C_2Cl_4$); $n = 0.5$. Alternatively, let $Cl_3 + C_2Cl_4 \longrightarrow C_2Cl_6 + Cl$ with $M + 2Cl \longrightarrow Cl_2 + M$ and $Cl + Cl_2 \longrightarrow Cl_3$.

11. At constant light intensity from 82°C to 132°C, the rate of disappearance of Br_2 in the photo-bromination of toluene (T) to yield benzyl bromide and HBr is

$$-\frac{dC_{Br_2}}{dt} = \frac{kC_{Br_2}^{1/2}C_T^{1/2}}{1 + n\left(\dfrac{C_{HBr}}{C_{Br_2}}\right)}$$

where k and n depend upon temperature thus:

$$\log k = 1.497 - \frac{1742}{T}$$

$$\log n = 3.007 - \frac{1176}{T}$$

[H. E. Anderson, Jr., H. A. Scheraga, and E. R. Van Artsdalen, *J. Chem. Phys.*, **21,** 1258 (1953)]. Propose a mechanism for this gaseous chain reaction that does not involve hydrogen atoms, and by comparison with the observed rate law discuss the relative efficiencies of Br_2 and toluene as third bodies in recombination of Br atoms.

Answer: $Br_2 + \gamma \xrightarrow{k_I} 2Br$; $Br + \phi CH_2H \xrightarrow{k_X} \phi CH_2 + HBr$; $\phi CH_2 + Br_2 \xrightarrow{k_H} \phi CH_2Br + Br$; $2Br + T \xrightarrow{k_T} T + Br_2$; $2Br + Br_2 \xrightarrow{k_{Br}} Br_2 + Br_2$; $\phi CH_2 + HBr \xrightarrow{k_{X'}} \phi CH_3 + Br$; $n = k'_X/k_H$; $k = k_X k_I^{1/2} k_T^{-1/2}$; toluene is much better third body.

12. By making suitable assumptions about activation energies of reactions in the chain mechanism for bromination of toluene in the previous problem, find the heat of formation of benzyl radical. For gaseous toluene, $\Delta H_f^0 = 12$ kcal mole^{-1}.
Answer: 50 kcal mole^{-1}.

13. Justify this statement: The partition function of a strongly adsorbed (i.e., chemisorbed) reactant on a solid catalyst is unity.

14. Let σ' be the empirically adjustable apparent diameter of species in a bimolecular reaction when $\alpha = 1$ in (18.21). If σ is the viscosity diameter (as in Table 18.1), show approximately that the volume in which reaction can occur is $(\pi/6)[\sigma'^3 - \sigma^3]$ and that the duration of the chemical collision is $2(\sigma' - \sigma)/u$ where u is the root mean square velocity of a molecule.

15. Explain what value is appropriate for J_{AC} and for K_{AC} in the London formula for ε' (18.29) when the complex $ABC^\ddagger$ is linear, and show that this energy ε' is less than ε' for a nonlinear complex of three atoms.
Answer: J_{AC} and K_{AC} are near zero.

16. Show that the scale parameter b' of (18.26) for the Morse function (18.25) is $\omega_e/[2r_e(B_eD_e)^{1/2}]$.

17. If a reaction involving a transfer of H from one molecule to another has an unusually great Arrhenius frequency factor s, and if the activated complex theory gives a low estimate of s, what process might be suspected?
Answer: Tunneling of proton through saddle.

18. By the theory of absolute reaction rates and then by the kinetic theory, estimate the order of magnitude of the apparent efficiency of collisions in a gaseous reaction at 300°K between an atom and a rigid diatomic molecule when the activated complex, rigid except for the pseudo-frequency along the reaction coordinate is: (a) linear; (b) nonlinear.
Answer: (a) 10^{-3}; (b) 10^{-2}.

19. Calculate and discuss the values of the transmission coefficients for the reactions of Table 18.2.

20. Show that the pseudo-frequency of vibration along the reaction coordinate is the same for passage in either direction across the energy saddle if the activated complex is the same for forward and for reverse reaction.

21. With the aid of Figure 18.3 and data elsewhere in the text calculate the rate constant for the reaction $H_2 + Cl \longrightarrow H + HCl$ and compare the result to the observed value $10^{11}\, e^{-6.1\times 10^3/RT}$ liter mole^{-1} sec^{-1}.

22. If the fundamental stretching vibration of ^1H on a large rigid molecule is 3000 cm^{-1}, what is the fundamental energy of the same vibration when ^2H replaces ^1H?
Answer: 2100 cm^{-1}.

23. Assume that the reaction $AB + C \longrightarrow ABC^\ddagger \longrightarrow A + BC$ involves a linear activated complex in which B is bonded with equal force constants to A and C in $ABC^\ddagger$. If the atomic weight of A is 10, if the total molecular weight of $A^{10}BC^\ddagger$ is 50, and if k_{10} is the rate constant when ^{10}B is used while k_{12} is the rate constant

when ^{12}B is used, what approximate factor attributable to this change of B occurs in the expression for the ratio k_{10}/k_{12}?
Answer: 1.09.

24. If $\psi(q, t)$ is the wave function of an activated complex for advancing time (clocks running forward), find the conditions that $\psi^*(q, -t)$ is the wave function for regressing (backward) time. Only the signs of t and i are adjustable, not charge, . . .
Answer: **H** must be real and all terms or factors containing $i = (-1)^{1/2}$ in the wave equation must be changed in sign.

25. Under what circumstances is the wave function $\psi(q, t)$ of an activated complex a linear function of time in the region of the complex's configuration at the saddle and, if $\psi = u(q)f(t)$, under what circumstances (the same set) is $u(q)$ a linear function of the reaction coordinate q in the region of the saddle maximum?
Answer: Flat top on saddle-pass and ε approximately equal to V.

APPENDIXES

APPENDIXES

APPENDIX A
VALUES OF PHYSICAL CONSTANTS

Defined Values

Meter	1 650 763.73 wavelengths of the unperturbed transition $2p_{10} - 5d_5$ in ^{86}Kr (in vacuo)
Kilogram	Mass of international kilogram (Sevres, France)
Second	1/31 556 925.9747 of the tropical year at 12^hET, 0 January, 1900 or 9 192 631 770 cycles of the hyperfine transition $(4,0 \rightarrow 3,0)$ of the ground state of ^{133}Cs unperturbed by external fields.
Degree Kelvin	Triple-point of water is 273.16°K (natural water)
Atomic Mass Unit	1/12 of the mass of one atom of ^{12}C
Acceleration of free fall	9.80665 m sec^{-1}
One Atmosphere	101 325 newtons per square meter
Calorie	4.184 joules or 4.184×10^7 ergs
Liter	1000.028 cm^3

Least Squares Values of 1963

c	2.997925(1)	$\times 10^8$ m sec^{-1}	$\times 10^{10}$ cm sec^{-1}
e	1.60210(2)	$\times 10^{-19}$ coulomb	
e	4.80298(7)		$\times 10^{-10}$ esu

N_o	6.02252(9)	$\times 10^{26}$ kmole^{-1}	$\times 10^{23}$ mole^{-1}
m	1.66043(2)	$\times 10^{-27}$ kg (amu)$^{-1}$	$\times 10^{-24}$ g (amu)$^{-1}$
m_e	9.10908(13)	$\times 10^{-31}$ kg (electron)$^{-1}$	$\times 10^{-28}$ g (electron)$^{-1}$
m_p	1.67252(3)	$\times 10^{-27}$ kg (proton)$^{-1}$	$\times 10^{-24}$ g (proton)$^{-1}$
m_p	1.00727663(8)	amu	amu
m_n	1.67482(3)	$\times 10^{-27}$ kg (neutron)$^{-1}$	$\times 10^{-24}$ g (neutron)$^{-1}$
m_n	1.0086654(4)	amu	amu
$\mathfrak{F}$	9.64870(5)	$\times 10^{4}$ coul mole^{-1}	
h	6.62559(16)	$\times 10^{-34}$ joule-sec	$\times 10^{-27}$ erg-sec
$h/2\pi$	1.054494(25)	$\times 10^{-34}$ joule-sec	$\times 10^{-27}$ erg-sec
R_∞	1.0973731(1)	$\times 10^{7}$ m^{-1}	$\times 10^{5}$ cm^{-1}
a_0	5.29167(2)	$\times 10^{-11}$ m	$\times 10^{-9}$ cm
μ_e	0.92732(2)	$\times 10^{-23}$ joule tesla^{-1}	$\times 10^{-20}$ erg oersted^{-1}
μ_N	0.505050(13)	$\times 10^{-26}$ joule tesla^{-1}	$\times 10^{-23}$ erg oersted^{-1}
R	8.31434(35)	$\times 10^{0}$ joule deg^{-1} mole^{-1}	$\times 10^{7}$ erg deg^{-1} mole^{-1}
k	1.38054(6)	$\times 10^{-23}$ joule deg^{-1}	$\times 10^{-16}$ erg deg^{-1}

AUXILIARY VALUES OF CONSTANTS (1963)

R_∞	13.60535(13) ev
R	0.082053 liter atm deg^{-1} mole^{-1} = 82.055 cm^3 atm deg^{-1} mole^{-1}
R	1.9872 cal deg^{-1} mole^{-1}
V_0	22 413.6 cm^3 mole^{-1}
1 ev	1.60210(2) $\times 10^{-19}$ joule = 1.60210(2) $\times 10^{-12}$ erg
1 ev	8065.73(8) cm^{-1}
1 ev	23.061(1) kcal mole^{-1}
1 amu	931.478(5) MeV

N. B. The digits enclosed in parentheses are the estimate of the standard deviation in the final digits of the quoted value. The probability that the quoted value lies more than this away from the true value is 0.3174; more than twice this away, 0.0456; more than three standard deviations away, 0.0026.

[Report to the Commission on Nuclidic Masses and Related Atomic Constants of the International Union of Pure and Applied Physics, June 24, 1963, by E. R. Cohen and J. W. M. DuMond. See also *Nat. Bur. Stds.* (U. S.) *Tech. News* **47**, 175 (1963) and E. R. Cohen and J. W. M. DuMond, *Revs. Modern Phys.* **37**, 537 (1965)]

APPENDIX B

ATOMIC MASSES RELATIVE TO $^{12}_{6}C$ = 12.00000

(REVISED TO 1965)

[Natural Mixture of Isotopes]

[By permission of International Union of Pure and Applied Chemistry]

Symbol and Name		Atomic No.	Atomic Mass	Symbol and Name		Atomic No.	Atomic Mass
Ac	Actinium	89		Ho	Holmium	67	164.930
Al	Aluminum	13	26.9815	H	Hydrogen	1	1.00797a
Am	Americium	95		In	Indium	49	114.82
Sb	Antimony	51	121.75	I	Iodine	53	126.9044
Ar	Argon	18	39.948	Ir	Iridium	77	192.2
As	Arsenic	33	74.9216	Fe	Iron	26	55.847c
At	Astatine	85		Kr	Krypton	36	83.80
Ba	Barium	56	137.34	La	Lanthanum	57	138.91
Bk	Berkelium	97		Lw	Lawrencium	103	
Be	Beryllium	4	9.0122	Pb	Lead	82	207.19
Bi	Bismuth	83	208.980	Li	Lithium	3	6.939
B	Boron	5	10.811a	Lu	Lutetium	71	174.97
Br	Bromine	35	79.904b	Mg	Magnesium	12	24.312
Cd	Cadmium	48	112.40	Mn	Manganese	25	54.9380
Ca	Calcium	20	40.08	Md	Mendelevium	101	
Cf	Californium	98		Hg	Mercury	80	200.59
C	Carbon	6	12.01115a	Mo	Molybdenum	42	95.94
Ce	Cerium	58	140.12	Nd	Neodymium	60	144.24
Cs	Cesium	55	132.905	Ne	Neon	10	20.183
Cl	Chlorine	17	35.453b	Np	Neptunium	93	
Cr	Chromium	24	51.996	Ni	Nickel	28	58.71
Co	Cobalt	27	58.9332	Nb	Niobium	41	92.906
Cu	Copper	29	63.546	N	Nitrogen	7	14.0067
Cm	Curium	96		No	Nobelium	102	
Dy	Dysprosium	66	162.50	Os	Osmium	76	190.2
Es	Einsteinium	99		O	Oxygen	8	15.9994a
Er	Erbium	68	167.26	Pd	Palladium	46	106.4
Eu	Europium	63	151.96	P	Phosphorus	15	30.9738
Fm	Fermium	100		Pt	Platinum	78	195.09
F	Fluorine	9	18.9984	Pu	Plutonium	94	
Fr	Francium	87		Po	Polonium	84	
Gd	Gadolinium	64	157.25	K	Potassium	19	39.102
Ga	Gallium	31	69.72	Pr	Praseodymium	59	140.907
Ge	Germanium	32	72.59	Pm	Promethium	61	
Au	Gold	79	196.967	Pa	Protactinium	91	
Hf	Hafnium	72	178.49	Ra	Radium	88	
He	Helium	2	4.0026	Rn	Radon	86	

Symbol and Name	Atomic No.	Atomic Mass	Symbol and Name	Atomic No.	Atomic Mass
Re Rhenium	75	186.2	Tb Terbium	65	158.924
Rh Rhodium	45	102.905	Tl Thallium	81	204.37
Rb Rubidium	37	85.47	Th Thorium	90	232.038
Ru Ruthenium	44	101.07	Tm Thulium	69	168.934
Sm Samarium	62	150.35	Sn Tin	50	118.69
Sc Scandium	21	44.956	Ti Titanium	22	47.90
Se Selenium	34	78.96	W Tungsten	74	183.85
Si Silicon	14	28.086	U Uranium	92	238.03
Ag Silver	47	107.868b	V Vanadium	23	50.942
Na Sodium	11	22.9898	Xe Xenon	54	131.30
Sr Strontium	38	87.62	Yb Ytterbium	70	173.04
S Sulfur	16	32.064a	Y Yttrium	39	88.905
Ta Tantalum	73	180.948	Zn Zinc	30	65.37
Tc Technetium	43		Zr Zirconium	40	91.22
Te Tellurium	52	127.60			

a Natural variation in isotopic abundance cause these ranges of atomic mass: H, 0.00001; B, 0.003; C, 0.00005; O, 0.0001; Si, 0.001; S, 0.003.
b Experimental uncertainty is believed to be 0.001.
c Experimental uncertainty is believed to be 0.003.

APPENDIX C

GAMMA FUNCTION*

A definite integral of common occurrence in physics and chemistry is called the gamma function. By definition it is

$$\Gamma(n) = \int_0^\infty x^{n-1}e^{-x}\,dx \tag{C.1}$$

Its value when $n = 1$ is simply

$$\Gamma(1) = \int_0^\infty e^{-x}\,dx = -e^{-x}\Big|_{x=0}^{x=\infty} = 0 + e^0 = 1 \tag{C.2}$$

If $n = 2$, its value is found by integration by parts as follows:

$$\Gamma(2) = \int_0^\infty x\,e^{-x}\,dx = \int_0^\infty x\,d(-e^{-x})$$

* A very lucid explanation is given by Woods, F. S., *Advanced Calculus*. Boston: Ginn & Company, 1934, p. 164 *et seq.*

$$\Gamma(2) = -\,x\,e^{-x}\Big|_{x=0}^{x=\infty} - \int_0^\infty (-e^{-x})\,dx$$

$$= -\lim_{x\to\infty}\left(\frac{x}{e^x}\right) + \int_0^\infty e^{-x}\,dx$$

$$= -\lim_{x\to\infty}\left(\frac{1}{e^x}\right) + (1) = 1 \tag{C.3}$$

Between $n = 1$ and $n = 2$, $\Gamma(n)$ reaches a single minimum at $\Gamma(1.46) = 0.8855$. By advanced methods of analysis it is possible to show that

$$\Gamma(\tfrac{1}{2}) = \sqrt{\pi} \tag{C.4}$$

This last result is frequently needed in physical applications.

A very valuable recursion formula for $\Gamma(n)$ results upon integration by parts, for

$$\Gamma(n+1) = \int_0^\infty x^n\,e^{-x}\,dx = \int_0^\infty x^n\,d(-e^{-x})$$

$$= -\,x^n\,e^{-x}\Big|_{x=0}^{x=\infty} - \int_0^\infty (-e^{-x})\,n\,x^{n-1}\,dx$$

$$= -\lim_{x\to\infty}\left(\frac{x^n}{e^x}\right) + n\int_0^\infty x^{n-1}\,e^{-x}\,dx$$

The limit is zero since, by l'Hospital's rule, the numerator eventually becomes finite while the denominator remains as e^x. Hence, the result is simply

$$\Gamma(n+1) = n\Gamma(n) \tag{C.5}$$

This recursion formula allows all values of $\Gamma(n)$ to be referred to values between $n = 1$ and $n = 2$. Numerous examples of the use of this formula and the gamma function are in the text.

The definition (C.1) and the recursion formula (C.5) yield a finite value for $\Gamma(n)$ except when n is zero or a negative integer. By (C.5),

$$\Gamma(n) = \frac{\Gamma(n+1)}{n} = \frac{\Gamma(n+2)}{n(n+1)} = \cdots$$

Continuation of this process when n is a negative integer eventually yields zero in the denominator. Thus $\Gamma(n)$ becomes infinite when $n = 0$ or when n is a negative integer. Of course, if n is a positive integer, then $\Gamma(n+1)$ is $n(n-1)(n-2)\ldots$, or $n!$.

APPENDIX D

LINE INTEGRATION; EXACT AND INEXACT DIFFERENTIALS*

A definite integral is a function of its limits when it is of the form

$$\int_a^b \frac{df(x)}{dx}\,dx = f(b) - f(a) \tag{1}$$

It is possible, however, for a definite integral of the form

$$\int_a^b \phi(x, y)\,dx \tag{2}$$

to depend not only on the limits a and b but also on the many possible values of y in the interval $a \leqslant x \leqslant b$. If the values of y are given as a function of x by the relation $y = F(x)$, then substitution of $F(x)$ for y in (2) gives an integral like (1) in one variable x. This is readily evaluated by (1) if the integration can be done. When the variable of integration is y, the expression analogous to (2) is

$$\int_{a'}^{b'} \chi(x, y)\,dy \tag{3}$$

In general, (2) and (3) seldom occur alone. Integrals of this type are commonly of the form

$$\int_{(a,a')}^{(b,b')} [\phi(x, y)\,dx + \chi(x, y)\,dy] \tag{4}$$

When the function $y = F(x)$ is specified, the integral (4) can be calculated. Because the curve $y = F(x)$ specifies that the integration be performed along a certain curve or *path*, the integral (4) is called a *line integral*.

The value of (4) generally depends upon the curve or path of integration. For example, let the integral be

$$I = \int_{(0,0)}^{(2,1)} [(y + 1)\,dx + (x^2)\,dy]$$

When $y = x/2$, substitution for y yields

$$I = \int_0^2 \left[\left(\frac{x}{2} + 1\right) dx + (x^2)\frac{dx}{2}\right] = \frac{13}{3}$$

* The matter of this appendix is highly abbreviated. For ample development, the student is referred to the latest editions of the two sources of this appendix, which were: Granville, W. A., P. F. Smith, and W. R. Longley, *Elements of the Differential and Integral Calculus.* Boston: Ginn & Company, 1941; Woods, F. S., *Advanced Calculus.* Boston: Ginn & Company, 1934 (New Edition: pp. 81–82 and 174–186. [Copyright 1962 by Emily Woods Ferguson]).

However, if the path be along $y = 0$ for $0 \leqslant x \leqslant 2$ and then along $x = 2$ for $0 \leqslant y \leqslant 1$, the integral along $y = 0$ becomes $\int_0^2 dx = 2$ while along $x = 2$ it becomes $\int_0^1 4\,dy = 4$. The second path along $y = 0$ and $x = 2$ thus yields $I = 6$, a value which differs from 13/3.

If the function $\phi(x, y)$ in (2) were merely y, then

$$\int_a^b \phi(x, y)\,dx = \int_a^b y\,dx$$

would be the area bounded by $y = \phi(x)$, $y = 0$, $x = a$ and $x = b$. Since curves like C_1 and C_2 of Figure D1 can be followed in two directions, it is necessary to define one direction as positive and the other as negative. When the curve bounds a certain region A, the positive direction along the curve C is that direction which keeps the region A on the left of a person traversing the curve. Integration along C_1, namely,

$$A_1 = \int_a^b y_1\,dx \tag{5}$$

would give the area A_1 bounded by C_1, $y = 0$, $x = a$, and $x = b$. Similarly, integration along C_2 with the region A on the left would give the area bounded by C_2, $y = 0$, $x = b$ and $x = a$. The expression for this area A_2 would be negative because dx is everywhere negative; hence,

$$-A_2 = \int_b^a y_2\,dx \tag{6}$$

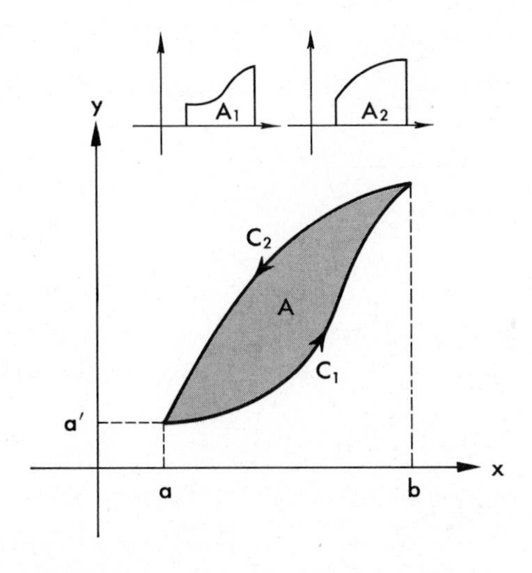

Figure D.1. Line Integral and Area

Since the infinitesimal element of area dA is $(y_2 - y_1)\,dx$ for the enclosed region A, this enclosed region has the area

$$A = \int_a^b (y_2 - y_1)\,dx = A_2 - A_1 \tag{7}$$

As C_1 and C_2 are traversed in the positive sense with the enclosed region on the left,

$$\oint y\,dx = \int_a^b y_1\,dx + \int_b^a y_2\,dx = A_1 - A_2 \tag{8}$$

where the symbol $\oint$ indicates integration in the positive sense along C along a closed path which begins and ends at (a, a'). By (5), (6), and (7), it follows that

$$\oint y\,dx = -A \tag{9}$$

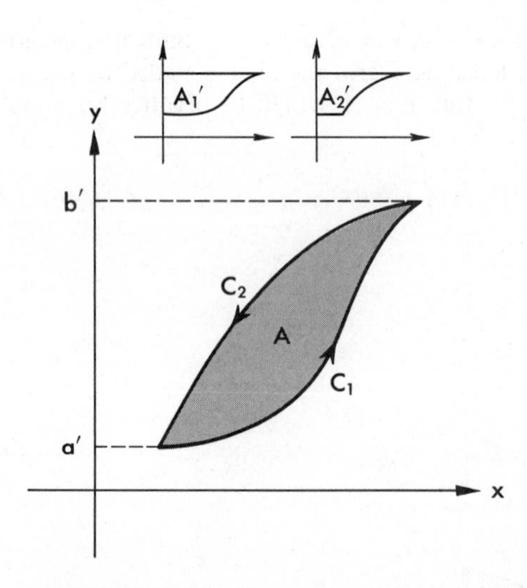

Figure D.2. Line Integral and Area Again

Similarly, it can be shown that

$$\oint x\,dy = +A \tag{10}$$

For if A_1' is the area bounded by C_1, $x = 0$, $y = a'$, and $y = b'$, then as in Figure D2,

$$A_1' = \int_{a'}^{b'} x_1\,dy$$

And for A_2' bounded by C_2, $x = 0$, $y = a'$ and $y = b'$,

$$-A_2' = \int_{b'}^{a'} x_2\,dy$$

Since $A = A_1' - A_2'$,

$$A = \int_{a'}^{b'} x_1\,dy + \int_{b'}^{a'} x_2\,dy = \oint x\,dy$$

for the region A is always on the left as the curve is followed from (a, a') along C_1 to (b, b'), thence along C_2 to (a, a').

From (9) and (10),

$$2A = \oint (x\,dy - y\,dx) \tag{11}$$

This formulation and (9) and (10) assume that there are only two points on the curve C for each value of x or y in the interval and that there is only one point on C at the ends of the interval. Equation (11) is, however, quite general, for any region can be divided into areas that satisfy these requirements. Moreover, the path of integration may consist of portions of two different curves.

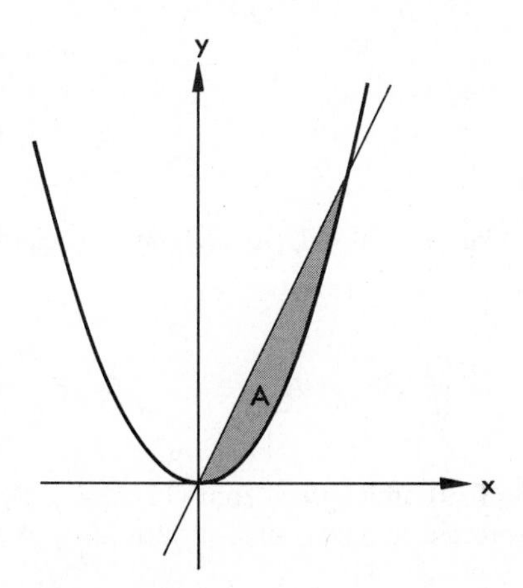

Figure D.3. An Area Calculated

The area bounded by the parabola $y = 2x^2$ and the line $y = 2x$ can be calculated by (11). As shown in Figure D3, these curves intersect at $x = y = 0$ and at $x = 1$, $y = 2$. Along the parabola where $y = 2x^2$ and $dy = 4x\,dx$,

$$\int_{(0,0)}^{(1,2)} (x\,dy - y\,dx) = \int_0^1 [x(4x\,dx) - (2x^2)\,dx] = \int_0^1 2x^2\,dx = \tfrac{2}{3}$$

Along the line where $y = 2x$ and $dy = 2\,dx$,

$$\int_{(1,2)}^{(0,0)} (x\,dy - y\,dx) = \int_1^0 [x(2\,dx) - (2x)\,dx] = 0$$

By (11),

$$A = \tfrac{1}{2} \oint (x\,dy - y\,dx) = \tfrac{1}{2}(\tfrac{2}{3} + 0) = \tfrac{1}{3}$$

Let $\phi(x, y)$ and $(\partial\phi/\partial y)_x$ be functions that are continuous in a region A and along a curve C as in Figure D1 or D2. If there are only two points on C for each value of x between the end points of the interval from a to b and if there is but one point on C at the end points a and b, then by (1),

$$\iint \left(\frac{\partial\phi}{\partial y}\right)_x dx\, dy = \int_a^b dx \int_{y_1}^{y_2} \left(\frac{\partial\phi}{\partial y}\right)_z dy$$

$$= \int_a^b [\phi(x, y_2) - \phi(x, y_1)]\, dx$$

$$= -\int_a^b \phi(x, y_1)\, dx - \int_b^a \phi(x, y_2)\, dx$$

Since $\phi(x, y_1)$ is C_1 while $\phi(x, y_2)$ is C_2, and since the limits establish the direction so as to keep the region A on the left, this is the line integral of $\phi(x, y)$ along C with reversed sign. That is,

$$\iint \left(\frac{\partial\phi}{\partial y}\right)_x dx\, dy = -\oint \phi(x, y)\, dx \tag{12}$$

Similarly, if $\chi(x, y)$ and $(\partial\chi/\partial x)_y$ behave like $\phi(x, y)$ and $(\partial\phi/\partial y)_x$ in the region A and along the curve C,

$$\iint \left(\frac{\partial\chi}{\partial x}\right)_y dx\, dy = +\oint \chi(x, y)\, dy \tag{13}$$

The signs of (12) and (13) resemble those of (9) and (10). From (12) and (13), the general form of the line integral can be expressed in terms of a surface integral over the region A as

$$-\oint [\chi(x, y)\, dy + \phi(x, y)\, dx] = \iint \left[\left(\frac{\partial\phi}{\partial y}\right)_x - \left(\frac{\partial\chi}{\partial x}\right)_y\right] dx\, dy \tag{14}$$

Equation (14) is a form of Green's theorem in the plane.

If everywhere in the region A

$$\left(\frac{\partial\phi}{\partial y}\right)_x = \left(\frac{\partial\chi}{\partial x}\right)_y \tag{15}$$

then the line integral of (14) around A, which can be any region suitably divided, is zero.

$$\oint [\chi(x, y)\, dy + \phi(x, y)\, dx] = 0 \tag{16}$$

On the other hand, if (16) is true, then (15) is also true. If (15) were not true, then it would be possible to choose the region A so that $(\partial\phi/\partial y)_x - (\partial\chi/\partial x)_y$ would be positive, with the result that the line integral would not be zero as supposed. Equation (15) is therefore the necessary and sufficient condition that the line integral around A be zero.

If (16) is true, the integral along C_1 between any two points is equal in magnitude but opposite in sign to the integral along C_2 for the return trip; for the sum of these two integrals is the round trip and must be zero. If the return trip along C_2 be performed in reverse, it becomes an alternate route from the initial state (a, a') to the final state (b, b'). Since these states and the alternate routes are quite arbitrary and are subject only to the conditions set forth in deriving (14), (15), and (16), the necessary and sufficient condition that a line integral (14) depend only on the initial and final states is that (15) or (16) be true.

The statements (15) and (16) can be formulated in another way in terms of an *exact differential*. The expression $\phi\, dx + \chi\, dy$ shall have the same meaning as above. If $\phi\, dx + \chi\, dy$ is an exact differential, then there exists some function $z = z(x, y)$ such that

$$dz = \phi\, dx + \chi\, dy \tag{17}$$

Then,

$$\left(\frac{\partial z}{\partial x}\right)_y = \phi \quad \text{and} \quad \left(\frac{\partial z}{\partial y}\right)_x = \chi \tag{18}$$

If the second mixed partial derivatives of z are found and if they are equal, as is generally true in physical applications, then

$$\frac{\partial}{\partial x}\left(\frac{\partial z}{\partial y}\right) = \frac{\partial^2 z}{\partial x\, \partial y} = \frac{\partial^2 z}{\partial y\, \partial x} = \frac{\partial}{\partial y}\left(\frac{\partial z}{\partial x}\right)$$

Or, by (18), $\partial\chi/\partial x = \partial\phi/\partial y$, which is the same as (15). On the other hand, let (15) be true. Then since $\phi = \phi(x, y)$,

$$\int \phi\, dx = f(x, y) + C(y) \tag{19}$$

The constant of integration $C(y)$ is a function of y because the integration was performed only upon x and $\int \phi\, dx$ depends on y. Let

$$z(x, y) = f(x, y) + C(y) \tag{20}$$

Then,

$$\frac{\partial z}{\partial y} = \frac{\partial f}{\partial y} + \frac{dC}{dy} \tag{21}$$

If z exists, (18) is true and all that remains is to determine C, which can be done by (21):

$$\frac{dC}{dy} = \chi - \frac{\partial f}{\partial y} \tag{21}$$

But dC/dy is not a function of x, so that differentiation of (21) gives

$$0 = \frac{\partial \chi}{\partial x} - \frac{\partial^2 f}{\partial x \, \partial y} \tag{22}$$

That is, by (19) and (22),

$$\frac{\partial \chi}{\partial x} = \frac{\partial^2 f}{\partial x \, \partial y} = \frac{\partial}{\partial y}\left\{\frac{\partial}{\partial x}\left[\int \phi \, dx - C(y)\right]\right\}$$

$$\frac{\partial \chi}{\partial x} = \frac{\partial \phi}{\partial y} \tag{15}$$

which is again (15). Since z is given by (20) and C is given by (21), the condition (15) is sufficient.

Since the integral of an expression that satisfies (15) is the integral of an exact differential dz, the function $z = z(x, y)$ exists and can be evaluated at the initial and final states. The value is thus independent of everything except the initial and final states.

If (15) or (16) is not satisfied, as sometimes happens in physical situations, then the expression $\phi \, dx + \chi \, dy$ is called an *inexact differential*. The value of an integral of an inexact differential depends not only on the initial and final states but also upon the path. Heat and work are examples of inexact differentials, and suitable examples and exercises illustrating the dependence upon the process as well as upon the initial and final states are given in the text.

Although heat and work depend upon the intermediate states of a changing system as it proceeds from a certain initial state to a certain final state, there are several thermodynamic functions that do depend only upon the initial and final states of a system. Accordingly, the increment in such a function, such as the energy, is independent of the process by which the change is effected. Any path that is mathematically convenient or conceptually simple provides a suitable path of integration and the unique increment in the value of the function between the two end states. Illustration of the behavior of exact differentials is, as for inexact ones, reserved to the main text.

Although heat is an inexact differential, it has been found that dividing the infinitesimal amount of heat absorbed reversibly by a system by the absolute temperature gives an exact differential. The reciprocal of the absolute temperature is called an *integrating factor*, for its use allows integration independent of the path. This fundamental mathematical nature of the laws of thermodynamics was discovered by Carathe'odory. Without the aid of fictitious engines, he was able to develop the laws of thermodynamics from a study of a certain differential equation.

INDEX

A

B

C

D

E

F

G

H

I

J

K

L

M

N

O

Q

R

S

U

V

X

Z

	f													
6														
5	90 Th	91 Pa	92 U	93 Np	94 Pu	95 Am	96 Cm	97 Bk	98 Cf	99 Es	100 Fm	101 Md	102 No	103 Lw
4	58 Ce	59 Pr	60 Nd	61 Pm	62 Sm	63 Eu	64 Gd	65 Tb	66 Dy	67 Ho	68 Er	69 Tm	70 Yb	71 Lu

	p			
	81 Tl	82 Pb	83 Bi	84 Po
	49 In	50 Sn	51 Sb	52 Te
	31 Ga	32 Ge	33 As	34 Se
3	13 Al	14 Si	15 P	16 S
2	5 B	6 C	7 N	8 O

PERIODIC TABLE OF THE ELEMENTS